A Note from the Publisher

W9-AZY-288

Prentice-Hall Biology explores the world of living things, beginning with the most simple and ending with the most complex. It examines the intricate interactions of living things from those of their atoms and molecules to those that occur in the largest of communities—biomes—and the entire earth. *Prentice-Hall Biology* is enhanced and enriched by the use of clear, detailed illustrations and the following special features. Page references provide an example of each feature.

- The book contains ten units and forty-eight chapters. The units are self-contained and can be studied in any order (page 13).

- Important science terms are introduced in boldface type and defined within the text. Other science terms are printed in italic type for emphasis. Phonetic pronunciations are given for many terms (page 27).

- A list of chapter objectives appears at the beginning of each chapter (page 262).

- Chapter sections create separate study units within each chapter. Each section ends with section review questions (pages 297–303).

- Forty-eight optional laboratory investigations that utilize easy-to-obtain materials reinforce the text content (page 183).

- Several highlights in each chapter focus on main ideas, concepts, and facts in the chapter (page 200). Sidelights provide intriguing bits of information (page 202).

- Thirty-three career descriptions emphasize the variety of opportunities for work in the field of biology (page 156). Fifteen close-ups provide students with a look at specific biologists and their work (page 320).

- Each chapter concludes with a chapter summary, a chapter vocabulary list, review questions, extensions and applications, and suggested readings (pages 184–185).

- Each unit culminates with "Perspectives in Biology," a feature that presents an open-ended topic for further study and discussion (page 55).

- A reference section, a glossary, and an index help students use and find biology terms and important information (pages 792–832).

To assure a highly readable book, the content for this text was selected, organized, and written at a level appropriate for the intended audience. The Dale–Chall and Fry readability formulas were used to control readability level.

PRENTICE-HALL BIOLOGY

The Comprehensive Coverage And Special Features You Expect...

...*Plus* DIAL–A–TEST,™
A Unique Customized Testing Service

DIAL-A-TEST,™ A UNIQUE CUSTOMIZED
TESTING SERVICE, SAVES TIME AND WORK

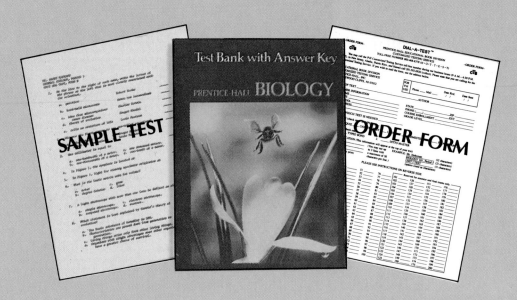

**PRENTICE-HALL BIOLOGY TEST BANK
WITH ANSWER KEY**

TO ORDER TESTS

COMPLETE ANCILLARY PACKAGE
PROVIDES MAXIMUM TEACHABILITY

**PRENTICE-HALL BIOLOGY
ANNOTATED TEACHER'S EDITION**

**PRENTICE-HALL BIOLOGY
LABORATORY MANUAL**

**PRENTICE-HALL BIOLOGY
LABORATORY MANUAL,
ANNOTATED TEACHER'S EDITION**

**PRENTICE-HALL BIOLOGY
TEACHER'S RESOURCE BOOK**

**PRENTICE-HALL BIOLOGY
COURSEWARE**

LIVELY INTRODUCTIONS PROVIDE
MOTIVATION AND DIRECTION

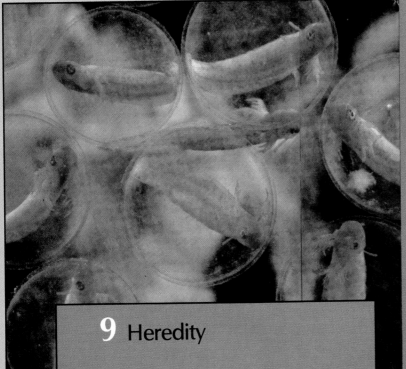

UNIT THREE

Variety and Continuity

For an overview of this unit, including field trip suggestions, a bibliography, and a list of audio-visual materials, see pages T-41 to T-51. You may want to check the Laboratory Investigations in this unit so that materials may be ordered, gathered, or prepared in advance.

Scientists estimate that about 5 million species of plants and animals live on the earth. This may not seem so amazing when you realize that beetles alone account for at least 500,000 species! Some scientists estimate that about 2 billion different kinds of plants and animals have lived on the earth throughout its history. If these estimates are correct, 99.75% of the plants and animals that ever lived on the earth do not exist today!

Every living thing fits into a particular environment. Each organism has special characteristics that enable it to live where it does. Most living things could not survive if their environment were to change greatly.

The ability of organisms to fit into a certain environment, the diversity of life, patterns of heredity, and the disappearance of millions of species can be explained by various scientific theories and observations. This unit will explore some of these theories and observations.

These salamanders are shown before and after hatching.

149

9 Heredity

Chapter Objectives   *After completing this chapter, you will be able to:*

a ■ Explain Mendel's principle of dominance and recessiveness. p. 152
b ■ State the law of segregation and the law of independent assortment. p. 154
c ■ Explain hybrid and purebred; genotype and phenotype. p. 153, p. 156
d ■ Apply the probability product rule to genetics problems. p. 157
e ■ Use Punnett squares to illustrate monohybrid and dihybrid crosses. p. 158
f ■ Explain incomplete dominance and give an example using a Punnett square. p. 161

For teaching aids for this chapter, including a chapter overview and teaching strategies, see pages T-41 to T-43. The page number next to each chapter objective refers to the text page where the information needed to fulfill the objective begins.

Young African elephants inherit their parents' traits.

You receive information in various ways. It is passed to you through computers, television, radio, telephones, books, magazines, and newspapers. You also receive information through the words of your parents, teachers, and friends. This information gives you knowledge of past and present.

There is another kind of information, genetic information, that makes you what you are—blond or brunette, blue-eyed or brown-eyed, tall or short. This information is provided by *DNA*, a complex molecule in cells. Information stored in the DNA molecules determines the structure and function of all living things. This information is passed from parent to offspring as *traits*, or characteristics. The passing of traits from parents to offspring is called **heredity** and causes offspring to resemble their parents.

The way traits are passed from parents to their offspring was a mystery for a long time. During the last 125 years, some of the mystery has been solved by research in the field of **genetics** (jə-NET-iks), the scientific study of heredity. Genetics is one of the most modern of the biological sciences.

150

VIVID UNIT OPENERS peak student interest and imagination and help capture their attention.

INTEREST-CATCHING CHAPTER OPENERS provide direction through attainable learning objectives keyed to the questions in the Test Bank.

HELPFUL ANNOTATIONS printed in red aid in lesson preparation, suggest strategies and activities, answer questions, and provide numerous other timely helps and direction throughout.

LOGICALLY ORGANIZED HEADINGS and subheadings create smooth, manageable lessons.

SPECIAL READABILITY AIDS in **boldface** and *italic type,* and controlled reading level enhance vocabulary development and comprehension.

The Digestive System

The breaking down of food into simple substances that can be absorbed into the bloodstream is called **digestion.** Digestion takes place in the digestive system, which is made up of two types of organs. *True digestive organs* are those through which the food actually passes. *Accessory digestive organs* play a role in digestion, but the food does not pass through them. Together, all of the digestive organs make up an efficient system for breaking down food and absorbing it. Without this system, the human body would be unable to release the energy from foods that it needs to carry out life functions. The body would also not be able to use the food for growth and repair.

The true digestive organs are the mouth, pharynx, esophagus, stomach, small intestine, and large intestine. The accessory digestive organs are the teeth, tongue, salivary glands, liver, gall bladder, and pancreas.

The Mouth

The mouth is made up of a hard, bony part and a soft, muscular section. The **hard palate** (PAL-it) is located at the front of the roof of the mouth. The hard palate separates the mouth from the nasal cavity. Along the back of the mouth, there is a section of muscle tissue, called the **soft palate.** When a person swallows, the soft palates prevents food from entering the nasal cavity. A tiny knoblike structure, called the *uvula* (YOO-vyə-lə), is suspended from the soft palate.

SALIVARY GLANDS The lining of the cheeks contain three pairs of **salivary glands.** The largest of these glands, the *parotid* (pə-RAHT-id) *glands,* are located in front of the ears. The *submaxillary* (sub-MAK-sə-ler-ē) *glands,* found beneath the tongue, open into the floor of the mouth. The third pair, the *sublingual* (sub-LING-gwəl) *glands,* are found in the front of the mouth below the tip of the tongue. They too have openings onto the floor of the mouth.

The three pairs of glands produce about 1.5 liters of *saliva* daily. Saliva is a mixture of water, **mucin** (MYOO-sin), and *ptyalin* (TĪ-ə-lin). Water makes up about 98% of saliva. Mucin is a slippery substance that lubricates food and makes it easier to swallow. Ptyalin is a digestive enzyme.

THE TONGUE Attached at the back of the mouth, the tongue takes up most of the mouth floor. It is made up of skeletal muscle covered with epithelial tissue. Scattered over the tongue are the **taste buds,** or *taste receptors.* Various types of taste buds react with different types of dissolved food. The tongue is able to detect four basic tastes, either

Figure 36-1 The salivary glands are located around the mouth. They secrete saliva, which contains enzymes that begin the chemical digestion of food.

Soft palate
Hard palate
Uvula
Nasal cavity
Parotid gland
Tongue
Pharynx
Sublingual gland
Epiglottis
Submaxillary gland
Windpipe

593

Nutritional S

Highlight

Nutrients are substances that provide a source of energy and materials for growth and repair of body tissues.

Food contains variou
tissues, to supply ener
body needs and uses n
are grouped into six c
all the nutrients neede

To stay strong and
diet. This type of die
body needs, and it is
groups are the *milk*
meat group, and the
anced diet, an average

At this point, you may want to assign to your students the second of the Extensions and Applications at the end of this chapter.

Four or more servings from the milk group
Two or more servings from the meat group
Four or more servings from the bread–cereals group
Four or more servings from the vegetable–fruit group

Figure 39-1 A balanced diet contains nutrients from each of the four basic food groups. These are the milk group, the meat group, the bread and cereal group, and the vegetable and fruit group.

635

SPECIAL CHAPTER

CONCEPT DEVELOPMENT,

HIGHLIGHTS provide emphasis for important concepts being developed.

ATTRACTIVE AND FUNCTIONAL ILLUSTRATIONS enhance interest, reinforce written content, and elicit student participation.

other watery places. **Mesophytes,** such as the philodendron, grow under moderately moist conditions.

SECTION REVIEW Answers on page T–69.

1. Name three external factors that affect plant growth.
2. What is photoperiodism? The critical dark period?
3. What is vernalization?

Responses to Stimuli

A plant's environment plays an important role in its growth and behavior. Environmental factors affecting a plant include habitat, light, availability of water, air, inorganic substances, and temperature. These factors affect plants by

SECTION REVIEWS provide ongoing evaluation and reinforcement of student comprehension throughout each chapter.

CAREERS introduce students to relevant applications and describe realistic opportunities in biology and related areas.

CAREER: Landscape Architect

Landscape architects often design outdoor land areas, such as parks, gardens, and forest campsites. The grounds along highways and around schools, offices, and other buildings are also designed by landscape architects.

Landscape architects first discuss with their clients how a particular piece of land is to be used. Together, the landscape architect and the client determine where sidewalks, play areas, and similar structures should be located. Then the landscape architect studies the physical site. Such factors as the slope of the land, the kinds of trees and soil present, and the amount of sunlight on each part of the site must be determined.

Once all the information is collected, the landscape architect prepares plans that show how the site is to be developed, along with the kinds of plants to be used in each area of the site. This planning requires extensive knowledge of plants. Landscape architects must know which plants will grow in different soils and climates. Landscape architects who work in large cities must also know which plants are likely to resist the damage of air pollution.

The landscape architect then discusses the plans with the client and with other people who are working on buildings on the site. This com-

munication helps to ensure that the finished land will be a pleasing and appropriate setting for the buildings.

Once a plan is approved, the landscape architect prepares detailed instructions for the contractor. The landscape architect will then oversee the work of the contractor to make sure that the plans are followed.

Landscape architects must have a bachelor's degree in landscape architecture. In all states, they must be licensed before they can practice. To receive a license, they must pass an exam, and they must show that they have received on-the-job training under the supervision of a licensed landscape architect.

For career information, write to The American Society of Landscape Architects, 1900 M Street, N.W., Suite 750, Washington, DC 20009.

FEATURES ENHANCE

INTEREST, AND FLEXIBILITY

SIDELIGHTS add interest to topic development and help keep students involved.

CLOSEUPS provide human interest by focusing on important work of current biologists.

ve cord contains a pair of glia, nerves lead to the

tter developed in crusta- The most sensitive of the ae and antennules, which . Located near the base of e, called a **statocyst,** con- is a ridge containing fine become attached to these s its position, these sand . The movement of the s and sends messages to the brain. The statocyst enables the crayfish to maintain its balance or to right itself when tilted.

A crayfish has a pair of **compound eyes,** which are eyes with more than one lens. In fact, each compound eye of a crayfish has about 2500 lenses. Although the images formed are not sharp, these eyes can detect movement very well. Due to their location on short movable stalks, the eyes also provide a wide field of vision. This feature helps crayfishes search for food and avoid predators.

Sidelight

One species of crayfish lives in lightless caves of Kentucky and is totally blind.

CLOSE-UP: Dr. Eduardo Macagno

Eduardo Macagno is a biologist who works in a modern lab at Columbia University in New York City. He is a professor in the Department of Biological Sciences. Macagno is studying the nervous systems of invertebrates, and he uses a computer. In particular, Macagno is studying the nervous system of *Daphnia,* which are tiny, freshwater animals, also called water fleas. *Daphnia* have a very simple nervous system. If Macagno can understand how *Daphnia* function, he will know more about the nervous systems of more complex animals.

Daphnia are so small that they are hard to study. Most are only 4 or 5 millimeters long. Moreover, to study their nervous system, Macagno must look at the individual nerve cells that make up the system. By using a microscope hooked up to a computer, Macagno is able to examine these cells.

"Before the computer, we had to make plastic models to help us understand the function and structure of the nerve cells." Macagno says. "It

took a very long time to make a model of a cell. Now we use a computer to draw the features of the cells."

After scanning sections of *Daphnia* tissue, the computer can instantly display information that took biologists weeks to uncover in the past. The computer that Macagno uses is one that he helped to develop at Columbia. It is only a few years old. With the computer, Macagno's research, as well as the research of other biologists, is moving ahead at new and impressive speeds.

CHAPTER AND UNIT

CONCEPT AND SKILL

LABORATORY INVESTIGATION 24

For additional information, see pages T-89.

Responses to Stimuli

Purpose One of the basic characteristics of living things is their ability to respond to environmental changes. Plants respond to such changes in two ways. A tropism is a response in which plants grow toward or away from a stimulus. A nastic movement is a movement that is independent of the direction of the stimulus. The purpose of this investigation is to observe these movements, along with the stimuli that cause them.

Materials *(per group)* ● Oxalis plant ● Corn seeds, soaked in water for 24 hours ● Shoe box ● Paper towels ● Petri dish ● Masking tape ● 2 colored pencils ● Grease pencil

Procedure **Part A** 1. Obtain an oxalis plant from your teacher. Examine the angle between the leaves and the stem. 2. Using one of the colored pencils, draw a straight vertical line about 10 cm long on a sheet of paper. Then draw a second, shorter line that intersects with the vertical line at the same angle that the oxalis leaves intersect with the stem. 3. Label the diagram, "Oxalis in the Light." 4. Place a shoe box over the plant and leave it undisturbed for 30 minutes. 5. Remove the box and observe the angle of the leaves relative to the stem. 6. Using the other colored pencil, make a second sketch indicating the angle between the leaves and the stem. Label this sketch, "Oxalis in the Dark." **Part B** 1. Obtain 4 corn seeds that have been soaked in water for 24 hours. Arrange the seeds with the embryo side down on the top half of a petri dish as shown in the figure. Keep the pointed ends of the corn seeds toward the center of the dish. 2. Place a paper towel against the seeds. 3. Pack the petri dish with crumpled paper towels so that when the top of the dish is put on, the seeds are held in place. 4. Dampen the paper towels, and cover the petri dish. 5. Seal the top of the petri dish to the bottom with a strip of masking tape. 6. Stand the dish on its edge so that one seed is at the 12-o'clock position. Mark the top of the petri dish with a

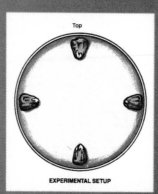

Top

EXPERIMENTAL SETUP

grease pencil. 7. Place your petri dish with the dishes of other class members in a place indicated by your teacher. Make sure that the dish remains on edge and in the right position. 8. Examine the germinating corn seeds every day for a week. Draw a sketch of them each d[...]

Observation[...] drawings in [...] the oxalis pl[...] Part B, in wh[...] grow? The [...] name of the [...] root?

394

LABORATORY INVESTIGATIONS provide the option of reinforcing and extending concepts through labs requiring easily obtainable equipment and materials. There are 48 labs, which are different from those in the Prentice-Hall Biology Laboratory Manual.

736

CHAPTER SUMMARY

The Biosphere Ecology is the study of the relationships between living things and their environment. These relationships take place in the biosphere, which is divided into smaller units called ecosystems. An ecosystem is an interacting system that consists of groups of organisms and their nonliving environment. Each ecosystem contains biotic and abiotic factors.

Ecosystems are made up of communities that include all the living organisms in a certain area. Communities consist of a number of populations. A population is a group of individuals of the same species that live in the same area. Each organism in a community has a habitat, or place in which it lives, and a niche, or a particular role within the habitat.

Biotic Interactions in the Environment Organisms are divided into three groups according to the way in which they obtain their food. Producers, or green plants, make their own food by the process of photosynthesis. Producers are also called autotrophs. Consumers feed directly or indirectly upon producers. Those that feed directly upon producers are called primary consumers or herbivores. Those that feed upon primary consumers are called secondary consumers or carnivores. Animals that feed on both plants and animals are called omnivores. Decomposers are organisms that break down organic material and return it to the environment. Consumers and decomposers are also called heterotrophs. Heterotrophic plants called saprophytes feed upon dead organisms or the waste products of living organisms. Animals that feed upon dead organisms are called scavengers.

In an ecosystem, energy from producers passes through a system of consumers. This flow of energy and organic materials through a number of organisms is called a food chain. Food chains that interconnect or overlap form a food web. Each feeding level in a food chain is called a trophic level. Producers belong

to the first trophic level, primary consumers belong to the second trophic level, secondary consumers belong to the third trophic level, and so on. Relationships among the different levels in food chains may be represented in ecological pyramids.

Members of a community interact with one another for the same materials. This is called competition. Intraspecific competition takes place among members of the same species. Interspecific competition results when two or more different species compete.

Certain factors help maintain an ecological balance in communities. Both competition and predator–prey relationships help to maintain the size of populations. Symbiosis is the interaction between two organisms that affects the survival of one or both. There are three types of symbiotic relationships. These types of relationships are commensalism, mutualism, and parasitism.

Abiotic Factors in the Environment Water, soil, temperature, and light are abiotic factors. All organisms need water to perform life functions. The type of soil determines the type of plants that grow in a given area. Average environmental temperatures affect the distribution of animals and plants around the world. The amount of sunlight determines the types of plants that can grow in an area. This, in turn, determines the types of animals that can live in the area.

Important Cycles in the Environment In addition to energy, more than 20 different substances must be present in an ecosystem for living things to carry on vital processes. The four most important of these are the elements hydrogen, oxygen, carbon, and nitrogen. These substances are constantly recycled within an ecosystem. Nutrient, or biogeochemical, cycles include the water cycle, the oxygen cycle, the carbon cycle, and the nitrogen cycle.

CHAPTER VOCABULARY

ammonification	denitrification	niche	prey
biomass	ecology	nitrification	producer
biosphere	ecosystem	nitrogen cycle	saprophyte
carbon cycle	food chain	nitrogen fixation	scavenger
commensalism	food web	oxygen cycle	symbiosis
community	habitat	parasitism	trophic level
consumer	host	population	water cycle
decomposer	mutualism	predator	

CHAPTER SUMMARIES provide timely review and reinforcement of important concepts.

CHAPTER VOCABULARY lists all new terms for ease of study and review.

EXTRAS REINFORCE
DEVELOPMENT

PERSPECTIVES IN BIOLOGY helps you present contemporary issues for students to explore, discuss, research, and investigate.

The Use of Food Additives

If you had lived about 100 years ago, most of the food that you ate would have come from your own farm or a neighbor's farm. Today, most people live in large cities that are not near farms. Food has to be transported, sometimes over long distances, to where it is needed.

Because of the great distances between farms and cities, care has to be taken during the transportation of food so that it does not spoil. To prevent spoilage, food manufacturers often add substances called food additives to food. Food manufacturers also use additives to improve the flavor, color, and texture of their products. Other additives, such as vitamin D, are added to food to increase its nutritional value.

Some food additives are made synthetically in the laboratory. Some snack foods are made up of only synthetic additives. Interestingly, however, most additives occur naturally. Salt, pepper, and sugar are examples of natural additives.

Some food additives may be dangerous to people's health. In 1970, the Food and Drug Administration (FDA) prohibited the sale of artificial sweeteners called cyclamates. The cyclamates were shown to cause cancer in laboratory animals. Six years later the FDA banned the use of red dye number 2 in foods, drugs, and cosmetics. Red dye number 2 has also been linked to cancer.

Food additives have also been blamed for other problems. Monosodium glutamate, a flavor enhancer, produces headaches in many people

part in the preparation of foods. For example, many natural fruits are not abundant or are available only during certain seasons, which restricts the use of natural fruit flavors. Manufacturers have developed synthetic fruit flavorings to overcome this problem and meet the needs and tastes of the consumer.

Nevertheless, many people are joining a growing movement to eat "natural" or "health" foods that are free of additives. Even neighborhood supermarkets offer these foods in special sections, enabling people to make their own choices as to what to eat.

Viewpoints

1. In 1977, the Food and Drug Administration took steps to limit the use of the artificial sweetener saccharin. It was found to cause cancer in laboratory animals. Foods that contain saccharin now carry a warning that it may be hazardous to your health. Should saccharin continue to be added to foods? Are there any other alternatives for people such as diabetics who must watch their intake of sugar?

2. Save the packages from the foods you eat during one day. Determine from the labels the additives you consumed and list them. Consult food and nutrition reference materials to find out whether these additives are natural or artificial. Determine whether or not they are considered unhealthy.

3. Interview a nutritionist or dietician. Before you interview, prepare a list of questions for the interview, such as the following: Do you try to avoid certain food additives in your selection of food? Are you concerned about additives?

4. Write to the Manufacturing Chemists' Association, Inc., 2501 M Street NW, Washington, DC 20037, and request a copy of the pamphlet "Food Additives: Who Needs Them?" Summarize the material in a visual presentation for the class.

147

737

REVIEW of FACTS and CONCEPTS Answers on page T–108.

On a separate sheet of paper, answer each of the following as completely as possible.

1. What is an ecosystem? Give an example of an ecosystem.
2. Why is sunlight needed to maintain an ecosystem?
3. What are the three groups of organisms that are classified according to the way in which they obtain their food? Give an example of an organism in each group.
4. Distinguish between an autotroph and a heterotroph.
5. Draw a food chain. Identify the different parts of the chain.
6. Describe an example of a food web.
7. Why does each trophic level in a food chain contain less energy than the level below it?
8. Explain how energy flows through a food chain in an ecosystem.
9. Why is it more energy-efficient for humans to eat plants instead of animals?
10. Briefly describe a predator-prey relationship.
11. Distinguish between the terms in each pair: habitat and niche; herbivore and carnivore; intraspecific competition and interspecific competition.

EXTENSIONS and APPLICATIONS For additional information, see page T–108.

1. Visit the library and research the effect of introducing certain foreign plants or animals into this country. Examples of some of these organisms are the Russian thistle, starling, English sparrow, gypsy moth, and European corn borer. Prepare an oral report showing how these organisms benefited or harmed the environment.
2. Investigate the environment near your home. Identify the ecosystems and how they are related. Identify some food chains and food webs and illustrate them in a chart. Note any recent changes in the ecological balance of the area.
3. Collect three different samples of soil from three different areas. Compare the color, particle size, and capacity to absorb water for each of the soils. Also compare the smell and texture of the soils. In each type of soil plant some seeds, giving them sufficient water. In which soil did the seeds grow best? Explain.
4. Find a large tree near your school or home. Observe the tree for a week and make a list of plants and animals that use the tree for shelter or food. What would happen to this ecosystem if one kind of organism were removed? Explain.
5. Obtain a small aquarium. Place a 1-centimeter layer of small stones in the bottom of the aquarium and cover it with 10 centimeters of soil. Obtain a few small green plants and carefully place them in the aquarium. Gently put in more soil to anchor the plants, and moisten with water. Do not pack the soil down tightly. In one part of the aquarium, place a small dish of water. Collect some earthworms, land snails, and small insects and place them in the aquarium. Cover the top of the aquarium with thin screening to prevent the escape of the small animals. Observe this ecosystem for a few weeks. Prepare a written report on the changes that occur.

SUGGESTED READINGS

Farb, P., *Ecology.* New York: Time-Life Books.
   In this introductory book, the author, an experienced naturalist, explains how living organisms on the earth form communities. Many photographs and diagrams are included.
McCombs, L.W., and N. Rosa, *What's Ecology?* Menlo Park, Calif.: Addison-Wesley.
   The authors describe nutrient cycles and the flow of energy through ecosystems. They also explain the factors that affect populations.
Meeker, J.W., *The Spheres of Life: An Introduction to World Ecology.* New York: Scribners.
   The author offers simple explanations of the basics of ecology and discusses reasons for environmental problems such as pollution.

REVIEW OF FACTS AND CONCEPTS contain questions designed to evaluate and reinforce understanding of chapter facts and concepts.

EXTENSIONS AND APPLICATIONS add further dimension to your course through various types of open-ended activities that extend facts or concepts, or apply them to new situations.

SUGGESTED READINGS include annotated bibliographies to encourage further student research and independent study.

COMPREHENSIVE CONTENT PROVIDES IN-DEPTH TOPIC COVERAGE

10 UNITS AND 48 CHAPTERS provide a full-year survey course allowing you to cover all important areas of biology.

FLEXIBILITY of self-contained units and chapters allows for choice of topics and sequence, and accommodates different ability ranges, teaching styles, and curriculum requirements.

UNITS

ONE	Introduction to Biology
TWO	Cells
THREE	Variety and Continuity
FOUR	Microbes
FIVE	Plants and Fungi
SIX	Invertebrates
SEVEN	Vertebrates
EIGHT	Human Structure and Function
NINE	Human Response and Development
TEN	Ecological Interactions

PRENTICE-HALL BIOLOGY

69937-1   Student Text
69938-9   Annotated Teacher's Edition
69939-7   Laboratory Manual
69941-3   Laboratory Manual, Annotated Teacher's Edition
69942-1   Teacher's Resource Book
69943-9   Test Bank with Answer Key
          Plus DIAL-A-TEST™: A Unique Customized Testing Service
          Biology Courseware

For further information, please write to:

PRENTICE-HALL, Inc.
Educational Book Division
Englewood Cliffs, N.J. 07632

PRENTICE-HALL BIOLOGY

ANNOTATED TEACHER'S EDITION

Sandra Gottfried
Science Instructor
Ona M. Wilcox School of Nursing
Middlesex Memorial Hospital
Middletown, Connecticut

Carol D. Hampton
Professor of Science Education
East Carolina University
Greenville, North Carolina

Carolyn H. Hampton
Professor of Science Education
East Carolina University
Greenville, North Carolina

Wayne Leibel
Adjunct Assistant Professor of
Biology
Boston College
Chestnut Hill, Massachusetts

Gerry Madrazo, Jr.
Instructional Supervisor of
Science, K-12
Guilford County Public Schools
Greensboro, North Carolina

LaMoine Motz
Director of Science, Health, and
Outdoor Education
Oakland Schools
Pontiac, Michigan

Dorothea Sinclair
Biology Teacher
Bishop Moore High School
Orlando, Florida

Gerald Skoog
Professor and Chairperson
of Secondary Education
Texas Tech University
Lubbock, Texas

Third Edition

ISBN 0-13-699380-X

10 9 8 7 6 5 4 3 2

PRENTICE-HALL OF AUSTRALIA, PTY. LTD., Sydney
PRENTICE-HALL CANADA INC., Toronto
PRENTICE-HALL HISPANOAMERICANA, S.A., Mexico
PRENTICE-HALL OF INDIA PRIVATE LTD., New Delhi
PRENTICE-HALL INTERNATIONAL, INC., London
PRENTICE-HALL OF JAPAN, INC., Tokyo
PRENTICE-HALL OF SOUTHEAST ASIA PTE. LTD. Singapore
EDITORA PRENTICE-HALL DO BRASIL LTDA., Rio de Janeiro
WHITEHALL BOOKS LIMITED, Wellington, New Zealand

CONTENTS

OVERVIEW OF *PRENTICE-HALL BIOLOGY*

Rationale and Approach

Science and technology play vital roles in meeting society's needs. Therefore, science fundamentals must be an important component of a student's general education. The presentation of such fundamentals should enable students to recognize the importance of basic scientific research and the application of scientific concepts to people's lives. *Prentice-Hall Biology* meets these educational goals as it presents the fundamentals of the science of biology.

Prentice-Hall Biology is a comprehensive program that includes all the subject matter of a general biology curriculum. Its structure is phylogenetic. Within the phylogenetic framework, the classification of life forms is treated in depth, as are the topics of cells, genetics, human biology, and the environment. Many special features enhance both teaching and learning for a wide range of interests and ability levels.

Readability and Comprehension

The reading level of *Prentice-Hall Biology* has been carefully monitored using both the Dale-Chall and the Fry scale. To aid readability and comprehension, important scientific terms introduced in the text are printed in boldface type at first mention. These boldface terms are repeated in a vocabulary list at the end of each chapter. Scientific terms of secondary importance are italicized for emphasis. Definitions accompany new terms, and phonetic pronunciations are provided where necessary.

Photographs, drawings, and tables visually reinforce the textual material, aiding readability and comprehension. In-text references to illustrations and tables help direct students as they read the text. Each illustration is accompanied by an explanatory caption. Tables have succinct titles that make their contents and structure immediately clear.

Features of the Student Text

The *Prentice-Hall Biology* text is divided into ten units. The ten units are divided into 48 chapters.

Flexible Units

Prentice-Hall Biology provides a flexible approach to the teaching of biology. The ten units of study are sufficiently self-contained so that they can be taught separately and in any order. Each unit begins with a two-page opening spread that includes an attractive full-color photograph, a brief overview of the topics covered in the unit, and a list of the chapters in the unit. At the end of each unit, a *Perspectives in Biology* feature presents contemporary issues in biology for study, discussion, and further investigation.

Comprehensive Chapters

Each of the 48 chapters of *Prentice-Hall Biology* opens with an appropriate full-color photograph, a list of *Chapter Objectives*, and a brief introduction to the chapter. The chapters are divided into teachable sections, each of which concludes with a *Section Review*—a series of questions designed to reinforce learning and comprehension. The use in each chapter of boldface type to introduce important scientific terms, accompanied by definitions and where necessary by phonetic pronunciations, and of italic type to emphasize other scientific terms also aids comprehension.

Interspersed throughout each chapter are *Highlights* and *Sidelights*. The Highlights pinpoint important ideas or concepts in the chapter. The Sidelights present interesting facts or additional information related to topics discussed in the chapter. In addition, each chapter contains a *Career* or *Close-up* feature. Each Career feature introduces students to a biological career related to the topic of the chapter. The Career feature includes a full-color photograph depicting a person actively engaged in his or her work, a discussion of the work done by people in the career, a description of the educational requirements, and an address to which interested students may write for additional information. Each Close-up feature introduces students to a particular person employed in a biological career and to his or her field of study. The Close-up feature is correlated to a topic discussed in the chapter. Each Close-up includes a photograph of the person and a description of his or her work.

End-of-Chapter Features

LABORATORY INVESTIGATIONS Each chapter in *Prentice-Hall Biology* concludes with an optional Laboratory Investigation that provides students with an opportunity to participate actively in investigating problems in biology. The Laboratory Investigations reinforce concepts presented in the text and in some cases supplement or extend the material already presented. The investigations can be performed with easy-to-obtain equipment and materials.

CHAPTER SUMMARY The Chapter Summary is organized according to the chapter sections. Important concepts presented in each section are reviewed.

CHAPTER VOCABULARY In the Chapter Vocabulary all boldface scientific terms presented in the chapter are listed for study and review.

REVIEW OF FACTS AND CONCEPTS The Review of Facts and Concepts consists of questions that reinforce understanding of scientific facts and concepts.

EXTENSIONS AND APPLICATIONS The Extensions and Applications present library, field, and laboratory investigations that extend facts or concepts presented in the chapter. Some exercises also require students to apply a concept presented in the chapter to a problem.

SUGGESTED READINGS The Suggested Readings section is an annotated listing of books for further reading. All the books included are related to the topics discussed in the chapter and are written at an appropriate reading level.

End-of-Text Features

REFERENCE SECTION Following the text is a Reference Section consisting of a description of the compound microscope and its use, the procedures for preparing a wet-mount slide and staining microscopic specimens, an explanation of the metric system, and a detailed chart of the five-kingdom system of taxonomy.

GLOSSARY An alphabetical listing of important scientific terms and their definitions is presented. Phonetic pronunciations, plurals, and adjectival forms are given where necessary.

NOBEL PRIZE WINNERS A chart, including the prizes in physiology or medicine and those in chemistry and physics that are related to biology, is given.

INDEX The Index provides students with an easy-to-use and comprehensive reference listing.

Features of the Annotated Teacher's Edition

The Annotated Teacher's Edition includes all of the material presented in the student text as well as several features that are designed to help you use the text effectively.

Overview of *Prentice-Hall Biology*

This section presents the rationale and approach of the program, discusses readability and aids to comprehension, lists the features of the student text and of the Annotated Teacher's Edition, and briefly describes the Laboratory Manual with its accompanying Annotated Teacher's Edition and the Test Bank with Answer Key.

Reading and Language Development in Science

This section discusses using *Prentice-Hall Biology* effectively, vocabulary development in biology, reading skills in biology, writing in the biology classroom, speaking in the biology classroom, and listening in the biology classroom. "Writing in the Biology Classroom" gives suggested formats for writing a laboratory report and a research paper. Instructional techniques for oral presentations, panel discussions, and class discussions are presented in "Speaking in the Biology Classroom."

Teaching and Scheduling Guides

Suggested teaching guides for low-level, average/college preparatory, and accelerated biology classes are presented. A suggested scheduling chart for a 180-day school year is also provided.

Safety Standards

General guidelines for laboratory safety, as well as specific safety guidelines for chemical storage and disposal, working with cultures, handling glassware and dissecting tools, and care of animals in the classroom, are included.

Field Trip Guidelines

This section discusses the development and implementation of field trips. Safety guidelines, a field trip checklist, and follow-up suggestions are included.

Unit and Chapter Discussions

This section presents a general overview of each unit and a summary of the main facts and concepts of each chapter. Several teaching strategies and activities are suggested for each chapter. Answers to the Section Review questions and Reviews of Facts and Concepts, as well as answers to the questions in the Observations and Conclusions section of each Laboratory Investigation, are provided. Teaching aids for the Extensions and Applications and Laboratory Investigations are also included.

Annotated Student Text

The Annotated Teacher's Edition provides answers printed in red for in-text questions and any questions posed in captions. Suggestions for review, discussion, or activities are also printed in red. Annotations referring to assigning Extensions and Applications and Laboratory Investigations are provided. The suggestions in the annotations may be modified to suit individual teaching situations and styles.

Laboratory Manual and Annotated Teacher's Edition

This consumable text provides 48 additional Laboratory Investigations correlated to the chapters in *Prentice-Hall Biology*. These Laboratory Investigations are designed to reinforce the concepts discussed in the student text. The investigations are more detailed and extensive than the Laboratory Investigations presented in the student text; however, all the equipment and materials required to complete the investigations may be easily obtained.

Each investigation includes a *Problem*, which is stated in the form of a question, a short introduction, a *Purpose*, which summarizes the aim of the investigation, a list of *Materials*, a step-by-step *Pro-*cedure, and an *Observations and Conclusions* section to help students record data and formulate conclusions based on the results of the investigation. All investigations also include suggested supplemental activities under the heading *For Further Investigation*. The activities listed in the For Further Investigation section may be used either in addition to the original Laboratory Investigation or instead of the original investigation.

Test Bank with Answer Key

The Test Bank is a complete evaluation program for *Prentice-Hall Biology*. The Test Bank is composed of 48 chapter tests. All test items are keyed to the Chapter Objectives listed in the student text.

The chapter tests are divided into three sections: *Vocabulary*, *Facts and Concepts*, and *Critical Thinking and Application*. There are more than 1500 questions, some with many parts, that provide more than 2400 individual items. Each test includes matching, multiple-choice, short-answer, and essay questions. The test items may be used to compose unit tests and final examinations.

READING AND LANGUAGE DEVELOPMENT IN SCIENCE

Using Prentice-Hall Biology Effectively

Students should feel comfortable about using *Prentice-Hall Biology*. Before beginning the course, devote some time to a discussion of the parts of the student text. Adequate preparation will reduce students' frustration in learning to use the text and will alert students to the special features that make *Prentice-Hall Biology* interesting and easy to read. Explain to the students that proper use of the textbook will make their study of biology more rewarding.

First, identify and locate for the students each of the parts of the text—the table of contents, the Reference Section, the chapters and units, the Glossary, and the Index. Make sure that the students know how to use each of these parts.

After you have explained the parts of the text, point out the features that appear in each chapter—the Chapter Objectives, the introduction, the section headings and subheadings, the Chapter Summary, the Chapter Vocabulary, and the Suggested Readings. Explain the usefulness of each of these features. In particular, you may want to stress that the various headings within each chapter can be used as an outline for the chapter. Other features that may be mentioned include boldface terms, phonetic pro-nunciations, Career and Close-up features, Laboratory Investigations, and Perspectives in Biology.

To find out whether the students understand how to use the text effectively, use questions and exercises such as the following:
1. Into how many units is the book divided? How many chapters?
2. What information is given in the Glossary?
3. How would you find out on what pages a discussion of flowers is located?
4. Why are some terms printed in boldface type?
5. Where would you find a list of the important terms in a chapter?
6. How many quarts in a liter? Where would you find this information?
7. Where would you find a list of careers?
8. Write the phonetic pronunciations of different scientific terms on the chalkboard. Have the students pronounce these terms.
9. Write a list of index topics on the chalkboard. Have the students find the pages on which these topics are discussed.

Vocabulary Development in Biology

The language used in the basic sciences of chemistry, physics, earth science, and biology includes what is probably the most difficult vocabulary in the secondary curriculum. The language of science is precise; there are no simple equivalents or synonyms for scientific terms. Students must appreciate and be able to cope with the inflexible and specialized vocabulary used in the sciences.

Vocabulary development is very important in the study of biology. When students have difficulty understanding vocabulary, they often lose interest in content. Biology teachers can do much to create interest in new words. Some ideas to help develop vocabulary follow.

1. Many biological terms are derived from Latin and Greek words. Students should be encouraged to research the meanings of basic root words, prefixes, and suffixes. Some words have fascinating histories that make the words easier to remember.
2. Use word associations to aid in the development of word-recognition skills. When using new words, try to relate them to words or concepts that are familiar to students.
3. Develop crossword puzzles, word-search puzzles, and acrostics to reinforce new science vocabulary.
4. Pronounce all new words and repeat the new terms in your lessons. Show students how to use the pronunciation key located at the beginning of the Glossary to read the phonetic pronunciations given in the text and Glossary.
5. Have students write unfamiliar words and their definitions on index cards or list them in a notebook. Students should include in their lists all the vocabulary words in the Chapter Vocabulary at the end of each chapter of the student text. Definitions may be taken either from the text itself or from the Glossary.

Reading Skills in Biology

Reading skills are central to the acquisition of information in most courses. Competence in science assumes the ability to comprehend handbooks, almanacs, encyclopedias, current scientific periodicals, and, of course, the science textbook. Because of the unfamiliar technical vocabulary of science, students have more difficulty reading in biology and the other sciences than they have in other subjects. Reading in science also presents other difficulties. Students must be able to isolate and organize basic scientific facts, to form hypotheses based on these facts, to develop and conduct experiments, and to formulate conclusions.

In biology, students should be provided with experiences and investigations that will enable them to develop problem-solving skills that are related to or dependent upon reading skills. Following are examples of problem-solving skills in science and the corresponding reading skills.

Science Problem-Solving Skill	Corresponding Reading Skill
Observing	Discriminating shapes and sounds
	Discriminating symbols and accents
Identifying	Recognizing letters, words, common prefixes, suffixes, and base terms
	Naming objects, events, and persons
Describing	Isolating and enumerating important characteristics
	Using appropriate terminology
	Using synonyms
	Comparing and contrasting characteristics
	Sequencing
	Arranging ideas
	Considering multiple factors
Designing Investigations	Asking questions
	Looking for potential relationships
	Following organized procedures
	Reviewing prior experiences
	Developing outlines
Collecting Data	Taking notes
	Surveying reference materials
	Using several parts of text or reference materials
	Recording data in a systematic fashion
	Developing precision and accuracy
Interpreting Data	Recognizing cause/effect relationships
	Organizing facts
	Summarizing new information
	Reasoning inductively and deductively
Communicating Results	Using graphic arts
	Logically arranging information in graphs and tables

	Sequencing ideas
	Acquiring knowledge of technical vocabulary
	Illuminating significant factors
Developing Conclusions	Generalizing
	Analyzing critically
	Evaluating information
	Recognizing main concepts and ideas
	Applying information to other areas or situations

An analysis of various science textbooks reveals that most contain specialized patterns of writing. Students must be aware of these unique patterns, which call for special approaches and different combinations of skills.

Classification In this pattern, living things are classified according to general headings and subdivisions. In recognizing this pattern, students will gain an insight into the logical organization of biological ideas.

Explanation of a Technical Process Usually, such an explanation is supported by diagrams, tables, or graphs that must be consulted repeatedly during the process of reading the text.

Cause and Effect In a cause-and-effect pattern, the student is given information that explains why certain things happen. To best develop these skills, students should first read to recognize causes and effects and then reread to determine how and why the causes had the effects they did.

Instructions for Conducting an Investigation or Experiment This pattern consists of following explicit directions, making observations, explaining what happens, and developing conclusions.

Scientific Method This pattern involves problem-solving situations that take the reader through a series of investigations conducted by one or several persons.

Writing in the Biology Classroom

Developing good writing skills is as important as developing good reading skills. Both are essential for effective communication. While using the *Prentice-Hall Biology* text, students will have frequent opportunities to display and develop their writing skills. The Laboratory Investigations and many of the Extensions and Applications require students to record information or write reports based upon their observations or research. The Section Reviews and

Reviews of Facts and Concepts are included not only for reinforcement and evaluation but also as opportunities to develop writing skills. Some suggestions for developing writing skills in science follow.

1. Students should answer questions in complete sentences.
2. Students should take notes on text material, lectures, discussions, and teacher and student demonstrations. These notes should summarize the information in a logical form.
3. Students should know why they are taking notes—to be able to answer questions, to write a report, to write a summary, to capture major concepts and ideas, to study for a test, or to prepare to do a Laboratory Investigation.
4. If students are taking notes from a chapter reading, they should read each paragraph and write down the main idea in their own words. They should also jot down the details that support the main idea.
5. Instruct the students to listen carefully to the titles or topics of lectures and discussions. Clearly identify the broad topics so that students can listen for main ideas and specific supporting details.
6. Emphasize that students should not attempt to copy every word of a lecture or reading; they should simply note key words.
7. Use signal words such as "first," "second," "third," "finally," "in summary," "next," "therefore," and "for example" during lectures.

Writing a Research Paper

A research project can lead to disciplined inquiry techniques that will serve science students throughout their academic careers and even in their everyday lives. Following are the basic steps to be followed in preparing a research paper.

1. Select a topic to be used as the basis of the report. Clearly state and define the topic.
2. Choose a central theme. State a concise title for the report.
3. Plan the project. Establish target dates for each phase of the project.
4. Plan a general outline.
5. Gather information. Index cards may be used to list and organize topics. Use the headings of the outline to key in information. *Note: Encourage students to use different kinds of references, such as magazines, books, newspapers, and encyclopedias. Suggest that students write to an appropriate agency or group for up-to-date information.*
6. Revise the outline, preparing a more detailed outline that can be used as a guide when writing a rough draft.
7. The final draft should include the following parts.

Title The title should concisely state the topic of the paper.

Introduction State the problem, clearly defining the topic.

Discussion The body of the report should be presented. Charts, tables, and graphs should be included when necessary.

Conclusions Summarize the results. Present facts that are significant to the conclusion.

Footnotes Include the author, title, place and date of publication, and page numbers for each reference.

Bibliography List alphabetically all the references used in writing the paper.

Writing a Laboratory Report

When writing a biology laboratory report, students should keep scientific method in mind. The following format is suggested; however, other formats may also be used.

Title State the name of the laboratory report or investigation.

Purpose State the problem. Describe the purpose of the investigation.

Gathering Known Information Make use of library reference books, filmstrips, periodicals, and other available materials.

Stating a Hypothesis Be sure the hypothesis supports the known information.

Materials and Methods List the materials that were used. Explain how the work was done, how data were gathered, how the experiment was designed, and what type of control was used. ***Note: Stress to students that anyone reading this section should be able to duplicate the experiment.***

Observations Present all observations made during the investigation. Prepare charts, tables, graphs, or diagrams to organize data.

Conclusions Based on the observations, present a conclusion or conclusions. The conclusions should either support or not support the hypothesis. The conclusions should also relate to the purpose.

Speaking in the Biology Classroom

The *Prentice-Hall Biology* program offers many opportunities to develop communication skills. When students are given the opportunity to express their thoughts orally or to interpret or comment upon the ideas of others, oral expression becomes an important aid to learning.

Presentations

Have students make oral presentations to their classmates about topics related to chapter sections. Students may also give oral presentations coupled with demonstrations concerning the results obtained from Laboratory Investigations, Reviews of Facts and Concepts, and Extensions and Applications.

Class Discussions

Encourage students to participate in class discussions. To guide the discussions, pose questions that reflect the various levels of performance objectives for each chapter and unit.

The following suggestions will help increase the participation of students who have difficulty in expressing themselves verbally in the classroom.
1. Give rules for class discussion.
2. Encourage students to ask questions in class.
3. Wait for students to respond (about three to five seconds). Do not call on the first student to raise his or her hand.
4. Ask some questions that call for short answers.
5. Where necessary, provide a hint, such as beginning the sentence for the student.
6. Help students who are reluctant to speak by addressing small groups within the class.

Panel Discussions

Students should be involved in panel discussions of ideas, which may come from Extensions and Applications or Perspectives in Biology features. The panel discussion may take the form of a debate. Although the art of debating is not new, its potential for dealing with controversial issues has not been realized fully in the science classroom. Classroom debating or panel discussions carried out in a friendly and noncompetitive way can have a number of benefits, such as stimulating critical thinking and logical processes, encouraging research and resourcefulness, increasing awareness of various world problems, clarifying values, instilling an inquisitive attitude, developing communication skills, and developing confidence and self-esteem.

Listening in the Biology Classroom

The ability to listen attentively and critically is crucial to success in the classroom. Good listening skills improve students' comprehension of subject matter and help develop operational understanding of basic science concepts. Good listening skills also increase students' general language facility.

Listening skills should be developed concurrently with speaking skills. Encourage good listening habits in students by being a good listener yourself. Wait after asking a question to allow the students to think about the question and to formulate a response. If no student offers a response to the question, rephrase it. Also, alternate between convergent (closed-ended) and divergent (open-ended) questions to allow for the development of more diverse thinking skills among students.

Listening constitutes a major portion of the communication process. To help students develop good listening skills, always establish motivation for every lesson and Laboratory Investigation. Give immediate and frequent positive feedback in response to appropriate behavior. Be sure that students understand the reasons for listening, such as the need to be able to follow directions, especially safety precautions in a laboratory. Encourage students to listen to questions asked by others in the class.

As a follow-up to these processes the teacher should provide opportunities for students to participate in activities that build on and develop concepts acquired during the lesson. These activities may include writing, reading, small-group discussions, and individual projects. Such types of activities are found in the Extensions and Applications feature provided in each chapter.

TEACHING AND SCHEDULING GUIDES

Teachers should be responsive to the requirements of particular situations and the needs of individual students. Modern educators are increasingly aware of the need for individualization of instruction. The continual growth of a mass educational system, however, makes individualization difficult to implement effectively in the classroom environment.

As a teacher of *Prentice-Hall Biology*, you will find that the program incorporates a flexible and manageable approach to teaching biology. *Prentice-Hall Biology* presents the facts and concepts of biology and teaches the necessary skills through chapter sections and special features that are adaptable to the diverse needs of students. A scheduling guide for low-level, average/college preparatory, and accelerated classes is provided here for reference.

Teaching a Low-Level Biology Class

The following guide offers some suggestions for instruction that will be helpful when teaching a course in biology for students who read below grade level.

Instructional Approach For each chapter, spend some class time on directed, individualized reading to help students with reading and comprehension problems. Use a slow, steady instructional pace, allowing sufficient class time for discussions and answering students' questions. Use daily reading assignments for homework. Provide daily review, including some motivational quizzes on the previous day's assignments. Have the students use the subheadings of the chapters as a basic outline. Encourage note-taking and suggest that students keep a vocabulary list of difficult words to assist vocabulary retention. The majority of class time should be devoted to reading and discussing chapter sections. Students should take active part in class discussions. Students should be given some time during each class period for supervised study.

Topics and Sections Emphasize the basic concepts treated in each chapter. Select relevant sections from the chapter and omit others (see the scheduling guide on pages T-13–T-19).

Laboratory Work Activity-centered learning situations are particularly effective. It is recommended that each class period include some laboratory activities, but such activities must be well planned. Specific instructions are necessary for successful results. Instructions for laboratory work may have to be read and discussed with the class. Students should be asked to investigate on their own, but they should be guided when necessary to prevent frustration. "Hands-on" laboratory activities will encourage students and sustain their interest. In-text Laboratory Investigations and basic investigations from the Laboratory Manual may be used.

Section Review Questions Assign Section Review questions during class time; have students work individually or in small groups to help develop cooperative learning skills. The questions also can be used as homework assignments. Students may answer questions orally or submit written responses.

Review of Facts and Concepts Answers to Reviews of Facts and Concepts should be written or discussed during class time. Omit questions that are above the ability of students. The questions can be used to initiate class discussion or to review for quizzes and chapter tests. Refer to the Chapter Vocabulary section for the key words of the chapter. Encourage students to learn the basic prefixes and suffixes of biological terminology.

Extensions and Applications Select projects that are appropriate for students' ability levels. Have students give brief oral reports. This type of activity will increase self-esteem and will result in greater achievement.

Suggested Readings Help students develop reading skills and learn to pronounce new words. Use low-level science reading materials.

Careers and Close-ups Refer to the suggestions for teaching an average biology class on this page.

Perspectives in Biology Have students read aloud from Perspectives and follow up with class discussion. Use Viewpoints that are activity-oriented.

Evaluation Give frequent short quizzes covering basic facts and concepts in one or several sections. Eliminate full-period testing as much as possible. Allow sufficient time for review before administering chapter or unit tests, which should be short. Shorter tests will improve achievement and encourage a positive self-concept. Avoid essay tests. Concentrate on direct-recall and short-answer tests. Test a few basic concepts at a time.

Teaching an Average Biology Class

The following guide offers some suggestions for instruction that will be helpful when teaching an average or college preparatory course in biology for students who read at or above grade level.

Instructional Approach Individualize instruction wherever possible; have students complete all Chapter Objectives; provide time for discussion of chapter sections, focusing on the Chapter Objectives. Students will usually acquire basic concepts on their own. Class time should be devoted to oral review of more difficult concepts. Individual projects can be assigned where appropriate. Gear projects to students' interests and ability levels.

Topics and Sections Introduce each chapter with a broad survey of all the major topics of the chapter. Advise students of the minimum requirements—Laboratory Investigations to be completed, Section Review questions and Review of Facts and Concepts questions to be answered, and assignments from Extensions and Applications or Suggested Readings to be completed.

Laboratory Work Assign in-text Laboratory Investigations and laboratory experiments from the *Prentice-Hall Biology* Laboratory Manual. Laboratory Investigations may be done during class time or during laboratory time. Select laboratory groups on the basis of students' cognitive and social abilities.

Section Review Questions Require written responses for all questions as homework. Devote class time to discussion of more difficult questions or questions raised by students.

Review of Facts and Concepts Use selected questions to initiate class discussion, which will relate facts to key ideas and expand upon basic concepts. Discussion of these questions may be useful in developing individual problem-solving and critical-thinking skills.

Extensions and Applications Extensions and Applications can be used as individual activities to further develop and apply chapter concepts. They may also be used for library research or laboratory investigations. Develop class or small-group discussions to stimulate problem-solving and critical-thinking skills and to broaden concepts.

Suggested Readings Some students may wish to investigate a specific area of interest. Encourage oral or written reports, panel presentations, and research papers. Also suggest that students read other books, periodicals, and newspapers for current science news topics.

Careers and Close-ups Use Careers and Close-ups to develop career awareness and knowledge about recent developments in science. Students should be encouraged to identify persons in the school community who work in a particular field of science.

Perspectives in Biology Use Perspectives to discuss relevant issues in biology; develop group discussions. These features are designed to illustrate how major biological concepts are applied to everyday problems and issues.

Evaluation Use frequent short quizzes and occasional long tests. Administer quizzes after one or more sections of a chapter have been studied and discussed. Administer a test after the completion of each chapter. Unit tests should be administered after a comprehensive review of each chapter in a unit.

Teaching an Accelerated Biology Class

The following guide offers some suggestions for instruction that will be helpful when using *Prentice-*

Hall Biology to teach an accelerated course in biology for students who read above grade level.

Instructional Approach All chapter objectives should be completed. All topics and sections should be covered. Emphasis should be placed on individualized learning of the ideas and concepts presented. Instruction time can be devoted to increasing student involvement through lectures, large-group and small-group discussions, and talks by visiting lecturers. Students should spend most of their course time on class presentation, research or independent projects, and laboratory investigations.

Topics and Sections If possible, all chapters should be covered. Topics of special interest to students or of unusual difficulty should be expanded. Special emphasis should be given to the Laboratory Investigations and Extensions and Applications provided at the end of each chapter.

Laboratory Work Students may present oral or written reports based upon the in-text Laboratory Investigations. Students should be assigned appropriate Laboratory Investigations from the *Prentice-Hall Biology* Laboratory Manual. Laboratory work should be highly individualized and should include library research. Students can also design and conduct their own experiments.

Section Review Questions Use Section Review questions for homework assignments, class discussion, and review. Supplement them with more detailed questions on related issues. Spend less time with drill-and-practice activities and more time developing individual problem-solving skills and critical thinking. Ask thought-provoking questions that will assist students in dealing effectively with new subject matter.

Review of Facts and Concepts Students should answer Review of Facts and Concepts questions on their own. These questions can be used to check comprehension of the key facts and concepts presented in each chapter. Select several questions from each chapter for class or small-group discussion. Use others as written homework assignments.

Extensions and Applications Use Extensions and Applications as individual assignments to aid students in extending and applying concepts developed in each chapter. These features may be used as springboards for individual or small-group projects, which can either be discussed in class or be presented as oral or written reports.

Suggested Readings The sources listed in the Suggested Readings sections are valuable references and resources for extending students' understanding of key concepts presented in the chapters. Have students select articles, books, or periodicals of interest for supplemental reading; or assign readings for oral and written reports and class discussion.

Careers and Close-ups Assign the careers and ideas presented in the Close-ups to individual students for further research. Individual projects can be conducted to find out more about a particular biological-science career. Invite a biologist, a botanist, or a practitioner of one of the other careers featured to speak to the class.

Perspectives in Biology Assign Perspectives for individual reading and use them as a springboard for class or small-group discussion or even for formal debates. Encourage students to do further research on particular topics that interest them.

Evaluation Give quizzes and full-period chapter and unit tests that include both multiple-choice and essay questions. Correlate test questions with Chapter Objectives, and include questions based on student laboratory experiences.

Suggested Scheduling and Planning Guide for Prentice-Hall Biology

The following scheduling guide is designed to assist in short-range and long-range planning of a balanced biology course for different ability levels. The scheduling guide suggests the number of class sessions, including laboratory sessions, for each chapter. It assumes 180 class sessions per school year, the equivalent of approximately 160 hours of combined classroom/laboratory instruction.

How much time is spent on each topic or section in a low-level class should depend upon students' abilities and needs and the discretion of the teacher. Emphasis should be placed on activity-oriented experiences rather than lectures. Students in an average class should be able to complete the course in about 180 days. Use optional topics and sections for discussion based upon students' abilities, interests, and needs. Students in an accelerated class should be able to complete the course in about 170 days. The remaining 10 days can be used for independent projects, additional laboratory work, or group projects approved by the instructor for class presentation.

The guide includes essential and optional topics or sections plus suggested laboratory topics. Suggested in-text Laboratory Investigations and Laboratory Manual investigations that relate to the topics and sections listed are provided. A basic biology curriculum will include the sections designated as essential topics. The optional sections contain material that expands and develops a particular concept or provides additional information that helps to enhance the understanding and appreciation of biology.

Laboratory Investigations, or parts of Laboratory Investigations, can be assigned at your discretion to suit particular circumstances.

KEY

LL: Low-level students
AVG: Average/college preparatory students
ACC: Accelerated students

ST: Student text
LM: Laboratory Manual

Chapter	Class Sessions	Topics/Sections		Lab Topics/Suggested Investigations
		Essential	Optional	
1	LL: 4	All sections	None	Scientific investigation: ST-1 The microscope: LM-1, Parts A and B
	AVG: 4 ACC: 3	All sections	None	Scientific investigation: ST-1 The microscope: LM-1, Parts A, B, and C
2	LL, AVG: 4 ACC: 3	All sections	None	Characteristics of living things: ST-2; LM-2
3	LL, AVG: 4 ACC: 3	All sections	None	Classification: ST-3; LM-3
4	LL: 4	States of and changes in matter Atoms and elements Compounds, molecules, and mixtures	Organic compounds	Mixtures and compounds: ST-4
	AVG, ACC: 4	All sections	None	Same as LL Organic compounds: LM-4
5	LL: 4	Cells: size, shape, organization, structure, and function	Prokaryotes and eukaryotes	Cell structures: ST-5; LM-5
	AVG, ACC: 4	All sections	None	Cell structures: ST-5; LM-5
6	LL: 4	Cell energy Homeostasis and passive transport	Homeostasis and active transport	Energy and maintenance of cells: ST-6; LM-6, Part A
	AVG, ACC: 4	All sections	None	Energy and maintenance of cells: ST-6; LM-6, Parts A and B
7	LL: 4	Photosynthesis and respiration	Fermentation	Photosynthesis: LM-7, Part A

Chapter	Class Sessions	Topics/Sections		Lab Topics/Suggested Investigations
		Essential	**Optional**	
	AVG: 4 ACC: 3	All sections	None	Photosynthesis: LM-7, Parts A and B Fermentation: ST-7
8	LL: 4	Cell reproduction Reproduction of organisms	Nucleic acids Protein synthesis	Mitosis: ST-8
	AVG: 4 ACC: 3	All sections	None	Same as LL Nucleic acids: LM-8
9	LL: 4	Basic Mendelian genetics Concepts of heredity	Probability Punnett squares	Simple monohybrid genetic problems: ST-9, Part A; LM-9, Part A
	AVG, ACC: 4	All sections	None	Genetics problems and probability: ST-9; LM-9, Parts A, B, and C
10	LL: 4	Chromosome theory Human genetics: multiple alleles, inherited diseases	Nature of genes	Human genetics: ST-10
	AVG, ACC: 4	All sections	None	Same as LL Genes and chromosomes: LM-10
11	LL: 3 AVG, ACC: 3	Plant and animal breeding	Genetic breeding	Plant and animal breeding: ST-11; LM-11
12	LL, AVG, ACC: 4	All sections	None	Variation and natural selection: ST-12; LM-12
13	LL: 3	Human and primate characteristics Neanderthal and Cro-Magnon cultures	Detailed discussion of biological history of human beings	Comparison of primates: ST-13; LM-13, Part B
	AVG: 3	Human and primate characteristics Brief discussion of biological history of human beings	Detailed discussion of biological history of human beings	Comparison of primates: ST-13; LM-13, Parts A and B
	ACC: 3	All sections	None	Same as AVG
14	LL: 4	Discovery of viruses Viral anatomy: plant and animal Viral diseases	Lytic cycle	Bacteriophage structure: ST-14

Chapter	Class Sessions	Topics/Sections		Lab Topics/Suggested Investigations
		Essential	**Optional**	
	AVG, ACC: 4	All sections	None	Same as LL Lytic cycle: LM-14
15	LL: 4	Characteristics of bacteria Life functions in bacteria	DNA transfer in bacteria	Classification of bacteria and bacterial growth: ST-15
	AVG, ACC: 4	All sections	None	Classification and characteristics of bacteria: ST-15 Bacterial growth: ST-15; LM-15
16	LL: 4	Sarcodines Paramecia	Flagellates Sporozoans	Structure and function of *Paramecium*: ST-16, Part B Food-getting and locomotion in *Amoeba* and *Blepharisma*: LM-16, Parts A and B
	AVG, ACC: 4	All sections	None	Structure, function, and growth of protozoans: ST-16; LM-16, Parts A, B, C
17	LL, AVG, ACC: 4	All sections	None	Disease transmission and prevention: ST-17; LM-17
18	LL: 5	Different types of algae Fungi Lichens	Slime molds	Structure of algae and fungi: ST-18; LM-18
	AVG: 5 ACC: 4	All sections	None	Structure and function of algae, fungi, and slime mold: ST-18; LM-18
19	LL: 2	Mosses Ferns	Liverworts Club mosses Horsetails	Structure of mosses and ferns: ST-19
	AVG, ACC: 2	All sections	None	Structure and identification of mosses and ferns: ST-19 Liverworts: LM-19
20	LL: 5	Seed-bearing plants: external features and specialized tissues	Detailed sections on angiosperms and gymnosperms	External structure of a gymnosperm: ST-20
	AVG: 5 ACC: 4	All sections	None	Characteristics of seed-bearing plants: ST-20; LM-20 Plant tissues: LM-20

Chapter	Class Sessions	Topics/Sections		Lab Topics/Suggested Investigations
		Essential	**Optional**	
21	LL: 3 AVG, ACC: 3	All sections	None	Root and stem structure: ST-21; LM-21 Root and stem structure and function: ST-21; LM-21
22	LL: 3	Leaf characteristics General discussion of photosynthesis	Leaf processes	Leaf anatomy: ST-22; LM-22
	AVG, ACC: 3	All sections	None	Leaf anatomy and physiology: ST-22; LM-22
23	LL: 4	Flowering plants: sexual reproduction	Artificial vegetative propagation	Anatomy of a flower: ST-23 Types of fruits and seeds: LM-23 Seed dispersal: LM-23
	AVG, ACC: 4	All sections	None	Same as LL
24	LL: 2	All sections	None	Phototropism and geotropism: ST-24
	AVG, ACC: 2			Same as LL Plant hormones: LM-24
25	LL: 4	Sponges Jellyfishes Hydras	Corals and sea anemones	External anatomy of a hydra: ST-25 External features of a sponge: LM-25
	AVG: 4	All sections	None	Anatomy and physiology of a hydra, hydra food-getting response: ST-25 Structure of a sponge: LM-25
	ACC: 4	All sections	None	Same as AVG Spicules: LM-25
26	LL: 4	Segmented worms	Flatworms Roundworms	Anatomy and physiology of an earthworm: LM-26
	AVG, ACC: 4	All sections	None	Same as LL Flatworms: ST-26
27	LL: 4	Mollusks General characteristics of echinoderms	Detailed explanation of physiology of echinoderms	Anatomy and physiology of a clam: ST-27

| Chapter | Class Sessions | Topics/Sections | | Lab Topics/Suggested Investigations |
		Essential	Optional	
	AVG, ACC: 4	All sections	None	Anatomy and physiology of a clam and a starfish: ST-27; LM-27
28	LL: 4	Crustaceans	Myriapods	External anatomy of a crayfish: LM-28 Daphnia: ST-28
	AVG, ACC: 4	All sections	None	Anatomy and physiology of a crayfish: LM-28 Daphnia: ST-28
29	LL: 4	Insects Difference between spiders and insects	Detailed discussion of arachnids	Anatomy of a grasshopper: LM-29 Ant colony: ST-29
	AVG, ACC: 4	All sections	None	Anatomy and physiology of a grasshopper: LM-29 Social insects: ST-29
30	LL: 4	Classification of fishes Bony fishes	Cartilaginous fishes	Respiration rate in fishes: ST-30 External anatomy of a perch: LM-30
	AVG, ACC: 4	All sections	None	Same as LL External and internal anatomy and physiology of a perch: LM-30
31	LL, AVG, ACC: 4	All sections	None	Metamorphosis in frogs: ST-31 Anatomy and physiology of a frog: LM-31
32	LL, AVG: 4	All sections	None	Classification of reptiles: ST-32 External features of a lizard: LM-32, Part A
	ACC: 4	All sections	None	Same as LL Anatomy and response of a lizard: LM-32
33	LL, AVG, ACC: 4	All sections	None	Feathers: ST-33 Bird adaptations: LM-33
34	LL: 6	All sections	None	Classification and characteristics of mammals: ST-34

Chapter	Class Sessions	Topics/Sections		Lab Topics/Suggested Investigations
		Essential	**Optional**	
	AVG: 6	All sections	None	Classification and comparison of mammals: ST-34
	ACC: 6	All sections	None	Same as LL and AVG Anatomy and physiology of a fetal pig: LM-34
35	LL, AVG: 4	All sections	None	Structure of a bone: ST-35 Types of muscles: LM-35, Part C
	ACC: 5	All sections	None	Same as LL and AVG Movement, bones, and muscles: LM-35, Parts A, B, and C
36	LL, AVG: 4	All sections	None	Absorption and surface area: ST-36 Starch digestion: LM-36, Part A
	ACC: 4	All sections	None	Same as LL and AVG Protein and fat digestion: LM-36, Parts A, B, and C
37	LL, AVG: 4	All sections	None	Blood circulation: ST-37 Composition of blood: LM-37, Part A
	ACC: 4	All sections	None	Same as LL and AVG Blood typing: LM-37, Part B
38	LL, AVG: 4	All sections	None	Pulse and respiration rate: ST-38
	ACC: 4	All sections	None	Same as LL and AVG Mechanics of breathing: LM-38
39	LL: 4	All sections	None	Energy needs and caloric intake: ST-39 Water and minerals in food: LM-39, Part A
	AVG, ACC: 4	All sections	None	Same as LL Vitamin C in food: LM-39, Parts A and B
40	LL, AVG, ACC: 3	All sections	None	Effects of adrenaline: ST-40 Hormones and growth: LM-40

Chapter	Class Sessions	Topics/Sections		Lab Topics/Suggested Investigations
		Essential	**Optional**	
41	LL: 4	All sections	None	Senses: LM-41, Parts A and B
	AVG, ACC: 4	All sections	None	Senses: LM-41, Parts A-D Reaction time: ST-41
42	LL: 4	All sections	None	Human growth: ST-42
	AVG, ACC: 4	All sections	None	Same as LL Embryology: LM-42
43	LL: 2	All sections	None	Human behavior: ST-43 Reflexes: LM-43, Part A
	AVG, ACC: 2	All sections	None	Human behavior: ST-43 Conditioning and habits: LM-43
44	LL, AVG: 3 ACC: 2	All sections	None	Alcohol, Drugs, and Tobacco: ST-44; LM-44
45	LL, AVG: 4 ACC: 3	All sections	None	Environmental factors Cycles in nature: ST-45; Abiotic factors: LM-45
46	LL, AVG, ACC: 3	All sections	None	Population density and growth: ST-46; LM-46
47	LL: 3	All sections	None	Climate: ST-47 Distribution: LM-47, Part A
	AVG, ACC: 3	All sections	None	Same as LL Distribution of organisms: LM-47
48	LL, AVG, ACC: 2	All sections	None	Pollution problems: ST-48; LM-48

SAFETY STANDARDS

In a biology program, students usually have many opportunities to engage in laboratory investigations and similar activities. Involvement in such activities requires strict attention to laboratory safety. Safety should be an integral part of the planning, preparation, and implementation of every biology program.

With careful planning, most of the potential dangers in an activity-oriented biology program can be coped with safely. The responsibility for the enforce-ment of safety rules in the biology classroom and laboratory is, of course, the teacher's, but students must do their part by following the rules. Careless-ness and a negative or apathetic attitude toward safety are the major causes of accidents.

The biology instructor is in a unique position to assist students in understanding and appreciating the importance of safety. Properly conducted class-room activities, experiments, and demonstrations can communicate to students how to anticipate and cope with problems that may arise. Good instruction can establish an educational environment in which safety awareness and practices become part of the lives of students.

For each Laboratory Investigation or activity, the instructor should provide the following:

- A pre-laboratory description of the investigation to be performed, including the necessary cautions and a discussion of the safety procedures and practices that should be followed
- Constant supervision of the students during laboratory activities
- A post-laboratory discussion of the investigation, including a review of the safety precautions taken

Guidelines for Using Materials and Equipment

To prevent accidents, both teacher and students must understand and practice recommended safety procedures. The following general guidelines may be helpful in establishing safety standards and procedures in your laboratory. You may want to add guidelines or modify these guidelines according to the regulations and policies of the state or school system in which you teach.

1. Whenever necesessary, perform an experiment or demonstration before allowing students to replicate the the activity. Look for possible hazards. Alert students to potential dangers. *Note: Safety instructions should be given each time an experiment is begun.*
2. Good housekeeping is essential in maintaining safe laboratory conditions.
3. Students' attitude toward safety is most important. Students should not fear doing experiments or using reagents and equipment, but they should respect them as sources of potential hazards.
4. Students should not perform unauthorized experiments. Students must never conduct experiments in the laboratory alone.
5. Teachers should set good safety examples when conducting demonstrations and experiments.
6. Exercise great care when smelling fumes or chemical materials in containers. Gently wave your hand over the opening of the container. This motion will cause the fumes to move toward your nose.
7. Use a suction bulb to fill pipettes with chemical reagents. Do not use mouth suction.
8. Long hair and loose clothing should be properly confined. Laboratory aprons should be worn.
9. Proper eye protection (goggles) should be worn by all persons performing, supervising, or observing activities that involve potential hazards to the eye.

10. Contact lenses should not be worn in the laboratory.
11. Use proper illumination for the microscope. *Caution: Do not use reflected sunlight.*
12. Make certain that hot plates and open burners are turned off when not in use.
13. All work surfaces in the laboratory should be thoroughly cleaned after each use.
14. Frequent safety inspections of the laboratory should be conducted. Any hazards should be reported in writing to the school principal.
15. One or more fire blankets, first aid kits, and fully charged fire extinguishers should be located in each laboratory/classroom.
16. Specimens preserved in formalin should be thoroughly washed before being handled. When removing specimens from formalin solution, wear rubber gloves or use forceps or tongs. Use goggles to protect against splashes.
17. Potassium cyanide should never be used as the killing agent in insect-killing jars. If alcohol, chloroform, or ether is used as the killing agent, students should be warned of its flammability and toxicity.

Cultures

During the study of microscopic organisms, students should have the opportunity to observe and culture these organisms. Some suggested guidelines for the storage, disposal, and handling of cultures follow.

1. Only nonpathogenic bacteria should be used in the classroom. Treat all microorganism cultures used in microbiological studies as if they were pathogenic.
2. Petri dish cultures should be sealed with tape.
3. Bacterial cultures should be killed before the petri dishes are washed. Most cultures can be killed by heating.
4. Contaminated culture media should be sterilized with a strong disinfectant and washed with a strong cleaning agent.
5. Always flame wire loops both before and after transferring microorganisms.

Storage of Chemicals

Proper storage of chemicals is important in the biology laboratory. Proper storage provides protection from fire and contamination, security against unauthorized access, and protection for the outside environment. Some suggested guidelines for storage follow.

1. Liquids should never be stored above eye level.
2. Large containers of toxic chemicals should be stored near the floor.
3. A recommended storage pattern is to separate inorganic from organic chemicals.
4. Storage areas should be well ventilated, dry, and cool (between 15 °C and 25 °C).

5. Flammable liquids should be isolated from oxidizing agents.
6. All jars and containers should be labeled properly. The areas in which the equipment and materials are stored should also be labeled.
7. Storage containers should not be crowded on storage shelves.
8. Inventory of all chemicals should be kept up to date.

Disposal of Chemicals

Safe and proper disposal of chemicals is important. The disposal of chemicals should be performed quickly; chemical wastes should not be permitted to accumulate. Check local and state regulations pertaining to chemical-waste disposal. The recommended general procedures for chemical disposal are listed in the *Laboratory Disposal Manual*, Manufacturing Chemists Assoc., 1825 Connecticut Avenue, N.W., Washington, DC 20009. Some general guidelines for chemical-waste disposal follow.
1. All materials disposed of by washing down the drain should be soluble in water.
2. Corrosive or caustic liquids can be disposed of by pouring the substances down the drain while flushing with copious amounts of water.
3. Flammable liquids should never be poured down the sink drain. Flammable vapors can accumulate in the plumbing and cause a serious explosion.
4. Common bases should be neutralized with dilute sulfuric acid. Wash the neutral solution down the drain with large amounts of water. Neutralize common acids with sodium carbonate, and wash them down the drain. *Caution: A neutralization reaction will give off heat.*
5. Use separate containers for flammable solid wastes and nonflammable wastes.

Glassware

Before doing any laboratory work, students should be properly instructed in the use and care of laboratory glassware. The precautions listed below should be followed when working with glassware in the laboratory.
1. Borosilicated glassware should be used in the laboratory. This type of glassware has low thermal expansion and high softening temperatures.
2. Broken or cracked glassware should be disposed of in a separate container marked "Broken Glass."
3. Use a dustpan and broom to pick up large pieces of broken glass. Wet cotton can be used to pick up small pieces of broken glass.
4. Glassware should be thoroughly cleaned after use. Students should never eat or drink from laboratory glassware.
5. Glass does not change temperature quickly. Heated glassware that has been cooling for no more than a few minutes can cause painful burns.

6. Packages of glass tubing should be carried and stored vertically. Glass tubing should never be forced into a rubber stopper.

Heating

Many investigations involve heating substances, melting substances, and evaporating liquids. Some safety guidelines that involve heating follow.
1. When heating a flask or beaker over an open flame, place the flask or beaker on a square of wire gauze resting securely on a ring clamp attached to a ringstand. *Note: Be careful while heating; the wire in the gauze produces hot spots that may break the bottom of the container.*
2. Most solids should be heated in an oven or water bath.
3. Melting is best done in a watch glass oven or in a test tube immersed in a water bath. In general, do not melt solids in test tubes. Many solids melt and vaporize within rather narrow temperature ranges and will spurt out of the test tube.
4. Use only Pyrex or other hard glass test tubes.
5. Never point the open end of a test tube toward your or another person's face when any substance is being heated in it.
6. Keep the test tube moving so that the material will heat evenly.
7. For heating the alcohol in chlorophyll-extraction experiments, use an immersion-type electric heater or a water bath heated by an electric hot plate instead of an open flame or a gas-heated water bath. *Caution: Keep open flames away from the alcohol. If the alcohol does ignite in a beaker, cover the beaker with a glass plate to extinguish the fire. If burning alcohol runs over the rim, use a fire blanket.*

Dissecting

If sharp instruments are to be used, the teacher must be sure that students are competent to use such instruments. Proper instruction will avoid accidents. Care should be taken when handling all dissection instruments.
1. Never use a scalpel, razor blade, or other cutting device that has more than one cutting edge.
2. Always cut down on a specimen against a waxed pan or similar container. Never hold a specimen in the hand while dissecting it.
3. Special care should be taken to avoid cuts and scratches when cleaning equipment.
4. Dissecting instruments and needles should be stored in a locked cabinet. Students should not remove instruments from the laboratory.

First Aid

First aid is the immediate care given to a sick or injured person before regular medical aid arrives.

The purpose of first aid is to protect rather than to treat; it is used in emergency situations where medical assistance is not immediately available. It is the responsibility of the teacher to know how to proceed in the event a student becomes ill or is injured in the classroom or laboratory. The American National Red Cross offers training in basic first aid.

The instructor should at all times operate on the premise that every accident is preventable. However, if an injury does occur, (1) promptly remove the victim from further harm, (2) proceed with appropriate first aid, and (3) report the incident to school authorities.

Establish first aid procedures to be followed in the event of an accident. All students and teachers should know the exact location of first aid kit(s), fire extinguisher(s), eyewash fountain(s), safety shower(s), and fire blanket(s). Signs should identify the location of safety equipment. Emergency instructions concerning fire, explosions, chemical reactions, spillage, and first aid procedures should be clearly posted near all storage areas. Safety posters should also be displayed in the biology laboratory.

Care of Animals in the Classroom

The observation of live animals helps students to understand life processes fully and to appreciate living things. Because most students are naturally attracted to animals and often respond to the classroom animals individually as pets, one of the most pleasant and rewarding aspects of teaching biology to students is the presence of living animals in the classroom.

Before introducing animals into the classroom, find out the policy of your local school district. Many schools require the permission of the principal to keep warm-blooded animals in a classroom and limit the time that the animals can be kept to fourteen days. In any case, all animals should be purchased from a reputable supply house. Wild animals should never be brought into the classroom; birds, raccoons, squirrels, opossums, and other wild animals may be disease carriers.

Before performing any experiment involving animals, check local and state regulations. Some states require certification before teachers are permitted to experiment with animals. The Society for the Prevention of Cruelty to Animals and/or the Humane Society should also be consulted. The HSUS pamphlet *Guiding Principles for Use of Animals in Elementary and Secondary Education* is available free from the Humane Society of the United States, 2100 L Street, N.W., Washington, DC 20037.

Safety procedures should be established to protect students from the hazards presented by classroom animals as well as to ensure the humane treatment of the animals. Indiscriminate use of animals in the classroom introduces unnecessary safety risks. The following guidelines for classroom animal use should prove helpful.

1. A science teacher or other qualified adult supervisor should assume primary responsibility for the conditions under which any study that involves live animals is carried out. If the school faculty does not include persons trained in the proper care of laboratory animals, the service of such a person should be sought on a consulting basis. Often a local veterinarian is willing to offer this kind of help.

2. Each animal study should have a clearly defined objective that relates to the teaching/learning of some scientific principle.

3. All animals used must be acquired lawfully in accordance with state and local statutes.

4. No animal studies involving anesthetic drugs, surgical procedures, pathogenic organisms, toxicological products, carcinogens, or radiation should be performed.

5. All mammals used in a classroom should be inoculated for rabies, unless purchased recently from a reliable scientific company.

6. Students should not bring their pets to the classroom for observation unless the activity has been arranged with the teacher.

7. Before an animal is brought into the classroom for observation, plans to provide proper habitat and food should be made. The animal's living quarters must be kept clean, free from contamination, and secure enough to confine the animal.

8. After an animal is no longer being used in the classroom, the cage should be thoroughly cleaned, using strong detergent and germicides. If possible, the cage should be boiled or scrubbed with very hot water.

9. Animals should be handled only if necessary and according to the particular type and habits of the animal. Special handling is required if the animal is frightened or excited, is feeding, is pregnant, or is with its young.

10. Students should scrub their hands after handling animals or a cage containing animals.

11. Students should be cautioned never to tease animals or to insert objects or their fingers through wire mesh cages. Any student bitten or scratched by an animal should report immediately to the school nurse. The animal should *not be destroyed* but should be kept until examined by authorities.

12. After a period of observation not longer than 14 days, animals should be returned to their natural environment.

13. Students should handle marine organisms carefully. Fishes, sea urchins, and mollusks can inflict painful wounds.

CONTROVERSIAL ISSUES

As with any field of endeavor, science has its controversies—controversies that spring naturally from the search for the truth about nature. These controversies are capable of being tested and resolved by scientific means, such as the development and testing of hypotheses, the performing of experiments, and the postulation, confirmation, or refutation, of theories. It is important that your students appreciate the fact that legitimate disputes among scientists exist and that such disputes tend to generate new thoughts and research, which helps promote the search for knowledge.

The presentation of topics in biology may also introduce controversies that are primarily of a social rather than a scientific nature. If topics in this text prompt discussions or questions that are essentially not part of your science curriculum, we would suggest you refer students to their social studies teachers, their parents, their religious leaders, or other more appropriate forums for the exploration of such controversies. A student should not be criticized or admonished for holding a point of view that differs from what currently is accepted by others. Factual knowledge and an open mind are the greatest guarantors of scientific progress, and we suggest that this attitude be the underlying theme of your classroom presentation of scientific topics.

The following is a list of four topics—or groups of topics—treated in this text, to which you might wish to give special attention. Page references are provided for your convenience.

1. Classification Systems (pp. 42-54). There are countless controversies among scientists regarding how living things should be classified. The controversies range from those that focus on the basic structure of the various classification systems to those involving the identification and naming of a specific organism. Both areas of controversy are dynamic, that is, ever changing. And both are functional, that is, they are designed to best fit the facts so that a better understanding of the organization of living things, and the place of each living thing in that organization, can be achieved. This text recognizes and presents a classification system structured on five kingdoms. Mention is even made of a six-kingdom system. Each of these classification systems has scientific merit. This text is organized around a five-kingdom system. Students, however, should be encouraged to explore other systems and, perhaps, prompted to invent—and logically support—alternative classification systems.

2. Evolution (pp. 15-16, 198-219). There are various scientific concepts and controversies concerning how living things evolved on our planet. However, there is virtually no dispute among scientists that the evidence so far uncovered supports the contention that living things have changed through time during the approximate 4.6 billion year history of the earth. You might point out to your students that scientists develop theories to explain or account for observed phenomena. To date, the theory of evolution best explains the observed phenomena. This theory, is, of course, capable of change and modification, as new scientific evidence emerges.

3. Drugs, Alcohol, and Tobacco (pp. 700-714). These are clearly very important topics related to the health and well-being of our nation's children. We suggest you approach these topics from a dispassionate and solidly factual and scientific point of view. Focus on scientific research and statistical evidence to shed light on the nature and danger of drugs, alcohol, and tobacco. Avoid "scare tactics" that cannot be supported by scientific findings. You may expect your students to have a wide variety of responses to the topic of drug abuse. Many may challenge values held by the adult community in regard to cigarette smoking, drinking alcoholic beverages, and using certain over-the-counter and prescription drugs. Point out that drug abuse is a problem all people face whether they are young or adults. And that, therefore, all people must work together to develop values that support health rather than undermine it.

4. Sexual Reproduction (pp. 142-143, 371-380, 678-689). The first reference is to a brief basic treatment of sexual reproduction in plants and animals. The second reference is to a discussion of plant reproduction. And the third reference is to human reproduction. In addition, sexual and asexual reproduction are discussed throughout the text as they apply to various kinds of living things. Obviously, it is impossible to teach biology without presenting discussions of one of the qualifying characteristics of living things, the ability to reproduce. In discussing sexual reproduction, you may wish to focus on the obvious biological advantages of the process, that is, the resulting diversity of offspring, which maximizes adaptability and the inheritance of positive traits. Present any supporting anatomical and physiological material in a straight-forward manner appropriate to a science classroom. The subject of human reproduction should be discussed as normally as you would discuss any other body system or process.

FIELD TRIP GUIDELINES

Field trips and outdoor activities are an essential part of the biology program. One of the most effective ways to study natural phenomena is to observe them in their own unique setting. A field trip can therefore be a valuable teaching and learning experience for the biology instructor and students. In order to make such activities safe and profitable, careful planning is required.

The instructor should have well-stated educational objectives and should conduct pre-trip preparation and effective follow-up activities and discussions. Every precaution should be taken to ensure the safety of the students and teaching personnel. Safety procedures should be taught as part of biology instruction; they should influence outside activities even when no direct supervision or control is possible. It should be kept in mind that class field trips are under school sponsorship and that the school has a responsibility for students' safety. Government agencies and private industrial or research facilities usually assume no legal liability for the safety of visitors on their premises.

Safety Guidelines

The following list of general safety guidelines can help make trips safer and more effective as teaching strategies. You may want to add other guidelines or modify these to suit your needs.

1. Visit the site yourself before the actual field trip. You should have a thorough knowledge of the area.
2. Establish rules for safe conduct before taking the trip.
3. No trip should be taken to any body of water unless at least one person is skilled in the latest methods of artificial respiration and the rules of water safety as described in first aid books such

as those developed by the American National Red Cross.
4. Water pollution is increasing in both freshwater and saltwater areas where field trips may be taken. If a student is accidentally scratched or receives a puncture wound in polluted water, first aid is required.
5. Insist upon proper dress and shoes for the terrain and weather.
6. Teachers and parents should provide supervision. The number of adults should be adequate for the size of the class. On any extensive trips, there should be at least one adult for every ten students. Students should remain under adult supervision at all times.
7. Instruct students about the potential dangers of the area, especially if the field trip is to be conducted near a lake or other body of water. Use the "buddy system."
8. A basic first aid kit should be standard equipment for any field trip. A snakebite kit should be carried if the field trip area contains poisonous snakes.
9. The proper consent forms should be completed and signed according to school policy and filed before departure. These may include parental and/or administrative (principal and teacher) consent forms.
10. Some field trips may require special equipment or materials, such as collection jars, containers, field books, and so on. Be sure these materials are gathered and packed in advance.
11. When necessary, include appropriate repellents to protect against mites, ticks, and mosquitoes.
12. It is generally safer if all students are transported by bus rather than in private vehicles.
13. If private land is used for the field trip, obtain the landowner's permission, in writing, before the trip.

UNIT AND CHAPTER DISCUSSIONS

UNIT ONE
Introduction to Biology

This unit introduces biology as the study of living things. Its theme is that, although life forms appear in remarkable diversity almost everywhere on the earth, they nevertheless exhibit basic similarities in structure and function. As students progress through this unit, they will be exposed to concepts and perform activities that will make them appreciate this theme.

The unit also presents biology as one of the major branches of science. Students discover how pure and applied research in biology differ and how each relates to everyday life. They learn how biologists use a scientific method, certain biological tools, and various techniques of measurement to conduct research. These introductory chapters also describe the achievements of the major biologists of the past. In addition, the levels of organization of life forms and the taxonomic hierarchy are presented. After completing the unit, students will have the background needed to continue their study of biology.

1 What Is Biology?

Chapter Objectives: See page 14.

Chapter Overview

For thousands of years, people have been curious about the earth's living things. This chapter introduces biology as the search for knowledge about these living things. It explains the contributions of some of the major participants in this search, such as Leeuwenhoek, Hooke, Pasteur, Darwin, Mendel, Morgan, Watson, and Crick. The chapter also identifies some of the branches of biology.

The principal topic of the chapter is the methods used in biological investigation. Although most scientists agree that there is no one scientific method, they do recognize certain important elements of such methods. In this chapter, several features of scientific methods are presented as a six-step process.

This chapter introduces the metric system, which is used throughout the book. The chapter also pre-

sents the characteristics of simple, compound, and electron microscopes. After completing this chapter, students will have gained an appreciation of the methods of scientific investigation.

Teaching Strategies and Activities

1. Before starting the chapter, ask the students to complete the following sentences: Science is _____. A scientist _____. Have the students compare and explain their answers in a forum-type discussion.
2. In regard to solving problems in our world today, is science limited or unlimited? Ask the students this question. They should indicate that science is limited as to what it can do, and they should state the reasons for these limitations. Discuss some of the limitations that the students name, and relate them to the solving of societal problems.
3. Ask the students to write out, in their own words, definitions of pure science and applied science. Lead a discussion on which, if either, is more important. Have the students list current problems that they think scientists could solve. Then focus the discussion on whether pure or applied science might lead to the solution of each problem.
4. Show slides of pictures taken through an electron microscope. To stimulate interest, have students try to identify the pictures before you explain them.

Answer Key to Section Reviews
The Science of Biology (p. 17)

1. Biology is the study of living things.
2. Leeuwenhoek contributed to the study of microbiology; Pasteur to bacteriology; and Mendel, Morgan, Watson, and Crick to genetics. Darwin's theory of evolution is also closely related to genetics.
3. Cells are the basic units of all living things. An organism is made up of one or more cells.

Biological Investigation (p. 22)

1. Scientists follow a logical and orderly series of steps to investigate a problem. The series of

steps usually involves stating the problem, gathering information, forming a hypothesis, conducting experiments, observing and recording information, and stating a conclusion.

2. Using a controlled experiment enables a scientist to recognize the effect of the experimental factor.

3. A hypothesis is a possible or working explanation for a given problem that agrees with all the available information.

4. Three common metric units are the meter (m), the liter (L), and the gram (g).

5. The microscope is one of the most important tools in biology because it can be used to view structures of living things that are not visible to the unaided eye. Students should name any two of the following: the compound microscope, the electron microscope, the simple microscope, or the magnifying glass.

Teaching Aids for Chapter End Features

Laboratory Investigation 1
A Scientific Investigation (p. 23)

Have the class wash the potatoes with a brush because some potatoes have a wax coating that can inhibit sprout growth. When setting up the experiment, remind the students that all factors except light must be the same for both potato halves.

OBSERVATIONS AND CONCLUSIONS 1. Sproutings should appear in both setups, but the potato halves in the dark should have a greater percentage of them. The reason is that light inhibits root growth in potatoes. 2. Potatoes do not need light to sprout. 3. Answers may vary. 4. The control consists of the potato halves in the dark, because potatoes normally grow underground in the absence of light. The experimental factor is the exposure to light of the other potato halves. 5. The data may vary. 6. Data from the class should be more reliable than data from a group because the class results are based on a greater number of trial experiments. 7. Answers may vary.

Review of Facts and Concepts (p. 24)

1. Swayed by superstition for centuries, people were fearful of natural events. Science developed slowly because people believed that natural events could be explained by folklore and magic.

2. *Leeuwenhoek* was the first to observe one-celled organisms. *Hooke* viewed and named cells. *Pasteur* discovered that microorganisms cause disease. *Darwin* developed a theory of evolution that explained, in part, why some organisms have a greater chance of survival than others. *Mendel* studied the transmission of characteristics from an organism to its offspring. *Morgan* studied how specific traits pass from one generation to the next. *Watson* and *Crick* discovered the helix-shaped structure of DNA.

3. *Botany* is the study of plants. *Zoology* is the study of animals. *Anatomy* is the study of the structures of plants, animals, and other organisms. *Physiology* is the study of life functions. *Embryology* is the study of the formation and development of organisms in their earliest stages. *Cytology, exobiology, marine biology,* and *paleontology* are also acceptable answers.

4. In a scientific investigation, biologists generally take the following steps. *State the problem*: In this step, biologists identify the problem at hand. *Gather information*: They collect whatever information is available, usually from books and scientific journals. *Form a hypothesis*: On the basis of the available information, researchers formulate a possible explanation for the problem under investigation. *Experiment*: To test the hypothesis, biologists conduct experiments. *Observe and record data*: Throughout the experiment, biologists observe results and record data. *State a conclusion*: Biologists review the recorded data to determine whether the hypothesis is supported. Their judgment becomes the basis for the conclusion drawn from the experiment.

5. In an experiment, the control setup is arranged as it would occur without human intervention. The factors in the experimental setup are exactly the same as those in the control setup, except for the experimental factor.

6. Data are used to develop the conclusions and sometimes the theories that scientists formulate. For scientists to state an accurate conclusion, they must observe and record data precisely.

7. The metric system is a standard system of measurements and measurement units used internationally by all scientists. Answers may vary.

8. See Figure 1-9 on page 20.

9. The compound light microscope has more than one lens and uses light to make the specimen visible. It magnifies objects hundreds of times. Instead of light, the electron microscope uses a beam of high-speed electrons to make a specimen visible. The electrons bounce off the specimen and form an image on a television screen or photographic surface. The electron microscope can magnify objects hundreds of thousands of times.

10. The *meter* (m) is a metric unit of linear measurement. The *liter* (L) is a metric unit of volumetric

measurement. *Magnification* is the apparent increase in size of a specimen under a lens. *Resolution* is a measure of the clarity and sharpness of the image. In a *scanning electron microscope* (SEM), the specimen appears three-dimensional. In a *transmission electron microscope* (TEM), the object appears flat and thin.

Extensions and Applications (p. 25)

1. You may want to divide the class into three groups and assign each group one of the fields for study. Each group should then prepare an oral report. The reports might discuss the origin and development of the field, its pioneers, or its contributions to the advancement of biology and to the betterment of society.
2. Before starting this activity, review "The Compound Microscope," pages 792–93, in the Reference Section. Then ask the students to describe what they see under each of the two instruments. They should note that, when viewed with a magnifying glass, the letter and the shapes in the photograph appear larger than with the unaided eye but otherwise do not change. Under the microscope, the images are even larger than under the magnifying glass. Also, students should note that the newspaper ink does not appear solid under the microscope and that the colored areas of the photograph are actually masses of black, yellow, red, and blue dots. The microscope provides greater magnification but poorer resolution than the magnifying glass. Students should note that, as they use lenses with progressively higher powers of magnification, the clarity of the image becomes poorer.
3. A few simple measures on the part of the teacher can improve the chance of success in this activity. Use radishes, lima or pinto beans, or any seeds that germinate quickly. Any common fertilizer will do, but make sure that it is mixed in the proper ratio for the amount of soil used. Plant the seeds in containers with holes for soil drainage. When setting up the experiment, the students should identify fertilizer as the experimental factor.

2 The Living Organism

Chapter Objectives: See page 26.

Chapter Overview

A major feature of this chapter is an explanation of how experimentation demonstrated the validity of the principle of biogenesis and thus refuted the idea of abiogenesis. Experiments conducted by Redi, Needham, Spallanzani, and Pasteur are described.

The remainder of the chapter is devoted to a discussion of the characteristics of living things. The cell and its protoplasm are discussed respectively as the basic structure and substance of living things. Other characteristics that distinguish living organisms from nonliving things are metabolism, growth and development, response to stimuli, reproduction, and adaptation. The chapter concludes with a discussion of the levels of organization in living things and the requirements of living things.

Teaching Strategies and Activities

1. Before beginning this chapter, take a walk around the school area with the class. Have the students make a list of the living and nonliving objects that they see, labeling each item in the list as either living or nonliving. Also tell the students to jot down the properties of each object. As the class studies the differences between living and nonliving things, have the students refer to their lists and correct their initial observations as necessary.
2. To stress the difference between growth and development, have the students observe the sprouting of some newly planted radishes, clover, rye grass, or navy bean seeds. After five to eight days of observation, ask the students to distinguish the growth of each plant from its development. Have the students define growth and development based on their observations.
3. Ask the students to list all the things that they need in order to live in their environment. From the list, have the students select the things they need daily.

Answer Key to Section Reviews

Abiogenesis and Biogenesis (p. 31)

1. Spontaneous generation, or abiogenesis, is the idea that some living things develop from nonliving materials.
2. The principle of biogenesis states that living things are produced only from other living things.
3. In Redi's first experiment, he tightly sealed his experimental set of jars. As a control, he left another set of jars open. Redi's second experiment was similar to the first. This time, however, he covered the experimental jars with a porous cloth, while he left the control jars open.
4. Spallanzani concluded that boiling actually made the broths more suitable for the growth of microorganisms.

5. Pasteur tested the hypothesis that the air contained spores, attached to dust particles, that remained inactive until they landed in an environment that could support life.

Characteristics of Living Things (p. 35)

1. Protoplasm is a complex system of cell parts and substances that function together to enable the cell to do work.
2. The metabolic functions are ingestion, digestion, assimilation, respiration, and excretion.
3. Growth is an increase in the size of an organism.
4. A *stimulus* is a change in the environment of a living organism. A *response* is the action or movement of the organism caused by the stimulus.
5. If a specific living thing did not reproduce, its kind would become extinct.
6. Adaptation is the process by which a kind of organism changes and becomes better suited to its environment.

Levels of Organization and Needs of Living Things (p. 38)

1. A *unicellular organism* is made up of only one cell. A *multicellular organism* is made up of more than one cell.
2. The levels of organization of living things are the cell, tissue, organ, organ system, and organism.
3. The primary source of energy for most living things is the sun.
4. A *producer* can make its own food. A *consumer* must obtain food by ingesting other organisms.

Teaching Aids for Chapter End Features

Laboratory Investigation 2
Distinguishing Between Living and Nonliving Things (p. 39)

Be sure to have a few solutions on hand. One should be a solution of liquid plant fertilizer. Another should be a nutrient solution, which can be mixed in several ways: in 1 L water, dissolve either 100 g of sucrose (table sugar), 100 mL of corn syrup, or 100 mL of molasses. Bromthymol blue (BTB) or phenolphthalein indicator solution should also be available.

Encourage the students to set up simple experiments to test the unknowns for signs of life. The students should at least examine all the unknowns under the magnifying glass. They should then go on to use the available materials for further testing. For example, suggest placing the dry yeast in a container of the nutrient solution. As a parallel test, the students might put sand into another container with the same solution. Alternatively, the students might bury some vegetable seeds and a few Styrofoam chips in soil and fertilize them.

Some objects that are suitable for this investigation are radishes, beans, peas, and grass seeds; dry powdered yeast; small pieces of rocks, minerals, and crystals; shells; fruits from ornamental trees and shrubs; pine cones; buttons; fruit seeds; nuts, both in and out of the shell; and Styrofoam packing chips.

OBSERVATIONS AND CONCLUSIONS 1. Answers will vary. **2.** Answers will vary. **3.** Answers will vary. Generally, the students should be able to group the unknowns correctly into living and nonliving categories. Some students may want to establish a third category—dead, or once living. **4.** Answers will vary. **5.** Answers will vary.

Review of Facts and Concepts (p. 40)

1. *Abiogenesis* is the idea that some organisms develop from nonliving materials. The principle of *biogenesis* states that living things are produced only from other living things.
2. In his first experiment, Redi tightly sealed the experimental set of jars. His second experiment was exactly the same as the first, but this time he covered the experimental jars with cloth that permitted air to enter but not flies.
   In the first experiment, Redi isolated the meat from the air as well as from the flies. The intended experimental factor, the exclusion of the flies, was therefore not the only factor that was varied. The second experiment was better in the sense that it varied only one factor, the flies.
3. Spallanzani claimed that organisms could have survived the short-term boiling during Needham's experiment. Spallanzani also thought that organisms could have entered the broth culture through the loosely sealed tops of the containers that Needham used.
4. Spallanzani sealed his flasks securely by melting the glass together at the mouths. He then placed the sealed flasks in boiling water for one hour. Supporters of abiogenesis claimed that boiling had destroyed the "vegetative force" needed for life.
5. Pasteur prepared several broths that would support the growth of microorganisms and poured each into a glass flask. He sealed the flasks and boiled them long enough to kill all the microorganisms present. The reopened flasks were then exposed to air that contained varying amounts of dust and spores. After several days, Pasteur discovered that the flasks exposed to the largest amount of dust contained the greatest number of

organisms. This result supported the idea that spores of microorganisms are attached to dust in the air.

In another experiment, Pasteur boiled a water, yeast, and sugar broth in flasks that had S-shaped necks. These curved necks trapped water and dust particles. At the same time, the boiling forced air out of the flasks, killed any microorganisms in the broth, and destroyed any spores in the necks. After leaving the flasks in contact with the air, Pasteur observed no living organisms in the broth.

Pasteur's experiments were conclusive because he isolated all the factors but air from the sterile broth, which remained contaminated until brought into contact with the trapped microorganisms in the S-curves of the flasks.

6. The structural characteristics of living things are cells, tissues, organs, and organ systems. The functional characteristics are metabolism, growth and development, response, and reproduction.
7. *Growth* is an increase in the size of an organism. As growth continues, the organism undergoes a series of changes in form and function called *development*.
8. Irritability is the ability of an organism to respond to a stimulus. Answers will vary.
9. A *variation* is a characteristic of an organism not possessed by others of its species. An *adaptation* is a variation that benefits an organism and therefore tends to persist in its species.
10. Cells make up tissues; tissues make up organs; organs make up organ systems.
11. The basic needs are energy, water, food, air, and living space.
12. All living things need energy to carry out life functions. Plants get their energy directly from sunlight. Animals get their energy by eating plants or other animals.
13. Overcrowding is the occupation of a niche by more organisms than can be supported by available food, water, and energy.

Extensions and Applications (p. 41)

1. *Caution: Do not overwater the soil sample.* Add only a little water at a time—10 mL or less.
2. To bring about the overcrowding, plant 15 to 20 seeds in a small flowerpot. As a control, place 5 to 7 seeds in another pot of the same size. Have the students keep careful records of their observations.
3. *Caution: Do not overwater the seeds in the five containers.* Be sure that the students leave enough room between the soil surface and the cellophane for the plants to grow.
4. Some organisms that were supposed to arise by means of spontaneous generation were maggots from rotting meat, frogs from pond mud, mice from wheat in a dirty shirt, fish from falling rain, insects from soil, earthworms from water-soaked soil, and lizards from rotting trees.

3 Classification of Organisms

Chapter Objectives: See page 42.

Chapter Overview

Chapter 3 examines the international classification system that biologists use to organize the estimated five million kinds of organisms on the earth. It was only through the development of taxonomy that scientists were able to discern order in the teeming world of living things.

In the eighteenth century, Linnaeus made an important contribution to taxonomy by dividing all organisms into the plant and animal kingdoms. Today, biologists classify organisms in seven major classification groupings: kingdom, phylum or division, class, order, family, genus, and species. Organisms fall into one category or another according to their homologous structures, biochemical likenesses, or genetic similarities. In this text, a five-kingdom system of classification (Animalia, Plantae, Protista, Monera, and Fungi) is used.

Teaching Strategies and Activities

1. Invite a taxonomist to visit the class and describe how animals are classified. Alternatively, invite a botanist or zoologist to perform the same function.
2. Set out before the class 15 specimens representative of the five kingdoms. Have students identify the organisms as either plants, animals, protists, monerans, or fungi. Be sure to have students state the reasons for their answers.
3. Lead a discussion on the problems of classifying organisms on the basis of similarities or differences in structure and function.

Answer Key to Section Reviews

History of Classification (p. 45)

1. Taxonomy is the science of classification of organisms.
2. Aristotle grouped animals as land dwellers, air dwellers, and water dwellers. He grouped plants according to their size, as herbs, shrubs, and trees.

3. Binomial nomenclature is a two-word system for scientifically naming an organism.

Modern Taxonomy (p. 47)

1. Homologous structures are body parts or organs of different organisms that have the same basic pattern and general relationship of parts but different functions.
2. Biologists use biochemical and genetic similarities to classify organisms.
3. The largest group is a kingdom; the smallest is a species.
4. The scientific name for a house cat is *Felis domesticus*.

Classification Systems (p. 49)

1. The kingdoms in the classification systems used by taxonomists are Plantae, Animalia, Protista, Monera, and Fungi.
2. Methanogens are organisms that do not need oxygen to survive. They produce methane.

Teaching Aids for Chapter End Features

Laboratory Investigation 3
Developing a Classification System (p. 52)

Keep the objects small. Buttons, shells, rocks, minerals, seeds, fruits, coins, or nuts would be good examples. The objects might be classified according to size (large/small), color (dark/light), and weight (light/heavy). Some students may want to subdivide the general property into more than two observable characteristics, such as size (large/medium/small).

OBSERVATIONS AND CONCLUSIONS 1. Answers will vary. **2.** Answers will vary. **3.** The first circle represents a kingdom; the second circles represent phyla. Each object stands for a genus and species. **4.** Follow the rules for binomial nomenclature. **5.** Answers will vary. **6.** Retail store managers use classification systems every day to arrange merchandise in sections and on shelves. The "classified" ads in the newspaper and the cataloging systems used by libraries are also classification systems.

Review of Facts and Concepts (p. 53)

1. Linnaeus used structural similarities to classify organisms.
2. Today, homologous structures, biochemical similarities, and genetic similarities are used to classify organisms.
3. The seven major classification groupings are kingdom, phylum or division, class, order, family, genus, and species.

4. A scientific name is made up of the genus and the species.
5. *Felis tigris* and *Felis leo* are the most similar because they are of the same genus.
6. Taxonomists classify organisms to provide a logical, internationally recognized system for naming organisms and for identifying relationships between groups of living things.
7. Some organisms are difficult to classify because they have characteristics that are not found in plants or animals or have characteristics of both plants and animals. Examples may include *Euglena*, fungi, or bacteria.
8. Scientists do not agree about the placement of organisms in the kingdoms or even on the number of kingdoms.
9. The five kingdoms are Protista, unicellular heterotrophic eukaryotes; Monera, unicellular autotrophic and heterotrophic prokaryotes; Plantae, multicellular autotrophic eukaryotes; Fungi, unicellular and multicellular heterotrophic eukaryotes; Animalia, multicellular heterotrophic eukaryotes.
10. A maple tree would belong in the kingdom Plantae; a mouse, in the kingdom Animalia; blue-green algae, in the kingdom Monera; a mushroom, in the kingdom Fungi; a human being, in the kingdom Animalia; a bacterium, in the kingdom Monera; and a mosquito, in the kingdom Animalia.

Extensions and Applications (p. 53)

1. First direct the students to make a list of the common names of ten animals and ten plants. Then have them use books in the library and the classroom to prepare a chart that lists the genus, the species, and the basis for each of the names.
2. Common misnomers are poison ivy, starfish, jellyfish, crayfish, shellfish, and ladybug. Unusual animals might include coral, sponges, sea cucumber, slime mold, and sea urchin.
3. Have students use Figure 3-1 as a guide.

Unit Teaching Aids

Perspectives in Biology

Animal Captivity: Zoos and Compounds Versus Preserves and Sanctuaries (p. 55)

1. A visit to a zoo or wildlife preserve might be arranged. Perhaps an interview with a zookeeper or game warden could also be arranged. After the zoo visit and interview, two panels of students could be formed and a debate held on the pros and cons of caging animals.

2. Charts or models of various zoo enclosures and an ideal zoo might be drawn or constructed by the students. Students should be able to explain the advantages and disadvantages of their enclosures and zoo.
3. After students receive material from various zoos, committees of students can be assigned two zoos to compare and contrast. An oral presentation can be made by each committee.

Field Trip Suggestions

1. Visit a zoo or botanical garden with the class. Focus the students' attention on how certain species are similar to each other, how they are classified or grouped, and how they have adapted to their environments.
2. Visit a milk- or cheese-processing plant to observe the pasteurization process or a research laboratory to watch scientists at work.
3. On a schoolground or neighboring area, organize the following activities. **a.** Have students make a map of the schoolground or nearby area, and indicate where birds commonly congregate. Correlate the birds' habitats to their food, water, and shelter needs. **b.** Compare how two trees of the same age get energy from the sun. **c.** Have the students make a survey of areas on the schoolground where plants do not grow. Determine which requirements for life are missing.

Audio-Visual Materials

Biology: Exploring the Living World, film, EBE
Classification, sound filmstrip, SSS
How to Use a Microscope, sound fimstrip, SSS
Scientific Method, film, EBE
Taxonomy, slide program, SSS
The Microscope, set/4 super 8mm film loops, PHM
The Scientific Method, sound filmstrip, PHM
Using Experiments as Tests of Hypotheses, slide program, HBJ
What Is Biology?, set/4 sound filmstrips, PHM

Reading Resources for Teachers

Asimov, I. *A Short History of Biology*. Garden City, N.Y.: Natural History Press.
Gabriel, M., and S. Fogel. *Great Experiments in Biology*. Englewood Cliffs, N.J.: Prentice-Hall.
Hanson, E. *Animal Diversity*. Englewood Cliffs, N.J.: Prentice-Hall.
Wilson, E., and T. Eisner. *Life on Earth*. Sunderland, Mass.: Sinauer Associates.

Cells

Each chapter of this unit contributes to a thorough introduction to cytology. Opening the unit, Chapter 4 provides the chemical concepts necessary for understanding cell functions. In Chapter 5, students explore the structures and functions of cells, along with the historical background of the cell theory. Chapter 6 concentrates on the processes by which a cell obtains, stores, transforms, and uses energy. Then, in Chapter 7, students follow the biochemical pathways for photosynthesis and cellular respiration. In Chapter 8, the topics of cell growth and reproduction are discussed. A description of the structure of DNA and RNA leads to a discussion of protein synthesis, mitosis, and meiosis.

4 Chemistry of Living Things

Chapter Objectives: See page 58.

Chapter Overview

Chapter 4 covers the fundamentals of chemistry that the students need to understand cell functions. The chapter begins with discussions of energy, matter, and the nature of physical and chemical changes. An explanation of the atomic structure of the elements leads to a discussion of bonding, compounds, molecules, and mixtures. The second part of the chapter focuses on the inorganic and organic substances that are important to living things. Emphasis is placed on discussions of carbohydrates, proteins, lipids, nucleic acids, and enzymes. A discussion of Oparin's hypothesis concludes the chapter.

Teaching Strategies and Activities

1. Define physical and chemical changes. Then demonstrate some simple physical and chemical changes. Ask your students to identify whether each change is physical or chemical.
2. Demonstrate the types of mixtures by preparing a solution, a suspension, and a colloid. As you make up these mixtures, introduce such topics as homogeneity versus heterogeneity, the separation of components in a mixture, particle size, and so on.
3. An understanding of the nature of organic substances has practical value. Make this point by asking students to bring in the labels of food packages from home. The objective is to learn how to read lists of ingredients and to determine

whether the foods contain proteins, lipids, or carbohydrates and in what quantities.

Answer Key to Section Reviews

Matter and Living Things (p. 66)

1. In a *physical change*, the form of matter changes, but the kind of matter stays the same. In a *chemical change*, the makeup of matter changes, forming a new substance or new substances.
2. The drawing must have 7 protons and 7 neutrons in the nucleus. The first energy level must contain 2 electrons, and the second must contain 5.
3. An isotope is an atom of an element that has a different number of neutrons and therefore a different atomic mass than other atoms of the element.
4. *Covalent bonds* result when atoms join by sharing electrons. *Ionic bonds* form when one atom transfers electrons to another atom.
5. An *element* is a substance that contains only one type of atom. A *compound* contains two or more chemically bonded elements. A *mixture* is made up of two or more substances that keep their chemical identities.
6. A *solution* is a homogeneous mixture in which the molecules or ions of the solute are evenly distributed throughout the molecules or ions of the solvent. A *suspension* is a heterogeneous mixture containing particles of a substance that are much larger than individual molecules or ions. A *colloid* is a homogeneous mixture containing particles that are larger than the molecules in a solution but smaller than the particles in a suspension.

Compounds Important to Living Things (p. 72)

1. All organic compounds contain the element carbon, whereas most inorganic compounds do not.
2. *Carbohydrates* are chains or rings of carbon atoms bonded to hydrogen and oxygen atoms. *Proteins* are made of molecules containing up to 20 different kinds of amino acids. *Amino acids* consist of an amino group ($-NH_2$), a carboxyl group ($-COOH$), and an R group of either a hydrogen atom or a group of hydrogen and carbon atoms. *Lipids* consist of three molecules of fatty acids bonded to a molecule of glycerol. *Nucleic acids* are special complex molecules that store genetic information. *Enzymes* are special proteins that help to speed up chemical reactions without themselves being changed.
3. *Dehydration synthesis* is a process by which small molecules bond to form larger molecules with the release of one molecule of water for every two molecules that bond. The reverse process, *hydrolysis*, breaks down large molecules into smaller ones with the addition of one molecule of water for every molecule that is broken down.
4. The two types of nucleic acids are deoxyribonucleic acid and ribonucleic acid.
5. Oparin's hypothesis proposes that solar energy caused the rearrangement of ammonia, methane, hydrogen, and water vapor in the earth's early atmosphere to form simple organic compounds. Stanley Miller, an American scientist, found evidence to support this hypothesis.

Teaching Aids for Chapter End Features

Laboratory Investigation 4
Observing Mixtures and Compounds (p. 73)

For Part A, elicit the characteristics of sulfur and iron from the class. Write the characteristics on the chalkboard. *Caution: For Part B, be sure that the students wear safety goggles. Liquids can splatter as they boil dry.* In Part C, the clay that you select must be very finely powdered. Clay particles that are too large will settle out quickly and spoil the results. In Part D, be sure students set the jars aside until the next class period so that the contents can gel.

OBSERVATIONS AND CONCLUSIONS 1. A magnet attracts the iron filings, separating them from the sulfur. 2. In Part C, the filter paper traps the larger clay particles but allows the smaller ones to pass. The filtrate in Part B is clear, while the filtrate in Part C is slightly cloudy. In both mixtures, the small molecules are able to pass through the filter paper. 3. In Part B, the mixture is a solution; in Part C, a suspension; in Part D, a colloid. 4. The salt remains. 5. The clay and water can be filtered. However, not all the clay particles can be removed because the smallest stay suspended indefinitely. 6. The larger clay particles settle to the bottom of the container. 7. The dissolved gelatin in jar 4 passes through the filter paper. If the gelatin doesn't dissolve completely, the filter paper traps some particles. The mixture in jar 5 eventually gels. 8. The sulfur and iron combine chemically to form iron sulfide. 9. Iron sulfide is a gray-black compound that is hard, granular, brittle, and not magnetic. Sulfur is a yellow, nonmagnetic powder, while iron filings are black, crystalline, magnetic, and powdery.

Review of Facts and Concepts (p. 74)

1. Biology is the study of living things, all of which are made up of chemical substances.

2. Anything that occupies space and has mass is matter. A *solid* has a definite shape and takes up a definite volume. A *liquid* does not have a definite shape, but it does have a definite volume. A *gas* has neither a definite shape nor a definite volume.

3. A *physical property* can be observed or measured, whereas a *chemical property* is not easily observed or measured. A chemical property shows how one kind of matter reacts with other matter.

4. The Law of Conservation of Matter states that during a chemical change, matter is neither created nor destroyed. Examples will vary.

5. Atoms make up elements.

6. The atomic model of sulfur has 16 protons and 16 neutrons in the nucleus. Starting with the innermost energy level, the energy levels have 2, 8, and 6 electrons, respectively.

7. For carbon-12, the nucleus contains 6 protons and 6 neutrons. The inner energy level contains 2 electrons, and the outer one has 4. The carbon-14 structure is exactly the same except that the nucleus has 8 neutrons.

8. The model for *covalent bonding* should show two atoms sharing electrons. The model for *ionic bonding* should depict the transfer of electrons from one atom to another.

9. A *solution* is a mixture in which the molecules or ions of the solute are evenly spread throughout the molecules or ions of the solvent. A *suspension* contains large particles that do not completely mix with another substance. In a *colloid*, the particles are larger than those in a solution but smaller than those in a suspension. Examples will vary.

10. All organic compounds contain the element carbon, whereas most inorganic compounds do not.

11. Any four of the following six kinds of compounds are acceptable. *Carbohydrates* are chains or rings of carbon atoms bonded to hydrogen and oxygen atoms. *Proteins* are made of molecules of up to 20 different amino acids. *Amino acids* consist of an amino group ($-NH_2$), a carboxyl group ($-COOH$), and an R group, which consists of a hydrogen atom or a group of hydrogen and carbon atoms. *Lipids* contain three molecules of fatty acids bonded to a molecule of glycerol. *Nucleic acids* are special complex molecules that store genetic information. *Enzymes* are special proteins that help to speed up chemical reactions without themselves being changed.

12. Carbohydrates and lipids are sources of energy.

13. See Figure 4-13 on page 69. During digestion, hydrolysis breaks down certain foods into molecules that are small enough to enter the cells.

14. See Figure 4-14 on page 69.

15. Both lipids and carbohydrates are composed of carbon, hydrogen, and oxygen, but lipids do not have the same hydrogen-to-oxygen ratio as do carbohydrates. Complex lipids may contain phosphorus and nitrogen.

16. *Deoxyribonucleic acid* contains the "genetic message" for the cell. *Ribonucleic acid* "reads" the message from DNA.

17. Enzymes are special proteins that enable chemical reactions to take place in the living cell. They are catalysts because they speed up reactions without being changed themselves. Without catalysts, these reactions would take place slowly or not at all.

18. Oparin's hypothesis states that energy bombarding the earth's early atmosphere may have given rise to simple organic compounds.

Extensions and Applications (p. 75)

1. Call ahead to a medical school or a medical center in your area and make appointments for students to visit various departments.

2. Assign the topics carbohydrates, lipids, and proteins to small groups in the class. Focus on the roles of the compounds in nutrition and on the food groups that contain them.

3. Hydrogen sulfide (H_2S) is an ionic compound. Carbon dioxide (CO_2) is a covalent compound. Magnesium oxide (MgO) is an ionic compound. Lithium chloride (LiCl) is an ionic compound.

5 Cell Structure and Function

Chapter Objectives: See page 76.

Chapter Overview

Chapter 5 explains how a cell is organized and how it functions. The opening section covers the development of the cell theory. The work of Hooke, Leeuwenhoek, Dutrochet, Dujardin, Schleiden, Schwann, and Virchow is discussed. The ensuing sections emphasize that, despite the diversity of cell size, shape, and organization, all cells carry out all life functions. The latter part of the chapter deals with the particulars of cell structures. Ending the chapter is a brief discussion of the distinction between prokaryotic and eukaryotic cells.

Teaching Strategies and Activities

1. In its organization and function, the cell is analogous to a factory. To illustrate this similarity, have groups of students design various floor plans for a factory. They should label the factory's hallways, rooms, machinery, and other

areas with both the proper factory names and the names of analogous cell parts—for example, "PRESIDENT'S OFFICE/NUCLEUS" or "HALLWAYS/ER." Have a representative of each group show the group's design and explain its workings to the class.

2. Have the class examine prepared slides of different kinds of cells. Students should make drawings of single cells and be able to compare and contrast them.

Answer Key to Section Reviews

Development of the Cell Theory (p. 77)

1. Robert Hooke was the first to describe cells.
2. The cell theory states that cells are the basic units of structure and function in all living things.

Size, Shape, and Organization of Cells (p. 79)

1. A *unicellular organism* is composed of only one cell. A *multicellular organism* is composed of two or more cells.
2. The microscope enlarged cells so that they could be seen and studied.

Cell Functions (p. 81)

1. Cell functions include nutrition, digestion, absorption, transport, biosynthesis, secretion, respiration, excretion, response, and reproduction.
2. *Biosynthesis* is the process of building new, larger chemical compounds from smaller ones. *Respiration* is a chemical process that breaks down organic compounds to release energy for use by cells. *Digestion* is a process that breaks down large food molecules into simple ones.
3. Most cells reproduce by fission.

Cell Structures (p. 90)

1. *Protoplasm* consists of the many different substances and structures in a cell. *Cytoplasm* is the clear, thick protoplasm that fills the space between the cell membrane and the nucleus. The *nucleoplasm* is the thick, protein-rich protoplasm in the nucleus.
2. Organelles are small, organized structures within cells. Examples will vary.
3. Plant cells have cell walls and plastids. Animal cells do not. Animal cells have centrioles and lysosomes. Most plant cells do not.
4. The nucleus directs all the cell's activities.
5. *Rough endoplasmic reticulum* has ribosomes attached to it, and it functions mainly in protein production and transport. *Smooth ER* has no

ribosomes, but it contains many enzymes necessary for cell metabolism.

6. Lysosomes join with food vacuoles to digest food molecules within the cell and to digest dead or injured cells.
7. The Golgi apparatus is a series of closely stacked, flattened sacs that packages substances that are to be secreted from the cell.
8. The two general classes of cells are prokaryotes and eukaryotes.

Teaching Aids for Chapter End Features

Laboratory Investigation 5
Examining Plant and Animal Cells (p. 91)

Caution: Remind students to use scalpels with care.

OBSERVATIONS AND CONCLUSIONS 1. Onion tissue has one cell layer. **2.** Onion cells are rectangular; cheek cells are irregularly shaped. **3.** Because cell structures are colorless and transparent, it is difficult to see them without staining them. **4.** The cell wall, the nucleus, and the nucleolus stain darker than other cell parts. **5.** The onion cell has a cell wall and a large vacuole, whereas the cheek cell has a cell membrane and small vacuoles. **6.** Onion cells are larger than cheek cells. **7.** Cytoplasm, a nucleus, nucleoli, and a cell membrane are common to both cells.

Review of Facts and Concepts (p. 92)

1. *Hooke* was the first to observe and name cells. *Leeuwenhoek* made the first observations of living unicellular organisms. *Dutrochet* found that groups of cells comprised the tissues of plants and animals. *Dujardin* stated that single-celled organisms were complete, self-sufficient living things. *Virchow* stated that all living cells come only from other living cells.
2. The cell theory states that living cells are the basic units of structure and function in all living things, and that cells come only from other living cells.
3. In cell specialization, the cells of an organism have different functions. The cells function together to benefit the organism.
4. In multicellular organisms, cells typically do specialized jobs, and they rely on other cells to perform some life functions. Unicellular organisms cannot rely on other cells and therefore must have a wide variety of subcellular organelles and a complex internal organization to live independently.

5. Cell metabolism is all the chemical processes and functions necessary for breaking down foods and building up cell substances.
6. The cell wall protects and supports a plant cell.
7. Selective permeability of the cell membrane maintains homeostasis.
8. Proteins are scattered within and throughout a double layer of lipid molecules.
9. The plant cell would have a cell wall, plastids, and probably a huge vacuole. The animal cell would not have these structures.
10. The cell membrane, cytoplasm, and nucleus are the three basic parts of most cells.
11. The mitochondria are complex, oval or rod-shaped structures that are made up of an outer membrane and an inner, folded membrane. A semifluid matrix fills the spaces between the folds. Mitochondria continue the oxidation of sugars for energy.
12. Vacuoles store food, enzymes, and waste materials. In plant cells, they often contain water. Some cells have contractile vacuoles, which pump out excess water.
13. *Leucoplasts* are white or colorless plastids that store oils, starches, and proteins. *Chromoplasts* are plastids that contain pigments. *Chloroplasts* function in photosynthesis.
14. The following are the chemical processes of cell metabolism and the organelles involved in each. *Nutrition and digestion:* vacuoles and lysosomes. *Absorption:* cell membrane. *Transport:* endoplasmic reticulum and Golgi apparatus. *Biosynthesis:* endoplasmic reticulum, ribosomes, and nucleus. *Secretion:* Golgi apparatus and cell membrane. *Respiration:* mitochondria. *Excretion:* contractile vacuole and cell membrane. *Response:* cell membrane. *Reproduction:* nucleus, microtubules, and centrioles.
15. A *prokaryotic cell* has few organelles and nuclear material that is not bounded by a membrane. The genetic material is scattered throughout the protoplasm or as strands of nucleic acid. A *eukaryotic cell* has many organelles and a distinct nucleus surrounded by a membrane.

Extensions and Applications (p. 93)

1. Have the students observe the specimens under both low and high powers of the microscope. *Note: Even under high power, the living microbes are almost transparent and may be difficult to see. To distinguish them, reduce the light on the substage illuminator.*
2. The students may include the work of such people as the French botanist Charles Brisseau-Mirbel and the German anatomist Lorenz Oken and the development of the microscope.

3. Students can find appropriate magazine articles by looking up "aging" or "lysosomes" in the *Readers' Guide to Periodical Literature.*
4. See "Preparing a Wet-Mount Slide and Staining Techniques," page 793, in the Reference Section.

6 Cell Energy and Maintenance

Chapter Objectives: See page 94.

Chapter Overview

Chapter 6 focuses on how cells obtain, store, transform, and use energy and on how cells transport the materials needed for life functions. The section on energy is introduced by a discussion of the types of energy. Students become familiar with the roles of enzymes and coenzymes, particularly ATP. They also become acquainted with the lock and key hypothesis and the induced fit theory, two possible explanations for enzyme-substrate reactions.

The sections on transport describe how cells maintain homeostasis. Processes of passive transport, such as diffusion and osmosis, operate without the benefit of energy. Other processes, such as endocytosis and exocytosis, illustrate active transport, which requires energy.

Teaching Strategies and Activities

1. To introduce the concept of a catalyst, add a pinch of manganese dioxide (MnO_2) powder to 5 mL of hydrogen peroxide (H_2O_2). Acting as a catalyst, the manganese dioxide splits the peroxide into water (H_2O) and oxygen (O):

$$2H_2O_2 \xrightarrow{MnO_2} 2H_2O + O_2 \uparrow$$

Caution: Do not pass the tube around the room. The reaction causes a great deal of heat.
2. Demonstrate the differences among isotonic, hypertonic, and hypotonic solutions. Cut three pieces of dialysis tubing, and tie off one end of each. Into the other ends, pour a physiologic saline (0.9%) solution, and then tie off the tubes. These solution-filled tubes are your "cells." To create an *isotonic* condition, place one "cell" into a beaker containing physiologic saline solution. For a *hypotonic* condition, place another "cell" into a beaker with distilled water. To make a *hypertonic* condition, put the third "cell" into a beaker of 10% saline solution.

Answer Key to Section Reviews

Cell Energy (p. 99)

1. The Law of Conservation of Energy states that energy can be neither created nor destroyed but can only be changed from one form to another.
2. Potential energy is stored energy.
3. A *catabolic reaction* breaks down molecules and releases energy. An *anabolic reaction* builds new molecules and uses energy.
4. A specific interaction occurs between the enzyme's active site and the substrate's reactive site.
5. A coenzyme is a nonprotein molecule found in some enzymes.
6. ATP stores energy and controls the release of energy within a cell.

Homeostasis and Passive Transport (p. 104)

1. Homeostasis is the ability of an organism to maintain a constant internal balance regardless of changes in its external environment.
2. Passive transport is the movement of substances into and out of the cell without the expenditure of cellular energy.
3. Brownian movement is the jiggling motion of dissolved particles of gases dissolved in one another or of solids, liquids, or gases dissolved in a liquid.
4. The rate and direction of diffusion are affected by concentration, pressure, and temperature.
5. An *isotonic* solution has the same concentration of solute as the protoplasm within a cell. If the solution outside the cell has a higher concentration of solute than that inside the cell, the solution is *hypertonic*. In a *hypotonic* solution, the concentration of solute is lower outside the cell than inside it.
6. Osmotic pressure is the pressure exerted on a cell by water outside of it.

Homeostasis and Active Transport (p. 106)

1. Active transport is the movement of molecules against the diffusion gradient.
2. Scientists think that materials are moved by carrier molecules.
3. The two forms of endocytosis are phagocytosis and pinocytosis.
4. Exocytosis is a process whereby large particles and molecules leave the cell.

Laboratory Investigation 6
Diffusion Through a Cell Membrane
(p. 107)

Prepare the gelatin "cells" the day before class. Mix two packages of colorless gelatin with about 10 mL of phenolphthalein. Pour the mixture into a clean, empty quart (946-mL) milk carton. Allow the gelatin to cool and gel.

At the start of class, lay the carton horizontally on a cutting surface. With a pencil, mark off as many cross sections as you have students or student groups. With a sharp knife, cut through the carton at the marks. Remove the pieces of carton from around the gelatin "cells."

OBSERVATIONS AND CONCLUSIONS 1. The "cell" begins to change to increasingly deeper shades of violet. 2. The ammonium hydroxide diffuses into the "cell." 3. The ammonia in the ammonium hydroxide solution becomes a gas and diffuses throughout the air in the beaker to the "cell."

Review of Facts and Concepts (p. 108)

1. A running person and a speeding train exhibit *kinetic energy*. A bicycle stopped at the top of a hill and a rock at the top of a cliff have *potential energy*. A burning match exemplifies *activation energy*.
2. *Catabolic reactions* break down molecules and release energy. *Anabolic reactions* synthesize new molecules and use energy.
3. Enzymes speed up chemical reactions. Without enzymes, reactions in organisms might progress too slowly or not at all. Enzymes also permit reactions to occur at the body temperature of an organism.
4. Vitamins make up all or parts of some coenzymes and enable vital chemical reactions to take place.
5. In the *lock and key hypothesis*, the enzyme's active site fits exactly with the substrate's reactive site. In the *induced fit theory*, the enzyme's active site must adjust to fit the substrate's reactive site.
6. In a molecule of ATP, a great deal of energy goes into the formation of the bonds between the first and second and between the second and third phosphate groups. When these high-energy bonds are broken, energy is released.
7. Answers will vary.
8. *Diffusion* is the movement of molecules, atoms, or ions from a region of higher concentration to a region of lower concentration. High concentrations, high pressures, and high temperatures increase the rate of diffusion.
9. Placed in an *isotonic solution*, a cell does not change. A *hypertonic solution* makes a cell lose water and shrink. A *hypotonic solution* makes a cell take in water, swell, and possibly burst.
10. *Diffusion* is the movement of molecules, atoms, or ions from a region of higher concentration to a region of lower concentration. *Osmosis* is the

diffusion of water molecules through a selectively permeable membrane.

11. *Turgor pressure* is the pressure exerted by plant-cell contents against the cell wall. *Plasmolysis* is the loss of turgor pressure. Turgor pressure stiffens plant tissues.

12. *Passive transport* is the movement of substances without the input of energy. *Active transport* requires the input of energy.

13. *Endocytosis* is the movement of molecules and particles into a cell. *Exocytosis* is the movement of substances out of a cell.

Extensions and Applications (p. 109)

1. The enzyme models can resemble the diagrammatic illustration on page 97.
2. To make the time differences more striking, use large beakers and only a few drops of food dye.
3. Ask the students to explain why the celery stalk stiffens in tap water but wilts in heavily salted water.

7 Photosynthesis and Respiration

Chapter Objectives: See page 110.

Chapter Overview

Chapter 7 traces the biochemical pathways of photosynthesis and respiration. After treating each process in detail, the chapter closes by describing the interrelationship of these two processes.

The section on photosynthesis follows the light reactions through the formation of ATP and NAD and the dark reactions through the formation of PGAL. The section on cellular respiration discusses anaerobic and aerobic respiration. The text explains the steps in the breakdown of glucose and the hydrogen-bonding role of NAD and FAD. In the aerobic phase, the detailed chemical pathways of the citric acid cycle and the electron transport chain are discussed. The closing discussion is on fermentation.

Teaching Strategies and Activities

1. Green plants contain pigments that can be separated by paper chromatography. To do so, macerate spinach in acetone with a mortar and pestle. Use "test tube chromatography" with nine parts of petroleum ether to one part of acetone.

Caution: Both compounds are poisonous. Be sure the room is well ventilated.

2. Alcohol fermentation produces a strong alcoholic odor. Put about a quarter-packet or cake of baker's yeast into a cotton-stoppered 50-mL sterile flask containing approximately 100 mL of sterile, fluid Sabouraud medium. Leave the flask in a warm place. The next day, pass the flask around the room, and ask the students to tell you what they smell.

3. Students can research the role of fermentation in industry. Individual students can be assigned to investigate the role of fermentation in the preparation of specific foods, such as cheese, sauerkraut, and sausage.

4. To illustrate three types of respiration in bacteria, melt three sterile tubes of tryptone glucose yeast-extract agar. To expel any dissolved oxygen in the agar, maintain the heat source at 100 °C for 10 minutes. Place the tubes in a 42 °C to 45 °C water bath to cool for 15 minutes. Inoculate each tube with several loopfuls of one of the following cultures: *E. coli, S. lutea,* or *C. sporogenes.* Gently swirl the inoculated agar; then put the tubes upright in a warm place for two days. Have the students observe the locations of bacterial growth. When grown in a tube of agar, aerobes appear only on the surface, anaerobes show up only in the deepest part of the agar, and facultative anaerobes spread throughout the agar.

Answer Key to Section Reviews

Photosynthesis (p. 116)

1. Photosynthesis is the process by which green plants use sunlight to make food.
2. Green plants absorb all but green wavelengths of light.
3. Accessory pigments are pigments that absorb light not absorbed by chlorophyll. Examples are carotenes and xanthophylls.
4. As electrons in the atoms of chlorophyll molecules absorb light energy, the electrons move to higher energy levels, "exciting" the chlorophyll.
5. Light reactions produce $NADPH_2$, ATP, and O_2. Dark reactions produce PGAL and RDP.

Cellular Respiration (p. 124)

1. Glucose molecules are the fuel for cellular respiration.
2. Cellular respiration is a process that converts the energy in food molecules into stored energy in ATP.
3. ATP supplies the energy for the breakdown of glucose. NAD is a hydrogen acceptor that is needed to form $NADH_2$.

4. Aerobic respiration produces 38 molecules of ATP, whereas fermentation yields only 2 molecules of ATP.
5. The end products of alcoholic fermentation are alcohol, carbon dioxide, and ATP. The end products of lactic acid fermentation are lactic acid and ATP.
6. The coenzymes NAD (used in cellular respiration) and NADP (used in photosynthesis) are similar in structure and function. An electron transport chain in which some of the electron carriers are similar is found in cellular respiration and photosynthesis.
7. Glucose is the main product of photosynthesis and the fuel for cellular respiration.

Teaching Aids for Chapter End Features

Laboratory Investigation 7
The Effect of Temperature on Yeast Fermentation (p. 125)

For the 20% glucose solution, dissolve 100 g of glucose (dextrose) in 50 mL of water. To prepare the bromthymol blue (BTB) solution, first make a 0.1% stock solution by dissolving 0.5 g of BTB in 50 mL of water. Then add enough of this stock solution to a liter of water to give it a blue-green color. Finally, add a drop or two of ammonium hydroxide to turn the solution a definite blue. As the students blow CO_2 into this solution, it should turn from blue to green to yellow. A similar reaction occurs, more slowly, as the fermentation process releases CO_2.

OBSERVATIONS AND CONCLUSIONS 1. In both cases, CO_2 is released. 2. Glucose is the raw material. 3. The CO_2 is released most rapidly at 35 °C. The BTB solution turns yellow faster at this temperature than at other temperatures. 4. An increase in temperature raises the rate of respiration.

Review of Facts and Concepts (p. 126)
1. The ultimate energy source of all living things is the sun.
2. A burning match releases energy quickly, and most of the energy is lost as heat. The breakdown of glucose includes reactions that capture and store a significant amount of the released energy. Both types of energy release involve the breaking of chemical bonds.
3. See Figure 7-5 on page 115.
4. Photosynthesis employs sunlight to convert carbon dioxide and water into glucose and oxygen.

During the light reactions, energy from the sun reacts with chlorophyll molecules to produce molecules of ATP and $NADPH_2$. The dark reactions use the energy in ATP and $NADPH_2$ to produce PGAL from CO_2. The PGAL can, in turn, provide energy directly, produce glucose, or remake RDP.
5. The light reactions require light; the dark reactions do not.
6. PGAL is a product of the dark reactions.
7. The amount of carbon dioxide and water, light intensity, and temperature affect the rate of photosynthesis.
8. Cellular respiration converts glucose and oxygen into carbon dioxide, water, and energy. This energy is stored in ATP molecules. The anaerobic phase converts glucose to pyruvic acid, with a net gain of 2 ATP molecules. In the aerobic phase, the pyruvic acid breaks down into CO_2 with the production of 36 molecules of ATP.
9. See Figure 7-10 on page 123.
10. An anaerobe can get only 2 ATP molecules from each molecule of glucose, while an aerobe gets 38 ATP molecules. An anaerobe must therefore process more food to obtain the same amount of energy.
11. *Autotrophs* use the energy of the sun to make their food directly; *heterotrophs* depend completely either on green plants or on other heterotrophs as their sources of food. *NAD* and *NADP* are both hydrogen acceptors; NADP appears in the light reactions of photosynthesis, and NAD in both phases of respiration. An *anaerobe* breaks down food molecules to obtain energy without using oxygen; an *aerobe* requires oxygen for this process.
12. Generalized equations for photosynthesis, cellular respiration, and alcoholic and lactic acid fermentations are given on pages 112, 117, 122, and 123 respectively.
13. Photosynthesis produces glucose. Cellular respiration breaks down glucose to produce ATP. In both processes, the coenzymes (NAD in cellular respiration and NADP in photosynthesis) are similar in structure and function. Cellular respiration produces 38 molecules of ATP; photosynthesis produces only 2 molecules of ATP.

Extensions and Applications (p. 127)
1. The visible colors are red, orange, yellow, green, blue, indigo, and violet.
2. Students must cover the front and the back of the leaf to exclude all light.
3. See Chapter 22, "Leaves."
4. The solutions turn blue, indicating that plants use carbon dioxide during photosynthesis.

8 Cell Growth and Reproduction

Chapter Objectives: See page 128.

Chapter Overview

Chapter 8 opens with a discussion of nucleic acids. The Watson-Crick DNA model serves as the basis for this discussion. The section on protein synthesis further explains the roles of nucleic acids in transcription and translation. The coverage of cell reproduction includes discussions of mitosis and meiosis, as well as of the formation of egg and sperm cells. The chapter concludes with sexual and asexual reproduction in animals and plants.

Teaching Strategies and Activities

1. Have the students make a DNA jigsaw puzzle by cutting pieces of cardboard to represent the parts of a DNA molecule. In cutting the pieces, use the following guidelines: (a) all phosphate and sugar pieces must have the same interlocking pattern; (b) the base-sugar fit must be standardized, allowing any base to fit any sugar; (c) the relative lengths of the four nitrogen bases must be such that a mismatch of a purine with a pyrimidine produces a rung that is shorter or longer than those of properly matched pairs.
2. Prepared slides of mitosis make an excellent introduction to this topic. As students look at individual cells, they can describe what they see. Ask students to speculate about what they think they are observing.

Answer Key to Section Reviews

Nucleic Acids (p. 132)

1. Deoxyribonucleic acid (DNA) and ribonucleic acid (RNA) are the two types of nucleic acid.
2. A nucleotide is a chemical unit in nucleic acid made up of a sugar, phosphate, and base.
3. Purines and pyrimidines are the two classes of nitrogen bases.
4. Replication is the ability of a molecule to build an identical copy of itself.
5. Ribosomal RNA (rRNA), messenger RNA (mRNA), and transfer RNA (tRNA) are the three types of RNA.

Protein Synthesis (p. 135)

1. *Transcription* is the process of making messenger RNA. *Translation* is the building of a protein based on the original DNA code.

2. A *codon* is a three-base messenger RNA code word for a specific amino acid. An *anticodon* is three transfer RNA bases that can bond to a complementary codon on messenger RNA.

Cell Reproduction (p. 141)

1. Interphase, prophase, metaphase, anaphase, and telophase are the five stages of mitosis.
2. A chromosome is a thick, rodlike strand of genes, which are made of DNA.
3. *Mitosis* produces two identical diploid cells. There is only one division in mitosis. *Meiosis* produces four haploid cells. There are two divisions in meiosis.
4. Gametogenesis is the development of gametes by the process of meiosis.
5. The *diploid number* is the normal number of paired chromosomes in a cell. The *haploid number* is half the normal number.

Reproduction of Organisms (p. 143)

1. Asexual reproduction is the formation of offspring from a single parent.
2. Budding, spore formation, and binary fission are forms of asexual reproduction.
3. In sexual reproduction, two haploid gametes unite to form a diploid zygote.
4. Fertilization is the joining of two haploid gametes.
5. In almost all multicellular animals, diploid cells produce haploid gametes through meiosis for sexual reproduction. Most plants have both haploid and diploid forms during their life cycles. The haploid cells produce haploid gametes by mitosis. In sexual reproduction, these gametes produce the diploid form of the plant.

Teaching Aids for Chapter End Features

Laboratory Investigation 8
Examining Mitosis in Onion Root Tip Cells
(p. 144)

Photographs of the various stages of mitosis may be displayed in the classroom.

OBSERVATIONS AND CONCLUSIONS 1. Answers may vary. 2. The chromosomes will not be distinct in interphase. 3. Most dividing cells are found just above the root cap and below the region of cell elongation. 4. Answers will vary. Eight times as many cells as the number of cells originally seen would be formed.

Review of Facts and Concepts (p. 146)

1. DNA contains the information needed to form and control the physical makeup and chemical processes of an organism.
2. The Watson-Crick model is a double helix that has sides made up of alternating sugar molecules and phosphate groups. The two sides of the helix are connected by either two purines or two pyrimidines.
3. RNA is single-stranded, while DNA is double-stranded. In RNA, uracil replaces the base thymine, which is found in DNA. The sugar molecules in RNA are ribose sugars; those in DNA are deoxyribose sugars.
4. DNA contains the sequence of bases that serves as a code for protein synthesis. RNA translates and assembles the specified proteins.
5. A portion of the DNA molecule "unzips." RNA nucleotides in the nucleoplasm bond to complementary bases on one of the unzipped DNA strands. RNA sugar molecules then bond with RNA phosphate groups.
6. Scientists know that at least 20 different amino acids are used to make up proteins. If a codon were only 1 base long, messenger RNA could code for only 4 amino acids. If a codon were 2 bases long, only 16 amino acids could be coded. However, if a codon is 3 bases, 64 3-letter word combinations are possible. A longer word is not necessary.
7. Transfer RNA picks up individual amino acids in the cytoplasm and brings them to the messenger RNA.
8. The types of proteins found in a living thing depend on the coding of its DNA. DNA "codes" vary from one species to another. Therefore, the proteins also vary.
9. The mRNA codon is UAC, and the tRNA anticodon is AUG.
10. See Figures 8-7 through 8-13 on pages 136–38.
11. A *cleavage furrow* is an indentation that pinches an animal-cell membrane inward. A *cell plate* grows from the center of the cytoplasm outward until it reaches the plant-cell wall.
12. In human gametes, there are 23 chromosomes.
13. The chromosomes do not double in the second meiotic division.
14. During egg formation, only one haploid egg cell will form. In sperm formation, one primary spermatocyte yields four haploid sperm.
15. *Asexual reproduction* is the formation, from a single parent, of an offspring that is exactly like its parent. In *sexual reproduction*, two haploid cells unite to form the first cell of a new organism, which has a mixture of the genetic characteristics of both parents.
16. Gametes from a haploid plant are formed by mitosis; spores are formed by meiosis.

Extensions and Applications (p. 146)

1. You may want to do this as a class project, assigning various groups different parts of the DNA molecule.
2. Have students do their drawings under high power. Ask them why several drawings from each stage are needed.
3. Models should be three-dimensional. Clay, pipe cleaners, or insulated wires can be used for chromosomes.
4. You can find the structure of insulin in many college-level introductory biology texts.

Unit Teaching Aids

Perspectives in Biology

The Use of Food Additives (p. 147)

1. Some of your students may want to write to the Food and Drug Administration in Washington, D.C. Students can prepare oral or written reports on the FDA's testing program.
2. Students can also compare the number of foods with and without additives on supermarket shelves.
3. In addition to nutritionists and dieticians, local farmers, health-food-store owners, and general grocers can also be interviewed. Questions regarding their recommendations for the public in general and their own personal preferences in foods can be asked.
4. Students may also write to manufacturers of cereals, candies, preserved fruits, or other foods for their policies and practices concerning food additives. Reports can then be presented to the class summarizing the food industry's responses.

Field Trip Suggestions

1. Arrange a field trip to a wooded area where class members can collect specimens for observation.
2. Visit a local medical school laboratory or university laboratory so that students may familiarize themselves with the careers of people who work with cells.
3. Plan a visit to a nursery or greenhouse. Have your students prepare a floor plan of the nursery or greenhouse. Then have them note the conditions of growth for several different plants.

Audio-Visual Materials

Basic Biochemistry, sound filmstrip, PHM
Cell Biology Series, set/3 films, Cor
Cell Respiration, set/2 sound filmstrips, PHM
Cell Structure, set/2 sound filmstrips, PHM
Diffusion and Osmosis, film, Cor
Energy Cycles in the Cell, film, MGH
Photosynthesis, set/2 sound filmstrips, PHM
The Biochemistry of Photosynthesis, slide program, DGAV
Water in Biology, film, BFA

Reading Resources for Teachers

Barry, J., and E. Barry. *Introduction to the Structure of Biological Molecules*. Englewood Cliffs, N.J.: Prentice-Hall.
Han, S., and J. Holmstedt. *Cell Biology*. New York: McGraw-Hill.
Henrickson, C., and L. Byrd. *Chemistry for the Health Professions*. New York: D. Van Nostrand Co.
Zelitch, I. *Photosynthesis, Photorespiration and Plant Productivity*. New York: Academic Press.

UNIT THREE
Variety and Continuity

Unit Three explores the theories, observations, and knowledge about the variety and continuity of life on the earth. Although the variety is brought about by constant change, life does retain a certain underlying continuity. This continuity is maintained because each generation passes its characteristics on to the next through the processes of heredity. Chapters 9, 10, and 11 present the fundamental facts and concepts of heredity and genetics.

There is much evidence that the plants and animals living today differ from those of the past. Some populations have become extinct, while others have changed gradually or relatively quickly as the result of natural processes. The same processes that ensure continuity also appear to produce differences among offspring and variety among life forms. Chapter 12 presents a discussion of how this variety may have come about during the history of life on the earth. The biological history of human beings is presented in Chapter 13.

9 Heredity

Chapter Objectives: See page 150.

Chapter Overview

Chapter 9 presents the main ideas of classical genetics. After introducing Mendel's experiments and conclusions regarding dominance, recessiveness, hybrids, and purebreds, the first section explains the laws of segregation and independent assortment. The second part of the chapter defines and illustrates fundamental terms in genetics, such as *allele*, *homozygous*, *heterozygous*, *genotype*, and *phenotype*. The role of probability and the product rule in genetics, as well as the use of Punnett squares in monohybrid and dihybrid crosses, is explained. A discussion of incomplete dominance concludes the chapter.

Teaching Strategies and Activities

1. Stimulate interest in heredity by asking such questions as, If nothing new had been discovered in the last 100 years about how characteristics are passed from one generation to another, how would our lives be different today? If you could control genetic processes so that you could design an "ideal" plant, what characteristics would this plant possess?

2. A model enables students to visualize genetic principles. Put about 50 beads of one color into one container and 50 of another color into a second container. (Beans, marbles, or circles of colored paper will also do.) The beads represent male and female gametes, with one color for the dominant trait and the other for the recessive. Each student or group of students should be given a pair of these containers.

   Direct the students to remove one bead from each container and pair them up. These pairings simulate fertilization in a number of monohybrid crosses and the formation of F_1 heterozygous organisms.

   To illustrate an F_1 cross, place 25 beads of each color in one container and 25 beads of each color in the other container. To create an F_2 generation, direct the students to remove one bead from each of the F_1 containers and pair them. The results are various homozygous and heterozygous combinations. Remind students to return the beads to their proper container before they remove the next beads. The class should record their results and compare them with the expected 3:1 phenotype ratio. A model of a dihybrid cross can be set up in a similar way.

Answer Key to Section Reviews

The Work of Gregor Mendel (p. 155)

1. A *dominant trait* shows up in the offspring of true-breeding organisms with contrasting traits. A *recessive trait* is masked.
2. A *hybrid* organism carries genes that are different for one or more characteristics. A *purebred* is an organism carrying genes that are alike for one or more characteristics.
3. The law of segregation states that gene pairs separate during gamete formation.
4. The law of independent assortment states that gene pairs separate independently from one another during gamete formation.

Concepts of Heredity (p. 162)

1. An allele is one of the contrasting genes for a single trait.
2. Genes in a *homozygous* allele pair are identical. Genes in a *heterozygous* allele pair are not identical.
3. The product rule states that the probability of two independent events both happening is equal to the probability of one event occurring multiplied by the probability of the other event occurring.
4. The possible genotypes are $\frac{1}{2}$ Bb and $\frac{1}{2}$ bb. Black (B) is dominant.
5. The gametes for round yellow seeds (RrYy) are RY, Ry, rY, and ry. The gametes for wrinkled green seeds (rryy) are all ry. The results are $\frac{1}{4}$ RrYy (round, yellow), $\frac{1}{4}$ Rryy (round, green), $\frac{1}{4}$ rrYy (wrinkled, yellow), and $\frac{1}{4}$ rryy (wrinkled, green).
6. In some gene pairs, the genes are neither dominant nor recessive.

Teaching Aids for Chapter End Features

Laboratory Investigation 9
Exploring Genetic Probability (p. 163)

Each student should bring two pennies and two nickels to class. If you see the need to do so, review monohybrid and dihybrid crosses, the basic laws of probability, and the Punnett square.

OBSERVATIONS AND CONCLUSIONS 1. The genotypes are Pp × Pp. The phenotypes are purple × purple. **2.** This is a monohybrid cross. **3.** The expected genotypes are 1 PP, 2 Pp, and 1 pp. The expected phenotypes are 3 purple and 1 white. **4.** The genotypes PP and Pp give the same phenotypes. **5.** The probability of white offspring is $\frac{1}{4}$. **6.** Answers will vary. The students' results

from tossing coins should approach the expected ratios. **7.** The genotypes are YyRr × YyRr. The phenotypes are yellow rough × yellow rough. **8.** This is a dihybrid cross. **9.** The expected genotypes are 1 YYRR, 2 YYRr, 1 YYrr, 2 YyRR, 4 YyRr, 2 Yyrr, 1 yyRR, 2 yyRr, and 1 yyrr. The expected phenotypes are 9 yellow rough, 3 yellow smooth, 3 white rough, and 1 white smooth. **10.** YYRR, YYRr, YyRR, and YyRr give yellow rough; YYrr and Yyrr give yellow smooth; yyRr and yyRR give white rough; yyrr gives white smooth. **11.** The probability of heterozygous offspring for both traits is $\frac{4}{16}$ or $\frac{1}{4}$. **12.** See answer for question 6. **13.** The tosses are random. **14.** Not necessarily. The likelihood of obtaining the same results would improve with more trials. As the students continue to toss the coin, the actual numbers come closer to the expected probability.

Review of Facts and Concepts (p. 164)

1. Genes are units of heredity.
2. Mendel could cross a plant with unknown genetic characteristics for a given trait with a true-breeding plant that exhibited the recessive trait. If the tested plant was a hybrid, some of the offspring would show the recessive trait.
3. The law of segregation states that paired genes separate, or segregate, as gametes form.
4. The three pairs are BB, Bb, and bb.
5. Aa, Yy, and Rr are heterozygous genotypes.
6. The phenotypes for green are GG and Gg; for yellow, the phenotype is gg.
7. The probability of a fifth daughter is $\frac{1}{2}$ or 50%.
8. According to the product rule, the probability is $\frac{3}{4} \times \frac{3}{4} = \frac{9}{16}$, or 56.25%.
9. The G allele will occur in 50% of the gametes; the g allele will occur in 50% of the gametes.
10. The possible genotypes are $\frac{1}{2}$ Bb (black) and $\frac{1}{2}$ bb (brown).
11. According to the product rule, the probability of four female babies is $(\frac{1}{2})^4 = \frac{1}{16}$. The probability of eight male babies is $(\frac{1}{2})^8 = \frac{1}{256}$.
12. Seventy-five tall plants would be expected.
13. The probability of a white lamb is $\frac{1}{2}$.
14. The possible gamete combinations are AB; AB and Ab; AB, Ab, aB, and ab; and Ab and ab.
15. In the F_1 generation, all the zygotes would be BbSs, or black and short-haired. In the F_2 generation, the probabilities are as follows: *Black, short-haired* $(\frac{9}{16})$—$\frac{1}{16}$ BBSS, $\frac{2}{16}$ BBSs, $\frac{2}{16}$ BbSS, $\frac{4}{16}$ BbSs. *Black, long-haired* $(\frac{3}{16})$—$\frac{1}{16}$ BBss, $\frac{2}{16}$ Bbss. *White, short-haired* $(\frac{3}{16})$—$\frac{1}{16}$ bbSS, $\frac{2}{16}$ bbSs. *White, long-haired* $(\frac{1}{16})$—$\frac{1}{16}$ bbss.
16. The possible gene combinations are ABCD, abcd, and ABcd. The combinations ABCDD, ABccD, and AaBb are not possible because a

normal gamete contains only one allele for each trait.

17. Because neither yellow (Y) nor white (W) is completely dominant, the F_1 generation is cream-colored (WY). If two cream-colored parents crossed in a WY × WY combination, $\frac{1}{4}$ of the offspring can be expected to be homozygous white (WW), $\frac{1}{4}$ can be expected to be homozygous yellow, and $\frac{2}{4}$ can be expected to be heterozygous and cream-colored. When crossed, the WW purebreds would breed true.

Extensions and Applications (p. 165)

1. The phenotype for RRYYTT is round, yellow seeds, tall stems; for rryytt, it is wrinkled, green seeds, short stems. The F_1 generation would have the genotype RrYyTt; its phenotype would be round, yellow seeds, tall stems. The F_2 generation of RrYyTt plants has eight possible gamete combinations: RYT, RYt, Ryt, ryt, rYt, rYT, ryT, and RyT.

   The offspring in the F_2 generation would be as follows: *Round, yellow, tall* (27)—1 RRYYTT, 8 RrYyTt, 4 RrYyTT, 4 RRYyTt, 4 RrYYTt, 2 RRYYTt, 2 RrYYTT, 2 RRYyTT. *Round, green, tall* (9)—4 RryyTt, 2 RRyyTt, 2 RryyTT, 1 RRyyTT. *Wrinkled, yellow, short* (3)—2 rrYytt, 1 rrYYtt. *Wrinkled, green, tall* (3)—2 rryyTt, 1 rryyTT. *Round, yellow, short* (9)—4 RrYytt, 2 RRYytt, 2 RrYYtt, 1 RRYYtt. *Round, green, short* (3)—2 Rryytt, 1 RRyytt. *Wrinkled, yellow, tall* (9)—4 rrYyTt, 2 rrYYTT, 2 rrYyTT, 1 rrYYTT. *Wrinkled, green, short* (1)—1 rryytt. The ratio is 27:9:9:9:3:3:3:1.

2. Assume that P = penny heads up, p = penny tails up, N = nickel heads up, and so on. On each set of flips, eight combinations are possible: PND, PNd, Pnd, pND, pnD, pnd, PnD, and pNd. Using the product rule, the probability of three heads-up coins (PND) is $\frac{1}{2} \times \frac{1}{2} \times \frac{1}{2} = \frac{1}{8}$. Each of the eight combinations could be expected to show up about 20 times if students flipped the three coins together 160 times (160 ÷ 8).

10 Genes and Chromosomes

Chapter Objectives: See page 166.

Chapter Overview

Chapter 10 presents the work of Sutton, Griffith, Morgan, Bridges, and other researchers, which led to the development of genetic principles. Gene mapping and linkage, sex determination and sex linkage, crossing over, and nondisjunction are explained in general terms. A brief discussion of gene and chromosome mutations follows.

The balance of the chapter explains how these genetic principles apply to human beings. The inheritance of blood types is used to explain multiple alleles. Similarly, sickle-cell disease and phenylketonuria (PKU) exemplify diseases caused by genetic "mistakes." Hemophilia and colorblindness illustrate the heredity of sex-linked traits. Examples of nondisjunction include Down's, Turner's, and Klinefelter's syndromes. A brief treatment of amniocentesis and ultrasound testing concludes the chapter.

Teaching Strategies and Activities

1. Challenge the students with genetic problems that involve each of the genetic principles discussed in this chapter.
2. During the past few years, much debate has centered around such issues as amniocentesis, genetic screening, and the influence of various chemicals and environmental factors on human growth and development. You can engage the class in a discussion of one or more of these topics by setting up an agree–disagree continuum on the board. Draw a long horizontal line on the board, with the word AGREE on one end and the word DISAGREE on the other. Above the line, write a statement of the position. Some examples are "Amniocentesis should be used to determine the sex of unborn fetuses"; "Genetic screening should be supported by public funds"; "Heavy fines should be levied against anyone caught dumping measurable quantities of mutagens into sewers and lakes." Students who wish to do so may then come to the board, one by one, to put their marks somewhere on the continuum. After taking positions, students are more apt to get involved in the discussion.
3. Display photographs of people engaging in various activities, such as singing, performing athletically or artistically, doing schoolwork, arguing, fighting, or doing mechanical work. Discuss whether heredity or environment contributes to a certain talent or behavior.

Answer Key to Section Reviews

The Chromosome Theory (p. 168)

1. According to the chromosome theory, hereditary traits are carried from one generation to the next by genes on chromosomes.
2. Sutton observed the independent and random separation of chromosomes during meiosis. He also noted that the normal number of chromosomes was restored during fertilization. Sutton

concluded that the activity of the chromosomes explained how Mendel's "factors" passed from one generation to the next.

The Nature of Genes (p. 173)

1. Refer to Figure 10-1 on page 168.
2. Avery, MacLeod, and McCarty concluded that DNA is the genetic material of living things and that DNA can transfer from one organism to another, changing the second organism's genetic makeup in the process.
3. A linkage group is all of the genes located on one chromosome.
4. The female gametes are X^R and X^r; the male gametes are X^R and Y. The offspring are $\frac{1}{4}$ $X^R X^r$ (red-eyed females), $\frac{1}{4}$ $X^r X^r$ (white-eyed females), $\frac{1}{4}$ $X^R Y$ (red-eyed males), and $\frac{1}{4}$ $X^r Y$ (white-eyed males).

Genetic Changes (p. 175)

1. A gene mutation is a mutation that affects only one gene.
2. Albinism is a condition in which an organism is not able to form an enzyme needed to make a pigment.
3. A chromosomal mutation is a genetic change involving the loss, addition, or trading of a piece of one chromosome or a change in the number of chromosomes.

Human Genetics (p. 182)

1. Multiple alleles are a group of alleles that control a certain trait.
2. Human blood types are determined by multiple alleles.
3. PKU (phenylketonuria) is caused by a recessive gene that does not permit the formation of the enzyme needed to break down phenylalanine.
4. Hemophilia is a condition in which the blood tends to clot slowly or not at all. People with this disease bleed severely even when they are only slightly injured. A defective sex-linked recessive gene on the X chromosome causes hemophilia.
5. *Trisomy* is a condition in which a zygote has an extra chromosome. *Monosomy* is a condition in which a zygote is missing a chromosome.

Teaching Aids for Chapter End Features

Laboratory Investigation 10
Observing Inherited Human Traits (p. 183)

The dominant traits are dark hair, the ability to roll the tongue sideways, the ability to roll the tongue backward, and a widow's peak. The attached earlobe is recessive. Body height and weight are influenced by the environment. You may want to have your students graph their data for height and weight.

OBSERVATIONS AND CONCLUSIONS **1.** As students try to match more and more traits, the probability that two students will have exactly the same characteristics decreases. **2.** Answers will vary. **3.** Probably, body weight has the widest range of distribution. Eating habits, amount of exercise, and other environmental factors influence body weight. **4.** More individuals should fall in the middle range and fewer individuals at the extreme ends of the curve. **5.** Although both height and earlobe attachment are inherited traits, body height is influenced by environmental factors, while earlobe attachment is not.

Review of Facts and Concepts (p. 184)

1. The grasshoppers that Sutton studied had only 12 chromosomes, but more than 12 characteristics. Each chromosome, therefore, had to carry several traits.
2. DNA is the genetic material of living things. DNA can transfer from one organism to another and, in the process, change the second organism's genetic makeup.
3. Homologous chromosomes are the paired chromosomes in cells that are identical in form and that usually carry the same number and sequence of genes. Refer students to Figure 10-2 on page 169.
4. $X^R X^R$, $X^r Y$, and $X^C X^C$ are genotypes that show sex-linked traits.
5. Cross a white-eyed female ($X^r X^r$) and a red-eyed male ($X^R Y$). Offspring are red-eyed females ($X^R X^r$) and white-eyed males ($X^r Y$).
6. Students should conduct a test cross with a homozygous white (bb) guinea pig.
7. Nondisjunction is the failure of a homologous pair of chromosomes to separate during mitosis or meiosis.
8. *Gene mutations* affect only a short segment of a chromosome. *Chromosomal mutations* involve large pieces of chromosomes or the number of chromosomes.
9. In *translocation*, a broken piece of a chromosome attaches to another chromosome. In a *deletion*, a chromosome loses and does not gain back a chromosome piece. In an *addition*, a chromosome gains extra genes. In an *inversion*, a chromosome breaks in two or more places, and, when the pieces go back together, the arrangement of genes changes.
10. The parents of the child could be $I^A i$ and $I^B i$ or $I^A i$ and ii or $I^B i$ and ii or both ii.
11. The possible offspring would be $\frac{1}{4}$ normal ($Hb^A Hb^A$), $\frac{1}{2}$ heterozygous ($Hb^A Hb^S$) who do not

suffer from the disease, and $\frac{1}{4}$ homozygous (Hb^SHb^S) who have sickle-cell disease.

12. The cause of colorblindness is a recessive allele linked to the X chromosome. In males, a single recessive allele (X^cY) can cause colorblindness. In females, two recessive genes must be inherited (X^cX^c).

13. *Monosomic* cells are missing a chromosome; *trisomic* cells have an extra chromosome.

14. The cause of *Down's syndrome* (trisomy-21) is an extra chromosome on the twenty-first pair of chromosomes. In *Turner's syndrome*, females have only one X chromosome (XO). In *Klinefelter's syndrome*, males have extra X chromosomes.

Extensions and Applications (p. 185)

1. Queen Victoria of England (1819–1901) had one son and three grandsons with hemophilia. Two of her daughters and at least four granddaughters were carriers.

2. Genetic textbooks, biology textbooks, and other reference books contain charts to test for colorblindness.

3. The sickle-cell gene provides some protection against the parasite that causes malaria, *Plasmodium falciparum*.

4. A review of recent research on twins may give the students working on this extension some ideas for their questionnaire.

11 Applications of Genetics

Chapter Objectives: See page 186.

Chapter Overview

This chapter focuses on the practical side of genetic research. The first half includes explanations of selection, mutation, hybridization, inbreeding, and polyploidy. The second half shows students how genetic engineers utilize recombinant DNA and certain types of bacteria to produce growth hormones, insulin, and interferon.

Teaching Strategies and Activities

1. Obtain several different catalogs containing pictures of fruit trees, ornamental trees and plants, and food crops. Have the students review these catalogs looking for claims related to the traits of the plants. Use a list of the claims as a springboard for a discussion of the benefits of genetic breeding.

2. Students can research the origins and development of some common plants, such as pineapple, sunflowers, lettuce, sugar cane, sorghum, triticale, figs, bananas, coconut, strawberries, coffee, tobacco, and grapes. Two useful references for this assignment are *Evolution of Crop Plants*, edited by N. W. Simmonds (Longman), and *Green Immigrants* by Claire S. Haughton (Harcourt Brace Jovanovich).

3. Invite to class either an animal breeder who works with horses or cattle or someone who breeds fish, pigeons, or rabbits for a hobby to discuss his or her work or hobby.

Answer Key to Section Reviews

Plant and Animal Breeding (p. 191)

1. Applied genetics has made possible the development of many plants and animals with improved characteristics.

2. Genetic breeding is the process of crossing a plant or animal that has desired traits with another that has either the same or different desired traits.

3. *Selection* is the process of selecting and breeding organisms with desired traits. *Hybridization* is the selecting and crossing of two genetically different but related organisms to develop offspring with the different desired qualities of each.

4. If $2n = 20$, then $n = 10$ and $3n = 30$.

5. Colchicine induces polyploidy in plants.

Genetic Engineering (p. 194)

1. Genetic engineering involves the addition or removal of specific genes in organisms.

2. Cloning is the production of genetically identical organisms.

3. A *restriction endonuclease* is an enzyme that removes specific segments of a DNA strand. A *plasmid* is a circular form of DNA in bacteria.

4. Answers will vary.

Teaching Aids for Chapter End Features

Laboratory Investigation 11

A Model for Animal Breeding (p. 195)

Before starting the model, explain these assumptions to the class: 1. Assume that there is no dominant or recessive gene. 2. FFmm represents the genotype most desirable for fleece production; ffMM represents the genotype most desirable for mutton production. 3. To ensure high fleece production in all the stock, the sheep breeder wants to develop a purebred line of sheep that all have the genes FF. When the sheep have the genotype FFMM, however, the food they eat is divided between the production of fleece and that of mutton, resulting in only moderate amounts of both.

OBSERVATIONS AND CONCLUSIONS 1. Answers will vary. Most groups will obtain a breeding pair of FFmm in four generations. 2. Answers will vary. Most groups will be able to come up with a pair of FFmm sheep within two or three generations. 3. In Part A, the sheep mate at random to produce offspring. In Part B, only the sheep with the desired traits become the parents of the next generation. 4. The genotype ffMM would result in high mutton production.

Review of Facts and Concepts (p. 196)

1. A wide range of genetic variability provides geneticists with more possibilities to develop organisms with improved characteristics.
2. Selection does not always work as a breeder might wish; recessive genes or some other combination of genes may unexpectedly give rise to undesired traits.
3. Only a very small percentage of mutants have proved to be useful.
4. Triticale is a cross between a wheat plant and a rye plant. The plant is a product of hybridization.
5. Breeders would use *hybridization* if they wanted offspring with the desired traits of two genetically different organisms. Breeders employ *inbreeding* to prevent the introduction of outside traits and to develop organisms that are homozygous for certain traits.
6. Inbreeding results in a population with little or no genetic variability. Although all the members of the population acquire the desired trait, they all become susceptible to the same threats to their well-being.
7. Polyploidy increases variations in plants.
8. The new plant is genetically identical to the parent plant.
9. See Figure 11-6 on page 192.
10. Certain bacteria can be engineered to accept DNA segments, and bacteria reproduce quickly.

Extensions and Applications (p. 196)

1. Refer students to "Vegetative Propagation," page 369, in Chapter 23.
2. Some thoroughbred horses to use as examples are Man o' War, War Admiral, and Secretariat.
3. *Scientific American, Science, Science 82, Discover, Time,* and *Newsweek* are some periodicals that publish articles about recombinant DNA technology.

12 Variation Through Time

Chapter Objectives: See page 198.

Chapter Overview

Throughout the history of the earth, organisms have undergone countless variations. Some of these variations have enabled certain species to survive and reproduce, while other variations have led to extinction. This is the theme of Chapter 12, which presents some of the evidence that indicates that organisms have changed throughout the earth's history. The chapter also presents the theories of evolution advanced by Lamarck, Darwin, and De Vries. The processes that change gene pools, such as adaptive shifts, migration, and isolation, are also explained. The closing section distinguishes between the two pathways of divergent and convergent evolution.

Teaching Strategies and Activities

1. Display photographs and specimens of 20–30 animals. Have individual students or student groups identify several adaptations for 15 or more of these animals. The adaptations should relate to life activities.
2. Design a laboratory investigation to demonstrate the variation in a species. For example, have students measure the lengths of pine needles or leaves from a tree. In each case, the students should record the data on a chart and make a graph of the results.
3. Obtain fossils of plants and animals. Have small groups of students observe the fossils and record as much information about each organism as can be discerned from its fossil. Ask students to describe the type of fossil in each case.

Answer Key to Section Reviews

Adaptations in Living Things (p. 200)

1. Sometimes a variation makes an organism better suited to its changing environment.
2. An adaptation is a helpful variation that is passed on from generation to generation.

Evidence of Evolution (p. 206)

1. Fossil evidence suggests that organisms living today are different from those which lived in the past.
2. Inland rocks contain fossils of ocean-dwelling animals. Fossils of warm-water corals turn up in the Arctic. Fossils of palm-tree leaves and ferns are found in cold regions of the earth.

3. Homologous organs and vestigial organs are used as anatomical evidence of evolution.
4. Biochemical research shows that living things with similar anatomical and embryological features have similar sequences of amino acids in certain proteins.

Theories of Evolution (p. 210)

1. Lamarck thought that traits acquired in one generation could be inherited by the next generation and that organs developed or disappeared depending on how often they were used.
2. Darwin's four hypotheses were: (a) the world is not static but changing; (b) living things change through time; (c) organisms with many common characteristics descended from a common ancestor; (d) evolutionary change is a result of natural selection.
3. Darwin thought that four factors were involved in evolution: overproduction, competition or the struggle for existence, variations, and natural selection.
4. De Vries thought that sudden mutations caused the development of new species.

Processes of Evolution (p. 214)

1. A gene mutation is a change in the genetic message of DNA.
2. An adaptive shift is a change in the frequency of occurrence of certain genes as the environment changes. As the frequency of a certain gene either increases or decreases, the shift changes the gene pool.
3. Natural and artificial barriers cause geographic isolation. Differences in the genetic composition of organisms cause genetic isolation. Isolation of either sort may lead to speciation.

Pathways of Evolution (p. 216)

1. Divergent evolution is the process whereby many different species develop from a common ancestor. Examples will vary.
2. Convergent evolution is the process whereby unrelated species develop similar characteristics. Examples will vary.

Teaching Aids for Chapter End Features

Laboratory Investigation 12
A Model for Natural Selection (p. 217)

You may want to have the students cut out the circles themselves.

OBSERVATIONS AND CONCLUSIONS 1. Answers will vary. 2. No, the blindfolded student randomly selects either color. 3. White has the greater frequency of survivors. Against the white background, the colored circles show up better than the white ones. 4. The removal of the circles represents predation. 5. Part A represents random selection; Part B represents nonrandom or natural selection. The blindfolded student selects the circles at random. The sighted student selects the circles that are easier to see against the white background. 6. In Part A, the frequency of each color would remain about the same. In Part B, the frequency of the white color would increase, and the frequency of the green color would decrease.

Review of Facts and Concepts (p. 218)

1. A *species* is a group of organisms that can interbreed. *Variations* are small differences that exist within the organisms in a species.
2. Answers will vary. Each adaptation noted should have survival value.
3. Inland rocks contain fossils of animals that lived in oceans. Fossils of tropical organisms appear in the Antarctic. Fossil remains of extinct organisms have been found. Fossils of animals that live today, such as horses, indicate that they were different in the past.
4. Radioactive decay is the breakdown of the nuclei of radioactive elements. The rate of radioactive decay of certain elements is the basis of radioactive dating. With this technique, scientists are able to measure how many years ago an organism lived.
5. The structure and arrangement of the bones and muscles are similar.
6. Answers will vary.
7. Organisms with variations that make them better suited to their environment than other organisms live to reproduce more of their kind. These helpful variations accumulate in the population from one generation to the next. Over a long period, the entire population will have the variation.
8. Lamarck thought that organisms changed to meet environmental needs. According to Darwin, organisms with suitable characteristics for a certain environment survived and reproduced.
9. *Microevolution* is a small and gradual change in a species. *Macroevolution* is a large and sudden change that produces a new species.
10. The organism's environment determines the value of a mutation. If the mutation gives an organism an advantage over others in a given environment, it is valuable. A mutation that reduces the organism's chances of survival and reproduction is not valuable. Answers will vary.

11. Recombination shuffles genes into different arrangements during meiosis. As a result, the offspring of sexually reproducing parents have many variations.

12. If all members of a population were genetically alike, an adverse change in the environment could destroy the whole population. If variations are present, some of the population may have a variation that is helpful in the changing environment. These organisms will survive and reproduce. A trait that was advantageous or neutral in the past may become harmful in the event of a change in the environment.

13. Organisms that migrate into and out of a population either add or subtract genes to or from the gene pool.

14. Mutations and genetic recombination could increase the variations in one or all of the isolated populations. Different environmental conditions could then "select" different variations in each of the populations. If the differences become so great that interbreeding can no longer occur between the separated populations, a new species is the result.

15. In *convergent evolution*, unrelated species develop similar adaptations for life in similar environments. In *divergent evolution*, different species develop from a common ancestor. Examples will vary.

Extensions and Applications (p. 219)

1. Arrange a field trip to a local area where students can look for fossils, which can provide clues to an area's past history. State and federal publications are also useful references for this assignment.

2. You may want to have small groups of students prepare different explanations of the extinction of the dinosaurs. Have each group also prepare a visual aid that expresses the explanation. Some explanations may include: (a) cold water from the landlocked Arctic Ocean poured over into the Atlantic Ocean, causing climatic changes and the disruption of food chains; (b) the world's climate warmed up considerably 65 million years ago owing to increased amounts of carbon dioxide in the atmosphere, and dinosaurs were unable to survive in the new conditions; (c) a huge asteroid hit the earth, darkening the sky for a lengthy period of time, and changing the climate; (d) alterations in the earth's magnetic field, which occur from time to time, left the earth unprotected from radiation, thereby killing off the dinosaurs; (e) a star that exploded near the earth destroyed the ozone layer; or (f) mammals became more dominant, and dinosaurs could not compete for food.

3. Students should use Figure 12-4 on page 201 as a model.

4. The students should note the relationship between the beak structures and the feeding habits of birds. The students should also note how the structures of legs, feet, and wings are suited to the environment.

13 Human History

Chapter Objectives: See page 220.

Chapter Overview

Chapter 13 begins by describing the characteristics and arboreal heritage of the primates. Certain anatomical, physiological, and behavioral characteristics that make human beings unique among the primates are briefly outlined. The discussion then presents the various theories of human biological history as they have been developed from studies of human fossils. The contrasting viewpoints of Johanson and White and of the Leakeys on the role of australopithecines in human biological history are presented. The chapter concludes with a description of the Neanderthals and Cro-Magnons.

Teaching Strategies and Activities

1. Collect and display photographs of people that show some of the small differences in human beings, such as skin and hair color, the shape of facial bones, hair texture, and the positioning or folding of the skin around the eyes. Discuss how some of these features could serve as adaptations for life in specific environments.

2. To single out just one of the many ways in which individuals differ, have the students compare their fingerprints. Students should clean their fingers with 70% ethanol. Then have them roll the tip of each finger from side to side on an office stamp pad and then on plain white paper. After making the prints, students should try to group the prints according to their patterns. Students should also contrast the prints. Reference to the Henry System, which recognizes five main groups of fingerprints, will help students to classify fingerprints.

3. Assign library research questions to small groups of students. Some possible questions follow. What are the trends in human height, weight, and cranial capacity? What causes aging in people? Do human beings have any instincts? How much is known about *A. afarensis, A. africanus, H. habilis,* and *H. erectus*? What happened to the Nean-

derthals? Who were the first human beings to live in North America? Students should display their findings on posterboards.

Answer Key to Section Reviews

Primate Characteristics (p. 221)

1. Most primates have opposable thumbs and flat nails. Both of these adaptations facilitate grasping.
2. Primates have well-developed color vision and can see fine detail even in dim light. They also have stereoscopic vision.

Human Characteristics (p. 225)

1. The shape of the foot is adapted to walking upright. The arch supports the weight of the body. The large toe is not opposable and therefore is suited for walking. Finally, the pelvis supports the upper body mass.
2. Bipedal animals walk on two limbs.
3. The pongids have large canines and premolars. Human teeth are generally smaller than those of pongids. In human beings, the teeth are arranged in a curved row. In pongids, the teeth are arranged in nearly parallel lines along the sides of the jaw.
4. Human beings do not have a definite breeding season. They also develop and age more slowly than do other primates.
5. The two classic examples of human behavioral characteristics are making and using tools and using symbols to form languages.

Biological History of Human Beings (p. 229)

1. The skull of A. africanus is larger than most non-human primate skulls but smaller than a modern human skull.
2. The skulls of H. habilis have thinner bones and are larger, higher, and rounder than those of the australopithecines.
3. "Lucy" was 105 cm tall and fully grown. The structure of her leg bones and pelvis indicates that she could walk erect. The skeleton shows a humanlike body and an apelike head.
4. The shape of the jaw, the shape and size of the teeth, the location of the opening where the spinal cord enters the skull, and the shape of the pelvis are some similarities between early hominids and modern humans.
5. The Cro-Magnons used tools and weapons, which indicates that they were good hunters. They made pottery, carved bones, and created cave paintings.

Teaching Aids for Chapter End Features

Laboratory Investigation 13
Studying the Hands of Primates (p. 230)

You may want to assign additional activities for Procedure 1.

OBSERVATIONS AND CONCLUSIONS 1. Generally, students should find that without opposable thumbs, many ordinary tasks become impossible or at least extremely difficult and time-consuming. **2.a.** All hands have five digits with claws or nails on each digit. **b.** *Shrew*: claws. *Tarsier*: enlarged pads on the tips of the digits. *Baboon*: nails on the ends of the digits and hands adapted for walking. *Orangutan*: elongated fingers and palm for climbing, as well as a short thumb. *Gorilla*: a short thumb and broad hand. *Human being*: a long, opposable thumb with short fingers. **c.** Nails replace claws on the digits. The thumb becomes larger in size and its location on the hand changes.

Review of Facts and Concepts (p. 231)

1. The characteristics of primates related to their arboreal heritage are hands adapted for grasping and stereoscopic color vision.
2. The human skeleton is better adapted for an upright position than the skeletons of other primates. The opposable thumb makes the human hand better suited for grasping. The human jaw has a different shape from the pongid jaw, and human teeth have a different shape and serve a different purpose from the teeth of the pongids. Human beings have larger and more complex brains than other primates. Two main physiological differences are that human beings have no definite breeding season and that they develop and age more slowly than other primates.
3. The human brain has a highly developed memory center and gives human beings a level of intelligence that is not matched by any other organism.
4. The position of the hole through which a spinal cord enters a skull indicates whether an organism walked upright. The study of fossil teeth can help determine what early hominids tended to eat.
5. A. robustus fossils are larger and weigh more than those of A. africanus. The jaws of A. robustus are also heavier and hold larger teeth than those of A. africanus.
6. H. habilis had an erect posture and humanlike hands. The skull of H. habilis is larger, higher, and rounder than those of the australopithecines, and the skull bones are thinner.
7. Johanson and White theorize that A. afarensis is the common ancestor of modern human beings

and of *A. africanus* and *A. robustus*. The Leakkys argue that the australopithecines were not the ancestors of modern human beings.

8. *Neanderthals* stood erect with an average height of 150 cm. Their bones were thicker and heavier than those of modern human beings. Most Neanderthal fossils are almost chinless, and some have sloped foreheads. *Cro-Magnons* were very similar to present-day human beings. About 173 cm tall, Cro-Magnons had high foreheads, small teeth, and large brain cavities.

9. Both the Neanderthals and the Cro-Magnons used fire and tools, lived in many different types of shelters, and hunted a variety of animals. Cro-Magnon culture, as evidenced by their pottery, carved bones, and paintings, was probably more complex than Neanderthal culture.

Extensions and Applications (p. 232)

1. Remind students that their presentations should recognize the multicultural nature of modern society.
2. In 1908, bone fragments of an unusually thick skull that was human in form were found in a gravel pit. Later an apelike lower jaw with two worn-down molars was also found. All of the deeply stained bones looked very old. Once the head was reconstructed, many considered it to be an important part of the record of human prehistory. In the late 1940s and early 1950s, however, it was discovered that the bones had been artificially stained and the molars filed down. The jaw was that of an orangutan. Piltdown man was obviously a fraud. Someone had modified the bones and planted them in the gravel pit.
3. If possible, students should review sources published over a 25- to 35-year time span. There is some evidence that artists working a few decades ago depicted early human beings as more brutish than those depicted by artists of today.
4. Students could summarize the material on a bulletin board.

Unit Teaching Aids

Perspectives in Biology

Sudden or Gradual Changes in Living Things (p. 233)

1. The most widely accepted theories of dinosaur extinction are macroevolutionary. They state that the dinosaurs could not adapt to a rapid (geologically speaking) change in their environment,

such as cooler worldwide temperatures or increased radiation from nearby exploding stars. Microevolutionists claim that plant-eating dinosaurs were not able to eat the new kinds of plants that developed slowly over millions of years. This problem was compounded by the rise of mammals, because the dinosaurs could not compete with the mammals for food. As the plant-eaters died out, so too did the meat-eaters that fed on them.

2. Many articles on macroevolution and microevolution have appeared recently in general scientific journals such as *Scientific American*, *Science*, *Nature*, and *Natural History*. More specific articles on these subjects may be found in journals such as *Annual Review of Ecology and Systematics*, *Evolution*, and *Paleobiology*. These latter journals may be found in large college or public libraries or may be ordered directly from their publishers.

Field Trip Suggestions

1. During the study of applied genetics, schedule a field trip to an agricultural experimental station, a plant nursery, a seed company, or a pet store.
2. As an introduction to Chapter 12, tour the natural history section of a museum.
3. Locate an area where the fossils and the geological history of the area can be found. A canyon or river bank is a suitable place. ***Caution:*** *Be sure to provide students with safety rules before visiting such an area. Use the buddy system.*

Audio-Visual Materials

DNA and Cell Reproduction, set/2 sound filmstrips, PHM
DNA: The Code of Heredity, sound filmstrip, HBJ
DNA: The Genetic Code, set/2 sound filmstrips, PHM
Elephant and Camel: Then and Now, sound filmstrip, HBJ
Evolution, set/6 sound filmstrips, DGAV
Evolution, set/6 sound filmstrips, PHM
Fossil Interpretation, super 8mm film loop, HBJ
Genetics Series, set/5 films, Cor
The Dinosaur Age, film, BFA
The Path to Genetics: Mendel's Laws, set/4 sound filmstrips, DGAV

Reading Resources for Teachers

Glass, B. *Genetic Continuity*. Lexington, Mass.: D. C. Heath Company.
Goodenough, U. *Genetics*. New York: Holt, Rinehart and Winston.

Mayr, E. *Evolution and the Diversity of Life*. Cambridge, Mass.: Harvard University Press.

Szalay, F., and E. Delson. *Evolutionary History of the Primates*. New York: Academic Press.

UNIT FOUR
Microbes

Although microbes are invisible to the unaided eye, these organisms have a great influence on the earth's living things. Chapters 14, 15, and 16 explore the worlds of viruses, bacteria, blue-green algae, and protozoans, respectively. Each chapter describes the structure, characteristics, and functions of one of these groups of microbes. Chapter 17 relates selected microbes to the diseases they cause. It also presents the body's defenses against disease, as well as methods for preventing and treating diseases.

14 Viruses

Chapter Objectives: See page 236.

Chapter Overview

Smaller than bacteria and too small for observation under the light microscope, viruses are tiny particles that contain hereditary material. The opening section of Chapter 14 provides a brief historical account of the discovery of viruses. Subsequent sections discuss the structural characteristics and classification of viruses. The distinctive characteristic of viruses is that they replicate only within living cells. This fact forms the basis for a discussion of the lytic cycle. The chapter closes with a section on plant and animal viral diseases.

Teaching Strategies and Activities

1. When bacteriophages infect a "lawn" of bacteria growing on an agar plate, the phages lyse the bacterial cells, producing clear areas called plaques. While discussing the stages of the lytic cycle, pass agar plates with plaques around the class. After your discussion, ask the students for ideas as to what the clear areas on the agar plates are.
2. Is the virus a living or nonliving thing? This question can serve as a general introduction to the chapter. Draw a picture of a virus on the chalkboard. Give a brief synopsis of its structure and manner of replication. Ask the students whether or not it is living. Have them support their answers.
3. Assign each student a plant or animal viral disease to research. Have each student give a two-minute oral report on the viral disease.

Answer Key to Section Reviews

Discovery of Viruses (p. 237)

1. The tobacco mosaic virus was the first virus to be isolated and identified.
2. Viroids are disease-causing agents that are simpler than viruses.

Viral Anatomy (p. 239)

1. A *capsid* is a layer of protein that surrounds most viruses. The repeating protein units of a capsid are called *capsomeres*.
2. Viruses are measured in nanometers.
3. In the past, viruses were classified according to the hosts they infected, the types of tissues they attacked, their methods of transmission, and the disease symptoms they produced.
4. The first viral classification grouping is the division.

Viral Replication and the Lytic Cycle (p. 242)

1. A bacteriophage is a virus that infects bacterial cells.
2. The lytic cycle is the process that occurs when a virus infects a cell.
3. Cell lysis is the bursting of the host cell.

Viruses and Disease (p. 244)

1. When a virus infects a plant, the plant tissues may become discolored or deformed. The plant may also develop tumors.
2. A *vector* is a transmitter of a virus. A *viral reservoir* is a source of a virus.
3. Animal viral diseases include equine encephalitis, blood poisoning, rabies, foot-and-mouth diseases, and cancer.

Teaching Aids for Chapter End Features

Laboratory Investigation 14
Constructing a Bacteriophage Model
(p. 245)

Floral wire is available at florists, hobby shops, and craft stores.

OBSERVATIONS AND CONCLUSIONS 1. The students should label the head, tail, protein coat, and attachment fibers. **2.** The acorn nut (head) would contain the nucleic acid. **3.** The pipe cleaner represents the sheath. **4.** The floral wire legs (attachment fibers) would be used to attach the phage to its host cell.

Review of Facts and Concepts (p. 246)

1. The study of viruses is called virology.
2. Iwanowski discovered that the tobacco mosaic virus was small enough to pass through a filter that trapped bacteria. Beijerinck discovered that TMV could reproduce only in a living tobacco plant.
3. Shadow casting is a special electron microscope technique used to study viruses.
4. The *nucleic acid core* carries genetic information. The *capsid* is a layer of protein that surrounds the core. The *capsomeres* are repeating protein units that make up the capsid. The *membranous envelope* surrounds the protein coat on some viruses.
5. Viruses have only one type of nucleic acid, not both types as do cells. Whereas the functions of the nucleic acids in cells may differ, the nucleic acids of viruses have only one function: the production of a new viral nucleic acid. In cells, DNA is always double-stranded and RNA is always single-stranded. In viruses, the DNA or RNA can be either single- or double-stranded.
6. Viral classification is based on the structural and chemical composition of viruses.
7. Bacteriophages have round, oval, or many-sided heads and hollow tails. Usually, the tail has fibers.
8. *Adsorption*: The bacteriophage attaches itself to a cell by means of its tail fibers. *Host cell penetration*: An enzyme in the tip of the tail makes an opening in the bacterium's cell wall, and the nucleic acid moves through the tubelike tail into the cell. *Eclipse*: The nucleic acid of the bacteriophage causes the cell to form new viral parts. *Formation of new phages*: The viral parts assemble to form new and complete phages. *Host cell rupture:* Lysozyme builds up and makes the cell wall increasingly thinner. Eventually the bacterium bursts, releasing the new phages.
9. A dual-host virus is a virus that an arthropod vector transmits from one vertebrate host to another vertebrate host.

Extensions and Applications (p. 246)

1. Students often think that electron microscopes are similar in size to light microscopes. Have students note the size and cost of an electron microscope.

2. As the students prepare their models, ask students to find out the answers to the following questions: How do viruses other than bacteriophages get into cells? Is the lytic cycle the same for most types of viruses?
3. Listed in the Suggested Readings are two good source books for this research, *The Viruses* and *Virus Hunters*.
4. Some questions that the students may ask follow. What is a parvovirus? Can pets be immunized against viruses? What are the contraindications of such immunization? Can pets infect humans with these viruses?

15 Monerans

Chapter Objectives: See page 248.

Chapter Overview

Monerans, such as bacteria and blue-green algae, are everywhere. This chapter acquaints students with the general characteristics of bacteria, including size, shape, general structure, and modes of movement. Discussions of nutrition and digestion, respiration, and growth and reproduction in bacteria follow. In the respiration section, the differences among aerobic, anaerobic, and facultative bacteria are explained. The conditions that bacteria require to survive and reproduce are discussed in the growth and reproduction sections. Endospore formation, DNA transfer by means of conjugation, transformation, and transduction are explained in subsequent sections. Students learn the importance of bacteria in the food industry, medicine, leather tanning, and agriculture. The chapter ends with a discussion of the characteristics of blue-green algae.

Teaching Strategies and Activities

1. Many bacteria are instrumental in the spoilage of food. Have students design experiments to test the effectiveness of various preservatives, such as salt, sugar, and vinegar. Do these substances stop the growth of bacteria in foods?
2. To introduce the concept of nutritional requirements for bacterial growth, prepare four agar plates containing: agar only (15 g purified agar + 1 L distilled water); agar + minerals (1 g $NH_4H_2PO_4$ [ammonium dihydrogen phosphate], 1 g KCl, and 1 g $MgSO_4$ per L); agar + minerals + glucose (10 g glucose per L); and agar + minerals + glucose + peptone (10 g peptone per L). Inoculate each plate with a bacterium, such as *E. coli*, and put the plates in a warm place overnight. The next day, pass the plates around the classroom. Some questions to ask follow. What

are the masses on some of the agar plates? Why haven't these masses covered the entire plate? Why do some plates have growth while others do not? What is in each of these types of media that the bacteria need? Will the bacteria grow as well in the light as in the dark?

4. Relate genetic engineering (Chapter 11) to what the students are now learning about bacteria.
5. Have students prepare a study of the treatment of sewage with bacteria. Some questions that can be answered in their reports follow. How is sewage treatment keeping America's rivers clean? Can sewage be recycled in any way? What are some methods of sewage treatment?

Answer Key to Section Reviews

Characteristics of Bacteria (p. 251)

1. The general shape of some bacteria can be seen under 1000×.
2. Bacteria are spherical, rod-shaped, or spiral-shaped.
3. The cell wall maintains the shape of a bacterium.
4. *Granules* are structures that store food. *Plasmids* are separate segments of DNA in some bacteria.
5. Spirochetes move by rotating with a spiral motion.

Life Functions in Bacteria (p. 251)

1. Photosynthetic bacteria use the sun's energy to make food.
2. A *saprophytic bacterium* feeds on dead organic matter. A *parasitic bacterium* feeds on other living things.
3. When cells use oxygen to break down substances, the process is called *aerobic respiration*. When they do not use oxygen, the process is called *anaerobic respiration*. *Staphylococcus epidermidis* is an aerobe. *Clostridium botulinum* is an anaerobe.
4. Ideal growth conditions include an adequate food and water supply, the appropriate aerobic or anaerobic condition, the proper temperature, sufficient moisture, and the absence of sunlight and harmful chemicals.
5. Bacteria usually reproduce asexually by binary fission.
6. F^+ bacteria have plasmids; F^- bacteria do not.

Importance of Bacteria (p. 256)

1. Bacteria can spoil food, contaminate water, and cause disease.
2. Bacteria change lactose into lactic acid in the milk used for cheese making.
3. Nitrogen-fixing bacteria change free nitrogen into nitrogen compounds. These compounds can then be used by other organisms for growth and development.

Cyanophytes (p. 258)

1. They both are prokaryotes.
2. Phycocyanin

Laboratory Investigation 15
Examining Bacterial Growth (p. 259)

Although you can purchase nutrient agar plates, preparing them saves costs. To prepare the agar plates, follow the mixing instructions on the containers of commercially prepared dry powdered nutrient agar. Autoclave the agar mixture at 121 °C under 15 psi for 15 minutes. Sterilize the glass petri dishes in a dry-air oven at 177 °C (350 °F) for two hours. After flaming the mouth of the agar container, pour the sterile medium into the sterile petri dishes.

OBSERVATIONS AND CONCLUSIONS 1. Answers will vary. The colonies of various bacterial species have different appearances. 2. Growth should appear in one to two days. 3. Answers will vary. 4. Identify the types by shape. 5. Bacteria grow and multiply where food and water are available under the appropriate temperatures.

Review of Facts and Concepts (p. 260)

1. Bacteria decompose complex substances into simpler substances. Bacteria also recycle substances.
2. *Streptococci* are chains of spherical bacteria. *Diplobacilli* are two rod-shaped bacteria attached end to end. *Staphylococci* are grapelike clusters of spherical bacteria. *Streptobacilli* are chains of rod-shaped bacteria that are strung end to end.
3. See Figure 15-3 on page 250.
4. Motile bacteria can move by means of flagella or by rotating.
5. *Autotrophic bacteria* make their own food from inorganic substances. *Heterotrophic bacteria* obtain food from their environment.
6. *Obligate anaerobes* are bacteria that undergo anaerobic respiration and cannot live in the presence of oxygen. *Obligate aerobes* are bacteria that need and use oxygen to undergo respiration. *Facultative bacteria* can live with or without oxygen.
7. In an actively growing culture, bacteria divide very quickly. Therefore, they do not age.
8. To slow down or stop bacterial growth, you can (1) remove the food and/or water source, (2) add

or take away oxygen, (3) heat or cool the culture, (4) add certain chemicals to the medium, or (5) keep the bacterial environment dry.

9. Bacterial endospores enable certain bacteria to survive unfavorable changes in their environment.

10. In both conjugation and transduction, DNA passes from one bacterium to another. In conjugation, this transfer takes place directly between the two bacteria. In transduction, a virus accomplishes the transfer.

11. In transformation, a live bacterium takes in DNA from a dead bacterium. In both conjugation and transduction, two living cells transfer DNA.

12. Answers will vary. The students may select three examples from those cited in the text.

Extensions and Applications (p. 261)

1. Students may also include Ferdinand J. Cohn, Friedrich Löffler, Sir Alexander Fleming, Paul Ehrlich, and the development of the electron microscope on their timeline.

2. You may want to use this assignment as a class field trip.

3. Most biological supply houses carry prepared slides of different bacteria. Good examples to use are *Bacillus* or *Clostridium* with an endospore stain; *Streptococcus* with a cell wall stain; *Pseudomonas* with a flagella stain; and a pathogenic bacterium, such as *Klebsiella pneumonia*, with a capsule stain.

16 Protozoans

Chapter Objectives: See page 262.

Chapter Overview

The protozoans are grouped into four phyla. The first two sections of this chapter discuss the sarcodines (Sarcodina) and ciliates (Ciliophora) respectively. *Amoeba* is used as the representative sarcodine, and *Paramecium* is used as the representative ciliate. The student studies the structure and the processes of food-getting, digestion, excretion, gas exchange, response, and reproduction in each organism. A discussion of the organisms in the phylum Mastigophora follows. The representative organism is *Euglena*. The chapter concludes with a discussion of the immobile, spore-forming sporozoans. *Plasmodium* is used as an example.

Teaching Strategies and Activities

1. Show several film loops of representative protozoans. Most film loops show the structures of various protozoans, as well as their methods of movement and food-getting.

2. The type of *Foraminifera* skeletons found in rock strata helps scientists estimate the date that a layer of rock was formed. Have students research how this concept helps prospectors locate oil-bearing rock strata.

3. Classification of the protozoans has always been a controversial topic among biologists. Have students research taxonomic schemes other than the one in the text and classify protozoa using various taxonomic approaches.

Answer Key to Section Reviews

The Sarcodines (p. 265)

1. A pseudopod is a projection of the cytoplasm of a sarcodine.

2. The amoeba feeds on small algae, other protists, and some microscopic multicellular animals.

3. Chemotaxis is a response to chemicals.

4. Amoebas reproduce by binary fission or by multiple fission.

The Ciliates (p. 269)

1. The pellicle is the hard membrane covering the outer surface of a paramecium.

2. Organisms use cilia for movement and food-getting.

3. Trichocysts are poisonous dartlike threads of protoplasm that are used to capture food and to anchor and defend a paramecium.

4. Paramecia reproduce asexually by binary fission and sexually by conjugation.

The Flagellates (p. 271)

1. Flagella are long, whiplike structures that are used for movement.

2. The eyespot is a light-sensitive reddish area located near the reservoir on the anterior end of the euglena.

3. The euglena reproduces asexually by longitudinal binary fission.

The Sporozoans (p. 272)

1. Sporozoans produce spores, have no means of locomotion, and are parasitic.

2. The sporozoan *Plasmodium* causes malaria in human beings. The *Anopheles* mosquito transmits the sporozoan.

Teaching Aids for Chapter End Features

Laboratory Investigation 16
Observing Examples of Living Protozoans
(p. 273)

If you have not already done so, show the students the proper technique for preparing wet-mount slides. Also demonstrate how to adjust the light source in the microscope to obtain the best contrast. *Note: Remind the students not to contaminate the droppers by using the same ones for different organisms.*

OBSERVATIONS AND CONCLUSIONS 1. The cytoplasm is constantly moving, and it is paler at the edges. **2.** The nucleus moves along with the cytoplasm. **3.** Drawings should show how the paramecium stops, reverses itself, turns, and continues forward in another direction. **4.** Paramecia swim in a spiraling motion. The cilia beat in a coordinated movement. **5.** *Euglena* is green. **6.** *Euglena* has an elongated body with a rounded anterior and a pointed posterior. **7.** The movement of *Euglena* suggests a flexible pellicle because *Euglena* not only moves in a twisting motion but also bends, contracts, and expands.

Review of Facts and Concepts (p. 274)

1. Typical protozoans are microscopic, unicellular organisms without cell walls. They have a membrane-bound nucleus and many organelles.
2. Protozoans are classified according to their method of movement.
3. *Ectoplasm* is the thin, clear cytoplasm of an amoeba that is close to the cell membrane. *Endoplasm* is the thick, grainy cytoplasm that makes up the inner part of the amoeba's cytoplasm.
4. An amoeba surrounds food with its pseudopodia.
5. The cyst enables an amoeba to resist unfavorable environmental conditions.
6. The paramecium moves by using cilia, which cause the microbe to move in a spiraling motion.
7. Contractile vacuoles pump excess water out of amoebas and paramecia.
8. See Figure 16-7 on page 269.
9. The function of the organelles in *Paramecium* can be compared to the function of organs in more complex organisms, which is not the case with *Amoeba proteus*.
10. The euglena moves by means of a flagellum.
11. Euglenas need bright light to carry on photosynthesis. Biologists think that the eyespot is light-sensitive.
12. Euglenas divide by longitudinal binary fission rather than across their width.
13. Students should follow the two-stage life cycle shown in Figure 16-11 on page 272.
14. The four major phyla of protozoans and an example of an organism in each phylum follow. Sarcodina: *Amoeba proteus*. Ciliophora: *Paramecium*. Mastigophora: *Euglena gracilis*. Sporozoa: *Plasmodium*.

Extensions and Applications (p. 275)

1. To record the types of protozoans in the jars, the students will need some sort of identification key, which may be found in a reference book. You may want to pose some of the following questions. Do photosynthetic protozoans appear in every sample? Explain. Would you expect to find different types of protozoans in samples taken from different places? If more than one species of a protozoan shows up in one sample, what might be the explanation?
2. If you have not done so already, explain to your students how to apply various substances to the slides. The technique is the same as staining cells. Staining techniques are given in the Reference Section on page 793.
3. This exercise may be used as a class activity, and will provide a good review of life functions in each of the protozoans.

17 Human Microbial Disease and Immunity

Chapter Objectives: See page 276.

Chapter Overview

Chapter 17 discusses how microbes cause diseases and how people spread, prevent, and treat diseases. The human body itself puts up the first line of defense against diseases. Bacteriostats, phagocytes, antibodies, antitoxins, and interferon are discussed as natural defenses of the body.

Students also learn how diseases spread through the air, in food or water, or by contact. Several common viral, bacterial, and protozoan diseases are discussed, including hepatitis, measles, food poisoning, tuberculosis, and African sleeping sickness. The closing discussion on disease control includes means of prevention, such as disinfectants, quarantines, and vaccines, as well as means of treatment, such as the use of chemotherapy and antibiotics.

Teaching Strategies and Activities

1. To introduce the role of disinfectants as a preventative measure, set up a demonstration of their effectiveness. Have students bring in either disinfectants or cleaning products that contain disinfectants. At the beginning of class, seed nutrient agar plates with a common microorganism, such as *B. cereus* or *S. lutea*. Soak a number of sterile filter paper disks (about 8 mm in diameter) in each disinfectant, and place the disks on the plates at least 15 mm apart. Incubate the plates in a warm place for 24 to 48 hours, and then observe them. Ask the students the following questions. Are there clear areas around any of the disks? What do these clear areas signify? How effective do household disinfectants seem to be against a common microbe? As a variation, compare the effectiveness of various brands of mouthwash against *S. salivarius* cultured on dextrose starch agar.

2. How do antibiotics kill or inhibit the growth of bacteria? Why don't antibiotics attack body cells as well? Have students research the answers to these and similar questions.

3. Assign each student a different viral, bacterial, or protozoan disease. Have each student prepare a one-minute oral report on the cause, symptoms, and treatment of the assigned disease.

Answer Key to Section Reviews

Natural Defenses of the Body (p. 279)

1. Bacteriostats are substances that help prevent the growth of microbes on the skin.
2. A phagocyte is a specialized amoebalike white blood cell that surrounds and destroys microbes in the human body.
3. *Antigens* are proteins that are foreign to the body. The body responds to antigens by producing *antibodies*.
4. Interferon is a protective substance that body cells produce when invaded by viruses.

Causes and Spread of Disease (p. 285)

1. Infectious microbes can be spread by air, by contaminated food or water, by direct contact with an infected person, or by indirect contact with a contaminated object.
2. Some examples of viral diseases are influenza, the common cold, viral hepatitis, and German measles.
3. Bacteria cause food poisoning.
4. Insects or other arthropod carriers transmit pathogenic protozoans to human beings.

Control of Disease (p. 289)

1. Quarantines interrupt the routes of disease transmission.
2. A vaccine is a substance that is injected into the body in order to produce immunity to a certain disease.
3. The different types of immunity are *inborn immunity* and *acquired immunity*. Passive immunity and active immunity are two types of acquired immunity.
4. Substances made for chemotherapy are usually made in a laboratory; antibiotics are produced by molds or bacteria.

Teaching Aids for Chapter End Features

Laboratory Investigation 17
A Model for Disease Transmission (p. 290)

Prepare the agar plates, swabs, water, and yeast culture before class begins. To prepare the sterile nutrient agar plates and cotton swabs, see the annotations for Laboratory Investigation 15. To prepare the sterile water, fill as many test tubes as you need half full of distilled water. Plug the tubes with cotton, and autoclave at 121 °C under 15 psi for 15 minutes. Cool the tubes before using them. To prepare the yeast culture, dissolve 20 g glucose in 200 mL distilled water. Add a package of dry yeast, and stir the mixture until the yeast cells are suspended.

OBSERVATIONS AND CONCLUSIONS 1. Both the control and the experimental side have bacterial colonies. On the experimental side, the yeast colonies appear grayish, slightly oval, and slightly raised. They grow faster and take up more space than do the bacterial colonies of the same age on the control side. 2. Answers will vary. Yeast colonies may possibly appear on the control side, but they should be more numerous on the experimental side. 3. The comparison enables the students to identify the yeast colonies from other microbes. 4. Yes, there is a pattern of transmission. The method of transmission is direct contact (handshaking). The plate for team member 1 should show the largest number of yeast colonies. The plates of each of the other team members, 2 to 4, should show progressively fewer colonies. 5. A dense and crowded human population greatly enhances the likelihood of disease transmission.

Review of Facts and Concepts (p. 291)

1. The structural defenses are the skin, bacteriostats, tears, mucous membranes, and cilia.
2. Phagocytes surround and then destroy microbes.

3. When an antigen enters the body, antibodies may either destroy the bacterial cell membranes or force the bacteria to clump together. Macrophages then surround and destroy the clumps.

4. *Indirect contact* refers to the spread of disease to a person by means of a contaminated object or an animal. *Direct contact* refers to the spread of disease by person-to-person contact.

5. The virulence of a virus depends on the ability of a virus to adsorb and to penetrate a cell, the ability of a virus to multiply and to spread in the organism, and the number of viral particles infecting the organism.

6. *Infectious hepatitis* is caused by the hepatitis A virus; it is spread by direct or indirect contact. *Serum hepatitis* is caused by the hepatitis B virus; it can be spread by means of contaminated objects such as hypodermic needles. Both diseases have similar symptoms.

7. *Endotoxins* are poisons that some bacteria release when they die and break apart. *Exotoxins* are poisonous substances that bacteria produce and secrete as they grow. Generally, exotoxins are more powerful poisons than endotoxins.

8. Food or water that is contaminated with infected feces transmits the amoebic dysentery protozoan. The sleeping sickness protozoan is transmitted by the tsetse fly.

9. *Preventative methods* of disease control are used before infection. *Therapeutic methods* are used after infection.

10. The three measures that can be taken to prevent disease are destroying the disease-causing agent, interrupting the route of transmission, and increasing the ability of the host to defend itself.

11. The *Salk vaccine*, administered by injection, contains inactive strains of the three polio viruses. The *OPV*, administered orally, contains live but less virulent strains of these three viruses.

12. *Passive immunity* results from injecting antibodies into a person's body. Passive immunity can prevent hepatitis. *Active immunity* arises from the body's production of antibodies, in response either to natural exposure to the disease or to an injection with vaccines. Mumps usually results in permanent active immunity.

13. An antibiotic is a chemical substance produced by a mold or bacterium that slows or stops the growth of microorganisms.

14. Viruses replicate within the cells of the host, whereas bacteria and protozoa grow outside the cells. Chemicals that damage the virus would probably also damage the host cells.

15. Some antibiotics cause side effects ranging from skin rashes to death. Bacteria can mutate so as to become resistant to a particular antibiotic.

Extensions and Applications (p. 292)

1. *Note: Incubate the plates in an inverted position.* The underlying question is why some of these plates show more growth than others.

2. Students may present their findings on a timeline. Additions can be made throughout the school year.

3. You may want to arrange to have groups of students survey the entire school during a week or two. Perhaps you can arrange to have a hall area designated as a polling center.

Unit Teaching Aids

Perspectives in Biology

A New Technology: Genetic Engineering (p. 293)

1. Students should prepare clear, concise charts that list the positive and negative points raised in each article that they use in their survey. Students should briefly explain to each person the ideas behind genetic engineering.

2. Students may want to write to the National Institutes of Health, Washington, DC 20014, for information on the guidelines for genetic engineering laboratories.

3. A comparison between the guidelines supplied by the National Institutes of Health and student guidelines may be used to stimulate class discussion.

Field Trip Suggestions

1. Visit a virology laboratory in a local medical center or university. Find out how scientists culture viruses, what scientists learn from viruses, and what careers are available in virology.

2. Tour a sewage treatment plant in your area to learn its role in controlling waterborne diseases. By what procedures can this facility control the spread of pathogenic microorganisms? What is the role of the treatment plant's bacteriology lab?

3. Visit a pharmaceutical company to see how antibiotics and other drugs are produced. Does the company function under governmental guidelines? How are the products tested after they are manufactured?

4. To enhance the students' understanding of the causes, spread, and control of disease, arrange a tour of a local reservoir or public water supply. The purpose of the trip is to determine how the water is treated to prevent its transmitting disease. If the students in your class use well water at home, have them find out what natural process purifies the water.

Audio-Visual Materials

Bacteria, film, Cor
Behavior of a Purple Bacterium, super 8mm film loop, HBJ
Biology: Disorders in Humans, set/6 sound filmstrips, PHM
Infectious Diseases Series, set/2 films, Cor
Locomotion in an Amoeba, super 8mm film loop, HBJ
Microorganisms That Cause Disease, film, Cor
Protozoa, film, Cor
Protozoa, set/24 super 8mm film loops, PHM
Viruses, film, Cor

Reading Resources for Teachers

DeKruif, P. *Microbe Hunters*. New York: Harcourt Brace Jovanovich.
Fraenkel-Conrat, H., and P. Kimball. *Virology*. Englewood Cliffs, N.J.: Prentice-Hall.
Sleigh, M. *The Biology of Protozoa*. London: Edward Arnold Publishers.
Wistreich, G., and M. Lechtman. *Microbiology and Human Disease*. Beverly Hills, Ca.: Glencoe Press.

UNIT FIVE
Plants and Fungi

This unit presents some of the major groups of plant life and some phyla of fungi. Chapter 18 discusses algae and fungi, including their economic importance and reproductive processes. Chapter 19 compares bryophytes (mosses and liverworts) with tracheophytes. The discussion of seed-bearing plants begins in Chapter 20 and continues throughout the remainder of the unit. The similarities and differences between gymnosperms and angiosperms, as well as those between monocots and dicots, are discussed. The focus of Chapter 21 is on the structure and function of roots and stems. Leaves, the sites of

photosynthesis, are the subject of Chapter 22. Plant reproduction is discussed in Chapter 23. The unit concludes with an explanation of plant growth and behavior in Chapter 24.

18 Algae and Fungi

Chapter Objectives: See page 296.

Chapter Overview

The student text classifies algae and fungi as plants because they have many plant characteristics, such as cell walls, but it recognizes the disagreement over their classification. For each division of algae represented in Chapter 18, a typical species is discussed. *Protoccus, Spirogyra, Ulothrix, Oedogonium,* and desmids show the diversity of the division Chlorophyta (green algae). The focus of the discussion of the division Chrysophyta (golden algae) is on diatoms. *Fucus* and *Sargassum* represent the division Phaeophyta (brown algae), as *Nemalion* and *Polysiphonia* do the division Rhodophyta (red algae). Fire algae (Pyrrophyta) are represented by *Gymnodinium*.

Like the discussion of the algae, the discussion of fungi uses typical species. The bread mold *Rhizopus stolonifer* represents the class of conjugating molds called Zygomycetes. Yeasts, morels, cup fungi, and powdery mildews reflect the variety of the class of sac fungi called Ascomycetes. The discussion of club fungi, Basidiomycetes, includes mushrooms, rusts, and smuts. *Penicillium* and *Aspergillus* illustrate the class of imperfect fungi called Deuteromycetes. Brief discussions of lichens and slime molds conclude the chapter.

Teaching Strategies and Activities

1. To stress the economic importance of algae and fungi, display some grocery items or commercial products derived from algae and fungi, their parts, or their extracts. Include toothpaste, jello, mushrooms, and baker's yeast.
2. Have the students research the uses of *Chlorella* and other green algae in space exploration.
3. Stimulate active learning by having the students collect or grow some fungi, algae, and slime molds. Students can also collect lichens from rocks or tree bark.

Answer Key to Section Reviews

Algae (p. 303)

1. Algae are simple plants that contain chlorophyll.
2. Plankton are tiny algae called desmids that float or drift near the surface of the water.
3. The divisions of algae and several examples of algae in each division follow. Green algae: *Chlorella, Protococcus, Spirogyra, Ulothrix, Oedogonium,* or desmids. Golden algae: diatoms. Brown algae: *Fucus* or *Sargassum.* Red algae: *Nemalion* or *Polysiphonia.* Fire algae: *Gymnodinium.*
4. Bioluminescence is a form of glowing light that living organisms produce.

Fungi (p. 309)

1. The four phyla of fungi are Zygomycetes, Ascomycetes, Basidiomycetes, and Deuteromycetes.
2. Imperfect fungi do not reproduce sexually.
3. Some diseases caused by fungi include athlete's foot, ear infections, wheat rust and corn smut in plants, and ringworm.

Lichens (p. 310)

1. A lichen is a symbiotic combination of a fungus and an alga.
2. Symbiosis is a mutually beneficial relationship between two members of different species.

Slime Molds (p. 310)

1. Slime molds grow in moist areas on decaying leaves, rotting logs, and other types of dead or decaying material.
2. During its life cycle, a slime mold alternates between fruiting and plasmodial stages. In the plasmodial stage, the entire slime mold mass, or plasmodium, resembles an amoeba. In the fruiting, or plantlike, stage, the plasmodium stops moving and develops fruiting bodies.

Teaching Aids for Chapter End Features

Laboratory Investigation 18
Investigating Algae and Fungi (p. 311)

To prepare bread mold cultures, crush several pieces of rabbit or hamster food into the top half of a small petri dish. Place a disk of white filter paper over the crushed food, and wet both the paper and the food thoroughly. Place the bottom half of the petri dish on the paper, and store the inverted dish in a dark place for several days. After three to four days, you should find half the dish filled with bread mold mycelia.

To prepare Lugol's iodine solution, dissolve 10 g of potassium iodide in 100 mL of distilled water. Add 5 g of iodine, and stir the mixture until the iodine is dissolved.

OBSERVATIONS AND CONCLUSIONS 1. Depending on the species of *Spirogyra,* one or two chloroplasts are in each cell. Chloroplasts carry on photosynthesis. **2.** Pyrenoids store starch. **3.** The walls in the filaments of bread mold appear only at the ends of the hyphae that form spore capsules (sporangia). **4.** In bread mold, the hyphae are colorless. **5.** Fungi do not have chloroplasts. **6.** *Algae* have chlorophyll and manufacture food by photosynthesis; their filaments have transverse walls. *Fungi* lack chlorophyll and therefore absorb food from their environment; their filaments lack transverse walls.

Review of Facts and Concepts (p. 312)

1. Algae contain chlorophyll and are autotrophic. Fungi are heterotrophic parasites and saprophytes. Neither algae nor fungi have true leaves, roots, or stems. Both algae and fungi reproduce sexually and asexually.
2. The various divisions of algae and the characteristics of each division follow. *Chlorophyta:* eukaryotic cells, chlorophyll usually not masked by other pigments, and detoxifying capability. *Chrysophyta:* various pigments such as carotenes, xanthophylls, and fucoxanthins. *Phaeophyta:* fucoxanthins. *Rhodophyta:* phycoerythrin. *Pyrrophyta:* unicellular, yellow-green to orange-brown, usually bioluminescence capability.
3. During conjugation, two adjacent filaments of *Spirogyra* form connecting tubes. The entire contents of one cell moves through a tube into the other cell, forming a zygote that later becomes a zygospore and eventually a *Spirogyra.*
4. In asexual reproduction, *Ulothrix* produces zoospores, which can move about in the water and develop into holdfasts that attach themselves to objects. Each holdfast then gives rise to a new filament. During sexual reproduction, *Ulothrix* forms isogametes instead of zoospores. When

5. Fungi are called heterotrophs because they do not produce food through photosynthesis.

6. Fungi ingest their food indirectly by releasing enzymes into their food. The enzymes digest the food, and the digested food is absorbed by the fungi.

7. The phyla of fungi and an example of an organism in each class follow. *Zygomycetes:* bread molds. *Ascomycetes:* yeasts, morels, cup fungi, and powdery mildews. *Basidiomycetes:* mushrooms, rusts, and smuts. *Deuteromycetes: Penicillium* and *Aspergillus*.

8. True fungi have branching filaments called hyphae. Masses of hyphae form mycelia. The mycelia form the fruiting bodies that contain the spore-producing organs.

9. The hyphae of bread mold are either plus or minus, and their tips act as gametes. When the tips of a plus hypha and a minus hypha come into contact, they form a zygote, which thickens into a zygospore and germinates.

10. In sexual reproduction, each yeast cell produces an ascus usually containing four or eight spores. Asexually, yeasts reproduce either by fission or by budding. In budding, some of the yeast material pushes out of the cell wall, forming a bud. This bud separates into several new cells. In fission, the yeast cell divides in half, forming two new yeast cells.

11. Fermentation is a process by which enzymes change sugars to ethyl alcohol. Yeasts cause fermentation.

12. The reproductive structure of the mushroom is the umbrella-shaped fruiting body, called the cap, which grows on a stalk. On the cap's underside are the gills. Millions of spores are produced on the surface of the gills. The stalk keeps the cap exposed to the air.

13. A lichen consists of a fungus and an alga. The fungus provides a means of attachment for the lichen and absorbs water and minerals that the alga uses for photosynthesis. In turn, the alga provides food for itself and the fungus.

14. During its life cycle, a slime mold alternates between funguslike (fruiting) and animal-like (plasmodial) stages. In the animal-like stage, the entire slime mold mass, or plasmodium, resembles an amoeba. In the funguslike or plantlike stage, the plasmodium stops moving and develops fruiting bodies.

15. *Isogametes* are gametes that are identical in appearance; *heterogametes* are gametes that are male or female sex cells. A *saprophyte* is an organism that feeds on dead or decaying matter; a *parasite* is an organism that feeds on the tissues of living things.

Extensions and Applications (p. 313)

1. Have each student present his or her food chain on a large piece of posterboard. Each food chain should show the role of algae (phytoplankton) as the producers of food for the primary consumers of food (zooplankton). From that point, the pictures should show various plankton eaters (secondary consumers), fishes (tertiary consumers), and human beings (ultimate consumers).

2. The best time to collect mushrooms, other fungi, and algae is after a heavy rain. If you have access to a pond or an area of stagnant water, collect algae from these sources.

3. *Caution: Students should avoid breathing in the spores.*

19 Mosses and Ferns

Chapter Objectives: See page 314.

Chapter Overview

The two divisions of terrestrial plants are discussed in this chapter. The mosses and liverworts of the bryophyte division have neither vascular systems nor true supported tissues such as roots, stems, or leaves. The section on bryophytes presents the general structures, life cycles, and methods of reproduction for mosses and liverworts.

In contrast, the plants of the tracheophyte division have roots, stems, leaves, and vascular systems. The section on tracheophytes presents four of the five tracheophyte subdivisions. In the first subdivision, psilopsids, *Psilotum* is used as a representative of the subdivision. The structural characteristics and life cycles of the next three subdivisions, ferns, club mosses, and horsetails, are discussed in this chapter. Chapter 20 deals with the fifth subdivision, seed-bearing plants.

Teaching Strategies and Activities

1. To generate interest in the plants of this chapter, collect and display mosses, liverworts, and ferns.

2. Have the students research and prepare a brief written report on the Carboniferous Period and

the Age of Ferns. Students should note the relationship of this period to fossil fuel formation.

3. The life cycles of the plants in this chapter may seem complicated to some students. Have small groups of students prepare posters or bulletin board displays on the life cycles of mosses, liverworts, and ferns. Assign displays on the economic importance of these plants to other class members.

Answer Key to Section Reviews

Bryophytes (p. 318)

1. Bryophytes are simple plants that lack specialized conducting and supporting tissues.
2. *Mosses* are tiny, leafy plants that grow in damp soil or on the shaded surfaces of rocks and trees. Mosses have rhizoids that function as roots. *Liverworts* are tiny green plants that look like flattened, branched leaves. The thallus of a liverwort is lobed.

Tracheophytes (p. 322)

1. The five subdivisions of tracheophytes are psilopsids (Psilopsida), ferns (Pteropsida), club mosses (Lycopsida), horsetails (Sphenopsida), and seed-bearing plants.
2. The *rhizome* is an underground stem that absorbs and conducts water and minerals for the plant. The *frond*, or leaf, consists of a *blade*, a *stipe*, and a *fiddlehead*. The frond is the site of photosynthesis.
3. A *sorus* is a minute, reddish-brown, circular structure that contains sporangia. A *sporangium* is a saclike structure that produces haploid spores.
4. The vascular tissue of a horsetail is arranged in a ring of small bundles. Horsetail stems have nodes and contain silica. Club mosses have none of these characteristics.

Teaching Aids for Chapter End Features

Laboratory Investigation 19
Investigating Mosses and Ferns (p. 323)

In most areas, you can find live specimens of mosses and ferns year round. The male moss plants can be identified by the rosette of leaves at the tip. In female mosses, the arrangement of leaves at the tip is irregular. You may not, however, find all the stages of the life cycle at one time. To supplement those you collect locally, you may have to order specimens. Fern prothalli are especially hard to find in natural settings. You can also grow prothalli in the classroom by sprinkling fern spores on a thin moist layer of soil in a terrarium. The spores need four to six weeks to germinate and grow to a suitable size for study.

OBSERVATIONS AND CONCLUSIONS 1. *Differences:* In mosses, the antheridia and archegonia are located at the ends of separate gametophyte plants. In ferns, both structures are located on a single prothallus. In the moss life cycle, the gametophyte generation is the more conspicuous, whereas in ferns, the sporophyte generation is the more conspicuous. *Similarities:* Both plants require water for fertilization to occur, and both reproduce sexually. **2.** Mosses do not have true roots, stems, leaves, or vascular leaves, as tracheophytes do. **3.** Moss and fern spores are tiny, dark bodies that can be seen clearly with a microscope. Fern spores are generally oval. Moss spores are usually tetrahedral. More specifically, the answers will vary since the color and texture of spores depend on the species observed.

Review of Facts and Concepts (p. 325)

1. The two major classes of bryophytes are mosses and liverworts. Answers will vary but may include *Polytrichum*, *Sphagnum*, and *Andreaea* for mosses and *Marchantia* for liverworts.
2. Vascular tissue enabled tracheophytes to live in drier environments, as well as to grow much larger than the primitive bryophytes.
3. The common names of the three orders of mosses are true mosses, peat moss, and rock moss.
4. In bryophytes, the zygote produced during the gametophyte generation develops into an embryo. In algae, the zygote develops into a mature alga. Unlike bryophytes, the entire cell of a unicellular alga functions as a gamete, and multicellular algae form gametangia. Bryophytes and algae are similar in that they both produce spores during their sporophyte stages. Bryophytes and some algae reproduce by undergoing alternation of generations.
5. Mosses undergo alternation of generations. See Figure 19-3 on page 317.
6. Mosses help keep the soil damp, allowing other plants to grow. Mosses return minerals to the soil and help prevent flooding in some areas.
7. Gemmae are tiny asexual reproductive bodies.
8. Psilopsids are the oldest known tracheophytes.
9. See Figure 19-9 on page 321.
10. *Mosses* are simple, nonvascular plants of the bryophyte division. *Club mosses* are tracheophytes that have true roots, stems, leaves, and vascular tissues.

11. Horsetail spores have chlorophyll.
12. *Haploid* refers to half the normal number of chromosomes in a cell; *diploid* refers to the complete number of chromosomes in a cell. A *rhizoid* is a rootlike structure; a *rhizome* is an underground stem. The *protonema* is a green, threadlike structure growing from the spore of a moss; the *prothallus* is the flat, green, heart-shaped structure growing from a fern spore.

Extensions and Applications (p. 325)

1. Mosses and ferns are ideal plants for a terrarium because they are not difficult to grow. All they need is a shaded, cool, moist place. *Note: Do not place the terrarium in direct sunlight.*
2. You may find some horsetails in dry environments, such as along roadsides. If students remember how horsetails get their name, they should be able to find these plants easily.

20 Seed-Bearing Plants

Chapter Objectives: See page 326.

Chapter Overview

The first section of this chapter identifies the characteristics of the seed-bearing plants. The seed-bearing plants are the most numerous of vascular plants and are well adapted for living in land environments. The external features of these plants are briefly discussed. The roots not only anchor these plants but also absorb water and minerals. The stems provide support, produce leaves, and contain vascular tissue. The leaves carry on the vital functions of photosynthesis, respiration, and transpiration. The flowers of angiosperms are the organs of reproduction. In addition to their external features, the specialized tissues of these plants are detailed. The section closes with brief discussions of annuals, biennials, and perennials.

The subsequent two sections of the chapter present the two classes of seed-bearing plants, the gymnosperms and the angiosperms. After a comparison of gymnosperms and angiosperms, the chapter concludes with a brief description of dicots and monocots.

Teaching Strategies and Activities

1. To focus the students' attention on plants in general, invite a forester, a member of a garden club, or a member of a conservation club to talk to your class on forest conservation, the lumber industry, growing seedlings, houseplants, or growing plants for fun.

2. Have students prepare a list of plants or parts of plants that they eat. Suggest that they include wild edible plants, such as dandelions and wild hickory nuts.
3. Have students prepare a display on the variety of seeds. Students should bring in examples of popular grocery items, such as beans or peas, as well as birdseed and sunflower seeds.
4. Have small groups of students plant different types of seeds, such as grass seeds, bean seeds, lentil seeds, and so on. Have the students identify the plants that result as monocots or dicots. These plants can be used to study the plant anatomy presented in the remaining chapters of Unit Five.

Answer Key to Section Reviews

Characteristics of Seed-Bearing Plants (p. 333)

1. A *gymnosperm* is a plant whose seeds do not develop within a protective wall. An *angiosperm* is a flowering plant whose seeds are protected by a fruit.
2. Some characteristics of seed-bearing plants are vascular systems and other specialized tissues; enclosed or exposed seeds; alternation of generations, with the sporophyte much larger than the gametophyte generation; true roots, stems, and leaves; and fertilization without water.
3. *Roots* anchor the plant in the soil and absorb minerals and water. In some plants, roots store food. *Stems* support the plant, produce the leaves, carry minerals and water from the roots to the leaves, and transport food made by the leaves to the roots. Stems may also serve as storage organs. *Leaves* perform photosynthesis, respiration, and transpiration. *Flowers* are the organs of reproduction.
4. *Epidermal tissue* covers and protects the tissues beneath it. *Meristematic tissue* is responsible for growth and differentiation. *Parenchyma tissue* stores food and water and takes part in photosynthesis. *Vascular tissue* conducts materials throughout the plant. *Supporting tissue* strengthens and supports parts of plants. *Cork* is the waxy and waterproof layer that prevents water loss.
5. *Annuals* are plants whose entire life cycles take place within one growing season. *Biennials* are plants that live for two growing seasons. *Perennials* are plants that live for more than two growing seasons.

Gymnosperms (p. 335)

1. The three major orders of gymnosperms are Cycadophyta (*Zamia*), Gingkophyta (*Gingko*

biloba), and Coniferophyta (pines, cedars, cypresses, firs, and hemlocks).

2. *Pollen cones* are found in clusters at the tips of the branches in the spring. *Seed cones* are larger and woodier than pollen cones.

Angiosperms (p. 336)

1. Flowers, seeds within fruits, large leaves, and complex vascular tissue make angiosperms a highly successful group of plants.

2. *Angiosperms* produce flowers, which later produce seeds enclosed by a fruit. *Gymnosperms* produce cones with seeds that are exposed on the surface. The xylem and phloem in angiosperms are more specialized than the xylem and phloem in gymnosperms. Unlike gymnosperms, angiosperms produce cotyledons.

3. *Monocots* have one cotyledon or seed leaf; *dicots* have two.

Teaching Aids for Chapter End Features

Laboratory Investigation 20
Investigating Gymnosperms (p. 337)

Two-year-old pistillate cones should have well-developed seeds. Soak enough seeds overnight so that you have at least one for each group of students.

OBSERVATIONS AND CONCLUSIONS 1. Answers will vary. The number of needles varies according to species. 2. The students should be able to recognize different species by the shapes and sizes of the cones, by the lengths of the needles, and by the number of needles per bundle. 3. The male cones are clustered at the ends of short lateral main branches. The female cones, which are larger than the male cones, appear on single, short lateral branches that are farther away from the ends of the main branches. 4. Pine pollen is much smaller than pine seeds. Both frequently have wings to keep them airborne for greater lengths of time.

Review of Facts and Concepts (p. 338)

1. A seed is a reproductive structure that contains a young plant and stored food and has a protective seed coat.

2. Seed-bearing plants, with their conducting tissues, are adapted to dry-land environments, and they do not need water for fertilization.

3. In the asexual stage, the sporophyte has diploid cells and forms the megaspore and microspore. The megaspore develops into the ovule. The microspore becomes the pollen grain. These gametes then join to become the gametophyte plant.

4. *Roots:* Aquatic roots grow in water; aerial roots grow above the soil; and fleshy roots store food. *Stems:* Herbaceous stems are soft, green, and fleshy; woody stems are hard. *Leaves:* Tendrils are long and slender structures that coil around the plant and nearby objects; spine leaves are slender, hard, conelike leaves that have lost their green color.

5. See Figure 20-5 on page 330.

6. Meristematic tissue differentiates into other specialized tissues.

7. *Differences:* In gymnosperms, tracheids make up most of the xylem. In angiosperms, the xylem consists primarily of vessel elements. The phloem of gymnosperms has no sieve plates, which are present in angiosperms. *Similarities:* The xylem and phloem of gymnosperms are similar to those of the woody angiosperms. In both groups, the phloem has companion cells. However, the sieve tubes are less specialized in gymnosperms.

8. The *male cones*, or pollen cones, are found in clusters at the tips of branches in the spring. The *female cones*, which produce seeds, are larger and woodier than the pollen cones.

9. A cotyledon is the first leaf (seed leaf) that the embryo of an angiosperm develops.

10. *Vegetative organs* perform all the life processes of a plant except reproduction; *reproductive organs* give rise to new plants. *Herbaceous stems* are soft, green, and fleshy; *woody stems* are hard. *Xylem* carries water and minerals from the roots to the leaves, and it also helps to support the plant; *phloem* conducts food from the leaves to all parts of the plant.

Extensions and Applications (p. 339)

1. Pollen grains from different flowers exhibit very distinctive shapes and structures. Most are sticky and indented. Some have hooklike spines.

2. The students may further classify angiosperms into monocots or dicots and gymnosperms into major groups or subgroups.

3. The stone cells are rigid.

21 Roots and Stems

Chapter Objectives: See page 340.

Chapter Overview

Chapter 21 presents the structure, adaptations, and functions of roots and stems. The section on roots opens with definitions of primary roots, secondary roots, fibrous roots, and taproots. The text describes the regions of the root tip and the two types of tissue in the root itself. The root adaptations covered are aquatic, aerial, and adventitious. In explaining the role of roots in the absorption of materials, the text reviews selective permeability, osmotic pressure, and active and passive absorption.

Stems are defined as bundles of tubes in the form of a single cylinder, the vascular bundle. In describing herbaceous stems, the text explains wilting in terms of turgor pressure. An extensive discussion of the structural features of woody stems, followed by an explanation of apical dominance, is included in the chapter. Stem adaptations including rhizomes, stolons, tubers, corms, and bulbs are also presented. The coverage of the translocation of materials includes a description of capillarity and the transpiration–cohesion theory.

Teaching Strategies and Activities

1. Obtain several tree-stem cross sections. Let the students examine the annual rings of the cross sections. Have them identify the dark heartwood rings and the light sapwood rings. Point out some unusual growth rings. For instance, thicker rings might indicate a period of rain and a good growing season.
2. Display some unusual roots and stems. Ask the students to identify the parts as roots or stems. Have them classify roots as fleshy, fibrous, aerial, adventitious, prop, or climbing. Students can also classify stems as rhizomes, stolons, tubers, corms, or bulbs. Some examples may include potato tubers, ginger rhizomes, tulip bulbs, beets, and ivy.
3. Have individual students or student groups either give a brief oral report or make posterboards showing industrial uses of stems and roots. For example, students could show how rubber is extracted from the bark of a tree in Malaysia or how the cork oak of Spain produces cork.
4. How are the structures of roots and stems related to their functions? To explore this question, take students to the nearest park or wooded area to observe stems and roots in their natural states.

Answer Key to Section Reviews

Roots (p. 345)

1. The root anchors the plant, absorbs minerals and water, and sometimes stores food for the plant.
2. A *taproot* is a primary root that becomes the main root as the plant grows. A *fibrous root* is a threadlike, highly branched secondary root that appears in some plants.

3. The *primary tissues* are made up of the epidermis, the cortex, and the vascular cylinder. The *secondary tissues* are composed of the vascular cylinder or cambium, which gives rise to two kinds of cells. One type remains part of the cambium, while the other forms the secondary xylem and phloem.
4. Aquatic, aerial, and adventitious roots are three root adaptations.
5. Roots absorb minerals by active transport.
6. *Active absorption* is the movement of water by osmosis. *Passive absorption* is the movement of water through the stem by transpiration.

Stems (p. 352)

1. The stem plays a role as part of the shoot, raising the leaves in the air and exposing them to sunlight. The stem also conducts food materials, produces new cells for growth and development, and stores food materials.
2. Turgidity is the condition of cells when they are full of water, causing turgor pressure against the cell walls.
3. Columnar, deliquescent, and excurrent are three stem branching patterns.
4. *Rhizomes* are stems that grow under the surface of the ground. *Stolons* are stems that grow either above or below ground and are longer or narrower than rhizomes. *Tubers* are enlarged underground stems. *Corms* are underground stems that grow vertically and are enclosed by several thin, scalelike leaves. *Bulbs* are short stems that are thicker than corms and are surrounded by thick leaves.
5. Translocation is the movement of water, minerals, and food within the plant.
6. The transpiration–cohesion theory assumes that, when a plant loses water through transpiration, the top of the plant exerts a "pull" on the bottom. Cohesion of water molecules then pulls water upward in the plant.

Teaching Aids for Chapter End Features

Laboratory Investigation 21
Observing the Structure of Roots and Stems (p. 353)

Plant the beans and corn two to three weeks in advance to ensure that they are large enough to use in Part B. Before using the plants in Part B, gently loosen each plant and wash off all the soil. If you place radish and grass seeds between wet paper towels in a dark place, the seeds will germinate in two to three days.

OBSERVATIONS AND CONCLUSIONS 1. The region of maturation has the longest root hairs. 2. Answers will vary. 3. Root hairs increase the surface area of the root. 4. The red ink remains concentrated in the vascular tissue of the stem. The xylem tissue transports the red ink up the stem. 5. In the stem of the monocot corn, vascular bundles are arranged throughout the stem area. In the stem of the dicot bean, the vascular bundles are arranged in a definite ring within the stem.

Review of Facts and Concepts (p. 355)

1. The *primary root* is the first root to develop. Smaller *secondary roots* grow from the primary root.
2. The *root cap* protects the root tip. The *meristematic region* gives rise to all new cells. In the *elongation region* newly formed cells begin to grow and develop, pushing the root cap deeper into the soil. In the *maturation region* the cells mature and become differentiated.
3. The *primary tissues* are the first group of cells that develop in a young root. The tissues that develop after a root's primary tissues have matured make up the *secondary tissues*.
4. Roots absorb water in two ways. In *active absorption*, water diffuses into root cells by osmosis. In *passive absorption*, water is drawn in as a result of transpiration.
5. *Permanent wilting* occurs when a plant loses water excessively, as during a long drought. *Temporary wilting* occurs when the plant loses more water through transpiration than it can replace through absorption. Temporary wilting usually occurs on a hot day.
6. The *bark* is a series of outer layers of living and dead tissues that cover and protect the stem. The *vascular cambium* is a single layer of cells located between the phloem and xylem. The *pith*, comprised mainly of parenchyma, is found at the center of the stem.
7. *Terminal buds* are large buds located at the ends of twigs or branches. *Lateral buds* are small buds that grow from the sides of woody stems, usually just above the point where a leaf joins the stem.
8. *Primary growth* is growth in the length of woody stems. *Secondary growth* is an increase in the diameter of woody stems.
9. *Woody stems* are hard and rigid. *Herbaceous stems* are soft and fleshy.
10. Each year, cambium cells develop a layer of new cells outside the xylem layers already there. Eventually, these layers grow outward and cover the head of the nail.
11. Two possible explanations are root pressure and capillarity. A more satisfactory theory is the transpiration–cohesion theory.
12. In extremely old trees, such as some giant sequoias, the xylem dies. The growth of living tissues therefore takes place in the outer portion of the stems.

Extensions and Applications (p. 355)

1. Arrange to observe a nearby field or park during the fall, winter, and spring. Students can then make comparisons of the types of plants during the three seasons.
2. Growth occurs mostly in the root tip, which has the most actively dividing cells. Adding a fungicide to the water used to soak the paper towel may be helpful.
3. The 4-H Club, local nurseries, and the agricultural extension office in your state may be able to provide pamphlets and information on hydroponics. Hydroponics kits are available from most biological supply companies.

22 Leaves

Chapter Objectives: See page 356.

Chapter Overview

Chapter 22 details the characteristics of leaves and the processes that the cells and tissues of a leaf carry out. In the section on characteristics, the students study the three groups of leaves and the reasons for the coloration and falling of leaves in autumn. The leaf structure discussion presents the major parts of the leaf, the differences between simple and compound leaves, and three types of venation. A discussion of the tissues in leaves follows. Defined and explained are the epidermis, mesophyll, and fibrovascular bundles. A brief discussion of leaf adaptations ends the section.

The section on leaf processes reviews photosynthesis, transpiration, and respiration. An explanation of guttation is also included.

Teaching Strategies and Activities

1. Obtain a collection of 30 different leaves. Mount each leaf on a sheet of white paper. Display the collection to the class as you explain the characteristics and structure of leaves. After the discussion, give each student a leaf. Have each student identify the group, leaf type, and vena-

tion of the leaf. Students can exchange leaves and record the group of each leaf until every student has seen and grouped all 30 leaves.

2. Have the class prepare a leaf collection. The display should have a key to the identification of leaves. Ask the students to write a comprehensive paragraph on each leaf and on the type of plant it represents.

3. In a class demonstration, extract chlorophyll from leaves. *Caution: Keep room well ventilated*. In a mortar, mix 3 g of fresh spinach leaves with 50 mL of 80% acetone for 5 minutes. Crush the leaves with the pestle. Have each student do a paper chromatography test on the extract.

4. Have the students observe the effect of colored lights on coleus plants. If necessary, review the lesson about the role of wavelengths in the light reactions of photosynthesis. Place one plant each under a green, a red, a yellow, and a "white" light. Filters used over a light source are also acceptable. Keeping the light on continually during the experiment, have the class members periodically observe the growth of each plant.

Answer Key to Section Reviews

Leaf Characteristics (p. 362)

1. Abscission is the shedding of a leaf or other plant organ.
2. A *simple leaf* is one in which the blade is not divided into sections. A *compound leaf* is divided into two or more leaflets.
3. Venation is the arrangement of the veins in leaves.
4. Answers may include spines, tendrils, succulent leaves, and insectivorous leaves.

Leaf Processes (p. 364)

1. *Photosynthesis* is the process by which a green plant uses sunlight to change water and carbon dioxide into oxygen and glucose. *Respiration* is the process of breaking down glucose and other food molecules to make use of their chemical energy.
2. *Transpiration* is the diffusion of water vapor from a leaf into the air through the stomata. *Guttation* is the forcing of liquid water out of the ends of the xylem of leaf veins.

Teaching Aids for Chapter End Features

Laboratory Investigation 22
The Structure of Leaves (p. 365)

Before beginning this investigation, demonstrate to the class how to strip the epidermis from the leaves.

OBSERVATIONS AND CONCLUSIONS 1. Answers will vary with the leaf type. The upper surface has more photosynthetic cells because this surface is exposed to sunlight. **2.** The palisade mesophyll cells are packed close together. The spongy mesophyll layer has loosely packed cells with large air spaces. **3.** The guard cells have chloroplasts. **4.** The students should be able to see the stomata.

Review of Facts and Concepts (p. 366)

1. Leaves may be broad, narrow, or needle-shaped.
2. In the cool temperatures of autumn, chlorophyll breaks down more easily than the other pigments that it masks. This breakdown unmasks the other pigments, such as xanthophyll and carotene.
3. Leaves are shed from trees when auxin production in the leaf slows down. When the stem contains more auxin than the leaf, abscission takes place, and the leaf falls.
4. *Stipules* support the stems of climbing plants and protect the leaf. The *petiole* is the stalk of a leaf and connects the stem to the blade of the leaf. The *blade* contains most of the green, photosynthetic cells.
5. Examples of plants with *simple leaves* may include maple, dogwood, sycamore, and apple trees. Examples of plants with *compound leaves* are poison ivy, Virginia creeper, buckeye, and black locust.
6. In *parallel venation*, the veins run parallel to the edge of the leaf and to each other. In *netted venation*, the veins spread out in a netlike pattern. In *pinnate venation*, small veins branch out from a midrib.
7. The *epidermis*, the outermost leaf tissue, covers the entire leaf and protects all the other tissues within it. The *mesophyll*, the middle layer, consists of the upper palisade and the spongy mesophyll. Photosynthesis takes place in this tissue. The *fibrovascular bundles* contain the xylem and phloem, which are the passageways for translocation.
8. The *palisade mesophyll* is made up of one row of elongated cells. The *spongy mesophyll* is made up of irregularly shaped cells with many air spaces between the cells.
9. Insectivorous plants also undergo photosynthesis.
10. In the light reactions of *photosynthesis*, light energizes the chlorophyll in the chloroplasts. In the dark reactions, glucose is formed. *Respiration* involves the breaking down of glucose and other food molecules to make use of their chemical energy.

11. During transpiration, the turgor of the guard cells controls the opening or closing of the stomata. When the guard cells are turgid, the stomata open. When the guard cells are flaccid, the stomata close.

Extensions and Applications (p. 367)

1. The shapes of the cutouts show up on the leaf where light has been prevented from striking. This activity shows that the leaf needs light to produce chlorophyll.
2. The stomate impressions on the cover slip should show that the stomata are open on a warm, sunny day. The stomata should be closed on the leaf kept in the dark.
3. Some insectivorous plants are bladderworts, Venus' flytraps, sundews, butterworts, and pitcher plants.

23 Reproduction in Flowering Plants

Chapter Objectives: See page 368.

Chapter Overview

The vegetative and reproductive stages in a flowering plant's life cycle form the basis for the organization of this chapter. A brief section on vegetative propagation presents several methods of natural propagation, as well as four methods of artificial vegetative propagation—cuttings, layering, grafting, and budding.

A discussion of sexual reproduction dominates the chapter. The section begins with a review of the roles of gametes, zygotes, and cotyledons. The generalized structures of flowers, such as the pedicel and the various parts of the receptacle, are outlined. A brief description of flower modifications precedes a detailed explanation of the reproductive process. The chapter concludes with a discussion of seeds, including structure, dispersal, and germination and growth.

Teaching Strategies and Activities

1. Develop the concept of asexual reproduction by discussing familiar plants in unfamiliar terms. For example, present the potato as a kind of stem or the sweet potato as a type of root. Then have the students grow several plants by vegetative propagation. A large chart can be used to summarize their observations.

2. Display and discuss samples of flowers. Use common flowers as well as the flowers of weeds and trees, such as those of wild daisies, dandelions, and maple and oak trees.
3. Have the students examine an ear of corn to determine why it is the product of a group of flowers. Study the silk, the tassel, and the corn grains. Locate the silk scars on a grain. Cut a cross section of the cob, and label the parts.
4. Develop a key for the identification of flowers that grow in your area.

Answer Key to Section Reviews

Vegetative Propagation (p. 371)

1. The *vegetative stage* is a form of asexual reproduction in which a plant grows roots, stems, and leaves. The *reproductive stage* is a form of sexual reproduction in which a plant develops flowers and seeds.
2. Examples of natural vegetative propagation are stolons, runners, plantlets, and reserve roots.
3. The four methods of artificial vegetative propagation are cuttings, layering, grafting, and budding.

Sexual Reproduction (p. 380)

1. The flower is the reproductive organ of an angiosperm.
2. The structures that develop from the receptacle are the sepals (calyx), petals (corolla), stamens, and pistil.
3. Pollination is the transfer of pollen from the anther to the stigma. Pollinating agents include wind and insects.
4. A *fruit* is a mature ovary. A *seed* is a mature ovule.
5. To germinate, seeds need sufficient moisture and oxygen and an appropriate temperature.

Teaching Aids for Chapter End Features

Laboratory Investigation 23
Flower Anatomy (p. 381)

Arrange in advance to pick up discarded flowers from a local florist.

OBSERVATIONS AND CONCLUSIONS 1. Answers will vary. 2. Answers will vary. 3. Monocot flowers have floral parts in multiples of three. Dicots have floral parts in multiples of four or five. 4. Answers will vary. Pollen grains differ from one plant species to another. 5. The number of chambers in the ovary of a flower varies from one to several.

Review of Facts and Concepts (p. 383)

1. *Cutting* is removing a vegetative organ from a parent plant and then rooting it in water or moist soil. In *layering*, moist soil is used to cover a plant's stems or branches, which then sprout adventitious roots. In *grafting*, a scion of one plant is attached to the stem of another plant. In *budding*, a bud on a piece of bark is implanted in a cut in the stem of another plant.
2. The grafted pear branch will bear pear fruit.
3. In *grafting*, the scion is cut so that its vascular cambium will be in close contact with that of the stock. In *budding*, a bud and some cambium take the place of the cutting used in grafting.
4. The *pedicel* serves as a stalk. The *receptacle* gives rise to four other structures. The *sepals*, collectively called the calyx, enclose the flower bud. The *petals*, collectively called the corolla, are usually the showy parts of a flower. The *stamen*, consisting of the filament and anther, is the male reproductive organ. The *pistil*, which contains the ovules, is the female reproductive part.
5. In *egg formation*, a diploid megaspore undergoes two meiotic divisions to form four haploid megaspores, but only one survives to form the embryo sac. Three mitotic divisions then result in the formation of polar nuclei and an egg. In *pollen formation*, each cell undergoes two meiotic divisions in the anther's pollen sac, producing four microscopic cells. Each microspore divides mitotically to form the tube nucleus and the generative nucleus and then develops into a pollen grain.
6. The micropyle is usually the entry point of the pollen tube.
7. *Pollination* is the transfer of pollen from an anther to a stigma. *Fertilization* is the union of one sperm nucleus with an egg nucleus.
8. A *monocot seed* has only one seed leaf. A *dicot seed* has two.
9. Wind, water, and animals can disperse seeds.
10. When a *monocot* seed germinates, the food in the endosperm provides nutrients for the growing plant. The coleoptile protects the plumule. The first leaves emerge and the stem grows upward. When these leaves unfold, photosynthesis begins. In *dicots*, the hypocotyl bends after the radicle emerges from the seed. When it reaches the surface of the soil, the hypocotyl becomes long and straight, pulling the cotyledons and plumule out of the soil. Once the young leaves emerge, photosynthesis begins.
11. Viability is the ability of a seed to germinate.
12. A *scion* is a piece of stem that is cut from a parent plant; the *stock* is the rooted stem onto which the scion is attached. A *calyx* consists of all the sepals on a receptacle; a *corolla* is the group of all the petals. A *megaspore* is a female plant gamete; a *microspore* is a male gamete. In *cross-pollination*, pollen is transferred from the anther of one plant to the stigma of another plant; in *self-pollination*, the transfer takes place on the same flower. The *epicotyl* consists of the embryonic leaves above the cotyledon of angiosperms; the *hypocotyl* is the embryonic stem below the cotyledon. The *plumule* consists of the epicotyl and its young leaves; the *radicle* is the primary embryonic root, found below the hypocotyl.

Extensions and Applications (p. 383)

1. A local 4-H Club or the state agricultural office may be able to provide pamphlets on propagation of plants.
2. Commercially available seeds may be used, particularly during the winter months.
3. The seeds in a warm, moist place should germinate. The point of the activity is that temperature, moisture, and light are important factors in seed germination.

24 Plant Growth and Behavior

Chapter Objectives: See page 384.

Chapter Overview

Chapter 24 defines plant growth as balanced metabolism. Behavior is described as a collection of responses to stimuli. Both the internal and the external factors that affect growth are discussed. The internal influences consist largely of hormones, such as the auxins, gibberellins, and cytokinins. Of the external factors, the text presents three in detail: light, temperature, and moisture.

The section on responses to stimuli discusses phototropism, geotropism, hydrotropism, thigmotropism, and chemotropism. The section closes with an explanation of nastic movement.

Teaching Strategies and Activities

1. Using houseplants or herbaceous garden plants as visual aids, ask students why roots grow downward and stems upward. Why do plants bend toward windows?

2. Several days before beginning this chapter, obtain two potted coleus plants. Use one as control, and spray the other with gibberellic acid. As the students view the results, ask them what they think caused the growth. Discuss the implications to agriculture.

3. Obtain a number of plants for a demonstration of photoperiodism. Certain kinds of morning glory plants, such as the Japanese morning glory, are short-day plants. Other short-day plants are Cornell, Crimson Rambler, and Scarlett O'Hara. Set aside a group of seedlings as a control. Grow the experimental group in a dark, lightproof box. To trigger a flowering response, expose the plants to several days or weeks of alternating short "days" and long "nights" (of at least 16 hours). Ask the students to record their observations. Discuss the results.

4. Ask students to prepare brief oral reports on the effect of light on plants.

Answer Key to Section Reviews

The Nature of Plant Growth (p. 385)

1. *Growth* is an increase in the number or size of cells. *Behavior* consists of a plant's responses to stimuli.
2. Growth occurs mostly in a plant's meristematic regions, located at the tips of roots and stems.

Internal Factors Affecting Growth (p. 388)

1. Hormones regulate plant growth by either promoting or inhibiting it.
2. *Auxins* regulate cell growth and development, inhibit abscission, stimulate the development of vascular tissues, and bring about cell elongation or enlargement. *Gibberellins* foster stem elongation. *Cytokinins* stimulate cell division.

External Factors Affecting Growth (p. 391)

1. Light, temperature, and moisture affect plant growth.
2. Photoperiodism is the response of a plant to the length of light and dark periods. The critical dark period is the maximum or minimum period of uninterrupted darkness that a particular plant needs to bloom.
3. Vernalization is the effect of low temperature on flowering.

Responses to Stimuli (p. 393)

1. Some tropisms and their stimuli are *phototropism* (light), *geotropism* (gravity), *hydrotropism* (water), *thigmotropism* (touch), and *chemotropism* (chemicals).

2. A nastic movement is a plant movement that is independent of the direction of a stimulus.

Teaching Aids for Chapter End Features

Laboratory Investigation 24
Responses to Stimuli (p. 394)

The leaves of *Oxalis* exhibit a photonastic response and fold downward during intervals of darkness.

OBSERVATIONS AND CONCLUSIONS 1. In the dark, *Oxalis* exhibits nastic movement (photonasty). **2.** The corn roots grew downward, toward gravity. The stems grew upward, away from gravity. Auxins concentrate on the lower side of the stem, stimulating growth there. The concentration of auxins on the lower side of the roots inhibits growth on the lower side of the roots. This unequal growth rate causes stems to turn upward and roots to turn downward. **3.** For stems, the growth response is called negative geotropism; for roots, it is called positive geotropism.

Review of Facts and Concepts (p. 395)

1. Growth and development are irreversible processes because the resulting mature stem, roots, and leaves cannot change back to their young meristematic forms.
2. See Figure 24-1a–24-1e, on page 386.
3. Some hormones that promote plant growth are auxins, indoleacetic acid, gibberellic acid, and kinetin. Some hormones that inhibit plant growth are abscisic acid, maleic hydrazine, and ethylene.
4. Light, temperature, moisture, gravity, chemicals, touch, and pressure affect plant growth and behavior.
5. Light energy is needed for photosynthesis. The length of a plant's exposure to light influences its flowering process. Through phototropic responses, light influences auxin production and, indirectly, stem elongation.
6. *Short-day plants* flower only when exposed to dark periods that are longer than the light periods. *Long-day plants* need longer light periods. *Day-neutral plants* are not affected by the relative durations of the light and dark periods. Examples will vary.
7. The optimum temperature is the temperature at which the life processes of a plant occur most rapidly and efficiently.
8. *Xerophytes* are plants that are adapted to dry and desert conditions. *Hydrophytes* are plants

that thrive in watery environments. *Mesophytes* are plants that grow under moderately moist conditions.

9. A *tropism* is a plant's growth response to environmental stimuli. A *positive tropism* is a growth response toward the stimulus. A *negative tropism* is a growth response away from the stimulus.

10. *Nastic movements* are plant movements that are independent of the direction of stimuli. *Tropisms* are growth responses to environmental stimuli.

Extensions and Applications (p. 395)

1. This extension demonstrates the effect of an external factor, light, and the effect of an internal factor, hormones. The control setup is the uncovered pot with the uncut plant. The three others constitute the experimental setup. The uncut plants inside the box should continue to grow toward the light coming in through the window. The cut plants, both inside and outside the box, should not grow at all, because they no longer have the source of their auxins.

2. The stem should respond negatively to gravity and bend upward. Try modifying the extension by introducing other stimuli, such as water, light, or chemicals.

3. Of particular interest is the history of gibberellins, which Japanese scientists discovered in rice plants.

Unit Teaching Aids

Perspectives in Biology

Chemical Versus Organic Farming (p. 397)

1. Stress to your students that not all chemical fertilizers contain the same type or amount of minerals. Also note that different fertilizers are designed to be used with different types of plants. The conclusions drawn by the students in this experiment will relate only to the ability of organic and inorganic fertilizers to promote the growth of plants.

2. Information about hydroponics may be found in the public and university libraries in your community. Literature can be obtained from the United States Department of Agriculture. Gardening magazines may also have articles on hydroponic gardening.

Field Trip Suggestions

1. Observe how commercial mushrooms are grown on a mushroom farm.
2. Take the students to ponds, lakes, swamps, estuaries, bogs, forests, and the banks of rivers and streams to observe the different types of plants that grow in each area. **Caution:** *Provide instructions on safety near water. Have students use the buddy system.*
3. A trip to a nursery, orchard, or lumberyard can be arranged. Students may be interested in finding out either how lumber is processed or how auxins are employed to make plants grow or bear fruit.
4. At a botanical garden or arboretum, identify as many native and foreign plants as time allows.

Audio-Visual Materials

Botany, set/32 overhead transparencies, DGAV
Early Land Plants, sound filmstrip, HBJ
From Blossom to Fruit, film, BFA
Plant Physiology, set/3 super 8mm film loops, PHM
Plant Tropisms and Other Movements, film, Cor
Seed Germination, film, EBE
Sexual Reproduction of a Flowering Plant, set/8 sound filmstrips, PHM
The Growth of Plants, film, EBE

Reading Resources for Teachers

Bold, H. *The Plant Kingdom*. Englewood Cliffs, N.J.: Prentice-Hall.
Galston, A. *The Life of the Green Plant*. Englewood Cliffs, N.J.: Prentice-Hall.
Lee, A. *Plant Growth and Development*. Lexington, Mass.: D. C. Heath Company.
Salisbury, F. *The Biology of Flowering*. New York: Natural History Press.

UNIT SIX

Invertebrates

This unit takes a phylogenetic approach to the invertebrate animals. Invertebrates represent more than 90% of all the animal species in the world. For each invertebrate phylum, students learn the structures and functions involved in various life processes. The sponges and coelenterates are discussed in Chapter 25. In Chapter 26, the emphasis is on the symmetry and the body cavity of flatworms, roundworms, and segmented worms. Chapter 27 deals with the diversity of both mollusks and echinoderms. In Chapter 28, the crustaceans and myriapods are discussed. The crayfish is used as the model of crustacean anatomy. The grasshopper is used as the model for insect anatomy in Chapter 29, in which arachnids and insects are discussed. Insect development, behavior, and control are also treated.

25 Sponges and Coelenterates

Chapter Objectives: See page 400.

Chapter Overview

The two characteristics of division of labor and interdependence first appear in sponges and coelenterates. Chapter 25 presents the sponges as the less complex of the two phyla. The features of sponge structure include the ostia, the osculum, a skeleton, and two layers of cells with an intermediate jellylike material. Digestion and reproduction in sponges are also discussed in Chapter 25. The functions of the osculum and the collar cells, as well as the circulation of food and materials, are explained. Asexual reproduction by budding or by gemmules and sexual reproduction are also treated.

Coelenterates have a slightly more complicated life cycle than do sponges. The general structural features of coelenterates include radial symmetry, a coelenteron, and tentacles with cnidoblasts and nematocysts. Specific subsections of the chapter are devoted to hydras, jellyfishes, and sea anemones and corals.

Teaching Strategies and Activities

1. Collect and display pictures of sponges, corals, hydras, and other coelenterates. Try to show the class slides or movies of living coelenterates obtaining food.
2. If you have a living sponge, trace the water currents through the sponge. This can be done by placing carmine red powder near the top of the sponge.
3. To show that sponges are organized at the cellular level, press pieces of the living sponge through cheesecloth and disperse the resulting mixture in dishes of the water in which the sponges were shipped. Within an hour or so, the cells begin to clump into small sponges. The freshwater sponge *Spongilla* works best for this demonstration.

Answer Key to Section Reviews
Sponges (p. 405)
1. Sponges are classified in the phylum Porifera.
2. Collar cells bring water into the sponge and filter out food particles.
3. Spicules are sharp, pointed, noncellular projections that support the sponge body.
4. Gemmules are groups of amoebocytes that are surrounded by a hard protective coat.
5. Regeneration is the ability to grow back missing parts or to replace old parts.

Coelenterates (p. 410)
1. The three classes of coelenterates are Hydrozoa, Scyphozoa, and Anthozoa.
2. *Cnidoblasts* are stinging cells on the tentacles of coelenterates. *Nematocysts* are spearlike threads within the cnidoblasts.
3. Hydras reproduce asexually by budding or sexually by producing eggs and sperm.
4. In strobilation, the sessile polyp form of the jellyfish produces medusas that stack like saucers.

Teaching Aids for Chapter End Features
Laboratory Investigation 25
Observing a Hydra (p. 411)

Note: Wash the brine shrimp before using them as food for the hydra because salt kills hydras. The shrimp can be washed by placing them into a fine mesh net that is suspended in a small container of aged tap water or aquarium water. In step 6, the 5% acetic acid solution is clear, distilled vinegar.

OBSERVATIONS AND CONCLUSIONS 1. Answers will vary. Six tentacles is the average number. **2.** Answers will vary. The hydra usually contracts all its tentacles when one is touched. The entire body should contract when it is touched. **3.** The nematocysts "fire," capturing the brine shrimp. The tentacle moves the shrimp to the mouth, where it is ingested. **4.** Under the microscope, the outer layer of the body wall is clearly visible. The coelenteron is inside the tubular body and tentacles. Yes, the coelenteron appears to extend into the tentacles. **5.** Answers will vary. When acetic acid is added, the tentacles should contract and fire their nematocysts. No, the nematocysts are not evenly distributed. Nematocysts occur in large numbers in the knobs of the tentacles.

Review of Facts and Concepts (p. 413)

1. A simple sponge has a hollow body with a large excurrent pore. The body is covered with incurrent pores. The body wall of the sponge consists of two cell layers separated by a layer of jellylike material.
2. The skeleton protects the sponge, supports its body, and gives the sponge its shape.
3. Sponges are grouped according to the chemical makeup of their skeletons.
4. Water currents, created by the flagella of the collar cells, draw microscopic food particles into the sponge. The many hairlike projections on the collar cells filter out the food particles. The cells themselves take the food into vacuoles.
5. Sponges produce asexually by budding and by forming gemmules.
6. *Amoebocytes* carry food and oxygen to other cells and secrete the substances that form the sponge skeleton. Epithelial cells make up the *epidermis. Porocytes* control the opening and closing of the ostia. The collar cells of the *inner cell layer* draw water into the sponge and filter out food particles.
7. Coelenterates are classified in the phylum Coelenterata. The coelenterates have a single, hollow digestive cavity.
8. Coelenterates have a tubelike, sessile polyp body form and a bell- or cup-shaped, swimming medusa body form.
9. Hydras lure their prey by extending and waving their tentacles. When the prey touches one of the tentacles, the contact releases nematocysts, which sting and paralyze the prey. The tentacles then contract, pulling the prey into the mouth of the hydra.
10. A nerve net is an irregular network of nerve cells.
11. Hydras reproduce sexually by producing eggs and sperm. Because hydras are dioecious, the sperm from a male hydra must swim to an egg of a female hydra.
12. Hydras and jellyfishes have three body layers and a nerve net, and they undergo both asexual and sexual reproduction. Unlike hydras, jellyfishes have true muscle cells, a medusa stage, and sense organs called the statolith and ocelli.
13. See Figure 25-10 on page 409.
14. Coral reefs form when corals die and leave behind their skeletons. These skeletons become cemented to one another in a mass, forming a reef. Refer to Figure 25-12 on page 410.
15. *Sponges* are organized at the cellular level, with a jellylike material between two cell layers. They are sessile organisms that have no digestive cavity and respond in a very simple way to stimuli. Sponges filter-feed. *Coelenterates*, organized at the tissue level, have an endoderm, an ectoderm, and an intermediate mesoglea. They can be sessile or free-swimming, and they have a nerve net. They have a digestive cavity with a single opening and are carnivorous animals.

Extensions and Applications (p. 413)

1. The clownfish, immune to the stinging cells of the sea anemone, uses the anemone for shelter. In return, the fish lures prey for the anemone to feed on. Hermit crabs place sea anemones on their shells. The crab gets added protection, and the anemone gains extra food. Snapping shrimp burrow into the crevices of coral for shelter.
2. Spicules may be straight rods or may have two or more rays.
3. You may want to have students give brief oral reports as well as submit written reports.
4. Although a synthetic sponge resembles a natural sponge, the natural sponge holds more water.

26 Worms

Chapter Objectives: See page 414.

Chapter Overview

Chapter 26 devotes one section to each of the worm phyla: the flatworms (Platyhelminthes), the roundworms (Nematoda), and the segmented worms (Annelida). Three classes of flatworms are presented in this chapter. The class Turbellaria is comprised of the free-living flatworms. The most common example is *Planaria*. Flukes, of the class Trematoda, are parasitic flatworms. The tapeworms, of the class Cestoda, are also parasitic. The reproductive cycle of the tapeworm in humans is stressed in this discussion. Discussions of the roundworms *Ascaris*, the hookworm, and the trichina worm, with their complex life cycles, are presented. The segmented worms include the earthworms, leeches, and sandworms. The anatomy of the earthworm, including nervous, digestive, circulatory, respiratory, excretory, and reproductive systems, is discussed.

Teaching Strategies and Activities

1. Present case studies of tapeworm, hookworm, elephantiasis, and Guinea worm infections. Perhaps students can also make a list of unusual facts about parasitic worms.
2. Have students prepare a presentation on the role

of leeches in past and present medical science practices.

3. *Tubifex* is an annelid worm that can regenerate its parts. Conduct a demonstration to illustrate regeneration.

4. During the discussion of earthworms, an earthworm farm can be set up. Students can keep drawings of the tunnels made by the worms. These worms can be used for the fourth of the Extensions and Applications on page 431.

Answer Key to Section Reviews

Flatworms (p. 419)

1. Planarians are grouped in the class Turbellaria.
2. The pharynx is extended from the mouth to draw in microscopic organisms.
3. Cephalization is the localization of the sense organs in the head area.
4. Tapeworms have a scolex, a neck, and proglottids.

Roundworms (p. 423)

1. Roundworms are classified in the phylum Nematoda.
2. The cloaca is a chamber in roundworms into which the digestive, excretory, and reproductive systems empty.
3. The life cycle of the hookworm begins when fertilized eggs pass out of a host with its feces. In the soil, the eggs hatch into larvae. The larvae enter a host through the skin, work their way through the bloodstream to the throat, and are swallowed. In the intestine of the host, they grow into mature worms. Their eggs pass from the host's body with the feces, initiating a new life cycle.

Segmented Worms (p. 428)

1. The coelom is a body cavity filled with fluid.
2. The clitellum is a swollen area toward the anterior end of the worm that is involved in reproduction.
3. The nervous system coordinates all movements and reactions in the earthworm by carrying impulses over definite nerve pathways.
4. *Nereis* uses its parapodia for swimming and burrowing.

Teaching Aids for Chapter End Features

Laboratory Investigation 26
Observing a Planarian (p. 429)

Once the regeneration part of the investigation is underway, change the aquarium water in the petri dishes at least three times per week. Do not feed the regenerating planaria until their regeneration is complete.

OBSERVATIONS AND CONCLUSIONS 1. The visible parts should include the anterior and posterior ends, the dorsal and ventral surfaces, the eyespots, the sensory lobes, the pharynx, and the digestive tract. **2.** The planarian moves away from light. **3.** Touched on a sensory lobe, the planarian contracts rapidly. Touched on the body, the planarian contracts less rapidly. **4.** The planarian should glide onto the piece of liver, and the pharynx may extend as the worm feeds. **5.** Parts of planaria should regenerate in the following sequence: first, the heads regenerate ends; second, the middles regenerate heads and ends; and last, the ends regenerate heads.

Review of Facts and Concepts (p. 431)

1. In comparison to sponges and coelenterates, worms have three layers of cells (not two), true organs and organ systems, and more complex nervous systems.
2. Bilateral symmetry means that the right and left sides of the worm's body are mirror images of each other.
3. The flatworm takes in food with its pharynx. The food is digested by enzymes in the intestine.
4. The excretory system of a flatworm consists of a series of tubes that lead to pores on the body surface. At the internal end of each tube is a single flame bulb. The cilia of the flame bulb send water and wastes through the tubes and out the pores.
5. In planaria, *sexual reproduction* occurs by mutual cross-fertilization between two planaria. *Asexual reproduction* occurs by fragmentation.
6. See Figure 26-3 on page 418.
7. The tapeworm is a ribbonlike flatworm consisting of a scolex, a neck, and a chain of square proglottids.
8. The tapeworm consists of a series of identical proglottids, whereas the segments of annelids contain various organs and body parts.
9. Oxygen and carbon dioxide pass directly into and out of nematodes through their body wall.
10. The eggs of *Ascaris* enter the human digestive system in contaminated food or water. In the intestine, the eggs hatch into larvae. The larvae burrow through the intestine, enter the bloodstream, and travel to the lungs and throat. After being swallowed, they return to the small intestine, where they mature and reproduce. Passed from the host in feces, the fertilized eggs start the cycle again.

11. Nematodes lack a circulatory system for distributing gases and food throughout their bodies. If they were too large, the gases and food could not reach all their cells. The earthworms have organ systems. Therefore, gases and food can be transported to all cells in very large species.

12. The life cycle of the hookworm begins when fertilized eggs pass out of a host with its feces. In the soil, the eggs hatch into larvae. The larvae enter a host through the skin, work their way through the bloodstream to the throat, and are swallowed. In the intestine of the host, they grow into mature worms. When the eggs pass from the new host, the cycle starts again.

13. Humans may get trichinosis by eating infected, undercooked pork.

14. The body of annelids is divided into many small, ringlike segments, which are not characteristic of flatworm and roundworm bodies. In addition to a coelom, the annelid body also contains a more complex nervous system and circulatory system.

15. The earthworm takes in food through the mouth by means of a muscular pharynx. Food passes through the esophagus, the crop, and the gizzard. In the gizzard food is ground up. In the intestine the food is digested.

16. The earthworm has a closed circulatory system. A large dorsal blood vessel carries blood to the anterior end, and the ventral blood vessel carries blood toward the posterior end. Along the lengths of both vessels, small paired vessels connect the dorsal and ventral blood vessels. Five pairs of aortic arches connect the dorsal and ventral blood vessels near the head, helping to move the blood by contracting and relaxing.

17. Nerve messages are sent along definite pathways in the earthworm.

18. Earthworms reproduce sexually by cross-fertilization. When two earthworms mate, mucus secreted by their clitella holds them together. In each earthworm, sperm is carried through the sperm ducts to the male genital pore. The two earthworms then exchange sperm cells. A few days later, eggs are passed through the oviduct to the female genital pore and into a mucus ring, where the stored sperm fertilizes them. The mucus ring slips off the anterior end of the earthworm and forms a cocoon containing 1 to 20 eggs.

Extensions and Applications (p. 431)

1. You may want to arrange to have a local veterinarian speak to the class about flatworm and roundworm infections in animals. The students could prepare a list of questions before the visit.

2. The life cycle of the liver fluke is given on page 418. Students will have to research the life cycle of the tapeworm.

3. *Elephantiasis* is an infection caused by the microfilaria larvae of a nematode. *Onchocerciasis* is caused by a nematode, and may result in blindness. *Schistosomiasis* is an infection caused by the fluke *Schistosoma*.

4. The clitellum is closer to the anterior end than to the posterior end. On a smooth surface, the worm is not able to anchor itself for extending and contracting.

5. Planarians prefer cool, clear streams and shallow ponds. They are also found on watercress farms. Students can use the planarians for the Laboratory Investigation.

27 Mollusks and Echinoderms

Chapter Objectives: See page 432.

Chapter Overview

Chapter 27 covers three of the six mollusk classes. The bivalves (class Pelecypoda), which have two hinged shells, are represented by clams, oysters, and scallops. The class Gastropoda includes univalve mollusks, such as snails, slugs, conchs, and whelks. Encasing the body of these organisms is a single shell. The mollusks of the class Cephalopoda are the most highly organized. Octopuses, squids, and nautiluses represent the class.

The echinoderms are discussed in the second section of this chapter. A discussion of the starfish dominates this part of the chapter. The chapter ends with a brief discussion of the brittle star, sea urchin, sand dollar, and sea cucumber.

Teaching Strategies and Activities

1. To stimulate student interest, display pictures of echinoderms and mollusks, as well as dried and preserved specimens.

2. Some of your students may have shell collections. Encourage them to bring in their collections and talk to the class about the shells. Students may also classify the shells as bivalves or univalves.

3. Have the students prepare reports on the many ways people have used mollusks and mollusk shells throughout history, including use as money, jewelry, food, and dyes.

4. Place a living starfish on a sheet of glass to show students the action of the starfish's tube feet.

Then place the starfish upside down in a tank of salt water so that the students can observe the animal's righting behavior.

Answer Key to Section Reviews

Mollusks (p. 439)

1. Annelids and mollusks both have coeloms and trochophore larvae.
2. The regions of the mollusk's soft body are the head, visceral mass, and foot.
3. Three characteristics used to classify mollusks are the presence or absence of a shell, the type of shell, and the type of foot.
4. *Bivalves* are mollusks whose shells have two parts. *Univalves* are mollusks with single shells.
5. Cephalopods are considered the most highly organized mollusks because they have a well-developed brain and sense organs. In addition, they have a closed circulatory system, and food moves through their digestive systems by means of muscle contractions.

Echinoderms (p. 442)

1. "Pentaradial" means radially symmetrical with five parts.
2. The water-vascular system is used for locomotion and food-getting.
3. Regeneration is the development of an entire animal from one of its parts or the regrowth of a new part to replace a missing one.
4. Other echinoderms include sea urchins, brittle stars, sea cucumbers, and sand dollars.

Teaching Aids for Chapter End Features

Laboratory Investigation 27
Observing a Mollusk (p. 443)

The valves of preserved clams often are pegged open to facilitate cutting the adductor muscles.

OBSERVATIONS AND CONCLUSIONS 1. The outer layer resembles a thin layer of shellac; the middle layer is chalky; and the inner layer is pearly. **2.** The incurrent siphon is below the excurrent siphon. **3.** Cilia on the gill surfaces move the particles forward to two thin fleshy folds. Ciliary action moves the food into the mouth. **4.** The posterior adductor muscle is larger than the anterior adductor muscle.

Review of Facts and Concepts (p. 444)

1. The trochophore larva is shaped like a top with a ring of cilia around its middle.

2. The outermost layer of the clam shell is called the *horny outer layer*. The middle layer is called the *prismatic layer*. The *pearly layer* is the inner layer.
3. In the respiratory system, water passes into the incurrent siphon, over the gills, and out the excurrent siphon. In an open circulatory system, the blood travels from the heart to small body cavities and to the tissues, organs, and gills and then returns to the heart. The nervous system is composed of three pairs of ganglia and sensory organs in the head region that respond to light and touch. Individual bivalves have either male or female reproductive structures.
4. Unlike clams, oysters attach themselves permanently to objects. Unlike clams, scallops move by opening and closing their valves, an action that jets water out at the hinge.
5. A pearl is formed when an object is caught between the mantle and the shell of an oyster. Part of the mantle surrounds the particle and secretes pearly layers of calcium carbonate.
6. Unlike other mollusks, cephalopods have closed circulatory systems. Also, food moves through the digestive system by means of muscle contraction instead of ciliary movement.
7. The members of the class *Pelecypoda* have two shells and a wedge-shaped foot. Mussels, clams, oysters, scallops, and shipworms are all acceptable examples. The members of the class *Gastropoda* have one shell, and the rear mantle cavity of an adult is located behind the head. The snails, slugs, conchs, and whelks are examples. The members of the class *Cephalopoda* include octopuses, squids, cuttlefishes, and chambered nautiluses. Most do not have shells, and the foot is located in the head region.
8. Echinoderms have an endoskeleton covered with a thin epidermal layer.
9. In both echinoderms and mollusks, the coelom is formed from the mesoderm. In echinoderms, projections of the coelom function as respiratory and excretory organs, whereas mollusks have separate organs for these functions.
10. Pressing against the shell of a mollusk, the tube feet of a starfish exert a steady pull on the shell. In half an hour or so, the adductor muscles of the mollusk tire and relax. The shell opens slightly, and the starfish turns its stomach inside out through the mouth. Then the starfish's stomach passes through the opening between the valves of the clam.
11. The respiratory system consists of projections of the coelom on the aboral surface. The nervous system consists of a nerve ring around the mouth, with nerves extending from the nerve ring into each of the starfish's five rays. At the tip of each ray is an eyespot. The reproductive

system of a starfish consists of a pair of gonads in each ray. An individual starfish is either male or female.

12. As predators, starfishes have damaged coral reefs as well as oyster, clam, and mussel beds. When present in large numbers, snails do great damage to garden plants and even to trees.

13. *Bivalve* means two-shelled; *univalve* means one-shelled. In *bilateral symmetry*, the two halves of the organism are mirror images of each other; in *radial symmetry*, there is a regular circular arrangement of body parts around a central area. The *trochophore* is the larval form in most mollusks; the *bipinnaria* is the larval form in the starfish.

Extensions and Applications (p. 445)

1. The nautilus occupies the outermost chamber of a series of chambers that comprise its shell. As the animal grows, it builds the outer wall forward and moves out of the current chamber, sealing itself off from its prior quarters. All the chambers are perforated by a long narrow tube. The vacated chambers contain a gas similar in composition to air, but with slightly less oxygen and slightly more nitrogen. This gas increases the buoyancy of the organism and facilitates swimming.

2. Both types of snails move by gliding on the foot. The radula in the mouth acts as a scraper to remove algae.

3. *Note: Stress conservation in shell collecting.* The populations of many snails have decreased because large numbers were killed for their shells.

28 Crustaceans and Myriapods

Chapter Objectives: See page 446.

Chapter Overview

Chapter 28 opens with a brief presentation of the identifying characteristics of arthropods. Arthropods have an exoskeleton, banded muscles, jointed appendages, and a reduced and divided coelom. Of the five main arthropod classes, this chapter discusses Crustacea, Chilopoda, and Diplopoda. The two other arthropod classes are discussed in Chapter 29.

In the discussion of crustaceans, the crayfish is the illustrative organism. Its external features are discussed. Detailed explanations of the crayfish's digestive, circulatory, respiratory, excretory, and nervous systems are provided. Sexual reproduction, molting, and regeneration in the crayfish are also discussed. The discussion of myriapods concentrates on centipedes (Chilopoda) and millipedes (Diplopoda).

Teaching Strategies and Activities

1. Begin the chapter by showing slides or photographs of as many arthropods as possible. Ask students to look for common features among the different species.

2. Students can raise their own crustaceans. Brine shrimp eggs hatch in 24 hours when placed in a 4% NaCl solution. Have the students observe the hatching shrimp under a dissecting microscope.

3. Dissect a crayfish to examine the internal systems of this crustacean. Have a few live crayfishes for students to observe. Students should try to determine locomotion, feeding, and defense behaviors of crayfishes.

4. Isopods prefer moist, dark environments. Students can study this preference by setting up a model of a natural environment. Cover half the bottom of an enamel pan with wet paper towels, and shade the same half with a piece of cardboard. Placing 10 sow bugs in the center of the pan, count how many sow bugs move to the dark, moist side and how many move to the light, dry side.

Answer Key to Section Reviews
Characteristics of Arthropods (p. 447)

1. Arthropods have hard exoskeletons, banded muscles, reduced coeloms, and jointed legs.

2. Molting is the periodic shedding of the exoskeleton.

3. The hemocoel is a cavity in arthropods that contains blood and surrounds the digestive system.

Crustaceans (p. 453)

1. Crayfishes have two fewer body segments than lobsters. Crayfishes live in fresh water, whereas lobsters live in salt water.

2. The divisions of the crayfish body are the cephalothorax and the abdomen.

3. *Maxillipeds* are appendages that hold and taste food. *Chelipeds* are large claws used for food-getting and for protection.

4. The green glands remove excess water and wastes from the blood of a crayfish.

5. Unlike the crayfish, the crab has a cephalothorax that is at least as wide as it is long. Also, the crab's abdomen is smaller than that of the crayfish, and it is turned up on the underside of the thorax.

Myriapods (p. 454)

1. "Myriapod" means "many legs."
2. The *tracheae* carry the gases of respiration directly to and from the body cells of myriapods. The *Malpighian tubules* remove wastes from the body cavity of most arthropods.

Teaching Aids for Chapter End Features

Laboratory Investigation 28
Observing a Crustacean (p. 455)

Green aquarium water is an acceptable substitute for the *Chlorella* culture.

OBSERVATIONS AND CONCLUSIONS 1. *Daphnia* swim rapidly. The drinking-straw chamber keeps the *Daphnia* in place. 2. When the temperature is decreased, the rate of heartbeat in *Daphnia* slows down. When the temperature is increased, the rate speeds up. 3. Students should be able to see the digestive tract. 4. The green alga cells give the digestive tract a green color.

Review of Facts and Concepts (p. 457)

1. Five main classes of arthropods are Crustacea, Chilopoda, Diplopoda, Arachnida, and Insecta.
2. An arthropod must periodically molt its exoskeleton because the exoskeleton does not grow as the arthropod grows.
3. *Isopods* are small terrestrial crustaceans, such as sow bugs. *Copepods* and *ostracods* are small aquatic crustaceans.
4. The crayfish's body consists of the *cephalothorax* and *abdomen*. *Antennules* help the crayfish to maintain its equilibrium and act as sense organs for touch and taste. The *antennae* are organs of touch and taste. The *mandibles* crush food. The first pair of *maxillae* hold the food during feeding. The second pair draw water over the gills. Three pairs of *maxillipeds* are used to hold and taste food. *Chelipeds* are used for food-getting and protection. Four pairs of walking legs are used for locomotion. *Swimmerets* aid in swimming and respiration. The *uropod* and the *telson* are used for backward movements.
5. The crayfish moves with walking legs and swimmerets. The telson and uropod enable the crayfish to move backward.
6. The crayfish has an open circulatory system, whereas the annelids have a closed system.
7. The nervous system of a crayfish is made up of a "brain" that consists of a pair of ganglia. Two nerves lead from the brain and join the ventral nerve cord. Each segment along this nerve cord contains a pair of jointed ganglia with nerves that extend to the appendages, muscles, and organs. The statocyst helps the crayfish to maintain its balance.
8. Before molting occurs, inorganic salts are removed from the exoskeleton and stored in the epidermis. At the same time, the new exoskeleton begins to form. The old exoskeleton cracks open, and the crayfish backs out. The inorganic salts are redeposited in the new exoskeleton.
9. *Annelids* have soft bodies, closed circulatory systems, large coeloms, and muscles arranged in sheets. *Crustaceans* have hard exoskeletons, reduced coeloms, open circulatory systems, and muscles in bands.
10. *Crabs* have a cephalothorax that is at least as wide as it is long and an abdomen that turns up on the underside of the thorax. Most crabs walk sideways. They can also swim with their flattened appendages. *Shrimps* have flattened bodies and large feathery swimmerets for swimming. The free-swimming, shrimplike larvae of *barnacles* attach themselves permanently to one place, filter-feeding for all of their adult lives. *Isopods* are terrestrial crustaceans that live in dark, moist places and breathe with gills.
11. *Centipedes* are carnivorous and have one pair of legs per body segment. *Millipedes* are herbivorous and have two pairs of legs per body segment.
12. Millipedes protect themselves by rolling into a ball or by secreting a foul-smelling liquid.
13. *Antennae* are organs of touch and taste; *antennules* are shorter organs of touch, taste, and balance. The *mandibles* crush food; the *maxillae* hold the food during feeding and draw water over the gills. The *gill chambers* contain the gills; the *gill bailer* draws water in and passes it over the gills.

Extensions and Applications (p. 457)

1. The crab burrows into the sand. Burrowing provides protection and moisture for the crab. When its feelers are touched, the animal backs away or raises its claws.
2. Krill are small crustaceans, called euphausids, that are the main food of baleen whales.
3. Answers may vary. In many reference books, Entomostraca and Malacostraca are listed as subclasses. In other books, subclasses may include Branchiopoda (fairy shrimp), Ostracoda (*Daphnia*), Copepoda (*Cyclops*, *Calanus*), Cirripedia (barnacles), and Malacostraca (large crustaceans). Some orders may include Branchiura (fish lice), Isopoda (pill bugs), Amphipoda (beach fleas), Euphausiacea (krill), and Decapoda (shrimp, lobster).

29 Arachnids and Insects

Chapter Objectives: See page 458.

Chapter Overview

The characteristics of spiders, which dominate the section on arachnids, are presented. These characteristics include open circulatory systems, hearts with ostia, Malpighian tubules, spinnerets, book lungs or tracheae, and spiracles. Mating habits and several special adaptations of the diving spider are discussed. The coverage of arachnids also includes scorpions, ticks, and mites.

The introduction to the discussion of insects includes the classification of insects, the three body regions, the exoskeleton, and the specialized mouthparts. The classic representative of Insecta is the grasshopper. The anatomy and physiology of the grasshopper are presented in detail. A discussion of insect development includes complete and incomplete metamorphoses. Social instincts, particularly the divisions of labor that are characteristic of ant, honeybee, and termite colonies, and defense mechanisms among insects are discussed. The chapter concludes with a comparison of chemical and biological methods for insect control.

Teaching Strategies and Activities

1. Take the students for a walk around the school grounds. Have students list all the types of insects and arachnids observed during the walk. Students can also collect appropriate specimens. Keep the insects in covered petri dishes or small jars lined with moist filter paper. The students can construct a key to identify local insects.
2. Begin the chapter by listing as many venomous insects and spiders as possible. Then inform the students about the ones that live in your area.
3. Organize a debate on the biological control versus the chemical control of insects.

Answer Key to Section Reviews

Arachnids (p. 462)

1. Arachnids have four pairs of legs, no antennae, and two body regions.
2. *Chelicerae* are clawlike fangs with poison glands. *Pedipalps* are a pair of appendages used for chewing and sensory functions.
3. Spiracles are openings in the abdomen of some spiders and insects that lead from the tracheae to the outside.
4. Types of spiders include the diving spider, hunting spider, fishing spider, and trapdoor spider.

5. Some arachnids other than spiders are scorpions, ticks, mites, and daddy-longlegs.

Insect Anatomy (p. 467)

1. The three regions of the grasshopper are the head, the thorax, and the abdomen.
2. The thorax divisions are the prothorax, mesothorax, and metathorax.
3. The tympanum is a membrane on the abdomen that enables the grasshopper to hear sounds.
4. The ovipositors of the female grasshopper are used to dig a hole and deposit the fertilized eggs.
5. Parthenogenesis is the development of eggs without fertilization.

Insect Development (p. 469)

1. Metamorphosis is the series of changes in appearance that insects undergo as they develop.
2. The stages of *incomplete metamorphosis* are egg, nymph, and adult. The stages of *complete metamorphosis* are egg, larva, pupa, and adult.
3. Juvenile hormone stimulates larval development and inhibits the development of an adult.

Insect Behavior (p. 472)

1. Division of labor is an arrangement in which each member of a society has a special job that is necessary for the survival of the colony.
2. Mimicry is the imitation of one insect by another insect.

Insect Control (p. 473)

1. An advantage of chemical control is that it is quickly effective in killing insects. Two disadvantages are that pesticides take a long time to break down into harmless substances and that they are stored in the fatty tissues of human beings and animals.
2. Advantages of biological control are that it attacks only the target pest, which cannot become resistant, and that biological control programs have no side effects on other organisms. Disadvantages are that such programs are expensive and that they can take years to produce results.
3. A pheromone is a chemical attractant given off by an insect.

Teaching Aids for Chapter End Features

Laboratory Investigation 29
Observing an Insect Colony (p. 474)

Have students devise ant traps and gather workers to place in observation chambers. One such trap consists of a darkened jar baited with food. A small piece of sponge placed inside the trap keeps the air humid. A cardboard runway extended from the lip of the jar to the soil increases the efficiency of the trap.

OBSERVATIONS AND CONCLUSIONS 1. All insects have an exoskeleton and a body comprised of a head, a thorax, and an abdomen. Insects usually have six pairs of jointed legs, simple and compound eyes, and one pair of antennae. Ants differ from other insects in that they have a narrow waist with a dorsal projection. Also, the workers are wingless; the reproductive males and females have wings, but only before mating. **2.** Sketches and answers will vary. **3.** Some activities in chambers may include storing food, tending eggs, and feeding larvae. **4.** The students should be able to discern the queen, female workers, and larvae. However, students may not be able to observe winged males, which emerge once a year and live only long enough to mate. **5.** The students should see that an ant colony is based on division of labor and mutual dependence among different types of ants.

Review of Facts and Concepts (p. 476)

1. The body of the spider is made up of a *cephalothorax* and an *abdomen*. The *chelicerae* are poisonous fangs, and the *pedipalps* are used for chewing and sensing. *Spinnerets* are used to make the web. For respiration, spiders have either *book lungs* or *tracheae*. *Spiracles* are openings in the abdomen of some spiders and insects that lead from the tracheae to the outside.
2. The silk glands produce a liquid silk that leaves the spider's body through the spinnerets. When the liquid silk passes to the outside, it hardens.
3. Arachnids have eight legs, no antennae, and two body parts. Insects have six legs, antennae, and three body parts.
4. Some adaptations of insects are wings, a chitinous but flexible exoskeleton, camouflage coloring, specialized mouthparts, ovipositors modified as stingers, legs with special pads for clinging to surfaces, and parthenogenesis.
5. Have the students make a table that lists the parts of the grasshopper that are given in the section on grasshoppers. In a second column, have them give the function of each part.
6. Like the crayfish, the grasshopper has an exoskeleton, mandibles and maxillae, an open circulatory system, compound eyes, a ventral nerve cord with ganglia, and jointed appendages.
7. *Incomplete metamorphosis* occurs in three stages. The insect begins as an egg, and then hatches and develops into a nymph. The nymph

grows to adult size. In *complete metamorphosis*, the insect changes from an egg into a segmented larva. The larva increases in size, molts, and enters the pupal stage. A cocoon covers some pupae. The adult emerges from the pupal stage.
8. In a honeybee society, the queen bee lays eggs. Several thousand sterile female worker bees gather food and care for the young bees. Drones mate with the queen.
9. Bees communicate with each other through food-sharing, "dancing," and transmission of queen substance.
10. Insect defense mechanisms include releasing foul-smelling liquids or irritating chemicals, stinging, biting, and mimicry.
11. The control organism may reproduce so fast that it becomes a pest itself.

Extensions and Applications (p. 476)

1. You may want to have the students present their information in a booklet.
2. The use of a net is best for catching insects. Bottles and jars with holes punched in the lids can be used to store the specimens.
3. Formerly regarded as a crustacean, the horse-shoe crab *(Limulus polyphemus)* is the sole survivor of an otherwise extinct group of arthropods intermediate between the trilobites and arachnids. It dates from the Devonian Period.

Unit Teaching Aids

Perspective in Biology
Triage Among Endangered Species (p. 477)

1. The information should be requested six to eight weeks in advance of the scheduled panel discussion. Some questions open to discussion could include: Should endangered species be protected? If so, how? By whom? With whose money?
2. Photographs of endangered species are available from various wildlife organizations, zoos, botanical gardens, aquaria, museums, and so on. A questionnaire can be prepared and then duplicated on the school copying machine.
3. There are actually three sides that may be taken in this debate: (1) Yes, endangered species should be protected by placement in zoos or preserves; (2) No, people should not interfere with the natural order of things and try to protect endangered species; and (3) Yes and no, people should protect endangered species, but in their natural habitats, not by placing them in zoos or preserves.

Field Trip Suggestions

1. Visit a natural history museum or aquarium to view sponges, coelenterates, mollusks, and echinoderms.
2. Visit a seafood market and have the students list all the types of mollusks for sale.
3. Visit a local pond or stream to collect crayfishes. If the school is near the ocean, collect crabs, shrimp, planktonic crustaceans.
4. To observe bees at work, visit an apiary. For a wider perspective on insects, take the class to the entomology department of a local university to see the insect collection there.

Audio-Visual Materials

Arthropoda, set/25 super 8mm film loops, PHM
Arthropods: Insects and Their Relatives, film, Cor
Echinoderms and Mollusks, film, Cor
Ephemera, film, BFA
Invertebrates, film, Cor
Mollusca, set/9 super 8mm film loops, PHM
Sponges and Coelenterates, film, Cor
The Honeybee, film, Cor
The Life of a Dragonfly, film, BFA
Worms: Flat, Round and Segmented, film, Cor

Reading Resources for Teachers

Barnes, R. *Invertebrate Zoology*. Philadelphia: W. B. Saunders Co.
House, M. *The Origin of Major Invertebrate Groups*. New York: Academic Press.
Lanham, U. *Insects*. New York: Columbia University Press.
Sherman, I., and V. Sherman. *The Invertebrates: Function and Form*. New York: Macmillan Company.

UNIT SEVEN
Vertebrates

The vertebrates, which include fishes, amphibians, reptiles, birds, and mammals, all have one characteristic in common: a vertebral column. Unit Seven presents the various classes of vertebrates from the simplest to the most complex.

Chapter 30 discusses the three classes of fishes. A detailed discussion of anatomy and physiology is also presented. Chapter 31 deals with the three orders of amphibians. The discussion focuses on the frog as a representative amphibian. Distinguished

from the amphibians by their scales, amniotic eggs, and internal fertilization, the reptiles are discussed in Chapter 32. The history, characteristics, and classification of birds (Aves) comprise Chapter 33. The last chapter in the unit, Chapter 34, presents the history, the characteristics, and fourteen of the orders of the class Mammalia.

30 Fishes

Chapter Objectives: See page 480.

Chapter Overview

Chapter 30 covers the classification of fishes. The three classes of fishes are discussed. The jawless fishes (Agnatha) are the most primitive of vertebrates. The parasitic lampreys and scavenging hagfishes represent this class in the text. The skates, rays, and sharks (Chondrichthyes) are cartilaginous fishes. Their paired fins and movable jaws set them apart from the agnathans. The bony fishes (Osteichthyes) include ray-finned fishes, lobe-finned fishes, and lungfishes.

The perch, a typical bony fish, is the focal point in the last half of the chapter. The discussion presents the perch's external features and internal structures. Each organ system is covered in turn. The final subsection explains the perch's breeding habits and development.

Teaching Strategies and Activities

1. Have the students research *Dunkleosteus*, a placoderm of the Devonian Period.
2. Invite a representative from the Fish and Wildlife Service to discuss the fishes in your area and their management.
3. Set up an aquarium in the classroom. The aquarium can be used for demonstrations of anatomy or behavior in fishes. As you give your presentation on fishes, refer to the anatomy and behavior of the specimens in the tank.
4. Observe some fish scales under a dissecting microscope. Many scales show dark rings that indicate the age of the fish.

Answer Key to Section Reviews
Classification of Fishes (p. 486)

1. The three classes of fishes are Agnatha, Chondrichthyes, and Osteichthyes.
2. The lamprey uses its suckerlike mouth to attach itself to the body of its host.

3. The skin of most sharks is rough and covered with placoid scales. Each of these scales is thin and disklike, with a hard, sharp point projecting from its center.

The Perch: A Representative Bony Fish
(p. 494)

1. Chromatophores are special skin cells that contain pigment granules.
2. The *dorsal fin* and the *anal fin* keep the perch from rolling while swimming. The *caudal fin* propels the perch. The *pelvic fins* and *pectoral fins* permit braking and steering.
3. The sexually mature female perch lays several hundred thousand eggs, and the male releases milt on the eggs. The fertilized eggs hatch in about 18 days, releasing fish larvae about 6 mm long.

Teaching Aids for Chapter End Features

Laboratory Investigation 30
Respiration Rate in Fishes (p. 495)

A class data table will have to be placed on the chalkboard at the beginning of the investigation. *Note: As water is added in steps 4 and 6, the small beaker with the fish tends to tip and float.* To prevent the small beaker from floating, one member of each team should hold it in position. Remove water from the large beaker, as necessary, to prevent it from overflowing.

OBSERVATIONS AND CONCLUSIONS **1.** Oxygen in the water diffuses into the capillaries in the gill filaments, and carbon dioxide diffuses out of the capillaries into the water. **2.** Operculum movements increase or decrease in direct proportion to the respiration rates. **3.** Stabilization prevents the goldfish from becoming excited and thereby allows the students to obtain more accurate data. **4.** The slowest operculum movements should occur at 0 °C, and the fastest at 32 °C.

Review of Facts and Concepts (p. 497)

1. *Jawless fishes* lack scales and paired fins. They have a cartilaginous skeleton, a single nostril, and a gill apparatus that looks like a series of holes. *Bony fishes* have jaws, scales, a skeleton of bone, paired fins, one or two nostrils on each side of the snout, and gills covered by an operculum.
2. *Lampreys* have wide, circular mouths with sharp, file-shaped teeth and muscular tongues.

Hagfishes have mouths that are smaller and less suckerlike than those of the lampreys. The mouths of hagfishes are surrounded by six barbels.
3. The members of the class Chondrichthyes have cartilaginous skeletons, movable jaws, paired fins, and no gill covering over the gill slits.
4. Skates and rays have flat bodies and are able to lie flat on the sea bottom, buried in the sand.
5. *Ovoviviparity* means that offspring are produced from eggs that hatch within the female's body. *Oviparity* means that offspring are produced from eggs that are hatched outside the female's body.
6. The lateral line functions as a series of touch receptors.
7. The swim bladder helps bony fishes to rise or sink in the water.
8. Perch scales are flat plates, and their outer surfaces have circular, bony ridges. Shark scales are disklike and have a hard, sharp point projecting from the center.
9. The five major regions of a bony fish's brain are as follows. The *olfactory lobes* receive sensory information from the nasal cavities. The *cerebrum's* function is not clearly understood. The *optic lobes* process visual information from the eyes. The *cerebellum* coordinates movement and controls balance. The *medulla oblongata* controls heartbeat.
10. The pyloric caeca increase the surface area of the intestine for food absorption.
11. An osmoregulator is a structure that keeps water and salts properly balanced in the fish's body.
12. In fresh water, a fish's body tends to lose salts and take in water. The kidneys of a freshwater fish excrete excess water and prevent salt from leaving the body. In sea water, a fish's body tends to lose water and take in salt. The kidneys of a saltwater fish work to keep water in the body.
13. Refer to Figure 30-11 on page 492.

Extensions and Applications (p. 497)

1. About 80 to 100 shark attacks occur in the world each year. The great white shark and the tiger shark account for more than half of these attacks.
2. Students should prepare a table to fill in during their visit.
3. In December 1938 a coelacanth *(Latimeria)* was captured in the nets of a fishing trawler off the South African coast. Eleven other coelacanths were captured between 1952 and 1956 near the Comoro Islands in the Indian Ocean.
4. Most vertebrate dissection guides include the anatomy of the shark.

31 Amphibians

Chapter Objectives: See page 498.

Chapter Overview

The first part of Chapter 31 is devoted to the classification of amphibians. In this chapter, amphibians are classified in three orders. The members of the order Apoda are legless and wormlike, with small eyes, no ears, and only a pair of tentacles for sensing their surroundings. The order Caudata includes the newts and salamanders, which have tails, clawless limbs, and no scales. Of particular interest are the oviparous breeding habits and development of salamanders. Amphibians that do not have tails as adults are members of the order Anura. The discussion of this order includes the distinguishing characteristics of frogs and toads. The remainder of the chapter examines the external features, skeleton, muscles, and organ systems of the frog. The chapter concludes with a description of the life cycle of a frog.

Teaching Strategies and Activities

1. Display live frogs and salamanders in the classroom while studying this chapter.
2. During a detailed frog dissection, relate the specimen's organs to those of human beings. After the dissection, have the students prepare a frog skeleton. To reconstruct the skeleton, the students must remove as much flesh from the bones as possible. Simmer the bones in vinegar and water for 30 minutes, and remove excess tissue with a toothbrush. Then assemble the bones with thin wire.
3. To demonstrate incomplete metamorphosis among salamanders, obtain a specimen of *Necturus* to show the students. Outline its life cycle on the chalkboard.

Answer Key to Section Reviews

Classification of Amphibians (p. 503)

1. The three amphibian orders are Apoda, Caudata, and Anura.
2. A blastopore is a hole that develops in the vegetal pole of the salamander blastula.
3. Hibernation is a state of winter rest during which an animal's body processes slow down.

The Frog: A Representative Amphibian
(p. 512)

1. The tympanum is the circular outer eardrum of the frog.
2. The frog's brain has olfactory lobes and a cerebrum that is divided into two halves. There are also large optic lobes behind which the cerebellum and medulla oblongata are located.
3. The *left atrium* of the heart receives oxygen-rich blood from the lungs through the pulmonary vein. The *right atrium* receives oxygen-poor blood from the body. The *ventricle* pumps the oxygen-rich blood out of the heart.

Teaching Aids for Chapter End Features

Laboratory Investigation 31
Observing Metamorphosis in Frogs (p. 513)

Toad eggs can also be used. As the tadpoles emerge, segregate groups of them according to their varying stages of development. ***Note:*** *After the investigation, return all eggs and tadpoles to their natural habitats.*

OBSERVATIONS AND CONCLUSIONS 1. The coating protects the egg from injury and from drying out. It also serves as food for the developing tadpole. 2. The caudal fin is used for swimming. After a point, it is no longer of use, and it is reabsorbed as food during development. 3. Young tadpoles have small, round mouths with a horny tip. Old tadpoles have a larger and wider mouth, as well as jaws. 4. A young tadpole has an eye on each side of its head. In older tadpoles with legs, the eyes are near the top of the head. 5. The tadpole takes water into the mouth, passes it over the gills, and pushes it out the spiracles on each side of its head. 6. The hind legs appear first. 7. Answers will vary according to the species of frog used in the investigation, the weather, and the temperature.

Review of Facts and Concepts (p. 515)

1. The members of the order Apoda are tropical, wormlike amphibians with no legs, small eyes, no ears, and wide mouths.
2. Amphibians of the order Caudata have slender and muscular bodies, long tails, four clawless limbs, and either smooth or rough skin without scales.
3. During cleavage, the fertilized egg divides into two halves that remain attached. Each of the two resulting cells divides again. Because of the

concentration of yolk in the vegetal pole of the embryo, the vegetal pole divides more slowly than does the animal pole. The upper part of the embryo therefore contains only a few large yolky cells, while the lower part has many small cells. The cells cleave until a blastula forms.

4. Amphibians in the order Anura have no tails, short bodies, and long, muscular hind legs.
5. Toads have dry, warty skin, whereas frogs have moist, smooth skin. Unlike frogs, toads have skin glands behind their eyes that secrete irritating or poisonous substances. Toads do not have teeth, but frogs do. The hind legs of toads are shorter than those of frogs. Frogs are streamlined, whereas toads are not.
6. Toads are not found in Australia or the polar regions.
7. Hibernation allows frogs to survive low temperatures.
8. The frog uses its hind legs for jumping and swimming. The forelegs cushion the frog's landing after a jump.
9. The frog's spine has one cervical vertebra, one sacral vertebra, seven trunk vertebrae, and the urostyle.
10. The frog respires directly through its skin. It also takes in air through the lining of its mouth and pharynx. The frog also utilizes its lungs for respiration.
11. Carbon dioxide leaves the frog's body mostly through the skin. The kidneys, the urinary ducts, the bladder, and the cloaca remove other wastes. Urea, collected in the liver, is passed into the intestine and excreted with the feces.
12. The frog's heart has three chambers, and the blood makes a double circuit. The perch's heart has only two chambers, and the blood completes only one circuit through the heart.
13. In the summer, the frog stores fat for use during hibernation.
14. The thumb pads are used to hold the female frog during mating.
15. Refer to Figure 31-11 on page 512.

Extensions and Applications (p. 515)

1. The frog primarily uses its hind legs for swimming and jumping. The forelimbs provide balance. In breathing, the frog uses the mouth, skin, and lungs. The frog catches the live insect with its sticky tongue and swallows it.
2. *Note: Change the water daily.* Keep the eggs at a constant 15 °C.
3. Certain dendrobatid frogs of Central America have poison glands. Darts dipped in the toxin can paralyze game in a few minutes.

32 Reptiles

Chapter Objectives: See page 516.

Chapter Overview

A brief history of the rise of the reptiles opens Chapter 34. A discussion of important reptile adaptations—scaly skin, internal fertilization, and a hard-shelled amniotic egg—is also included. Within this section, descriptions of *Brontosaurus, Triceratops, Tyrannosaurus,* and *Pterodactyl* are presented.

The section on the classification of modern reptiles includes a discussion of each of their four orders. Representing the order Rhynchocephalia is the tuatara. Turtles and tortoises are distinguished in the order Chelonia, as are nonpoisonous and poisonous snakes in the order Squamata. The lizards, such as the chameleon, gecko, Komodo dragon, and Gila monster, are also discussed. Finally, the crocodiles and alligators of the order Crocodilia are presented.

Reptilian anatomy is discussed in general. This discussion includes external features as well as various organ systems.

Teaching Strategies and Activities

1. Obtain an anole, and let the students observe its color changes when it is placed on different backgrounds.
2. Obtain mounted skeletons of a snake, lizard, and turtle. Have the students point out the various modifications that help each reptile to move and protect itself.
3. Discuss some of the unusual reptiles of the Galapagos Islands, such as the marine iguana and giant Galapagos tortoise.

Answer Key to Section Reviews

The History of Reptiles (p. 519)

1. A cotylosaur was a primitive, terrestrial reptile.
2. Land-dwelling reptiles owe their success to a scaly skin, internal fertilization, and a hard-shelled egg.
3. Some types of dinosaurs are *Brontosaurus, Triceratops, Tyrannosaurus,* and *Pterodactyl.*

Classification of Reptiles (p. 526)

1. A herpetologist is a scientist who studies reptiles and amphibians.

2. The tuatara has dark olive skin and yellow spines on its back. The tuatara grows to be 70 cm long. An unusual feature of the tuatara is that it has a parietal body, or third eye, beneath the skin in the middle of its head.

3. The parts of a tortoise shell are the carapace and the plastron.

4. *Snakes* have no legs, no ear openings, and immovable eyelids. *Lizards* have legs, external ear openings, and movable eyelids.

Anatomy of the Reptiles (p. 532)

1. The lungs of a tuatara have few compartments. The left lung of a snake is either smaller than the right lung or nonexistent. A lizard's lungs have numerous small chambers, but they do not have blood vessels running through them.

2. The elimination of wastes in the form of uric acid conserves a reptile's internal water.

3. The heart of most reptiles has two atria and a single ventricle. The ventricle is partially divided by a septum.

4. Water snakes, rattlesnakes, and garter snakes are ovoviviparous. Skinks and night lizards are viviparous.

Teaching Aids for Chapter End Features

Laboratory Investigation 32
Classifying and Comparing Reptiles (p. 533)

Encourage students to bring old books and magazines from home to supplement the class supply. *Note: The picture sources can be used in Laboratory Investigation 34.*

OBSERVATIONS AND CONCLUSIONS 1. Lizards have movable eyelids, legs with five clawed toes on each foot, and external ear openings. Snakes have no eyelids, no legs, and no external ear openings. **2.** The feature that distinguishes turtles and tortoises from other reptiles is a shell. **3.** Answers will vary. **4.** Answers will vary. **5.** All reptiles have a body covering of scales or bony plates, are air-breathers, have hearts with a partially divided ventricle, and are cold-blooded. **6.** The feet of reptiles have five toes with claws, and they are covered with scales and/or bony plates.

Review of Facts and Concepts (p. 534)

1. The general reptilian characteristics are a body covering of horny scales or plates, lungs, a partial septum dividing the ventricle of the heart, a body temperature that varies with the temperature of the environment, and, with the exception of snakes and some lizards, four limbs with claws on the toes.

2. The three adaptations that enabled reptiles to be so successful on land are scaly skin, internal fertilization, and a hard-shelled egg.

3. The tuatara is virtually no different from its Mesozoic ancestors.

4. Turtles and tortoises have a shell, no teeth, and a hard beak. Tortoises have short, stumpy legs with claws. Turtles have legs that serve as paddles.

5. Lizards usually have legs, movable eyelids, and external ear openings. Snakes are legless, and they lack external ear openings and movable eyelids.

6. Snakes move by *lateral undulation*, by *rectilinear movement*, by *concertina movement*, and by *sidewinding*. Students may give detailed explanations of these movements.

7. Alligators have broad, round snouts, whereas the snouts of crocodiles taper to a point. Also, the crocodile's large fourth tooth protrudes over the upper jaw when its mouth is closed, but the alligator's fourth tooth is hidden.

8. The limbs of many amphibians cannot lift the belly of the amphibian high off the ground, resulting in an awkward sprawling gait. Frogs and toads have specialized limbs for leaping and hopping. The longer and stronger legs of reptiles extend beneath the body instead of to either side. Consequently they can lift the body, permitting fast locomotion.

9. In comparison with that of an amphibian, the reptilian brain has a larger and more complex cerebrum and better-developed olfactory lobes. The reptilian optic lobes, cerebellum, and medulla are all about as well developed as those of an amphibian.

10. The kidneys of reptiles extract very little water from the blood when they filter it, thus conserving body water for life on land. Land-living reptiles excrete their nitrogenous wastes in the form of uric acid instead of water-soluble ammonia.

11. The hard outer shell and chorion of the reptilian egg retain moisture but allow gas exchange. The allantois stores the nitrogen wastes and contains many blood vessels that are used in respiration. The egg has a large yolk.

12. The large yolk allows the reptile to grow more completely within the egg and to hatch as a miniature adult. Therefore, reptiles do not have to undergo larval stages.

Extensions and Applications (p. 535)

1. Some theories that are used to explain the extinction of dinosaurs follow. One theory states that a

gradual cooling of the climate made it too cold for the large reptiles. Other theories state that insect larvae destroyed plants and the dinosaurs starved, or that a lethal heat wave resulted from the earth's collision with an asteroid.

2. The body temperatures of the reptiles change when the animals are placed in the sun. The temperatures of the birds and mammals do not.

3. Students should include the genus and species of each reptile that they use.

4. A field guide to reptiles and a first aid book should have the necessary information.

33 Birds

Chapter Objectives: See page 536.

Chapter Overview

Chapter 33 devotes a section each to the history, the characteristics, and the anatomy of birds. A discussion is presented of one of the earliest birds, *Archaeopteryx*. The text explains the characteristics of particular bird species as adaptations of particular lifestyles or environments.

The discussion of bird anatomy begins with the external structures of flight, such as the types of feathers, the wings, the strong pectoral muscles, and the fused spine. The last part of this section discusses the nervous, digestive, excretory, respiratory, circulatory, and reproductive systems of birds. The remainder of the chapter describes breeding habits, incubation, and the care of hatchlings.

Teaching Strategies and Activities

1. Display pictures of various bird species, bird nests, eggs, and feathers. Actual nests, eggs, and feathers may also be displayed.

2. Play tapes of bird songs, and discuss how birds learn the songs of their species.

3. Construct either bird feeders in the winter or birdhouses and nest boxes in the spring. Have students observe the types of birds that use the bird feeders, birdhouses, or nest boxes.

Answer Key to Section Reviews

The History of Birds (p. 538)

1. Feathers were lighter than other types of protective body covering, and so they did not hinder flying. Feathers also control the exchange of heat between the bodies of birds and the air.

2. *Archaeopteryx* had feathers and feet for perching, as do modern birds, but it also had teeth and a long tail, as do reptiles.

3. Explorers killed many of the dodos on Mauritius. Newly introduced pigs and goats successfully competed with the remaining dodos for food on the island.

Characteristics of Birds (p. 540)

1. Talons are the sharp claws found on birds of prey.

2. Seed-eating birds have thick beaks, and insect eaters have small pointed beaks. Ducks have spoon-shaped beaks for feeding in water, while woodpeckers have beaks adapted for drilling holes and getting at tree-dwelling insects.

3. The syrinx produces a bird's song. Air expelled from the lungs passes over membranes in the syrinx that vibrate and make sounds. Muscles that control the membranes of the syrinx change the sound's pitch.

Anatomy of a Bird (p. 548)

1. The parts of a contour feather are the *quill*, the *shaft*, the *barbs*, and the *barbules*.

2. During incubation, the embryo develops in the *amnion*. The embryo is attached to the *allantois*, which carries out respiration and receives the waste products of the embryo. When incubation is complete, the hatchling cracks the shell open.

3. *Precocial birds* are hatchlings that are well formed and are able to take care of themselves. *Altricial birds* are hatchlings that are helpless and must be fed and cared for in the nest.

Teaching Aids for Chapter End Features

Laboratory Investigation 33
Examining Feathers (p. 549)

Provide each group with samples of the three main types of feathers. Before class, sort the feathers into sets. Place a piece of masking tape on each feather and number the feathers. Prepared microscope slides may be substituted for the actual feathers.

OBSERVATIONS AND CONCLUSIONS 1. The fluffiness and softness of a down feather make it ideal for pillow stuffing. 2. The contour feather is used mainly during flight. This type of feather is found on the wings and tail of a flying bird. 3. The filoplume is also known as a pinfeather because of its similarity in size and thinness to a pin.

Review of Facts and Concepts (p. 550)

1. The fossil record indicates that reptiles appeared on the earth before birds. Moreover, birds retain or share certain characteristics of reptiles. Both birds and reptiles lay shelled, amniotic eggs. The scales on the legs of birds are similar to the scales of reptiles. Bird and reptilian organ systems are also similar.

2. *Archaeopteryx* had the feathers and the perching feet of a bird, and it also had the teeth and long tail of a reptile.

3. Four major groups of birds are perching birds (robins, jays, and sparrows), water birds (ducks and geese), birds of prey (eagles, hawks, and owls), and flightless birds (ostriches, penguins, emus, and cassowaries).

4. Scientists think that the bright color of male birds attracts females of the species.

5. Singing and calling are means of communication. Songs and calls mark the territories of birds, attract mates, or warn of danger.

6. Homologous structures are structures that have the same point of origin in evolutionary development. Examples are the wing of a bird and the forelimbs of other vertebrates.

7. A *contour feather* has a hollow quill and a shaft with barbs that are hooked to one another by barbules. *Down feathers* have quills and reduced shafts. *Filoplumes* have single hairlike shafts that end in a few barbs. *Bristles* are hairlike feathers with short quills, thin shafts, and few or no barbs.

8. When the bird swallows, the food goes down the *esophagus* to the *crop*, where the food is moistened and passed on to the *stomach*. In the first part of the two-part stomach, the *proventriculus*, digestive fluids act on the food. The second part of the stomach, the *gizzard*, crushes the food. The food goes to the *small intestine*, which absorbs the nutrient molecules. The undigested food goes to the *rectum*, to the *cloaca*, and out of the body.

9. Air sacs make respiration more efficient in birds during flight.

10. See Figure 33-12 on page 548.

Extensions and Applications (p. 551)

1. *Passenger pigeons* not only were trapped for food but also were used as live targets in shooting galleries. The last of these pigeons died in 1914. The *Hawaiian o'o*, which was prized for its feathers, was trapped and killed by settlers. Farmers destroyed the *Carolina parakeet* because it ate their unripe fruit. Other people either shot this bird for sport or collected it as a cage bird. The last one died in 1914. The *moa* was hunted and eaten by natives of New Zealand. With the introduction of dogs and rats to the island, these new predators killed the chicks of the moa and destroyed its eggs.

2. If your area doesn't have a local chapter of the Audubon Society, ask the state chapter to send you information.

3. A pan of water in the incubator keeps the eggs from drying out. Make the saline solution from 9 g sodium chloride and 991 mL of distilled water, and keep the solution at 39 °C. Students should be able to see the heart, backbone, eye, and wingbud.

34 Mammals

Chapter Objectives: See page 552.

Chapter Overview

Chapter 34 treats the history, characteristics, and classification of mammals. It presents the concept that the first mammals, which were very small, probably developed from the therapsids. Modern mammals have hair, mammalian glands, a well-developed brain, two pairs of limbs, four-chambered hearts, lungs, and five-sectored vertebral columns. These characteristics are discussed as well as mammalian reproduction, parental care, migration, hibernation, and dormancy.

The classification section is a comprehensive listing of the three major mammalian groups. The monotremes are the first group. This group includes the duck-billed platypus and spiny anteater, which are primitive, egg-laying mammals with no external ears. The second group consists of the marsupials, such as the kangaroo and opossum. Placental mammals comprise the third group, containing more than 20 orders. Of these 20 orders, the section describes 13.

Teaching Strategies and Activities

1. In anticipation of the chapter's Laboratory Investigation, collect as many pictures of mammals as you can. Before beginning the chapter, let the students group the pictures based only on external characteristics. The class can then reorganize the pictures in the Laboratory Investigation after completing the chapter.

2. Discuss the plight of endangered mammals, such

as the blue whale, manatee, duck-billed platypus, and gray wolf.

3. Have students research and then debate the pros and cons of whaling. Play a recording of whale sounds.

Answer Key to Section Reviews

The History of Mammals (p. 553)

1. Mammals are probably descended from the therapsids.
2. The Cenozoic Era began 65 million years ago.

Characteristics of Mammals (p. 558)

1. Unlike the heart of most vertebrates, the mammalian heart has four chambers.
2. The gestation period is the time required for an embryo to develop fully.
3. During *hibernation*, mammalian body temperatures drop, and their hearts slow down. In *dormancy*, the heart rate and breathing slow down, but the body temperature remains unchanged.

Classification of Mammals (p. 565)

1. Monotremes are primitive, egg-laying mammals that lack external ears.
2. The only North American marsupial is the opossum.
3. The placenta is an embryonic structure that supplies nourishment to the embryo.
4. Refer to Figure 34-12 on pages 566–67.

Teaching Aids for Chapter End Features

Laboratory Investigation 34
Classifying and Comparing Mammals
(p. 568)

Use the same picture sources as in Laboratory Investigation 32.

OBSERVATIONS AND CONCLUSIONS 1. Monotremes lay eggs; marsupials have a pouch in which the young develop and mature after birth. Marsupials have external ears; monotremes have no external ears. 2. The pouch in which the young develop after birth distinguishes marsupials from other mammals. 3. Of all the mammalian orders, Insectivora, Rodentia, and Lagomorpha have the most similar external characteristics. 4. All mammals are warm-blooded and have mammary glands, hair, a four-chambered heart, two pairs of limbs, lungs for breathing, and a five-part vertebral column.

Review of Facts and Concepts (p. 569)

1. All mammals are warm-blooded and viviparous and have mammary glands, hair, a well-developed cerebrum and cerebellum, four-chambered hearts, two pairs of limbs, lungs for breathing, diaphragms, and a five-part vertebral column.
2. Air enters the *trachea*, which divides into two *bronchi*. Each bronchus subdivides into *bronchioles* and then into *air sacs*. Each air sac contains *alveoli* where gas exchange takes place.
3. Female mammals feed their newborn young with milk secreted from mammary glands. While the young are still in the female's care they are trained to carry out many activities.
4. Mammals migrate in search of warm weather and food.
5. Marsupials are pouched mammals whose young are born only partially developed, completing their development in the pouch. The opossum, kangaroo, Tasmanian devil, bandicoot, and koala are examples of marsupials.
6. Skin from the bat's back and abdomen stretches over the arms and long fingers to form wings. The bat also has a large breastbone to anchor its powerful flying muscles.
7. Carnivores have muscular legs to chase their prey, claws for holding prey, powerful jaws for tearing flesh, and sharp teeth for biting and cutting.
8. *Incisors* are for biting off flesh, and *canines* for tearing. *Molars* grind food. Some carnivores have specialized teeth called *carnassials* that are used to cut through muscle.
9. Rodents and lagomorphs are very numerous because they reproduce quickly and can easily outrun their predators.
10. Cetaceans are adapted for a water-dwelling life with flippers, dorsal fins, and no hind limbs.
11. See Figure 34-12 on pages 566–67.

Extensions and Applications (p. 570)

1. Students may present brief oral reports of their research.
2. Students may present their observations to the class as an oral report.
3. Students may want to find out the symbols used in these experiments.
4. All mammals have some hair, mammary glands, a four-chambered heart, two pairs of limbs, and a diaphragm. They also have many structures that occur in other vertebrates, such as a vertebral column, lungs, a stomach, an intestine, and kidneys.

Unit Teaching Aids

Perspectives in Biology

Language in the Higher Animals (p. 571)

1. Students may present their findings on the work of Roger Payne, John Lilly, and Allen and Beatrice Gardner as brief oral reports. The class can then discuss the views and work of these scientists.
2. Students may want to observe communication in children of different ages, such as an infant that is a few months old, a one-year-old, and a four-year-old.
3. Students should observe a pet animal for several days. Students should note similarities in communication among different pets.

Field Trip Suggestions

1. To observe aquaculture, visit a fish farm or state fish hatchery.
2. Living fish can be viewed at a marine park or aquarium.
3. To see living reptiles, visit a serpentarium at a zoo or a reptile farm.
4. To observe birds, visit the bird house at the local zoo. If you are not near a zoo, take a nature walk in a park, near a lake, or in the woods. Using binoculars, have students look for and identify birds. There are many bird-watching guides that can be purchased in book stores.
5. To see preserved mammal specimens, either go to a natural history museum or visit a taxidermist's shop. Try to arrange a visit to a museum's workshops where animal specimens are studied and prepared for display.

Audio-Visual Materials

Animals with Backbones, sound filmstrip, Eye
Frog Anatomy, set/10 super 8mm film loops, PHM
Fur, Fins, Teeth and Tails, set/6 sound filmstrips, SSS
Investigating Hibernation, film EBE
Reptiles Are Interesting, film, FBA
The Chick Embryo, film, EBE
Unusual Mammals of Australia, sound filmstrip, HBJ

Reading Resources for Teachers

Dethier, V., and E. Stellar. *Animal Behavior*. Englewood Cliffs, N.J.: Prentice-Hall.

Romer, A. *The Vertebrate Body*. Philadelphia: W.B. Saunders Co.
Schaefer, J. *An American Bestiary*. Boston: Houghton Mifflin.
Webster, D., and M. Webster. *Comparative Vertebrate Morphology*. New York: Academic Press.

UNIT EIGHT
Human Structure and Function

Unit Eight is the first of two units devoted to the human organism. Chapter 35 treats the skeletal, muscular, and integumentary systems. Chapter 36 discusses the digestive system, and Chapter 37 covers the circulatory system. The systems for respiration and excretion are the subject of Chapter 38. Finally, Chapter 39 applies what students have learned in the previous four chapters to a discussion of the body's needs for adequate nutrition, exercise, and sleep.

35 Human Body Structure

Chapter Objectives: See page 574.

Chapter Overview

Chapter 35 presents the skeletal, muscular, and integumentary systems as components of body organization that work together. The chapter begins with definitions of connective, muscle, epithelial, and nerve tissue. Opening the section on the human skeleton is an explanation of its four functions, followed by a description of the axial and appendicular divisions and a discussion of how bones are formed. The text analyzes the structure of bone, which is described as a combination of living and nonliving matter, and explains how ball-and-socket, hinge, pivot, and gliding joints work. The next section deals with the muscular system, which consists of skeletal, smooth, and cardiac muscles. The structure and function of these three types of muscles are explained. Covering both the skeletal and the muscular system is the integument, whose layers are described. Also explained are the structure and functions of hair, hair follicles, and oil and sweat glands.

Teaching Strategies and Activities

1. Display a plastic model of a human skeleton or models of parts of a skeleton. Many biological supply houses have models of bones, skulls, and so on.
2. In the summer, many people become preoccupied with getting a suntan to improve their appearance. Use a discussion of suntanning to introduce the integumentary system.
3. Obtain some X-rays from a local physician or hospital, and use them as the basis for starting a discussion of this chapter.

Answer Key to Section Reviews

Organization in the Human Body (p. 576)

1. The four basic types of tissues in the human body are connective, muscle, epithelial, and nerve tissue.
2. Blood carries food, oxygen, and wastes throughout the body.
3. The epithelial tissue forms the skin on the outside of the body and lines many body cavities.
4. See Figure 35-2 on page 576.

The Skeletal System (p. 582)

1. The functions of the skeleton are support and shape, movement, protection of the internal organs, formation of blood cells, and storage of minerals.
2. The *axial skeleton* has 80 bones and runs through the central axis of the body. All the other bones are directly or indirectly connected to it. The *appendicular skeleton*, containing 126 bones, consists of the bones of the legs, hands, and feet and the pelvic and pectoral girdles.
3. Ossification is the process of forming bone, in which bone cells replace cartilage cells.
4. A long bone contains both spongy and compact bone tissue. Dense compact bone surrounded by the tough, fibrous periosteum makes up the shaft of the long bone. Spongy bone, covered by thin layers of compact bone and cartilage, constitutes the knobby ends of a long bone. Haversian canals, containing blood vessels and nerves, run throughout the compact bone tissue. A long bone also has a marrow cavity down the center of the shaft, filled with nerves, blood vessels, and marrow.
5. In a *ball-and-socket joint*, the rounded head (ball) of one bone fits into the cuplike socket of another bone, permitting circular motion with free movement in all directions. A *hinge joint*, which resembles the hinge of a door, allows movement back and forth in only one direction. In a *pivot joint*, a ring-shaped bone surrounds a peglike pivot, permitting rotational movement about the pivot. In a *gliding joint*, a bone with either a slightly curved or a nearly flat surface slides along another bone with a corresponding shape. This joint provides flexibility.

The Muscular System (p. 586)

1. *Skeletal muscle* is made of long bundles of closely packed muscle fibers that move bones. *Smooth muscle* is made of long, spindle-shaped cells found in the walls of some blood vessels and of the digestive system. Because these muscles move without conscious control, they are called involuntary. *Cardiac muscle* consists of muscle cells that branch in a laced network. Contracting rhythmically and spontaneously, cardiac muscle is responsible for the heart's pumping action.
2. As a muscle contracts, the actin filaments slide past the myosin filaments, which do not move.
3. Flexors bend joints; extensors straighten them.

The Integumentary System (p. 588)

1. Melanin is found in the bottom layer of the epidermis. Melanin determines skin color and protects the skin from the sun by screening out ultraviolet radiation.
2. *Sweat glands* rid the body of excess water, salts, and nitrogen wastes and help to regulate body temperature. Secretions of the *oil glands* keep the hair and skin soft.
3. The functions of skin include protection, response, and storage.

Teaching Aids for Chapter End Features

Laboratory Investigation 35
Observing the Structure of Bones (p. 589)

Soak some of the bones in vinegar or dilute hydrochloric acid solution for several weeks before this investigation. The vinegar (acetic acid) or hydrochloric acid reacts with the inorganic salts in the bones, leaving them soft and flexible. Rinse and dry the soaked bones before using them in class. *Caution: The students must be very careful when slicing bones for slides.*

OBSERVATIONS AND CONCLUSIONS 1. Yes, cartilage tissue surrounds the ends of long bones. Unlike bone, cartilage is soft and flexible. 2. The bones become soft and flexible because the acid reacts with the calcium salts in the bone. 3. Answers will vary depending on the bones studied. The students should look for spongy and compact bone cells, the various types of marrow, Haversian canals, cartilage, and the periosteum. 4. Answers will vary with the bones used. Students should explain that the differences in structure are related to the function of the bone.

Review of Facts and Concepts (p. 590)

1. *Connective tissue* supports and connects different parts of the body. *Muscle tissue* contracts. Skeletal muscle produces voluntary contractions, while smooth muscle is responsible for involuntary contractions. Cardiac muscle is responsible for the heart's spontaneous and rhythmical contractions. *Epithelial tissue* protects the body and lines the body cavities. *Nerve tissue* conducts impulses.
2. *Compact bone* is very dense and hard. *Spongy bone* is softer, and there are spaces in it.
3. The functions of the skeleton are to support and give shape to the body, contribute to the movement of body parts, protect the internal organs, form blood cells, and store minerals.
4. The *axial skeleton* includes the skull, vertebral column, and rib cage. The *appendicular skeleton* consists of the arm, leg, hand, and feet bones directly or indirectly attached to the axial skeleton by means of the pelvic and pectoral girdles.
5. Human bone contains bone cells, blood vessels, fat cells, and cartilage.
6. The shaft of a long bone consists of dense compact bone surrounded by the tough, fibrous periosteum. Spongy bone, covered with thin layers of compact bone and cartilage, makes up the knobby ends.
7. The types of joints are *ball-and-socket* (femur and pelvic girdle, humerus and pectoral girdle), *hinge* (knee or elbow), *pivot* (neck vertebrae), and *gliding* (wrist or ankle).
8. *Skeletal muscles* are made up of multinucleate muscle cells consisting of fibrils that contract voluntarily for skeletal movement. *Smooth muscles* contain spindle-shaped cells, each with a single nucleus organized into tissue that contracts involuntarily. *Cardiac muscles*, found only in the heart, consist of branched cells in a laced network. Cardiac muscle contracts spontaneously and rhythmically to make the heart pump. All three types of muscle tissue are alike in that they do work by contracting.
9. *Flexor muscles* contract to close hinge joints. *Extensors* contract to open or straighten the same joints. The biceps is a flexor; the triceps is an extensor.

10. Bones are connected to each other by ligaments. Ropelike tendons connect muscles to bones. The bones, ligaments, tendons, and muscles work together to move the body.
11. The integumentary system consists of the skin, the hair, the nails, and the sweat and oil glands.
12. Answers will vary but may include the cornea and the sole of the foot.

Extensions and Applications (p. 591)

1. The drumstick is a fusion bone unique to birds. It is composed of a tibia and a small fibula that is free at the thigh end but fused at the "stick" end. Despite its orientation to the bird's body, the drumstick is not the femur. The femur articulates with the pelvis and tibia, and it is held nearly horizontal in a living bird.
2. Students should pinch the balloons alternately to shorten the length first of one and then of the other. This simulates the contraction of opposing muscles.
3. A bucket or bushel basket could represent the pelvis. The antenna connection of a portable TV or radio is a good model of a ball-and-socket joint. The cranium could be represented by a lunch box or some other durable package. The elbow works much like the movable arm of a drafting lamp or a door hinge, and the spine closely resembles a flexible gooseneck lamp or the metal casing of high-voltage electrical wire.

36 Digestion

Chapter Objectives: See page 592.

Chapter Overview

Chapter 36 introduces the students to the human digestive system and its processes. Beginning with the distinction between true and accessory digestive organs, the section on the digestive system explains the role of the salivary glands, the tongue, and the teeth. Information detailing the role of the pharynx and esophagus in the movement of food to the stomach is then presented. The anatomy of the small and large intestines, the liver, and the pancreas is also discussed.

In the second half of the chapter, the mechanical and chemical breakdown of food in the digestive system is explained. The steps of the process that take place in the mouth, in the stomach, and in the intestines are followed. The chapter ends with an explanation of absorption.

Teaching Strategies and Activities

1. Despite what advertisements state, an acid stomach is both normal and necessary for digestive enzymes to function properly. Yet TV commercials for popular antacids stress the coating action or acid-neutralizing capabilities of various products. To initiate a discussion on enzymatic digestion, conduct an experiment that tests such products. Have students bring in a collection of popular antacids. Mix a solution of vinegar and water to a pH of 4. (Normally, the stomach's pH is about 1.5 to 2.5.) Then pour the solution into as many containers as you have antacids. Put an antacid in each container, labeling the containers appropriately. To evaluate each antacid's effectiveness, simply test the pH of the solutions at set intervals.

2. The idea of bacteria living in close association with a multicellular organism is intriguing, and it can be a useful springboard for a discussion of the digestive system. Discuss the role of bacteria in the digestive systems of human beings, horses, and cows.

Answer Key to Section Reviews

The Digestive System (p. 598)

1. Saliva is a mixture of water, ptyalin, and mucin. Three pairs of salivary glands produce saliva.
2. The pyloric valve allows food to move into the small intestine and prevents food from backing up into the stomach.
3. The *small intestine* consists of the duodenum, the jejunum, and the ileum. The *large intestine* is divided into the ascending colon, the transverse colon, and the descending colon. The sigmoid colon links the descending colon to the rectum.
4. The liver produces bile. The pancreas produces pancreatic fluid and insulin.

The Mechanisms of Digestion (p. 602)

1. *Pepsin* is an enzyme that splits protein into simpler groups of amino acids called peptones and proteoses. *Hydrochloric acid* provides the proper environment for pepsin to act, allows iron to be absorbed, and destroys bacteria.
2. The liver changes carbohydrates into glucose and then regulates the release or storage of this energy-rich compound. Excess glucose can be changed into glycogen, which is either stored in the liver or transformed into fat. The liver also transforms nitrogen wastes into urea for excretion by the kidneys. As an accessory digestive organ, the liver produces bile, which aids in digestion.

3. Pancreatic fluid contains trypsin, amylase, and lipase. *Trypsin* continues the breakdown of proteins into peptides. *Amylase* breaks down undigested starch into maltose. *Lipase* acts on emulsified fat drops, changing them to fatty acids and glycerol.
4. *Amylase* breaks down starches, *sucrase* breaks down sucrose, and *trypsin* breaks down proteoses and peptones.
5. After being broken down to its simplest form, food is absorbed through the villi of the intestinal wall. Completely digested foods pass into capillaries and lacteals.

Teaching Aids for Chapter End Features

Laboratory Investigation 36
The Effects of Surface Area on the Rate of Absorption (p. 603)

Clear plastic 2-liter soft drink bottles with the tops cut off can be substituted for the large glass jars. To prepare the starch solution, add 3 g of soluble starch to 500 mL of water. Bring the solution to a boil and remove it from the heat, stirring thoroughly. Add the boiled starch solution to 5 L of cold water and stir. Store the solution in a refrigerator until it is used. To prepare the iodine solution, add 1 g of iodine crystals and 3.5 g of potassium iodide to 300 mL of distilled water. Stir until the solids are dissolved.

OBSERVATIONS AND CONCLUSIONS 1. In each jar, the starch solution changes from clear to blue-black. The iodine molecules pass through the membrane into the starch solution, causing the color change. 2. The color changes faster in the jar with the longer piece of dialysis tubing. 3. The longer piece of tubing has more surface area, thereby allowing more iodine to pass through the membrane. 4. The iodine molecules are moving from an area of greater concentration into an area of lesser concentration. 5. There is a direct relationship between the surface area and the rate of absorption. Increasing the surface area increases the rate of absorption. In the investigation, the longer tube had more surface area than the short tube. In the small intestine, the villi increase the surface area.

Review of Facts and Concepts (p. 604)

1. Digestion is the breaking down of food into simple substances that can be absorbed into the bloodstream.

2. *True digestive organs* are the organs through which food actually passes. *Accessory digestive organs* play a role in digestion, but food does not pass through them.

3. The *soft palate* prevents food from entering the nasal cavity. The *epiglottis* prevents food from entering the windpipe.

4. The three salivary glands are the parotid, the submaxillary, and the sublingual glands. Saliva begins the digestion of food and lubricates the food for swallowing.

5. The tongue aids chewing by constantly pushing food between the teeth and by moving chewed food toward the back of the mouth for swallowing.

6. See Figure 36-3 on page 594. The four types of teeth are incisors, canines, premolars, and molars.

7. Chewing creates more total surface area on the food, which allows the digestive enzymes to work on the food more efficiently. Also, chewing prevents large pieces of food from lodging in the pharynx.

8. Food passes through the mouth, the pharynx, the esophagus, the stomach, the small intestine, and the large intestine.

9. Inside the stomach, many folds allow the organ to expand as it fills.

10. The *small intestine* consists of the duodenum, jejunum, and ileum. The *large intestine* includes the ascending colon, transverse colon, descending colon, and sigmoid colon.

11. In the *mouth*, ptyalin breaks down starch. In the *stomach*, pepsin breaks down proteins. In the *small intestine*, trypsin, amylase, and lipase from the pancreas break down proteins, starches, and fats, respectively.

12. Peristalsis moves food through the digestive system regardless of gravity's presence or absence.

13. The *liver* produces bile, a fluid that aids in digestion by emulsifying fats. The *pancreas* secretes a pancreatic fluid containing trypsin, amylase, and lipase, which break down proteins, starches, and fats, respectively.

14. Food absorption occurs in the small intestine. Villi are fingerlike projections of thin epithelial cells in the small intestine. Inside each villus, an extensive capillary network surrounds a lymphatic vessel called a lacteal. Blood and lymph carry the nutrients away from epithelial cells of the villi to the rest of the body. The blood also absorbs water, vitamins, and some salts.

15. The large intestine absorbs water and bile salts.

16. During digestion, ptyalin in the mouth would start to break down the starch in bread into simple sugars. Amylase in the small intestine would continue the process. The sugars of jelly would undergo a similar process. The various proteases (trypsin, peptidase, and pepsin) would break down milk proteins into amino acids. Lipase would break down the emulsified milk fat into fatty acids and glycerol. Finally, lactase would break down the milk sugar, lactose.

Extensions and Applications (p. 605)

1. In 1822, Alexis St. Martin, in the service of the American Fur Company, was accidentally shot in the left side by a musket from only a yard away. Dr. William Beaumont, at the time stationed at the same post, nursed St. Martin back to health. The patient not only lived but returned to good health, except for a 6.35-cm hole in his left side. In 1825, Beaumont began a series of experiments that enabled him to observe the gastric process, obtain gastric contents at various stages of digestion, and generally study the digestive process in the stomach.

2. The amphipathic molecules of detergent, with polar and nonpolar ends, can interact with the polar water molecules and the nonpolar fat molecules, causing the oil to emulsify. Bile has the same function in the intestine. By dispersing fat into smaller globules, bile effectively increases the surface area available for the digestion of fats by lipase.

3. By crushing the sugar cube, you increase the number of individual pieces while decreasing their average size. In so doing, you increase the total surface area, allowing greater and faster interaction between the sugar and the water.

37 Circulation

Chapter Objectives: See page 606.

Chapter Overview

Chapter 37 presents a discussion of the components of the circulatory system, the pathways of body fluids, and the functions of the lymphatic system. The text reveals that the circulatory system delivers nutrients and oxygen to the body, removes wastes, assists in maintaining a proper pH balance, regulates the body's water content and temperature, and helps to fight infection. A description of blood composition leads to an explanation of blood characteristics, clotting, and the importance of Rh factors and cross-matching in transfusions.

The structure of the heart is described. An explanation of how the heart beats and produces blood pressure is also presented. A distinction between arteries and veins is made. A final section explains the role of the lymphatic system.

Teaching Strategies and Activities

1. Display models of the heart and diagrams and charts of the circulatory system to help the students visualize the extensiveness and complexity of the circulatory system.
2. To begin the chapter, ask the students to explain why they think the circulatory system is so named.
3. Explaining the nature of a heart attack can lead to a more general discussion of the circulatory system and its importance.

Answer Key to Section Reviews

The Circulatory System (p. 612)

1. Plasma is the liquid portion of the blood.
2. *Red blood cells* have no nuclei, contain hemoglobin, and are shaped like doughnuts without holes in the middle. RBCs carry oxygen and some carbon dioxide. *White blood cells* are colorless, amoebalike cells with nuclei. WBCs help fight infection. *Platelets* are small, colorless cell fragments that initiate the clotting process and seal small leaks in capillaries.
3. When platelets come into contact with an injured blood vessel, they release the enzyme thromboplastin. Thromboplastin acts on prothrombin to change it into its active form, thrombin. Thrombin cleaves fibrinogen into fibrin. which forms a netlike trap over the site of injury.
4. *Antigens* are substances that are found on the surfaces of certain red blood cells. *Antibodies* are proteins circulating in the plasma that attack foreign antigens. Karl Landsteiner discovered blood antigens.
5. The Rh factor is an antigen commonly found on red blood cells.

The Path of Body Fluids (p. 618)

1. The four chambers are the left and right atria and the left and right ventricles. The left atrium receives oxygenated blood from the lungs; the right atrium receives deoxygenated blood from the body. The left ventricle pumps oxygenated blood to the body; the right ventricle pumps deoxygenated blood to the lungs.
2. The *S-A node* sets and regulates the heartbeat. The *A-V node* controls ventricular contraction.

3. The *systolic pressure* is the blood pressure exerted by the contraction of the ventricles. The *diastolic pressure* is the blood pressure exerted between these contractions.
4. *Arteries* carry blood away from the heart. *Veins* return blood to the heart. *Capillaries* connect the arteries and veins and are the sites of most gas, nutrient, and waste exchanges.
5. The *pulmonary circulation* delivers blood to and from the lungs. The *systemic circulation* delivers nutrients and oxygenated blood to body tissues and removes wastes from them.

The Lymphatic System (p. 618)

1. The lymphatic system collects fluid from tissues, transports it back into the circulatory system, and in the process filters out bacteria and other foreign substances.
2. The thoracic duct collects lymph from most of the body and empties it into the surrounding veins.
3. Lymph nodes filter bacteria out of the circulating lymph. The tonsils and adenoids are two lymph nodes.

Teaching Aids for Chapter End Features

Laboratory Investigation 37
Observing Blood Circulation (p. 619)

Note: Remind the students to keep the fish wet by adding water to the cotton as necessary. The webbed foot of a living frog or the tail of a tadpole may also be used for this investigation.

OBSERVATIONS AND CONCLUSIONS 1. The blood cells travel through the capillaries single file. 2. Capillary walls are one cell layer thick. Arteries and veins have walls that are more than one cell layer thick. 3. The gills of the fish have an extensive network of capillaries. The gills absorb oxygen and release carbon dioxide as water passes over them.

Review of Facts and Concepts (p. 620)

1. The circulatory system helps to maintain the proper acid-base (pH) balance, transports oxygenated blood and nutrients to body tissues, removes wastes, regulates the water content of the body, and helps to fight infection.
2. Blood is considered a tissue because it is made up of several different kinds of cells that work together.
3. Blood is the medium that carries nutrients and oxygen to the body cells and removes wastes from such cells.

4. *Plasma* is the slightly yellowish liquid part of the blood. *White blood cells* are colorless nucleated cells. *Red blood cells* are doughnut-shaped, reddish cells. *Platelets* are colorless cell fragments.
5. White blood cells are larger than red blood cells. WBCs are colorless, whereas RBCs are red. Mature WBCs contain nuclei, while RBCs have none.
6. Phagocytes engulf and digest bacteria and damaged red blood cells.
7. See Figure 37-3 on page 609.
8. The four blood types are A, B, AB, and O. They are distinguished on the basis of the presence of cell surface antigens.
9. *Universal donors* are people with blood group O. These individuals do not have either A or B antigens and can donate blood to people of any other blood group. *Universal recipients* are individuals of blood group AB. These individuals produce neither anti-A nor anti-B antibodies and therefore can receive blood from people with any of the other major blood groups.
10. Cross-matching assures compatibility of blood types. If cross-matching were not done, there would be a chance that the recipient's blood in a transfusion would agglutinate.
11. The human circulatory system is considered a closed system because the blood travels around the body through a network of blood vessels. It does not move freely in the body cavity.
12. Refer to Figure 37-8 on page 613.
13. Refer to Figure 37-11 on page 617.
14. The sinoatrial (S-A) node sets and regulates the heartbeat by sending impulses along the atrial walls to the atrioventricular (A-V) node at the base of the right atrium. The A-V node then signals the ventricles to contract.
15. Blood pressure is highest in the vessels that carry blood away from the heart (the arteries). It is the lowest in blood vessels that carry blood to the heart (the veins).
16. In the *pulmonary circulation*, blood flows between the heart and the lungs. In the *systemic circulation*, the blood carries nutrients and oxygen to the body and removes wastes.
17. Subdivisions of the systemic circulation are the coronary circulation, renal circulation, and portal circulation.
18. The lymphatic system is an open system, while the circulatory system is a closed system.
19. Tonsils protect the digestive and respiratory tracts against infection.
20. An *atrium* is a heart chamber that receives blood from the body or lungs; a *ventricle* is a heart chamber that pumps blood away from the heart. An *artery* carries blood away from the heart; a *vein* carries blood to the heart. The *systole* is the period of contraction of the ventricles; the *diastole* is the period of relaxation between contractions.

Extensions and Applications (p. 621)

1. Write or call your local Red Cross chapter, and discuss these questions with a representative.
2. As you gradually loosen the cuff, a faint vibration is heard through the stethoscope. When you hear this vibration, the mercury column is registering the systolic pressure. As you loosen the cuff, the sound becomes louder. When the pressure in the cuff drops just below diastolic pressure, the sound vanishes.
3. The body's immune system causes poorly matched tissues to be rejected when transplanted. The body does not recognize artificial hearts and valves as foreign, however, and so the recipient's immune system does not reject them.
4. Caution the students to be careful with a scalpel.

38 Respiration and Excretion

Chapter Objectives: See page 622.

Chapter Overview

Chapter 38 devotes one section to a discussion of the respiratory system and another to the excretory system. Respiration, which is distinguished from breathing, is described as being external, internal, or cellular. Students learn the nature and functions of each respiratory structure in the order in which air passes through them. Also covered are the roles of the diaphragm and intercostal muscles in breathing, the nature of the gas exchange in the alveoli, and the respiratory center's control of breathing. Metabolism is presented as a process that is served by respiration.

Similarly, students learn the structures of the excretory system by following the path of fluids through the kidney. The excretory system is described as also including the skin with its sweat glands, the liver, and the lungs.

Teaching Strategies and Activities

1. Many students have probably experienced muscle fatigue and weakness as a result of strenuous activity. Have students recount their experiences. Relate these events to the effects of lactic acid accumulation. The resulting discussion can be an interesting introduction to metabolism, anaerobic metabolism, and oxygen debt.

2. Many people have experienced asthma, pneumonia, or other respiratory difficulties at some time in their lives. Discuss these common maladies as a springboard for a more general discussion of the respiratory system.
3. Construct a model to illustrate the mechanics of breathing. Use Figure 38-2 on page 625 as a guide.

Answer Key to Section Reviews

Respiratory System (p. 628)

1. Respiration is the delivery of oxygen to the cells, the elimination of carbon dioxide, and the release of energy in cells.
2. The principal respiratory organs are the lungs.
3. Diffusion is the movement of substances from an area of high concentration to an area of low concentration.
4. Artificial respiration is the manual or mechanical stimulation of respiratory movements and the exchange of gases until a person can breathe naturally.

Excretory System (p. 630)

1. A nephron is the basic structural and functional unit of the kidney.
2. Nitrogenous wastes are removed from the blood by filtration and reabsorption.
3. Other organs of excretion are the lungs, liver, and skin.

Teaching Aids for Chapter End Features

Laboratory Investigation 38
Measuring Pulse and Respiration Rates

(p. 631)

Note: Be sure students do not use their thumbs to take the pulse of other students. The pronounced pulse in the thumb may interfere with pulse detection elsewhere.

OBSERVATIONS AND CONCLUSIONS 1. Walking causes a moderate increase in both pulse and respiration rates. 2. Running causes an even greater increase in the rates. 3. Both rates generally average higher in females.

Review of Facts and Concepts (p. 632)

1. *External respiration* is the exchange of gases between the lungs and the blood. *Internal respiration* is the exchange of gases between the

blood and the cells. *Cellular respiration* is the release of energy in the cells.
2. The *nasal chamber* is the entrance to the respiratory system. The *pharynx, trachea,* and *bronchi* are air passages. The *lungs* are the organs where gas exchange occurs.
3. The paired lungs are divided into lobes. The right lung is composed of three lobes, while the left has two lobes. Both lungs are enclosed in a membrane called the pleura. The lungs are located in the thoracic cavity.
4. When a human being inhales, the diaphragm contracts and is pulled down from its resting bowed position, and the intercostal muscles pull the ribs upward and outward. These actions increase the chest cavity's volume and decrease the internal air pressure, which allows air to enter the lungs. During exhalation, these muscles relax, reducing the chest cavity volume and increasing the internal air pressure, thereby moving air out of the lungs.
5. Gas exchange occurs between the alveoli and the capillaries. Oxygen dissolves in the water film on the alveoli. The oxygen moves through the walls of the capillaries into the blood. Carbon dioxide moves from the blood through the capillary walls and into the alveoli. The exchange takes place through diffusion.
6. Anaerobic respiration is respiration in the absence of oxygen. When a person engages in vigorous physical activities, the muscle cells may not get enough oxygen to meet their needs. These cells then obtain energy through anaerobic respiration. This process generates lactic acid and produces a condition known as oxygen debt.
7. The respiratory center of the medulla oblongata controls the muscular movements of breathing. As the carbon dioxide levels in the blood increase, the blood becomes more acidic, triggering the respiratory center's impulses to increase the breathing rate. When the carbon dioxide levels drop, the respiratory center slows down the breathing rate.
8. Vital capacity is the largest volume of air a person can breathe.
9. Oxygen debt is the amount of oxygen that the muscles need to rid themselves of the lactic acid built up through anaerobic respiration.
10. Metabolism is the sum of all the chemical processes that occur in the body. The two phases of metabolism are *anabolism* and *catabolism*.
11. Growth occurs when anabolism is greater than catabolism.
12. Basal metabolism is the work the body does in maintaining life functions and their associated chemical reactions. The BMR is the minimum

amount of energy needed to accomplish these tasks.

13. Carbon monoxide causes oxygen deprivation in cells, drowsiness, and possibly death.

14. Cigarette smoke may damage the lining of the upper respiratory tract and the lungs and destroy the cilia that filter foreign substances from inhaled air.

15. Each kidney is made up of a cortex and an inner medulla. The cortex is made up of nephrons, and the medulla is made up of pyramids.

16. By means of filtration in the glomerulus, the nephrons remove waste materials from the blood. As this filtrate passes through the loop of Henle, the capillaries reabsorb leftover food materials by active transport and water by osmosis. The remaining substances, constituting the urine, empty into the collecting tubules.

17. Sweat glands located in the skin excrete water, salts, and urea as perspiration.

Extensions and Applications (p. 633)

1. You may want to have some students prepare brief oral reports based on the materials sent by your local chapter of the Tuberculosis and Respiratory Disease Association.

2. As a diver goes deeper into the water, the surrounding water pressure increases. The increased pressure allows the diver's blood to dissolve increased amounts of air. A rapid ascent causes an abrupt drop in pressure and gas solubility. As a result, the dissolved gases (particularly nitrogen) are released from the blood as bubbles, which cause serious tissue damage and may even result in death. To avoid the bends, a diver must ascend slowly, stopping often to allow the gradual equilibration of gas solubility and pressure.

3. A short review of osmosis and diffusion would help students to understand the dialysis process.

39 Nutrition and Health

Chapter Objectives: See page 634.

Chapter Overview

Chapter 39 integrates what students know about the human body with what they should know about maintaining good health. The discussion of nutritional substances in the first part of the chapter lists the four food groups and how much of each group an average young adult needs each day. The text explains the nature and functions of proteins, carbohydrates, fats, vitamins, and minerals. A discussion of the importance of water concludes the section.

The section on maintaining good health and physical fitness explores the effects on the body of exercise, sleep, and weight control. The section concludes with a discussion of heart disease, cancer, and mental illness.

Teaching Strategies and Activities

1. Display photographs of many different kinds of foods. Have the students classify the foods in the proper food group.

2. "Day" people retire early and wake early. "Night" people normally stay up late at night and wake up late in the morning. Conduct a survey of the class to determine how many students belong to each category. Then, after explaining that both types of people require sleep, ask whether the sleep of each type is identical in quality. Let the class debate the question as a lead-in to a discussion of what sleep is and what it does for the body.

3. Have students list the foods that they have eaten during a day. Check the list against a balanced diet that contains foods from each of the four food groups. How many students ate a balanced diet? Discuss the importance of a balanced diet.

Answer Key to Section Reviews

Nutritional Substances (p. 640)

1. *Carbohydrates* are energy sources for cellular metabolism. Cereals, breads, fruits, and some vegetables are excellent sources of carbohydrates. *Fats* are an energy source, and they insulate the body. Common sources of fats are nuts, butter, bacon, cheese, vegetable oils, and fatty meats. *Proteins* help to build and repair tissues and make enzymes, some hormones, and antibodies. Protein sources include soybeans, eggs, fish, and lean meats.

2. See Figure 39-2 on page 638.

3. *Major minerals* are minerals that the body needs in large quantities. *Trace elements* are minerals that the body needs only in small amounts.

Maintaining Good Health (p. 643)

1. Regular exercise helps tone muscles, strengthen the heart, reduce blood pressure, decrease cholesterol level, and improve circulation. Sleep reduces fatigue, relieves tension, and restores energy, especially to the nervous system.

2. Weight control is the process either of losing excess body fat or of not putting on excess weight in the first place.

3. Three major health problems are heart disease, cancer, and mental illness.

Teaching Aids for Chapter End Features

Laboratory Investigation 39
Determining Daily Energy Needs (p. 644)

Many food product companies supply calorie charts free of charge. Most bathroom scales register in pounds; therefore, students will have to convert their body weights from pounds to kilograms.

OBSERVATIONS AND CONCLUSIONS 1. When you take in more calories than you use, you gain weight. When you use more calories than you take in, you lose weight. 2. Weight can be maintained by taking in the same amount of calories that you use.

Review of Facts and Concepts (p. 645)

1. A nutrient is a substance that the body needs to repair tissue, to supply energy, or to carry out life processes.
2. *Proteins* are needed to build and repair tissues and to make enzymes, some hormones, and antibodies. *Carbohydrates* are the primary energy source for cellular metabolism. *Fats* are used for energy and as insulation. *Vitamins* help regulate body processes, promote growth, and aid in the general upkeep of the body. *Minerals* give strength to soft tissues, bones, and teeth. They also aid the growth of body cells. *Water* is needed to transport substances in the body and for biochemical reactions to take place.
3. The four basic food groups are the *milk group* (milk and other dairy products), the *meat group* (eggs, fish, beef, poultry), the *bread-cereals group* (bread, cereal, or wheat germ), and the *vegetable-fruit group* (vegetables and fruit).
4. For a balanced diet, an average young adult should daily consume four or more servings each from the milk, bread-cereals, and vegetable-fruit groups and two or more servings from the meat group.
5. Two common *monosaccharides* are glucose and fructose. Lactose, maltose, and sucrose are *disaccharides*. Cellulose and glycogen are *polysaccharides*.
6. Excess carbohydrates are stored first in the muscles and liver, then in the rest of the body.
7. The *fat-soluble vitamins* are A, D, E, and K. The *water-soluble* vitamins are C and the B-complex vitamins.
8. A vitamin-deficiency disease is a condition caused by an inadequate supply of a certain vitamin. Examples include scurvy, beriberi, and rickets.
9. Some major minerals are sodium, calcium, phosphorus, and potassium. Some trace elements are iron, iodine, and copper.
10. Exercise affects circulation by lowering blood pressure, strengthening the heart, and improving the efficiency of the respiratory system. Exercise also makes muscles stronger and better toned.
11. *Sleep* reduces fatigue, relieves tension, and allows energy to be restored, especially to the nervous system.
12. To *lose weight*, a person should take in fewer calories than are used up. To *gain weight*, a person should take in more calories than are used.
13. Two causes of heart disease are hypertension and arteriosclerosis.
14. Cancer is a disease involving abnormal cell growth.
15. Symptoms of mental illness include severe and prolonged periods of depression, worry, or anxiety and alcoholism, drug addiction, and criminal behavior.

Extensions and Applications (p. 646)

1. The public library is a good source of this material. Also try bookstores that carry the more popular weight-loss strategies in paperback form.
2. Suggest to the students that they scan the lists of ingredients supplied with packaged foods.
3. The addresses or phone numbers of these organizations should be in the phone book.

Unit Teaching Aids

Perspectives in Biology
Holistic Medical Treatment (p. 647)

1. Information on most of these practices may be obtained from the various organizations or professional groups that espouse them. Opposing viewpoints may often be obtained from some of the more traditional organizations, such as the American Medical Association. Personal interviews with practitioners or administrators of these practices may also be arranged.
2. This demonstration is designed to be performed by individual students at home, but it can also be done in small groups or as a class activity. A variation of the demonstration can be performed by substituting various kinds of television programs for the music.

Field Trip Suggestions

1. The X-ray room and laboratory of the local hospital are interesting places to visit, especially if some of the personnel can take the time to explain their work.
2. Visit a paramedic or first aid squad station. Arrange to have a squad member demonstrate some of the equipment.
3. Arrange to visit a reputable weight control or physical fitness center. The representatives of such groups might speak about their programs to the class.

Audio-Visual Materials

Blood: The Inside Story, set/4 sound filmstrips, DGAV
How Blood Clots, film, BFA
Human Blood Typing, super 8mm film loop, PHM
Human Physiology Series, set/22 sound filmstrips, PHM
Muscle Series, set/3 films, EBE
Physiology, set/20 overhead transparencies, DGAV
The Human Body: A Machine at Work, set/8 sound filmstrips, DGAV

Reading Resources for Teachers

Baren, M., D. Wenck, and P. Dewan. *Nutrition.* Englewood Cliffs, N.J.: Prentice-Hall.
Gray, H. *Gray's Anatomy.* New York: Bounty Books.
Hole, J. *Human Anatomy and Physiology.* Dubuque, Iowa: Wm. C. Brown Company.
The Illustrated Encyclopedia of the Human Body and How It Works. New York: Exeter Books.

UNIT NINE

Human Response and Development

Survival depends ultimately on how successfully human beings interpret and interact with their external environments. Unit Nine presents the finely tuned and integrated systems underlying human physiology, behavior, and reactions to chemical substances. Chapter 40 explains the network of reactions comprising the endocrine system. The nervous system is the subject of Chapter 41; reproduction and development are the focus of Chapter 42.

Human behavior, emotions, and attitudes are discussed in Chapter 43. Chapter 44 presents a discussion of the effects of alcohol, drugs, and tobacco on the human body.

40 The Endocrine System

Chapter Objectives: See page 650.

Chapter Overview

Chapter 40 deals with the structure of the endocrine system and with its feedback process. The endocrine glands—the thyroid, the parathyroids, the pituitary, the hypothalamus, the adrenals, the pancreas, the gonads, and the thymus—are described in turn, and their secretions, functions, and locations are identified. A discussion of the feedback process, which is essential to homeostasis, concludes the chapter.

Teaching Strategies and Activities

1. The "fight-or-flight" reaction is partially caused by the function of the adrenal gland and the hormone adrenaline (epinephrine). Discuss this commonly experienced response as a springboard to the topic of the endocrine system.
2. Make a large diagram of the human body that illustrates the location of the endocrine glands and their relationships with other parts of the body. Using the diagram, stress that the hormones of the endocrine glands have their principal effect on target tissues that are situated far away from the glands.

Answer Key to Section Reviews
Endocrine Structure (p. 658)

1. A hormone is a chemical substance that regulates the activities of body organs and cells.
2. The pituitary gland is called the master gland.
3. Acromegaly is a condition caused by an oversecretion of growth hormone during adulthood.
4. The ovaries secrete estrogen and progesterone.

Feedback Process (p. 658)

1. In the endocrine feedback process, one gland secretes a hormone that stimulates another gland. This second gland in turn secretes a hormone that inhibits the production of the hormone from the first gland.
2. The pituitary secretes thyroid-stimulating hormone (TSH), which stimulates the thyroid to se-

crete thyroxine. When the concentration of thyroxine reaches a certain level in the bloodstream, the production of TSH slows down.

Teaching Aids for Chapter End Features

Laboratory Investigation 40
Measuring the Effects of Adrenaline
(p. 659)

Stethoscopes and sphygmomanometers may be borrowed from the medical office in the school. The Health Activities Project (HAP), produced by the Lawrence Hall of Science, University of California (Berkeley), has developed inexpensive plastic stethoscopes and sphygmomanometers that may be purchased and used in this investigation. Before collecting data in this investigation, teach students to use the stethoscopes and sphygmomanometers. *Caution: Any students with cardiac or other health problems should act as observers or recorders, not as subjects.*

OBSERVATIONS AND CONCLUSIONS 1. The exercise causes the pulse and respiration rates to increase, just as an increase in adrenaline would. **2.** Group data will be similar. There should be little, if any, difference between subjects. After vigorous exercise, however, overweight students may show higher blood pressures and pulse rates than lean or average-sized students. As time passes, the pulse and blood pressure return to normal.

Review of Facts and Concepts (p. 660)

1. The endocrine system is a chemical control system that regulates many body functions.
2. *Endocrine glands* secrete hormones directly into the bloodstream. *Exocrine glands* release their secretions through ducts.
3. The thyroid gland is located in the neck below the larynx. It regulates general metabolism and controls blood calcium levels and bone phosphate levels.
4. *Hypothyroidism* is a condition in which the thyroid gland is underactive. *Hyperthyroidism* is a condition in which the thyroid gland is overactive.
5. *Cretinism* is a condition resulting from a lack of thyroxine since birth. When the same type of deficiency occurs during adulthood, the condition is called *myxedema*.
6. If the parathyroids are injured or underactive, the calcium and phosphorus levels in the blood drop. The muscles then undergo continuous contractions or spasms (tetany).

7. The pituitary is often called the master gland because it secretes hormones that control most of the other endocrine glands and a variety of body processes.
8. Refer to Figure 40-5 on page 657.
9. In *pituitary dwarfism*, caused by a deficiency of HGH, body growth is stunted, but mental development is normal. In *thyroid-induced dwarfism*, caused by a lack of thyroxine from birth, both mental and physical development are retarded.
10. Specialized nerve cells of the hypothalamus produce hormones that stimulate the posterior lobe of the pituitary.
11. Refer to Figure 40-5 on page 657.
12. Addison's disease is an ailment caused by a hypofunctioning of the adrenal cortex.
13. The islets of Langerhans in the pancreas secrete insulin directly into the bloodstream; other tissues in the pancreas produce digestive enzymes that travel through ducts to organs of the digestive system.
14. Hypoglycemia is a condition characterized by abnormally low blood sugar levels.
15. Gonads secrete sex hormones and produce gametes.
16. Adrenaline triggers physiological changes in the body, such as increased heart rate. These changes make the body better able to meet the challenge of sudden stress or danger.
17. See Figure 40-6 on page 658.

Extensions and Applications (p. 661)

1. Banting and Best discovered and isolated insulin in the 1920s.
2. Some hormones that have been synthesized since the 1940s include auxin, cortisone, and the sex hormones. Not all hormones can be synthesized, however.
3. Selye's research showed how the body reacts to the stress of general living conditions and how people can adjust to energy depletion in the body.

41 The Nervous System

Chapter Objectives: See page 662.

Chapter Overview

Chapter 41 opens with a discussion of the structure and functions of the nervous system. This first section presents the basic unit of structure, the neuron, and analyzes the nature of nerve impulses. A discussion of the two parts of the central nervous system, the brain and the spinal cord, follows. A brief discussion of the peripheral nervous system as the link between the central system and the limbs, neck, and trunk is then presented. A description of the two divisions of the autonomic nervous system and of their functions concludes this section.

In a section on the senses, the text presents the structure of the eye. The senses of smell and taste are presented as chemical senses. The various aspects of the sense of touch are discussed. Finally, the structure of the ear and its functions as an organ of hearing and balance are presented.

Teaching Strategies and Activities

1. Use the knee jerk reflex to demonstrate the action of neuronal circuits and to lead into the nervous system's circuitry in general.
2. Engage student interest by explaining the observations on human brain function of Wilder Penfield, a brain surgeon. During brain operations, Penfield stimulated various regions of the cerebral cortex of conscious patients, who were then able to recall past episodes in their lives in extreme detail. Their incredibly realistic recollections involved all sensory modalities, to the extent that the patients believed themselves to be actually reliving the events. The same event could be recalled repeatedly by stimulating the same region.
3. Assemble a group of optical illusions and vision or color charts. Have your students examine and discuss the illusions and charts.

Answer Key to Section Reviews

Structure and Function of the Nervous System (p. 664)

1. The three main parts of a neuron are the dendrites, the axon, and the cell body.
2. *Axons* carry impulses away from the cell body. *Dendrites* carry impulses toward the cell body.
3. A neuron is polarized when it has a positive electric charge on the outside of its cell membrane and a negative electric charge on the inside.

Central Nervous System (p. 668)

1. The major parts of the brain are the cerebrum, the cerebellum, and the brain stem.
2. The pons and the medulla oblongata are the two parts of the brain stem.
3. The spinal cord serves as the major connection between the brain and the rest of the body and regulates reflexes.

Peripheral and Autonomic Nervous Systems (p. 670)

1. The two sets of nerves in the PNS are the spinal nerves and the cranial nerves.
2. A reflex arc is a pattern of stimulus and response that includes incoming sensory impulses and outgoing motor impulses.
3. The sympathetic and parasympathetic systems are the two systems of the autonomic nervous system.

The Senses (p. 674)

1. With the help of the ciliary body, the shape of the lens is changed to bring objects into focus.
2. The olfactory bulbs are two small sections of the brain that receive and interpret impulses from the smell receptors.
3. The *outer ear* consists of a funnel-shaped auricle, which leads to the ear canal and the eardrum. The *middle ear* is made up of the malleus, incus, and stapes. In the *inner ear*, a series of semicircular canals connects with the cochlea.
4. The semicircular canals are set at right angles to one another in three different planes and are filled with fluid. When a person's head changes position, the movement of the fluid causes hair cells to send an impulse to the cerebellum, which then sends the necessary adjustment signals to the body to maintain balance.

Teaching Aids for Chapter End Features

Laboratory Investigation 41
Investigating Reaction Time (p. 675)

Note: Check to see that students are following the instructions for their hand position and the position of the ruler.

OBSERVATIONS AND CONCLUSIONS 1. The rate of falling is about the same for all rulers. The faster the student's reaction time, the shorter the distance that the ruler will fall. 2. Reaction time varies. Some students react more quickly than others. 3. The formula is: distance = (initial velocity) (change in time) + $\frac{1}{2}$ (acceleration due to gravity) (change in time)^2. Simplified, this equation is: change in time = $\sqrt{\text{(distance/491)}}$.

Review of Facts and Concepts (p. 676)

1. The *central nervous system* reacts to internal and external stimuli and coordinates the body's

activities. The *peripheral nervous system* carries messages to and from the central nervous system.

2. *Sensory nerves* carry impulses to the brain and spinal cord. *Motor nerves* carry impulses from the central nervous system to the muscles and glands. *Mixed nerves* contain both sensory and motor nerve fibers.

3. A *receptor* collects stimuli and transforms them into nerve impulses. An *effector* responds to nerve impulses. A *conductor* provides a pathway between a receptor and an effector.

4. The *cell body* contains the nucleus and is the base for receiving and sending impulses. *Dendrites* are branching fibers that carry impulses toward the cell body. *Axons* are long fibers that branch at their ends. Axons conduct impulses away from the cell body.

5. A nerve impulse is an electrochemical signal that moves along a neuron.

6. The cerebrospinal fluid acts as a shock absorber for the brain and distributes nutrients and gases to the brain cells.

7. A concussion is a brain bruise caused by a severe blow to the head.

8. The three major divisions of the brain are the cerebrum, the cerebellum, and the brain stem.

9. The cerebrum is divided into two hemispheres separated by a deep groove. Each hemisphere is divided into the frontal, parietal, occipital, and temporal lobes.

10. The outer surface of the cerebrum, called the cortex or gray matter, consists of nerve cell bodies. The inner surface, or white matter, consists mostly of axons.

11. The cerebellum, located below the occipital lobe of the cerebrum, controls balance, coordination, and muscle tone.

12. The medulla oblongata serves as a conducting pathway between parts of the brain and regulates respiration, blood pressure, and heartbeat.

13. The spinal cord is the principal connection between the brain and the rest of the body. The spinal cord also regulates reflexes.

14. The peripheral nervous system provides a link between the central nervous system and the arms, legs, neck, and trunk.

15. A reflex arc is a pattern of stimulus and response that involves incoming sensory impulses and outgoing motor impulses.

16. The *sclera* is the outermost layer of the eye. It is made of dense white connective tissue and the cornea. The *choroid* is the middle layer. It includes the iris, lens, and muscles (such as the ciliary body). The *retina* is the inner layer. It consists of rods and cones.

17. See Figures 41-11 and 41-12 on page 672.

18. The two functions of the ear are hearing and balance.

19. The Eustachian tube equalizes air pressure in the middle ear with that of the environment.

Extensions and Applications (p. 677)

1. The point where the optic nerve connects with the retina is devoid of sensory rods and cones, and that point is effectively a "blind spot" on the retina.

2. *Note: Students should use a clean cotton applicator for each solution.*

3. Students may want to write to various foundations or research organizations to obtain the most recent information about nervous system disorders.

42 Reproduction and Development

Chapter Objectives: See page 678.

Chapter Overview

The first half of Chapter 42 deals with the structures and functions of the male and female reproductive systems. The production and storage of sperm and the composition of seminal fluid are described. The structures and functions of the female system, as well as the stages of the menstrual cycle, are also presented.

The second half of the chapter covers the stages of human development from conception to adulthood. The discussion of embryonic development includes explanations of the cleavage process, as well as a description of the tissues surrounding the embryo. Definitions and discussions of infancy, childhood, adolescence, and adulthood end the chapter.

Teaching Strategies and Activities

1. Explain to the class the theory of preformation, which was accepted by scientists from about 1600 to 1900. According to this notion, the human embryo is preformed in the gamete, and it merely grows to adult size. Contrast this theory with current knowledge of conception and development.

2. Write the terms INFANCY, CHILDHOOD, ADOLESCENCE, and ADULTHOOD on the chalkboard. Ask

the students when each begins and ends. Then ask them to give characteristics of each period of development.

Answer Key to Section Reviews

The Reproductive System (p. 681)

1. The paired *testes*, suspended in the scrotum, are the site of testosterone and sperm cell production. The *seminiferous tubules* produce and store sperm in the *epididymis*. During ejaculation, sperm pass through the *vas deferens* to the *urethra*, where they exit the body from the *penis*. Along the way, the sperm mix with nutrients from the seminal vesicle, secretions from the prostate gland, and a lubricant from Cowper's gland to become collectively what is known as *semen*.

2. The paired *ovaries* produce eggs and the hormones estrogen and progesterone. The eggs travel through the *Fallopian tubes* to the *uterus*. Fertilization takes place in the Fallopian tubes, and development of the fertilized egg takes place in the uterus. The uterus narrows to the necklike *cervix*, which opens into the *vagina*.

Stages of Development (p. 686)

1. The gestation period of human beings is 280 days.
2. As the *zygote* travels down the Fallopian tube to the uterus, the zygote undergoes *cleavage*. In a few days, rapid cell division transforms the zygote into a *morula*. The next stage, the *blastula*, consists of a hollow ball of cells. The following stage, the *gastrula*, contains the primary germ layers that eventually become the tissues of a fully formed human being.
3. Infancy is characterized by a tremendous rate of increase in weight and height. The arms and legs grow into proportion with the head and trunk, the skull bones fuse, and teeth appear. Motor skills and coordination develop slowly.
4. *Adolescence* is characterized by a growth spurt. The sex organs mature, and secondary sex characteristics develop. In *adulthood*, the body completes its growth in height, and the body systems mature.

Teaching Aids for Chapter End Features

Laboratory Investigation 42
Observing Human Growth (p. 687)

After the students have recorded their data in Table 1, guide the class through the procedure for setting up the graph.

OBSERVATIONS AND CONCLUSIONS 1. Males and females double their size at about age 4. 2. Females grow more rapidly than males between the ages of 10 and 12. Males grow more rapidly than females between the ages of 14 and 16. 3. Answers will vary. 4. Answers will vary. 5. Answers will vary. The fewer students in each group, the less reliable the data.

Review of Facts and Concepts (p. 688)

1. The specialized reproductive cells are called gametes. Male gametes are called sperm; female gametes are called ova.
2. The testes are flattened, oval structures found in the scrotum. Each testis contains tightly coiled seminiferous tubules held together by connective tissue.
3. Each sperm cell has an oval head that contains a nucleus and a total of 23 chromosomes. Behind the head is a body connected to a tail.
4. The ovaries are located on the right and left side walls of the abdominal cavity. These glands produce female gametes and the hormones estrogen and progesterone.
5. The Fallopian tubes are the passageways for the ova, connecting the ovaries to the uterus.
6. Refer to the section "Ovarian and Uterine Cycle" on page 681.
7. During fertilization, a single sperm cell unites with an egg cell.
8. The stages of embryonic development are the morula, blastula, and gastrula.
9. See Figure 42-4 on page 682.
10. The *chorion* surrounds the embryo and attaches the embryo to the uterus. The *amnion* surrounds the embryo and contains the amniotic fluid, which keeps the embryo moist and acts as a shock absorber. The *yolk sac* produces blood cells until the liver becomes functional. The *allantois* also forms blood cells, and becomes part of the umbilical cord.
11. *Identical twins* result when, during cleavage, the cells of a single fertilized ovum divide into two separate parts. *Fraternal twins* result when the ovary releases two ova that are fertilized by different sperm.
12. Puberty is the beginning of adolescence.
13. *Infancy* is the stage of development that begins with birth and extends to the end of the first year. *Childhood* begins with the second year and ends with puberty. Beginning with puberty, *adolescence* extends through the growth spurt and the attainment of sexual maturity. *Adulthood* includes the time from adolescence to death.

Extensions and Applications (p. 689)

1. When having students do this extension, be sure to check their completed letters so that you may provide them with your support and guidance.
2. Alcohol ingested during the last trimester gives rise to fetal alcohol syndrome. Cigarette smoking increases the level of carbon monoxide in the blood, stunting fetal growth and often triggering premature birth. Heroin ingestion may cause fetal convulsions, fetal addiction, or miscarriage.
3. To avoid tiring the infant, advise your students to do these studies over a period of time.
4. If you have a set of twins in a class, you may want to have them diagram a family tree to find out whether their family history reflects such a tendency.

43 Human Behavior

Chapter Objectives: See page 690.

Chapter Overview

Chapter 43 categorizes human behavior as involuntary, emotional, or acquired. The basic human physical and psychological needs are presented in a brief section. The interrelationship of emotions and physiological activity, as evidenced by blushing, "butterflies" in the stomach, or sweaty palms from emotional stress, is discussed. In conclusion, a discussion of acquired behavior, including habits, mannerisms, and attitudes, is presented.

Teaching Strategies and Activities

1. To introduce the topic of human behavior, you can demonstrate the concept of personal space. While talking with a student, slowly move closer and closer. The student, feeling physical and emotional discomfort, may step back. A person can sometimes "chase" another person around a room by continually invading his or her personal space. Have the students conduct their own experiments with this phenomenon. Are all personal spaces of similar size? Does the size change depending on the situation or the person?
2. Discuss the relationship between sports and human behavior, especially aggressive behavior. Many team sports, such as football and basketball, are commonly described as forms of ritual aggression. Football, in particular, bears a relation to normal animal aggression, which usually takes the form of threat displays, such as facial grimaces and body posturing.

Answer Key to Section Reviews

Involuntary Behavior (p. 691)

1. Involuntary behavior is behavior that does not depend upon will or choice and does not have to be learned.
2. A taxis is a response that arises because of irritability.

Basic Human Needs (p. 692)

1. Human physical needs include food, air, water, sleep, clothing, and shelter.
2. Human psychological needs include social contact, realization of potential, self-esteem, and the respect of others.

Emotional Behavior (p. 695)

1. *Positive emotions* include love, contentment, and joy. *Negative emotions* include anxiety, fear, and anger.
2. The three basic emotions are love, fear, and anger.
3. Answers will vary but may include blushing, "butterflies," and sweaty palms.

Acquired Behavior (p. 696)

1. Acquired behavior is behavior that is conscious, voluntary, and learned.
2. Habits are learned responses that become almost automatic through repetition.
3. Prejudice is an emotional and usually negative opinion of a person or group of people.

Teaching Aids for Chapter End Features

Laboratory Investigation 43
Investigating Human Behavior (p. 697)

In this investigation, students can observe and discuss the human behaviors exhibited during a problem-solving activity.

To prepare for the investigation, cut tangram puzzle pieces out of posterboard by using the pattern shown on the next page. Prepare six tangram puzzles for each team of six students.

Place the pieces for each tangram puzzle into one of the small envelopes, but do not give a few members of each team a complete puzzle, and distribute the extra pieces among the other envelopes. Then put the six small envelopes for each team into a larger envelope. Tell students that they must use seven pieces to complete their puzzles.

Ask some of the students to act as observers. The observers are to move around the room and re-

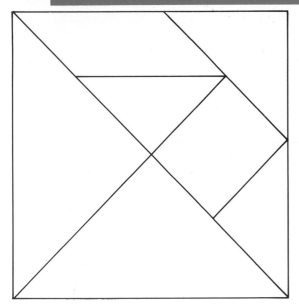

cord their observations of the behaviors exhibited during the problem-solving activity. They should not talk with the other students or help them in any way.

At the end of twenty minutes, ask the teams to stop working on the puzzles. Ask each of the observers to give a brief report. Then let the puzzle-solvers supplement or refute the observations.

OBSERVATIONS AND CONCLUSIONS 1 and 2. *Nonsupportive behaviors* may include hurrying, disobeying the rules, and grabbing pieces from teammates. *Supportive behaviors* may include concentrating, working quietly, obeying the rules, and giving up tangram pieces to teammates. 3. Giving tangram pieces to other team members would probably be the most useful type of behavior. 4. Responses will vary.

Review of Facts and Concepts (p. 698)

1. Behavior is anything an organism does or any response it makes.
2. Some *external stimuli* are noise, odor, and light. Some *internal stimuli* are hunger, thirst, pain, and fatigue.
3. Involuntary behavior is behavior that is unlearned, unconscious, and automatic.
4. A taxis is a response that arises because of irritability. Examples will vary.
5. Reflex behavior is a simple automatic response that usually involves only a small number of nerves.

6. *Physical needs* are needs that must be satisfied for the individual to stay healthy and alive. *Psychological needs* are needs that are necessary for mental well-being.
7. Psychologists define emotions variously as motives, as bodily changes, and as feelings.
8. Emotional behavior patterns affect the body, and physiological factors can cause emotions. Illustrations will vary.
9. With intelligence and reasoning, human beings can draw conclusions, learn, and base decisions on previous experience.
10. Acquired behavior is conscious, voluntary, learned behavior.
11. *Habits* are learned responses that become almost automatic with repetition. *Mannerisms* are patterns of acquired behavior in which an individual develops an unusual or affected way of behaving or moving.
12. Conditioning is a form of behavior modification in which a response initially associated with one stimulus becomes associated with a second, unrelated stimulus.
13. An attitude is a readiness to respond in certain ways toward persons, events, or ideas.
14. In *stereotyping*, an individual holds a fixed idea that involves casting groups of people in a mold. In *prejudice*, an individual forms an emotional, unfounded, and usually negative attitude toward a person or group of people, often before experiencing or considering the facts.

Extensions and Applications (p. 698)

1. Students may present their research as an oral report.
2. ***Note:*** *Be sure students set up their experiments according to scientific method.*
3. This application may be used as a supplemental laboratory investigation.

44 Alcohol, Drugs, and Tobacco

Chapter Objectives: See page 700.

Chapter Overview

Chapter 44 presents the negative effects of drug use. The text examines a wide variety of drugs as well as alcohol and tobacco. Alcoholism is presented as a disease whose stages include such symptoms as blackouts, amnesia, alcoholic psychosis, and cirrhosis of the liver. Also explained are physiological and psychological approaches to therapy. In the section on drugs, the student learns the nature, sources, and effects of inhalants, depressants, tranquilizers, hallucinogens, cannabis, stimulants, and narcotics. Treatment for drug abuse is also discussed. The discussion on tobacco lists and explains the effects of nicotine, tars, and carbon monoxide and examines the United States Surgeon General's report on the effects of cigarette smoking.

Teaching Strategies and Activities

1. Make your presentation of the negative effects of drug use factual and nonmoralizing. Avoid preaching.
2. Have the students cut out and mount advertisements for over-the-counter drugs, alcohol, and tobacco products. Ask them to explain how the advertisements make the use of these products appealing.
3. Invite a representative from a mental health or law enforcement agency to speak to your classes about alcohol or drug addiction.

Answer Key to Section Reviews

Alcohol (p. 703)

1. Alcohol acts as a depressant to the central nervous system, reducing judgment, memory, emotion, speech, vision, motor skills, muscular coordination, and balance. It also slows down the heart, digestive, and respiratory rates.
2. *Alcoholism* is a disease that involves an abnormal intake of alcohol and a loss of control of alcohol consumption. *Alcoholic psychosis* is a mental disturbance brought on by long-term alcohol use.
3. Symptoms of alcoholism include blackouts, brief episodes of amnesia, alcoholic psychosis, and cirrhosis of the liver.

Drugs (p. 707)

1. A drug is any substance that causes a change in body function.
2. Seven groups of drugs are inhalants, depressants, tranquilizers, hallucinogens, cannabis, stimulants, and narcotics.
3. A *depressant* is a drug that temporarily decreases the action of the central nervous system. A *stimulant* is a drug that temporarily increases the action of the central nervous system.
4. A hallucinogen is a drug that produces sensory distortions.
5. A narcotic is a drug that depresses the action of the central nervous system, reducing pain.

Tobacco (p. 711)

1. Some components of tobacco are nicotine and tar.
2. The immediate effects of cigarette smoking are increased heart rate, constriction of blood vessels, lowering of skin temperature, dilation of the pupils, and irritation of the linings of the nose, throat, and mouth.
3. Cigarette smoking causes the heart to work harder because of arterial constriction. This can cause damage to the heart. Smoking also destroys the alveoli and bronchial cilia, opening the door to respiratory illnesses such as emphysema, chronic bronchitis, and lung cancer.

Teaching Aids for Chapter End Features

Laboratory Investigation 44
Investigating the Hazards of Smoking
(p. 712)

Clear plastic bottles are best for this investigation because they allow the student to observe the action taking place inside. If old felt-tip pens are not available, you may use glass tubing with a diameter large enough to insert a cigarette. Use clay to hold the cigarette tightly in the pen or tubing.

OBSERVATIONS AND CONCLUSIONS 1. The non-filter-tipped cigarettes should produce more stain on the cotton than the filter-tipped ones, because the nonfilter type allows all the chemicals in the smoke to pass through. 2. The filter type of cigarette produces less stain because the filter traps some of the chemicals. 3. The lungs of a smoker become coated with the chemicals contained in the inhaled smoke.

Review of Facts and Concepts (p. 713)

1. Ethyl alcohol is produced by fermentation.
2. Alcohol reduces the ability of neurons to transmit impulses between the brain and the body. Alcohol may impair judgment, memory, emotion, speech, vision, motor skills, muscular coordination, and balance.
3. Alcohol is classified as a depressant because it reduces the activity of bodily functions.
4. Alcoholism is considered a disease because it causes disturbances of body function and has characteristic symptoms.
5. Alcoholism causes destruction of liver tissue.
6. *Physiological therapy* for alcoholism involves physical withdrawal from alcohol dependence. *Psychological therapy* includes counseling, through which the alcoholic understands and learns to cope with the problem.

7. See Figure 44-4 on pages 708–9.
8. Drug treatment methods include methadone treatment for heroin addiction and psychological help in treatment communities.
9. The Surgeon General reported that cigarette smoking is the most important cause of lung cancer.
10. Yes; cigarette smoking causes the heart to work harder because the arteries constrict. This can lead to heart disease.

Extensions and Applications (p. 714)

1. Students may want to write to local chapters of rehabilitation organizations for pamphlets and brochures.
2. You may want to establish a student committee to organize this event. Perhaps the project can be done as a general assembly for the school.
3. Local and national chapters of these organizations usually have brochures and pamphlets that they provide without charge. Students can find addresses in the telephone directory.

Unit Teaching Aids

Perspectives in Biology

The ESP Debate (p. 715)

1. Answers to these questions can be used to open up a discussion or debate about psychic phenomena.
2. Stress to your students that these experiments do not prove that ESP exists.
3. In this exercise, students should set up their experiment according to scientific method. Again, stress that these experiments do not prove that a person is telepathic. Remind your students that reliable methods for testing ESP have not been established.

Field Trip Suggestions

1. Arrange a visit to a neurological laboratory in a local hospital or nearby university or college. Arrange to have a staff member explain how an EEG works.
2. A visit to a pharmacy might be used to establish the difference between prescription drugs and illegal drugs. Perhaps the pharmacist can explain why prescriptions are needed to purchase some drugs.

Audio-Visual Materials

Biological Rhythms: Studies in Chronobiology, film, EBE
Endocrine Glands, film, EBE
Human Birth, Growth and Development, set/7 sound filmstrips, PHM
Human Body Series, set/12 films, Cor
Human Physiology Series, set/22 sound filmstrips, PHM
Learning About Human Behavior, film, Cor
The Ears and Hearing, film, EBE

Reading Resources for Teachers

Decoursey, R. *The Human Organism*. New York: McGraw-Hill.
Ferster, C. *Behavior Principles*. Englewood Cliffs, N.J.: Prentice-Hall.
Rugh, R., and L. Shettles. *From Conception to Birth*. New York: Harper and Row.
Worick, W., and W. Schaller. *Alcohol, Tobacco and Drugs: Their Use and Abuse*. Englewood Cliffs, N.J.: Prentice-Hall.

UNIT TEN

Ecological Interactions

This last unit introduces students to the complex interrelationships in the environment. Chapter 45 deals with basic elements of the environment. The biosphere, ecosystems, communities, populations, habitats, niches, and biotic and abiotic factors are defined and discussed. Chapter 46 focuses on how ecosystems and their populations change. Students learn the various types of succession and rhythms and the mathematics of population changes. The major biomes of the earth, along with their characteristic climates and life forms, constitute the subject matter of Chapter 47. Finally, Chapter 48 discusses the conservation of both renewable and nonrenewable resources.

45 The Environment

Chapter Objectives: See page 718.

Chapter Overview

Chapter 45 introduces students to the components and types of interrelationships in the environment. The opening section, on the biosphere, discusses ecosystems, communities, populations, habitats, and niches. The following section explains the roles of producers, consumers, and decomposers in food chains and food webs. Students learn how energy decreases at each succeeding level of an ecological pyramid. Competition, predator–prey relationships, and symbiotic relationships are also discussed. The next section identifies the four main abiotic factors in the environment—water, soil, temperature, and light. The chapter closes with descriptions of the water, oxygen, carbon, and nitrogen cycles.

Teaching Strategies and Activities

1. Begin this chapter with a walk around the school grounds or through a nearby grassy or wooded area. Point out to the class some of the plants and animals that depend on one another. Your observations can be the springboard for discussions of ecosystems, populations, and habitats.
2. Have the students identify communities, populations, and ecosystems in the school area. Encourage the students to develop ecology trails around the grounds, placing identification labels on as many plants as possible. Labels can also identify the habitats of various animals. Have the students make up trail guides identifying various populations of organisms and their roles in the food chains of one or more ecosystems.
3. To introduce the concept of the niche, have each student study an organism that is easily found in your area, such as a beetle, a spider, or a grasshopper. Have the students answer these questions: Where does this organism live? How is its body adapted to live in this place? What other organisms live near or with this organism? How do these organisms interact? What is the principal food of the organism?

Answer Key to Section Reviews

The Biosphere (p. 721)

1. The biosphere is the thin zone that contains all living things on the earth.
2. An ecosystem is an interacting system consisting of living things and their nonliving environment.
3. A *habitat* is the place where an organism lives. A *niche* is the environmental role that the organism plays in its habitat.

Biotic Interactions in the Environment (p. 728)

1. A *producer* is an organism that makes its own food. A *consumer* is an organism that feeds directly or indirectly on producers. A *decomposer*

is an organism that breaks down organic material and returns it to the environment.
2. A *food chain* is the flow of energy and organic materials from organism to organism. A *food web* consists of interconnected and overlapping food chains.
3. The transfer of energy in a food chain is a *pyramid of energy*. A *pyramid of biomass* shows the amount of matter that can be supported at each trophic level. A *pyramid of numbers* shows the number of organisms at each trophic level.
4. Predators are animals that feed upon other living animals, which are called prey.
5. Symbiosis is a relationship between two organisms in which each contributes to the survival of the other. The three types of symbiotic relationships are commensalism, mutualism, and parasitism.

Abiotic Factors in the Environment (p. 730)

1. Four abiotic factors in the environment are water, soil, temperature, and light.
2. The two main ingredients of soil are humus and particles of weathered rock.
3. *Exotherms* are cold-blooded animals. *Endotherms* are warm-blooded animals. Examples will vary.

Important Cycles in the Environment (p. 734)

1. *Precipitation* is the movement of water from the atmosphere to the earth. *Evaporation* is a process by which some of the molecules on the surface of a liquid become gas.
2. Four nutrient cycles are the water cycle, the oxygen cycle, the carbon cycle, and the nitrogen cycle.
3. *Nitrogen fixation* is the process by which certain bacteria change atmospheric nitrogen directly into nitrates and nitrites. *Denitrification* is the process by which nitrites, nitrates, and ammonia are converted into nitrogen, which is returned to the atmosphere.

Teaching Aids for Chapter End Features

Laboratory Investigation 45
The Role of Green Plants in the Water Cycle (p. 735)

Prepare cobalt chloride paper by immersing sheets of filter paper in a 5% aqueous solution of cobalt chloride. Dry the paper in an oven at 40 °C. Cut the paper into strips approximately 12 mm × 35 mm. Store the dried strips in an airtight container.

OBSERVATIONS AND CONCLUSIONS 1. Tumbler B is the control because it does not contain a green plant. 2. The color of the blue cobalt paper in tumbler A changes to pink. The change is caused by the moisture from the leaf. 3. Water collects on the interior of setup A. 4. Water returns to the atmosphere by transpiration, as well as by evaporation. In this experiment, the leaf recycles the water in the tumbler by transpiration, just as plants return water to the atmosphere.

Review of Facts and Concepts (p. 737)

1. An ecosystem is an interacting system that consists of groups of organisms and their nonliving environment. Examples will vary.
2. Sunlight is the primary source of energy in an ecosystem.
3. Classified according to how they obtain food, the three groups of organisms are producers (green plants), consumers (animals), and decomposers (bacteria or fungi).
4. An *autotroph* is an organism that makes its own food. A *heterotroph* feeds on other organisms or on the wastes of other organisms.
5. Answers will vary. The illustrations should show producers, consumers, and decomposers.
6. Examples will vary.
7. Energy is lost at each trophic level because each organism in a level uses some of the energy locked in the chemical bonds of its food to carry on its own life functions. Also, there is always a loss of energy in the form of heat in any system of energy transfer.
8. The flow of energy in an ecosystem follows the direction of the food chain from producers to consumers to decomposers.
9. It is more efficient to eat plants instead of animals because plants are the first level of a food chain and have the highest level of energy.
10. Predators are animals that feed on other animals called prey. This interaction is called a predator–prey relationship.
11. A *habitat* is a place where an organism lives in a community; the role or occupation of the organism within the habitat is its *niche*. *Herbivores* are plant eaters; *carnivores* are flesh eaters. *Intraspecific competition* is competition among individuals of the same species; *interspecific competition* is competition among two or more different species.

Extensions and Applications (p. 737)

1. Students should find that several foreign plants or animals introduced into the United States have caused environmental problems. You may want to have the students address how these effects could be minimized.
2. Have the entire class identify as many ecosystems as possible. Then divide the class into groups and have each group study one of the ecosystems and identify some food chains and food webs within it. After the group work is done, have the entire class work together to identify the relationships of these ecosystems.
3. Have the students set up and label their soil samples. The labels should include where the samples were found, who found them, and at what time of year they were found.
4. Be sure that the students do not overlook the forms of life that may be growing on and within the tree itself.
5. A list of questions may help guide the students in preparing their reports. Some questions may include: What effect does light have on this ecosystem? What effect would the removal of the earthworms have on the system? Does the number of each type of organism change over time? What role do the land snails play in this ecosystem?

46 Succession and Population Changes

Chapter Objectives: See page 738.

Chapter Overview

The first section of Chapter 46 explains ecological succession in general, citing lakes and sand dunes as examples, and distinguishes between primary succession and secondary succession. Biological rhythms are the topic of the next section. Rhythms discussed include circadian rhythms, lunar rhythms, and annual rhythms. The last section, on population changes, offers a mathematical formula for expressing changes in population size. In addition, students learn such basic concepts as biotic potential, carrying capacity, growth curves, and limiting factors. Students also become aware of density-dependent and density-independent factors. The chapter closes with a discussion of human population.

Teaching Strategies and Activities

1. For lead-in information on what is being done to preserve sand dunes and the shoreline, write to the National Seashore Visitors Center, Route 6, Eastham, Massachusetts 02642.

2. Have the students answer a questionnaire with the following types of questions: When do you sleep best? (9:00 P.M.–5:00 A.M.? 11:00 P.M.–7:00 A.M.? 1:00–9:00 A.M.?) When do you feel most alert and do your best work? (5:00–9:00 A.M.? 7:00–11:00 A.M.? 9:00 A.M.–1:00 P.M.?) Using the information gathered from the questionnaire, expand the discussion to include circadian rhythms and the students' own biological clocks.

3. To introduce the concepts of population density and distribution, have each student pick a species of plant or animal and determine its habitat and its population density in that habitat. Ask such questions as: Is your species found in only one type of climate or in many different climates? If the organism lives in only one climate, how is it adapted to that one climate? What is the organism's food source? Do other organisms in this area have the same food source? Does this organism always live in a climax community? Is it always found with certain other species of organisms?

Answer Key to Section Reviews

Ecological Succession (p. 742)

1. Ecological succession is the series of changes that an ecosystem undergoes during its development.
2. *Pioneer plants* are the first plants to dominate a developing ecosystem. *Climax species* are the dominant organisms in a climax community.
3. *Primary succession* is the development of a community in an area with no previous community. *Secondary succession* is the development of a community in an area where a previous community was removed.

Time Rhythms and Cycles in Biotic Communities (p. 747)

1. A *circadian rhythm* is a 24-hour cycle of an organism's activity.
2. The moon exerts a gravitational pull on the earth and causes tides. Many organisms are adapted to the rising and falling tides.
3. *Hibernation* is a state of winter inactivity. *Estivation* is a period of summer inactivity.
4. Some animals migrate in search of warmth, water, or food.

Population Changes (p. 750)

1. *Immigrants* are organisms that move into an area. *Emigrants* are organisms that move out of an area.
2. Limiting factors such as food supplies, living space, and water supplies prevent organisms from reaching their biotic potential.
3. Carrying capacity is the population size that an environment can support.
4. *Density-dependent factors* are factors that are directly related to the density of a population. *Density-independent factors* are factors that have an effect on populations regardless of their densities.
5. Scientists predict that the earth's population will be more than 6.2 billion by the year 2000.

Teaching Aids for Chapter End Features

Laboratory Investigation 46
Succession and Population Density in Microorganism Cultures (p. 751)

For Part A, distribute corks with slits already cut in them, in order to save time and to minimize the chances of the students' injuring themselves. During the study, replace the water lost through evaporation with aged tap water. To prepare the aged tap water, keep ordinary tap water in an open container for several days. In Part B, supply the students with picture keys to help them identify the different organisms.

OBSERVATIONS AND CONCLUSIONS Part A:
1. Answers will vary. 2. Answers will vary. 3. As organisms live, grow, and carry on metabolic activities, they change the environment, making it more favorable for the growth and development of other organisms. As organisms reproduce, they use up their food supply, release wastes into the culture, and crowd out others. **Part B: 1.** For the first few days the increase in numbers cannot be detected or is very slow. 2. Answers will vary, but there should be a large increase in the number of organisms at one point or another. 3. Toward the end of the observation period, the number of organisms will decrease. 4. The graph resembles an upside-down U.

Review of Facts and Concepts (p. 753)

1. Succession of a community arises from changes within the structure of the community, which usually are caused by the community itself.
2. Pioneer plants help to change rock into soil, anchor the soil, and make the soil more fertile.
3. A climax community is stable. No major changes occur unless there are severe climate changes, natural disasters, or disturbances by people. The death and birth rates of the different organisms remain about the same. There are no major

changes in the kinds of species or the structure of the community.

4. *Primary succession* is the development of a community in an area where there has been no previous community. *Secondary succession* occurs in an area from which a previous community has been removed.

5. A biological clock is an internal mechanism that controls the cyclic rhythms of an organism's activities.

6. *Nocturnal organisms*, such as owls and bats, are active at night. *Diurnal organisms*, such as hawks, are active during the day.

7. (a) The skunk exhibits a circadian rhythm. (b) The crabs have a lunar rhythm. (c) The mouse exhibits an annual rhythm. (d) The opening and closing of the poppy is a circadian rhythm. (e) The grunions move according to a lunar rhythm.

8. Hibernation and estivation are alike in that they are both states of inactivity. They differ in that hibernation occurs in winter, while estivation occurs in summer.

9. Animals migrate in search of warmth, water, and food. Examples will vary.

10. Four factors that determine the change in the size of a population are the birth rate, the death rate, the rate of immigration, and the rate of emigration. The change in the example would be zero.

11. Limiting factors such as food supply, living space, and water supply prevent organisms from reaching their biotic potential.

12. This type of a population growth curve would probably indicate a climax community at its carrying capacity.

13. The population growth curve in a natural environment should show a gradual rise until the population reaches a stable level. A population curve in a closed environment should show a gradual rise, a stable level, and then a gradual decline.

14. The population density is 0.375 deer per hectare.

15. Some advantages of a high-density population are greater genetic diversity leading to positive evolutionary adaptations, better protection within the group, and a lower chance of extinction.

16. Competition is density-dependent because competition for food, water, and living space increases with population density. A flood is density-independent because population size will be affected by a flood regardless of its density.

17. Most of the limiting factors that affect other organisms also affect the human population. Other factors are the development of new technologies,

sources of food, housing, communications, and transportation networks.

Extensions and Applications (p. 753)

1. You may want to have students take photographs of the area that can then be used in a display and in future classes.

2. In their study of migration patterns, the students should note the distance covered in the migration.

3. Students should list the types of plants and animals that first returned to the area.

4. Current encyclopedias are the best source of information.

47 Biomes

Chapter Objectives: See page 754.

Chapter Overview

In this chapter, biomes are defined as large geographical regions that biologists classify and describe on the basis of climate and characteristic plant and animal life. A short introductory section on biogeography explains how plants and animals are dispersed and shows how geographical, ecological, and behavioral barriers prevent their dispersion. Terrestrial biomes are discussed in the next section. These biomes include the tundra, coniferous forests, deciduous forests, tropical rain forests, and deserts. The chapter concludes with a section on aquatic biomes. The marine biome and its life zones are presented. The freshwater biomes of lakes, ponds, rivers, and streams are discussed. The section ends with a discussion of estuaries.

Teaching Strategies and Activities

1. Have students research the desert biome in North America. Ask them to explain the adaptations of one desert plant and one desert animal to desert life.

2. To introduce the concept of behavioral barriers and territoriality, begin your lecture with a particular territorial behavior. For example, ask students, Why do birds sing? Then ask the students when they think this territorial behavior would be most evident. What advantages do territorial behaviors give animals? What disadvantages? Do people exhibit any kind of territorial behavior?

After this discussion, assign independent study projects on the territorial behaviors of particular birds, mammals, or insects.

3. Have students prepare a bulletin board showing the differences between the types of trees in coniferous and deciduous forests. Display a map of the United States showing the areas in which these trees grow.

Answer Key to Section Reviews

Biogeography (p. 757)

1. Biogeography is the study of the distribution of plants and animals throughout the world.
2. *Active dispersal* is the movement of organisms by their own energy. *Passive dispersal* is the movement of organisms by other animals, wind, moving water, or other physical factors.
3. The three types of barriers that prevent the dispersal of organisms are geographical, ecological, and behavioral barriers.

Terrestrial Biomes (p. 765)

1. The three major climate zones of the earth are the tropical zone, the temperate zone, and the polar zone.
2. Ecotones are transition zones between biomes.
3. Permafrost is the permanently frozen soil of the tundra.
4. The trees in a coniferous forest are cone-bearing trees. The trees in a deciduous forest have broad leaves that are shed in the fall.
5. Vertical stratification is the characteristic of forests in which different kinds of plants grow at different heights above the forest floor.
6. Savannahs are grasslands that are scattered with trees.
7. The major terrestrial biomes are the tundra, coniferous forests, deciduous forests, tropical rain forests, grasslands, and the desert.

Aquatic Biomes (p. 770)

1. The two marine environments are the pelagic and the benthic.
2. Four factors that affect life in the marine biome are sunlight, temperature, salinity, and water pressure.
3. The saltwater biome contains dissolved salts. The freshwater biome contains little or none of the salts and other minerals found in the ocean. Lakes, ponds, rivers, and streams are several freshwater environments.
4. An estuary is a zone between a freshwater biome and a marine biome.

Teaching Aids for Chapter End Features

Laboratory Investigation 47
Climatograms (p. 771)

To facilitate the location of points in constructing the climatogram, use graph paper with 1-cm squares. Students can then estimate points by subdividing the squares using a metric ruler.

OBSERVATIONS AND CONCLUSIONS Part A:
1. The warmest month in both Albuquerque and Columbus is July.   2. The driest months in Albuquerque are November, January, and February; in Columbus, the driest month is October.   3. The coldest month in Albuquerque is January; in Columbus, February.   4. The rainfall is the lowest in Albuquerque during January, February, and November; in Columbus, during October.   5. Albuquerque has the warmer summers, and Columbus has the colder winters.   6. Columbus has the higher annual rainfall.   7. The greater fluctuations in average monthly rainfall occur in Columbus.   8. Albuquerque is in the desert biome; Columbus is in the temperate deciduous forest biome.   **Part B: 1.** The matchups are as follows: temperate deciduous forest—B; tundra—D; tropical rain forest—no climatogram represented; desert—E; taiga—A; grassland—C.   2. Answers will vary.   3. Answers will vary.

Review of Facts and Concepts (p. 772)

1. Some ways that organisms are dispersed are flying, swimming, and being transported by another animal, by the wind, or by moving water.
2. (a) An ecological barrier would prevent the fern spore from being dispersed. (b) An ecological barrier would stop the starfish. (c) A geographical barrier would prevent the kangaroo from migrating. (d) A behavioral barrier would prevent the snowshoe hare from going far from where it was born.
3. The dominant forms of vegetation in the tundra are grasses, lichens, mosses, and short, woody shrubs. Trees do not grow because the growing season is too short and because the permafrost prevents them from rooting and developing.
4. The taiga is the northernmost area of the coniferous forest. The dominant trees in coniferous forests are cone-bearing trees.
5. Refer to "Deciduous Forests," pages 760–61.
6. The tropical rain forest has the highest biomass of any biome because of its high level of rainfall and warm temperatures.

7. Most *grasslands* have no trees; a *savannah* is a type of grassland that is scattered with trees.

8. Plants are adapted in several ways to live in a desert biome: *succulents* can store water in their stems, which are covered with a thick outer skin and with spines that reduce evaporation; *perennials* have a waxy coating that reflects heat and prevents water loss; *annuals* mature quickly during the brief moist spells, flower, and die. Many desert animals burrow underground during the hottest part of the day or are active only at night when temperatures are relatively low.

9. *Sagebrush* is found in the desert. *Caribou* roam the tundra. *Sequoias* grow in coniferous forests. *Kangaroos* inhabit grasslands. *Beech* and *maple trees* grow in deciduous forests.

10. The main abiotic factors affecting the types of organisms in aquatic biomes are the amount of available oxygen and carbon dioxide, the temperature, the presence of dissolved materials, and the amount of sunlight.

11. Organisms that live in the intertidal zone must be able to live without water for some of the time. They must also be able to attach themselves to rocks or burrow into the sand so they will not be washed out to sea.

12. The penetration of sunlight, low water pressure, and a relatively constant water temperature make the neritic zone the most productive life zone in the ocean.

13. The absence of sunlight, extreme water pressure, little food, and cold temperatures limit the kinds of organisms that can live in the abyssal zone.

14. *Oligotrophic lakes* are deep and contain little plankton. These lakes have small amounts of nutrients and a good oxygen supply. *Eutrophic lakes* are shallow and contain large populations of plankton, many nutrients, and a low oxygen supply.

15. The water movement and the type of stream or river bed affect the types of organisms living in it.

16. Most of the plants in estuaries are marsh grasses, seaweeds, and phytoplankton. Some of the animals that live in estuaries are shrimp, oysters, clams, crabs, and many kinds of fishes.

Extensions and Applications (p. 773)

1. Avoid having different students use the same plants and animals. After students prepare their maps, you may want to have them transfer their information to a large class map outline.

2. Have the students prepare labels indicating where each plant was found, what type of plant it is, who found it, and on what date it was found.

3. Make sure the students research procedures for preparing an aquatic or terrestrial biome. Constructing a type of biome that is not available naturally in your area might be interesting.

48 Conservation

Chapter Objectives: See page 774.

Chapter Overview

The opening section of this chapter distinguishes between renewable and nonrenewable resources. Food is presented as a variable renewable resource. The discussion of soil examines contouring, terracing, strip cropping, and windbreaks as soil conservation methods. A description of water as a resource follows. The text discusses fossil fuels as nonrenewable sources of energy and in relation to alternative sources of energy such as solar energy, ocean waves, geothermal energy, or wind. Also presented as renewable resources are plants and wildlife.

The discussion of environmental pollution begins with definitions of biodegradable and nonbiodegradable substances. Under the heading of atmospheric pollution, the text explains temperature inversions, the greenhouse effect, photochemical smog, and radiation pollution. Next follows a discussion of water pollution, which includes sewage, agricultural pollution, and industrial pollution. Brief discussions on land pollution and pollution controls conclude the chapter.

Teaching Strategies and Activities

1. Generally, the number of bacteria present in soil is a direct indicator of the soil's fertility. Have the students bring in samples of soil from various places. Students should weigh out 1 g of each type of soil. Place the soil sample into a bottle containing 99 mL of sterile saline, cap it, and shake it vigorously for 2 minutes. Then have the students transfer 1 mL of the suspension into another bottle of 99 mL of sterile saline. Tell them to shake this bottle vigorously for another 2 minutes and then place 1 mL of the solution into a sterile empty petri dish. Pour in liquid nutrient agar that has been cooled to about 45 °C, and gently swirl to mix. When the mixture hardens, put the plates upside down in a warm place for a

week. Then count the colonies and compare the number of bacteria in each soil sample. How do the samples compare in numbers of bacteria?

2. Divide the class into four groups. Assign one pair of groups the topic of fossil fuels versus nuclear power, and the other two groups solar versus geothermal power. Each pair of groups should then prepare for a debate.

3. Does your area have a particular pollution problem? What factors cause this problem? Ask the students to do written reports on the problem and its possible solutions.

Answer Key to Section Reviews

Natural Resources (p. 780)

1. Conservation is an activity in which attempts are made to find ways of satisfying the needs of human beings while doing the least damage to the environment and the organisms that live in it.
2. *Renewable resources* are resources that can be used and replaced. *Nonrenewable resources* cannot be replaced.
3. *Erosion* is the carrying away of soil by natural forces. *Depletion* is the removal of organic matter and minerals from the soil.
4. Soil conservation methods include crop rotation, contour farming, terracing, strip cropping, and the use of windbreaks.
5. Desalination is the process of removing salts from seawater.

Environmental Pollution (p. 786)

1. Pollution is the contamination of the atmosphere, water, or soil with undesirable materials.
2. *Biodegradable substances* are capable of being naturally broken down by living things in the environment. *Nonbiodegradable substances* are not broken down by living things.
3. Biomagnification is the buildup of chemicals in members of a biological system.
4. Answers will vary.
5. Thermal pollution is the addition of undesirable heat to the water of a lake or river.

Pollution Controls (p. 787)

1. A catalytic converter is a device in an automobile that chemically changes carbon monoxide and unburned hydrocarbons in the exhaust to carbon dioxide and water vapor.
2. Control methods for atmospheric pollution include charcoal filters, chemical filters, and catalytic converters.

Teaching Aids for Chapter End Features

Laboratory Investigation 48
Densities of Polluted and Unpolluted Water (p. 788)

Several days before the investigation, "pollute" a sample of tap water by adding various foreign substances, such as organic matter, sand, clay, salt, empty cans, or paper.

OBSERVATIONS AND CONCLUSIONS 1. Sample A should be clear. Sample B should be cloudy. 2. The "polluted" water should have the higher density. 3. Answers will vary. 4. After a second refiltering, the density of the "polluted" water should be closer to that of distilled water. The filter paper traps particles, thereby reducing the density of the "polluted" water.

Review of Facts and Concepts (p. 790)

1. Natural resources are the living and nonliving "materials" of the earth.
2. Plants, animals, soil, water, and air are examples of renewable resources. Coal and petroleum are two nonrenewable resources.
3. Once trees are removed, their root systems die, and the soil can be easily blown away or washed away.
4. Constantly growing a single kind of crop on the same land may deplete the soil of specific organic materials and minerals.
5. Windbreaks act as barriers to the wind.
6. Desalination is the process of removing salt from seawater. Disadvantages are that the process is expensive and that it uses large amounts of energy.
7. Three fossil fuels are coal, oil, and natural gas.
8. Sources of energy other than the burning of fossil fuels are geothermal energy, ocean waves, wind, and sunlight.
9. An endangered species is an organism that is close to extinction. Examples will vary.
10. Reforestation is the practice of renewing the forest by seeding and planting new trees to replace mature trees that have been cut down.
11. A temperature inversion occurs when a cool layer of air becomes trapped below warm air.
12. Carbon dioxide in the atmosphere prevents solar heat from leaving the atmosphere. This process is known as the greenhouse effect.
13. Photochemical smog is a mixture of smoke, gases, and fog caused by chemical reactions of hydrocarbons initiated by the light from the sun.

14. Eutrophication is an oxygen-depletion process that takes place in a body of water.
15. Answers will vary. Students should include a food chain of sorts to explain their answers. Another example is that pesticides usually do not break up in the environment and disappear. Falling to the ground after being sprayed in the air, pesticides can be washed into streams and other bodies of water that empty into oceans. In this way, they can travel to areas far away from the original spraying and affect animals in distant regions.
16. Acid rain forms when moisture from the air combines with nitrogen oxide gases and sulfur dioxide gases and falls to the earth with rain or snow.
17. Answers will vary.

Extensions and Applications (p. 790)

1. Students can repeat the activity in various indoor locations.
2. You may want to perform this exercise as a student field trip.
3. Select specific organisms that are the targets of pesticides, and assign them to groups of students. Ask students to find out what methods are used to control the organisms. Have the students express their opinions on whether the spraying of large areas, such as entire towns, is good or bad for the area's ecology. The students should back up their opinions with researched material.

Unit Teaching Aids

Perspectives in Biology

Oceans as a Food Resource Versus Ecological Balance (p. 791)

1. The nutritive values of foods are available from many sources. Two good starting points for this research are encyclopedias and college-level textbooks in the field of nutrition. Additional information may be available from museums, aquaria, and professional organizations such as the American Dietetic Association in Chicago, Illinois. Information regarding the use of seaweeds in various cultures is available from the above

sources as well as from the information offices of the embassies of countries such as Japan, Indonesia, and so on.
2. A debate format may be useful here. Information may be requested from the U.S. Department of Agriculture in Washington, D.C.

Field Trip Suggestions

1. Visit a local aquarium. If there is no aquarium in your area, visit a local pet store that sells fishes. Ask questions of aquarium or store personnel about the care of sea life in captivity.
2. A trip to a museum of natural history is certainly appropriate during a unit on ecology. Many natural history museums offer exhibits dealing with ecology.
3. If a visit to a botanical garden is possible, have the students try to identify specific ecosystems as they walk through the garden.

Audio-Visual Materials

Distributions of Plants and Animals, film, EBE
Ecology at Work: A Study of the Sea Otter, set/3 sound filmstrips, PHM
Ecology at Work: The Case of the Bighorn Sheep, set/2 sound filmstrips, PHM
Ecology: Interactions and Environments, set/7 sound filmstrips, PHM
Ecosystem in Darkness, sound filmstrip, HBJ
Investigations in Ecology, slide program, DGAV
New Ways to Grow Plants, sound filmstrip, HBJ
Plant-Animal Communities Series, set/4 films, Cor
Succession: From Sand Dune to Forest, film, EBE
What Is Ecology?, sound filmstrip, PHM

Reading Resources for Teachers

Ehrlich, P., et al. *Ecoscience: Population, Resources and Environment*. San Francisco: Freeman.
Kormondy, E. *Concepts of Ecology*. Englewood Cliffs, N.J.: Prentice-Hall.
Time-Life Series. *The World We Live In*. New York: Time, Inc.
Troeh, F., J. Hobbs, and R. Donahue. *Soil and Water Conservation*. Englewood Cliffs, N.J.: Prentice-Hall.

GUIDE TO MATERIALS AND SUPPLIERS

Laboratory Materials and Equipment

Item	Quantity per Class of 32 Students	Laboratory Investigation
Acetic acid (5%)	100 mL	25
Agar, nutrient	12 100-mL pkgs	15, 17
Alcohol lamps or Bunsen burners	8	4, 15, 17, 28
Ammonium hydroxide solution, dilute	100 mL	6
Ant colony	8	29
Bags, plastic, with ties	16	1
Balances, triple-beam	8	48
Balls, small rubber	8	33
Beakers		
100-mL	24	7, 28, 48
250-mL	8	6, 21, 30
500-mL	24	4, 7, 46
1000-mL	8	30
Bolts or screws, ¼″ × 1½″, round-head	32	14
Bones, assorted (beef, pork, and chicken)	8 sets	35
Bones, assorted, soaked in vinegar	8 sets	35
Bottles with screw-on cap	16	13
Bottles, clear plastic, squeeze	8	44
Bottles, 207-mL (7-oz)	8	29
Bottles, 2-L plastic	8	29
Bromthymol blue solution	2 liters	2, 7
Calorie chart	32	39
Cheesecloth	1 pkg	6
Cigarettes		
filter-tipped	1 pkg	44
unfiltered	1 pkg	44
Clams	32	27
Clam shells	32	27
Clay, modeling	1 kg	44
Clay, powdered	1 kg	4
Cobalt chloride test paper	1 pkg	45
Corks, no. 12	8	46
Cotton	3 boxes	16, 29, 37
Cotton swabs, sterile	1 bag	15, 17, 44
Cover slips	20 boxes	5, 16, 18, 19, 20, 21, 22, 23, 25, 26, 27, 28, 35
Cultures		
Amoeba	2	16, 46
Blepharisma	1	46
brine shrimp	1	25
Chlorella	1	28
Daphnia	1	28

Item	Quantity per Class of 32 Students	Laboratory Investigation
Euglena	2	16, 46
Hydra	1	25
Paramecium	2	16, 46
Planaria	1	26
Rhizopus	1	18
Spirogyra	1	18
yeasts	1	17
Dialysis membrane	1 small roll	36
Dissecting kits	32	5, 18, 19, 21, 22, 23, 27, 28, 29, 45, 48
Envelopes		
small	32	43
large	6	43
Eyedroppers	48	5, 7, 15, 16, 18, 22, 23, 25, 26, 28, 46
Feathers, assorted	8 sets of 3 types	33
Ferns, sporophyte and gametophyte generations	32 of each generation	19
Filter paper	1 pkg	4, 48
Floral wire	12 meters	14
Flowers, two species	32 of each species	23
Frog eggs and tadpoles	8 sets	31
Funnels	8	4, 30, 36, 48
Gelatin, powdered	2 kg	4, 6
Glucose solution (20%)	300 mL	7
Goggles, safety	32	4
Goldfish	16	30, 37
Graduated cylinders		
25-mL	8	36
100-mL	16	6, 7, 48
Hot plate	1	30
Ice	8 5-lb bags	7, 26, 28, 30
Ink, red	1 bottle	21
Iodine solution	1 16-oz bottle	5, 18, 36
Iron filings	1 1-lb jar	4
Jars		
small, with lid	40	4, 31
large (½-gal–1-gal), with lid	20	12, 31, 36, 37
Labels	1 box	46
Leaves, five species	32 of each species	22
Lens paper	1 pkg	8
Liver, fresh beef	1 pkg	28
Magnets, bar	8	4
Magnifying glasses or hand lenses	32	2, 3, 18, 19, 20, 21, 26, 27, 28, 29, 31, 33
Matches	1 box	44
Medicine droppers	48	5, 7, 15, 16, 18, 22, 23, 25, 26, 28, 46
Meter sticks	16	10
Methyl cellulose solution	1 4-oz bottle	16
Methylene blue stain	1 4-oz bottle	5, 15, 27
Microscopes	32	

Item	Quantity per Class of 32 Students	Laboratory Investigation
Microscope slides		
depression	50	16, 25, 26
flat	10 boxes	5, 15, 18, 19, 20, 21, 22, 23, 26, 27, 28, 35
Microscope slides, prepared		
dicot leaf	32	22
monocot leaf	32	22
onion root tip	16	8
Mosses, sporophyte and gametophyte generations	32 of each generation	19
Nets, aquarium	8	31
Nuts		
¼-inch	32	14
acorn, ¼-inch	32	14
Onions, small	8	5
Pan or dish, shallow	8	29
Paper		
black construction	8 8″ × 12″ sheets	29
green construction	20 8″ × 12″ sheets	11, 12
white construction	200 8″ × 12″ sheets	3, 11, 12, 26, 34
graph	250 sheets	42, 46, 47
typing	8 sheets	20
waxed	1 box	45
Pen, felt-tip (tip and insides removed)	8	44
Pencils		
colored	16 each of two colors	24, 42
grease	32	7, 15, 17, 24, 26, 45
Petri dishes	40	15, 17, 24, 26, 37
Petroleum jelly (Vaseline)	1 large jar	28, 45
Phenolphthalein solution (1%)	2 16-oz bottles	2, 6
Pictures		
mammals (assorted)	8 sets	34
reptiles (assorted)	8 sets	32
Pine cones, female (2 yrs)	8	20
Pine branches with male and female cones	8 each	20
Pine branches with needles (two species)	8 of each species	20
Pipe cleaners, 15 cm long	32 pieces	14
Plants		
bean	8	21
corn	8	21
oxalis	8	24
Plant leaf with stem	16	45
Plastic wrap	1 roll	29
Pliers, needle-nose	16	14
Potatoes, medium-sized	8	1
Razor blades, single-edged	40	21, 23, 26, 35, 46
Ring stands with clamps	8	48
Rods, glass stirring	8	36
Rubber bands	20	6
Rubber stoppers, one-hole test tube	24	7
Rulers, metric	32	14, 41, 42, 47

Item	Quantity per Class of 32 Students	Laboratory Investigation
Sand, beach	2 kg	2
Salt	2.4 kg	4
Scale, bath or medical	1	10, 39
Scissors	32 pairs	5, 19, 21, 28, 36
Screwdrivers	16	14, 27
Seeds		
corn	1 bag	24
grass	1 bag	21
pine	1 bag	20
radish	1 bag	21
Shoeboxes	8	24
Soil		
potting	2 kg	2
sandy	2 kg	29
Sphygmomanometers	8	40
Spoons, plastic	16	2
Starch solution	20 liters	36
Stethoscopes	8	40
Straws, drinking	1 box	7, 28
String	10 meters	36
Sugar solution	1 liter	2
Sulfur, powdered	1 1-lb box	4
Tangrams (Chinese geometric puzzles)	32	43
Tape, masking	4 rolls	13, 24, 29, 34, 44, 45, 46
Tape measures	16	42
Test tubes	40	4, 7
Test tube holders	8	4, 15
Test tube racks	8	4
Thermometers, Celsius	8	7, 30
Toothpicks, flat	1 box	5, 15, 25, 26, 28
Towels, paper	2 rolls	1, 4, 5, 18, 24
Trays		
cardboard	16	2
dissecting	32	27
Tripods	8	28
Tubing, rubber (to fit over wide end of dropper)	10 meters	7
Tumblers, plastic, large	64	45
Washers, metal		
1/4-inch	64	14
$\frac{5}{16}$-inch	32	14
Water		
aquarium	1 L	26
distilled	1 L	48
polluted	1 L	48
pond	10 L	31
sterile	1 L	17
tap, aged	10 L	46
Wire gauze	8	28
Wire loops	64	17
Yeast, dry, packaged	12 pkgs	2, 7

Laboratory Preparations

Many of the solutions, test papers, and stains used in the Laboratory Investigations can be prepared in the school laboratory. The directions for making these preparations are provided in the Unit and Chapter Discussions. However, you may find it useful to mix stock solutions at the beginning of the school year. Instructions for preparing many of the laboratory solutions, reagents, test papers, and so on that are used in the in-text Laboratory Investigations follow.

Agar Plates

Mix 15 g of agar powder in 1 L of distilled water. Autoclave the agar mixture at 121 °C under 15 psi for 15 minutes. Sterilize the petri dishes in a dry-air oven at 177 °C for 2 hours. Pour the agar into the sterilized petri dishes.

Aged Tap Water

Store tap water in a large, open container for at least 24 hours before using it.

Bromthymol Blue Solution

Add 0.5 g of bromthymol blue to 500 mL of distilled water. Then add enough of this solution to 1 L of water to turn the water blue-green. Add 0.4% sodium hydroxide, one drop at a time, until the water turns a definite blue.

Cobalt Chloride Paper

Immerse sheets of filter paper in a 5% aqueous solution of cobalt chloride. Dry the paper in an oven at 40 °C. Cut the paper into strips approximately 12 mm × 35 mm. *Note: Store the strips in an airtight container.*

Cobalt Chloride Solution 5%

Dissolve 5 g of cobalt chloride in 100 mL of distilled water.

Gelatin "Cells"

Mix 2 packages of colorless gelatin with 10 mL of phenolphthalein. Pour the mixture into a clean, empty quart (946-mL) milk carton. Allow the gelatin to cool and gel. *Note: Keep refrigerated until needed.*

Glucose Solution

Dissolve 100 g of dextrose in 500 mL of distilled water.

Iodine Solution

Add 1 g of iodine crystals and 3.5 g of potassium iodide to 300 mL of distilled water. Stir until the solids are dissolved.

Lugol's Solution

Dissolve 10 g of potassium iodide in 100 mL of distilled water. Then add 5 g of iodine crystals, and stir until the solids are dissolved. *Note: Keep refrigerated until needed.*

Methylene Blue Stain

Dissolve 0.3 g of methylene blue in 30 mL of absolute (95%) alcohol. Add 100 mL of distilled water. Set the solution aside for 24 hours before using.

Nutrient (Sugar) Solutions *(3 variations)*

a. Dissolve 100 g of table sugar (sucrose) in 1 L of water.
b. Dissolve 100 mL of corn syrup in 1 L of water.
c. Dissolve 100 mL of molasses in 1 L of water.

Sodium Hydroxide Solution 0.4%

Add 1 L of distilled water to a flask. Dissolve 4 g of sodium hydroxide pellets in the water. *Caution: During the preparation of this solution, heat is given off. Also, sodium hydroxide solution is caustic.*

Starch Solution

Add 3 g of soluble starch to 500 mL of water. Boil the mixture until the starch dissolves. Add the boiled starch solution to 5 L of cold water. Stir.

Test Tube Chromatography Solution

Mix 9 parts petroleum ether to one part acetone. *Caution: Both compounds are poisonous. Keep room well ventilated.*

Yeast Culture

Dissolve 20 g of glucose in 200 mL of distilled water. Add a package of dry yeast. Stir the mixture until the yeast cells are suspended.

Suppliers of Laboratory Materials and Equipment

Carolina Biological Supply Company
Burlington, NC 27215

Damon Corporation
Educational Division
80 Wilson Way
Westwood, MA 02090

Edmund Scientific Company
101 East Gloucester Pike
Barrington, NJ 08007

Fisher Scientific Company
Stansi Educational Materials Division
4901 West LeMoyne Avenue
Chicago, IL 60651

Hubbard Scientific Company
1946 Raymond Drive
Northbrook, IL 60062

LaPine Scientific Company
6001 Knox Avenue
Chicago, IL 60629

Nasco International, Inc.
901 Janesville Avenue
Fort Atkinson, WI 53538

Nova Scientific Corporation
111 Tucker Street
P.O. Box 500
Burlington, NC 27215

Prentice-Hall, Inc.
Educational Book Division
P.O. Box 900
Englewood Cliffs, NJ 07632

Sargent-Welch Scientific Company
7300 North Linder Avenue
Skokie, IL 60077

Science Kit, Inc.
777 East Park Drive
Tonawanda, NY 14150

Ward's Natural Science Establishment, Inc.
P.O. Box 1712
Rochester, NY 14603

Suppliers of Audio-Visual Materials

BFA
BFA Educational Media
2211 Michigan Avenue
Santa Monica, CA 90404

Cor
Coronet Films
65 East South Water Street
Chicago, IL 60601

DGAV
Denoyer-Geppert Audio-Visuals
5235 Ravenswood Avenue
Chicago, IL 60640

EBE
Encyclopaedia Britannica Educational Corporation
425 North Michigan Avenue
Chicago, IL 60611

Eye
Eye Gate
146-01 Archer Avenue
Jamaica, NY 11435

HBJ
Harcourt Brace Jovanovich
757 Third Avenue
New York, NY 10017

MGH
McGraw-Hill Films
1221 Avenue of the Americas
New York, NY 10020

PHM
Prentice-Hall Media
ServCode ZT
150 White Plains Road
Tarrytown, NY 10591

SSS
Science Software Systems, Inc.
11899 West Pico Boulevard
West Los Angeles, CA 90064

PRENTICE-HALL Biology

PRENTICE-HALL
BIOLOGY

Sandra Gottfried

Science Instructor
Ona M. Wilcox School of Nursing
Middlesex Memorial Hospital
Middletown, Connecticut

Gerry Madrazo, Jr.

Instructional Supervisor
  of Science, K-12
Guilford County Public Schools
Greensboro, North Carolina

LaMoine Motz

Director of Science, Health,
  and Outdoor Education
Oakland Schools
Pontiac, Michigan

Joseph Olenchalk

Chairman, Science
  Department
Antioch Senior High School
Antioch, California

Dorothea Sinclair

Biology Teacher
Bishop Moore High School
Orlando, Florida

Gerald Skoog

Professor and Chairperson
  of Secondary Education
Texas Tech University
Lubbock, Texas

Prentice-Hall, Inc., Englewood Cliffs, New Jersey

Supplementary Materials

Annotated Teacher's Edition

Laboratory Manual

Annotated Teacher's Edition,
   Laboratory Manual

Test Bank with Answer Key

DIAL-A-TEST:™ Customized Testing Service

Teacher's Resource Book

Biology Courseware

Third Edition

ISBN 0-13-699372-9

10 9 8 7 6 5 4 3

Prentice-Hall of Australia, Pty. Ltd., Sydney
Prentice-Hall Canada, Inc., Toronto
Prentice-Hall Hispanoamericana, S.A., Mexico
Prentice-Hall of India Private Ltd., New Delhi
Prentice-Hall International, Inc., London
Prentice-Hall of Japan, Inc., Tokyo
Prentice-Hall of Southeast Asia Pte. Ltd. Singapore
Editora Prentice-Hall do Brasil Ltda., Rio de Janeiro
Whitehall Books Limited, Wellington, New Zealand

Cover Photograph: This photograph shows a honeybee (*Apis mellifera*) about to land on a flower. After landing on it, the honeybee sucks up a drop of nectar with its long tongue. The nectar that the honeybee collects is brought back to the hive and is used to make honey. (S. Dalton/Animals Animals)
Back Cover: (from top to bottom) **Col. 1,** S. Wilson/ DPI; E.R. Degginger; A. Lax/Photo Researchers; T. Nebbia/DPI; E. Stone; **Col. 2 ,** M. Kage/Peter Arnold; M. Kage/Peter Arnold, D. Woodward/Taurus Photos; Dagmar/Focus on Sports; S. Wilson/DPI

Contributors

LABORATORY INVESTIGATIONS

Carol D. Hampton
Professor of Science Education
East Carolina University
Greenville, North Carolina

Carolyn H. Hampton
Professor of Science Education
East Carolina University
Greenville, North Carolina

CAREERS

Jenny Tesar
Bethel, Connecticut

CLOSE-UPS

Janet Taylor
Montclair, New Jersey

PERSPECTIVES IN BIOLOGY

Warren Marchioni
Biology Instructor
Montclair High School
Montclair, New Jersey

Reading Consultant

Patricia N. Schwab
Chairman, Department of Education
Guilford College
Greensboro, North Carolina

Unit Reviewers

Linda Laine   (Units 1, 4)
Science Department Chairman
Minneapolis Public Schools
Minneapolis, Minnesota

Joseph S. Bonita   (Units 2, 3)
Supervisor of Science
Kingston City School District
Kingston, New York

Harry J. Gross   (Unit 5)
Chairman, Science Department
Beaverton High School
Beaverton, Oregon

Julia C. Williams   (Units 6, 7)
Science Department Head
Biology Teacher
Reidsville Senior High School
Reidsville, North Carolina

Maria C. Vismor   (Units 8, 9)
Biology Teacher
Open Campus East
DeKalb School System
Stone Mountain, Georgia

Jane Abbott   (Unit 10)
Science Department Chairperson
Waterville High School
Waterville, Maine

Contents

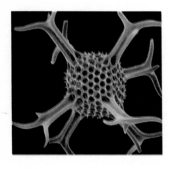

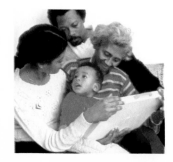

LABORATORY INVESTIGATIONS

CAREERS

CLOSE-UPS

NOBEL PRIZE WINNERS

Preface

Prentice-Hall Biology is designed to meet the needs of students in a full year introductory course in high school biology. The text can be used effectively with students of varying abilities and different interests. It can also be adapted easily to a wide range of teaching styles.

The structure of the text allows for flexibility in presenting the material. Early units present such basic topics as biological classification and scientific methodology, cell structure and function, and the variety and continuity of life. Other units deal with the simplest organisms, the protists, as well as more complex forms of life, the plants and animals. Two units focus on the anatomy, physiology, and development of human beings and one unit treats ecological interactions. The units need not be taught in order but can be adapted to any sequence that best meets the curriculum.

The text includes important features that are designed to enhance student mastery of the material. Each chapter includes many pedagogical aids. For example, science terms are emphasized by boldface or italic type. Other aids include chapter objectives, section review questions, marginal notes, and end-of-chapter exercises. In addition, Careers and Close-ups provide students with views of working scientists. Each chapter includes an optional laboratory investigation that allows the student to participate actively in the acquisition of scientific knowledge.

Prentice-Hall Biology gives students the opportunity to behave like scientists in order to learn science and its applications. The text is the basic tool for stimulating research from which students gain first-hand knowledge of scientific methodology. In doing research, students also benefit by learning to work independently or as group members to achieve meaningful objectives.

Prentice-Hall Biology presents science as a process that involves research, experimentation, and the development of theories, which can hold great explanatory and predictive power. These theories are presented in an intellectually honest way as scientists have conceived them. All theories are tentative and await further modification and refinement. This approach reflects the challenges and intellectual rewards available to students in the ever-changing discipline of science.

UNIT ONE

Introduction to Biology

For an overview of this unit, including field trip suggestions, a bibliography, and a list of audio-visual materials, see pages T–25 to T–31. You may want to check the Laboratory Investigations in this unit so that materials may be ordered, gathered, or prepared in advance.

Living things can be found on or beneath the surface of the earth, thousands of meters beneath the oceans, or kilometers into the atmosphere. Each kind of living thing is unique. Living things vary in size from single-celled living things, such as an amoeba, to many-celled living things, such as the blue whale. Every kind of living thing has distinct physical characteristics and kinds of behavior. However, all living things have basic similarities in structure and function. The fact that certain types of structures and functions are necessary to life accounts for these similarities.

1   What Is Biology?

2   The Living Organism

3   Classification of Organisms

Like all birds, mallards have unique characteristics such as feathers. Mallards also have characteristics that they share with other organisms such as the presence of limbs.

1 What Is Biology?

Experiments provide biologists with scientific information.

Chapter Objectives *After completing this chapter, you will be able to:*

a ■ Explain what is meant by the science of biology. p. 15
b ■ List and describe some of the major contributors to the science of biology. p. 15
c ■ Explain what is meant by scientific method. p. 17
d ■ Explain the meaning of hypothesis and theory. p. 18
e ■ State the importance of the metric system. p. 19
f ■ Compare the characteristics of light and electron microscopes. p. 21

For teaching aids for this chapter, including a chapter overview and teaching strategies, see pages T–25 to T–27. The page number next to each chapter objective refers to the text page where the information needed to fulfill the objective begins.

For hundreds of years, people were fearful of natural events. To account for unexplained happenings, they often turned to notions from folklore or magic, such as the existence of "spirits" in the bloodstream to explain the movement of blood. Overshadowed by superstition and fear, the development of *science* proceeded slowly. In time, science became an organized, ongoing inquiry into the world of living and nonliving things. This inquiry has produced an understanding of the facts and processes of nature.

Scientific study is usually divided into two parts. *Pure science* involves the search for basic knowledge about living and nonliving things. *Applied science* uses this knowledge in practical ways. For example, scientists searching for basic knowledge may discover the effect of different types of soil on the growth of certain plants. Scientists may then apply this information to determine what kind of fertilizer should be developed to produce the greatest growth of a particular crop.

You may want to have your students gather some specific information on folklore and superstitions that were used to explain the occurrence of natural events.

The Science of Biology

One of the most important qualities of human thought is curiosity. Throughout history, people have been challenged by the mysteries of their bodies and of the living things around them. They were curious about how living things developed, grew, reproduced, and died. They wanted to know what caused disease and how to fight it. They wanted to know how life was produced and what sustained it. They wanted to solve the riddles of the vast diversity of life on the planet. Urged on by their curiosity, they began to try to figure out the functions of different **organisms,** or living things. The study of living things is called **biology.**

Important Biologists

Biology did not begin to emerge as a true science until well into the seventeenth century. Following are some biologists who have made major contributions to the science of biology.

At this point, you may want to have your students find out how other scientists, such as William Harvey, Alexander Fleming, Louis Agassiz, and Robert Koch, contributed to the science of biology.

Figure 1-1 Louis Pasteur discovered that diseases were spread by bacteria. What other contribution did Pasteur make to the science of biology?

Pasteur disproved the idea that small organisms develop from nonliving material.

Anton van Leeuwenhoek (LĀ-vən-hook) Using his hand-held *microscope,* van Leeuwenhoek, a seventeenth-century Dutch merchant, was the first person to see one-celled organisms. A microscope is an instrument that enlarges the image of very small objects so that they can be studied. Throughout his life, van Leeuwenhoek drew and described microscopic organisms as well as the microscopic parts of larger organisms, such as flies and other insects. Van Leeuwenhoek is sometimes referred to as the father of *microbiology.* Microbiology is the study of *microorganisms,* or microscopic organisms.

Robert Hooke Hooke, a seventeenth-century British scientist, also viewed small units of organisms through a microscope. Hooke recognized these units as the basic structures of all living things and named them **cells.**

Louis Pasteur Pasteur, a nineteenth-century French scientist, disproved the idea that small organisms developed from nonliving material. He also showed that microorganisms caused disease. Pasteur's work led to the development of the science of *bacteriology,* the study of one-celled organisms called *bacteria.*

Charles Darwin Darwin, a British scientist, wrote a book called *On the Origin of Species by Natural Selection,* published in 1859. In this book, Darwin discussed a theory of *evolution,* or change, in plants and animals.

15

Figure 1-2 Working with fruit flies, Thomas Hunt Morgan studied the processes by which characteristics are handed down from one generation to the next.

Among other things, his theory explains that organisms with slight advantages over other organisms have a greater chance of survival.

Gregor Mendel Mendel was an Austrian monk who lived in the nineteenth century. He grew pea plants to see how the offspring resembled their parents. His work led to the development of the science of *genetics*. Genetics is the study of the transmission of characteristics from an organism to its offspring.

Thomas Hunt Morgan Morgan was an American geneticist who studied how specific characteristics were passed from generation to generation. Morgan worked with a small insect called the fruit fly. In 1926, Morgan published his findings in a book entitled *The Theory of the Gene*.

James D. Watson and Francis Crick Watson is an American biologist and Crick is a British biologist. In 1953, they discovered the structure of *DNA*, the basic substance of *heredity*, or inherited characteristics. By assembling a model of DNA, they were able to explain how DNA stored and passed on hereditary information.

Branches of Biology

At this point, you may want to assign to several students the first of the Extensions and Applications at the end of this chapter.

The science of biology includes a tremendous amount of knowledge about living things, and the field is divided into many branches. Following are some examples of these branches.

Figure 1-3 Two of the main branches of biology are botany and zoology. Botany is the study of plants and zoology is the study of animals.

Botany is the study of plants.

Zoology is the study of animals.

Anatomy is the study of the structure of plants, animals, and other organisms.

Physiology is the study of the functions of plants, animals, and other organisms.

Some branches are further divided into more specialized areas of study. Following are some examples.

Cytology is the study of cells.

Embryology is the study of the formation and development of organisms in their earliest stages.

Exobiology is the study of the possible existence of living things in the universe other than on the earth.

Marine biology is the study of living things in oceans.

Paleontology is the study of prehistoric plants and animals.

Figure 1-4 Ornithology, the study of birds, is a specialized branch of biology.

SECTION REVIEW   Answers on page T–25.

1. Define biology.
2. Which scientists contributed to the science of microbiology? Bacteriology? Genetics?
3. Explain the relationship between cells and organisms.

Biological Investigation

Relationships and patterns exist among living things. By careful experimentation and observation, some of these relationships and patterns can be discovered. Once they have been found, scientists can use them as a basis for solving problems.

How do biologists and other scientists begin to solve problems? They approach the problem and make observations in a logical and orderly manner.

A Scientific Method

Usually, scientists follow a given procedure in solving a problem. However, most scientists agree that there is no single scientific method. Instead, there are many related scientific methods, each of which was developed by an investigator attempting to solve a particular problem. Even though scientists follow a logical and orderly series of steps in solving problems, they may still fail to find the answers they seek.

Figure 1-5 Before a scientist attempts to solve a problem, all the important information related to the problem must be gathered and understood.

STATING THE PROBLEM   The first step in solving a problem is to identify and state the problem. The problem may be stated as a question—"Do green plants need sunlight to survive?"

GATHERING INFORMATION ON THE PROBLEM   After the problem is stated (or the question asked), a scientist carefully gathers all the material that is related to it. Much of this information is found in books, scientific journals, and magazines. For example, books and articles on botany might be consulted for information about green plants and their need for sunlight.

FORMING A HYPOTHESIS   After reading and studying all the material relating to the problem, the scientist arrives at a tentative explanation, or a **hypothesis** (hī-PAHTH-ə-sis). The hypothesis should account for and agree with all the information the scientist has already collected. If there is more than one hypothesis, the scientist chooses what appears to be the best one. A hypothesis for the example problem might be "Green plants need sunlight to survive."

EXPERIMENTING   In order to determine whether the hypothesis is correct, the scientist devises an experiment to test the effect of only one factor. This factor is called the **experimental factor.** The experimental factor in the example is sunlight.

The scientist usually sets up a second experiment along with the first, or experimental, setup. This second experiment is called the **control.** All of the factors are the same in both setups except the one factor being tested. By using a control, the scientist can recognize the effect of the experimental factor. In the example, the experiment can be performed with two similar green plants in the same type of soil. The control plant is placed in the sunlight. The experimental plant is placed in a dark place. Both plants are given the same amount of water. Because all conditions except light are the same for both plants, any difference that is later observed is the result of the difference in light conditions.

OBSERVING AND RECORDING INFORMATION   Throughout the experiment, the scientist records all observations. These records almost always include written notes and may also include drawings, photographs, graphs, and tables. The recorded information is called the *data*. Some of the data that might be recorded in the experiment to find whether sunlight is necessary for green plants include the amount of

Figure 1-6 Scientists use computers to organize, store, and retrieve vast amounts of information related to their research.

At this point, you may want to have your students do the Laboratory Investigation at the end of this chapter.

water given to each plant, how often each plant was watered, and the appearance and growth of each plant during the experiment. In this experiment, the scientist would have observed that the plant in the dark did not grow as well as the one in sunlight and eventually died.

Today, various types of computers help the scientist record, organize, and store important data. Suppose, for example, a scientist was doing an experiment that involved hundreds of plants. A computer would help the scientist handle the data more quickly and easily.

STATING A CONCLUSION Data are beneficial only when used to develop conclusions. Once the scientist has tested the hypothesis and collected data based on carefully made observations, a conclusion or conclusions are stated. In the example, the conclusion would be that sunlight is needed for the survival of the plant. This conclusion is based on the data that were recorded during the experiment.

Figure 1-7 The radish plant on the left was grown in the light while the radish plant on the right was grown in the dark. What conclusions can you draw from the appearance of the plants?

Radish plants grow better in light than in darkness.

As more and more data are collected that support a hypothesis, the hypothesis becomes a **theory**. A theory ties together many facts, explains their relationships, and suggests a possible explanation supported by considerable experimentation. All theories are subject to further testing, analysis, and revision. New data can strengthen or weaken a theory.

Figure 1-8 In the United States, distances and other measurements are often given in both the English and metric systems.

Biological Measurements

When gathering and recording specific data, the biologist uses units of measure. The *metric system* is a standard system of measurements and measurement units that is used internationally by all scientists. The metric system is a decimal system similar to the monetary system of the United States. It is based on multiples of ten.

Have your students list some everyday uses of the metric system of measurements.

Prefix	Meaning	Symbol
kilo-	1000	k
hecto-	100	h
deci-	0.1	d
centi-	0.01	c
milli-	0.001	m

Figure 1-9 Common Prefixes Used in the Metric System

In the metric system, a common unit of linear measurement is the *meter* (m). To measure *volume*, or the space an object takes up, the *liter* (1) is used. The *gram* (g) is a metric unit that is used to measure *mass*, the amount of matter in an object. Temperature is measured in the metric system in *degrees Celsius* (°C).

Prefixes are added to the units of the metric system to form larger or smaller units. For example, the prefix *milli-* means one-thousandth. Therefore, a millimeter (mm) is equal to one-thousandth of a meter. Figure 1-9 gives a list of common prefixes used in the metric system. The Reference Section at the end of this book contains a list of some of the more commonly used units of the metric system.

Biological Tools

Scientists use many tools in biological research, such as balances, dissecting instruments, and computers. One of the most important tools is the microscope. This instrument provides information about the basic structure of living things.

CAREER: Biology Teacher

High school biology provides students with their first comprehensive study of the world of living things. Biology teachers help students discover the many different kinds of life on the earth. Students learn how plants and animals function and why each lives in a certain environment. Biology teachers also help students appreciate the nature and value of scientific research.

Biology teachers generally teach a course of study that has been approved by their school district. They develop lesson plans that include lectures, discussions, films, laboratory work, tests, and other activities.

As well as teaching biology, teachers meet with parents and school personnel to discuss the progress of their students. By participating in workshops and continuing to take courses, biology teachers keep up to date on new developments in biology and in education.

In order to teach high school biology, a person must have a bachelor's degree. Many states require a master's degree as well. The person must be licensed by the state in which he or she

plans to teach. Each state has its own requirements for obtaining a license. These requirements include a good background in biology and education, as well as practice teaching under the supervision of a licensed teacher.

Some biology teachers teach in colleges, universities, and medical schools. While they do not need to be licensed, they generally need an advanced degree, such as a doctorate, in order to remain on the faculty. These teachers often combine their teaching with research work.

For further career information, write to National Association of Biology Teachers, 11250 Roger Bacon Drive, Reston, VA 22090.

Have you ever used a magnifying glass to read very small print? If you have, you actually used a type of microscope. A magnifying glass is considered a simple microscope because it has only one *lens*. A lens is a curved piece of glass that bends light rays as they pass through it. By bending the light rays, a lens enlarges the image of the object being viewed. Compound microscopes have more than one lens.

THE COMPOUND LIGHT MICROSCOPE The **compound light microscope** uses light to make the *specimen*, or object being studied, visible. Two important factors influence the function of a microscope. *Magnification* is the increase in size of the image of the specimen. *Resolution* is a measure of the clarity and sharpness of the image. Unfortunately, the more an image is magnified, the poorer is its resolution. The image becomes less sharp. This is a disadvantage of the compound light microscope.

Compound light microscopes were developed in the sixteenth century. Zacharias Janssen, a Dutch eyeglass-maker, is often credited with making the first compound microscope. Anton van Leeuwenhoek, a seventeenth-century scientist, further developed microscopes. His microscopes could enlarge objects by as much as 300 times. With his microscopes, van Leeuwenhoek viewed organisms that had never before been seen. Among his discoveries were microorganisms such as *protozoans* and bacteria.

The modern compound microscope has many lenses. See Figure 1-11. The *eyepiece* is found at the top of the microscope. Compound microscopes usually have from one to four *objectives* located at the bottom of the tube. Each objective contains lenses. Both eyepiece and objectives are marked with a numeral followed by the symbol ×. This indicates the number of times the lenses magnify a specimen. If the eyepiece is marked 10×, it magnifies an object 10 times. The total magnification of an object is determined by multiplying the magnifications of the eyepiece and the objective being used. The maximum useable magnification of a light microscope is more than 1000×.

THE ELECTRON MICROSCOPE Instead of using a beam of light to make the specimen visible, the **electron microscope** uses a beam of high-speed *electrons*. Electrons are negatively charged particles. These particles bounce off the specimen and form an image on a television screen or photographic plate. The first electron microscopes were used in 1931. Today, electron microscopes are found in many research laboratories and hospitals.

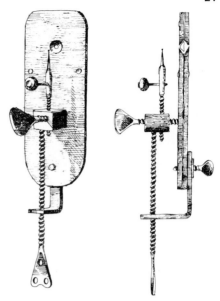

Figure 1-10 Van Leeuwenhoek's simple microscope shown from the back (left) and the side (right) could magnify objects a few hundred times.

At this point, you may want to assign to several students the second of the Extensions and Applications at the end of this chapter.

Figure 1-11 In compound light microscopes, light rays pass through the lenses of the objective and the eyepiece. By bending the light rays, the lenses can enlarge the image of a specimen a thousand times.

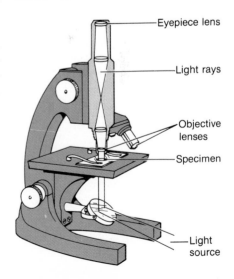

Eyepiece lens

Light rays

Objective lenses

Specimen

Light source

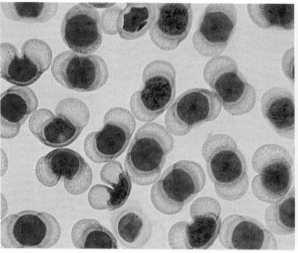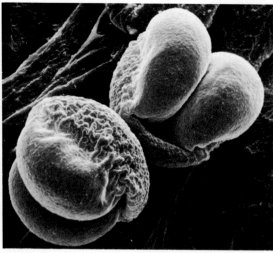

Figure 1-12   Pine pollen grains on the left are seen through a compound light microscope (400X). The pine pollen grains on the right were photographed through a scanning electron microscope (2000X). What advantage does the scanning electron microscope have over the compound light microscope?

The image of the specimen is larger and appears three-dimensional.

Sidelight

When a specimen is prepared for use with an electron microscope, it is sliced with a diamond knife into sections that are only a few millionths of a centimeter thick.

Electron microscopes can magnify objects hundreds of thousands of times. With electron microscopes, biologists can study the tiny details of the internal structure of cells. In addition to providing greater magnification, electron microscopes provide better resolution than do light microscopes.

There are two kinds of electron microscopes. In a *transmission electron microscope* (TEM), the object being viewed appears flat and thin. In a *scanning electron microscope* (SEM), the surface of the object appears three-dimensional and is seen in sharp focus. Therefore, the scanning electron microscope is better for seeing detail on the surface of an object. A disadvantage of electron microscopes is that they cannot be used to study living cells. The techniques that are used to prepare the specimen destroy cells.

SECTION REVIEW   Answers on pages T–25 to T–26.

1. How does a scientist usually investigate a problem?
2. What is the importance of a controlled experiment?
3. Define hypothesis.
4. Name three common units of measurement in the metric system.
5. Why is the microscope one of the most important tools in biology? Name two types of microscopes.

A Scientific Investigation

Purpose Scientists try to solve problems in a logical and orderly way. The purpose of this investigation is to apply a scientific method to find out whether or not light is necessary for the sprouting of potatoes.

Materials *(per group)* ● 1 medium-sized potato
● 2 plastic bags with twist ties ● Knife
● 2 paper towels

Procedure **1.** With the members of your group, discuss whether or not the potato needs light to sprout. On a sheet of paper, write a hypothesis based on your discussion. **2.** Copy the table on your paper. **3.** Carefully cut the potato in half. Count the number of eyes on each potato half and record the information in the table. **4.** Fold each paper towel repeatedly until you have a rectangle about 12 cm by 8 cm. Moisten the towels with water. Place a folded paper towel in each of the plastic bags. **5.** Place a potato half in each plastic bag with the cut surface on the paper towel. Tie each bag with a twist tie. **6.** Place one of the bags in a place that will receive light. Put the other bag in a dark place. **Note:** *Be sure that the potato halves remain on top of the paper towels and that both halves are kept at the same temperature.* **7.** After one week, open each bag and count the number of sprouts. Record the information in your table. **8.** To obtain the percentage of eyes sprouting, divide the number of sprouts by the number of eyes and multiply the result by 100. Record the results in the appropriate place in your table. **9.** Have one person from your group go to the chalkboard to record your group's data in the table that has been drawn by your teacher.

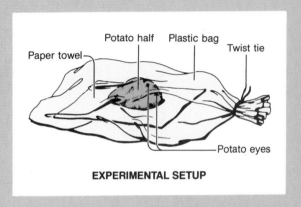

EXPERIMENTAL SETUP

Observations and Conclusions **1.** Compare the sprouts grown in the light with those grown in the dark. Is there a significant difference between the number of sprouts grown in the two potato halves? Explain your answer. **2.** Based on your observations, state a conclusion for this investigation. **3.** Compare the hypothesis that you stated at the beginning of this investigation with your conclusion. Does the experiment support your hypothesis? Why or why not? **4.** Which part of the investigation is the control? What is the experimental factor? **5.** After all the groups have recorded their data on the board, find the average percentages of sprouting for potato halves grown in light and for those grown in the dark. Record the class averages in a new table on the chalkboard. **6.** Which set of data is more reliable, that of your group or that of the class? Why? **7.** Do the results of your investigation agree with the results of the class? Explain your answer.

	Number of Eyes	Number of Eyes Sprouting	Percent of Eyes Sprouting
Light			
Dark			

CHAPTER SUMMARY

The Science of Biology   Science is defined as an organized, on-going inquiry into the world of living and nonliving things. Scientific study is divided into pure science and applied science. Pure science involves the search for basic knowledge about living and non-living things. Applied science uses this knowledge in practical ways.

Biology, the study of living things, is one of the main branches of science. Biology did not emerge as a true science until the smallest living unit of an organism, the cell, was discovered in the seventeenth century. Since then, the science of biology has made great strides.

Biological Investigation   Scientists usually follow a scientific method to solve a particular problem. After the problem is stated, scientists gather information concerning the problem and a hypothesis is formed. In order to determine whether the hypothesis is correct, scientists conduct experiments. During experimentation, scientists record observations and state conclusions. If scientists collect more and more data that support the hypothesis, the hypothesis becomes a theory.

All scientists use the international units of measure of the metric system. Scientists use the microscope to discover information about living things. The microscope enlarges the image of very small objects so that they can be studied. The light microscope uses lenses to magnify objects hundreds of times. The electron microscope uses beams of electrons to magnify objects hundreds of thousands of times.

CHAPTER VOCABULARY

biology
cell
compound light microscope
control
electron microscope

experimental factor
hypothesis
organism
theory

REVIEW of FACTS and CONCEPTS   Answers on pages T–26 to T–27.

On a separate sheet of paper, answer each of the following as completely as possible.

1. Why did scientific knowledge develop slowly centuries ago?
2. List some of the major contributors to biology. What were their contributions?
3. Name five branches of biology. What is studied in each branch?
4. Name and describe the steps that are often used in a scientific investigation.
5. Distinguish between the experimental setup and the control setup in an experiment.
6. Why is recording data important in a scientific investigation?
7. What is the metric system? Give two examples of metric measurements.
8. List some of the common prefixes that are added to units of the metric system. Give the meaning of each prefix.
9. Compare the characteristics of the compound light microscope with those of the electron microscope.
10. Distinguish between the following pairs of terms: meter and liter; magnification and resolution; scanning electron microscope and transmission electron microscope.

EXTENSIONS and APPLICATIONS   For additional information, see page T–27.

1. During the last 40 years, biologists have made great advances, especially in the fields of molecular biology, genetic engineering, and biochemistry. Choose one of these fields and find out more information about one specific development. Explain how this development contributed to the advancement of biology.

2. Using a magnifying glass and a compound light microscope, look at a lower-case letter from a piece of newspaper and a color photograph from a magazine. Sketch what you see for each. What are the differences in magnification and resolution of each instrument?

3. Devise an experiment to find out the effects of plant food on the growth of bean seeds. Include a control in your experiment. On posterboard, construct an outline showing the steps of the scientific method you used during this experiment. Include a table that summarizes your observations. State your conclusion and explain how you reached it.

SUGGESTED READINGS

Asimov, I., *A Short History of Biology*. Westport, Conn.: Greenwood Press.
This survey of the science of biology begins with the ancient Greeks and proceeds forward through time to the most recent discoveries. Along the way, readers are introduced to famous contributors to biology.

Dethier, V.G., *To Know a Fly*. San Francisco, Calif.: Holden-Day.
A biologist explains how to investigate the behavior and physiology of the common fly. Some experimental approaches of science are clearly illustrated.

Handler, P., ed., *Biology and the Future of Man*. London: Oxford University Press.
The range of the life sciences, beginning with the origin of organic molecules and ending with the possible role of biology in the future, is discussed.

Stehli, G., *The Microscope and How to Use It*. New York: Dover Publications.
This is an excellent source on the microscope and how to use it. It also contains many suggestions for investigations using the microscope.

2 The Living Organism

Newly hatched brine shrimp swim in a salt solution.

Chapter Objectives *After completing this chapter, you will be able to:*

a ▪ Explain the difference between abiogenesis and biogenesis. p. 27
b ▪ Describe the experiments of Redi and Spallanzani and explain their importance. p. 27
c ▪ Explain how Pasteur's experiments disproved the theory of abiogenesis. p. 30
d ▪ Distinguish between living and nonliving things. p. 32
e ▪ Explain the levels of organization in organisms. p. 36
f ▪ Describe the needs of living organisms. p. 37

For teaching aids for this chapter, including a chapter overview and teaching strategies, see pages T–27 to T–29. The page number next to each chapter objective refers to the text page where the information needed to fulfill the objective begins.

If you went outside for a walk, you could easily make a list of the living and nonliving things that you saw. However, some organisms appear to be nonliving. A pit of a cherry and brine shrimp eggs appear to be nonliving. Yet, if you plant the cherry seed, it grows and eventually becomes a living tree. When they are placed in water, brine shrimp eggs hatch into small shrimp. Biologists know that a nonliving thing, such as a pebble, cannot produce a living thing. Therefore, the cherry pit and the brine shrimp eggs are living because they produce living things.

What distinguishes a living thing from a nonliving thing or a living organism from a dead organism? These are questions that biologists have been asking for hundreds of years. Today, biologists explain life in terms of certain physical characteristics and chemical properties.

Abiogenesis and Biogenesis

Before the middle of the seventeenth century, most people thought that some living things developed from nonliving materials. This idea was known as **abiogenesis** (ā-bī-ō-JEN-ə-sis), or *spontaneous generation*. Some people thought that organisms such as frogs and fish were made from the mud at the bottom of a pond. For many years, people thought that decaying meat turned into *maggots*, a wormlike stage in the life cycle of a fly. Some people thought that flies actually formed from dead animals. It is not surprising that people believed these stories because few people had actually investigated the reproduction and development of organisms. It is difficult, for example, to observe flies laying eggs. If this activity were not observed, it might seem natural to assume that maggots were formed by spontaneous generation.

Today, most people know that living things are produced only from other living things. This idea is called the **principle of biogenesis.** After hundreds of experiments, biologists have found no evidence to support abiogenesis, but they have gathered much evidence to support biogenesis.

At this point, you may want to assign to several students the fourth of the Extensions and Applications at the end of this chapter.

You may want to review the scientific method discussed in Chapter 1 and relate the steps to Redi's experiments.

Redi's Experiments

During the seventeenth century, Francesco Redi, an Italian physician, was not convinced that flies developed from decaying meat. Redi thought that flies came from eggs laid by other flies. In 1688, he developed an experiment to test his hypothesis. In four different large, wide-mouthed jars, he placed pieces of a snake, a fish, and an eel, and a slice of veal. He also prepared a second set of jars, which also contained pieces of snake, fish, eel, and veal. Redi tightly sealed one set of jars. This was the *experimental set.* He left the other set of jars open. This was the *control set.* In this way, Redi could see what happened to exposed, decaying meat and what happened when the meat was not exposed to the air. He also used more than one jar of each type because he knew that the more experimental setups there were, the more reliable the results were likely to be.

Flies gathered in the open jars of decaying meat and laid eggs. After several days, Redi noticed maggots in the open jars. In the sealed jars, there were none. Based on these observations, Redi concluded that maggots hatched from the eggs laid by flies.

Many people argued that Redi's experiment did not disprove abiogenesis. They stated that air was necessary for living things to form and that Redi had kept air out of the

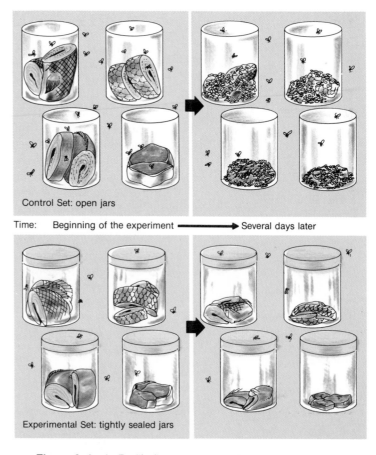

Figure 2-1 In Redi's first experiment, he allowed air and flies to enter a control set of jars containing meat. Redi sealed a second set of identical jars. No maggots appeared in this experimental set of jars. Redi's critics claimed that spontaneous generation did not occur because air was kept out of the experimental jars.

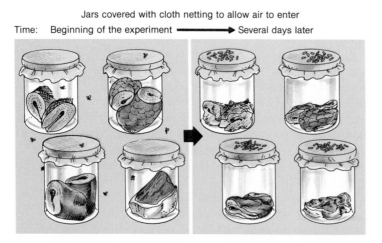

Figure 2-2 In Redi's second experiment, the experimental jars were covered with fine cloth netting that allowed air but not flies to enter the jars. Maggots were found on the netting but not on the meat in the jars. Redi concluded that maggots developed from eggs laid by flies.

sealed jars. Redi then developed a second experiment using pieces of the same kinds of meat in jars. This time he covered the jars in the experimental set with cloth netting that permitted air to enter, but kept out the flies. Redi set up a control set of jars without lids. Flies entered the jars without lids and laid eggs. The meat decayed in both jars, but maggots appeared only on the meat in the control set. Therefore, Redi had found evidence to support the hypothesis that "life comes from life."

Even though Redi cast doubt on the idea of abiogenesis, the controversy of abiogenesis versus biogenesis continued to rage. Critics stated that Redi's experiment disproved abiogenesis only in maggots, not in all living things.

Needham's Experiments

In the eighteenth century, John Needham, an English scientist, conducted experiments to support his ideas of abiogenesis. He was influenced by Anton van Leeuwenhoek's discovery of microorganisms. John Needham thought these small organisms developed from spontaneous generation, and he performed experiments to support his idea.

In his experiments, Needham boiled meat for several minutes to make a broth. Needham thought that boiling would kill any living things in the broth. He left the broth to cool in flasks and then loosely sealed the flasks with cork stoppers. After several days, Needham looked at the broth under a microscope and found it swarming with living microorganisms. He repeated his experiment with various vegetable broths and other meat broths. His results were always the same. Needham concluded that the new microorganisms formed by spontaneous generation.

Spallanzani's Experiments

A number of years after Needham's experiments, Lazzaro Spallanzani, an Italian priest and biologist, developed an experiment to disprove Needham's idea of abiogenesis of microorganisms. Spallanzani claimed that organisms could have survived the short-term boiling during Needham's experiment. He also thought that organisms could have entered the broth culture through the loosely sealed tops of the containers.

Spallanzani's experiment was unlike Needham's in two important ways. Spallanzani securely sealed his broth-containing flasks by melting the glass together at the mouths. He also placed the sealed flasks in boiling water for one hour. Even after the broths cooled, nothing could get into

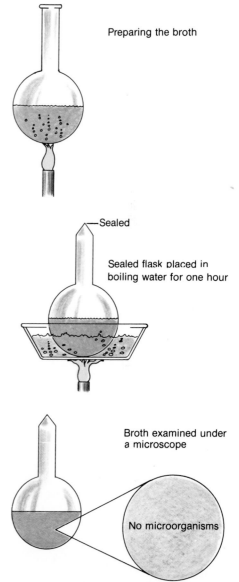

Figure 2-3 No microorganisms grew in Spallanzani's flasks because the broth was boiled long enough to kill any microorganisms in it, and the flasks were sealed to prevent air from entering.

Preparing the broth

Sealed

Sealed flask placed in boiling water for one hour

Broth examined under a microscope

No microorganisms

them from the outside, as Spallanzani thought had happened in Needham's experiments. After several days, Spallanzani observed his broth under a microscope. None of the broth samples contained living organisms. Based on these results, Spallanzani concluded that organisms did not arise by spontaneous generation.

Most of the supporters of abiogenesis did not accept the experiments of Spallanzani as proof of biogenesis. They claimed that the boiling destroyed the "vegetative force" or "active principle" in the broth that caused living organisms to develop.

Spallanzani set up another experiment in which he filled flasks with a vegetable broth but did not seal them. He boiled one set of flasks for half an hour, another set for one hour, a third set for one and a half hours, and a fourth set for two hours. Spallanzani reasoned that fewer microorganisms would be present in the fourth set if boiling destroyed the "vegetative force" or "active principle."

Spallanzani loosely sealed the flasks and set them aside for several days. When he examined the broths under a microscope, he discovered microorganisms in all of the flasks. In fact, there were more microorganisms in the flasks that had been boiled the longest. Spallanzani concluded that far from destroying the "vegetative force" or "active principle," boiling made the broths better suited for the growth of microorganisms. Spallanzani concluded that the boiling dissolved more of the seeds from which he had made his broth, thus making the food supply richer. However, many scientists still did not accept Spallanzani's experiments. The argument continued for another half a century until a French scientist began experiments to disprove abiogenesis.

Pasteur's Experiments

In 1864, Louis Pasteur, a French chemist, conducted a series of experiments to prove that life is not produced from nonliving materials. From his experiments, Pasteur concluded that the air contained inactive microorganisms called *spores*. He hypothesized that the spores were attached to dust particles in the air. The spores remained inactive until they landed in an environment that could support life, such as a broth.

In his first set of experiments, Pasteur prepared several broths that would support the growth of microorganisms. Each broth was placed in a glass flask. The flasks were sealed and boiled long enough to kill all of the microorganisms that might be present. Then Pasteur opened the flasks and left them in places where the air would most

You may want to have your students repeat Spallanzani's second experiment in the classroom laboratory.

Have your students state the problem, list the known information, state the hypotheses, list the observations, and state the conclusions for Pasteur's experiments.

Highlight

Pasteur's experiments proved that (1) microorganisms exist in the air; (2) the ability of a broth to support the growth of microorganisms is not destroyed by boiling; (3) if a broth is exposed to filtered, sterile air, no living organisms will grow in the broth.

likely contain varying amounts of dust and spores. He opened the flasks at high and low altitudes and in places such as meadows or along dusty roads.

After several days, Pasteur examined the broth in the flasks and found that the greatest number of microorganisms had grown in flasks that had been placed in areas with the largest amount of dust. He also found that more organisms developed in flasks that were left open at low altitudes than in those opened at high altitudes. The results supported Pasteur's hypothesis that microorganisms were attached to dust particles in air.

Nevertheless, Pasteur's critics were not convinced by his results. They claimed that air itself could give rise to microorganisms. Pasteur designed another experiment under controlled laboratory conditions to challenge this claim. See Figure 2-4. In this experiment, Pasteur boiled a water, yeast, and sugar broth in flasks that had long S-curved necks. Boiling forced air out of the flasks and killed any microorganisms present in the broth. The steam killed any microorganisms or spores present in the neck of the flask. As the flasks cooled, air reentered them. Water and dust particles were trapped in the bend of the S-curved necks. Therefore, the broths remained *sterile*. That is, they contained no living things. When Pasteur examined the broths, he observed no microorganisms even though the broths had been in contact with the air. Only after the flasks were tipped and the broth came into contact with the trapped dust and water in the S-curve of the flasks did microorganisms grow in the broths.

Pasteur proved that boiling did not destroy the ability of the broth to support microorganisms. He also showed that air did not contain any "active principle" or "vegetative force" that gave rise to life. Life could be produced only by life. The living spores of microorganisms on dust particles in the air were responsible for the life in Pasteur's flasks. Pasteur finally disproved the centuries-old theory of abiogenesis.

SECTION REVIEW   Answers on pages T–27 to T–28.

1. What is meant by spontaneous generation?
2. What is the principle of biogenesis?
3. How did Redi's control set and experimental set differ in his two experiments?
4. What effects did boiling have on the growth of microorganisms in Spallanzani's second experiment?
5. What hypothesis did Pasteur test during his experiments?

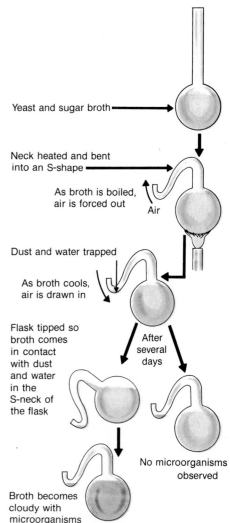

Yeast and sugar broth

Neck heated and bent into an S-shape

As broth is boiled, air is forced out

Air

Dust and water trapped

As broth cools, air is drawn in

Flask tipped so broth comes in contact with dust and water in the S-neck of the flask

After several days

No microorganisms observed

Broth becomes cloudy with microorganisms

Figure 2-4   In Pasteur's experiment, the broth remained sterile even though it was continuously exposed to air. The argument that air alone could give rise to microorganisms was finally proven wrong, as was the concept of spontaneous generation.

Characteristics of Living Things

Living things are distinguished from nonliving things by a number of characteristics. Among the most obvious characteristics possessed by living things is a unit of structure called the *cell.* Some cells, like those of microorganisms, function independently. Other cells, like those in the human body, work together. The *viruses* are the only forms of life that do not possess cells. They are referred to as *subcellular.* Viruses are discussed in Chapter 14.

Scientists recently have learned more about the similarities in the internal structure of cells. Inventions such as the electron microscope have made it possible to examine the contents of individual cells. Scientists have discovered that every cell is made up of a very complex system of parts and substances. These parts and substances function together to enable the cell to do work. Taken together, the parts and substances are called **protoplasm.** The protoplasm in different cells has different properties and is made of different substances. For example, the protoplasm in an oak leaf cell is different from that in a human skin cell. The protoplasm in a human skin cell is also different from that in a human brain cell.

Although protoplasm is the material of life, it is not itself alive. When the parts of protoplasm work together in a cell to produce organized chemical activity, life is said to exist. The chemical activities that occur in living cells are called *life functions.* These functions distinguish living things from nonliving things.

Metabolism

All living things perform many chemical activities essential to life. Together, all of these activities are called **metabolism.** Metabolism takes place in two major phases.

Figure 2-5 The basic units of structure and function in all living things are cells. Salamander liver cells are shown in the left photograph. Moss plant cells are shown in the right photograph.

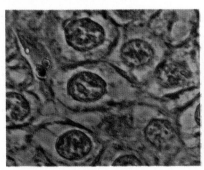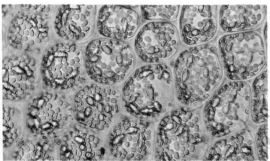

During **anabolism** (ə-NAB-ə-liz′m), simple substances combine with other simple substances to form complex substances. Anabolism involves storage of energy, production of new materials, and growth. During **catabolism** (kə-TAB-ə-liz′m), complex substances break down. Energy is released and food substances are used. Anabolism and catabolism occur continuously and involve several metabolic functions.

Ingestion   Living things take in substances such as oxygen, carbon dioxide, food, and water. The process of taking in substances is called **ingestion.**

Digestion   During **digestion,** complex food substances are broken down into simple substances that can be used by the cells of the organism. Foods can be broken down by such actions as grinding and churning or by the action of chemicals.

Assimilation   The production of living materials from the chemical substances that make up food is called **assimilation.** The new living materials are used for growth, repair, and maintenance.

Respiration   Most living organisms use oxygen to produce energy. When food is combined with oxygen, energy to do work is produced. The process of **respiration** releases stored energy in food substances.

Excretion   When an organism breaks down substances, waste materials are produced. The process of eliminating waste material is called **excretion.**

Growth and Development

An increase in size is called **growth.** Some nonliving things, such as crystals and icicles, are said to grow. They "grow" through the addition of more of the same material to their surfaces. In an organism, growth results from an increase in the number and size of cells. Food, water, minerals, and other substances are used to form new protoplasm. Therefore, growth can also be described as a process that increases the amount of protoplasm within an organism.

As an organism grows, a series of changes in form and function also occur. This series of changes is called **development.** An acorn develops into a tree. A child develops into an adult. Most organisms have a limited period of growth and development. For example, a lima bean seed planted in moist soil begins to grow in five to seven days. The seed

Figure 2-6   Many changes occur in the form and functions of a frog during its growth and development. A young bullfrog tadpole (*top*) is adapted for life in water. An older bullfrog tadpole (*bottom*) has developed legs. A bullfrog tadpole develops into an adult bullfrog in two to three years.

Sidelight

The seed of a giant California sequoia weighs 85 milligrams. After growing and developing for more than 1000 years, the sequoia has a mass about 600 billion times that of the original seed.

Figure 2-7 A mimosa plant responds to the stimulus of touch by folding its leaves.

On the chalkboard, place a list of stimuli to which people respond. Ask your students to give a possible response to each of the stimuli.

Figure 2-8 All living things produce offspring. Asexually reproducing organisms produce offspring that are identical to their parents. Sexually reproducing organisms, such as these lions, produce offspring that are similar to their parents but are not exactly like them.

grows and develops into a bean plant with specialized parts over a period of weeks.

Response

All living things react to *stimuli*. Stimuli are changes in the *environment*, or surroundings, of living organisms. Some common stimuli that affect plants and animals are light and temperature. Other stimuli are changes in the chemical composition of soil, water, or air surrounding an organism. The action or movement of the organism caused by the stimulus is called a *response*. Certain cells in some organisms are highly specialized to respond to stimuli. The ability of an organism to respond to a stimulus is called **irritability.**

Different organisms respond to a given stimulus in different ways. The response of an organism also varies with the nature and intensity, or strength, of the stimulus. For example, some single-celled organisms, such as *Euglena*, respond to light by moving toward it. When touched, a mimosa plant responds by folding up its leaves. If you touch something hot or sharp, you respond by pulling your hand away.

Reproduction

Every living organism produces other organisms, or offspring, of the same kind. This process is called **reproduction.** Only living organisms can reproduce. It is one of the most important functions of living organisms. Because all individual living things of a given kind have limited life spans, all their kind would become extinct if they did not reproduce.

Living things reproduce in many different ways. However, there are two basic forms of reproduction. **Sexual reproduction** usually requires two parents. **Asexual reproduction** requires only one. Reproduction can be as simple as an organism dividing into two parts. This type of asexual reproduction is common in single-celled organisms. Some plants, such as geraniums and African violets, can grow from part of a stem, root, or leaf of the parent plant, which is a form of asexual reproduction. In organisms that reproduce sexually, each parent forms special sex cells called *gametes*. When the gametes from the two parents combine, *fertilization* occurs. The fertilized cell produced by this combining process eventually develops into a complete organism.

To one extent or another, size, form, and behavioral *traits*, or characteristics, are passed on from parent organisms to their offspring. The transferring of these traits from one generation to another is called **heredity.** Although sexually reproducing organisms produce similar offspring, the offspring are not exactly like their parents.

Adaptation

Various factors in an organism's environment support or threaten its survival. Organisms of the same kind have certain traits that enable them to survive in a particular environment. From time to time, a change in their environment may occur. The change may be sudden, such as a forest fire, or slow, such as changes in soil or weather conditions. If organisms are not suited to the change, they move to a new environment, change, or die. Organisms do not usually change suddenly. They change over many generations. These changes occur as a result of **variations,** or differences, in organisms.

The offspring of sexually reproducing organisms have variations. Most variations are neither helpful nor harmful. For example, different eye and hair colors do not affect the ability of people to survive. However, some variations give organisms a better chance to survive. If a helpful variation is passed on to the next generation, the organisms of that generation have a better chance for survival. After several generations, all of the organisms of that kind may have the helpful variation. The process by which a kind of organism changes and becomes better suited to its environment is called **adaptation.**

Organisms survive because they change. But they do not change in order to survive. For example, giraffes did not develop long necks in order to eat the leaves from tall trees. A variation produced giraffes with long necks. This enabled long-necked giraffes to reach leaves on tall trees easier than could giraffes with shorter necks. The longer-necked giraffes were better suited to an environment where food was high off the ground. They survived to reproduce long-necked giraffes. The shorter-necked giraffes did not obtain enough food and, therefore, they did not survive to reproduce more of their kind.

Figure 2-9 Every organism has special characteristics, or adaptations, that enable it to survive in its environment. Would these organisms be able to survive in one another's environment? Explain.

No. Student explanations will vary.

Explain to your students that an adaptation can also refer to an inherited trait that makes an organism better suited to its environment. Students should be aware that all living things have adaptations. You may want to show photographs or slides of different organisms. Ask your students to give some of the special adaptations of each organism.

At this point, you may want to have your students do the Laboratory Investigation at the end of this chapter.

SECTION REVIEW   Answers on page T–28.

1. What is protoplasm?
2. List the metabolic functions of living organisms.
3. What is growth in an organism?
4. What is meant by stimulus and response?
5. Why must all living things reproduce?
6. What is adaptation?

Levels of Organization and Needs of Living Things

The structure of organisms is complex and varies from one kind of organism to another. Organisms can be studied according to the level at which they are organized.

Cells   The cell is the first level at which life is organized. Living things that are made up of only one cell are called **unicellular organisms.** Organisms that are made up of more than one cell or many cells are called **multicellular organisms.** Some organisms are made up of billions of cells.

Tissues   In multicellular organisms, cells are organized in specialized groups. Different kinds of cells work closely together and depend on one another to perform a particular function. Groups of specialized cells, or an organization of cells that are alike in structure and func-

CLOSE-UP: *John Behler*

John Behler was 10 years old when his family moved to Oklahoma. He lived in a dry, prairie area where box turtles crawled across roads, and colorful lizards lounged on rocks. Behler could not help noticing them, and he became interested in these reptiles. Soon he filled his room with a small collection of snakes, lizards, and turtles.

"Some people keep hamsters," Behler said, "others watch birds. I wanted something wild that I could hold and look at close up."

Today, John Behler is a biologist. He is Curator of Herpetology at the Bronx Zoo in New York City, where he runs the Reptile House, which holds 150 species of reptiles and amphibians. Herpetology is the study of reptiles and amphibians. Part of Behler's job is to see that the animals are cared for properly and live in the right kinds of environments.

As a biologist, Behler is always looking for new species or new information about old species. He often travels around the world. He has been to Fiji collecting sea snakes, to New Guinea studying crocodiles, and to Africa to look at the Goliath frog, which can weigh 3.5 kilograms and is the largest frog in the world.

Behler also watches animals living in marshes and bogs near his home. "Biology is the study of life," he says, "and the best way to study life is to go out and look at it yourself."

tion, are called **tissues.** Because they are organizations of cells, tissues are the second level of organization. The human body, for example, contains many types of tissues, such as bone, muscle, and nerve tissues. Each type of tissue has a special function. For example, bone tissue provides structure. Muscle tissue is necessary for movement. Nerve tissue carries impulses from nerve to nerve and to and from the spinal cord and brain. In multicellular organisms, the specialization of cells in each type of tissue can also be referred to as a *division of labor*.

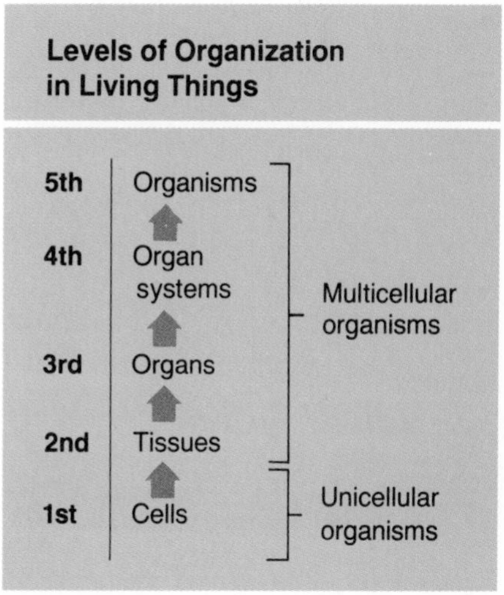

Organs Within complex organisms such as human beings, tissues can function alone or with other tissues. Two or more different kinds of tissues that work together make up an **organ.** Organs, such as the heart, lung, hand, or stomach, are the third level of organization in living things. Complex multicellular animals and plants have organs.

Organ System Organs do not usually work alone. A group of organs often works together to perform a certain function and is called an **organ system.** Organ systems are the fourth level of organization. An example of an organ system is the human *circulatory system*. The heart and various blood vessels are the parts of this organ system. Together, they work to carry blood with its important oxygen and food supply throughout the body. In complex multicellular organisms, organ systems carry out almost all metabolic functions.

Organism The fifth level of organization of living things is an *organism*. An organism is a combination of organ systems. Other levels of organization group organisms according to their relationship to one another. Groups of the same organism that can interbreed are called *populations*. Different populations that live together and interact in different ways make up *communities*. The different communities in a certain geographic area with a particular climate make up a *biome*. All of the earth's biomes make up the largest level of organization, the *biosphere*.

In their complex interrelationships, living things depend on one another and on the environment. In order to survive, both as individual organisms and as groups of organisms, living things have certain needs that must be met.

Energy All living things need energy to carry out their activities. Energy used by most living things comes ei-

Figure 2-10 Living things contain five levels of organization.

Figure 2–11 The sun is the primary source of energy for most living things. What living things obtain their energy directly from the sun? Green plants

The number of living things and their distribution around the world (biogeography) are influenced by the environment. Some environmental factors that affect living things are climate, type of soil, amount of available water, and other animals and plants in the environment.

To illustrate the effects of overcrowding on producers, you may want to assign to several students the second of the Extensions and Applications at the end of this chapter.

ther directly or indirectly from the sun. *Solar energy,* or energy from the sun, is stored in food substances. The energy is transferred from one organism to another through feeding patterns called *food chains.* For example, plants obtain their energy directly from the sun, insects eat plants, frogs eat insects, snakes eat frogs, and hawks eat snakes. Energy is transferred from the sun to the plants to the insects to the frogs to the snakes and then to the hawks.

Water and Food All living things need water to function properly. Plants obtain water from soil and air. They make their own food from materials including carbon dioxide and nitrogen in water, soil, and air. The process of food-making in green plants is called *photosynthesis.* Living organisms that are able to make their own food are called **producers.** Animals are *dependent organisms.* They obtain water from foods or by drinking it. They obtain food by eating plants or other animals. In a food chain, dependent organisms are called **consumers.**

Air Most living things require one or more gases found in the earth's *atmosphere,* or air. Two of the most important gases are oxygen and carbon dioxide. Without oxygen, respiration cannot take place. Without carbon dioxide, photosynthesis cannot take place.

Living Space Every organism requires a certain amount of living space. The particular environment in which an organism lives and how the organism interacts with its environment are referred to as the organism's *niche.* If too many organisms occupy the same niche, *overcrowding* occurs. When overcrowding occurs, the organisms must compete for the same available food, energy, and water. The losers of this competition do not receive the proper amount of food, energy, and water and die.

SECTION REVIEW   Answers on page T–28.

1. What is the difference between a unicellular organism and a multicellular organism?
2. List the levels of organization of living things from simple to complex.
3. What is the primary source of energy for most living things?
4. What is the difference between a producer and a consumer?

Distinguishing Between Living and Nonliving Things

Purpose Living things have certain characteristics that distinguish them from nonliving things. These characteristics can be observed and measured. The purpose of this investigation is to examine and test a collection of unknown objects to determine whether they are living or nonliving.

Materials *(per group)* ● Collection of 5 unknowns ● 2 solutions provided by your teacher ● Soil ● Sand ● Plastic spoons ● Cardboard trays ● Magnifying glass ● A variety of small containers

Procedure **1.** Obtain the collection of 5 unknowns from your teacher. Each is marked with a symbol. **2.** Copy the table. Fill in the identifying symbols of each of your unknowns. **3.** Carefully examine each of the unknowns for signs of life. **CAUTION:** *Do not taste any of the unknowns. Some of them may be poisonous.* **4.** Sort the unknowns into 2 groups, living and nonliving, to represent your hypotheses.

5. In the blank spaces at the top of the columns of your table, fill in the general characteristics used to determine the placement of the unknown in each group. Then fill in the specific characteristics for each unknown. **6.** Using any of the materials provided, set up experiments to determine whether your hypotheses are correct.

Observations and Conclusions **1.** Carefully describe the experiments you do and record the results you obtain. If any of your experiments require several hours or days to provide results, set them in a place where they will not be disturbed. **2.** Record any changes that you observe for each unknown. Prepare a table to organize your observations. **3.** After you have completed all of your experiments, regroup the unknowns as living and nonliving. Are your hypotheses supported? Explain your answers. **4.** Do you think that you proved that some of the unknowns are nonliving? Explain your answer. **5.** Summarize your conclusions and compare them with the conclusions of other groups.

Unknown	Characteristics			Hypothesis	
				Living	Nonliving

CHAPTER SUMMARY

Abiogenesis and Biogenesis   For many years, there were two major theories of reproduction in organisms. The idea of abiogenesis states that some organisms develop from nonliving material. The principle of biogenesis states that living things are produced only from other living things.

In the seventeenth and eighteenth centuries, scientists such as Francesco Redi and Lazzaro Spallanzani conducted a series of experiments that supported the hypothesis of biogenesis. John Needham conducted experiments that seemed to support the hypothesis of abiogenesis. In 1864, Louis Pasteur conducted a series of laboratory-controlled experiments that proved that life is produced only from other living things.

Characteristics of Living Things   Living things have several characteristics and functions that distinguish them from nonliving things. All living things contain protoplasm, which is organized into cells. All living things perform many chemical activities that are collectively called metabolism. Taking place continuously, metabolism occurs in two phases called anabolism and catabolism. Metabolism includes ingestion, digestion, assimilation, respiration, and excretion.

Living things grow by forming new protoplasm. While they grow, living things also undergo a series of changes called development. Other characteristics of living things are response, reproduction, and adaptation. Reproduction is one of the most important functions of living things. If life is to continue, organisms must reproduce.

Levels of Organization and Needs of Living Things   Organisms have different levels of structural organization. The first level of organization is the cell. Tissues are the second level of organization. Tissues are groups of cells that are alike in structure and function. Organs are the third level of organization. Organs are groups of different tissues that work together. Organs working together to perform a certain function form an organ system, the fourth level of organization. Organisms are the fifth level of organization. Other levels of organization, which represent interactions among organisms and the environment, are populations, communities, biomes, and the biosphere.

In order to survive, all living things must meet certain needs. Living things need energy, water, food, air, and living space, among other things. Energy is obtained directly or indirectly from the sun.

CHAPTER VOCABULARY

abiogenesis	excretion	principle of biogenesis
adaptation	growth	producer
anabolism	heredity	protoplasm
asexual reproduction	ingestion	reproduction
assimilation	irritability	respiration
catabolism	metabolism	sexual reproduction
consumer	multicellular organism	tissue
development	organ	unicellular organism
digestion	organ system	variation

REVIEW of FACTS and CONCEPTS   Answers on pages T–28 to T–29.

On a separate sheet of paper, answer each of the following as completely as possible.

1. What is the difference between abiogenesis and biogenesis?
2. Explain the difference between Redi's two sets of experiments. Why could the second experiment be said to be better than the first?
3. Why did Spallanzani think Needham's experiment and results were incorrect?
4. Describe Spallanzani's experiment to disprove Needham's work. Why did supporters of abiogenesis not accept Spallanzani's first experiment?

5. Describe the experiments of Louis Pasteur. Why were his experiments so conclusive?
6. List the structural and functional characteristics of living things.
7. What is the relationship between growth and development?
8. What is meant by irritability? Give three examples of stimulus and response in human beings.
9. What is the relationship between variations and adaptations?
10. Explain the relationship between cells, tissues, organs, and organ systems.
11. List the basic needs of living things.
12. How are food and energy related to the survival of an organism?
13. What is meant by overcrowding?

EXTENSIONS and APPLICATIONS For additional information, see page T–29.

1. Collect soil samples from different areas around your neighborhood, such as a wooded area, your backyard, a flowerbox, and a grassy field. Place each sample in a jar. Label the jars with a description of the place from which the soil was taken. Add some water and seal each jar. Keep a daily record, including sketches, of the different plants and animals that appear over 1 or 2 weeks.
2. Prepare an experiment with a control that will show the effect of overcrowding on producers. Use seeds such as lima bean or radish seeds.
3. Find out how different colors of light affect the growth of plants. Plant several of the same kind of seeds in five different containers. The surface of the soil in the containers should be at least 10 cm from the top of the containers. After the seedlings are about 2.5 cm above the soil, cover the tops of the containers with sheets of cellophane of different colors, such as red, blue, green, and yellow. Leave one container uncovered as the control. Keep a careful daily record of the appearance of each set of plants.
4. Prepare a report on various stories that were told in the past about spontaneous generation. In your report, include the type of organism that was thought to develop by spontaneous generation and the material from which the organism was supposed to have developed.

SUGGESTED READINGS

Asimov, I., *Life and Energy*. New York: Bantam Books.
   In this book, the author discusses how an organism acquires and uses energy to survive.
Bates, M., *The Forest and the Sea*. New York: Random House.
   Two different major environments are compared in this book. The dependency of organisms on the physical and chemical components of their surroundings is described.
Krutch, J.W., *The Great Chain of Life*. Boston: Houghton Mifflin.
   Many forms of organisms and their requirements for life are discussed in this book.
Nicolle, J., *Louis Pasteur: The Story of His Major Discoveries*. New York: Basic Books.
   Pasteur's greatest contributions to science, including his experiments that proved the principle of biogenesis, are described.

3 Classification of Organisms

Flowers can be grouped according to similar features.

Chapter Objectives   *After completing this chapter, you will be able to:*

a ▩   State two reasons why taxonomists classify organisms. p. 43

b ▩   Describe the work of Carolus Linnaeus. p. 44

c ▩   Explain binomial nomenclature. p. 44

d ▩   List the bases of modern scientific classification. p. 45

e ▩   List the seven major classification groupings. p. 46

f ▩   Explain why taxonomists use different classification systems. p. 47

g ▩   Give some general characteristics of the protist, moneran, plant, fungi, and animal kingdoms. p. 48

For teaching aids for this chapter, including a chapter overview and teaching strategies, see pages T–29 to T–30. The page number next to each chapter objective refers to the text page where the information needed to fulfill the objective begins.

Scientists estimate that as many as five million different kinds of plants, animals, and microorganisms may inhabit the earth. Some organisms look very similar but are really very different. Other organisms look very different but are really very similar. As the science of biology developed, scientists began to realize that the only way to make sense out of these biological riddles was to find a way to *classify*, or group, living things according to their characteristics. By doing this, the relationships among living things could be more easily understood.

For example, are fish and whales closely or distantly related? The same question can be asked about bats and birds, or worms and snakes, or octopuses and clams. It turns out that the only closely related pair of animals is the one made up of the most different looking creatures, octopuses and clams. Only through the development of a logical classification and naming system did scientists begin to see a kind of order in the world of living things.

History of Classification

Of the two million living things that have been discovered on the earth, about 1.5 million have been classified and named. The classification and naming system scientists use today was developed in the eighteenth century.

The development of an international classification system solved several problems. One problem involved the naming of organisms. If an organism did not have a name that all scientists used—and this was frequently true—long lists of characteristics were needed to describe the organism. Organisms had different names in different languages. Sometimes organisms even had different names in the same language, which is still true today. For example, in different parts of the United States the same type of turtle is called a box turtle, a gopher, and a dry-land terrapin. Moreover, in another part of the country the word gopher names a kind of rodent. To make matters more confusing, some organisms were given *misnomers*, or misleading names. Examples of misnomers are the names starfish, jellyfish, and crayfish. These organisms are not fish at all. All this caused a great deal of confusion and made it difficult for scientists to communicate with each other.

Another problem solved by a scientific classification system was the identification of the relationships among organisms. For example, are bats closely related to birds because both animals fly? Are whales closely related to fish because they both swim in the sea? Or are whales and bats more closely related to each other than to either birds or fish? The science of classification, which today is called **taxonomy**, helped provide the answers. It also provided a logical, international system for the naming of organisms.

Early Classification Systems

Since people first began to observe and explore their surroundings, they probably grouped living things in simple ways. They might have grouped plants, for example, in two categories, edible and poisonous. Although groupings like this were not very scientific, they were practical.

About 350 B.C., Aristotle, a Greek philosopher and naturalist, began to classify living things more scientifically. He classified animals in three groups according to their natural environments: land dwellers, air dwellers, and water dwellers. He classified plants in three groups according to their size: herbs, shrubs, and trees. For almost 2000 years, people used Aristotle's groups to classify organisms.

In the seventeenth century, an English biologist named John Ray grouped the organisms he knew in a systematic order. Ray recognized that all of the characteristics of an organism had to be identified before it could be classified. His work included a classification system for plants that became the basis for modern plant taxonomy. He was the first person to use the term **species** for a group of animals that can interbreed.

The Work of Carolus Linnaeus

In 1758, Carolus Linnaeus, a Swedish botanist, made an important contribution to the science of taxonomy. Linnaeus developed a classification system based on the structural similarities of organisms. He placed organisms into two major **kingdoms**, or groups, the plant and animal kingdoms. He further divided the kingdoms into smaller groups and these groups into still smaller groups. The smaller the group, the more alike were the living things in it.

Highlight

The scientific name of an organism is formed from its genus and species name.

Aware of the confusion caused by organisms having more than one name, Linnaeus developed a naming system that all scientists eventually came to use. The *scientific name* of an organism consisted of two Latin words. The first word referred to a larger category of organisms called a **genus.** The second word referred to a smaller category called a *species*. The two words describe the characteristics of an organism, or refer to the person who named it or the place where it was found. Linnaeus' two-word naming system was called **binomial nomenclature.** Linnaeus used Latin words because Latin was the language of science.

Figure 3-1 The scientific name of an organism consists of a noun that identifies the genus and an adjective that identifies the species.

A COMPARISON OF COMMON AND SCIENTIFIC NAMES OF FIVE ORGANISMS

Common Name	Scientific Name	Meaning of Genus and/or Species Name
Spotted skunk	*Spilogate putorius*	Smelly spotted weasel
Rhinoceros	*Rhinosceros bicornis*	Nose with two horns
Anteater	*Myrmecophaga jubata*	Ant eater with a mane
White clover	*Trifolium repens*	Three-leafed creeper
Pink rhododendron	*Rhododendron californicum*	Rose tree found in California

Biologists still use binomial nomenclature and, usually, Latin words to name organisms. If they use a word in another language, they latinize it, or give it a Latin form. For example, a species of toad found in America is called *Bufo americanus. Bufo* is the Latin word for toad and *americanus* is a latinized form of the word American. Some scientific names of organisms come from the Greek language. An example is *Drosophila*, which means dew-loving and is the genus name of fruit flies.

SECTION REVIEW   Answers on pages T–29 to T–30.

1. What is taxonomy?
2. How did Aristotle group organisms?
3. What is meant by binomial nomenclature?

Modern Taxonomy

Biologists still use obvious structural characteristics, such as feathers and hair, to classify organisms. They also use less obvious characteristics. Some of the general similarities they look for follow.

Homologous (hō-MAHL-ə-gəs) *Structures*   Structures that have the same basic pattern and general relationship of their parts are said to be *homologous.* For example, the bone structures of the wing of a bat, the arm of a human being, and the flipper of a whale are homologous. Therefore, biologists consider these organisms to be closely related and classify them closely.

Biochemical Similarities   One of the newest branches of biology is *biochemistry,* the study of the chemical makeup of living things. Biologists know that closely related organisms have similar chemical makeups. For example, sheep, horses, and yeasts may contain a certain kind of chemical. But the structure of the chemical is more similar in the sheep and horses than in the sheep and yeasts. This leads scientists to conclude that sheep and horses are more closely related to one another than to yeasts.

Genetic Similarities   One of the most reliable ways to determine how closely two organisms are related is to examine the structure of *DNA.* DNA is the chemical that passes traits from one generation to the next. The greater the similarity in the structure of the DNA of two organisms, the closer the organisms are related.

Figure 3-2 The horseshoe crab was originally thought to be a true crab. However, biochemical studies of the horseshoe crab's blood revealed that the organism was more closely related to spiders.

Figure 3-3 The species in the same genus are very similar to one another. What similarity can you see in the leaves of these three different species of maple trees?

The leaves are broad and flat and have a handlike shape.

At this point, you may want to assign to the class the third of the Extensions and Applications at the end of this chapter.

Classification Groupings

To classify organisms, biologists today use seven major classification groups, many of them the same ones Linnaeus used. The largest groups are called *kingdoms*. Each kingdom is divided into smaller groups called **phyla** (singular: phylum). In the plant kingdom, **divisions** are used more often than phyla. Each phylum or division is divided into **classes**. Within each class are **orders**. In turn, each order is divided into **families**. A family consists of many related *genera* (singular: genus). A genus is usually divided into more than one *species*. The two words of the name of an organism show its genus and species. The genus name is capitalized and the species name begins with a small letter. For example, the genus *Canis* includes wolves, coyotes, and dogs. The species names are *Canis lupus* (wolf), *Canis latrans* (coyote), and *Canis familiaris* (dog). These kinds of organisms are classified as different species because normally they do not breed with each other.

Usually, the seven main groups are all that are needed to classify an organism. However, biologists can further break up the groupings by using the prefixes *super-* and *sub-*. For example, the species dog, *Canis familiaris*, is broken down into more than 100 breeds, such as Irish setter, collie, and German shepherd. These breeds are given a subspecies name, such as *matris-optimae* for a collie. Other groupings are used that may be smaller or larger than a species. These include *group, tribe, variety,* and *form*.

Classifying an Organism

If you examine the classification groupings for the house cat, you will notice that each group represents a more specific set of characteristics. A cat moves from place to place and obtains food from its environment, two general characteristics of animals. Therefore, the cat is considered a member of the kingdom *Animalia*. Because the cat has a hollow nerve cord that extends down its back, it is placed in the phylum *Chordata*. The cat also has a backbone. Therefore, it is classified in the subphylum *Vertebrata*. The class grouping for a cat is *Mammalia*. The animals in this class have several characteristics, including fur or hair and production of milk for their offspring. A cat is primarily a meat-eating animal. Therefore, it is placed in the order *Carnivora*. The family name for the cat is *Felidae*. The scientific name, or genus and species, is *Felis domesticus*. The species name *domesticus* indicates that the organism is domesticated, or tame.

	Human	Yogurt-making bacterium	Edible mushroom	Dandelion	Paramecium
Kingdom	Animalia	Monera	Fungi	Plantae	Protista
Phylum	Chordata	Eubacteriacea	Basidiomycetes	Tracheophyta	Ciliophora
Class	Mammalia	Schizomycetes	Homobasidiomycetes	Anthophyta	Ciliatea
Order	Primates	Eubacteriales	Agaricales	Asterales	Hymenostomatida
Family	Hominidae	Lactobacillaceae	Agaricaceae	Compositae	Paramecidae
Genus	*Homo*	*Lactobacillus*	*Agaricus*	*Taraxacum*	*Paramecium*
Species	*H. sapiens*	*L. bulgarius*	*A. campestris*	*T. officinale*	*P. caudatum*

Figure 3-4 Classification of Five Different Organisms

SECTION REVIEW Answers on page T-30.

1. What are homologous structures?
2. What kinds of similarities among organisms do biologists use to classify a living thing?
3. Of the seven major classification groups, which contains the largest number of different organisms? Which contains the smallest number of different organisms?
4. What is the scientific name for a house cat?

Classification Systems

Before microscopic organisms were discovered, organisms were classified in only two kingdoms, *Plantae* and *Animalia*. Problems in classification arose when microscopic organisms could not be easily classified as plants or animals. Other organisms, such as fungi, were also known to have characteristics not found in plants or animals.

In 1866, Ernst Haeckel, a German biologist, proposed that all single-celled organisms be classified in a separate kingdom. He called the kingdom *Protista*, meaning first, or earliest. However, taxonomists did not begin using the protist kingdom grouping until 1960.

Some taxonomists use classification systems that have more than three kingdoms. One system adds the fourth kingdom *Monera* (muh-NIR-uh) for single-celled organisms that do not have a well-defined *nucleus*, or control center.

Highlight

The subspecies or variety name may be added as a third part of the scientific name.

Explain to your students that in the classification system, the number of different groupings increases from kingdom to species. However, the number of kinds of organisms in each group decreases. For example, at the kingdom level there are three groups that contain every kind of organism. However, at the species level, there are millions of groupings but only one kind of organism in each grouping.

At this point, you may want to have your students do the Laboratory Investigation at the end of this chapter.

48

Stress to your students that classification systems are not perfect. Keeping an open mind about how organisms should be classified permits biologists to change and refine the systems so that new and better systems may be established.

Sidelight

More than 900,000 insects have been classified. If their scientific names were listed in this text, the list would be more than 18,700 pages long.

Examples of organisms placed in this kingdom are bacteria and blue-green algae.

Other taxonomists use a fifth kingdom, *Fungi*, to classify such organisms as mushrooms and molds. these organisms have many characteristics of plants, but they do not make their own food. This book is organized around a five-kingdom classification system. See Figure 3-5.

PROTISTA   The protist kingdom includes the protozoans. Many protists are unicellular microscopic organisms. However, some protists live in colonies that are large enough to be seen with the unaided eye. Protists are *eukaryotes* (YOO-kar-ē-ōts), or organisms with a true nucleus.

MONERA   The moneran kingdom includes all bacteria and the blue-green algae. Monerans are unicellular *prokaryotes* (PRŌ-kar-ē-ōts). Prokaryotes are organisms that do not have a true nucleus. Although most bacteria are **heterotrophic** (het-ər-ə-TRAHF-ik), or unable to make their own food, some are **autotrophic** (awt-ə-TRAHF-ik). That is, they make their own food from simple substances. Blue-green algae are also autotrophic.

CAREER: Museum Technician

Museum technicians prepare museum collections and exhibits. Technicians clean and preserve animal and plant specimens and carefully mount and arrange them in glass cases. They label and assign catalog numbers to the mounted specimens. When an exhibit is replaced, technicians carefully remove and store the old specimens.

Museum technicians may also work with fossils that have been recently discovered. They use electric drills, chisels, and other tools to remove the fossils from the surrounding rock. Museum technicians also restore the skeletal parts of fossil organisms, using clay, plaster, and other materials. Sometimes, a museum technician constructs copies of entire fossil skeletons.

A bachelor's degree in a specialized field of science is usually required for a position as a museum technician. Museum technicians with biology backgrounds usually work in natural history museums. These museums vary greatly in size and in the comprehensiveness of their col-

lections. Most natural history museums are owned by cities, counties, or states, while others are privately owned. Other employment positions are available in the natural history departments of colleges and universities.

For further career information, write to American Association of Museums, 1055 Thomas Jefferson St. NW, Washington, D.C. 20007.

PLANTAE   Most plants are multicellular organisms with specialized tissues and organs. Plants are autotrophic and contain *chlorophyll*. Chlorophyll is a green pigment necessary for making food. Each plant cell is surrounded by a rigid *cell wall*.

FUNGI   Most fungi are multicellular organisms that have simple structures. All fungi are eukaryotes, and heterotrophic. The organisms in this kingdom include the mushrooms, molds, and yeasts.

ANIMALIA   The animal kingdom is made up of only multicellular organisms. The organisms in this kingdom are the most complex. Most have tissues, and most have organs and organ systems. Animal cells do not have cell walls and do not contain chlorophyll. Animals are heterotrophs.

Plantae	All multicellular plants
Animalia	All multicellular animals
Protista	Most of the one-celled organisms
Monera	Bacteria and blue-green algae
Fungi	Fungi and molds

Figure 3–5   Five-kingdom Classification System

Figure 3-6   The insect in this photograph is an example of a heterotroph because it cannot make its own food. The plant is an autotroph because it contains chlorophyll and can make its own food.

SECTION REVIEW   Answers on page T–30.

1. Name the kingdoms in the classification systems taxonomists use.
2. What are methanogens?

Figure 3-7 A Five-Kingdom Classification System of Organisms (major phyla only)

KINGDOM PROTISTA

Phylum *Sarcodina* *Amoeba, Radiolaria,* and *Foraminifera.* Unicellular microscopic organisms. Move by means of extensions of cytoplasm called pseudopodia. Heterotrophic.

Phylum *Ciliophora* *Paramecium, Stentor,* and other ciliates. Microscopic unicellular organisms. Move by means of hairlike structures called cilia. Heterotrophic.

Phylum *Mastigophora* *Euglena, Volvox,* and other organisms with whiplike tails called flagella. Move by means of flagella. Many are unicellular. Some live in colonies. Chlorophyll present in some species.

Phylum *Sporozoa* *Plasmodium.* Nonmotile. Parasitic organisms. Produce spores for reproduction.

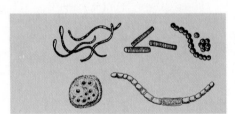

KINGDOM MONERA

Phylum-*Eubacteriacea* Bacteria. Extremely small microscopic organisms. Some form clusters or chains. No distinct nucleus. Most are heterotrophic.

Phylum *Cyanophyta* Blue-green algae. Mostly one celled. Contain chlorophyll. No distinct nucleus.

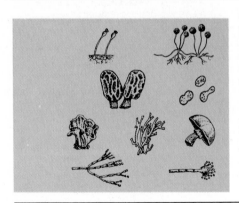

KINGDOM FUNGI

Phylum *Zygomycetes* Bread molds. Multicellular. Produce spores and zygospores for reproduction. Heterotrophic.

Phylum *Ascomycetes* Morels, yeasts, and cup fungi. Most are multicellular. Some are unicellular. Heterotrophic.

Phylum *Basidomycetes* Mushrooms, rusts, and smuts. Multicellular. Heterotrophic.

Phylum *Deuteromycetes* *Penicillium* and *Aspergillus.* Reproduction by spores on simple hyphae. Heterotrophic.

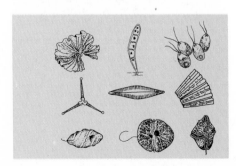

KINGDOM PLANTAE

Division *Chlorophyta* Green algae. Most are microscopic. Grow in salt and fresh water. Some exist as colonies and form a a green film on the surface of lakes and ponds.

Division *Chrysophyta* Yellow-green and golden algae, diatoms. Usually one cell, but some live in colonies.

Division *Pyrrophyta* Dinoflagellates. One-celled organisms. Produce a poisonous red substance. Have the ability to move from place to place.

Division *Phaephyta* Brown algae. Largest algae. Multicellular organisms.

Division *Bryophyta* Mosses and liverworts. Small, multicellular plants. Do not have true roots, stems, or leaves.

Division *Tracheophyta* Horsetails, ferns, conifers, *Ginkgo,* all flowering plants. Have vascular tissues that carry food and water throughout the plant.

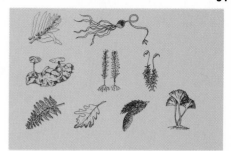

KINGDOM ANIMALIA

Phylum *Porifera* Sponges. Body wall made up of two cell layers. No nervous system. Many pores in body wall. Do not move from place to place. Mineral skeleton.

Phylum *Coelenterata* Jellyfish, sea anemones, *Hydra,* corals. Saclike animals. Single opening for taking in food and eliminating waste products. Tentacles and stinging cells.

Phylum *Platyhelminthes* Flat worms. Flattened bodies. Three cell layers. Many live in the bodies of other organisms.

Phylum *Nematoda* Round worms, rotifers. Small slender bodies with three cell layers. Some are microscopic, but multicellular.

Phylum *Bryozoa* Sea mosses. Colonial organisms that look like flowers. Tentacles around mouth. Three cell layers. Primitive nervous system.

Phylum *Brachiopoda* Lampshells. Marine animals. Body enclosed in a two-piece shell. Two fleshly stalks with tentacles.

Phylum *Mollusca* Snails, clams, squids, mussels, octopuses. Soft bodies with a shell that covers all or part of their bodies. Have a digestive, circulatory, excretory, and respiratory system.

Phylum *Annelida* Segmented worms, such as the earthworm. Long bodies divided into segments. Three cell layers. Two body openings. Simple circulatory system.

Phylum *Arthropoda* Spiders, insects, millipedes, centipedes, and crustaceans. Jointed appendages and chitinous exoskelton.

Phylum *Echinodermata* Sea lilies, starfishes, sea urchins, sand dollars, sea cucumbers. Outer skeleton with spines. Many have arms or rays. All are marine animals. Many have tube feet for movement.

Phylum *Hemichordata* Acorn worms. Body divided into three sections. Many have gill slits on either side of their bodies. Burrow in mud and sand.

Phylum *Chordata* Tunicates, fishes, reptiles, birds, mammals, amphibians. Possess a rodlike structure called a notochord at some stage in their life. Paired appendages. Nerve cord that extends down the back.

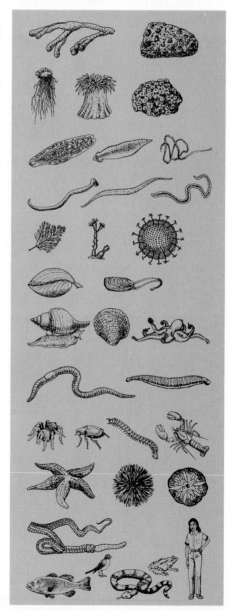

Developing a Classification System

Purpose Biologists developed a classification system for grouping and naming living things. The system is organized according to the characteristics of organisms. The purpose of this investigation is to develop a classification system for a random group of objects and to gain an understanding of how this is done.

Materials (*per 2 students*) ● Collection of 12 objects ● Magnifying glass ● Large sheet of white construction paper

Procedure **1.** Obtain a collection of 12 objects from your teacher. **2.** Draw a large circle in the top center of the sheet of construction paper. Write the names of the 12 objects in this circle. **3.** Choose a general property of objects, such as size. Separate the group of objects into two subgroups based on two specific observable characteristics of the general property, such as large and small. **4.** Draw 2 circles below the large one, and list the names of the objects in each of the subgroups. Write the general property between the 2 circles. To the side of each circle, note the specific characteristic used to divide the groups. **5.** Choose another general property and then specific characteristics of the general property. Divide the two groups of objects into four subgroups. List the objects in four circles underneath the other circles.
6. Continue subdividing the objects until only one object remains in a circle. **Note:** *Be sure to label each row of circles with a general property and each circle with the specific characteristics of that property.*
7. Choose an object in the classroom and place it in your classification system.

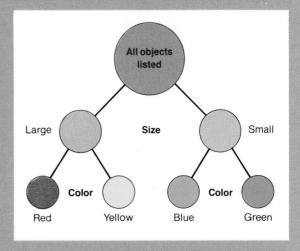

Observations and Conclusions **1.** What are some of the characteristics of the objects? **2.** How many divisions did it take to separate all of the objects in the collection? **3.** Which biological classification grouping would the first circle represent? the second two circles? each object? **4.** Choose one of the objects and devise a scientific name for it based on your classification system. **5.** How well did your classification system work for the classroom object you chose in procedure 7? Did you make changes in the system for it to work? If so, what changes were necessary? **6.** List examples of classification systems you use every day.

CHAPTER SUMMARY

History of Classification For almost 2000 years, organisms were classified according to a system established by Aristotle. In the seventeenth century, John Ray, an English biologist, established a classification system for plants that became the basis of the system scientists use today. In the eighteenth century, Carolus Linnaeus, a Swedish botanist, developed a classification system based on the structural similarities of organisms. Linnaeus also established a system for naming organisms, binomial nomenclature, which is still used.

Modern Taxonomy Today, organisms are classified according to structural characteristics, biochemical similarities, and genetic similarities. Organisms are classified in seven major groupings. These groups, from largest to smallest, are kingdom, phylum, class, order, family, genus, and species.

Classification Systems The five-kingdom system of classification used in this text includes the kingdoms *Protista, Plantae, Animalia, Monera,* and *Fungi.*

CHAPTER VOCABULARY

autotrophic	family	order
binomial nomenclature	genus	phylum
class	heterotrophic	species
division	kingdom	taxonomy

REVIEW of FACTS and CONCEPTS   Answers on page T–30.

On a separate sheet of paper, answer each of the following as completely as possible.

1. What type of characteristics did Linnaeus use to develop his classification system?
2. List several characteristics of organisms that are used today to classify living things.
3. List the seven major classification groupings from largest to smallest.
4. What classification groupings are used to form the scientific name of an organism?
5. Which two organisms are the most similar: *Felis tigris* (tiger), *Ovis canadensis* (bighorn sheep), *Felis leo* (lion), and *Cervus canadensis* (elk)? Explain your answer based on your understanding of classification groupings.

6. Why do taxonomists classify organisms?
7. Why are some organisms difficult to classify? Give an example.
8. What are some problems in classifying organisms in kingdoms?
9. Name and describe the kingdoms used in the five-kingdom classification system.
10. In which kingdom of the five-kingdom · system would each of the following belong: a maple tree, a mouse, blue-green algae, a mushroom, a human being, a bacterium, and a mosquito?

EXTENSIONS and APPLICATIONS   For additional information, see page T–30.

1. Using library reference books, find the genus and species names for 10 different kinds of plants and 10 different kinds of animals. What is the basis for each genus and species name?
2. Divide a sheet of paper into four equal columns. In the first column, list several uncommon plants and animals. Also include in this column several misnomers for plants and animals, such as star-

fish. Ask 10 to 15 people whether they think each name refers to a plant or an animal. Record the results in the second column. Ask the same people what kind of plant or animal the organism is, such as shrub, tree, mammal, rodent, fish, or reptile. Record the results in the third column. In the fourth column, give the correct kingdom—plant or animal—and the actual type of plant or animal, such as class, order, or family. Prepare a report that summarizes the different views people have about these organisms.

3. Choose an animal or plant that you would like to study. Find out the organism's classification groupings. Then, try to find out what character-istics are used to classify the organism in each grouping. Make a chart of your findings. The chart should consist of columns headed with the terms class, order, genus, and species. In each column, write the characteristics of the organism that belong under the heading.

SUGGESTED READINGS

Bailey, L.H., *How Plants Get Their Names*. Detroit: Gale Research Co.
    Basic botanical nomenclature is introduced in this book. The author explains the confusion that results from using misleading common names for plants, and the advantages of a scientific classification system.

Editors of Time-Life Books, *A Guide to the Natural World*. New York: Time-Life Books.
    The history of taxonomy is discussed in the introductory chapter. The remainder of the book is a catalogue of the major divisions of the natural world, including many photographs of living things.

Gotch, A.F., *Mammals—Their Latin Names Explained*. New York: Sterling Publishing Co.
    This book explains the basic principles of animal classification used today. The scientific names of animals are given, along with a brief explanation of why the species was given its name.

Hanson, E.D., *Animal Diversity*. Englewood Cliffs, N.J.: Prentice-Hall.
    Descriptions of many different types of animals are provided in this book.

Animal Captivity: Zoos and Compounds Versus Preserves and Sanctuaries

Animals have been displayed in zoos and compounds for thousands of years. For the most part, these animals were kept in cages where people could easily see them. Many people think that keeping animals in cages is harmful to the health of the animals. These people point to the fact that infectious diseases increase among caged animals. This is possible because animals that live in a controlled environment have a lowered resistance to disease.

Scientists and other people are concerned that the natural behavior of animals changes when the animals are made to conform to unnatural daily patterns. In zoos, caged animals are conditioned to eat at specific times, instead of when they are hungry. As feeding time approaches, they become agitated and pace in their cages, which does not happen in the wild. Researchers have also found that animals become frustrated and unresponsive in an enclosed environment. In some cases, the animals do not mate or reproduce.

Recently, alternative zoos have been established. Officials in these zoos put the animals in large open preserves or sanctuaries designed to simulate the animals' natural habitat. Human visitors view the animals from minitrains or from walking paths. The preserves of large animals, such as bears and lions, are often surrounded by a moat over which the animals are unable to jump. Not only do these exhibits allow animals to behave naturally, they also provide a view of the animals as they would live in their natural environments.

Some people feel that animals should never be held in captivity. They believe that animals should remain in their natural habitats and sanctuaries protected by laws and patrolled by game wardens. Other people, including many scientists, believe that zoos provide important benefits. One of these benefits is wildlife conservation. Endangered species can be bred in zoos so that their increased numbers may someday be returned to the wild. For example, the Hawaiian goose, a once endangered species that was successfully bred in a zoo, has since been returned to the wild.

Viewpoints

1. Visit the nearest zoo or sanctuary and observe the ways in which different animals are displayed. Do you think some types of animals should be caged while others should not be caged? Discuss your reasons.

2. What are some ways, other than in cages, that animals can be exhibited? What are some advantages and disadvantages to these methods of exhibition?

3. Contact the following zoos and request maps and information on their physical setup.

> Arizona-Sonora Desert Museum
> Tucson, AZ 85704
>
> Bronx Zoo
> Bronx, NY 10460
>
> Brookfield Zoo
> Brookfield, IL 60513
>
> Fort Worth Zoological Park and Aquarium
> Fort Worth, TX 76110
>
> Milwaukee County Zoological Park
> Milwaukee, WI 53226
>
> Minnesota Zoological Garden
> Apple Valley, MN 55124
>
> San Diego Zoo
> San Diego, CA 92112

Compare and contrast the physical setups of the zoos. Which zoo appears to exhibit different groups of animals in the best ways? Why?

UNIT TWO

Cells

For an overview of this unit, including field trip suggestions, a bibliography, and a list of audio-visual materials, see pages T–31 to T–41. You may want to check the Laboratory Investigations in this unit so that materials may be ordered, gathered, or prepared in advance.

You can easily see that living things, such as trees and butterflies, are different from nonliving things, such as rocks and water. A characteristic that living things share is cells. Cells are the building blocks of organisms. Some organisms, like the amoeba, are made up of only one cell. Complex organisms, such as people, contain trillions of cells.

Cells are also the basic unit of function in living things. Cells are like tiny factories. They make almost everything an organism needs, such as parts for growth and reproduction. Cells are also energy transformers. They change unuseable forms of energy to forms that can be used to do cell work. In addition, cells act like tiny computers, storing information that can produce an entirely new organism.

4   Chemistry of Living Things

5   Cell Structure and Function

6   Cell Energy and Maintenance

7   Photosynthesis and Respiration

8   Cell Growth and Reproduction

These glistening marine organisms are single-celled foraminifera, which build many-chambered shells.

4 Chemistry of Living Things

The light of glowworms is the product of a chemical reaction.

Chapter Objectives *After completing this chapter, you will be able to:*

a ▨ Explain the importance of chemistry to the study of biology. p. 58
b ▨ Define matter and list its properties. p. 59
c ▨ Describe the structure of atoms. p. 60
d ▨ Distinguish between elements, compounds, and mixtures. p. 61
e ▨ Compare solutions, suspensions, and colloids. p. 64
f ▨ State the difference between inorganic and organic compounds. p. 66
g ▨ Describe the structure of carbohydrates, proteins, amino acids, lipids, nucleic acids, and enzymes, and explain their importance in living things. p. 67
h ▨ State Oparin's hypothesis. p. 72

For teaching aids for this chapter, including a chapter overview and teaching strategies, see pages T–31 to T–33. The page number next to each chapter objective refers to the text page where the information needed to fulfill the objective begins.

The study of the composition and interaction of substances is called **chemistry.** The air you breathe, the water you drink, and the living things you see—in fact all living and nonliving things—are made up of chemical substances.

The sciences of biology and chemistry are closely related. In fact, biology cannot be understood properly without some background in chemistry. To study the structure and functions of cells, for example, you need to know about the kinds of substances that make up cells and how the substances interact. In the cells of some organisms, such as glowworms, the interaction of special substances produces light.

Matter and Living Things

Anything that occupies space and has *mass* is called **matter.** Mass is a measure of the amount of matter in an object. All living things are made up of matter. Cells are made up of matter. To survive, cells take in matter in the form of food.

Some of the matter that the cell takes in as food is changed chemically to produce *energy.* The cell uses this energy to carry out its activities, including growth, development, and reproduction. As a cell grows, it also uses food to make new cell parts and cell chemicals.

States and Changes of Matter

Matter exists in three states: *solid, liquid,* and *gas.* A solid has a definite shape and takes up a definite amount of space, or *volume.* A liquid does not have a definite shape, but it does have a definite volume. Like a liquid, a gas takes on the shape of the container it is in. However, a gas does not have a definite volume. It spreads out to fill its container.

Matter has definite *physical* and *chemical properties.* Some physical properties are color, boiling point, and hardness. They can be observed or measured easily. Chemical properties are not so apparent and are often more difficult to observe and measure. The ability of wood to burn is an example of a chemical property. A chemical property shows how one kind of matter reacts with other matter.

Matter undergoes both *physical* and *chemical changes.* In a physical change, the form of the matter changes, but the kind of matter stays the same. For example, water changes from a liquid to a solid when it freezes. Its physical properties change, but its chemical properties do not. Even in the form of ice, it is still water. A chemical change, also known as a *chemical reaction,* changes the makeup of the

A fourth state of matter, plasma, exists but does not ordinarily occur on the earth. Plasma, which is a high-energy state of matter, is found naturally in outer space and in the interiors of stars.

On the chalkboard, write a list of examples of physical and chemical changes. Ask your students to classify them as physical or chemical changes. Have them discuss the reasons for their choices.

Figure 4-1 A physical change occurs when solid water turns to liquid water. The form of the matter changes but not its composition. A chemical change occurs when wood burns, because the composition of matter changes.

matter. When a piece of wood burns, the carbon in the wood reacts with oxygen to produce an altogether different kind of matter, carbon dioxide.

Although different kinds of matter form during a chemical reaction, the amount of matter remains the same. This principle is the basis of the *Law of Conservation of Matter*, which states that during a chemical change, matter is neither created nor destroyed. For example, the amount of the different kinds of matter that form as wood burns is the same as the amount of matter in the wood plus the oxygen that combined with it during burning.

Atoms and Elements

For 2000 years, matter was thought to consist of small individual units. In 1805, John Dalton, an English chemist, presented scientific evidence that all matter is indeed made up of tiny units called **atoms.** For almost a century afterward, scientists thought that an atom was a solid object without parts. This belief was shattered in 1897 when scientists discovered *subatomic particles* within the atom. Figure 4-2 shows the relationship of the subatomic particles of an atom.

The center of the atom is called the *nucleus*. The nucleus is made up of two major types of subatomic particles, **protons** and **neutrons.** Protons have a positive electrical charge. Neutrons have no charge. Therefore, the nucleus has an overall positive charge.

The third major type of subatomic particle, the **electron,** is found outside the nucleus. Electrons are negatively charged. The electrons in an atom are found in *energy levels* in the space around the nucleus. The electrons in the energy level nearest the nucleus have the lowest amount of energy. The electrons located farthest away from the nucleus have the most energy. Each energy level can have a maximum number of electrons. The energy level nearest the nucleus can have only 2 electrons, while the second energy level can contain 8 electrons. The maximum number of electrons in the remaining energy levels is also fixed.

NAMES OF ELEMENTS An **element** is a substance that contains only one type of atom. Scientists have identified more than 100 elements. The name of each element is expressed by a *symbol*. The symbols for many elements consist of the first letter or first two letters of the English names of the elements. For example, the symbol for the element hydrogen is H, while the symbol for the element helium is He. Other symbols come from the names of the elements in

Sidelight

Scientists have discovered more than 100 different kinds of subatomic particles. Three examples are muons, positrons, and pions.

Stress the fact that Figure 4-2 is a model of an atom and is not a representation of how the atom actually looks.

Figure 4-2 Model of an Atom Containing 4 Protons, 4 Electrons, and 5 Neutrons

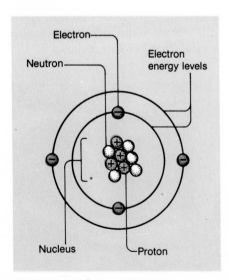

Have the students find out the symbols for the names of other elements such as tin, gold, potassium, and copper. Also, have them explain the derivation of these symbols.

Latin or other languages. The symbol for silver, Ag, comes from the Latin word *argentum*. The German word *Wolfram* provides tungsten with the symbol W.

STRUCTURE OF ELEMENTS Figure 4-3 shows models of the atoms for the three simplest elements: hydrogen, helium, and lithium. The hydrogen atom has 1 proton in its nucleus and 1 electron in the first energy level outside the nucleus. The most common form of hydrogen atom does not have any neutrons. All other atoms have neutrons. The helium atom contains 2 protons and 2 neutrons in its nucleus and 2 electrons in the first energy level. An atom of lithium has 3 protons, 4 neutrons, and 3 electrons. Two electrons are in the first energy level and the third electron is in the second energy level.

Atoms of the same element always contain the same number of protons. The number of protons in an atom is characteristic of that element. Do you see the pattern in the number of protons in hydrogen, helium, and lithium? Hydrogen has 1, helium has 2, and lithium has 3. The number of protons in an atom determines its *atomic number*. The atomic number of hydrogen is 1, of helium 2, of lithium 3.

Because atoms are matter, they have mass. *Atomic mass number* is equal to the sum of the protons and neutrons in the nucleus of an atom. (Electrons do not contribute significantly to the total mass of an atom.) Look at Figure 4-3 again. The atomic mass number of hydrogen is 1, because it has 1 proton and no neutrons. Helium has 2 protons and 2 neutrons, so its atomic mass number is 4. The atomic mass number of lithium is 7 because it has 3 protons and 4 neutrons. An atom of iron has 26 protons and 30 neutrons in its nucleus. What is its atomic mass number? Its atomic number? The atomic mass of iron is 56; its atomic number is 26.

ISOTOPES Atoms of the same element can have different numbers of neutrons and as a result have different atomic masses. Such atoms are called **isotopes.** The atomic structures of the three isotopes of hydrogen are shown in Figure 4-4 on page 62. Each isotope has 1 proton and 1 electron. They are all atoms of hydrogen because they all have 1 proton. However, they have different numbers of neutrons. Ordinary hydrogen has no neutrons, deuterium has 1, and tritium has 2.

Notice that the isotopes of hydrogen have different names. Usually, different isotopes have the same name followed by the atomic mass number of the isotope. Oxygen-18 is an important isotope in the study of certain activities of living things, such as how green plants make their own food. Oxygen-18 contains 10 neutrons and 8 protons.

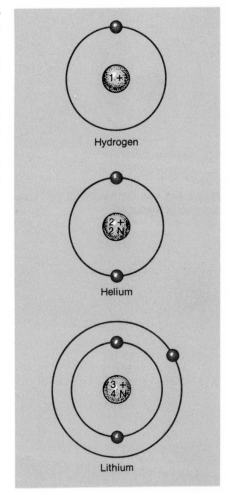

Figure 4-3 Atomic Models of the Three Simplest Elements, Hydrogen, Helium, and Lithium

At this point, you may want to assign to several students the first of the Extensions and Applications at the end of this chapter.

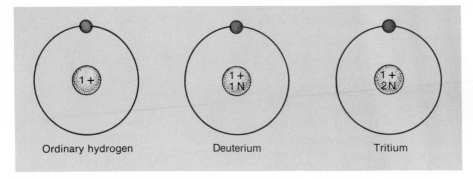

Figure 4–4 Atomic Models of the Three Isotopes of Hydrogen

Compounds and Molecules

When the number of protons and electrons in an atom is the same, the atom is electrically neutral. For example, in a neutral atom of helium, the number of positively charged particles, or protons, equals the number of negatively charged particles, or electrons.

An atom that has the maximum number of electrons in its outermost energy level is very *stable*, or unreactive. An atom that does not have a filled outermost energy level can become more stable by sharing or transferring electrons in *chemical bonds* with other atoms. When two or more elements are chemically bonded, a **compound** is formed. Water is a compound in which atoms share electrons. Ordinary table salt is a compound in which atoms transfer electrons.

Ask students to identify some common objects found in the classroom or at home as elements or compounds.

Figure 4–5 In a molecule of water, 2 hydrogen atoms share their electrons with 1 oxygen atom.

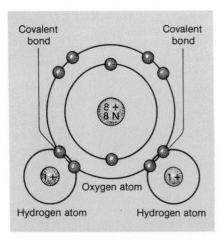

COVALENT BONDING Atoms that join by sharing electrons are said to form **covalent bonds.** The bonded set of atoms is called a **molecule.** Two atoms of hydrogen covalently bonded to 1 atom of oxygen, for example, form a molecule of water. A molecule is the smallest unit of a compound that can exist and still behave like that compound. For example, a water molecule "behaves" like water while the separate atoms of hydrogen and oxygen do not.

What happens when hydrogen and oxygen atoms bond and become a water molecule? An atom of hydrogen has 1 electron in its first and only energy level. As stated earlier, the first energy level of an atom is filled when it has 2 electrons. To fill its energy level, the hydrogen atom needs 1 more electron. An atom of oxygen has 6 electrons in its second and outermost energy level. To have a full outer energy level, the oxygen atom needs 2 more electrons. Through covalent bonding, the 2 atoms of hydrogen and 1 atom of oxygen all complete their outer energy levels. Look at Figure

4-5. Each pair of shared electrons forms a covalent bond. How many covalent bonds are there in a molecule of water?

If only 2 atoms are joined by covalent bonding, a *diatomic molecule* is formed. Diatomic molecules can be formed by atoms of different elements or atoms of the same element that have unfilled outer energy levels. Hydrogen is an example of an element whose atoms form diatomic molecules. Each atom of hydrogen shares its 1 electron with another hydrogen atom. When bonded in this way, each atom has a filled outer energy level.

IONIC BONDING Atoms form **ionic bonds** when electrons are transferred from one atom to another. Therefore, one atom in an ionic bond loses electrons while another atom gains them. Because the resulting atoms no longer have equal numbers of protons and electrons, they are electrically charged. The atom that loses electrons has a positive charge. The atom that gains electrons has a negative charge. Such electrically charged atoms are called **ions.**

Sodium chloride, or table salt, is a compound formed by the ionic bonding of sodium and chlorine atoms. When an atom of sodium and an atom of chlorine join, the sodium atom gives up its 1 electron to the outer energy level of the chlorine atom, as shown in Figure 4-6. When the sodium loses the electron in its outer energy level, its filled second energy level becomes its outer energy level. By gaining an electron, the outer level of the chlorine atom becomes filled. However, neither atom is neutral any longer. The sodium atom has 1 more proton than it has electrons and is now a positive ion with a charge of +1. The chlorine atom now has 1 more electron than it has protons and is a negative ion with a charge of −1.

CHEMICAL FORMULAS The chemical makeup of a compound, either covalent or ionic, can be expressed in a *formula*. A formula uses chemical symbols to show the kinds of elements that make up the compound. A formula also shows the number of atoms of each element in the compound. The formula for water, for example, is H_2O. The H stands for hydrogen and the O for oxygen. The numeral 2 after the symbol for hydrogen is called a *subscript*. It indicates that 2 atoms of hydrogen are present in a molecule of water. When only 1 atom of an element is present, a subscript is not used. The formula H_2O shows 1 atom of oxygen.

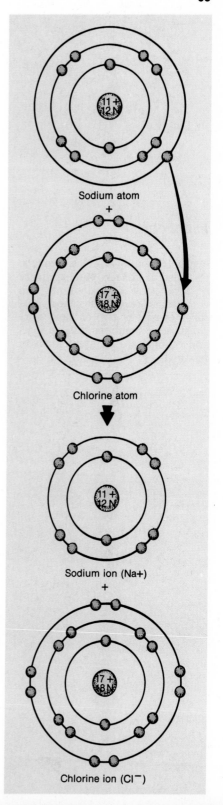

Sodium atom
+

Chlorine atom

Sodium ion (Na+)
+

Chlorine ion (Cl⁻)

Figure 4-6 Sodium and chlorine ions form when an atom of sodium transfers 1 electron to an atom of chlorine.

At this point, you may want to assign to several students the third of the Extensions and Applications at the end of this chapter.

There are 8 hydrogen atoms and 4 oxygen atoms.

Highlight

Matter is made up of atoms. It may be classified as either a pure substance or a mixture. All elements and compounds are pure substances. Mixtures consist of two or more pure substances. Solutions, suspensions, and colloids are different kinds of mixtures.

Formulas can also express numbers of molecules. In the formula, $2H_2O$, for example, the numeral 2 before H_2O indicates 2 molecules of water. This number is called a *coefficient*. To find out the total number of hydrogen atoms in 2 molecules of water, multiply the coefficient by the subscript for hydrogen: $2 \times 2 = 4$. Do the same for oxygen: $2 \times 1 = 2$. How many hydrogen atoms are there in 4 molecules of water? How many oxygen atoms? Formulas for ionic compounds are expressed the same way.

Mixtures

All samples of matter can be classified either as pure substances, such as helium, sodium chloride, or water, or as **mixtures.** A mixture is made up of two or more substances. Although the quantities of the substances in a mixture may vary, each substance in the mixture keeps its own chemical identity.

The substances in a mixture can be separated from each other by physical means, for example, *filtration* and *evaporation*. In filtration, a mixture is placed in a filter. When a mixture of sand and water is filtered, the particles of sand are trapped by the filter because they are too large to pass through. The molecules of water pass through because they are small enough to do so. In evaporation, molecules escape as gas from the surface of liquids. If the water in the sand and water mixture is allowed to evaporate, only the sand remains.

Mixtures may be *homogeneous* (hō-mə-JĒ-nē-əs) or *heterogeneous* (het-ər-ə-JĒ-nē-əs). In homogeneous mixtures, such as salt and water, every part of the mixture looks the same. The molecules or ions of one substance are spread evenly throughout the molecules or ions of another substance. In a heterogeneous mixture, such as concrete, some sections of the mixture look different from other sections. This is because different substances are concentrated in different sections of the mixture.

SOLUTIONS   A **solution** is a homogeneous mixture in which one substance is dissolved in another substance. The substance that is dissolved is called the *solute* (SAHL-yoot), while the substance that does the dissolving is called the *solvent* (SAHL-vənt). When the solute is dissolved, its molecules or ions are evenly spread throughout the molecules or ions of the solvent. Both the solute and the solvent can pass through a filter. Solutions are the "best-mixed" mixtures.

An example of a solution is sugar water. The sugar is the solute and the water is the solvent. When the sugar is dis-

Figure 4-7 A solution forms when crystals of copper sulfate dissolve in water.

solved in the water, its individual molecules separate from one another. The sugar molecules spread evenly throughout the molecules of the water. The chemical makeup of the sugar and water molecules remains unchanged. If more and more sugar were added to the solution, the solution would become *saturated.* That is, no more sugar could be dissolved in the water. Any additional sugar would settle to the bottom of the container. The *plasma,* or liquid portion of the blood, is another example of a solution. Plasma is a water solution made up of various substances.

When an ionic compound, such as table salt, is dissolved in water, its ions separate from one another and enter the solution. This process is known as *dissociation.* A simple equation shows the dissociation of table salt in water.

$$NaCl \xrightarrow{\text{water}} Na^+ + Cl^-$$

SUSPENSIONS   A **suspension** is a heterogeneous mixture. It contains particles of a substance that are much larger than individual molecules or ions. In a suspension, the substances do not completely mix and most of the particles settle out. However, some of the particles are permanently suspended and do not settle out. This results in a cloudy appearance of the mixture.

An example of a suspension is clay in water. When clay is mixed with water, very little clay actually dissolves. The mixture appears cloudy because some of the clay particles are permanently suspended in the water. If the suspension is filtered, the water will pass through the filter paper but the clay will not.

Many materials that are important in living things form suspensions in liquids. In the bloodstream, for example, red and white blood cells form a suspension in plasma. The constant movement of the blood in the body keeps the blood cells from settling out.

COLLOIDS   A **colloid** (KAHL-oid) is a homogeneous mixture. A colloid contains particles that are larger than the

The mixture appears cloudy because some of the clay particles are permanently suspended in the water.

Figure 4-8 A suspension forms when clay is added to water. Why does this mixture appear cloudy?

Figure 4-9 Gelatin is an example of a colloid.

At this point, you may want to have your students do the Laboratory Investigation at the end of this chapter.

molecules in a solution but smaller than the particles in a suspension. Colloidal particles may consist of clusters or groups of atoms, ions, or molecules. They may also be single giant molecules. Because the *cytoplasm*, or liquid portion of the cell, contains many giant molecules, it is an example of a colloid. Gelatin and homogenized milk are also examples of colloids.

SECTION REVIEW   Answers on page T-32.

1. What is the difference between a physical change and a chemical change?
2. Draw a model of an atom of nitrogen (atomic number 7, atomic mass 14).
3. What is an isotope?
4. Describe covalent and ionic bonding.
5. Distinguish between elements, compounds, and mixtures.
6. Name and give the characteristics of the three types of mixtures.

Compounds Important to Living Things

More than 99% of the atoms in the human body are atoms of hydrogen, oxygen, carbon, and nitrogen. These and other elements are combined by tiny structures within each cell to form thousands of different compounds.

Plants and animals are made up mostly of the same four kinds of atoms. For example, green plants use atoms of hydrogen, oxygen, carbon, and nitrogen to make sugars, starches, and proteins. These compounds are used for food and energy by most living things.

Inorganic Compounds

Most **inorganic compounds** are composed of elements other than carbon. The most abundant inorganic compound in all living things is water. Because it can dissolve many substances, water is sometimes called the "universal solvent." In addition, water transports various substances throughout living things. Most cellular chemical reactions occur in a watery environment.

Another important inorganic compound is carbon dioxide. Carbon dioxide is an exception to the "no carbon" rule for inorganic compounds. Although the percentage of carbon dioxide in the atmosphere is small, it is an important source

Highlight

Compounds may be classified as organic or inorganic. All organic compounds contain the element carbon. Inorganic compounds may or may not contain carbon. Most inorganic compounds do not contain carbon.

of carbon and oxygen. Carbon is found in many of the chemical compounds of living organisms. Oxygen is essential to the survival of most living things.

Organic Compounds

All **organic compounds** contain the element carbon. Organic compounds usually also contain hydrogen or both hydrogen and oxygen. They may also contain other elements, such as nitrogen, phosphorus, or sulfur.

Before 1828, scientists thought that organic compounds could be made only by chemical reactions in living organisms. At that time, a German chemist, Friedrich Wöhler, proved this idea to be wrong. Using inorganic chemicals in his laboratory, he was able to make the organic compound found in urine called *urea* (yoo-RĒ-ə).

Organic compounds can be described using *structural formulas*. These formulas show the number and kind of atoms in one molecule of a compound. They also show how the atoms are attached to one another. The structural formula for a molecule of *methane* (METH-ăn), a simple organic compound, is shown in Figure 4-10. Methane is the main ingredient of natural gas. In the structural formula for methane, the carbon atom has 4 lines around it. The lines represent covalent bonds. In a methane molecule, a carbon atom fills its outermost energy level by bonding with 4 hydrogen atoms. The chemical formula for methane is CH_4.

Many important organic compounds are found in and produced by living things. All living things are made up mostly of water and organic compounds. A discussion of some of these compounds follows.

CARBOHYDRATES One family of organic compounds is **carbohydrates.** These compounds contain the elements carbon, hydrogen, and oxygen. Look at the structural formula for a carbohydrate in Figure 4-11 on page 68. A carbohydrate molecule is a chain or a ring of carbon atoms bonded to hydrogen and oxygen atoms. Each carbon atom has 4 bonds. Oxygen atoms have 2 bonds, while hydrogen has 1. In each carbohydrate molecule, there are 2 atoms of hydrogen for every atom of oxygen.

One class of carbohydrates is called the *monosaccharides* (mahn-ə-SAK-ə-rīdz), or simple sugars. *Mono*saccharides contain *one* sugar molecule. The most common monosaccharide is *glucose*. Living cells use glucose to produce energy for cell work. The major source of glucose is fruits. Other simple sugars are *fructose* and *galactose*. Both of these monosaccharides are also made by plants. The chemical formula

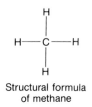

Structural formula
of methane

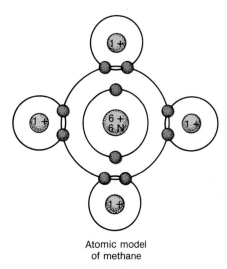

Atomic model
of methane

Figure 4–10 In a molecule of methane, 4 atoms of hydrogen share their electrons with 1 atom of carbon.

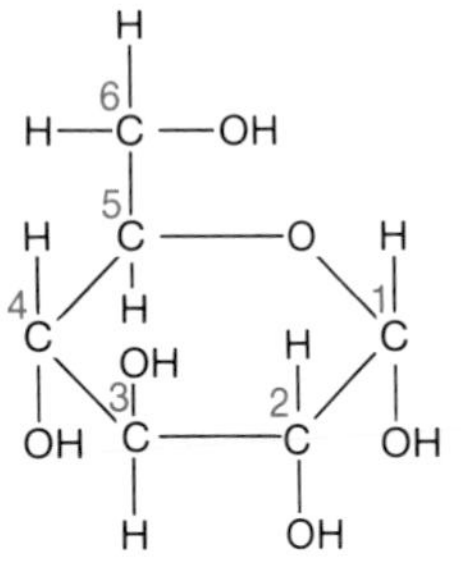

Ring structure

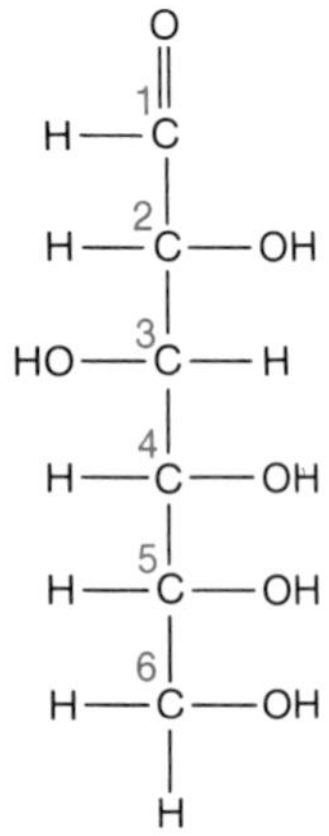

Chain structure

Figure 4-11 The structural formula for glucose may be shown in the form of either a ring or chain. What is the chemical formula for glucose? $C_6H_{12}O_6$

Figure 4-12 The dehydration synthesis of a molecule of glucose and a molecule of fructose forms 1 molecule of sucrose and 1 molecule of water.

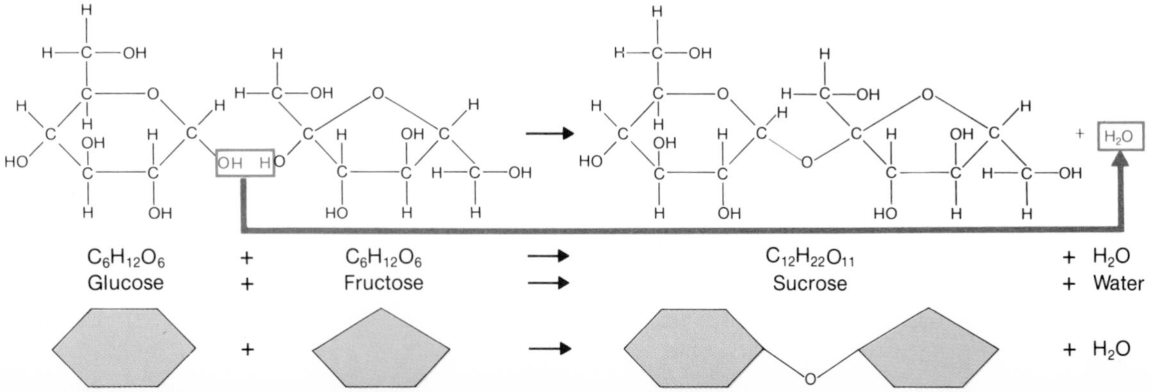

for these types of monosaccharides is $C_6H_{12}O_6$. However, the structural formula of each is different.

Another class of carbohydrates is the *disaccharides*, or double sugars. *Di*saccharides are composed of *two* monosaccharides. Two common examples of disaccharides are *sucrose*, or table sugar, and *maltose*, or malt sugar. Disaccharides are formed by a process called **dehydration synthesis** (dē-hī-DRĀ-shən SIN-thə-sis), shown in Figure 4-12. During dehydration synthesis, small molecules bond to form larger molecules. For every 2 monosaccharide molecules that bond to form a disaccharide, 2 hydrogen atoms and 1 oxygen atom are released as a molecule of water.

The *polysaccharides* are another class of carbohydrates. *Poly*saccharides are formed by the dehydration synthesis of *many* monosaccharides. *Cellulose* (SEL-yoo-lōs), found in fruits and vegetables, is an example of a polysaccharide. *Starches*, also polysaccharides, are found in certain parts of plants. A starch may be changed to a simple sugar and used by an organism as an immediate source of energy, or it may be stored for future use. Another polysaccharide, *glycogen*, is sometimes called animal starch because it is stored in the liver and muscle cells of animals. When energy is needed, the glycogen is broken down to form glucose.

Just as larger molecules of carbohydrates can be formed by dehydration synthesis, they can also be broken down by a process called **hydrolysis** (hī-DRAHL-ə-sis). Hydrolysis takes place when water is added. Figure 4-13 shows that hydrolysis is the exact opposite of dehydration synthesis.

The hydrolysis of carbohydrates and other substances that an organism takes in as food occurs during *digestion*, or the breaking-down process of food. Food must be broken down into smaller molecules before it can enter a cell. Once inside a cell, the smaller molecules bond to form larger molecules by dehydration synthesis. These larger molecules can then be used to form new cell parts.

$C_6H_{12}O_6$	+	$C_6H_{12}O_6$	→	$C_{12}H_{22}O_{11}$	+	H_2O
Glucose	+	Fructose	→	Sucrose	+	Water
	+		→		+	H_2O

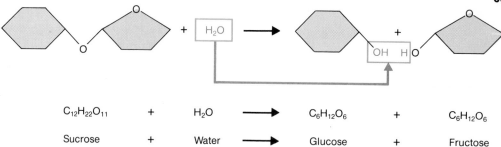

$$C_{12}H_{22}O_{11} \quad + \quad H_2O \quad \longrightarrow \quad C_6H_{12}O_6 \quad + \quad C_6H_{12}O_6$$

Sucrose $\quad + \quad$ Water $\quad\longrightarrow\quad$ Glucose $\quad+\quad$ Fructose

Figure 4-13 The hydrolysis of 1 molecule of sucrose forms 1 molecule of glucose and 1 molecule of fructose.

PROTEINS AND AMINO ACIDS The second group of organic compounds important in biology are the **proteins** and **amino acids.** The word protein comes from the Greek word *proteios*, which means "of first importance." Proteins are used to build and repair the cells of living things. They are also used in cell growth and maintenance. Meats, poultry, fish, and cheese are examples of foods containing large amounts of protein.

Proteins include the elements carbon, hydrogen, oxygen, and nitrogen. Sulfur is also found in some proteins. Only small amounts of other elements, such as phosphorus, iron, and zinc, are found in proteins.

Proteins are made of molecules of up to about 20 different kinds of amino acids strung together like beads. Hundreds of these amino acids may bond together in different combinations to form proteins. A molecule of an amino acid is made up of three groups of atoms. One group is called an *amino group.* The structural formula for an amino group is

$$-N\substack{\diagup H \\ \diagdown H}$$

Its chemical formula is $-NH_2$. The second group is called a *carboxyl group.* The structural formula for this group is

$$-C\substack{\diagup\!\!\!= O \\ \diagdown O-H}$$

Figure 4-14 Peptide bonds form during the dehydration synthesis of amino acids.

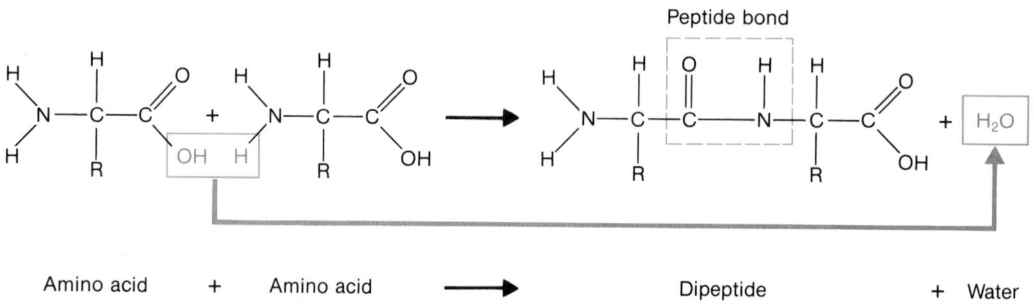

Amino acid $\quad+\quad$ Amino acid $\quad\longrightarrow\quad$ Dipeptide $\quad+\quad$ Water

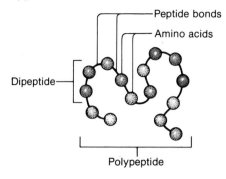

Figure 4-15 Amino acids are linked by peptide bonds. Groups of two amino acids are dipeptides. Groups of more than two are polypeptides.

Its chemical formula is –COOH. The third group, called an *R group*, consists of a hydrogen atom or a group of hydrogen and carbon atoms. Different amino acids have different R groups.

Amino acids, like carbohydrates, bond by the process of dehydration synthesis. A *dipeptide* is formed when the amino group of one amino acid bonds with the carboxyl group of another. The bond that forms between the two groups is called a *peptide bond*. A peptide bond joins a carbon atom with a nitrogen atom. This process is shown in Figure 4-14 on page 69. When more than two amino acids bond, they form a large molecule called a *polypeptide*. When many polypeptides bond, they form a protein. See Figure 4-15.

LIPIDS Compounds that are oily, greasy, waxy, or fatty are called **lipids.** In living organisms, lipids form part of the cell membrane. For animals, they provide protection, in-

CAREER: Biochemist

Scientists who study the chemistry of living things are called biochemists. The work of biochemists helps us to understand many life processes, such as metabolism, reproduction, and heredity. Their work also gives us important information about the effects of food, drugs, and other chemicals on living things. By performing chemical tests on living things, biochemists develop new and better ways to study chemical changes that occur in plants and animals.

In laboratories, biochemists may use highly complex electronic and automated equipment. These machines can quickly analyze compounds or chart changes in the behavior of a cell or organism. Some biochemists who work in hospitals perform chemical tests on the blood and other body fluids of patients. The information that they gather from these tests helps doctors diagnose and treat certain illnesses.

An important part of the work of biochemists is reporting their findings to other scientists. Their findings usually appear as written reports in professional journals or as oral reports presented at scientific meetings. Because of constant new developments, it is essential that biochemists keep up to date in their field.

A bachelor's degree, with a major in chemistry or biochemistry, is needed to become a bio-

chemist. In many instances, a doctorate, with a specialization in a particular area of biochemistry, is required. Biochemists may specialize in research. The agriculture, food, and pharmaceutical industries employ biochemists as researchers. In addition to doing research, biochemists may teach at colleges and universities. Other biochemists work for federal and state agencies. These agencies test new products for safety and establish standards for production and testing procedures.

For further career information, write to American Society of Biological Chemists, 9650 Rockville Pike, Bethesda, MD 20014.

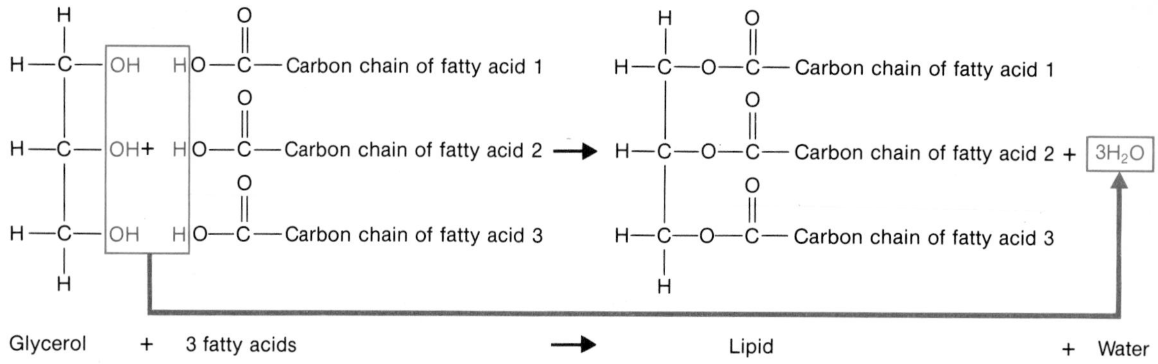

Glycerol   +   3 fatty acids   ⟶   Lipid   +   Water

Figure 4-16 A lipid forms by the dehydration synthesis of 3 molecules of fatty acids and 1 molecule of glycerol.

sulation, and energy. Salad and cooking oils, butter, and mayonnaise are foods that contain lipids or *fats*.

Like carbohydrates, lipids contain the elements carbon, hydrogen, and oxygen, although lipids do not have the same hydrogen-to-oxygen-atom ratio as do carbohydrates. Phosphorus and nitrogen also occur in some complex lipids. Lipids are formed by the dehydration synthesis of three molecules of *fatty acids* and a molecule of *glycerol*. See Figure 4-16. Fatty acids are long chains of carbon and hydrogen atoms that contain a carboxyl group. Glycerol is an example of a compound called an *alcohol*. All alcohols contain a *hydroxyl group*—an oxygen atom bonded to a hydrogen atom. The chemical formula for a hydroxyl group is −OH.

At this point, you may want to assign to several students the second of the Extensions and Applications at the end of this chapter.

NUCLEIC ACIDS   The special complex molecules that determine the transmission of characteristics in cell reproduction are called **nucleic acids.** Nucleic acids store genetic information, control cellular activity, and direct the making of proteins. There are two types of nucleic acids. *Deoxyribonucleic acid* (dē-ahk-sē-rī-bō-noo-KLĒ-ik AS-id), or *DNA*, contains the material that carries the "genetic message"—manufacturing instructions for the cell. A type of *ribonucleic acid* (rī-bō-noo-KLĒ-ik AS-id), or *RNA*, "reads" the message from DNA. With the help of this type of RNA and others, the amino acids in the cell are bonded in the proper order to produce different cell proteins.

ENZYMES   Cells make special proteins called **enzymes.** Enzymes enable many cellular chemical reactions to take place. Enzymes act as **catalysts,** chemicals that help to speed up reactions without themselves being changed.

Enzymes are *specific*, that is, they have certain jobs. For example, the enzyme that hydrolyzes maltose is *maltase*. Notice that the prefix of the name (*malt-*) is derived from the compound on which the enzyme works. The names of enzymes usually end in -*ase*. See Figure 4-17 on page 72.

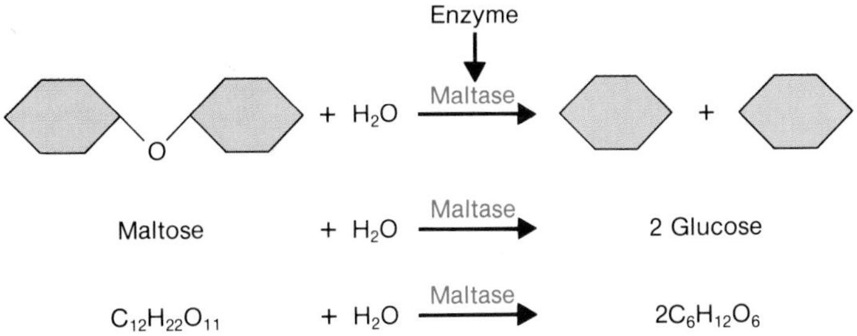

72

Enzyme

Maltose + H_2O $\xrightarrow{\text{Maltase}}$ 2 Glucose

$C_{12}H_{22}O_{11}$ + H_2O $\xrightarrow{\text{Maltase}}$ $2C_6H_{12}O_6$

Figure 4-17 The enzyme maltase hydrolyzes maltose. What is the name of the enzyme that hydrolyzes sucrose? Sucrase

Figure 4-18 Miller's experiment provided evidence that simple compounds, which may have been present in the earth's early atmosphere, could react to form amino acids.

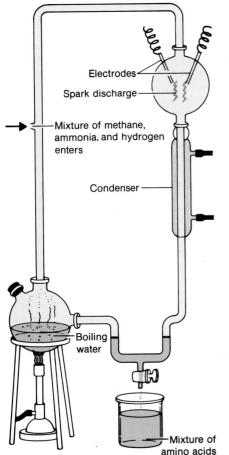

Electrodes
Spark discharge
Mixture of methane, ammonia, and hydrogen enters
Condenser
Boiling water
Mixture of amino acids

Oparin's Hypothesis

Many scientists today think that organic molecules developed chemically from nonliving matter billions of years ago. One *hypothesis*, or explanation, of the chemical origin of organic substances was published by the Russian biochemist Alexander Ivanovich Oparin in 1938. His hypothesis proposed that the atmosphere of the earth was once made up of ammonia, methane, hydrogen, and water vapor. He also thought that the earth was bombarded with energy in the form of heat, ultraviolet light, and lightning. He thought that this energy caused the breaking and the joining of chemical bonds, forming simple organic compounds such as the amino acids. After a time, more complex molecules were formed. Eventually, self-reproducing molecules like nucleic acids developed. This explanation is now the most widely held concept of the origin of organic substances.

In 1953 Stanley Miller, an American scientist, found evidence to support Oparin's hypothesis. In his laboratory, Miller put a mixture of ammonia, methane, hydrogen, and water vapor in a sealed container and then sent electrical sparks through it. Soon after, amino acids appeared. Since then many scientists have performed similar experiments and have produced a large variety of organic compounds. These experiments do not prove that these events took place long ago, but they show that such events could have taken place.

SECTION REVIEW   Answers on page T–32.

1. What is the difference between organic and inorganic compounds?
2. What are the characteristics of carbohydrates, proteins, amino acids, lipids, nucleic acids, and enzymes?
3. What is dehydration synthesis? Hydrolysis?
4. Name the two types of nucleic acids.
5. What is Oparin's hypothesis? Who found evidence to support Oparin's hypothesis?

LABORATORY INVESTIGATION 4 For additional information, see page T–32.

Observing Mixtures and Compounds

Purpose Many substances in living things are found in mixtures. For example, cytoplasm is largely a colloidal mixture. The purpose of this investigation is to determine some of the properties of different kinds of mixtures and compounds.

Materials (*per group*) ● Iron filings ● Powdered sulfur ● Salt ● Powdered clay ● Powdered gelatin ● Bar magnet ● Beaker ● Funnel ● Filter paper ● Paper towels ● Heat source ● 5 small jars numbered 1 to 5 with lids ● Test tubes ● Test-tube holder and rack ● Safety goggles

Procedure   Part A   1. Obtain 7 g of iron filings and 4 g of sulfur from your teacher. Observe and list the physical characteristics of each of these substances. **2.** After mixing the iron and sulfur together, devise a way to separate them. **3.** Remix the substances and set them aside. **Part B   1.** Half fill jar 1 with water. Add some salt to the water. **2.** Cover the jar and shake vigorously until the salt is dissolved. Continue adding salt until no more salt will dissolve. Observe and list the characteristics of the salt and water mixture. **3.** To determine whether the salt and water mixture can be separated, filter the mixture into a beaker. **4. CAUTION:** *Be very careful when heating materials. Wear safety goggles.* Using a heat source, slowly evaporate all the liquid in the beaker. **5.** Record your results. **Part C   1.** Half fill jar 2 with water. Add some clay to the water. Cover the jar and shake it vigorously for 30 seconds. **2.** Pour half of the clay and water into jar 3. Set this jar aside for now. **3.** Without heating the water, devise a way to separate the clay and water. **4.** Compare the mixtures in jars 2 and 3. **5.** Record your observations. **Part D 1.** Obtain 2 to 3 g of gelatin from your teacher. **2.** Half fill jar 4 with water. Add the gelatin. **3.** Shake vigorously until the gelatin is completely dissolved. **4.** Pour half of the mixture into jar 5. Set this jar to the side for now. **5.** Filter the mixture in jar 4. **6.** Compare the mixtures in jars 4 and 5. **7.** Record your observations. **Part E   1.** Place the sulfur and iron filings mixture from Part A into a test tube.

2. CAUTION: *Use safety goggles for Part E.* Gently heat the iron and sulfur mixture. When a distinct glow appears in the mixture, remove the test tube from the heat. **3.** Allow the test tube to cool for 5 to 10 minutes. Then wrap the test tube in a paper towel and have your teacher crack it with a hammer. **4.** Observe and list the characteristics of the substance formed.

Observations and Conclusions   1. In Part A, how can you separate the iron filings from the sulfur? **2.** How do the mixtures in Parts B and C differ? How are they alike? **3.** In Part B, what type of mixture is formed? In Part C? In Part D? **4.** What happens to the salt in Part B after the liquid is evaporated? **5.** How can you separate the clay and water without heating the water? Can you recover all of the clay particles? Explain your answer. **6.** In Part C, what changes can you observe in jar 3 by the end of the class? **7.** In Part D, what happens to the mixture in jar 5 when it is filtered? What happens to the mixture in jar 4 after it remains undisturbed for a time? **8.** After heating, what happens to the sulfur and iron in Part E? What is the new substance called? **9.** How is the substance in Part E different from the mixture of iron and sulfur in Part A?

73

CHAPTER SUMMARY

Matter and Living Things   Matter is defined as anything that occupies space and has mass. Within the cell, matter can be changed chemically to produce energy and perform cellular activities.

All matter is made up of atoms. Most kinds of atoms contain three types of subatomic particles: protons, neutrons, and electrons. An atom is the smallest particle of an element. An element is a substance that contains only one type of atom. Isotopes are forms of the same element that differ in the number of neutrons.

When two or more elements chemically combine, a compound forms. Compounds are formed by covalent or ionic bonding. Covalent bonding is the sharing of electrons between atoms. Ionic bonding is the transfer of electrons from one atom to another. The charged atoms that form during ionic bonding are called ions.

Mixtures are made up of two or more substances that do not chemically react. Three types of mixtures are solutions, suspensions, and colloids.

Compounds Important to Living Things   Living things contain two groups of compounds: inorganic and organic. Most inorganic compounds are composed of elements other than carbon. Organic compounds contain the element carbon and usually hydrogen or both hydrogen and oxygen.

The organic compounds may be divided into five groups: carbohydrates; proteins and amino acids; lipids; nucleic acids; enzymes. Carbohydrates are used mainly for energy and are divided into three classes: monosaccharides, disaccharides, and polysaccharides. Proteins are used to build, repair, and maintain cellular parts. The building blocks of proteins are called amino acids. Lipids, or fats, are used to form certain cell parts and also are used for protection and insulation in organisms. Lipids are composed of glycerol and fatty acids. The nucleic acids DNA and RNA transmit characteristics from one cell to another and control cellular activity. Enzymes are special proteins that regulate chemical reactions in living organisms.

Small organic molecules can form larger ones by joining together by dehydration synthesis. These large molecules may be broken down into smaller ones by hydrolysis.

Many scientists now think that organic molecules arose from nonliving matter billions of years ago. One widely accepted explanation is Oparin's hypothesis.

CHAPTER VOCABULARY

amino acid	element	molecule
atom	enzyme	neutron
carbohydrate	hydrolysis	nucleic acid
catalyst	inorganic compound	organic compound
chemistry	ion	protein
colloid	ionic bond	proton
compound	isotope	solution
covalent bond	lipid	suspension
dehydration synthesis	matter	
electron	mixture	

REVIEW of FACTS and CONCEPTS   Answers on pages T–32 to T–33.

On a separate sheet of paper, answer each of the following as completely as possible.

1. Why is the study of chemistry so important to the understanding of biology?
2. What is matter? Describe the three states of matter.
3. Distinguish between a physical and a chemical property of matter.
4. State the Law of Conservation of Matter. Give an example.

5. How is an atom related to an element?
6. Draw the atomic model of sulfur (atomic number 16, atomic mass number 32).
7. Draw atomic models for the isotopes carbon-12 and carbon-14 (atomic number 6). What is the difference between these two atoms?
8. Using atomic models, distinguish between covalent and ionic bonding.
9. Distinguish between solutions, suspensions, and colloids. Give a specific example for each of these mixtures.
10. How are inorganic and organic compounds different?
11. List four groups of organic compounds and the characteristics of each group.
12. What groups of substances are considered sources of energy?
13. Using structural formulas, illustrate the process of hydrolysis. Why is this process important to living cells?
14. Draw a generalized structural formula for an amino acid. Identify the parts of this molecule.
15. How are lipids and carbohydrates similar? How are they different?
16. Name the two types of nucleic acids. What is their importance in the cell?
17. What are enzymes? Why are they referred to as catalysts? What would happen to cellular reactions if there were no enzymes?
18. Explain Oparin's hypothesis.

EXTENSIONS and APPLICATIONS   For additional information, see page T–33.

1. Visit a local medical center to investigate some of the uses of isotopes in medicine and research. Make a report to the class on your findings.
2. Find out more information about carbohydrates, proteins, and lipids in the diet. Discuss the importance of these substances in maintaining good health.
3. Construct models of the following covalent and ionic compounds: hydrogen sulfide (H_2S), carbon dioxide (CO_2), magnesium oxide (MgO), and lithium chloride ($LiCl$). You will need to consult a chemistry text to find out the number of sub-

atomic particles and energy levels in each atom. On posterboard, draw a circle to represent the nucleus of each atom. Write the number of protons and neutrons in each circle. Draw the correct number of energy levels around each nucleus. To represent the electrons, cut out discs of construction paper about the size of a quarter. Put a small piece of double-backed tape on each disc. Place the discs in the proper positions of the electrons in the energy levels of each atom. Show how each compound is formed by sharing or transferring electrons.

SUGGESTED READINGS

Asimov, I., *Building Blocks of the Universe*. New York: Abelard.
 A brief description of the more than 100 elements is presented. Emphasis is placed on such elements as oxygen, carbon, hydrogen, and nitrogen.
Baker, J.J.W., and G.E. Allen, *Matter, Energy, and Life*. Reading, Mass.: Addison-Wesley.
 The fundamentals of chemistry needed to understand certain processes of biology are covered.
Farago, P., and J. Lagnado, *Life in Action—Biochemistry Explained*. New York: Alfred A. Knopf.
 The chemical processes that made life possible are explored. Recent biochemical discoveries that have opened up new possibilities in controlling disease, genetics, aging, and ecology are also discussed.
Judson, H.F., *The Eighth Day of Creation*. New York: Simon and Schuster.
 The author equates the current revolution in biological thought with that in physics earlier in this century. The discoveries in molecular biology are traced through interviews with many of the scientists who contributed to them.

5 Cell Structure and Function

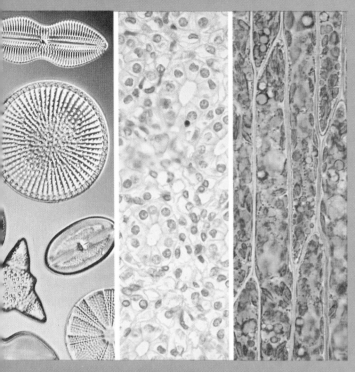

Diatoms, the human kidney, and moss are made of cells.

Chapter Objectives *After completing this chapter, you will be able to:*

a ■ Outline the major contributions to the study of cells. p. 77

b ■ State the cell theory. p. 77

c ■ List the life functions of a cell. p. 80

d ■ Identify the basic structures in a typical cell. p. 81

e ■ Describe the functions of the various cell structures. p. 82

f ■ Compare a prokaryotic cell and a eukaryotic cell. p. 90

For teaching aids for this chapter, including a chapter overview and teaching strategies, see pages T–33 to T–35. The page number next to each chapter objective refers to the text page where the information needed to fulfill the objective begins.

The **cell** is the basic structural and functional unit of all living things. Cells are living units of matter and can reproduce. They contain organic compounds, including proteins, lipids, and carbohydrates. Cells also contain large amounts of inorganic materials, such as water and simple salts.

The study of cells is called **cytology,** or *cell biology.* Cytologists study cells to learn about organisms in the same way that chemists study atoms to learn about matter.

Since most single cells cannot be seen with the unaided eye, the science of cytology did not begin until the microscope was invented in the seventeenth century. In fact, this new science did not progress much until microscopes with greater magnification were built in the nineteenth century.

Development of the Cell Theory

The study of cells began in the middle of the seventeenth century when Robert Hooke, an English scientist, looked at thin slices of cork under a microscope. Hooke reported his observations in 1665 in an article called *Micrographia*. Hooke wrote that a thin slice of cork appeared to be made up of "boxes," or "cells." He used the word cell to describe structural appearance only. No one yet knew that cells were both the structural and the functional units of living things.

At about the same time, a Dutch inventor and scientist, Anton van Leeuwenhoek (vahn LĀ-vən-hook), was using a microscope to study objects such as blood, rainwater, and scrapings from his teeth. Van Leeuwenhoek observed and made drawings of small organisms in his tooth scrapings that he called "animalcules." Beginning in 1676, he sent a series of letters to the Royal Society of London describing the microscopic structure of these organisms. The smallest of these "animalcules" are known today as *bacteria*, one-celled microscopic organisms.

In 1824, a French scientist, R.J.H. Dutrochet (doo-truh-SHĀ), stated that all plant and animal tissues were made up of groups of cells. He explained that tissue growth was due to the growth of individual cells, both in size and in number.

Working at about the same time as Dutrochet, Felix Dujardin (doo-zhar-DAN), a French biologist, was studying living single-celled organisms. In 1835, he stated that single-celled organisms were complete, self-sufficient living things. He also said that the living parts of all cells were made up of a "pellucid substance," which is now called *protoplasm*.

In 1838, Mathias Schleiden, a German botanist, announced that all plants were made up of cells. One year later, Theodor Schwann, a German zoologist, reported that all animals were made up of cells. Schleiden and Schwann then proposed that cells were the basic units of structure and function in all living things. This concept came to be known as the *cell theory*.

Biologists have continued to expand the cell theory since it was first stated. In 1855, a German physician, Rudolf Virchow, stated that all living cells come only from other living cells. This idea is called the *principle of biogenesis* (bi-ō-JEN-ə-sis).

Highlight

Today, the cell theory states that (1) cells are the basic unit of structure and function in living things; (2) living cells are produced from other living cells; (3) the activity of an entire organism depends on the total activity of its independent cells.

SECTION REVIEW   Answers on page T–34.

1. Who first described cells?
2. What was the cell theory proposed by Schleiden and Schwann?

Size, Shape, and Organization of Cells

Cells vary in size. Some cells, such as the yolk of an ostrich egg, are large enough to be seen with the unaided eye. However, most cells are too small to be seen without the aid of a microscope.

Cells also have different shapes. Some are shaped like long boxes, spheres, or discs. Others are rod-shaped or spiral-shaped. Still others, such as the amoebas, do not have a definite form and change shape all the time. Most plant cells are shaped like long boxes, but there is a great diversity of shape among animal cells. The shape of both animal and plant cells is related to their function. For example, human red blood cells are shaped like doughnuts with a thin solid center instead of a hole. This shape provides these cells with a very large surface area for their volume. Therefore, red blood cells are able to pick up a large amount of oxygen in the lungs. By contrast, human nerve cells are very long and

Figure 5-1 Cells have various shapes and functions. In multicellular organisms, cells are specialized and function together. In unicellular organisms, a single cell exists as a free-living organism that functions alone.

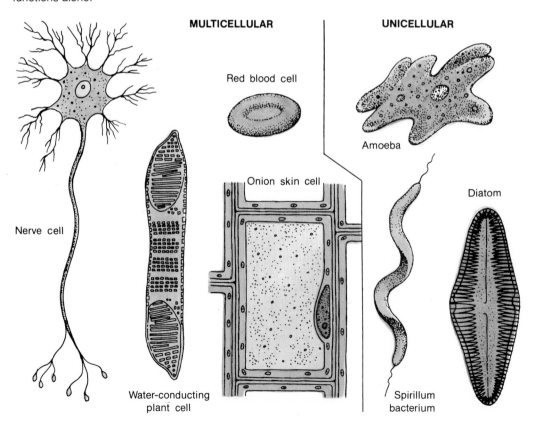

MULTICELLULAR UNICELLULAR

Red blood cell

Amoeba

Onion skin cell

Diatom

Nerve cell

Water-conducting plant cell

Spirillum bacterium

have many branches. This shape permits nerve cells to transmit messages more efficiently from the brain and spinal cord to distant parts of the body, and vice versa.

Besides varying in size and shape, cells vary in the ways they are organized. Some cells function alone and are called *unicellular organisms*. These include bacteria and *Amoebas*. Other cells join to form various kinds of colonies. Some colonies consist of only one kind of cell. They are called *identical colonies*. An example is *Volvox*, which lives in water.

Although the cells in *Volvox* are all of the same kind, some perform different functions than do others. Scientists observe that a *Volvox* colony moves through the water toward a light source. This happens in an orderly way because cells at the front of the colony have better-developed light-sensitive *eyespots* than do cells at the back of the colony. However, reproduction is carried out only by a few cells at the back of the colony. These different functions are signs of *cell specialization*. That is, the cells have different functions that help the entire organism to survive.

Cell specialization is more complex in an organism such as the Portuguese man-of-war. The Portuguese man-of-war is a colony like *Volvox*, but unlike *Volvox* the man-of-war is made up of different kinds of cells. For example, some of its cells produce a poison and a kind of stinger. Other cells form the structure of the organism's tentacles. Because the Portuguese man-of-war colony is made up of such different cells, it is called a *diversified colony*.

More complex cell specialization is a characteristic of *multicellular organisms*, such as human beings. In multicellular organisms, every kind of cell depends on every other kind of cell for its survival and for the survival of the entire organism. In human beings, for example, red blood cells carry oxygen to all body cells to release energy vital to cell functions. Using this energy, nerve cells send messages to muscle cells in organs, such as the heart. The heart muscle cells contract and send red blood cells to the lungs for oxygen. The red blood cells then carry oxygen to all the other cells in the body. All of the body's cells work together to keep the body functioning normally.

Sidelight

The largest cell is the yolk of an ostrich egg. It is about the size of a baseball. However, most cells are only about 0.0025 centimeters long and therefore microscopic.

SECTION REVIEW   Answers on page T–34.

1. What is the difference between a unicellular organism and a multicellular organism?
2. Based on what you know about the sizes of cells, why was the development of the microscope important to cytology?

Cell Functions

Although the cells in multicellular organisms are specialized, every cell must also be able to carry out the chemical processes and functions necessary to life. These processes and functions include the following.

Nutrition and Digestion   All living things need food for *nutrition*. Nutrition is the use of food for energy and growth. Every cell needs food and energy to carry out its functions. Within cells, large food molecules must be *digested*, or broken down into simple forms, before they can be used by the cells. Some cells, such as those of green plants, make their own food, using carbon dioxide, water, and other nutrients. Organisms that cannot make their own food must get their food from the environment.

Absorption   Cells take in food, oxygen, and other necessary substances from their surroundings through a process called *absorption*.

Transport   Once molecules of food, oxygen, and so on are absorbed, they can be moved within the cell. In multicellular organisms, some cells have the ability to transport substances from one place to another.

Biosynthesis   Cells are continuously making new compounds for use in cell growth, repair, and reproduction. The process of building new, larger chemical compounds from smaller ones is called **biosynthesis.** For example, cells make the enzymes needed to help many chemical reactions take place. These chemical reactions produce new compounds.

Secretion   In a multicellular organism, newly made substances are not necessarily used within the cell that makes them. The vitamins and hormones that a cell makes, for example, may be needed in other parts of the organism. Therefore, cells must be able to *secrete* (si-KRĒT), or release, substances within the organism. Once the substances are secreted, they can be used locally or carried to other parts of an organism by a transport system.

Respiration   Energy is released when the bonds of organic compounds are broken during the chemical process of *respiration*. The energy that is released is used by the cell to carry out all life functions.

Sidelight

The term *biosynthesis* is often used interchangeably with the term *nutrition*. Some scientists consider the cell's conversion of raw materials from the environment into useable substances or products a part of nutrition.

Excretion Waste products are formed during cell functions. Cells get rid of waste products through *excretion*. If waste products are not removed, they eventually poison the cell and interfere with other life processes. Individual cells must rid themselves of wastes. In multicellular organisms, specialized groups of cells eliminate wastes from the whole organism.

Response All cells react to their environment. Many factors, such as chemicals, temperature, and light, act as *stimuli* that affect the activities of cells. Even simple unicellular organisms respond to stimuli. *Euglena*, for example, responds to light.

Reproduction Most cells reproduce by *fission*. During fission, one cell divides to form two new identical cells. In a unicellular organism, cell reproduction results in the formation of new organisms. In a multicellular organism, fission results in an increase in the number of cells. *Body cells*, such as the cells that make up your skin, reproduce this way.

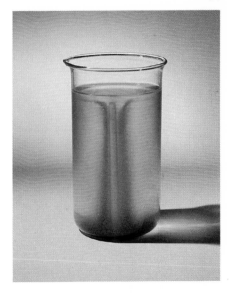

Figure 5-2 The sides and top of this beaker were covered with a can in which a vertical slit was cut. The euglenas in the beaker moved out of the darkened areas and also avoided the area of the slit where bright light entered The euglenas moved to the areas of semidarkness on either side of the slit and on the bottom of the beaker. (LIFE SCIENCE LIBRARY—*The Cell*, photograph by Sol Mednick, Time-Life Books, Inc., publisher.)

SECTION REVIEW   Answers on page T–34.

1. List several of the processes and functions of a cell.
2. What are the differences between biosynthesis, respiration, and digestion?
3. By what process dò most cells reproduce?

Cell Structures

The term **protoplasm** is used to describe the materials in a cell. Protoplasm is not a single substance. It is made up of many different substances and structures. The makeup of protoplasm varies in different types of cells.

Using the most recent techniques for cell study, cytologists have discovered many organized structures within cells. These small structures are called **organelles.** The term organelle means "little organ." Organelles carry out the life functions of the cell.

Some cells have specialized organelles that are not found in other cells. For example, some plant cells have special organelles for making carbohydrates. Some cells contain more organelles than other cells. For example, cells that produce many complex proteins, such as the hormone *insulin*, need more organelles for making proteins than do other types of simpler cells.

Throughout your discussion of cell structures, you should stress to your students that just as the cell is separated from its environment by a membrane so are the organelles separated from the cell's environment by membranes.

Cell Wall

The **cell wall** is the nonliving outermost structure of most plant cells. Animal cells do not have cell walls. The cell wall is one of the major differences between an animal cell and a plant cell.

The cell wall of a plant cell provides protection and support for the cell. It is made up mostly of *cellulose* (SEL-yoo-lōs), a carbohydrate that is made by plant cells. The cell wall also contains other substances, such as *pectin* and *lignin*, that make the wall harder. Although the cell wall is hard, it allows water, oxygen, carbon dioxide, and other dissolved materials to pass through it.

With the aid of the electron microscope, cytologists have discovered that the cell wall is made up of two or more layers. In soft plant parts, such as leaves and soft fruits, cell walls have two layers. The cell walls of harder plant parts, such as stems, may have more than two layers.

The first layer of a cell wall to be formed is called the *middle lamella.* The middle lamella is formed where two cells meet. It is formed by both cells and holds the cells tightly together.

Pectin is found in the middle lamella of many fruits. As a fruit ripens, it becomes softer. This softness occurs as the pectin in the fruit begins to dissolve. As the pectin continues to dissolve, the cells that make up the fruit become less tightly held together.

On either side of the middle lamella, thin *primary walls* form. In harder plant parts, the cells form other layers called *secondary walls*. Secondary walls are made up of cellulose and lignin. They provide more support and protection for individual cells and for the entire plant.

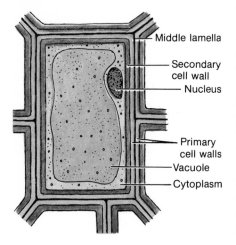

Figure 5-3 The wall of a plant cell has a primary wall, a middle lamella, and a secondary wall.

Middle lamella

Secondary cell wall

Nucleus

Primary cell walls

Vacuole

Cytoplasm

Cell Membrane

The **cell membrane,** or *plasma membrane,* is the boundary of an animal cell. Plant cells also have a cell membrane located just inside the cell wall. Unlike the cell wall, the cell membrane is part of the cell's living substance.

One of the most important functions of the cell membrane is to regulate the movement of materials in and out of the cell. Everything that the cell needs, from nutrients to gases, must enter the cell through the cell membrane. All waste products and secretions must exit through the cell membrane.

The cell membrane is generally *permeable* to small molecules and ions and *impermeable* to large molecules. A permeable membrane allows substances to pass through it.

Large molecules pass in and out of a cell by special transport processes, which are discussed in Chapter 6.

Because the cell membrane regulates which substances pass in and out of the cell, it is a *selectively* permeable membrane. This kind of control is important to *homeostasis.* Homeostasis is the ability of a cell to maintain a stable internal environment as changes occur in the environment outside the cell.

Cell membranes are made of lipid and protein layers. Cell membranes differ in the amount and chemical makeup of the proteins and lipids that they contain.

The *fluid mosaic model* is the most generally accepted description of the arrangement of lipids and proteins in the cell membrane. Figure 5-4 shows a fluid mosaic model. Proteins are scattered within and throughout a double layer of lipid molecules. Lipid and protein molecules can move within the membrane, although the lipids tend to be more moveable than the protein molecules. Most scientists think that lipid and protein molecules aid in the transport of certain materials through cell membranes.

Animal cells also have *cell coats*. Cell coats are formed by carbohydrates bonded to the protein and lipid molecules of the cell membrane. The compounds formed are *glycoproteins* (carbohydrates and protein) and *glycolipids* (carbohydrates and lipids). Under an electron microscope, a cell coat looks like a fuzzy layer on the surface of the cell. Cell coats may help cells respond to their environment.

Figure 5-4 The fluid mosaic model shows an arrangement of lipid and protein molecules in the cell membrane. The arrangement of the molecules accounts for some of the properties of the cell membrane.

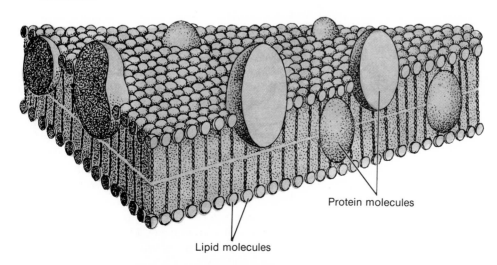

Protein molecules

Lipid molecules

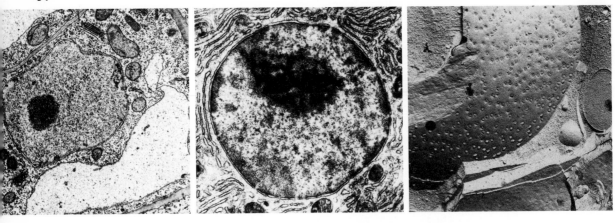

Figure 5-5 The nucleus is surrounded by a double-layered nuclear membrane and contains a dark nucleolus (*left*). Small openings called nuclear pores perforate the nuclear membrane (*center*). A scanning electron micrograph reveals many nuclear pores on the surface of a nuclear membrane (*right*). What is the function of these pores?

The nuclear pores permit materials to pass in and out of the nucleus.

Nucleus

The **nucleus** is a large oval or spherical structure within the cell. It is made up of proteins, enzymes, and hereditary material. The nucleus is the control center of the cell. It directs all of the activities of the cell, including reproduction.

Most cells contain one nucleus. However, some cells, such as certain muscle cells in human beings, may have more than one nucleus. Other cells, such as the one-celled protozoan *Paramecium*, always have two nuclei. The red blood cells of mammals do not have a nucleus for most of their lives. Once a red blood cell matures, it loses its nucleus. Since a cell cannot live very long without a nucleus, cells without a nucleus have a limited life span. They also cannot reproduce or repair themselves.

Highlight

The nucleus is the control center of the cell.

NUCLEAR MEMBRANE The nucleus is surrounded by a thin, double-layered membrane called the *nuclear membrane*. The two layers are separated by a space. The nuclear membrane is a boundary that separates the **nucleoplasm** from the rest of the cell. However, the membrane is not solid and permits materials to pass in and out of the nucleus. The nucleoplasm is the thick, protein-rich protoplasm in the nucleus. The nuclear membrane enables the nucleus to maintain an environment different from the environment of the rest of the cell.

NUCLEOLUS Within the nucleus, there may be a small body called the **nucleolus** (noo-KLĒ-ə-ləs). Some nuclei contain more than one nucleolus. The nucleolus is made up of RNA and protein. It plays an indirect role in making proteins.

CHROMATIN MATERIAL   Also within the nucleus is a large, irregular mass of thin threads called the **chromatin material.** Chromatin is made up of DNA, RNA, and proteins. It forms the *chromosomes* during cell reproduction. Chromosomes direct the activities of the cell and pass on the traits of the cell to new cells.

Cytoplasm

The clear, thick protoplasm that fills the space between the cell membrane and the nucleus is called the **cytoplasm.** In a living cell, the cytoplasm is always moving. The cytoplasm is a *colloid* in which the organelles of the cell are suspended. All of the materials needed by a cell are moved within the

CAREER: Cytologist

People who study the structure and growth of cells are called cytologists. Using special equipment, they slice pieces of tissue into very thin sections and stain them with special dyes. Staining makes parts of a cell easier to see. Because some parts of a cell absorb more stain than others, staining enables cytologists to differentiate parts of the cell.

Using microscopes, cytologists study the different parts of cells and their functions. Cytologists often study specific kinds of cells. Some do research in the physiology of one-celled organisms. Others study plant cells or human cells.

Cytology has important medical applications, for example in the diagnosis of cancer. An early sign of cancer is the rapid growth of abnormal cells. Detecting such cells enables a doctor to diagnose and begin treating cancer long before the disease can be found by other methods.

Cytologists generally have medical or Ph.D. degrees. Those in entry-level positions are called cytotechnicians. They have completed at least two years of college, or they have had two years of work-study experience in a program approved by the Accrediting Bureau of Medical Laboratory Schools.

Many cytologists work for universities and medical schools. Some work in hospitals or private laboratories. Some work for government agencies, such as the National Institutes of Health.

For further career information, write to American Society of Cytology, Health Sciences Center, Suite 810, 130 South 9th Street, Philadelphia, PA 19107.

cytoplasm. Many life functions, including the making of proteins, are carried out in the cytoplasm.

RIBOSOMES Cells contain small organelles that are the site for making proteins. These are called **ribosomes.** All cells need proteins for growth, repair, and many metabolic functions. Many ribosomes float freely in the cytoplasm.

ENDOPLASMIC RETICULUM The **endoplasmic reticulum,** or ER, is a canal-like membrane system within the cytoplasm. Some of the ER is attached to the nuclear membrane and the cell membrane.

On some of the ER, the surface is dotted with ribosomes that contain large amounts of RNA. The endoplasmic reticulum that has ribosomes attached to it is called *rough ER.* If the ER has no ribosomes attached to it, it is called *smooth ER.*

The main functions of rough ER are protein production and transport. Proteins can be transported to various parts of the cell through the rough ER. Materials can also be carried to the outside of the cell through this membrane system. Smooth ER contains many enzymes that are necessary for **cell metabolism,** the breaking down of foods and the building up of cell substances.

Figure 5-6 This electron micrograph shows the canal-like structure of the endoplasmic reticulum and the double-walled membrane and cristae of a mitochondrion. Compare the labeled drawings of these structures with the electron micrograph.

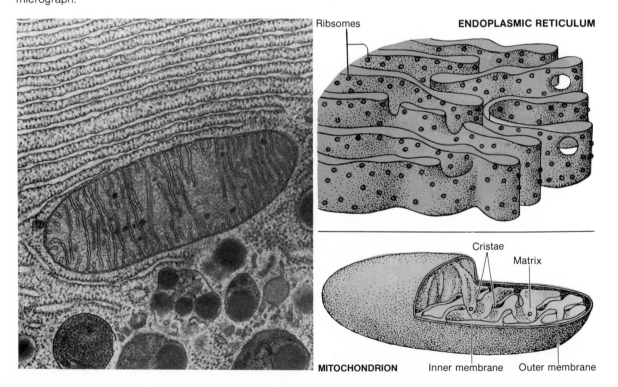

Ribsomes

ENDOPLASMIC RETICULUM

Cristae

Matrix

MITOCHONDRION   Inner membrane   Outer membrane

MITOCHONDRIA   The **mitochondria** (mīt-ə-KAHN-drē-ə) are complex, oval rod-shaped structures. They are among the largest organelles in the cell. Each mitochondrion is made up of an outer membrane and an inner membrane. The inner membrane has many folds in it called *cristae* (KRIS-tē). A semifluid *matrix* fills the space between the cristae. The matrix contains DNA and ribosomes. Together, these are used to make proteins for growth and for the reproduction of the mitochondria.

Mitochondria are often referred to as the powerhouses of the cell. The main function of the mitochondria is to continue the *oxidation,* or breakdown, of sugars that starts in the cytoplasm. The mitochondria supply most of the energy for the cell. Cells that need a great deal of energy have more mitochondria than cells that need less energy. For example, muscle cells contain many more mitochondria than do bone cells.

Explain to your students that mitochondria are somewhat independent organelles in that they can make proteins for their own growth and reproduction.

Sidelight

Some cells, such as a human liver cell, contain more than 1000 mitochondria.

VACUOLES   Both plant and animal cells have **vacuoles** (VAK-yoo-ōlz). A vacuole is a spherical, membrane-bounded organelle. Plant cells often have one large vacuole that takes up 80% to 90% of the cell. Animal cells have only a few small vacuoles. Small vacuoles are often called *vesicles*.

Vacuoles have many different functions. They usually store food, enzymes, and other materials needed by the cell. They are also the temporary dumping sites for waste products. The large vacuoles in plant cells are often filled with water. Some unicellular organisms have specialized vacuoles called *contractile vacuoles*. Contractile vacuoles act as water pumps, removing excess water from the cell.

LYSOSOMES   Small round organelles that contain enzymes are called **lysosomes** (LĪ-sə-sōmz). They are found in the cytoplasm of animal cells but have not been widely observed in plant cells.

Lysosomes are able to join with food vacuoles. The enzymes in the lysosomes digest food molecules. The membrane surrounding a lysosome prevents the enzymes from escaping and digesting the entire cell. However, lysosomes do digest whole cells when they are injured, exposed to certain chemicals, or die. These organelles are also helpful in destroying bacteria.

GOLGI APPARATUS   In 1898, an Italian scientist, Camillo Golgi (kə-MIL-ō GŌL-jē), discovered an organelle made up of a series of closely stacked, flattened sacs. This organelle, which is called the **Golgi apparatus,** may contain 3 to 20 sacs.

88

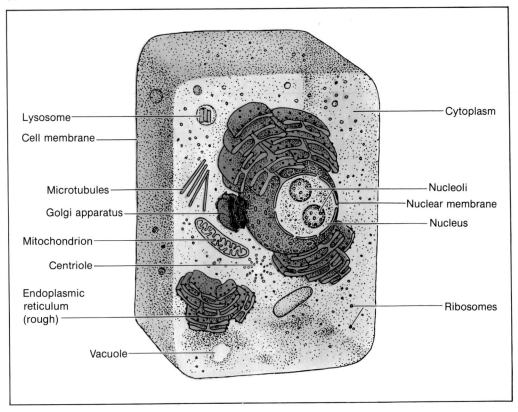

Figure 5-7 Model of a Typical Animal Cell

The Golgi apparatus packages substances that are to be secreted from the cell. Other substances, such as proteins, are transported from the endoplasmic reticulum to the Golgi apparatus. The Golgi apparatus then packages large groups of protein molecules in vesicles. Although the cell secretes most of these packages of protein molecules, scientists think that some remain in the cell as lysosomes.

PLASTIDS   Plant cells and some unicellular organisms contain **plastids.** Plastids are organelles that make or store food. A white or colorless plastid called a *leucoplast* (LOO-kə-plast) stores oils, starches, and proteins. Leucoplasts are common in seeds.

A type of plastid where food is made or stored is a *chromoplast.* Chromoplasts contain different kinds of pigments that give them color. The most familiar chromoplasts are the *chloroplasts.* Chloroplasts contain the pigment *chlorophyll* that gives most plants their characteristic green color.

Sidelight

Chromoplasts give carrots their orange-red color and tomatoes their red color.

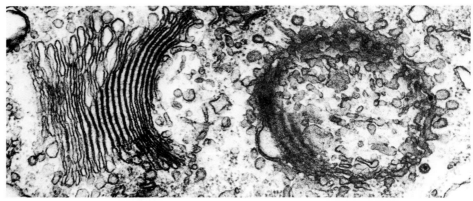

Chloroplasts are large, double-membraned organelles that vary in size and shape among different organisms. Within the chloroplasts are membranes called **grana**, which are made up of layers of chlorophyll, proteins, and lipids.

MICROTUBULES AND MICROFILAMENTS In animal cells, thin, hollow cylinders made of protein called **microtubules** (mī-krə-TOOB-yoolz) perform many jobs. Cytologists think that they help maintain the shape of animal cells by acting as a kind of cell "skeleton." Microtubules may also provide channels for the movement of substances in cells. These structures also form *spindle microtubules*, which are involved in cell reproduction.

Smaller, thin protein fibers in the cytoplasm are called **microfilaments.** They are involved in changes in the shape of cells. The contraction of muscle cells is caused by microfilaments. In plant cells, microfilaments are involved in the

Figure 5-8 The electron micrograph shows a cross section *(left)* and a top view *(right)* of a Golgi apparatus. Compare the drawing of the Golgi apparatus with the electron micrograph.

At this point, you may want to have your students do the Laboratory Investigation at the end of this chapter.

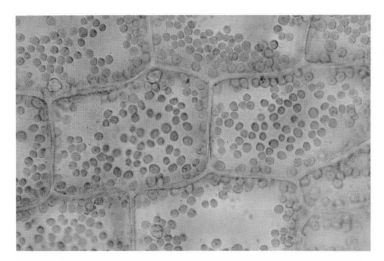

Figure 5-9 Chloroplasts float in the cytoplasm of plant cells.

movement of the protoplasm. Cytologists do not fully understand how microfilaments cause movement or changes in the shape of cells.

CENTRIOLES   Most animal cells and some plant cells have two small organelles called **centrioles** (SEN-trē-ōlz). The centrioles appear to be necessary for cell reproduction in cells that possess them.

In a cell that is not dividing, or reproducing, the centrioles are found near the Golgi apparatus. In a dividing cell, the centrioles move to opposite ends of the cell.

Prokaryotes and Eukaryotes

Cytologists group cells in two general classes according to their internal structure. The simplest cells are called **prokaryotes** (PRŌ-kar-ē-ōts). The word prokaryote means "before the nucleus." Prokaryotic cells contain nuclear material, although the material is not enclosed in a nuclear membrane. Bacteria and blue-green algae are typical prokaryotes. Cells that have a more organized structure are called **eukaryotes** (YOO-kar-ē-ōts). The word eukaryote means "true nucleus." The nucleus is enclosed in a membrane. Eukaryotic cells are found in animals and most plants.

Eukaryotic cells have many organelles that perform different functions. Prokaryotic cells do not have most of the organelles found in eukaryotic cells. The hereditary material of a prokaryotic cell is not in the form of chromosomes. Instead, it is scattered through the cytoplasm or appears as a strand of nucleic acid.

Although many prokaryotes have a cell wall, its composition is different from that of the cell wall of plants. As simple as the structure of prokaryotes may seem, they are cells that are capable of carrying out all life functions and exist as free-living organisms.

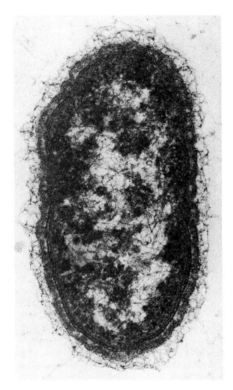

Figure 5-10   The cell in this electron micrograph has a nuclear area rather than a distinct nucleus.

SECTION REVIEW   Answers on page T-34.

1. What is the difference between protoplasm, cytoplasm, and nucleoplasm?
2. What are organelles? Give two examples.
3. How do plant and animal cells differ?
4. What is the function of the nucleus?
5. Name the two types of endoplasmic reticulum and their functions.
6. What are the functions of lysosomes?
7. What is the Golgi apparatus?
8. Name the two general classes of cells.

Examining Plant and Animal Cells

Purpose   A knowledge of cell structure is important in understanding cell functions. The structural similarities and differences among plant and animal cells can be seen easily with a light microscope. The purpose of this investigation is to examine the basic structure of a plant cell and an animal cell.

Materials *(per group)*   ● 1 small onion ● Forceps
● Scalpel ● 2 glass slides ● Methylene blue stain
● 2 cover slips ● Microscope ● Several flat
toothpicks ● Iodine solution ● 2 medicine
droppers ● Paper towels ● Scissors

Procedure   Part A: Onion Cells   1. Using the scalpel, cut the onion into quarters. Use the forceps to remove a piece of the thin layer of transparent epidermal tissue from the inner surface of the onion. **2.** Place a drop of water on one slide. Then, cut off a small piece of the epidermal tissue and place it *flat* in the drop of water. Cover it with a cover slip. **3.** Examine the onion tissue under the low and high powers of the microscope. **4.** Remove the slide from the microscope. Place a drop of iodine stain near one edge of the cover slip. Touch a piece of paper towel to the *opposite* edge. The stain will be drawn under the cover slip and into the tissue. **5.** Reexamine the stained onion tissue under the low and high powers of the microscope. Make drawings of the onion cells under low and high power. Label all of the cell structures that you observe.   **Part B: Cheek Cells   1.** Using the broad end of a flat toothpick, gently scrape the inside of your cheek.   **2.** Place one drop of water on the second slide. Carefully mix the scrapings in the drop of water. **Note:** *The edge of the toothpick will probably look as though there is nothing on it.* Cover the drop of water and scrapings with a

cover slip.   **3.** Examine the mixture under the low and high powers of the microscope.   **4.** Remove the slide from the microscope. Using the same staining technique as in Part A, stain the cheek cells with methylene blue.   **5.** Reexamine the cheek cells under the low and high powers of the microscope. Make drawings of the cheek cells under low and high power. Label all of the cell structures that you observe.

Observations and Conclusions   1. How many cell layers make up the onion tissue?   **2.** What is the general shape of the onion cells? The cheek cells? **3.** Why do you have to stain the cells?   **4.** Which parts of the cell stain darker than the other parts? **5.** What differences can you see in the cells? **6.** Which cells are larger?   **7.** What structures do both cells have in common?

CHAPTER SUMMARY

Development of the Cell Theory The study of cells, called cytology, began when the microscope was invented in the seventeenth century. Robert Hooke and Anton van Leeuwenhoek were the first scientists to describe what are now known as cells. In the nineteenth century, Schleiden and Schwann established the cell theory, which states that cells are the units of structure and function in all living things. Rudolf Virchow added that all living cells come only from other living cells.

Size, Shape, and Organization of Cells Some cells exist as free-living, unicellular organisms. Some unicellular organisms live in organized colonies of identical cells. Some organisms, such as the Portuguese man-of-war, are diversified colonies of the same cell species. In complex multicellular organisms, the cells exhibit cell specialization. These cells are dependent on one another.

Cell Functions Every cell must be able to carry out the chemical processes and functions necessary to life. These processes and functions are nutrition and digestion, absorption, transport, biosynthesis, secretion, respiration, excretion, response, and reproduction.

Cell Structures All cells are made up of protoplasm. The protoplasm includes the cell membrane, the nucleus, cell organelles, and the cytoplasm. The nonliving part of most plant cells is the cell wall. The nucleus is a cell's control center. The cytoplasm carries out many cell life functions. Within the cytoplasm are organelles, small structures that have distinctive shapes and functions. Organelles include the endoplasmic reticulum, mitochondria, vacuoles, lysosomes, the Golgi apparatus, plastids, microtubules, microfilaments, and centrioles.

Cells are classified in two general groups, prokaryotes and eukaryotes. A prokaryotic cell has a nuclear area without a membrane and few organelles. A eukaryotic cell has a distinct nucleus surrounded by a membrane and many organelles. Most types of cells are eukaryotes.

CHAPTER VOCABULARY

biosynthesis	endoplasmic reticulum	nucleoplasm
cell	eukaryote	nucleus
cell membrane	Golgi apparatus	organelle
cell metabolism	grana	plastid
cell wall	lysosome	prokaryote
centriole	microfilament	protoplasm
chromatin material	microtubule	ribosome
cytology	mitochondria	vacuole
cytoplasm	nucleolus	

REVIEW of FACTS and CONCEPTS   Answers on pages T–34 to T–35.

On a separate sheet of paper, answer each of the following as completely as possible.

1. What were the contributions of Hooke, van Leeuwenhoek, Dutrochet, Dujardin, and Virchow to the development of the understanding of the cell?
2. List the main ideas of the cell theory.
3. What is cell specialization?
4. Based on your knowledge of cells, explain this statement: "Unicellular organisms are often more complex than the individual cells of multicellular organisms."

5. What is meant by cell metabolism?
6. What is the function of the cell wall in plant cells?
7. Why is it important for the cell membrane to be selectively permeable?
8. Explain the fluid mosaic model of the cell membrane.
9. If you were given a plant cell and an animal cell, how could you tell the difference?
10. Name the three basic parts of most cells.

11. Explain the structure of the mitochondria. What is their function?
12. What are the functions of vacuoles in different types of cells?
13. What are the different types of plastids? How do they differ?
14. Name the chemical processes and functions that are part of cell metabolism. Which organelles are involved in each process or function?
15. How do prokaryotic cells and eukaryotic cells differ?

EXTENSIONS and APPLICATIONS   For additional information, see page T–35.

1. Using a light microscope, observe some of the objects that Hooke and van Leeuwenhoek observed, such as cork, rain water, scrapings from your teeth, and prepared slides of blood. Make drawings of what you observe. In several reference books, find pictures of Hooke's and van Leeuwenhoek's work. Compare them with your drawings.
2. Prepare a time line that illustrates the events that led to the cell theory.
3. The aging process is a recent area of study in biology. Find out more about the role of lysosomes in the process of aging. Find current articles in magazines about aging. Prepare an illustrated report that could be presented to your class.
4. Pick some leaves and petals from several different plants. Make wet mount slides of thin slices of the leaves and petals. Observe the slides under the microscope. Prepare a set of drawings. Note any differences and similarities.

SUGGESTED READINGS

Cudmore, L.L.L., *The Center of Life: A Natural History of a Cell.* New York: Quadrangle/The New York Times Book Co.
The author describes the process involved in the development of a single cell as it develops into a complex, self-sustaining organism.
Gillie, O., *The Living Cell.* New York: Funk and Wagnalls.
The structures and functions of cells are explained with numerous illustrations and photomicrographs that make the book easy to follow and interesting to read.
Swanson, C.P., and P. Webster, *The Cell.* Englewood Cliffs, N.J.: Prentice-Hall.
Basic cellular anatomy and reproduction are clearly explained with drawings and photographs.

6 Cell Energy and Maintenance

All living things use energy to perform activities.

Chapter Objectives *After completing this chapter, you will be able to:*

a ■ State the difference between kinetic and potential energy. p. 95
b ■ Explain the role of enzymes in biochemical reactions. p. 95
c ■ State the structure and importance of ATP. p. 97
d ■ Define homeostasis. p. 99
e ■ Describe the difference between diffusion and osmosis. p. 101
f ■ Explain the changes in cells in different solutions. p. 102
g ■ Explain the importance of turgor pressure in plant cells. p. 103
h ■ Explain the processes of active transport. p. 104

For teaching aids for this chapter, including a chapter overview and teaching strategies, see pages T–35 to T–37. The page number next to each chapter objective refers to the text page where the information needed to fulfill the objective begins.

The work of the billions of cells in your body keeps you alive. Every cell is constantly using *energy*. Energy is the ability to cause change or do work. For example, muscle cells use energy to enable you to walk, breathe, pump blood, and even to speak. When the muscles are working hard, muscle cells need even more energy. In the brain, cells are constantly using energy to sort information, guide body movements, and control vital life functions. Every activity or movement requires energy. Even when you are sleeping, energy is needed to maintain life functions.

Where do you get the energy to run a race, to play baseball, or even to talk or get up in the morning? All living things get their energy either directly or indirectly from the sun. Plants get their energy directly from the sun. Animals get their energy indirectly from the sun through the foods they eat. The foods contain stored energy that comes directly or indirectly from the sun.

Cell Energy

Every cell in your body is like a miniature factory that produces many different chemical reactions. Some of these chemical reactions use energy, while others release energy. Your body needs energy to permit muscle movement, to maintain body temperature, to make new molecules, and to control body functions.

One of the most important jobs of each cell is to provide energy. However, cells do not make energy. The *Law of Conservation of Energy* states that energy can be neither created nor destroyed but can only be changed from one form to another. Therefore, cells must obtain energy from the environment and change it into a useable form. What are the types of energy? How does a cell change energy from one form to another?

Types of Energy

You may want to have your students discuss various forms of energy, such as heat, light, electrical, nuclear, mechanical, and chemical.

All living cells transform **potential energy,** or stored energy, into a useable form. Potential energy is stored energy. It can be released from a chemical bond to be used to do work. When cells need energy, they break chemical bonds and change potential energy into immediately useable forms.

Energy is needed to break the chemical bonds in which the potential energy is stored. The energy needed to trigger this process is called **activation energy.** An example of activation energy is the energy of a lighted match held under a sheet of paper. The paper has potential energy stored in the chemical bonds of its substances. The energy from the match flame causes these bonds to start breaking. Energy stored in the bonds is released in the forms of light and heat as the paper burns.

Enzymes and Chemical Reactions

You may want to discuss some of the factors that affect the rate of enzyme action. Among these factors are temperature, the amount of substrate, and pH.

Within an organism, biochemical reactions that result in the breakdown of molecules and the release of energy are called **catabolic reactions.** Digestion and cellular respiration are examples of catabolic reactions. Other biochemical reactions called **anabolic reactions** synthesize, or build, new molecules. Cell repair and growth involve anabolic reactions. Energy is needed for these reactions to occur.

Anabolic reactions usually take place only if catabolic reactions occur at the same time. However, the chance of anabolic and catabolic reactions occurring simultaneously

96

Enzymes are needed to start almost every chemical reaction that takes place in living things.

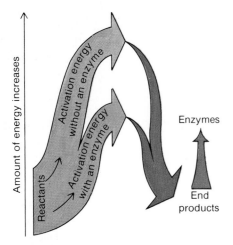

Figure 6-1 Enzymes lower the activation energy needed to begin a reaction and also increase the rate of the reaction.

At this point, you may want to assign to several students the first of the Extensions and Applications at the end of this chapter.

and on their own is very small. To survive, cells must not only make these reactions occur together, but when and where they are needed. What causes these reactions to begin? What causes them to occur together? What controls them?

Within an organism are special molecules called *enzymes*. Enzymes act as catalysts, speeding up the rate of reactions that might otherwise progress too slowly to be of use to the organism. Enzymes are released unchanged at the end of the reaction.

Enzymes lower the activation energy without adding heat. They permit reactions to occur at a temperature that is normal for an organism. In an experiment in a test tube, heat energy can be used to speed up a reaction. In a living organism, heat energy cannot be used because excess heat would either be harmful to the organism or destroy the enzymes.

NAMES OF ENZYMES Enzymes are usually named for the reaction they cause or for their *substrate*. A substrate is the substance upon which the enzyme acts. Most enzyme names end in the letters *-ase*. The enzyme *sucrase* is named for the substrate *sucrose*. Some enzymes are named for the reaction they cause and their substrate, such as the enzyme *DNA polymerase*, which helps make molecules of DNA.

Enzymes that were named before the late nineteenth century do not have the *-ase* ending. Some of these names are still used today, such as *pepsin* and *trypsin*. These two enzymes break down proteins in the digestive system.

LOCK AND KEY HYPOTHESIS Every enzyme is made up of a different protein and has a specific shape. Each enzyme reacts with a specific substrate. The part of the enzyme that reacts with the substrate is called the *active site*. The part of the substrate that reacts with the enzyme is called the *reactive site*. Scientists do not know exactly how enzymes work. However, they have proposed several explanations for enzyme-substrate reactions.

In 1894, the *lock and key hypothesis* was proposed to explain the reactions of enzymes and substrates. This hypothesis states that the active site of a certain enzyme fits exactly with the reactive site of a specific substrate. Figure 6-2 shows a model of the lock and key hypothesis.

In 1958, the *induced fit theory* was introduced. This theory states that the active site of an enzyme must adjust to fit the reactive site of the substrate. As the enzyme and the substrate join, the enzyme may change slightly in shape to fit the substrate better.

LOCK AND KEY HYPOTHESIS

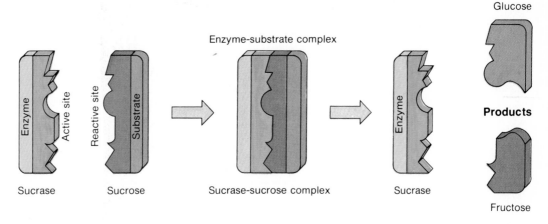

Figure 6-2 In the lock and key hypothesis, an enzyme and its substrate fit together like two pieces of a jigsaw puzzle.

In both the lock and key hypothesis and the induced fit theory, a specific interaction occurs between the enzyme's active site and the substrate's reactive site. During the interaction, the enzyme and the substrate are joined by weak chemical bonds that are made and broken easily. Look at the equation for the breakdown of sucrose by sucrase.

$$\text{sucrase + sucrose} \longrightarrow \text{sucrase-sucrose complex} \longrightarrow$$
$$\text{sucrase + glucose + fructose}$$
$$\text{enzyme + substrate} \longrightarrow \text{enzyme-substrate complex} \longrightarrow$$
$$\text{enzyme + product}$$

COENZYMES Many enzymes are made up of protein and a nonprotein part. A nonprotein molecule found in some enzymes is called a **coenzyme.** Coenzymes are organic molecules that work with enzymes. A coenzyme bonds weakly to the protein part of an enzyme, and can join and leave it easily. Coenzymes are needed for certain chemical reactions to take place.

Some coenzymes are made of vitamins or their parts. Organisms cannot make most vitamins and must take them in as part of their food. If vitamins are lacking, certain coenzymes cannot be made and the organism's metabolism does not function normally.

ATP

One of the most important coenzymes in every living thing is *adenosine triphosphate*, or **ATP.** ATP is important because it can store energy and control the release of energy within a cell. ATP is composed of a *base*, a *sugar*, and three

Sidelight

Vitamin deficiency diseases are caused by a scarcity or absence of certain vitamins in the diet. Scurvy is a vitamin deficiency disease caused by a lack of vitamin C.

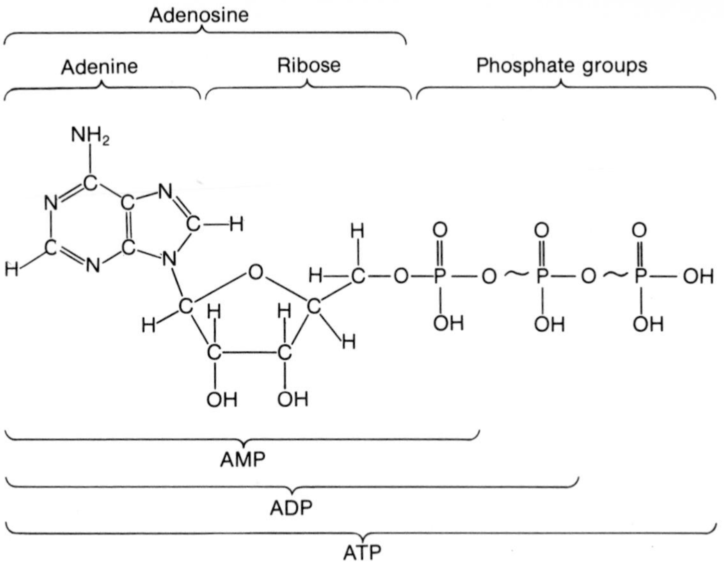

Figure 6-3 Structural Formulas for AMP, ADP, and ATP.

phosphate groups. The base of ATP, called *adenine,* is made up of the elements nitrogen, carbon, and hydrogen. These elements are covalently bonded. Bonded to the base is a sugar molecule called *ribose.* Adenine and ribose form *adenosine.* The molecule of ATP is completed by the three phosphate groups. If the molecule has only one phosphate group, it is *adenosine monophosphate,* or **AMP.** If only two phosphate groups are present, the compound is *adenosine diphosphate,* or **ADP.**

In a molecule of ATP, the bonds holding the second and third phosphate groups are called *high-energy bonds.* A great deal of energy is needed to attach these phosphate groups in the ATP molecule. High-energy bonds are indicated by the symbol $\sim(P)$. The (P) represents a phosphate group. Energy is released when these high-energy bonds are broken. When the bond that attaches the third phosphate is broken, the most energy is released. During this reaction, ATP is changed to ADP, a free phosphate group, and energy. If you think of ATP as $A-P\sim P\sim P$, the reaction would be as follows.

$$A-P\sim P\sim P \rightarrow A-P\sim P + (P) + energy$$

Only under certain conditions does the cell use ADP as an energy source. If the bond is broken between the two phosphate groups of the ADP molecule, the ADP changes to AMP. This reaction can be represented as follows.

$$A-P\sim P \rightarrow A-P + (P) + energy$$

Highlight

Energy needed by living things is obtained when the high-energy bonds of ATP are broken. ATP is converted to ADP which in turn can be converted to AMP.

When a high-energy phosphate is changed to a low-energy phosphate, the process is called hydrolysis. When a low-energy phosphate is changed to a high-energy phosphate, the process is called phosphorylation.

The bond holding the phosphate group of AMP to the rest of the molecule has very little energy. The cell does not usually use this bond as a source of energy.

In the cells, the ATP picks up and stores energy from any catabolic reaction and then releases this energy for any anabolic reaction. The energy for anabolic reactions is provided when ATP changes to ADP. As bonds are broken during catabolic reactions, energy is released. This released energy can be used immediately by a cell to bond a phosphate group onto a molecule of ADP, reforming ATP. The energy is then stored in the third phosphate bond until it is needed. In this way, ADP and ATP control the cell's energy production through a continuous cycle of energy storage and release.

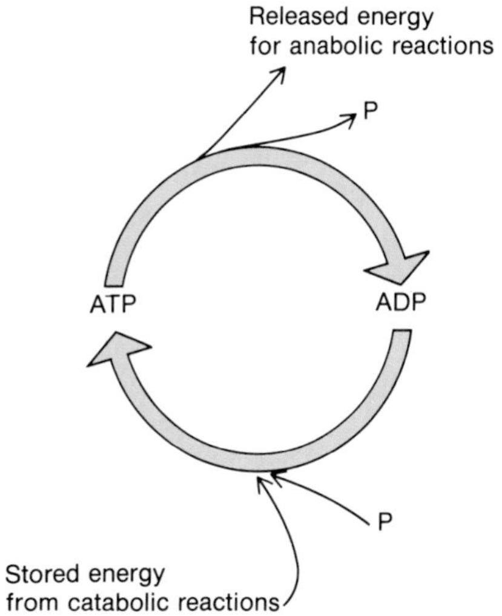

SECTION REVIEW   <small>Answers on page T–36.</small>

1. What does the Law of Conservation of Energy state?
2. What is potential energy?
3. What is meant by catabolic reaction? Anabolic reaction?
4. How are the lock and key hypothesis and induced fit theory similar?
5. What is a coenzyme?
6. What is the importance of ATP in living things?

Figure 6-4 Cell energy is stored and released in a continuous cycle.

Homeostasis and Passive Transport

If you took your temperature either while lying on the beach on a hot summer day or while walking on a cold, snowy day, it would be about 37 °C. Unless you have a *fever*, your temperature always stays about the same. Maintaining a constant body temperature is an example of **homeostasis** (hō-mē-ō-STĀ-sis). Homeostasis is the ability of an organism to maintain a constant internal balance regardless of changes in its external environment. Homeostasis is necessary for survival. If an organism cannot keep its internal environment relatively constant, it cannot survive.

Homeostasis occurs at all organizational levels within an organism—from cells to organ systems. In complex organisms, such as human beings, the organ and body systems work closely together to maintain the proper balance of oxygen, salts, water, and other substances the body needs. The organs and body systems also work to maintain the proper body temperature, blood pressure, and heart rate.

Many scientists consider homeostasis one of the most important processes in biology. Stress to your students that every organism encounters changes in its environment and within itself and must adjust to the changes that upset its internal balance. You may want to have your students try to give examples of homeostasis in people or in other organisms.

At the cellular level, each individual cell exists in a fluid environment. Food molecules, oxygen, water, and other materials must be able to pass into and out of the cell. Each cell must constantly work to maintain homeostasis. The cell must keep its cytoplasm at a constant pressure within its membrane or the cell may shrink or burst. However, there are times when environmental factors prevent cells from maintaining a proper balance. For example, some saltwater fish cannot survive in fresh water. The cells of these fish cannot maintain a proper internal balance of water and salt in a freshwater environment.

There are several ways in which the proper balance of substances is maintained in cells. One way is through a process called **passive transport.** In passive transport, energy is not required to move substances in and out of the cell through its membrane. The movement of oxygen into your cells and the removal of carbon dioxide from them is an example of passive transport.

CLOSE-UP: *Dr. Louise Slade*

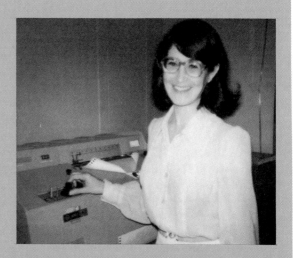

Dr. Louise Slade is a biochemist whose special interest is enzyme research. Dr. Slade's laboratory is not located on a university campus or at a research institute. Instead, it is in a technical center in Tarrytown, New York, operated by one of America's largest food companies. The company prepares and packages food that you eat every day, such as cereals, chocolate, and frozen vegetables. It also works to find new kinds of food, such as new sources of food protein. This is Dr. Slade's job.

Dr. Slade uses enzymes to change substances that the human body cannot easily digest into nutritious food. Enzymes are proteins that cause chemical changes to occur in certain substances. For example, gelatin is made from the protein in cowhide and pigskin that enzymes have changed chemically into food protein. However, gelatin has little nutritional value by itself. It cannot replace such protein sources as meat. One of Dr. Slade's projects is to find a protein that gels like a gelatin but also provides high-quality nutrition. Dr. Slade is exploring milk whey, soybeans, and seaweed as sources of protein. When transformed by enzymes, these substances have potential as more nutritious protein foods than they now are.

"As traditional protein sources, such as meat, become increasingly expensive, and as supplies become limited, the idea is to find new protein sources to replace the old," she states. Dr. Slade's knowledge of enzymes is important to her search for new protein sources.

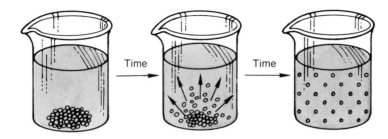

Time   Time

Figure 6-5   When a solid substance that can dissolve in water is placed in a beaker of water, the solid eventually diffuses throughout the water until molecules of the solid are evenly distributed throughout the water.

Diffusion

One type of passive transport is **diffusion.** In diffusion, molecules, atoms, or ions move from a region of higher concentration to a region of lower concentration. The movement is possible because the molecules, atoms, or ions have **kinetic energy,** or energy of motion. Within a given space, molecules, atoms, ions, and even small particles constantly move in a straight path. When they hit something, such as another molecule, the wall of a container, or a cell membrane, they bounce off the object or membrane and continue in another direction. Under a microscope, this movement is seen as a jiggling motion called *Brownian movement,* named after an English botanist, Robert Brown. Eventually, this random movement causes the particles to spread evenly throughout the space. This movement is a property of particles of gases dissolved in one another, and of solids, liquids, or gases dissolved in a liquid.

Diffusion is important for the movement of some substances through the cell membrane. Because the cell membrane is *selectively permeable,* it permits only certain substances to diffuse in and out of the cell. Substances such as oxygen and food molecules pass into cells. Waste products, such as carbon dioxide, pass out of cells. The process of diffusion moves oxygen from red blood cells into body cells. Red blood cells coming from the lungs have a high concentration of oxygen. Body cells have a low concentration of oxygen because they continuously use oxygen to carry out life processes. Carbon dioxide becomes more highly concentrated in body cells, where it is produced, than in red blood cells. Diffusion moves carbon dioxide out of the body cells.

Several factors affect the rate of diffusion and the direction of the movement.

Concentration Diffusion takes place from areas of higher concentration to areas of lower concentration. The greater the differences in concentration, the more rapidly diffusion takes place.

At this point, you may want to have your students do the Laboratory Investigation or the second of the Extensions and Applications at the end of this chapter.

Highlight

The rate and direction of diffusion are affected by concentration, pressure, and temperature.

Pressure Diffusion takes place from areas of higher pressure to areas of lower pressure. High pressure forces molecules closer together. Molecules move faster and become more concentrated, which increases the rate of diffusion.

Temperature Diffusion takes place from areas of higher temperature to areas of lower temperature. As the temperature of a substance is increased, the molecules diffuse more rapidly.

Osmosis

You may want to set up a demonstration of osmosis using water and a sugar solution.

Another type of passive transport is **osmosis.** Osmosis is the diffusion of water through a selectively permeable membrane. Water molecules can easily pass through a cell membrane. The movement of water in and out of a cell plays a major role in maintaining cell homeostasis. However, the cell cannot control this movement. The water molecules move from an area of high concentration of water to an area of low concentration of water by their own kinetic energy.

Water can dissolve many substances. The concentration of *solute*, or dissolved substances, affects the movement of water in and out of a cell. If a solution outside the cell has the same concentration of solute and the same concentration of water molecules as the contents of a cell, the solution is **isotonic.** The movement of water molecules into and out of the cell is equal, and the cell neither loses nor gains water. If the solution outside the cell has a higher concentration of solute and a lower concentration of water than the solution inside the cell, the solution is **hypertonic.** More water moves out of the cell than enters it, and the cell shrinks. In a **hypotonic** solution, the concentration of solute is lower outside the cell than inside. As a result, more water rushes into

Highlight

Isotonic solutions have the same concentration of solute and water molecules as found in the contents of a cell. Hypertonic solutions have a higher concentration of solute molecules and a lower concentration of water molecules than the contents of a cell. Hypotonic solutions have a lower concentration of solute molecules and a higher concentration of water molecules than the contents of a cell.

Figure 6-6 During osmosis, water molecules move by their own kinetic energy through a selectively permeable membrane from an area of high concentration of water to an area of low concentration of water.

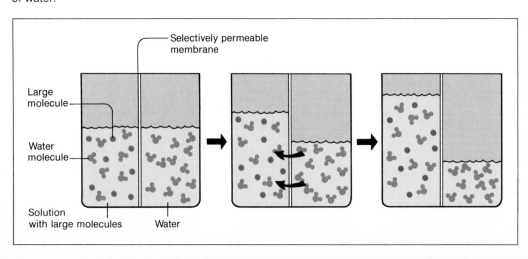

Selectively permeable membrane

Large molecule

Water molecule

Solution with large molecules

Water

the cell than leaves it, causing the cell to swell and possibly burst.

OSMOTIC PRESSURE When the molecules of a solute outside the cell are too large to pass through the cell membrane, the concentration of the solute outside the cell increases. As this concentration increases, the concentration of water outside the cell decreases. Therefore, water inside the cell moves out of the cell at a more rapid rate. Eventually, a point is reached where the water outside the cell exerts a pressure that is equal to the pressure exerted by the water leaving the cell. The pressure exerted by the water outside the cell is called **osmotic pressure.** At this time, no more water leaves the cell than enters it. Osmosis continues in both directions at an equal rate.

TURGOR PRESSURE A plant cell has one large vacuole that contains a hypertonic solution. Usually, the fluid that surrounds the plant cell is hypotonic. Therefore, water molecules move from the surrounding fluid (area of high concentration of water) through the cell wall and membrane into the vacuole (area of low concentration of water) by osmosis. As water enters the vacuole, the vacuole swells and pushes the cytoplasm and nucleus against the cell wall. Water continues to enter the cell until the pressure within the cell equals the pressure outside the cell. The pressure exerted by the cell contents against the cell wall is called **turgor pressure.**

Because the cell wall does not stretch very much, turgor pressure causes the cell to become stiff. In plants, these stiff cells help support soft tissues, such as soft stems, petals, and leaves. If there is not enough water in the environment, turgor pressure cannot be maintained, and the soft tissues wilt.

Animal cells do not have a rigid cell wall. Instead, they have a flexible membrane that expands with an increase in turgor pressure. If the cells do not get rid of some of the water, the cell membrane eventually bursts. Many unicellular animals, such as paramecia and amoebas, live in ponds and other hypotonic freshwater environments. These organisms have specialized structures called *contractile vacuoles*. These vacuoles act as small water pumps, collecting extra water and pumping it out of the cell.

Plasmolysis

Loss of turgor pressure is called **plasmolysis.** In plant cells, the movement of water from the cell vacuole causes the cell contents to shrink away from the cell wall. Shrinking

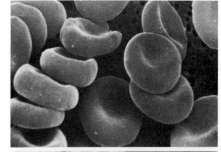
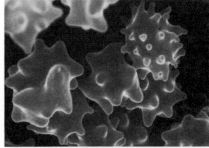
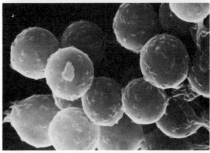

Figure 6-7 Red blood cells have a disk shape in isotonic solutions (*top*). In hypertonic solutions, red blood cells shrink and their cell membranes form folds (*center*). In hypotonic solutions, red blood cells swell and become spherical (*bottom*).

Figure 6-8 If a plant does not receive enough water, its cells begin to lose turgor pressure, and its soft tissues begin to wilt.

At this point, you may want to assign to the class the third of the Extensions and Applications at the end of this chapter.

and swelling of cells can be demonstrated using a stalk of celery, salt, and a glass of water. If a high concentration of salt is dissolved in water and the celery is placed in the solution, the cells in the celery stalk lose water through osmosis, causing the stalk to wilt. If the celery stalk is placed in tap water, water enters the vacuoles by osmosis. Turgor pressure is restored, and the celery stalk becomes stiff again.

SECTION REVIEW   Answers on page T–36.

1. What is homeostasis?
2. What is meant by passive transport?
3. What is Brownian movement?
4. What factors affect the rate and direction of diffusion?
5. What is an isotonic solution? a hypotonic solution? a hypertonic solution?
6. What is osmotic pressure?

Homeostasis and Active Transport

Cells maintain homeostasis by controlling the substances that pass in and out of the cell. Sometimes molecules need to be transported into and out of cells against the *diffusion gradient*. The diffusion gradient is the direction in which molecules naturally move by diffusion. Movement against the diffusion gradient requires energy and is called **active transport.** Scientists do not know exactly how active transport works. However, many theories state that cells have *carrier molecules* that transport substances through the cell membrane.

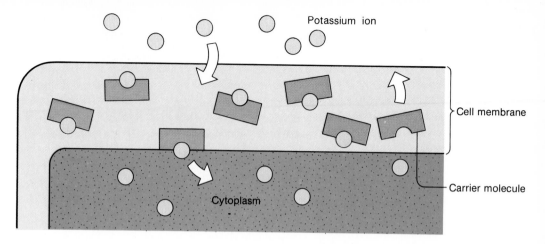

Potassium ion

Cell membrane

Carrier molecule

Cytoplasm

One example of active transport is the movement of sodium ions out of animal cells. Animal cells must keep the concentration of sodium ions inside the cell lower than the concentration in the surrounding tissue fluid. Therefore, sodium ions move from solutions of lower concentration to solutions of higher concentration.

Figure 6-9 Scientists think that carrier molecules react chemically with some molecules or ions that are to be transported across the cell membrane into or out of the cell. In this example, the carrier molecules release potassium ions and then return to the outer part of the cell membrane to pick up more potassium ions.

Endocytosis

One type of active transport in cells is **endocytosis** (en-dō-sī-TŌ-sis). Endocytosis is a method of moving molecules and particles that are too large to pass through the cell membrane into the cell. These molecules and particles include lipids, proteins, some amino acids, and some ions. During endocytosis, particles outside the cell become surrounded by the cell membrane. The cell membrane forms a pocket around the particle and then pinches closed.

There are two types of endocytosis. In **phagocytosis** (fag-ō-sī-TŌ-sis), extensions of cytoplasm called *pseudopodia*

Figure 6-10 During phagocytosis, an amoeba extends a pseudopod toward a paramecium (*left*). The pseudopod begins to surround the paramecium (*center*), eventually engulfing it completely (*right*).

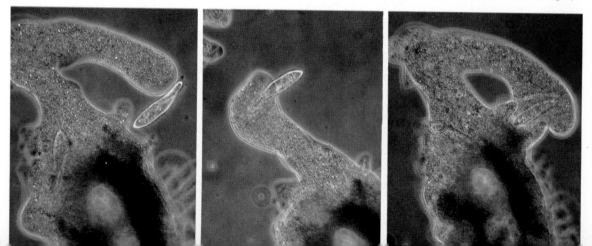

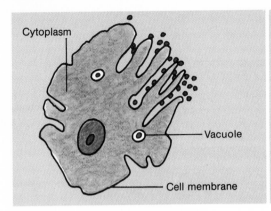
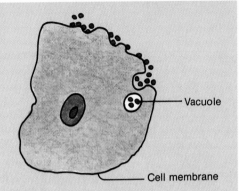

Figure 6-11 During pinocytosis, particles that are adsorbed on the cell's surface move into channels in the cell membrane where vacuoles form (*left*). Vacuoles can also form directly on the surface of the cell membrane enclosing adsorbed particles (*right*).

Figure 6-12 During exocytosis, vacuoles fuse with the cell membrane and permit substances to leave the cell.

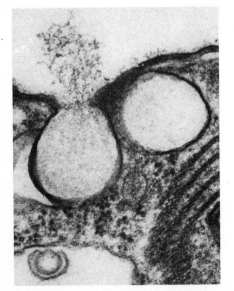

(soo-də-PŌ-dē-a), meaning false feet, surround large particles. The pocket forms a vacuole. Usually, this vacuole joins with a lysosome, which digests the contents of the vacuole. The amoeba and the human white blood cell are examples of phagocytic cells. In some human white blood cells, called *macrophages*, bacteria are taken in and destroyed. These cells use phagocytosis to fight disease.

Another type of endocytosis is **pinocytosis** (pī-nō-sī-TŌ-sis). During pinocytosis, smaller particles and liquids are taken into the cell. However, the cell does not surround the material with pseudopodia. Instead, the material is *absorbed*, or collected, on the surface of the cell membrane. The membrane folds inward with the material, forming a channel. Vacuoles form at the end of the channel or directly on the membrane surface.

Exocytosis

Some molecules and particles within cells, such as lipids, wastes, hormones, and enzymes, are too large to leave the cell through the cell membrane. These large particles and molecules leave the cell by **exocytosis** (ek-sō-sī-TŌ-sis). During exocytosis, molecules or particles are encased in vacuoles within the cell. Once in a vacuole, these materials are moved to the cell membrane. An opening forms in the cell membrane that allows the substances to leave the vacuoles. The proteins packaged by the Golgi apparatus leave the cell by exocytosis.

SECTION REVIEW   Answers on page T–36.

1. What is meant by active transport?
2. How do scientists think materials are moved into and out of a cell against the diffusion gradient?
3. What are the two forms of endocytosis?
4. What is exocytosis?

LABORATORY INVESTIGATION 6 For additional information, see page T–36.

Diffusion Through a Cell Membrane

Purpose   One of the most important processes that occurs in a cell is diffusion. Diffusion regulates what enters and leaves the cell. The purpose of this investigation is to illustrate the process of diffusion through a cell membrane.

Materials *(per group)*   ● 250-mL beaker ● Rubber band ● Gelatin "cell" ● 100-mL graduated cylinder ● Piece of cheesecloth (15 cm x 15 cm) ● 10 mL dilute ammonium hydroxide solution

Procedure   **1.** Copy the table shown in this investigation into your notebook.   **2.** Using the graduated cylinder, obtain 10 ml of ammonium hydroxide solution. **CAUTION:** *Avoid contact with the skin or prolonged inhalation of the vapors. Keep the room well ventilated.* Carefully pour the ammonium hydroxide solution into the beaker.   **3.** Place the cheesecloth over the opening of the beaker. Hold it in place by putting the rubber band around the beaker and the cheesecloth.   **4.** Place the gelatin "cell" on top of the cheesecloth. The "cell" contains phenolphthalein, which shows the presence of bases, such as ammonium hydroxide, by changing color. **Note:** *Do not allow any ammonium hydroxide to come in direct contact with the "cell."*   **5.** Observe and record any changes that occur within the "cell" at 2-minute intervals for 10 minutes.

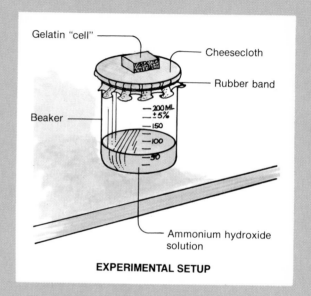

EXPERIMENTAL SETUP

Observations and Conclusions   **1.** What happens to the "cell" after 2 minutes? After 6 minutes? After 10 minutes?   **2.** Does the ammonium hydroxide diffuse into the "cell" or does the material in the "cell" diffuse into the beaker?   **3.** How does the ammonium hydroxide cause the "cell" to undergo changes without touching it?

	After 2 minutes	After 4 minutes	After 6 minutes	After 8 minutes	After 10 minutes
Color changes					

CHAPTER SUMMARY

Cell Energy   Energy is the ability to cause change or do work. Every cell needs energy and the ability to transform energy into a useable form. Potential energy, or stored energy, is changed to forms of energy that are immediately usable by the cell or organism.

Living things must also regulate and store the energy released during chemical reactions. Enzymes catalyze reactions in living things. Enzymes also permit anabolic and catabolic reactions to occur simultaneously. Substances called coenzymes are also needed for some of these reactions. One of the most important coenzymes is ATP. ATP is the energy-storing molecule in every living thing. The high-energy bonds in ATP are used for storing and releasing energy.

Homeostasis and Passive Transport   Cells must maintain homeostasis. Homeostasis is the ability of an organism to maintain an internal balance regardless of changes in the external environment. It occurs at all levels within an organism. Cells maintain homeostasis by controlling the molecules that pass into and out of them. During passive transport, substances pass into and out of a cell without using energy. Diffusion and osmosis involve passive transport. Diffusion is the movement of materials from areas of higher concentration to areas of lower concentration. Osmosis is the diffusion of water through a selectively permeable membrane.

Homeostasis and Active Transport   Some molecules need to be transported into and out of cells against the diffusion gradient. This movement requires energy and is called active transport. Endocytosis, a form of active transport, is used to move molecules and particles into cells. Another form of active transport called exocytosis is used to move molecules and particles out of cells.

CHAPTER VOCABULARY

activation energy	diffusion	osmosis
active transport	endocytosis	osmotic pressure
ADP	exocytosis	passive transport
AMP	homeostasis	phagocytosis
anabolic reaction	hypertonic	pinocytosis
ATP	hypotonic	plasmolysis
catabolic reaction	isotonic	potential energy
coenzyme	kinetic energy	turgor pressure

REVIEW of FACTS and CONCEPTS   Answers on pages T–36 to T–37.

On a separate sheet of paper, answer each of the following as completely as possible.

1. Which form of energy is involved in each of the following: a person running, a bicycle stopped at the top of a hill, a burning match used to light a Bunsen burner, a rock at the top of a cliff, and a speeding train?
2. What are the differences between catabolic reactions and anabolic reactions?
3. How is an enzyme a catalyst? Why are enzymes important to living things?
4. What is the role of vitamins in metabolism? In chemical reactions within the body?
5. What is the major difference between the lock and key hypothesis and the induced fit theory?
6. Explain how a molecule of ATP stores and releases energy.
7. Give an example of homeostasis in people and in a single cell.
8. What is diffusion? How is diffusion affected by concentration, pressure, and temperature?
9. What changes would occur in a cell placed in an isotonic solution? A hypertonic solution? A hypotonic solution?

10. What is the difference between diffusion and osmosis?

11. What is turgor pressure? What is plasmolysis? How does turgor pressure affect plant cells?

12. What is the difference between passive transport and active transport?

13. What is the difference between endocytosis and exocytosis?

EXTENSIONS and APPLICATIONS For additional information, see page T–37.

1. Make three-dimensional models that illustrate the lock and key hypothesis and the induced fit theory. Mount the models on posterboard. Label all necessary stages and parts. Prepare a display for your classroom.

2. Observe the effect of temperature on the rate of diffusion. Fill a beaker with tap water at room temperature, another with ice water, and a third with hot water. Add equal amounts of food dye to each beaker. Observe how long it takes for the molecules of dye to diffuse evenly throughout the water in each beaker.

3. Complete a series of experiments in plasmolysis. Place a stalk of celery in a glass of tap water and a stalk in a glass of heavily salted water. Repeat the same procedure with cuttings from several other plants. Note the difference in the plants after 24 hours.

SUGGESTED READINGS

Berger, M., *Enzymes in Action*. New York: Thomas Y. Crowell.
   The roles that enzymes play in certain biochemical reactions are described. Ideas on the possible uses of enzymes in the future are also discussed.
Goldsby, R., *Cells and Energy*. New York: Macmillan.
   The production, use, and storage of energy by living cells is explored.
Pfeiffer, J., and the Editors of Time-Life Books, *The Cell*. New York: Time-Life Books.
   This illustrated book explains the many activities that take place in cells. It includes a chapter on cell energy.

7 Photosynthesis and Respiration

Sunlight is the basic source of energy for all life.

Chapter Objectives *After completing this chapter, you will be able to:*

a ▓ Distinguish between autotrophs and heterotrophs. p. 111
b ▓ Discuss the role of light and chlorophyll in photosynthesis. p. 111
c ▓ List some factors that affect the rate of photosynthesis. p. 116
d ▓ Summarize the processes of photosynthesis and respiration. p. 111
e ▓ Compare photosynthesis and respiration. p. 123

For teaching aids for this chapter, including a chapter overview and teaching strategies, see pages T-37 to T-38. The page number next to each chapter objective refers to the text page where the information needed to fulfill the objective begins.

Look up at the sky on a clear day and you will see the sun blazing 149.6 million kilometers away. Incredibly, even at that enormous distance, you can feel the sun's heat energy. But there is more that comes from that distant star than the energy of heat. The sun is also a source of another form of energy called light. Sunlight is what makes life on earth possible.

Green plants capture sunlight and store the energy in chemical bonds. When human beings or animals eat green plants, the chemical bonds in the plants are broken and the energy is released. The energy is used to make possible all the functions of living things.

Photosynthesis

Green plants convert the sun's light energy into chemical energy by the process of **photosynthesis.** Organisms that capture the sun's energy directly and use it to make food, such as plants, are called **autotrophs** (AWT-ə-trahfs). Organisms that use the sun's energy indirectly, such as human beings and other animals, are called **heterotrophs** (HET-ər-ə-trahfs). Heterotrophs are completely dependent on green plants as their source of food and energy from the sun.

During photosynthesis, green plants use the raw materials carbon dioxide and water to produce food in the form of energy-rich compounds, mainly glucose. Another product of this process is oxygen. Most of the oxygen in the earth's atmosphere is produced by green plants. A substance in green plants called **chlorophyll** is necessary for photosynthesis. Chlorophyll is a green pigment that gives green plants their

You may want to explain to your students that complex plants contain two types of chlorophyll: a blue-green chlorophyll **a** ($C_{55}H_{72}O_5N_4Mg$) and a yellow-green chlorophyll **b** ($C_{55}H_{70}O_6N_4Mg$).

Figure 7-1 During photosynthesis, a green plant uses the raw materials carbon dioxide and water in the presence of chlorophyll and sunlight to produce oxygen and glucose.

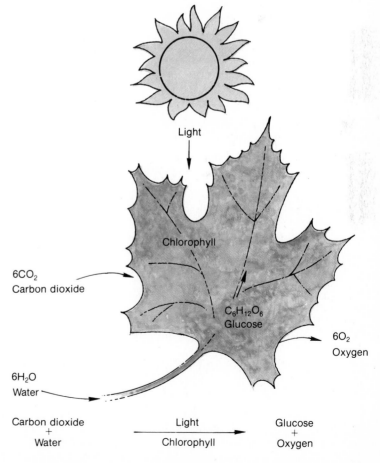

Light

Chlorophyll

$6CO_2$
Carbon dioxide

$C_6H_{12}O_6$
Glucose

$6O_2$
Oxygen

$6H_2O$
Water

Carbon dioxide + Water	Light Chlorophyll →	Glucose + Oxygen

characteristic color. The overall process of photosynthesis is represented by the following equation.

$$6CO_2 + 6H_2O \xrightarrow[\text{light}]{\text{chlorophyll}} C_6H_{12}O_6 + 6O_2$$

This equation shows that for every 6 molecules of carbon dioxide and every 6 molecules of water, a green plant produces 6 molecules of oxygen and 1 molecule of glucose. In this equation, only the reactants and products of photosynthesis are shown. The actual process of photosynthesis is a series of reactions that change the reactants to products. These reactions can be divided into two main groups: reactions that require light energy and reactions that do not.

Light Reactions

Chemical reactions that use light energy are called **light reactions**. During these reactions, light energy from the sun is captured and changed into chemical energy.

To appreciate how green plants capture the sun's energy, it is helpful to understand some of the properties of light. Light travels as a wave. The distance between one point on a wave and the corresponding point on the next wave is called a *wavelength*. Sunlight, or white light, is made up of many different wavelengths. Each wavelength has a characteristic color. The colors in white light can be sepa-

Sidelight

Scientists estimate that the total production of glucose by the earth's plants, both on land and in the sea, is about 91 billion metric tons a year.

Before you begin an explanation of the light and dark reactions of photosynthesis, you may want to prepare a summary of these reactions on posterboard or on a transparency for an overhead projector.

At this point, you may want to assign to several students the first of the Extensions and Applications at the end of this chapter.

Figure 7-2 After a rainfall, tiny droplets of water remain suspended in the air. These droplets act like prisms that separate sunlight into colors and form a rainbow.

rated by passing the white light through a *prism*. A prism is a solid piece of glass that has a triangular cross section. When sunlight passes through a prism, the wavelengths of light are separated into colors. The colors compose the visible part of the *spectrum* (SPEK-trəm).

Figure 7-2 shows the separation of sunlight into its various colors. The shorter the wavelength of light the more energy it has. Blue light, for example, has a shorter wavelength than red light. Therefore, blue light has more energy than does red light.

In green plants, various wavelengths of light are absorbed or reflected by pigments, or compounds that have color. Chlorophyll, the primary pigment in green plants, absorbs mainly red and blue wavelengths and reflects mostly green wavelengths. The color that is reflected is the color that the eye sees. This is why green plants look green.

Plants also contain other pigments, such as the orange *carotenes* (KAR-ə-tēnz) and yellow *xanthophylls* (ZAN-thə-filz). These pigments vary in amount and type from one plant to another and are called *accessory pigments*. They absorb wavelengths of light that are not absorbed by chlorophyll. Some types of bacteria contain a special kind of chlorophyll called *bacteriochlorophyll*. This pigment enables some bacteria to make their own food.

The process of photosynthesis occurs in plant cell organelles called **chloroplasts.** Within the chloroplasts are tiny stacked structures called *grana*. The grana contain chlorophyll and accessory pigments. Inside the grana the electrons in the atoms of chlorophyll molecules absorb energy from blue and red wavelengths of light. As an electron absorbs energy, it moves to a higher energy level and the chlorophyll molecule is said to be "excited." The electron "jumps" from the excited chlorophyll molecule, leaving an electron "gap" behind. This gap is filled by an electron from another chlorophyll molecule. In the process, energy is released.

Figure 7-3 Plants contain pigments other than chlorophyll. Some of these pigments give the leaves of the coleus plant a purple color.

Figure 7-4 This micrograph shows a chloroplast (23,000X), in which photosynthesis takes place. Light reactions occur in the grana, which appear as dark gray bands. The grana contain pigments, such as chlorophyll. Dark reactions occur with the help of enzymes produced by the stroma, which appear as light gray areas. The drawing provides a different view of these structures.

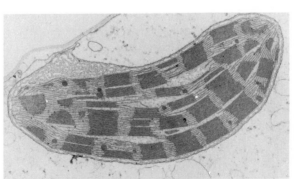

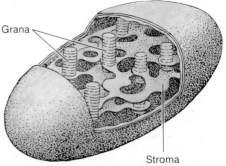

Grana

Stroma

A number of reactions occur while the electron from one chlorophyll molecule is moving to another chlorophyll molecule. In one series of reactions, the electron is passed along a series of *coenzymes* that form an **electron transport chain.** The coenzymes act as electron acceptors. After passing along the coenzymes, the electron eventually returns to its original energy level by filling a gap in a chlorophyll molecule. The energy that is released during this series of transfer reactions is sufficient to bond phosphate groups to molecules of *ADP* in the chloroplast. This results in the formation of the energy-storing compound *ATP.* The ATP provides the energy needed to make glucose in reactions that do not use light energy.

During photosynthesis, water molecules are broken down. The energy for this reaction comes from the excited chlorophyll molecule. A molecule of water is broken down to oxygen, electrons, and hydrogen ions. The oxygen is given off as a gas. The electrons and hydrogen ions combine to form uncharged hydrogen atoms. These atoms join with molecules of *nicotinamide adenine dinucleotide phosphate,* or **NADP.** Two hydrogen atoms join with NADP to form 1 molecule of $NADPH_2$. NADP is a hydrogen acceptor and is used to carry hydrogen atoms into the next group of photosynthetic reactions.

You may want to review the ATP cycle discussed in Chapter 6.

Highlight

Three groups of reactions occur during the light reactions of photosynthesis: (1) the splitting of water into hydrogen and oxygen; (2) the production of ATP; (3) the combining of hydrogen atoms with NADP.

Dark Reactions

Photosynthetic reactions in which no light energy is used are called **dark reactions.** Figure 7-5 shows the relationship of light and dark reactions. The dark reactions manufacture the other product of photosynthesis, glucose, by bonding carbon dioxide to the hydrogen atoms carried by $NADPH_2$. The energy that bonds these atoms is provided by molecules of ATP that were made in the light reactions. The dark reactions also use enzymes as catalysts. These enzymes are in the *stroma,* a semifluid portion of the chloroplast.

The first step in the dark reactions is the bonding of carbon dioxide and a 5-carbon sugar called *ribulose diphosphate,* or **RDP.** When these two compounds bond, an unstable 6-carbon compound is formed. This compound immediately breaks down into two 3-carbon molecules of *phosphoglyceric acid,* or **PGA.** Each molecule of PGA then reacts with the hydrogen atoms in $NADPH_2$. This reaction produces two 3-carbon molecules of *phosphoglyceraldehyde,* or **PGAL.** PGAL can be thought of as the intermediate product of photosynthesis because the plant uses it as a direct source of energy. Some of the PGAL is used to produce glucose. PGAL is also used to reform RDP to keep the cycle of dark reactions going.

Figure 7–5 Light and Dark Reactions of Photosynthesis

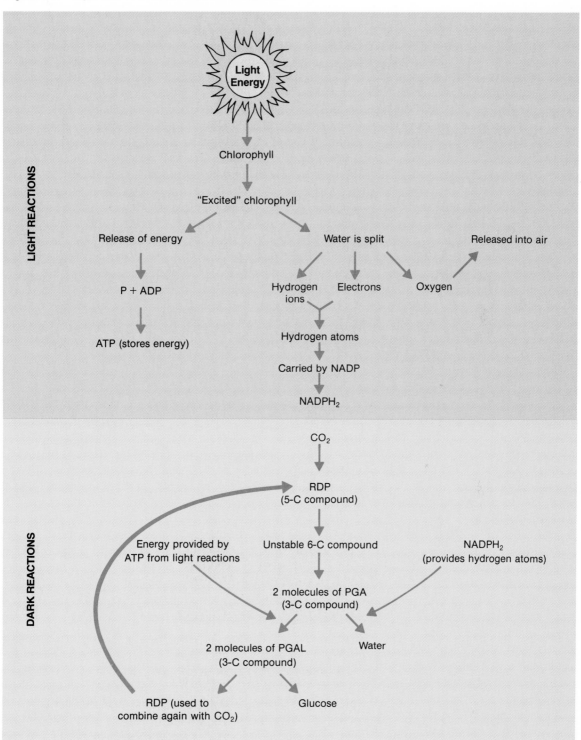

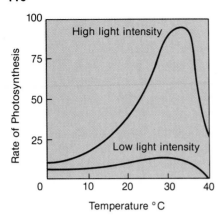

Figure 7-6 Effects of Temperature and Light Intensity on the Rate of Photosynthesis

Sidelight

In leaves of plants that require bright sunlight, the rate of photosynthesis tends to be proportional to the light intensity received by the leaves, up to a maximum of one-third to one-half of full sunlight.

At this point, you may want to assign to several students the second of the Extensions and Applications at the end of this chapter.

Factors Affecting Photosynthesis

Carbon dioxide and water are needed for photosynthesis. Changes in the availability of any of these materials affect the rate of photosynthesis. The amount and *intensity*, or strength, of sunlight also affect the rate of photosynthesis, as does temperature. See Figure 7-6.

Carbon dioxide is needed in the dark reactions to form PGAL. If carbon dioxide were absent, the dark reactions would stop, and no PGAL or glucose could be made. To a point, the rate of photosynthesis varies with the amount of carbon dioxide available. The rate of photosynthesis also depends upon the availability of other raw materials.

Green plants use water to provide hydrogen atoms that bond to NADP, changing it to $NADPH_2$ in the light reactions. If these reactions do not take place, for example during a drought, photosynthesis stops. When the plant again absorbs water, the rate of photosynthesis increases until it reaches a maximum level of activity.

Sunlight is the energy source for photosynthesis. Without it the molecules of chlorophyll cannot become excited to begin the light reactions. As the intensity of light increases, more energy becomes available to the chlorophyll molecules. This causes an increase in the rate of photosynthesis.

Temperature also affects the rate of photosynthesis. If enough light, water, and carbon dioxide are present, the rate of photosynthesis increases as the temperature increases from 0 °C to 30-35 °C. The enzymes that catalyze photosynthetic reactions work less efficiently at colder and warmer temperatures. If the temperature is lower than 0 °C or higher than 35 °C, the enzymes begin to break down. This causes a decrease in the rate of photosynthesis.

SECTION REVIEW   Answers on page T–37.

1. What is photosynthesis?
2. What wavelengths of light are absorbed by green plants?
3. What are accessory pigments? Give two examples.
4. Explain how a chlorophyll molecule becomes excited in the chloroplast.
5. List the products of the light and dark reactions of photosynthesis.

Cellular Respiration

The cells of all living things need energy to perform cell work. The energy-rich molecule in cells is ATP. Cells must take energy, such as that in the chemical bonds in food, and incorporate it into the chemical bonds of ATP. This process is called **cellular respiration,** and it occurs in the mitochondria of the cell.

Whether an organism is an autotroph or a heterotroph, energy is needed to break down food molecules. In heterotrophs, large food molecules are broken down into smaller ones, such as glucose, by digestion. After digestion has taken place, molecules of glucose and other simple substances enter the cells. In autotrophs, food is already in its useable form, glucose. The glucose molecules are the fuel for cellular respiration. During cellular respiration, glucose molecules are broken down to release energy. This energy is used to produce the energy-rich molecules of ATP.

Like photosynthesis, cellular respiration occurs in a series of chemical reactions. Each reaction is catalyzed by a specific enzyme. Following is the overall equation for cellular respiration.

$$C_6H_{12}O_6 + 6O_2 \xrightarrow{\text{enzymes}} 6CO_2 + 6H_2O + ATP$$

Highlight

Both plants and animals use the energy released during respiration to build and maintain their cellular materials.

Figure 7-7 The substances of photosynthesis and respiration are recycled in nature.

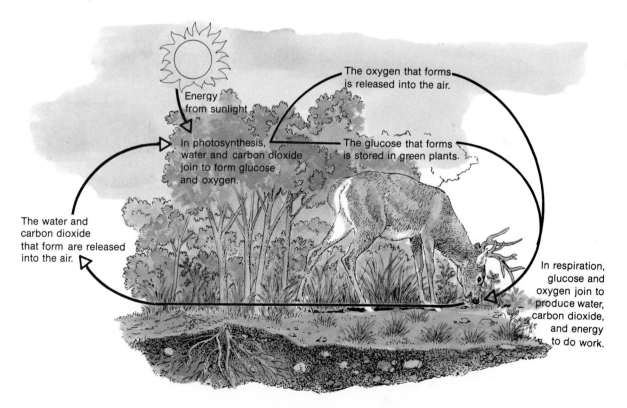

Energy from sunlight

The oxygen that forms is released into the air.

In photosynthesis, water and carbon dioxide join to form glucose and oxygen.

The glucose that forms is stored in green plants.

The water and carbon dioxide that form are released into the air.

In respiration, glucose and oxygen join to produce water, carbon dioxide, and energy to do work.

This equation shows that 1 molecule of glucose and 6 molecules of oxygen react to form 6 molecules of carbon dioxide, 6 molecules of water, and energy. The equation shows only the reactants and products of cellular respiration. It does not reveal all the reactions in the process of cellular respiration. To help understand the reactions of cellular respiration, scientists have divided them into two phases.

Anaerobic Phase

You may want to discuss obligate and facultative anaerobes with your students. These bacteria are dealt with in more detail in Chapter 15.

The first phase of cellular respiration does not require oxygen and is called the **anaerobic** (an-er-ō-bik) **phase.** This phase takes place in the cytoplasm of the cell in a series of reactions, which is shown in Figure 7-8 on page 120. During

CAREER: Agronomist

People who study plants and try to find ways to develop better crops are called agronomists. They help to increase food production to meet the needs of an increasing world population. One way to do this is to develop strains of plants that produce higher food yields or are resistant to insects and diseases. Another way to grow more productive plants for food is to improve the soil so that it can better support the growth of crops.

Agronomists who are primarily concerned with the breeding, physiology, and management of crops are called crop scientists. Agronomists who seek ways to improve the soil are called soil scientists. Even within these areas there is room for specialization. For example, some soil scientists study ways to enrich soil with solid wastes. Others try to determine how long it takes pesticides to break down in soil. Still others work with cities and towns on park development, highway landscaping, and land-use plans.

Although many positions require additional education or training, a bachelor's degree is all that is needed to enter the field of agronomy. Agronomists must keep up to date with developments in many areas of biology, including ecology, entomology, genetics, and biochemistry. Knowledge of geology, meteorology, and agricultural engineering also is important.

Government agencies and agricultural colleges are major employers of agronomists. Many agronomists trained in the United States work in other countries helping to solve agricultural problems throughout the world. Agronomists who work for agricultural companies inform farmers about new products and suggest ways to improve the yields of crops.

For further career information, write to American Society of Agronomy, 677 South Segoe Road, Madison, WI 53711.

these reactions, glucose is broken down into smaller molecules that can enter the mitochondria for the second phase of respiration. The anaerobic phase of respiration releases a very small amount of energy. However, some bacteria and yeasts use this phase as their only source of energy. These organisms are called **anaerobes** (an-ER-ōbs).

The first reaction in the anaerobic phase of cellular respiration is the breaking of some of the bonds of a glucose molecule. The energy that is used to break these bonds is supplied by 2 molecules of ATP. The energy from the splitting of the glucose bonds is enough to change 4 molecules of ADP to 4 molecules of ATP. The net gain of ATP molecules in this reaction is 2. When the glucose molecule splits, 2 molecules of a 3-carbon compound are formed. This compound is called *pyruvic acid* and has the formula $CH_3COCOOH$. Four atoms of hydrogen are also released. These atoms are picked up by a coenzyme called *nicotinamide adenine dinucleotide*, or **NAD.** NAD is similar to the NADP used in photosynthesis. A molecule of NAD accepts 2 atoms of hydrogen and becomes $NADH_2$. Two molecules of NAD are needed to carry the 4 atoms of hydrogen. $NADH_2$ is an energy-rich compound that is used in the second phase of cellular respiration.

Aerobic Phase

The second phase of cellular respiration is called the **aerobic** (er-ō-bik) **phase.** This phase requires oxygen. Organisms that need oxygen to perform cellular respiration are called **aerobes** (ER-ōbs). Animals, plants, and most protists are examples of aerobes.

The aerobic phase is divided into two major reactions. The **citric acid cycle** is named after the first substance, citric acid, that is formed during the reaction. As the word cycle suggests, the series of reactions begins and ends with the same substance. Look at the citric acid cycle in Figure 7-8 on page 120. The cycle is also known as the *Krebs cycle* in honor of Hans Krebs, a British scientist, who first worked out these reactions in 1937.

The citric acid cycle completes the breakdown of glucose that began in the anaerobic phase. The pyruvic acid that was formed in that phase is transported from the cytoplasm of the cell to the fluid of the mitochondria. This active transport uses the energy of 1 molecule of ATP to transport each pyruvic acid molecule.

Before the citric acid cycle can begin, the pyruvic acid is chemically changed to a 2-carbon compound. This compound is called *acetic acid*. The acetic acid eventually bonds with a

In the anaerobic phase of cellular respiration, the reaction that breaks down glucose is called glycolysis.

Highlight

Cellular respiration occurs in two phases. The anaerobic phase does not require oxygen. The aerobic phase requires oxygen. The product of the two phases is 38 molecules of ATP.

Figure 7-8 Anaerobic and Aerobic Phases of Cellular Respiration

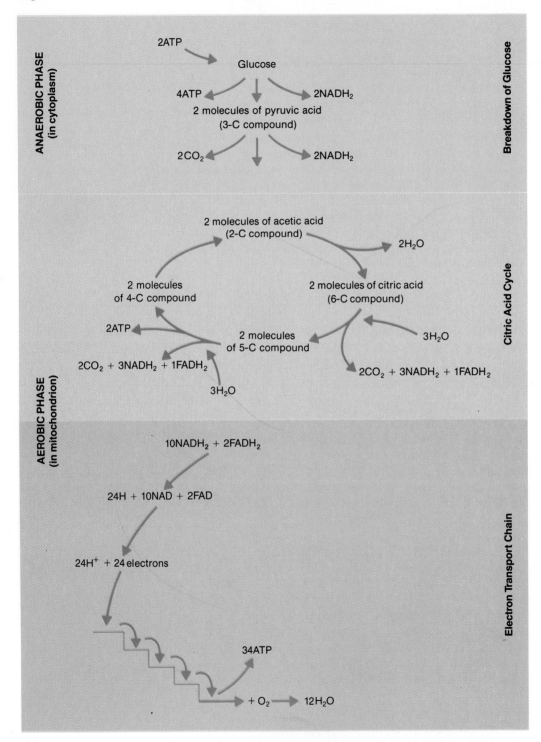

4-carbon molecule to form the 6-carbon molecule citric acid. During the reaction, a carbon atom bonds with oxygen and a molecule of carbon dioxide is given off as a product. In addition, 4 hydrogen atoms bond with NAD to form 2 $NADH_2$.

For each molecule of glucose that is broken down in the anaerobic phase, 2 molecules of citric acid are produced. This occurs because 1 glucose molecule is changed into two 2-carbon molecules that enter the cycle. In the cycle, each citric acid molecule is broken down to a 5-carbon molecule and finally into the original 4-carbon molecule. In this process, 4 molecules of carbon dioxide are released. In addition, a total of 6 molecules of water (3 for each molecule of citric acid) are used in the cycle. Look closely at Figure 7-8 again. Sixteen atoms of hydrogen (8 atoms of hydrogen for each molecule of citric acid) also are released. Six molecules of NAD and 2 molecules of *FAD* are needed to carry the 16 atoms of hydrogen. Two molecules of ATP also are produced.

The second major reaction of the aerobic phase of cellular respiration, the electron transport chain, involves a series of electron acceptors. Look at the electron transport chain in Figure 7-8. The acceptors are attached to the inner membranes of the mitochondria. The reactions along the series of acceptors supply most of the ATP that is produced during cellular respiration.

The electron transport chain accepts electrons and hydrogen ions from the energy-rich molecules $NADH_2$ and $FADH_2$. The electrons and ions are passed from one electron acceptor to another in the chain. As they are passed along, energy is released. Thirty-four molecules of ATP are formed during the reactions of the electron transport chain. So far, the total number of hydrogen atoms that have been released by these reactions is 24. The 24 hydrogen atoms form 24 hydrogen ions and 24 electrons. These particles usually pair up to form 12 pairs of hydrogen ions and 12 pairs of electrons. Near the end of the electron transport chain, each atom of oxygen accepts 2 hydrogen ions and 2 electrons to form a molecule of water. Oxygen is the final electron acceptor in the electron transport system.

When the 12 molecules of hydrogen bond with the 6 oxygen molecules, 12 molecules of water are produced. Six water molecules are used within the various reactions of respiration. Therefore, the net gain of water molecules is 6. Lastly, 6 carbon dioxide molecules are produced, 2 from the conversion of pyruvic acid to acetic acid and 4 from the citric acid cycle.

The result of both phases of cellular respiration is 38 molecules of ATP. Two molecules of ATP were produced in

Sidelight

After pyruvic acid breaks down to form 2 molecules of acetic acid, the acetic acid joins with 2 molecules of a 2-carbon compound called coenzyme A and forms acetyl-co-A. Actually, it is this compound that releases the 4 hydrogen atoms and bonds with a 4-carbon molecule to form citric acid.

the anaerobic phase, 2 were produced by the citric acid cycle, and 34 were produced by the electron transport chain.

Fermentation

Some organisms do not possess the enzymes that are necessary for the aerobic phase of cellular respiration. Therefore, they can obtain energy only from the anaerobic phase. The type of cellular respiration that these organisms perform is called **fermentation.** These organisms cannot break down pyruvic acid to produce energy. Instead, they change the molecules of $NADH_2$ to NAD during the anaerobic phase. The breaking of the bonds between NAD and H_2 supplies enough energy for the remainder of the anaerobic phase to occur.

ALCOHOLIC FERMENTATION In organisms such as yeast, one of the products of fermentation is alcohol. This type of fermentation is called *alcoholic fermentation*. The breakdown of glucose to pyruvic acid occurs just as in the anaerobic phase of respiration. As the pyruvic acid is changed to alcohol, a molecule of carbon dioxide is released and $NADH_2$ is converted to NAD. Alcoholic fermentation is represented by the following equation.

$$C_6H_{12}O_6 \xrightarrow{\text{enzymes}} 2C_2H_5OH + 2CO_2 + 2ATP$$

glucose $\longrightarrow$ ethyl alcohol + carbon dioxide + energy

The products of alcoholic fermentation are useful in the baking industry. Dough rises because the yeast reacts with the glucose in the dough, forming carbon dioxide. The heat of an oven causes the carbon dioxide to expand, leaving the baked product full of holes and very light. The alcohol evaporates into the air.

LACTIC ACID FERMENTATION The muscle tissue of animals requires a good deal of energy, especially during heavy exercise. Normally, muscle cells use oxygen for cellular respiration. However, sometimes the circulatory system of an animal cannot bring enough oxygen to the muscle cells to keep them functioning efficiently. This forces muscle cells to rely on an anaerobic respiration process called *lactic acid fermentation* to supply needed energy. The glucose in these cells is converted to pyruvic acid just as in the normal anaerobic phase. However, because there is not enough oxygen present, the muscles then go into what is known as *oxygen debt*.

Figure 7-9 In baking, carbon dioxide, a product of fermentation, causes dough to rise or expand.

At this point, you may want to have your students do the Laboratory Investigation at the end of this chapter.

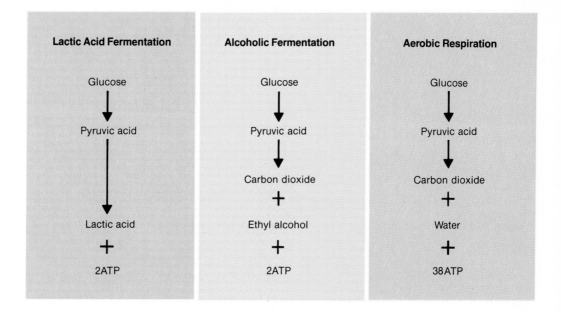

Lactic Acid Fermentation	Alcoholic Fermentation	Aerobic Respiration
Glucose	Glucose	Glucose
↓	↓	↓
Pyruvic acid	Pyruvic acid	Pyruvic acid
↓	↓	↓
	Carbon dioxide	Carbon dioxide
	+	+
Lactic acid	Ethyl alcohol	Water
+	+	+
2ATP	2ATP	38ATP

Figure 7-10 Comparison of Lactic Acid Fermentation, Alcoholic Fermentation, and Aerobic Respiration

Under these conditions, pyruvic acid is changed to lactic acid and energy is released. The buildup of lactic acid in muscle cells causes the soreness felt in muscles after strenuous exercise. Aerobic respiration occurs again when enough oxygen is available. Lactic acid is turned back into pyruvic acid as the oxygen debt is paid off. The following equation shows the general process of lactic acid fermentation.

$$C_6H_{12}O_6 \xrightarrow{\text{enzymes}} 2CH_3CHOHCOOH + 2ATP$$

glucose $\longrightarrow$ lactic acid + energy

In comparing the equations for alcoholic and lactic acid fermentation, you will notice that they both produce 2 molecules of ATP. This indicates that most of the energy of fermentation remains within the chemical bonds of its products. Compare this with the 38 molecules of ATP that are produced by aerobic respiration. It is easy to see that aerobic respiration is a more efficient way of obtaining energy.

Comparing Photosynthesis and Cellular Respiration

Figure 7-11 on page 124 shows the relationship between photosynthesis and cellular respiration. The main product of photosynthesis, glucose, is the fuel for cellular respiration. The main product of respiration, ATP, is the fuel for pho-

Stress to your students that both autotrophs and heterotrophs require glucose as a source of energy.

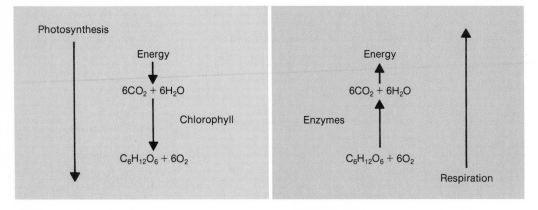

Figure 7-11 Comparison of Photosynthesis and Cellular Respiration

tosynthesis. Green plants use the sun's energy to make glucose. Animals get their glucose fuel from plants.

Photosynthesis and cellular respiration have some similarities. The coenzymes NAD of cellular respiration and NADP of photosynthesis are similar in structure and function. An electron transport chain in which some of the electron carriers are similar occurs in both processes.

One of the major differences between the systems is that the production of ATP is lower in photosynthesis than in cellular respiration. Photosynthesis produces only 2 molecules of ATP, while cellular respiration produces 38 molecules of ATP. Also, the reaction mechanisms for each process are different.

Photosynthesis and cellular respiration work together to provide useable energy for all living things. Glucose is the energy connection between the two processes.

At this point, you may want to assign to several students the fourth of the Extensions and Applications at the end of this chapter.

SECTION REVIEW Answers on pages T–37 to T–38.

1. Why do cells need glucose?
2. Define cellular respiration.
3. What is the function of ATP and NAD in cellular respiration?
4. Why is aerobic respiration considered more efficient than fermentation?
5. How are alcoholic fermentation and lactic acid fermentation different?
6. How are the processes of photosynthesis and cellular respiration similar?
7. Why is glucose considered a connection between photosynthesis and cellular respiration?

The Effect of Temperature on Yeast Fermentation

Purpose   In cells, energy is released from food molecules by the process known as cellular respiration. Certain organisms, such as yeast, perform a type of cellular respiration called fermentation. The purpose of this investigation is to determine how temperature affects the rate of fermentation in yeast cells.

Materials (*per group*)   ● ½ package of dry yeast ● 30 mL of 20% glucose solution ● 200 mL of bromthymol blue solution ● 3 medicine droppers ● 3 test tubes ● 3 one-hole rubber stoppers to fit test tubes ● 3 large beakers ● 100-mL graduated cylinder ● 3 pieces of rubber tubing (35 cm long) ● Warm water ● Ice ● Thermometer ● Wax marking pencil ● Drinking straw ● 3 small beakers

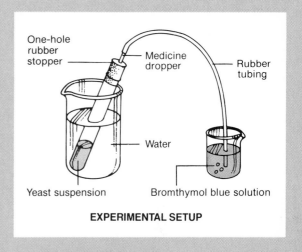

EXPERIMENTAL SETUP

Procedure   **1.** Using the graduated cylinder, add 50 mL of bromthymol blue solution to a small beaker. Insert the drinking straw into the solution and gently blow into the bromthymol blue solution until it changes color. Note the change in color. Rinse the beaker and the graduated cylinder so they may be reused. **2.** Copy the table in your notebook.   **3. CAUTION:** *Wrap paper towels around the medicine droppers and use a gentle rotating action to insert the droppers.* Wet the pointed ends of the medicine droppers and carefully insert them into the large end of the 3 one-hole stoppers. Attach a length of rubber tubing to the wide end of each dropper.   **4.** Using the graduated cylinder, add 50 mL of bromthymol blue solution to each of the three small beakers. Rinse the graduated cylinder.   **5.** Add the yeast and add 30 mL

of the glucose solution to one of the test tubes. Swirl the contents of the tube until the yeast is fully suspended.   **6.** Pour 10 mL of the yeast suspension into each of the remaining 2 test tubes. This should result in 3 test tubes, each containing 10 mL of yeast suspension. Label the test tubes 1, 2, and 3 with a wax marking pencil.   **7.** Prepare 3 water baths in the large beakers. Use warm water and ice to adjust the water baths to the temperatures indicated in the table. Use the thermometer to make sure that the temperatures are what they should be.   **8.** Insert a rubber stopper with the attached medicine dropper and rubber tubing into each test tube.   **9.** Place each test tube in the appropriate water bath and place the free end of each rubber tube into a beaker of the bromthymol blue solution. See the experimental setup.   **10.** Begin timing each test tube as soon as the 3 setups are completed. Record the length of time that is required for the color of the bromthymol blue solution to change to yellow in each of the test tubes.

Observations and Conclusions   **1.** What product is released into the bromthymol blue solution when you breathe through the straw? What end product is released by the fermenting yeast?   **2.** What is the raw material for the fermentation reaction?   **3.** At which temperature is the end product released most rapidly? How do you know?   **4.** How does temperature affect the rate of respiration in yeasts?

Test Tube	1	2	3
Temperature	10 °C	22 °C	35 °C
Time in minutes for the color change of bromthymol blue			

CHAPTER SUMMARY

Photosynthesis In photosynthesis, green plants use carbon dioxide, water, and light energy from the sun to produce glucose and release oxygen. The sun's energy, or light energy, is converted to chemical energy in the bonds of glucose. Photosynthesis occurs in plant cell organelles called chloroplasts. They contain chlorophyll, a green pigment that captures the energy from the sun. Organisms that use light energy to make their own food are called autotrophs. Heterotrophs are organisms that cannot make their own food and must obtain their food either directly or indirectly from green plants.

The process of photosynthesis occurs in a series of complex chemical reactions. These reactions have been divided into two main groups. During the light reactions, light energy is captured and changed to chemical energy and oxygen is released. During the dark reactions, the energy from ATP helps to form bonds between carbon dioxide and the hydrogen atoms that are carried by NADP. PGAL is produced and is used to make glucose.

Cellular Respiration In cellular respiration, glucose is broken down by a cell to produce energy. The chemical reactions of cellular respiration are divided into two phases. The anaerobic phase breaks down glucose into smaller molecules and produces 2 molecules of ATP. The aerobic phase requires oxygen. In this phase, the citric acid cycle continues the breakdown of glucose. The electron transport chain provides most of the energy for respiration.

Some organisms obtain their energy in a type of anaerobic respiration called fermentation. Yeast cells undergo alcoholic fermentation. Lactic acid fermentation occurs in the muscle cells of animals that do not receive enough oxygen for a normal aerobic phase.

The main product of photosynthesis, glucose, is the fuel for cellular respiration. Both processes involve coenzymes that have similar structures and functions, NAD in cellular respiration and NADP in photosynthesis. A major difference between the two processes is that cellular respiration produces 38 molecules of ATP, while photosynthesis produces 2 molecules of ATP.

CHAPTER VOCABULARY

aerobe	chloroplast	NAD
aerobic phase	citric acid cycle	NADP
anaerobe	dark reactions	PGA
anaerobic phase	electron transport chain	PGAL
autotroph	fermentation	photosynthesis
cellular respiration	heterotroph	RDP
chlorophyll	light reactions	

REVIEW of FACTS and CONCEPTS   Answers on page T–38.

On a separate sheet of paper, answer each of the following as completely as possible.

1. Discuss the following statement: Life on the earth depends on the energy from the sun.
2. How is the release of energy from a burning match different from the release of energy from glucose? How is it similar?
3. Show how light and chlorophyll take part in photosynthesis.
4. Briefly outline the process of photosynthesis.
5. How did the light and dark reactions of photosynthesis receive their names?

6. Why is PGAL considered a product of photosynthesis?
7. List some factors that affect the rate of photosynthesis.
8. Briefly outline the process of cellular respiration.
9. What is the difference between the aerobic phase of cellular respiration and fermentation?
10. Why does an anaerobe require more food than an aerobe?
11. Distinguish between the following pairs of terms: autotroph and heterotroph; NAD and NADP; and anaerobe and aerobe.
12. Write a generalized equation for each of the following processes: photosynthesis, cellular respiration, alcoholic fermentation, and lactic acid fermentation.
13. Compare the processes of photosynthesis and cellular respiration.

EXTENSIONS and APPLICATIONS   For additional information, see page T–38.

1. Separate sunlight into its different colors by using a prism. On a separate sheet of paper, use colored pencils to draw and label the visible spectrum.
2. In order to verify whether or not light is needed for photosynthesis, obtain a green plant and cover a leaf of the plant with black construction paper. Use a small paper clip to hold the construction paper on the leaf. Give the plant sunlight and water as needed for about 2 weeks. Observe what happens to the covered leaf and keep a record of your observations. How do you know that light is needed for photosynthesis?
3. Using reference materials in the library, find out what types of pigments other than chlorophyll are in different kinds of plant leaves. Why are you able to see these pigments in autumn?
4. In a medium-sized test tube, add enough bromthymol blue to come within 2.5 cm of the mouth of the test tube. Insert a straw and gently blow into the bromthymol blue solution until it changes color. The change in color indicates the presence of carbon dioxide. Place a sprig of an aquatic green plant, such as *Elodea,* into the solution. Stopper the test tube and put it in a place that will receive sunlight. Leave it there for about 5 days. Look at the test tube each day and record any observations. Did the bromthymol blue change back to its original color? Why or why not?

SUGGESTED READINGS

Asimov, I., *Photosynthesis.* New York: Basic Books.
This book provides an overview of the important chemical process of photosynthesis.
McElroy, W.D., *Cellular Physiology and Biochemistry.* Englewood Cliffs, N.J.: Prentice-Hall.
This book contains a concise review of the chemistry of life at the cellular level. Step-by-step explanations of life processes are included on nutrition, fermentation, respiration, and metabolism.
Rosenberg, J.L., *Photosynthesis.* New York: Holt, Rinehart and Winston.
This book explains how plants convert tremendous amounts of solar energy into chemical energy that provides food for animals and people. It also includes an examination of the process of food-making in green plants.

8 Cell Growth and Reproduction

Courtesy Carolina Biological Supply Company

These frog egg cells are undergoing their first division.

Chapter Objectives *After completing this chapter, you will be able to:*

a ■ Recognize the importance of nucleic acids in living things. p. 129

b ■ Explain the structural and functional differences between DNA and RNA. p. 129

c ■ Describe the process of protein synthesis. p. 132

d ■ Outline the processes of mitosis and meiosis. p. 135

e ■ State the differences in the processes of mitosis and meiosis. p. 135

f ■ Distinguish between asexual and sexual forms of reproduction. p. 141

g ■ Relate the processes of mitosis and meiosis to asexual and sexual forms of reproduction. p. 141

For teaching aids for this chapter, including a chapter overview and teaching strategies, see pages T–39 to T–40. The page number next to each chapter objective refers to the text page where the information needed to fulfill the objective begins.

A basketball player who is 1.9 meters tall was once a single cell! A giant California redwood that is more than 76 meters tall was once a single cell! A tremendous amount of cell growth and reproduction is necessary to change a single cell into a complex multicellular organism made up of trillions of cells.

Growth is an increase in the size of a living thing. In unicellular organisms, growth is an increase in the size of the cell. In multicellular organisms, growth is an increase in the size and number of cells. To produce the large number of cells that make up multicellular organisms, the cells split during cell reproduction. This complex process takes place over and over again. Each cell produced is exactly like its parent cell. In addition, in complex multicellular organisms such as human beings, the cells that appear very early undergo changes that lead to the formation of specialized cells. In another kind of cell reproduction, sex cells are formed in multicellular organisms.

Nucleic Acids

Cell growth and reproduction are controlled by *nucleic acids*, two organic compounds that control all activities of a cell. The cells of all except one group of organisms contain both nucleic acids. The viruses are an exception and contain only one nucleic acid.

DNA

One type of nucleic acid is *deoxyribonucleic* (dē-ahk-sē-rī-bō-noo-KLĒ-ik) *acid*, or **DNA.** DNA is found in the nucleus or in the nuclear region of a cell. Every organism contains different DNA. DNA is often referred to as the "code of life" because it contains the information needed to form and control the physical makeup and chemical processes of every part of an organism. For example, DNA determines the external characteristics and necessary enzymes of an organism.

Although the chemical makeup of DNA was known by 1950, biologists did not know how the atoms of a DNA molecule were arranged. Maurice H.F. Wilkins of King's College in London had determined the three-dimensional patterns of the atoms in DNA. In 1953, James D. Watson, an American biologist, and Francis H.C. Crick, an English biophysicist, both working at Cambridge University in England, used Wilkins' data to develop a model of DNA that agreed with all of the information known about it. Research by other scientists has provided evidence to support Watson and Crick's model of the structure of DNA. Their model is still accepted today. For their work, Watson, Crick, and Wilkins were awarded the Nobel Prize.

STRUCTURE OF DNA The Watson and Crick DNA model is made up of two long coiled strands of molecules that are attached to each other by smaller molecules. The structure of the molecule is called a *double helix* (DUB-'l HĒ-liks). If this molecule could be uncoiled, it would look somewhat like a ladder. The sides of the DNA ladder are made up of alternating sugar molecules and phosphate groups. The sugar is a 5-carbon *deoxyribose* sugar. Each phosphate group is a phosphorus atom with 4 oxygen atoms bonded to it. Each "rung" of the DNA ladder is made up of two *nitrogen bases*. Nitrogen bases are organic compounds containing the element nitrogen. Together, each sugar, phosphate, and base make up a **nucleotide.**

Nitrogen bases are grouped in two classes. The **purines** (PYOOR-ēnz) are *adenine* (AD-'n-ēn) and *guanine* (GWAH-nēn).

Sidelight

In a human being, a typical DNA molecule is made up of about 5 billion pairs of nucleotides. Therefore, a single DNA molecule contains about 20 billion bits of information.

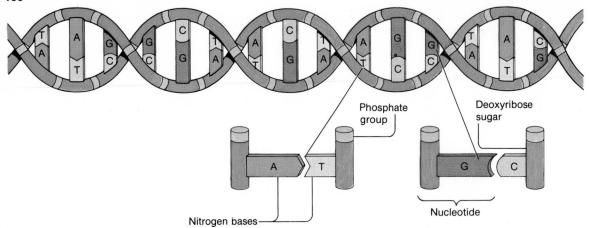

Figure 8–1 The Watson–Crick DNA model is made up of two coiled strands of nucleotides that are attached to each other.

The **pyrimidines** (pi-RIM-ə-dēnz) are *cytosine* (SĪT-ə-sēn) and *thymine* (THĪ-mēn).

In the DNA molecule, a purine and a pyrimidine make up each rung of the ladder. The bases are bonded to each other and the deoxyribose sugar. Adenine bonds only with thymine, and cytosine bonds only with guanine. The base pairs are said to be complementary to each other. This pairing assures that the rungs are the proper size. If two purines were paired, the rung would be too long. Two pyrimidines would form a rung that is too short.

REPLICATION OF DNA   DNA has the ability to build an identical copy of itself. Before a cell divides, a complete copy of its DNA is made. This process is called **replication.** The duplicate molecule of DNA goes into the new cell.

The chemical bonds joining the nitrogen bases of a DNA molecule are weak hydrogen bonds that can be broken easily. During replication, a DNA molecule "unzips," or splits down the middle, along the weak bonds. Then, nitrogen bases from the cytoplasm attach to their complementary bases on the two DNA strands. Replication starts at some point within the strand and proceeds in both directions, moving toward the ends of each strand. Sometimes replication begins in several places.

RNA

Another type of nucleic acid is *ribonucleic* (rī-bō-noo-KLĒ-ik) *acid,* or **RNA.** RNA is involved in the manufacture of proteins. The structure of RNA is similar to that of DNA. In

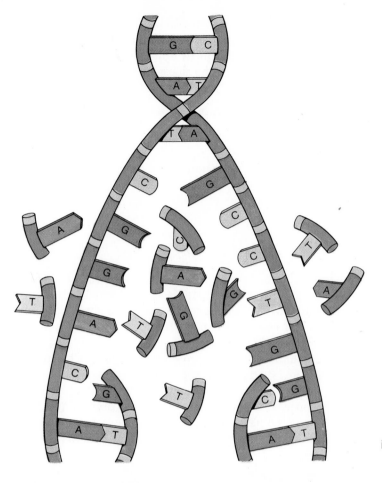

Figure 8-2 During DNA replication, two identical strands of DNA are formed.

fact, DNA is the pattern that is used to make RNA. However, RNA has three significant differences.

RNA is a single strand. Each strand is made up of repeating units of a phosphate group, a sugar, and a nitrogen base. The strand does not bond to a complementary strand as in a DNA molecule.

The base thymine is not found in RNA. Another nitrogen base called *uracil* (YOOR-ə-sil) is found in its place. Uracil is complementary to adenine.

The sugar molecules in RNA are ribose sugars. Ribose sugars have one more oxygen atom than do deoxyribose sugars.

Cells contain three different types of RNA. **Ribosomal RNA,** or rRNA, makes up part of the ribosomes. **Messenger RNA,** or mRNA, brings the *code*, or message, of DNA from

Highlight

The two nucleic acids are DNA and RNA. Three different types of RNA found in cells are ribosomal RNA, messenger RNA, and transfer RNA.

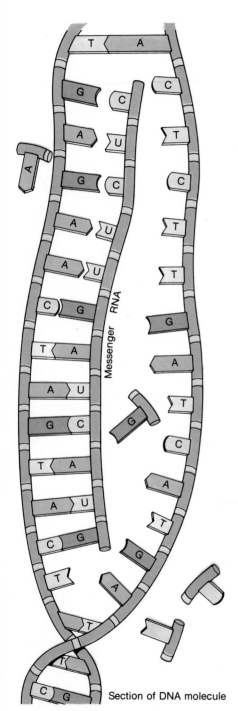

Figure 8-3 A single strand of messenger RNA is formed during transcription. In the process, the DNA code is transferred to the strand of RNA.

the nucleus to the ribosomes. The code dictates the order in which amino acids must be linked to make a specific protein. **Transfer RNA,** or tRNA, "picks up" and carries amino acids to the messenger RNA at the ribosomes.

SECTION REVIEW   Answers on page T–39.

1. What are the two types of nucleic acid?
2. What is a nucleotide?
3. What is a purine? A pyrimidine?
4. Define replication.
5. Name the three types of RNA.

Protein Synthesis

All living cells contain proteins. The proteins in the cells of living things are different. In fact, different kinds of proteins are found in the same organism. For example, the proteins in a leaf cell are different from the proteins in a stem cell of the same plant.

Cells manufacture the proteins they need. The making of proteins is called **protein synthesis.** Using combinations of amino acids, cells build many different kinds of proteins. The sequence of DNA bases is a code for protein synthesis. Therefore, DNA determines which proteins are made in a cell. RNA is necessary to put the proteins together.

Transcription

The process of making messenger RNA is called **transcription.** DNA is used as the *template,* or pattern. Each sequence of three bases in a single strand of DNA is a "word" in the DNA code.

During transcription, a small part of the DNA molecule that codes for a needed protein unzips. RNA nucleotides in the nucleoplasm bond to complementary bases on one of the two DNA strands. The RNA sugar molecules bond with the RNA phosphate groups to form a single strand of messenger RNA. The code words of the DNA bases are copied onto the strand of messenger RNA. Each combination of three bases on the messenger RNA is a **codon,** or 3-letter code word, for a specific amino acid. The order of DNA code words determines the order of amino acids needed to make specific proteins. The strand of messenger RNA then separates from the DNA and moves into the cytoplasm.

How did scientists determine that each codon was made up of 3 bases? Scientists know that at least 20 different

Second Base in Code Word

First Base in Code Word		A	G	U	C	Third Base in Code Word
A		Lysine	Arginine	Isoleucine	Threonine	A
		Lysine	Arginine	Methionine	Threonine	G
		Asparagine	Serine	Isoleucine	Threonine	U
		Asparagine	Serine	Isoleucine	Threonine	C
G		Glutamic Acid	Glycine	Valine	Alanine	A
		Glutamic Acid	Glycine	Valine	Alanine	G
		Aspartic Acid	Glycine	Valine	Alanine	U
		Aspartic Acid	Glycine	Valine	Alanine	C
U		"Stop" codon	"Stop" codon	Leucine	Serine	A
		"Stop" codon	Trytophan	Leucine	Serine	G
		Tyrosine	Cysteine	Phenylalanine	Serine	U
		Tyrosine	Cysteine	Phenylalanine	Serine	C
C		Glutamine	Arginine	Leucine	Proline	A
		Glutamine	Arginine	Leucine	Proline	G
		Histidine	Arginine	Leucine	Proline	U
		Histidine	Arginine	Leucine	Proline	C

You may want to have your students figure out the 16 possible 2-base codon combinations of adenine, guanine, thymine, and cytosine to show that a 2-base codon system could not be used to code for each of the 20 amino acids found in proteins. Stress to your students that the 64 combinations of a 3-base codon are more than enough to code for these amino acids. Using Figure 8-4, have your students find the codons for a number of amino acids.

Figure 8-4 The genetic code gives the triplet codon for each amino acid or "stop" codon. Note that there is more than one codon for each amino acid. For example, leucine has 6. There are also 3 "stop" codons.

amino acids are used to make proteins. Both DNA and RNA have 4 bases. If a codon was only 1 base long, messenger RNA could code for only 4 amino acids. If a codon was 2 bases long, only 16 amino acids could be coded because there are only 16 different ways the 4 bases could be combined into 2-base groups. However, if a codon is 3 bases, 64 3-letter word combinations are possible. A longer word is not necessary. Scientific experiments support the concept of a 3-base codon, or *triplet codon.*

Scientists have also been able to find out which triplet codons code for which amino acids. This *genetic code* is shown in Figure 8-4. You can easily see that there is more than 1 codon for most amino acids. For example, the amino acid *leucine* has 6 different codons. Some codons do not stand for an amino acid at all. These codons mark the end of a protein in much the same way as a period ends a sentence.

Translation

The codons of messenger RNA are needed for the building of proteins in the cytoplasm of a cell. This process is called **translation** because the original code of DNA is "translated" into a protein. During translation, messenger RNA temporarily binds to the ribosomes. The ribosomes appear to move along the messenger RNA and "point out" each codon to transfer RNA. The job of transfer RNA is to pick up individual amino acids in the cytoplasm and bring them to the messenger RNA.

Transfer RNA is a single strand of RNA that loops back on itself. One end of the transfer RNA molecule can bond to a codon on the messenger RNA. Each transfer RNA unit can

Figure 8-5 Transfer RNA is a single strand of RNA that loops back on itself. The anticodon, made up of 3 bases, attaches itself to one end of the model. An amino acid can bond at the other end of the model.

Figure 8-6 During translation, transfer RNA picks up the proper amino acids and places them in the correct position to form a specific protein chain. Messenger RNA is the template that has been coded for the proper amino acid sequence.

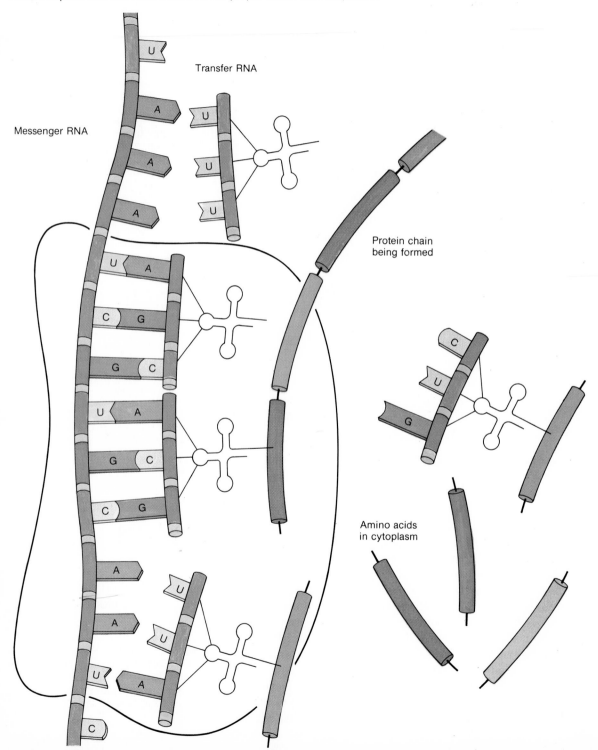

Transfer RNA

Messenger RNA

Protein chain being formed

Amino acids in cytoplasm

bond to a complementary messenger RNA codon. Three transfer RNA bases are called an *anticodon*. Each transfer RNA molecule also bonds to a specific amino acid. Therefore, at least 20 different transfer RNA molecules are needed to pick up each of the 20 amino acids. Special enzymes direct the correct amino acid to bond to the proper transfer RNA. The energy needed for this reaction to occur is provided by ATP.

When the anticodon of transfer RNA bonds to the proper codon of messenger RNA, each amino acid is placed in the proper order to form a specific protein. After an amino acid is placed in the forming protein, a *peptide bond* is formed between each amino acid. Then, the weak bond between the transfer RNA and the amino acid is broken. The transfer RNA is free again and can pick up another amino acid in the cytoplasm. The process of protein synthesis continues until a "stop" codon is reached. Once the protein is complete, it leaves the ribosome to be used within the cell or is secreted to other parts of the organism.

Highlight

During transcription, the DNA code is tranferred to a strand of messenger RNA. During translation, the DNA code on the messenger RNA is translated into a protein. The order of the triplet codons codes for the proper order of the amino acids needed to build a specific protein.

After your class finishes the sections Nucleic Acids and Protein Synthesis, you may want to assign to students the fourth of the Extensions and Applications at the end of this chapter.

SECTION REVIEW   Answers on page T–39.

1. What is transcription? Translation?
2. What is a codon? An anticodon?

Cell Reproduction

Proteins are needed by all living things to perform various life functions, including cell growth. As proteins and other organic compounds are produced in the cell, the cell increases in size. Growth is one factor that triggers *cell reproduction.* Other factors are not fully understood by scientists but probably involve interactions among the cell's nucleus, cytoplasm, and environment.

When a cell undergoes reproduction it divides. The original cell is called the *parent cell.* The new cells that are formed are called the *daughter cells.* During cell division, both the nuclear material and the cytoplasm are duplicated. Each new cell contains all the replicated cell parts of the parent cell, including DNA, which passes on the genetic code of the cell or organism to the daughter cells or offspring.

You may want to explain to your students that as a cell grows its volume and surface area increase. However, the volume increases more than does the surface area. If a cell continued to increase in size, the surface area eventually would be too small to permit food, oxygen, and wastes to enter and leave through its cell membrane. Scientists know that when a certain ratio is reached between volume and surface area of a cell, the cell divides.

Mitosis

The process in which a cell divides into two cells is called **mitosis,** or *simple cell division.* In unicellular organisms, mitosis produces new organisms. In multicellular organisms,

Highlight

Mitosis is simple cell division. During mitosis, a cell divides into two daughter cells that each contain the same number of chromosomes as does the parent cell.

You may want to explain to your students that as a cell grows its volume and surface area increase. However, the volume increases more than does the surface area. If a cell continued to increase in size, the surface area eventually would be too small to permit enough food, oxygen, and wastes to enter and leave through its cell membrane. Scientists know that when a certain ratio is reached between volume and surface area of a cell, the cell divides.

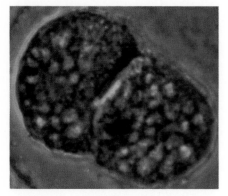

Figure 8-7   During interphase, the chromosomes appear as a grainy mass of chromatin material.

Some biologists consider prophase to begin when the centrioles start to move to opposite ends of the cell.

Figure 8-8   During mitosis, two chromatids are held together by centromeres.

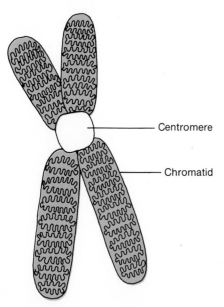

Centromere

Chromatid

mitosis increases the number of body cells in an organism or replaces them.

Much of the activity of mitosis occurs in the cell's nucleus. Thick strands called *chromosomes* appear in the nucleus. Chromosomes contain the genetic code in the form of *genes*, or the units of heredity made of DNA. The duplicated nuclear material is evenly distributed to the daughter cells. In this way, the *traits*, or characteristics, of the parent cell are passed on to the daughter cells. This is called *genetic continuity*.

Mitosis may last 30 minutes to several hours depending on the type of cell and environmental conditions. When a cell undergoes mitosis, it does not pause or rest. Mitosis is a complex, continuous process. However, mitosis is discussed in stages to make the process easier to understand.

INTERPHASE   During **interphase,** the cell is not dividing, although it is performing all life functions, such as cell respiration and protein synthesis. Although interphase is not involved with the actual separation of the cell into two new cells, the cell is preparing itself for the next division. During late interphase, the DNA replicates, and the chromosomes double. The cell then contains two sets of genes on the chromosomes. Although the nucleus is clearly visible under a microscope during interphase, the chromosomes appear only as a grainy mass of chromatin material.

In this stage, nucleoli are visible in the nucleus. During late interphase, the centrioles in animal cells begin to separate and move to opposite ends of the cell. Scientists think that they play a role in the separation of the chromosomes. Most plant cells do not have centrioles.

PROPHASE   During **prophase,** the cell gets ready for the separation of its nuclear material. The tangled, thin chromatin material begins to shorten and thicken. By the end of prophase, distinct rodlike chromosomes are visible. Each chromosome is made up of two strands called **chromatids.** These identical strands are made up of DNA. Each chromosome has a structure called a **centromere.** In some unknown way, the centromeres hold the chromosomes together.

By late prophase, the centrioles have moved to opposite ends of the nucleus. Microtubules form that may extend from one centriole to the other or only part of the way. These structures are called *spindle microtubules*. Eventually, they attach to the centromere of each chromosome. Other microtubules extend from the centrioles in all directions, forming a starlike pattern called an **aster.** These microtubules are called **aster rays** and do not connect to any other

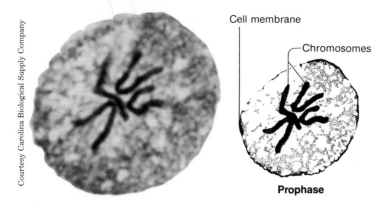

Cell membrane

Chromosomes

Prophase

Courtesy Carolina Biological Supply Company

Figure 8-9 During prophase, the chromosomes are clearly visible and begin to move to the equatorial plane of the cell.

Figure 8-10 During metaphase, the chromosomes are lined up along the equatorial plane of the cell.

structure. Aster rays form in animal cells, but they do not form in plant cells.

The chromosomes begin to move to an area halfway between the two centrioles along the *equatorial plane* of the cell. At this time, the nuclear membrane begins to disappear, and the nucleoli are usually not visible under a microscope.

METAPHASE During **metaphase,** the chromosomes complete the move to the equatorial plane. The centromeres of the chromosomes attach to the spindle microtubules. Metaphase ends when the centromeres divide and the chromatids become separate chromosomes.

ANAPHASE The main event of **anaphase** is the separation and movement of the two sets of chromosomes to opposite ends of the cell. The spindle microtubules appear to pull the chromosome pairs apart. The chromosomes appear to be dragged by their centromeres with the ends of the chromosomes trailing behind. Scientists do not yet understand how the chromosomes move. However, they do know that the spindles and centromeres are needed for this movement. Division of the cytoplasm often begins at the end of anaphase.

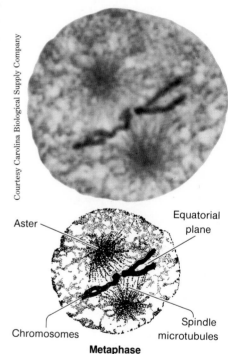

Courtesy Carolina Biological Supply Company

Aster

Equatorial plane

Chromosomes

Spindle microtubules

Metaphase

Courtesy Carolina Biological Supply Company

Chromosomes

Anaphase

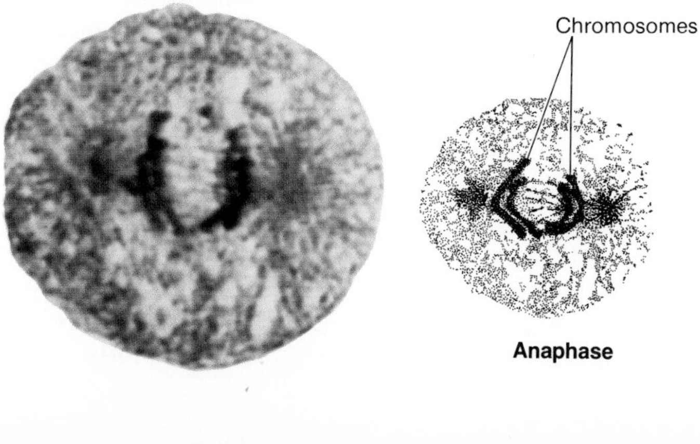

Figure 8-11 During anaphase, the chromosomes begin to move to opposite ends of the cell.

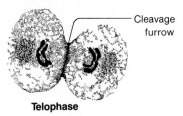

Courtesy
Carolina Biological Supply Company

Cleavage
furrow

Telophase

Figure 8-12 At the end of telophase, the cell has divided into two daughter cells.

Figure 8-13 In this onion root tip cell, the cell plate forms in the center of the cytoplasm.

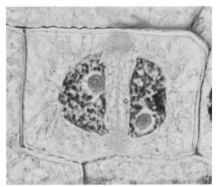

Courtesy Carolina Biological Supply Company

Highlight

Meiosis is also called reduction division. During meiosis a cell divides into two cells that each contain half the number of chromosomes as did the parent cell.

At this point, you may want to have your students do the Laboratory Investigation at the end of this chapter.

TELOPHASE The last stage of mitosis is called **telophase.** During telophase, the chromosomes are at opposite ends of the cell. New nuclear membranes form around the chromosomes. As the chromosomes begin to disappear and the chromatin material reforms, the nucleoli slowly appear. The spindle microtubules and astral rays disappear. The division of the cytoplasmic material is usually completed.

In animal cells, a *cleavage furrow* begins to form during anaphase. The cleavage furrow is an indentation that pinches the cell membrane inward. During telophase, the furrow deepens until the cell is pinched in half, forming two new daughter cells.

The rigid cell walls of plant cells cannot be pinched inward. Instead, plant cells form a structure called a *cell plate* in the center of the cytoplasm. The cell plate grows outward until it reaches the cell wall. The cell is then divided into the daughter cells.

Mitosis is complete when the daughter cells enter the interphase stage. At this point, mitosis can begin again.

Meiosis

The diploid number of chromosomes in human beings is 46. The haploid number of chromosomes in human beings is 23. You may want to explain to your students that the diploid number is restored during fertilization.

Every new cell that is produced by the process of mitosis has the same type and number of chromosomes as does the parent cell. The chromosomes always occur in pairs, and the shape and gene sequence on each chromosome are the same. Each pair of chromosomes is referred to as *homologous.* The normal number of homologous chromosomes in a cell is called the **diploid number** (2n). Your body cells are examples of diploid cells.

The main function of the process of **meiosis** (mī-ō-sis) is to produce cells with only half the normal number of chromosomes, referred to as the **haploid number** (n). During meiosis, four cells are produced from one cell. In animals, the cells produced by meiosis are called **gametes,** or sex cells. The development of gametes by the process of meiosis is called **gametogenesis** (ga-mēt-ə-JEN-ə-sis). Some plants also produce gametes, but the sex cells of most plants are **spores.**

During meiosis, DNA is replicated. Then the cell undergoes two cell divisions. Many of the changes that occur during meiosis are similar to those that occur during mitosis. Meiosis is also a continuous process, but it has been separated into two major divisions containing various stages to make the process easier to understand.

FIRST MEIOTIC DIVISION The first meiotic division is similar to the process of mitosis. However, the events of the first prophase are slightly different than in mitosis.

Interphase DNA is replicated.

Prophase I The chromatin material shortens and thickens. Double-stranded chromosomes appear. By the end of prophase I, double-stranded homologous chromosomes pair up and twist around each other. The pairing process is called **synapsis.** Because each chromosome pair is double-stranded, there are a total of four chromatids. This is called a **tetrad.** Synapsis does not occur in mitosis.

Metaphase I During metaphase I, the paired homologous chromosomes line up on the equatorial plane.

Anaphase I The homologous chromosomes of each pair move to opposite ends of the cell. The chromatids of each chromosome do not separate as they do in mitosis. They remain double-stranded.

Telophase I Two new nuclei form. Once the two daughter cells have separated, the first meiotic division is completed.

At this point, a stage of meiosis referred to as **interkinesis** (in-tər-ki-NĒ-sis) occurs. This stage is similar to interphase except that the genetic material is not replicated.

SECOND MEIOTIC DIVISION The second meiotic division occurs quickly and is similar to mitosis. Basically, the chromatids separate, and the cytoplasm divides.

Prophase II The chromosomes shorten, thicken, and become visible under a microscope.

Metaphase II The chromosomes move to the equatorial plane.

Anaphase II The chromatids of each chromosome separate and move to opposite ends of the cell.

Telophase II Four haploid daughter cells are formed. The second division is complete.

Formation of Egg and Sperm Cells

Egg cells are produced in the *ovaries* of the female organism. The process of egg formation is called *oogenesis* (ō-ə-JEN-ə-sis). During oogenesis, a diploid cell in the ovaries called a *primary oocyte* (ō-ə-sīt) undergoes meiosis. In the first meiotic division, a large cell called the *secondary oocyte* and a smaller cell called the first **polar body** are produced. The secondary oocyte undergoes a second meiotic division, forming a large cell called an **ootid** and a second polar body.

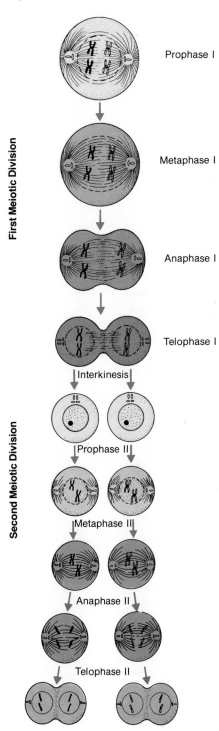

Figure 8-14 Stages of Meiosis

First Meiotic Division — Prophase I, Metaphase I, Anaphase I, Telophase I

Interkinesis

Second Meiotic Division — Prophase II, Metaphase II, Anaphase II, Telophase II

Sometimes, the first polar body divides into two second polar bodies. The ootid develops into the mature haploid egg cell, or **ovum.** The polar bodies do not develop into egg cells. The ovum contains more cytoplasm than the polar bodies. The extra cytoplasm is used as food during early development of a new organism.

In the male organism, diploid cells called *primary spermatocytes* are produced in the *testes*. These cells undergo a form of meiosis called *spermatogenesis*. At the end of spermatogenesis, four haploid male sex cells, or **sperm,** are produced from a parent cell.

After the first meiotic division, each primary spermatocyte produces two *secondary spermatocytes*. These two

CAREER: Science Editor

Scientists must communicate their ideas and discoveries to other scientists, policy makers, and the general public. Usually this information is published in books, magazines, and newspapers. Sometimes the information is broadcast as a daily newscast or as a special television program.

Science editors are responsible for coordinating and preparing material for publication or broadcast. An editor may assign a writer to prepare a manuscript on a specific topic. Sometimes scientists will be asked to write about their theories or discoveries.

Once the material has been written, it is called a manuscript. When science editors receive a manuscript from a writer, they make changes in the manuscript that will help make the material clearer and easier to read. In addition, they correct grammar and spelling errors. Editors must also make sure that the facts are accurate. After the manuscript has been edited, the editors may choose photographs or have drawings made to illustrate the manuscript.

Science editors have different responsibilities depending on the type of publisher they work for. A textbook editor may spend up to three years developing and producing a single book. A science editor on a daily newspaper may have to handle several articles every day.

Some science editors cover all branches of science while others specialize in one area, such as medicine, agriculture, or space science.

Technical editors work only on technical publications. These publications are designed to be read by people who are experts on the subjects covered in the publications. Some editors work only on children's books or general interest magazines.

Science editors have at least a bachelor's degree in one area of science and have taken background courses in other sciences. They may also have taken courses in journalism. Science editors who work on textbooks often have teaching experience, which helps them to understand the needs, abilities, and interests of the students who will use the books.

For further career information, write to National Association of Science Writers, Inc., Post Office Box 294, Greenlawn, NY 11740.

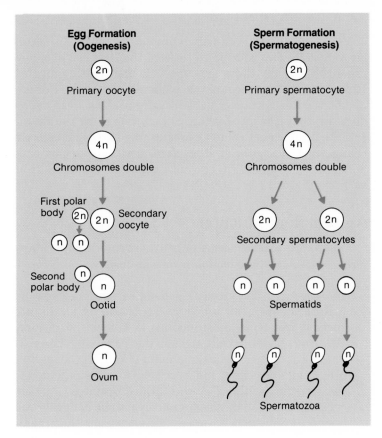

Figure 8-15 Eggs and sperm cells are formed by meiotic division. How does the end result of oogenesis and spermatogenesis differ?

At the end of oogenesis, a single egg cell is formed from each primary oocyte. At the end of spermatogenesis, four sperm cells are produced from each primary spermatocyte.

cells produce four *spermatids*, which develop into *spermatozoa*, or sperm. They are made up mainly of a head of nuclear material and a long, whiplike tail called the *flagellum*. The flagellum is used for movement.

SECTION REVIEW   Answers on page T–39.

1. Name the five stages of mitosis.
2. Describe the structure of a chromosome.
3. How do mitosis and meiosis differ?
4. What is gametogenesis?
5. What is meant by the diploid number of chromosomes? The haploid number?.

Reproduction of Organisms

Some plants and animals reproduce asexually. **Asexual reproduction** is the formation of offspring from a single parent. The offspring of an organism that reproduces asexually is exactly like its parent.

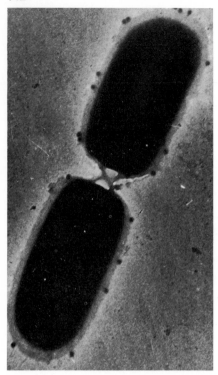

Figure 8-16 This bacterium, called *E. coli*, has almost completed binary fission.

Figure 8-17 A zygote is formed when an egg cell and a sperm cell unite. The symbol N stands for the haploid number of chromosomes. The symbol 2N stands for the diploid number of chromosomes.

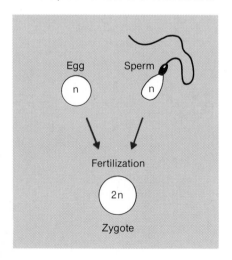

Most plants and animals reproduce sexually. In **sexual reproduction,** two cells unite to form the first cell of a new organism. Usually these cells are male and female gametes. However, in some organisms gametes are alike. For example, the unicellular protist called *Paramecium* can reproduce by *conjugation.* During conjugation, two paramecia fuse. In a somewhat complex process, the two organisms exchange nuclear material. Therefore, both cells act as male and female. Eventually, two new cells are produced from each original cell.

Stress to your students that mitosis is involved in all forms of asexual reproduction. Forms of asexual reproduction include cloning and vegetative propagation.

Asexual Reproduction

There are several forms of asexual reproduction. Many forms of asexual reproduction involve mitosis.

Budding In the process of **budding,** the nucleus and cytoplasm of a cell are duplicated, and two cells are formed from one cell. Budding is a form of mitosis. However, budding cells are not the same size. The parent cell is larger than the daughter cell. The daughter cell, or bud, is usually pinched free from the parent cell. Because the daughter cell was formed by mitosis, the hereditary material in the parent cell and the daughter cell is exactly the same. Examples of organisms that reproduce by budding are hydra, jellyfish, sea anemones, yeasts, and some fungi.

Spores Small, round haploid reproductive cells produced by plants during meiosis are called **spores.** These asexual structures grow into *haploid organisms.* Haploid organisms are made up of cells that have half the normal number of chromosomes. In some plants, such as mosses and fungi, spores grow into multicellular plants. In other plants, such as ferns and seed-bearing plants, the haploid spores quickly divide by mitosis and produce gametes.

Binary Fission A process similar to mitosis is **binary fission.** During binary fission, a cell splits into two new cells of equal size. This is the simplest form of asexual reproduction. Unicellular organisms, such as blue-green algae and bacteria, reproduce this way.

Sexual Reproduction

During sexual reproduction, two haploid gametes unite to form a **zygote** (zī-gōt), or fertilized egg. The joining of the two haploid gametes is called *fertilization.* The zygote contains the diploid number of chromosomes. Each gamete provides half the number of chromosomes.

ANIMALS   Almost all multicellular animals exist as *diploid organisms* throughout their lives. That is, every cell in their body contains the diploid number of chromosomes. However, they produce haploid gametes through meiosis for sexual reproduction. When these cells unite to form a diploid zygote, repeated mitotic divisions and *cell differentiation* produce a new diploid individual. Cell differentiation is the formation of many different types of cells, such as skin cells and muscle cells. These cells have special functions. Although they contain the full amount of DNA, the only part of the DNA that is active is that which codes for the cell's special functions.

Some multicellular animals, such as the jellyfish, reproduce both sexually and asexually. The asexual form and the sexual form look different from one another. Each form is a different stage in the life cycle of the animal.

PLANTS   Most plants have a haploid form and a diploid form during their life cycles. In some plants, the haploid form dominates the life cycle. In others, the haploid form exists for only a short period of the life cycle. Figure 8-19 shows the life cycle of different types of plants. Mosses and fungi have long haploid stages. Ferns and seed-bearing plants exist as diploid organisms throughout most of their life cycles. Most flowering plants have a short haploid stage, during which they are small organisms made up of few cells.

Unlike animals, plants do not produce gametes directly by meiosis. Instead, haploid gametes are produced during mitosis. This is the only situation in which haploid cells are produced by mitosis. The cells then fuse to form a diploid zygote. The zygote develops into the diploid form of the plant. During the diploid stage of the life cycle of the plant, haploid spores are produced by the process of meiosis. The spores develop into the haploid form of the plant. The haploid form of the plant then produces gametes.

SECTION REVIEW   Answers on page T–39.

1. Define asexual reproduction.
2. What are three forms of asexual reproduction?
3. What is sexual reproduction?
4. Define fertilization.
5. How does sexual reproduction in plants and animals differ?

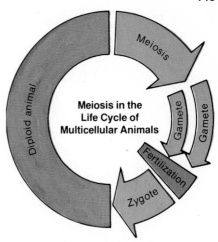

Figure 8-18   In multicellular animals, gametes are produced by the process of meiosis. After fertilization, the zygote undergoes many mitotic divisions to become a diploid multicellular organism.

Have your students compare the plant life cycles shown in Figure 8-19. Stress the differences in the length of the haploid and diploid stages.

The length of the haploid stage varies among plants.

Figure 8-19   Compare the life cycles of different types of plants. What difference can you see between the haploid and diploid stages of the life cycles?

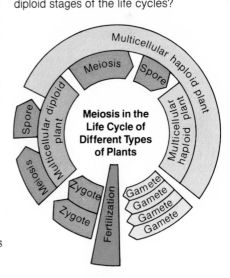

For additional information, see page T–39.

Examining Mitosis in Onion Root Tip Cells

Purpose Cells reproduce by dividing. In mitosis, the nucleus and cytoplasm of a cell are divided into two equal parts. Although plant and animal cells have several structural differences, the process of mitosis is essentially the same in both. The purpose of this investigation is to observe mitosis in plant cells.

Materials *(per 2 students)* ● Prepared onion root tip slides (stained) ● Microscope ● Lens paper

Procedure **1.** Obtain a stained slide of onion root tip. Gently clean it with lens paper to remove any smudges and fingerprints. **2.** Examine the slide with the low power of the microscope. Look over the entire surface of the tip for cells that are in different stages of mitosis. **3.** Using the high power of the microscope, examine the stained cells more carefully. You should notice many cells in different stages of division.
4. Prepare and label laboratory drawings of individual cells that exhibit the following characteristics.
a. Chromosomes appear as a grainy mass.
b. Nuclear membrane has disappeared, and chromosomes appear as short, thick strands in cytoplasm. **c.** Chromosomes are aligned along equatorial plane. **d.** Chromosomes appear as V-shaped groups at opposite sides of cell. **e.** Cell plate is developing, and chromosomes are less distinct.
5. Find other cells in stages of mitosis between the stages in each of your five drawings. **Note:** *Because mitosis is a continuous process, it is possible to have several drawings for each stage of mitosis.*

Observations and Conclusions **1.** In which stage of mitosis do most of the root cells appear to be? **2.** In what ways is the interphase stage different from the other stages of mitosis? **3.** As you examine the onion root tip under high power, in which area do most cells appear to be undergoing mitosis? **4.** Approximately how many cells are visible in the microscope field? If each of these cells underwent three successive divisions, how many daughter cells would be produced?

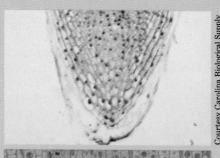

Courtesy Carolina Biological Supply Company

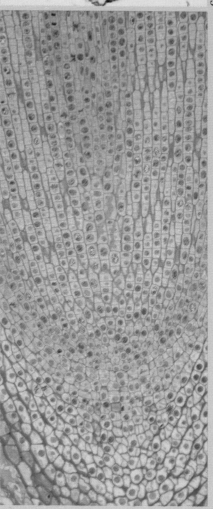

CHAPTER SUMMARY

Nucleic Acids The cells of all living things except viruses contain two types of nucleic acids: deoxyribonucleic acid (DNA) and ribonucleic acid (RNA). DNA contains all of the information needed to make and control every part of an organism.

A model of DNA was proposed in 1953 by James D. Watson and Francis H.C. Crick. The model consists of two coiled chains of nucleotides called a double helix. Each nucleotide is made up of a deoxyribose sugar, a phosphate group, and one of four different nitrogen bases.

The DNA in a cell replicates itself before a cell divides. Therefore, each new cell contains identical DNA molecules. DNA is also used as a pattern to produce a complementary chain of RNA. RNA is involved in the manufacture of proteins.

Protein Synthesis Three types of RNA are used to make proteins: messenger RNA (mRNA), ribosomal RNA (rRNA), and transfer RNA (tRNA). During transcription, the code words of DNA are copied onto a strand of messenger RNA. The RNA sequence of bases is a code used to manufacture specific proteins. Each 3-base codon on the single-stranded RNA is a code for an amino acid. During translation, messenger RNA bonds to the ribosomes. Ribosomal RNA is found in the ribosomes. Amino acids in the cytoplasm are picked up by transfer RNA and carried to the messenger RNA. As each amino acid is placed on the forming protein, a chemical bond forms. When the protein is completed, it leaves the ribosome and is used within the cell or secreted to other parts of the organism.

Cell Reproduction When a cell reproduces, it divides. Mitosis is a form of cell reproduction. In a unicellular organism, mitosis produces new organisms. In a multicellular organism, mitosis increases the number of cells and replaces cells. During mitosis, the DNA and cytoplasm duplicate and separate into two identical cells. The two daughter cells each have the same number of chromosomes as the parent had. Mitosis is a continuous process that is described in five stages: interphase, prophase, metaphase, anaphase, and telophase.

Some cells reproduce through meiosis. The main function of meiosis is to produce sex cells, or gametes, which have only half the number of chromosomes of the parent cell. Meiosis begins similarly to mitosis. However, meiosis has two cell divisions. Egg and sperm cells are produced by meiosis.

Reproduction of Organisms Many plants and animals reproduce asexually. The offspring are formed from one parent and are identical to the parent. Some forms of asexual reproduction are budding, spore formation, and binary fission.

Most animals and some plants reproduce sexually. Some organisms reproduce sexually at one time in their life cycle and asexually at another time. During sexual reproduction, two gametes unite to form the first cell of an organism.

CHAPTER VOCABULARY

anaphase	interkinesis	replication
asexual reproduction	interphase	ribosomal RNA
aster	meiosis	RNA
aster rays	messenger RNA	sexual reproduction
binary fission	metaphase	sperm
budding	mitosis	spore
centromere	nucleotide	synapsis
chromatid	ootid	telophase
codon	ovum	tetrad
diploid number	polar body	transcription
DNA	prophase	transfer RNA
gamete	protein synthesis	translation
gametogenesis	purine	zygote
haploid number	pyrimidine	

REVIEW of FACTS and CONCEPTS   Answers on page T–40.

On a separate sheet of paper, answer each of the following as completely as possible.

1. Why is DNA called the "code of life?"
2. Describe the Watson-Crick model of DNA.
3. List the three differences between DNA and RNA.
4. What are the roles of DNA and RNA in protein synthesis?
5. How is messenger RNA formed during transcription?
6. Each codon on messenger RNA represents a specific amino acid or a "stop." How does this indicate that a molecule of DNA must have 3-letter code words?
7. What is the role of transfer RNA in translation?
8. Why are different proteins found in different living things?
9. If a code on a DNA chain is ATG for a specific amino acid, what is the messenger RNA codon? The transfer RNA anticodon?

10. List the stages of mitosis. Briefly describe what happens in each stage.
11. How does the formation of a cleavage furrow in animal cells differ from the formation of a cell plate in plant cells?
12. All cells in the human body except the gametes have 46 chromosomes. During meiosis, how many chromosomes are found in each gamete?
13. How does the second meiotic division differ from mitosis?
14. What are the differences between egg formation and sperm formation?
15. What are the major differences between asexual and sexual reproduction?
16. By what process are gametes from the haploid plant formed? By what process are the spores from the diploid plant formed?

EXTENSIONS and APPLICATIONS   For additional information, see page T–40.

1. Make a three-dimensional model of a DNA molecule that can be displayed in your classroom. Look up a photograph of the Watson-Crick model to use as a reference.
2. Using prepared slides of plant and animal cells, make a series of laboratory drawings of the stages of mitosis that you can see under the microscope. Label each drawing with the stage and

a sentence that explains what is occurring. **Note:** *Include several drawings for each stage.*
3. Make a series of labeled models of cells undergoing mitosis or meiosis.
4. Look up the structure of the human protein insulin. Using different colored construction paper, make a model of a single strand of DNA that would code for insulin.

SUGGESTED READINGS

Readings from Scientific American, *The Living Cell*. San Francisco, Calif.: W.H. Freeman.
   This book is a collection of articles on the structure and function of cells, including cell division and growth.
Sayre, A., *Rosalind Franklin and DNA*. New York: W.W. Norton.
   The life of Rosalind Franklin and her contribution to the discovery of the structure of DNA are discussed.
Watson, J.D., *The Double Helix*. New York: New American Library.
   One of the Nobel Prize-winning scientists who helped discover the structure of DNA relates a personal view of how it was accomplished.

The Use of Food Additives

If you had lived about 100 years ago, most of the food that you ate would have come from your own farm or a neighbor's farm. Today, most people live in large cities that are not near farms. Food has to be transported, sometimes over long distances, to where it is needed.

Because of the great distances between farms and cities, care has to be taken during the transportation of food so that it does not spoil. To prevent spoilage, food manufacturers often add substances called food additives to food. Food manufacturers also use additives to improve the flavor, color, and texture of their products. Other additives, such as vitamin D, are added to food to increase its nutritional value.

Some food additives are made synthetically in the laboratory. Some snack foods are made up of only synthetic additives. Interestingly, however, most additives occur naturally. Salt, pepper, and sugar are examples of natural additives.

Some food additives may be dangerous to people's health. In 1970, the Food and Drug Administration (FDA) prohibited the sale of artificial sweeteners called cyclamates. The cyclamates were shown to cause cancer in laboratory animals. Six years later the FDA banned the use of red dye number 2 in foods, drugs, and cosmetics. Red dye number 2 has also been linked to cancer.

Food additives have also been blamed for other problems. Monosodium glutamate, a flavor enhancer, produces headaches in many people who are sensitive to it. Even sugar, a natural additive, has been viewed as a cause of hyperactivity in some children. An excess of sugar also causes dental caries in children and adults.

It is important to note that many additives benefit the consumer. Some enable foods to have a longer shelf life. Others protect foods from bacterial growth and permit seasonal foods, such as blueberries, to be available throughout the year. In addition, some food additives play an important part in the preparation of foods. For example, many natural fruits are not abundant or are available only during certain seasons, which restricts the use of natural fruit flavors. Manufacturers have developed synthetic fruit flavorings to overcome this problem and meet the needs and tastes of the consumer.

Nevertheless, many people are joining a growing movement to eat "natural" or "health" foods that are free of additives. Even neighborhood supermarkets offer these foods in special sections, enabling people to make their own choices as to what to eat.

Viewpoints

1. In 1977, the Food and Drug Administration took steps to limit the use of the artificial sweetener saccharin. It was found to cause cancer in laboratory animals. Foods that contain saccharin now carry a warning that it may be hazardous to your health. Should saccharin continue to be added to foods? Are there any other alternatives for people such as diabetics who must watch their intake of sugar?

2. Save the packages from the foods you eat during one day. Determine from the labels the additives you consumed and list them. Consult food and nutrition reference materials to find out whether these additives are natural or artificial. Determine whether or not they are considered unhealthy.

3. Interview a nutritionist or dietician. Before you interview, prepare a list of questions for the interview, such as the following: Do you try to avoid certain food additives in your selection of food? Are you concerned about additives?

4. Write to the Manufacturing Chemists' Association, Inc., 2501 M Street NW, Washington, DC 20037, and request a copy of the pamphlet "Food Additives: Who Needs Them?" Summarize the material in a visual presentation for the class.

UNIT THREE

Variety and Continuity

For an overview of this unit, including field trip suggestions, a bibliography, and a list of audio-visual materials, see pages T–41 to T–51. You may want to check the Laboratory Investigations in this unit so that materials may be ordered, gathered, or prepared in advance.

Scientists estimate that about 5 million species of plants and animals live on the earth. This may not seem so amazing when you realize that beetles alone account for at least 500,000 species! Some scientists estimate that about 2 billion different kinds of plants and animals have lived on the earth throughout its history. If these estimates are correct, 99.75% of the plants and animals that ever lived on the earth do not exist today!

Every living thing fits into a particular environment. Each organism has special characteristics that enable it to live where it does. Most living things could not survive if their environment were to change greatly.

The ability of organisms to fit into a certain environment, the diversity of life, patterns of heredity, and the disappearance of millions of species can be explained by various scientific theories and observations. This unit will explore some of these theories and observations.

These salamanders are shown before and after hatching.

9 Heredity

Chapter Objectives *After completing this chapter, you will be able to:*

a ▪ Explain Mendel's principle of dominance and recessiveness. p. 152
b ▪ State the law of segregation and the law of independent assortment. p. 154
c ▪ Explain hybrid and purebred; genotype and phenotype. p. 153 , p. 156
d ▪ Apply the probability product rule to genetics problems. p. 157
e ▪ Use Punnett squares to illustrate monohybrid and dihybrid crosses. p. 158
f ▪ Explain incomplete dominance and give an example using a Punnett square. p. 161

For teaching aids for this chapter, including a chapter overview and teaching strategies, see pages T–41 to T–43. The page number next to each chapter objective refers to the text page where the information needed to fulfill the objective begins.

Young African elephants inherit their parents' traits.

You receive information in various ways. It is passed to you through computers, television, radio, telephones, books, magazines, and newspapers. You also receive information through the words of your parents, teachers, and friends. This information gives you knowledge of past and present.

There is another kind of information, genetic information, that makes you what you are—blond or brunette, blue-eyed or brown-eyed, tall or short. This information is provided by *DNA*, a complex molecule in cells. Information stored in the DNA molecules determines the structure and function of all living things. This information is passed from parent to offspring as *traits*, or characteristics. The passing of traits from parents to offspring is called **heredity** and causes offspring to resemble their parents.

The way traits are passed from parents to their offspring was a mystery for a long time. During the last 125 years, some of the mystery has been solved by research in the field of **genetics** (jə-NET-iks), the scientific study of heredity. Genetics is one of the most modern of the biological sciences.

The Work of Gregor Mendel

Modern laws of heredity were established from the research of Gregor Mendel. Mendel was an Austrian monk, scientist, and mathematician. For eight years, during the middle of the nineteenth century, Mendel experimented with garden pea plants to see if there was a pattern in their heredity. Similar plant breeding experiments had been done before Mendel's work. However, Mendel was among the first to keep careful records and to complete mathematical studies of his work.

In 1866, Mendel published the results of his observations and experiments. However, his studies were ignored and eventually forgotten until the early 1900s. At that time, three scientists working in three countries reached conclusions similar to Mendel's. Scientists recognized the importance of Mendel's work, and the study of genetics as a branch of biology began.

Mendel's Experiments

Mendel worked with many different kinds of plants in his first experiments. However, he decided to focus on the heredity of pea plants in his later experiments. He did this because pea plants grew rapidly and produced many seeds. These characteristics allowed Mendel to study several generations and many offspring during a short period of time. Mendel observed and kept records of seven traits from one generation to the next. These traits were seed shape, seed color, seed coat color, pod shape, pod color, flower position, and stem length. Some plants had long stems, while other plants had short stems. Some plants had smooth seeds while others had wrinkled seeds, and so on. Mendel chose these traits because they occurred in contrasting pairs and were easy to observe.

The structure of the flowers of the pea plants made it easy to control the reproductive process of the plants. In flowering plants such as the pea, the *female gametes*, or egg cells, are found at the base of the *pistil*. The pistil is the female reproductive structure. The male reproductive structure is called the *stamen* and produces pollen. Pollen contains the *male gametes*, or sperm cells. The flower of a pea plant has both a stamen and a pistil. Figure 9-1 shows the parts of a pea flower. Pollen from the stamen falls on the pistil of the same flower or on other flowers of the same plant. This process is called *self-pollination*. The pollen from the flowers of one pea plant can also be carried by the wind

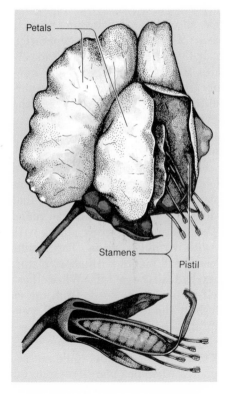

Figure 9-1 In one of his experiments, Gregor Mendel prevented self-pollination in pea plants by pinching off the pollen-containing stamens of the flowers. He then cross-pollinated these pea plants with pollen from the stamens of other pea plants with the traits he wanted to study.

or on the legs of insects to the pistil of another plant. This process is called *cross-pollination.*

SOME MENDELIAN STUDIES To study the results of self-pollination, Mendel covered flowers so that pollen from other plants could not reach the pistils. Mendel noticed that in successive generations of self-pollinated plants, the seven traits remained the same. Plants with yellow seeds produced plants with yellow seeds. Plants with round seeds produced plants with round seeds. Mendel called these plants "true-breeding" plants.

Mendel continued his studies by crossing true-breeding plants that had contrasting traits. In one experiment, he pinched off the stamens of a plant that produced only wrinkled seeds. He then took pollen from a plant that produced only round seeds and dusted it onto the pistil of the plant with wrinkled seeds. Mendel referred to these two plants as the *parental generation*, or P_1.

Mendel discovered that all of the offspring in the next generation had round seeds. Mendel called this generation the *first filial generation*, or F_1. Mendel repeated this experiment for each of the traits. He discovered that the F_1 generation always showed only one of the traits of the P_1 generation. One of the parental traits seemed to disappear in the F_1 generation. What happened to this trait? Why did it seem to disappear?

Mendel allowed the plants of the F_1 generation to self-pollinate. Mendel called the plants of the next generation the *second filial generation*, or F_2. When he opened the pods of the F_2 generation of plants, he was surprised to find that some plants had wrinkled seeds and some plants had round seeds. How could seeds that were round grow plants with round seeds and plants with wrinkled seeds? The results were similar when he crossed tall plants with short plants. The F_1 generation plants had all been tall. When these plants were allowed to self-pollinate, the seeds from the F_1 generation produced both short and tall plants in the F_2 generation, but no plants of intermediate height.

DOMINANCE AND RECESSIVENESS Mendel could not see what happened in the gametes when pea plants reproduced. He knew of the existence of *cells*, the basic unit of living things, but he did not know anything about cell reproduction. His work was based on the hypothesis that *factors*, or units, carried the traits that he was studying. Today, those factors, or units of heredity, are called **genes.**

From his observations, Mendel knew that the offspring of true-breeding plants with contrasting traits showed the

	Seed Shape	Seed Color	Seed Coat Color	Pod Shape	Pod Color	Flower Position	Stem Length
Dominant	Round	Yellow	Colored	Inflated	Green	Axial	Long
Recessive	Wrinkled	Green	White	Constricted	Yellow	Terminal	Short

Figure 9-2 The chart shows the seven characteristics that Mendel studied in pea plants. Each characteristic had a contrasting pair of traits. What is the dominant trait of each pair? The dominant traits in pea plants are round seed shape, yellow seed color, colored seed coat, inflated pod shape, green pod color, axial flower position, and long stem length.

trait of only one parent plant. He called this trait the **dominant** trait. He referred to the trait that seemed to disappear as the **recessive** trait.

Scientists use symbols to represent different forms of a trait. Dominant traits are represented by capital letters. For example, green pods are represented by "G." Recessive traits are represented by lower-case letters. Yellow pods are represented by "g." These symbols indicate that green pods are dominant over yellow pods. Likewise, tallness (T) in pea plants is dominant over shortness (t).

Figure 9-3 shows a P_1 cross of plants with yellow pods and plants with green pods. The F_1 generation that results has green pods. Therefore, the dominant trait for pod color is green. When plants of the F_1 generation self-pollinate, some of the plants of the F_2 generation have green pods and some have yellow pods. The recessive trait for pod color, yellow, reappears.

Today, an organism that carries genes that are alike is said to be **purebred.** An organism that carries genes that are

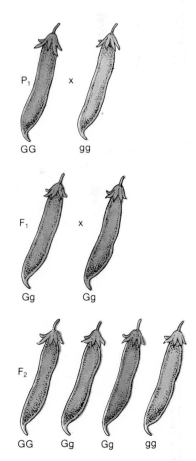

Figure 9-3 Mendel discovered that one trait seemed to disappear in the F_1 generation. However, the trait reappeared in the F_2 generation. What did Mendel call this trait? Recessive

154

Highlight

The dominant trait is the trait that shows up in the F₁ generation when two purebred organisms with contrasting traits are crossed. The recessive trait is the trait that seems to disappear in the F₁ generation of the same cross.

You may want to review meiosis with your students before you discuss Mendel's laws.

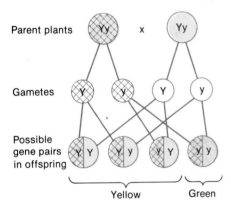

□ gene from male

Figure 9-4 Gene pairs separate, or segregate, during meiosis. What is the difference between the Yy and the yY gene pairs?

The Y gene is supplied by the male and the y gene by the female in the Yy zygote. The Y gene is supplied by the female and the y gene by the male in the yY zygote.

different is called a **hybrid.** Thus, Mendel's parental generation of pea plants were purebred. The plants in the F₁ generation were hybrid plants because they were offspring of parents with different traits.

Dominant and recessive traits have been discovered in many plants and animals. Scientists use Mendel's *principle of dominance and recessiveness* to explain why certain organisms are similar or not similar to their parents.

Mendel's Laws

Mendel tried to explain his observations by developing *hypotheses* (hī-PAHTH-ə-sēz), or explanations for what he saw. In time, his hypotheses provided consistent explanations for what he observed as patterns of heredity. After being supported by the results of many different experiments, some of Mendel's hypotheses became known as *theories.* Today, because these theories are accepted explanations of facts, they are known as *laws.*

LAW OF SEGREGATION On the basis of his experiments, Mendel hypothesized that there must be a pair of factors for each trait. The two units control or account for the trait. Scientists today call the two units a *gene pair.* For example, if a pea plant that has green seeds is the offspring of plants with yellow seeds, the factor accounting for the green color must be present in the parents. A parent plant with the gene pair Yy would have yellow seeds but would be carrying a recessive gene (y) for green seeds. The trait would be masked in the parent but could be passed on to the offspring. The possible gene pairs for seed color are YY, Yy, yY, and yy. Yy and yY represent the same gene pair but indicate that in each case the genes were contributed by different parents. Both combinations are usually written with the dominant gene first (Yy).

Modern knowledge of *chromosomes* and *meiosis* can help explain Mendel's hypothesis. Chromosomes are structures that carry the code for inherited traits in the form of *genes.* Ordinary cells contain pairs of chromosomes, and, therefore, pairs of genes. However, during meiosis, when sex cells form, chromosome pairs separate. The paired genes that are on the *paired* chromosomes also separate, or *segregate.* The gametes that are formed each receive only one gene for a particular trait. For example, one-half of the gametes of a pea plant with a yellow/green (Yy) gene pair for seed color have a gene for yellow (Y). The other half of the gametes carry a gene for green (y). During reproduction, single gametes unite to form a *zygote,* or fertilized gamete. A gene pair is formed again. When this offspring plant produces gametes, its gene pairs separate again.

Mendel's hypothesis that the pairs of factors for each trait separate as gametes form explained the results of many other experiments that involved the crossing of hybrid plants. In 1900, Mendel's hypothesis became known as the **law of segregation.**

LAW OF INDEPENDENT ASSORTMENT   The results of Mendel's experiments led him to the hypothesis that each of the seven traits he was studying was controlled by a pair of genes. He also hypothesized that these different pairs of genes separated from each other during gamete formation. For example, when a tall plant with yellow seeds forms gametes, the genes for stem length separate independently from the genes for seed color.

Mendel's theory that gene pairs separate independently from one another during gamete formation is now known as the **law of independent assortment.** According to this law, genes are shuffled around and form different combinations. The possible number of different combinations of gene pairs is very large in living things that have thousands of genes. The differences between individuals of the same species are the result of the independent assortment and shuffling of gene pairs that Mendel first described.

The seven pairs of genes that Mendel studied separated independently because they were on different pairs of chromosomes. If these genes were all on the same pairs of chromosomes, they would not separate independently.

SECTION REVIEW   Answers on page T–42.

1. What is meant by a dominant trait? A recessive trait?
2. What is the difference between a hybrid and a purebred organism?
3. Which of Mendel's laws states that gene pairs separate during gamete formation?
4. What does the law of independent assortment state?

Concepts of Heredity

Scientists who study the patterns and processes of heredity in living things are called *geneticists* (jə-NET-ə-sists). Geneticists use certain terms and concepts to communicate the results of their studies. They use the term **allele** (ə-LĒL) to refer to a gene for a single trait. For example, in pea plants, yellow (Y) is the dominant allele for seed color. Green (y) is

---

Highlight

The law of segregation states that the pair of genes for each trait separates, or segregates, during gamete formation. The law of independent assortment states that different gene pairs separate independently from one another during gamete formation.

The possible gene combinations are yellow seed/tall stem, yellow seed/short stem, green seed/tall stem, and green seed/short stem.

Figure 9-5 During meiosis, the chromosomes double and then separate. Different gene pairs on different chromosomes separate independently. What are the possible gene combinations of the gametes shown in this illustration?

LAW OF INDEPENDENT ASSORTMENT

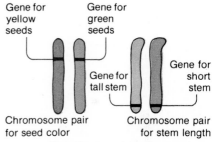

Gene for yellow seeds

Gene for green seeds

Gene for tall stem

Gene for short stem

Chromosome pair for seed color

Chromosome pair for stem length

Two chromosome pairs

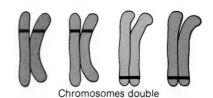

Chromosomes double

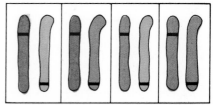

Four different gametes are possible

the recessive allele. The genes that represent tallness (T) and shortness (t) in pea plants are also alleles.

In an allele pair, each gene is on a separate chromosome. When the genes in an allele pair are identical (YY or yy), the zygote is said to be **homozygous** (hō-mō-zī-gəs), or pure for that trait. If the genes in the allele are not identical (Yy), the zygote is **heterozygous** (het-ə-rə-zī-gəs).

The combinations of alleles or genes for a trait are called **genotypes** (JĒN-ə-tīps). For example, YY and Yy are the genotypes for yellow seed color and yy is the genotype for green seed color in pea plants.

The visible characteristics of organisms that genotypes produce are called **phenotypes** (FĒ-nə-tīps). Different genotypes may have the same phenotype. In pea plants, for example, YY and Yy represent two different genotypes for seed color, but a YY plant and a Yy plant would both have yellow seeds. They would have the same phenotype.

Highlight

A genotype is the combinations of alleles or genes for a trait. A genotype is homozygous or heterozygous. A phenotype is the visible characteristics of an organism that a genotype produces.

Ask your students to give the genotypes for various phenotypes and the phenotypes for various genotypes. This exercise will help reinforce terminology and concepts of heredity.

CAREER: Geneticist

A geneticist is a scientist who studies heredity. Some geneticists do basic research. Research geneticists try to learn what factors affect inherited traits. They perform experiments to determine the principles of inheritance. In their work, they may study the relationships between heredity and other aspects of life, such as aging and reproduction. Other geneticists apply the principles of genetics to solve everyday problems. Applied geneticists try to use genetics to improve life. They may develop crops that grow faster than other crops, yield more food, or resist certain diseases.

Much of a geneticist's work is done in a laboratory. However, some geneticists may work in "field laboratories," such as wheat fields in which test crops are grown. Geneticists direct lab technicians and other helpers.

Geneticists may specialize in a particular branch of genetics. For example, molecular geneticists study the chemicals that make up genes and chromosomes. Population geneticists study how hereditary factors influence the development of populations and races. Genetic engineers work with genetic material in cells to develop organisms with new traits.

Geneticists are highly trained. They usually have a master's degree in genetics. Most positions require a doctorate with specialization in a branch of genetics.

Colleges, universities, and medical schools employ many geneticists. They combine research with teaching duties. Other geneticists work for state or federal government agencies, such as departments of agriculture or health. Some geneticists work for pharmaceutical companies or other private companies.

For further career information, write to American Genetic Association, 818 18th Street NW, Washington, DC 20060.

Probability

Geneticists use *probability* to predict possible genotypes and phenotypes. Probability is the chance that something will or will not happen. Probabilities are expressed in fractions or percentages. For example, the chance that a flipped coin will land heads up is ½, or 50%, because there are only two possibilities, heads or tails. The probability of a gamete receiving a Y gene from a Yy parent is ½, or 50%.

The results of one chance event do not affect the next. Each event happens independently of the next event. For example, if a coin lands heads up ten times in a row, the probability of it landing heads up on the next flip still remains ½, or 50%. The first ten flips do not influence the result of the eleventh.

The probability of independent events occurring at the same time is determined in a different way. If a nickel and a penny are flipped at the same time, they can turn up in one of four possible combinations.

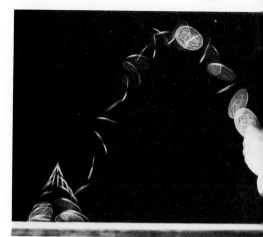

Figure 9-6 The probability of a coin landing heads up is 50%. The probability of a coin landing tails up is 50%.

Possibilities

	1	2	3	4
Penny	Heads	Heads	Tails	Tails
Nickel	Heads	Tails	Tails	Heads

Figure 9-7 The predicted probability of phenotypes and genotypes can be seen in the F_1 and F_2 generations of a P_1 cross of a pea plant that is homozygous yellow for seed color and a pea plant that is homozygous green for seed color.

The probability of a heads-heads combination is ¼, while the probability of a tails-tails combinations is also ¼. The probability of two independent events both happening is equal to the probability of one event occurring multiplied by the probability of the other event occurring. This is called the *product rule*. For example, the probability of the nickel landing heads up is ½. The probability of the penny landing heads up is ½. Therefore, the probability of both a penny and a nickel landing heads up is ½ × ½, or ¼. What would be the probability of three coins, a penny, a nickel, and a dime, all landing heads up? ½ × ½ × ½ = ⅛

Geneticists use probability to predict the percentages of possible genotypes resulting from crosses of plants or animals. Figure 9-7 shows a cross of a pea plant that is homozygous yellow (YY) for seed color with one that is homozygous green (yy). The YY parent produces only Y gametes. The yy parent produces only y gametes. Therefore, all of the F_1 offspring will be heterozygous yellow (Yy).

When the F_1 generation is crossed, the female gametes from one plant are ½Y and ½y. The male gametes from the

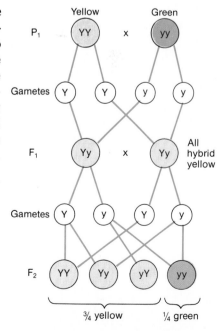

At this point, you may want to assign to the class the second of the Extensions and Applications at the end of this chapter.

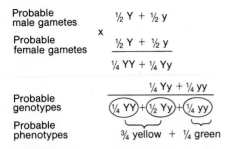

Probable male gametes	½ Y + ½ y
	x
Probable female gametes	½ Y + ½ y
	¼ YY + ¼ Yy

	¼ Yy + ¼ yy
Probable genotypes	(¼ YY) + (½ Yy) + (¼ yy)
Probable phenotypes	¾ yellow + ¼ green

Figure 9–8 The product rule can be used to find the predicted probability of phenotypes and genotypes.

Explain to your students that probability can also be expressed as a ratio. To determine a ratio, divide each quantity by the smallest quantity. Use the example of 100 plants given at the end of the Probability section to explain how to obtain a 3:1 phenotype ratio (75 [yellow] ÷ 25 = 3 and 25 [green] ÷ 25 = 1) and the 1:2:1 genotype ratio (25 [YY] ÷ 25 = 1; 50 [Yy] ÷ 25 = 2 ; 25 [yy] ÷ 25 = 1).

Figure 9–9 Punnett squares can be used to show the results of crosses. They can also be used to predict the percentages or probabilities of possible genotypes and phenotypes each time a cross is made.

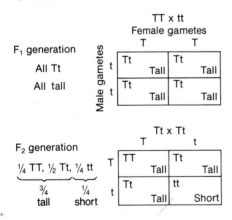

Throughout this section, assign a number of simple monohybrid and dihybrid crosses to your class as homework to make sure that your students understand how to use Punnett squares and how genes separate in these crosses.

other plant are also ½Y and ½y. To predict the genotypes of the F_2 generation, use the product rule. Multiply the probabilities for the different male gametes by the probabilities for the female gametes.

If 100 plants are produced in the F_2 generation, the probability is that 75 will have yellow seeds and 25 will have green seeds. Fifty of the plants with yellow seeds are likely to be heterozygous (Yy) and 25 of the plants are likely to be homozygous (YY). All of the plants with green seeds will be homozygous (yy). The predicted results and the actual results rarely match exactly. Probability shows what is likely to happen, but not necessarily what actually happens.

Punnett Squares

Relate the information provided in Punnett squares to the process of meiosis.

A special chart devised by the mathematician R.C. Punnett shows the possible combinations resulting from a cross of two organisms. These charts are called *Punnett squares*.

The Punnett square in Figure 9-9 has the female gametes listed along the top and the male gametes listed along the left side. Male gametes are paired with female gametes to form zygotes. Each box in the chart represents a possible zygote. The method of matching male and female gametes follows the product rule.

The Punnett square in Figure 9-9 shows that in the P_1 cross, all the female gametes are tall (T) and all the male gametes are short (t). As a result, all of the offspring in the F_1 generation are heterozygous tall (Tt). In the F_1 cross, the square shows that ½ of the gametes for the male are T and ½ t, which is the same for the female. The offspring of the F_1 cross, or the F_2 generation, will probably be ¼ homozygous tall (TT), ¼ homozygous short (tt), and ½ heterozygous tall (Tt). Punnett squares predict the percentages of possible genotypes and phenotypes of the offspring each time a cross is made. Because the gametes combine randomly, or by chance, the percentages observed in the offspring may be more or less than the percentages predicted.

MONOHYBRID CROSSES A cross that involves one set of contrasting traits is called a **monohybrid cross**. Monohybrid crosses involve differences in only one pair of alleles. For example, a guinea pig with homozygous black hair (BB) is crossed with another having homozygous white hair (bb). The gametes of the parent with the genotype BB carry the B allele. The gametes of the parent with the genotype bb carry the b allele. All of the zygotes formed will have the allele pair Bb. Because black (B) is dominant and white (b) is recessive, all of the F_1 generation will be heterozygous black (Bb).

When crossing two of the F_1 generation (Bb × Bb), the possible gametes that each parent can form are B or b, as shown in Figure 9-10. The possible genotypes of the offspring are BB, Bb, and bb. Based on probability, the ratio of the possible genotypes is 1:2:1, or ¼ BB, ½ Bb, and ¼ bb. This ratio can also be expressed in percentages, 25% BB, 50% Bb, 25% bb. The ratio of the phenotypes is 3:1, or 75% black and 25% white. For every three black guinea pigs there is likely to be one white guinea pig.

In a monohybrid cross of two heterozygous parents, 25% of the offspring are likely to be homozygous for the dominant trait BB. Fifty percent of the offspring are likely to be heterozygous Bb and the remaining 25% are likely to be homozygous for the recessive trait (bb). In any monohybrid

Highlight

A monohybird cross involves parents with one pair of contrasting traits. The expected genotype ratio is 1:2:1. The expected phenotype ratio is 3:1.

Figure 9-10 A monohybrid cross of guinea pigs with contrasting hair color is shown. What is the phenotype ratio of black-haired guinea pigs to white-haired guinea pigs? The phenotype ratio is 3:1.

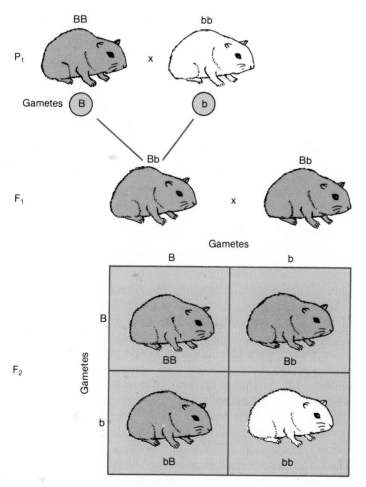

P₁ Generation		F₁ Generation	F₂ Generation Results	Actual Ratio	Predicted Ratio
Dominant	**Recessive**				
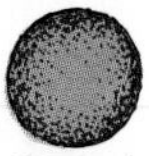 Round	 Wrinkled	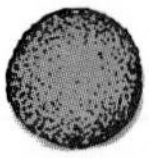 Round	5474 round 1850 wrinkled	2.96:1	3:1
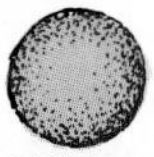 Yellow	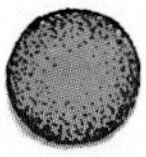 Green	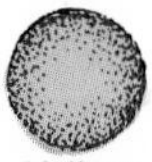 Yellow	6022 yellow 2001 green	3.01:1	3:1
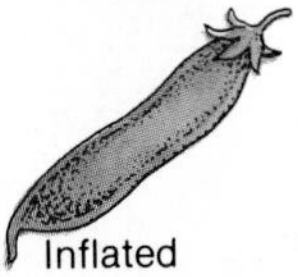 Inflated	 Constricted	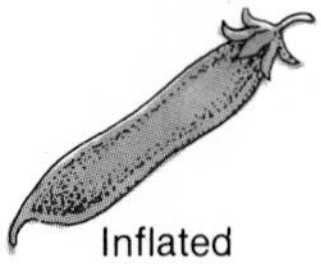 Inflated	882 inflated 299 constricted	2.95:1	3:1
 Green	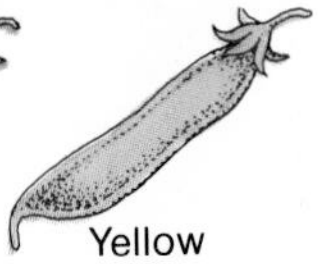 Yellow	 Green	428 green 152 yellow	2.82:1	3:1
 Long stem	 Short stem	 Long stem	787 long 277 short	2.84:1	3:1

Figure 9–11 Mendel's results in the F₂ generations of monohybrid crosses of pea plants resulted in 3:1 ratios. Compare the actual ratios with the predicted ratios.

cross, a 1:2:1 genotype ratio and 3:1 phenotype ratio can be expected.

DIHYBRID CROSSES A cross that involves two different sets of contrasting traits is called a **dihybrid cross.** Dihybrid crosses involve two pairs of alleles. Mendel crossed pea plants that were homozygous for round, yellow peas with others that were homozygous for wrinkled, green peas. All of the pea seeds produced were round *and* yellow. Only the dominant traits showed up in the first generation. F₁ generation plants were then allowed to self-pollinate. The plants that resulted developed 556 peas. Mendel found 315 round yellow, 101 wrinkled yellow, 108 round green, and 32 wrinkled green peas in the pods of the plants. The ratio of these different seed types was about 9:3:3:1.

Figure 9-12 explains Mendel's results. The plants with round, yellow peas (RRYY) can produce only RY gametes. The plants with wrinkled, green peas (rryy) can produce only

Highlight

A dihybrid cross involves parents with two pairs of contrasting traits. The expected phenotype ratio is 9:3:3:1. There are nine different genotypes.

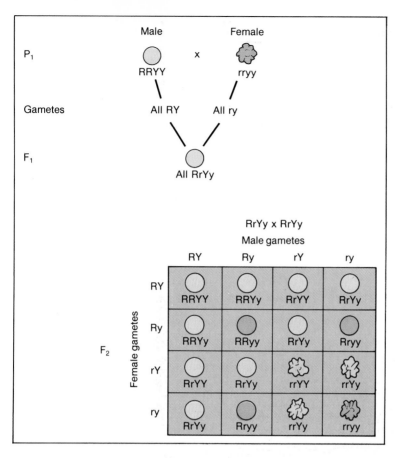

Figure 9-12 In a dihybrid cross, the phenotype ratio is always 9:3:3:1.

ry gametes. During fertilization the RY and ry gametes unite to form RrYy zygotes. Therefore, all the F_1 generation plants have round yellow seeds.

The F_1 generation (RrYy) can produce four different types of gametes: RY, Ry, rY, or ry. These four types are possible because the genes for seed shape (R and r) separate independently from those for seed color (Y and y). The Punnett square in Figure 9-12 shows male and female gametes and the possible genotypes and phenotypes. Nine different genotypes and four different phenotypes are possible. The ratio of the four phenotypes is 9:3:3:1, the predicted ratio for a dihybrid cross.

INCOMPLETE DOMINANCE In some gene pairs, the genes are neither dominant nor recessive. These genes show **incomplete dominance.** For example, when a homozygous red (RR) four o'clock flower is crossed with a homozygous white (WW) flower, the offspring are all pink (RW). Note

At this point, you may want to have your students do the Laboratory Investigation at the end of this chapter.

At this point, you may want to assign to the class the first of the Extensions and Applications at the end of this chapter.

Figure 9-13 Nine different genotypes and four different phenotypes are possible in a dihybrid cross.

Gentoype	Phenotype	
1/16 RRYY	round, yellow	
2/16 RrYY	round, yellow	
2/16 RRYy	round, yellow	9/16
4/16 RrYy	round, yellow	
1/16 RRyy	round, green	
2/16 Rryy	round, green	3/16
1/16 rrYY	wrinkled, yellow	
2/16 rrYy	wrinkled, yellow	3/16
1/16 rryy	wrinkled, green	1/16

162

Figure 9-14 In four o'clock flowers, neither the red gene nor the white gene for color is dominant. When these two genes are present in the same plant, a pink flower results.

Figure 9-15 In shorthorn cattle, neither red hair nor white hair is dominant. A shorthorn with a gene for red hair and a gene for white hair is roan, or reddish brown. In Andalusian fowl, neither black feathers nor white feathers are dominant traits. When a gene for black feathers and a gene for white feathers are present, the fowl appears to have blue feathers.

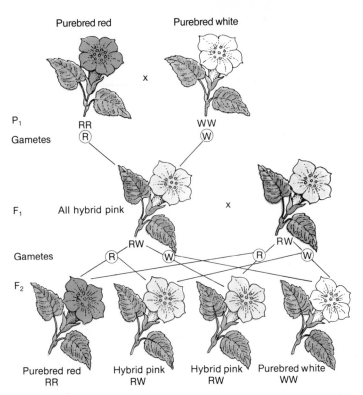

that the symbols used for each allele are different capital letters. When plants with pink flowers (RW) are crossed, the flowers of the offspring are about 25% red, 50% pink, and 25% white, a 1:2:1 ratio. Neither the red nor the white gene is dominant. When the offspring have a red-white gene pair, the flowers are pink. Therefore, the offspring have a phenotype that is different from either parent. Similar incomplete dominance occurs in other organisms, such as a species of chicken called Andalusian fowl and a species of shorthorn cattle.

SECTION REVIEW   Answers on page T–42.

1. What is an allele?
2. What is the difference between a homozygous and a heterozygous allele pair?
3. What is the product rule?
4. In a Punnett square, show the cross between a heterozygous black guinea pig and a white guinea pig. Which trait is dominant?
5. In a Punnett square, show the cross between a pea plant that is heterozygous for round yellow seeds and one that is homozygous for wrinkled green seeds.
6. What is meant by incomplete dominance?

LABORATORY INVESTIGATION 9

For additional information, see page T–42.

Exploring Genetic Probability

Purpose When a coin is tossed, it can land either heads up or tails up. The probability of the coin landing either way is ½, or 50%. The probability of two coins landing heads up or tails up can be used to find the genotype and phenotype ratios, or probability, of offspring from a monohybrid cross. By using four coins, the genotype and phenotype ratios of offspring from a dihybrid cross can be found. The purpose of this investigation is to study how probability is applied to the science of genetics.

Materials *(per student)* ● 2 pennies ● 2 nickels

Procedure Part A 1. Copy the table on a sheet of paper. You will use this table to organize your observations. **2.** In pea plant flowers, the color purple is dominant over white. Using a Punnett square, determine the probable color of the flowers of offspring whose parents are each heterozygous for the trait. Record the expected genotype probability on the table. **3.** Obtain two pennies. Each penny represents the parental heterozygous genotype. Let heads represent the gene for purple and tails represent the gene for white. **4.** Toss the coins simultaneously 50 times. The result of each toss represents the genotype of a new offspring. Record the results of each toss in the tally column of the table. **5.** When you finish, divide the results of each genotype by the total of tosses (50) to obtain the experimental probability.
Part B 1. In corn plants, rough seed shape is dominant over smooth seed shape and yellow seeds are dominant over white seeds. In a Punnett square, determine the probable seed shape *and* color of offspring whose parents are each heterozygous for the

traits. **2.** Obtain two pennies and two nickels. Let the pennies represent the parental heterozygous genes for seed color (heads = yellow; tails = white) and the nickels represent the parental heterozygous genes for seed shape (heads = rough; tails = smooth). Each combination of nickel and penny represents one parental heterozygous genotype. **3.** Prepare a table that will help you organize your observations. Record the expected genotype probability on the table.
4. Toss the pair of coins 100 times. Record the results of each toss. **5.** When you finish, divide each result by the total (100) to obtain the experimental probability.

Observations and Conclusions. **1.** In Part A, what is the genotype of each parent? The phenotype? **2.** What type of cross is this? **3.** What are the expected probabilities for the genotypes of the offspring? The phenotypes? **4.** Which genotypes give the same phenotype? **5.** What is the probability that the offspring will be white? **6.** Compare the expected probability with the experimental probability. **7.** In Part B, what is the genotype of each parent? The phenotype? **8.** What type of cross is this? **9.** What are the expected probabilities for the genotypes of the offspring? The phenotype? **10.** Which genotypes give the same phenotype? **11.** What is the probability for offspring that are heterozygous for both traits? **12.** Compare the expected probability with the experimental probability. **13.** In Parts A and B, why are there differences between the predicted and experimental results? **14.** If you carried out this investigation again, would your results be the same? If there were more tosses of the coins? Explain your answers.

Coin Combinations (Offspring Genotypes)	Tally	Expected Probability	Experimental Probability
Penny Penny Heads Heads			
Penny Penny Heads Tails			
Penny Penny Tails Tails			

CHAPTER SUMMARY

The Work of Gregor Mendel The study of how hereditary information is passed on from one generation to another is called genetics. Gregor Mendel's work provided the basis for modern laws of heredity. Mendel crossed purebred plants with contrasting traits and noticed that all of the offspring had only one of the traits, while their offspring had both traits. Mendel referred to the trait that appeared in the first generation as dominant. The trait that disappeared in the first generation and reappeared in the second generation he referred to as recessive. This is known as the principle of dominance and recessiveness.

Mendel discovered that gene pairs separate when gametes form. According to the law of segregation, one gene from each pair goes to each gamete. Today, geneticists know that the genes Mendel studied were on different chromosomes. Geneticists also know that different chromosomes separate independently during meiosis.

Concepts of Heredity Geneticists call genes that control contrasting traits alleles. The combinations of alleles for a trait are called genotypes. A gene pair with identical alleles is homozygous. A gene pair with contrasting alleles is heterozygous. Geneticists use probability to predict the ratios of genotypes and phenotypes of a zygote. Punnett squares show the possible combinations resulting from a cross. In a monohybrid cross of two heterozygous parents, 25% of the offspring can be expected to be homozygous for the dominant trait. Fifty percent will be heterozygous, and the other 25% will be homozygous for the recessive trait. In a monohybrid cross, the ratio of a dominant phenotype to a recessive phenotype is 3:1. A dihybrid cross involves two different sets of traits. The expected genotype and phenotype ratios can also be predicted from a knowledge of the parents' genotypes and phenotypes.

In some gene pairs, neither gene is dominant or recessive. These gene pairs show incomplete dominance. For example, a cross of homozygous red and homozygous white four o'clock flowers yields plants with pink flowers. If the pink flowers are crossed, red, pink, and white flowers result.

CHAPTER VOCABULARY

allele	**heredity**	**law of segregation**
dihybrid cross	**heterozygous**	**monohybrid cross**
dominant	**homozygous**	**phenotype**
gene	**hybrid**	**purebred**
genetics	**incomplete dominance**	**recessive**
genotype	**law of independent assortment**	

REVIEW of FACTS and CONCEPTS Answers on pages T–42 to T–43.

On a separate sheet of paper, answer each of the following as completely as possible.

1. What are genes?
2. Explain how Mendel could tell whether or not a plant was a hybrid.
3. What is the law of segregation?
4. The contrasting traits for hair color in guinea pigs are black (B) and white (b). What are the gene pairs possible for hair color?
5. Which of the following genotypes are heterozygous: AA, Aa, Yy, yy, Rr, RR?
6. Green (G) is the dominant color for pods of pea plants. Yellow (g) is recessive. What are the phenotypes of the following allele pairs: GG, Gg, gg?

7. A family has four daughters. What is the probability that a fifth child would be a female?
8. If peas that are heterozygous for both tall stems and green seed pods are crossed, the probability is that 75% of the offspring will be tall. The probability is also that 75% of the offspring will have green seed pods. What is the percentage of the offspring that are likely to be tall and have green seed pods?
9. In a plant with genotype Gg for pod color, what percentage of the gametes will have the G allele? The g allele?

10. Use a Punnett square to determine the possible genotypes of the F₁ generation when a heterozygous black (Bb) rabbit is crossed with a homozygous brown (bb) rabbit.

11. The probability that a baby will be male or female is ½. What is the probability that all four babies born in a hospital one morning will be female? What is the probability that all eight babies born another day will be male?

12. Short stems (t) are recessive to tall stems (T) in peas. Two pea plants that are heterozygous for the allele are crossed (Tt × Tt). One hundred seeds from the two plants are collected and planted. How many of the plants in the next generation can be expected to have tall stems?

13. White (W) hair is dominant over black (w) hair in sheep. A white male and a black female are parents of a black lamb. What is the probability that their next lamb will be white?

14. What gamete combinations are possible when the following groups of alleles separate in meiosis: AABB, AABb, AaBb, Aabb?

15. Black (B) hair is dominant over brown (b) hair in rabbits. Short (S) hair is dominant over long (s) hair. If a homozygous black short-haired rabbit is crossed with a homozygous brown long-haired rabbit, what would be the genotype and phenotype of the F₁ generation? List the ratio of each genotype and phenotype possible in the F₂ offspring of crosses between animals of the F₁ generation.

16. A woman received the genes aBcD from her father and the genes AbCd from her mother. Which of the following gene combinations could be present in her gametes: ABCD, abcd, ABCDD, aBccD, ABcd, AaBb?

17. A yellow guinea pig is crossed with a white guinea pig. All of the offspring are cream-colored. The cream-colored animals are crossed. Sixteen yellow, 33 cream, and 15 white animals are born. Explain these results. Explain how a white breed could be developed by starting with two cream-colored parents. Draw a Punnett square to illustrate your explanation.

EXTENSIONS and APPLICATIONS   For additional information, see page T–43.

1. Using Punnett squares, find out the possible genotypes and phenotypes for a cross involving three traits in pea plants. Let R represent the dominant gene for round seeds and r the recessive gene for wrinkled seeds. Let Y represent the dominant gene for yellow seeds and y the recessive gene for green seeds. Let T represent the dominant gene for long stems and t the recessive gene for short stems. For the P₁ generation, the cross is RRYYTT and rryytt. What is the phenotype of each parent? What is the genotype and phenotype for all offspring in the F₁ generation? Using Punnett squares, find out the possible genotypes and phenotypes for the F₂ generation.

2. Let a penny, a nickel, and a dime represent chromosome pairs. On each coin let the heads side represent one allele and the tails side represent the contrasting allele. What combinations are possible during gamete formation? What is the probability that all of the coins will land heads up? What is the probability that the penny and the nickel will land heads up and the dime tails up? Flip each of the three coins 160 times to test your answers.

SUGGESTED READINGS

Bornstein, J. and S., *What Is Genetics?* New York: Julian Mesner.
    This book is an introduction to genetics that includes many explanatory illustrations.

Fried, J.J., *The Mystery of Heredity.* New York: John Day.
    The history of and theories behind modern genetics are explained in this book.

Pedder, I.J., and E.G. Wynne, *Genetics: A Basic Guide.* New York: W.W. Norton.
    This reference guide will help you answer questions that you may have about genetics.

Winchester, A.M., *Heredity: An Introduction to Genetics.* New York: Barnes and Noble.
    This guide to genetics and its applications explains how to solve genetics problems and includes a chapter on probability.

10 Genes and Chromosomes

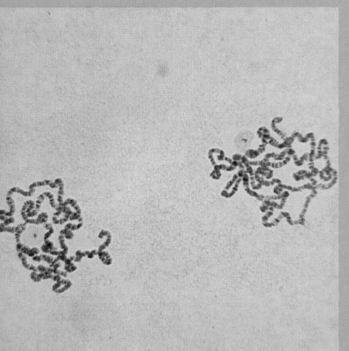

These chromosomes are from a fruit fly's salivary gland.

For teaching aids for this chapter, including a chapter overview and teaching strategies, see pages T–43 to T–45. The page number next to each chapter objective refers to the text page where the information needed to fulfill the objective begins.

A new human life begins from one fertilized cell. This cell possesses all the hereditary information needed to develop into a complex organism. Early in genetic research, scientists discovered that units of hereditary material called genes possess the information needed for a cell to perform its vital functions. This information passes from one generation of cells to the next by genetic messages. Assuming that the environment is favorable to the normal development of life, the continuity of life is maintained.

Every now and then, however, genetic information provides an unusual message for cells. Genes or chromosomes may be missing or changed, or there may be more than the normal number. When this happens, an organism can become abnormal. Diseases can result. Today, geneticists are finding out more and more about the way genes and chromosomes function, which will help solve many of the inherited disorders of human beings.

The Chromosome Theory

Although Gregor Mendel could not see or know what happened in cells, he developed the basic laws of heredity. He hypothesized that units, or factors, carried traits from one generation to the next. He did not describe these factors or prove that they existed in cells. Later scientists determined that these factors were real particles in the gametes of organisms.

In 1902, a graduate student at Columbia University, Walter S. Sutton, made a connection between Mendel's hypotheses and his own observations. He suggested that Mendel's factors might be *chromosomes* or parts of chromosomes. He suggested this hypothesis while studying meiosis in the cells of a grasshopper. Grasshoppers, he noted, have 12 pairs of chromosomes. When Sutton observed meiosis in grasshopper cells, he saw that each gamete received one chromosome from each pair. He also noted that the chromosomes separated randomly and independently of one another. Finally, he observed that after the male and female gametes united in fertilization, the zygote had the original number of chromosomes, 12 pairs or 24 chromosomes. Sutton concluded that chromosomes carried hereditary factors from one generation to the next. These factors accounted for the traits of an organism.

According to Sutton, Mendel's hypotheses could be explained by the following concepts.

1. A pair of factors determines each characteristic in an organism.
2. One factor from each pair is in a gamete.
3. Independent assortment of factors occurs during meiosis.
4. Pairing of factors during fertilization occurs to restore the original number of factors.
5. Individual factors remain unchanged from one generation to the next.

Some biologists argued that Sutton's hypothesis was wrong. They knew that organisms had more traits than chromosomes. For example, grasshopper cells have 12 pairs of chromosomes, but grasshoppers have more than 12 different traits or characteristics. Sutton concluded that each chromosome carried factors for several traits, and that these factors were small particles located on the chromosomes.

You may want to have several students investigate the work of Theodor Boveri. Boveri was a German scientist who conducted genetics experiments similar to Sutton's and reached the same conclusions as Sutton.

Highlight

The chromosome theory states that genes are located on chromosomes.

SECTION REVIEW   Answers on pages T–43 to T–44.

1. What is the chromosome theory?
2. How did Sutton's observations of chromosomes compare with the behavior of Mendel's factors?

The Nature of Genes

In 1911, the Danish plant scientist Wilhelm Johannsen used the term *gene* in place of factor, trait, or characteristic. However, for many years there was much disagreement and confusion about genes. Many biologists argued that genes did not exist. Others said genes were tiny particles on chromosomes.

Transformation in Bacteria

Today, biologists consider genes to be segments of DNA molecules that carry hereditary instructions for structure and function. This conclusion was reached, in part, through experimentation with a type of bacteria called pneumococcus. In 1928, Fred Griffith, an English bacteriologist, reported a puzzling result to one of his experiments. Griffith had been working with two types of pneumococcus organisms. When Griffith injected mice with strain S bacteria, the mice got pneumonia and died. When they were injected with strain R, the mice did not get pneumonia. The mice also survived if they were injected with strain S bacteria that had been killed with heat. However, if the mice were injected

Highlight

During the twentieth century, experiments conducted by many scientists have shown that genes are individual particles on chromosomes. The genes are arranged in a single line on each chromosome.

Figure 10-1 The results of Griffith's experiments showed that bacterial transformation had occurred in pneumococcus bacteria.

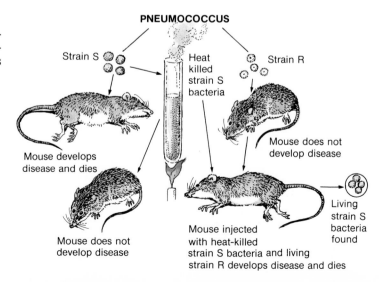

PNEUMOCOCCUS

Strain S

Heat killed strain S bacteria

Strain R

Mouse develops disease and dies

Mouse does not develop disease

Mouse does not develop disease

Mouse injected with heat-killed strain S bacteria and living strain R develops disease and dies

Living strain S bacteria found

with live strain R bacteria and heat-killed strain S bacteria, the mice got pneumonia and died. Laboratory tests showed that the dead mice had live strain S bacteria in their blood. Evidently, something had passed from the dead bacteria to the live ones, transforming them from harmless strain R organisms to deadly strain S organisms. Griffith did not know what had caused the transformation.

In 1944, Oswald Avery, Colin MacLeod, and Maclyn McCarty of the Rockefeller Institute demonstrated that DNA was the material that transformed the bacteria. The work of the Rockefeller researchers led them to two conclusions. (1) DNA is the genetic material of living things. (2) DNA can transfer from one organism to another and, in the process, change the second organism's genetic makeup.

In 1951 and 1952, Alfred Hershey and Martha Chase of the Carnegie Laboratory of Genetics provided more evidence to support the conclusions reached by Avery, MacLeod, and McCarty. The Carnegie researchers discovered that a certain virus could inject its DNA into bacteria. No other part of the virus entered the bacteria. A few minutes after the injection of the viral DNA, new viruses could be seen in the bacteria. The scientists concluded that DNA carried genetic instructions. The viral DNA had taken over the manufacturing processes of the bacteria and forced them to make more viruses.

Mapping Genes and Gene Linkage

In the 1930s, geneticists began studying the chromosomes of the larvae of the fruit fly, *Drosophila melanogaster* (drə-SOFF-uh-luh MELL-an-ə-gas-ter). The chromosomes of the fruit fly are among the largest found in animal cells and are easily seen through a microscope. Using complex methods, geneticists have produced chromosome maps for *Drosophila*. This kind of map shows the location of individual genes on a chromosome.

Figure 10-2 shows the location of several genes on a *Drosophila* chromosome. The location of a specific gene on a chromosome is called a *locus* (plural: loci). For example, the locus for body color in *Drosophila* is on the tip of the chromosome. The chromosome carries the gene for either yellow or gray body color at this locus.

In cells, chromosomes are found in pairs. The chromosomes in each pair are **homologous** (hō-MAHL-ə-gəs). Homologous chromosomes are identical in form, and usually carry the same number and sequence of genes.

The chromosome in Figure 10-2 carries genes for many characteristics. Taken together, the genes on a chromosome

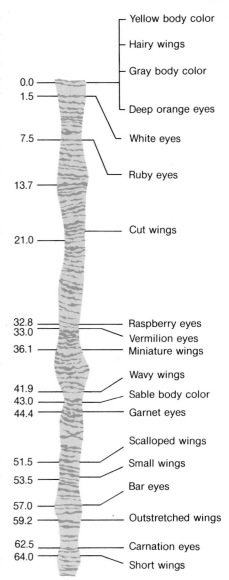

Figure 10-2 A chromosome map of *Drosophila melanogaster* shows many gene loci.

Sidelight

A human cell has perhaps 100,000 different genes attached in a single line on each chromosome.

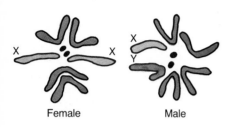

Figure 10-3 A *Drosophila* has four pairs of chromosomes. How many autosomes does the *Drosophila's* cells have?

Three pairs of autosomes, or six individual autosomes

Have your students examine the two <u>Drosophilia</u> shown in Figure 10-4. Ask your students to list the differences between the male and the female. Students should notice that the male is smaller and has a darker and blunter posterior end than has the female.

Figure 10-4 In *Drosophila*, there is a 50:50, or 1:1, chance of obtaining a male or female offspring. Which parent determines the sex of the offspring in *Drosophila*? The male

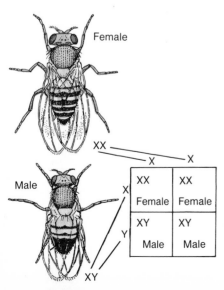

are called a *linkage group* and are inherited as a group. Geneticists know that individual genes on the same chromosome do not segregate independently, as Mendel thought. Instead, chromosomes segregate independently of one another during meiosis. In human beings, many thousands of genes are located on a single chromosome. These genes make up a linkage group.

Morgan's Investigations

In 1910, Thomas Hunt Morgan, an American zoologist, was experimenting with *Drosophila melanogaster*. One day he found a white-eyed male among the red-eyed flies in one of his breeding bottles. Until this point, all of his flies had had red eyes. Morgan bred the white-eyed male with a red-eyed female. All of the F_1 generation had red eyes. Morgan concluded that red was dominant over white for eye color in fruit flies.

Morgan bred the F_1 hybrid red-eyed flies with one another. Of the resulting F_2 generation of flies, 50% were red-eyed females, 25% were red-eyed males, and 25% were white-eyed males. Although Morgan expected a 3:1 ratio of red eyes to white eyes, he was surprised that all the flies with white eyes were male. Eye color seemed to be linked to the sex of the fly. Morgan hypothesized that the gene for eye color separated with the gene for sex when gametes formed.

SEX DETERMINATION Morgan also found that *Drosophila* has four pairs of chromosomes. As shown in Figure 10-3, the four pairs of chromosomes in females match up and appear homologous. In males, one of the pairs does not match. This pair contains a rod-shaped *X chromosome* and a hook-shaped *Y chromosome*. The X and Y chromosomes determine the sex of the offspring. An XX zygote is female and an XY zygote is male. The X and Y chromosomes are called **sex chromosomes**. All other chromosomes are called **autosomes**.

The Punnett square in Figure 10-4 shows a prediction of the offspring in *Drosophila*. All of the gametes produced by the female have an X chromosome. The male gametes have either an X or a Y chromosome. Based on the combinations of gametes, the Punnett square shows that the probability of a female or XX zygote is 50%. The chance of a male or XY zygote is also 50%.

SEX LINKAGE Traits for characteristics other than sex that are carried by genes on sex chromosomes are called **sex-linked traits**. In *Drosophila*, eye color is sex-linked. The gene

Female

	X^R	X^R
X^r	$X^R X^r$ Red-eyed female	$X^R X^r$ Red-eyed female
Y	$X^R Y$ Red-eyed male	$X^R Y$ Red-eyed male

Male

Female

	X^R	X^r
X^R	$X^R X^R$ Red-eyed female	$X^R X^r$ Red-eyed female
Y	$X^R Y$ Red-eyed male	$X^r Y$ White-eyed male

Male

for eye color is carried by, or linked to, the X chromosome. The Y chromosome does not carry a gene for eye color.

The first Punnett square in Figure 10-5 shows the P_1 generation and the F_1 generation of a sex-linked trait for eye color. The symbol X^R indicates that the gene for red eyes is carried on the X chromosome. The red-eyed female parent has the genotype $X^R X^R$. The symbol X^r indicates that the recessive gene for white eyes is also carried by the X chromosome. The white-eyed male parent has the genotype $X^r Y$. In the F_1 generation, all the female ($X^R X^r$) and male ($X^R Y$) offspring have red eyes.

For the F_2 generation, an $X^R X^r$ female was crossed with an $X^R Y$ male. The second Punnett square in Figure 10-5 shows that the genotypes of the female offspring are either $X^R X^r$ or $X^R X^R$. They all have red eyes. The male offspring are either red-eyed ($X^R Y$) or white-eyed ($X^r Y$). White-eyed female offspring ($X^r X^r$) are possible if a heterogenous red-eyed female ($X^R X^r$) or a homogenous white-eyed female ($X^r X^r$) is crossed with a white-eyed male ($X^r Y$).

TEST CROSSES The red-eyed female that Morgan experimented with could have been either heterozygous ($X^R X^r$) or homozygous ($X^R X^R$) for eye color. To find out which was the case, Morgan performed a **test cross.** In a test cross, the organism being tested is crossed with another organism that is recessive for the trait being studied. If the organism being tested is homozygous dominant for the trait, all the offspring will have the dominant phenotype. If the organism is heterozygous for the trait, some of the offspring will show the dominant phenotype and some the recessive phenotype. For example, if the offspring of a cross between a red-eyed female and a white-eyed male *Drosophila* are all red-eyed, the female is homozygous ($X^R X^R$). If some of the offspring are white-eyed, the female is heterozygous ($X^R X^r$).

Stress to your students that test crosses can be done for traits that are not sex-linked. Have your students do several test crosses for genotypes of various sex-linked and nonsex-linked traits.

Figure 10-5 Eye color is sex-linked in *Drosophila.* What would the P_1 generation have to be if all of the offspring could only have white eyes?

The P_1 generation would have to be $X^r X^r \times X^r Y$.

Figure 10-6 In a test cross, the organism being tested is crossed with an organism that exhibits the recessive trait. In this example, the test organisms are an $X^R X^R$ female and an $X^R X^r$ female that are being crossed with an $X^r Y$ male.

Female

	X^R	X^R
X^r	$X^R X^r$ Red-eyed female	$X^R X^r$ Red-eyed female
Y	$X^R Y$ Red-eyed male	$X^R Y$ Red-eyed male

Male

Female

	X^R	X^r
X^r	$X^R X^r$ Red-eyed female	$X^r X^r$ White-eyed female
Y	$X^R Y$ Red-eyed male	$X^r Y$ White-eyed male

Male

You may want to review meiosis as you discuss crossing over and nondisjunction.

Crossing Over

Individual genes on a chromosome can be separated and exchanged. The exchange of genetic material from one chromosome to another is called **crossing over.** Crossing over often happens when homologous chromosomes become twisted during meiosis. Sometimes these twisted chromosomes break apart. Figure 10-7 shows chromosomes exchanging genes. Because different genetic combinations form, crossing over is also called *recombination*.

Figure 10-7 also shows how the chromosomes are sorted independently in meiosis. Recombination and independent assortment continually shuffle the genes in a population. Therefore, many different combinations of genes are possible in organisms that reproduce sexually.

Nondisjunction

Sometimes a homologous pair of chromosomes does not separate during mitosis or meiosis. This failure to separate is called **nondisjunction.** Nondisjunction can occur in sex chromosomes and autosomes. When nondisjunction occurs, the new gametes or cells do not receive equal numbers of chromosomes. One cell may receive one or more extra chromosomes. The other cell has less than the normal number of chromosomes. Nondisjunction results in abnormal phenotypes.

Nondisjunction was first observed in *Drosophila.* Vermilion, or scarlet, eye color is recessive and red eye color is dominant in *Drosophila.* Calvin Bridges, a graduate student working with Morgan, crossed vermilion-eyed female (X^rX^r) with red-eyed male (X^RY) *Drosophila.* The offspring included the expected red-eyed females (X^RY^r) and vermilion-eyed males (X^rY). However, about one of every two thousand *Drosophila* was either a red-eyed male or a vermilion-eyed female offspring.

According to the prediction in the Punnett square shown in Figure 10-8, neither red-eyed males nor vermilion-eyed females should have been present. Vermilion-eyed female offspring would have the genotype X^rX^r. Because the male parents were X^RY, both X chromosomes would have had to come from the female parent! Red-eyed male offspring would have the genotype X^RY. However, the female parents all had the genotype X^rX^r and could not produce X^R gametes. Both the X^R and Y chromosomes would have had to come from the male parent.

When Bridges looked at the chromosomes under a microscope, he found out what had happened. The vermilion-eyed

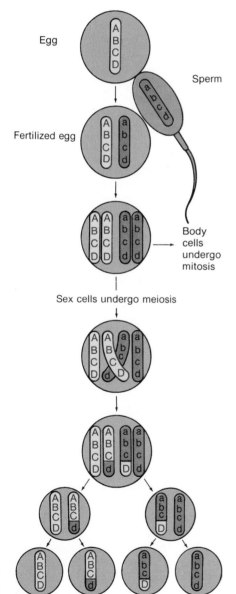

Figure 10-7 Crossing over occurs during meiosis. In meiosis, homologous chromosomes twist around each other.

Egg

Sperm

Fertilized egg

Body cells undergo mitosis

Sex cells undergo meiosis

females had two X chromosomes and one Y chromosome. They had an extra sex chromosome. The red-eyed males had only an X chromosome. Bridges observed that during meiosis the homologous pair of X chromosomes had not separated. As a result, some of the eggs of the vermilion-eyed females had two X chromosomes, while some had none. When one of the eggs with two X chromosomes (X^rX^r) combined with a Y gamete, the offspring was a vermilion-eyed female (X^rX^rY). These flies usually died.

When an egg with no sex chromosome combined with an X gamete, the offspring was a red-eyed male (X^R0). These flies lived but could not produce offspring. When an egg with no sex chromosome combined with a Y gamete, the zygote died. Nondisjunction occurs in many other animals and plants. Nondisjunction in human beings will be discussed later in this chapter.

SECTION REVIEW   Answers on page T–44.

1. Briefly explain Griffith's experiment with bacterial transformation.
2. What conclusions did Avery, MacLeod, and McCarty reach about DNA and bacterial transformation?
3. What is a linkage group?
4. In a Punnett square, cross a heterozygous red-eyed female *Drosophila* with a white-eyed male. Remember that eye color is a sex-linked trait.

Nondisjunction

Prediction

	Female	
	X^r	X^r
Male X^R	X^RX^r Red-eyed female	X^RX^r Red-eyed female
Y	X^rY Vermilion-eyed male	X^rY Vermilion-eyed male

Actual

	Female	
	X^rX^r	O
Male X^R	$X^RX^rX^r$ Red-eyed female	Sterile X^RO Red-eyed male
Y	Died X^rX^rY Vermilion-eyed female	Died YO

Figure 10–8 To explain the presence of vermilion-eyed female *Drosophila* and red-eyed males, the two X chromosomes of the female parent had to pass into a single gamete.

Genetic Changes

Genes, which are segments of DNA, usually make copies of themselves without mistake during cell division. Genetic messages are passed from one generation to the next, which causes offspring to resemble their parents. However, mistakes do happen. Sometimes one nucleotide in DNA may be switched with another. Also, one or more nucleotides may be left out or added. These changes in the DNA, or genes, are **mutations.**

An organism that has a mutation is called a *mutant.* Most mutations are recessive. Mutations that occur in the sex cells can be passed on from one generation to another. Some mutations cause major changes in the life functions and structure of an organism. These changes may be either helpful or harmful, although most are harmful. A mutant organism tends to be less well adapted.

Mutations that cause an organism to die are called lethal mutations.

Mutations can be caused by radiation, some viruses, high temperatures, certain chemicals, and environmental pollutants. Any substances or conditions that disrupt the normal formation of DNA are called mutagens.

Highlight

Mutations are changes in the hereditary message of the DNA molecule. Genetic changes may be caused by gene mutations or chromosomal mutations.

Figure 10–9 Albinism can occur in animals, such as koalas, and plants, such as blueberries.

Gene Mutations

A mutation that affects only one gene is called a *gene mutation*, or *point mutation*. Much has been learned about mutations and the action of genes by studying *Neurospora* (noo-rō-SPOR-ə). *Neurospora* is a common pink mold that grows on bread and other substances. In the 1940s, two American scientists, George W. Beadle and Edward L. Tatum, exposed some spores of this mold to X-rays. Some of the treated spores did not grow. The scientists hypothesized that the X-rays caused mutations in these spores. These mutations seemed to have stopped the mold from forming substances necessary for growth. Beadle and Tatum continued their experiments to try to identify the substances that could not be synthesized by the mutant spores. The researchers discovered that the substances were *enzymes*. Enzymes are proteins that catalyze chemical reactions in living things.

From these experiments, Beadle and Tatum developed the *"one gene-one enzyme" hypothesis*. They concluded that one and only one gene controls the synthesis of each enzyme. The one gene-one enzyme hypothesis explains much about gene action. However, it is now known that genes are involved in more than protein synthesis.

A gene mutation common to many organisms causes **albinism**. Albinism is a condition in which an organism is not able to form an enzyme needed to make a pigment. In animals, a gene mutation causes melanin not to be produced. Melanin is responsible for skin, hair, and eye color. Albinos have white hair and pinkish skin and eyes.

Chromosomal Mutations

Some genetic changes are caused by *chromosomal mutations*. Chromosomal mutations involve large pieces of chromosomes or the number of chromosomes in a cell. In a chromosomal mutation, several genes may be added, lost, or traded. As a result, chromosomal mutations can cause changes in cells and organisms. Changes in chromosomes increase the variety of individuals in a species. Chromosomal changes may be harmful to individuals.

Chromosomes become twisted during meiosis, and sometimes pieces break off. A broken piece may attach to another chromosome through *translocation*. Translocation can involve chromosomes that are or are not homologous. New genetic combinations result from translocation.

A chromosome that loses a piece does not always gain back another piece. This results in a *deletion*. In a deletion, genes are lost. In an *addition*, a chromosome gains genes.

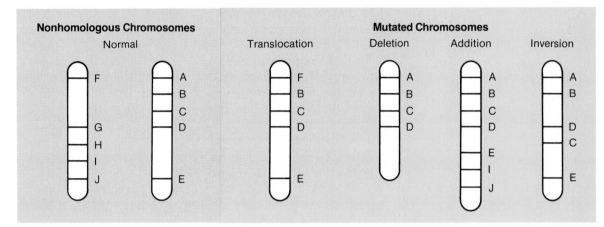

Nonhomologous Chromosomes

Normal

Mutated Chromosomes

Translocation   Deletion   Addition   Inversion

Sometimes a chromosome breaks in two places. If the three pieces go back together, an *inversion* may occur. In an inversion, the arrangement of the genes is changed. Usually, an inversion has no harmful effects on a living thing.

Figure 10-10 Chromosomal mutations are caused by translocations, deletions, additions, and inversions in nonhomologous or homologous chromosomes.

SECTION REVIEW   Answers on page T–44.

1. What is a gene mutation?
2. What is albinism?
3. What is a chromosomal mutation?

Human Genetics

Many factors make the study of human genetics complex. Genetic studies require data from many successive generations. *Drosophila*, bacteria, many plants, and small animals, such as mice, produce many generations in a short time. For example, five generations of mice can be produced in a number of months. As a result, much can be discovered about their heredity. However, the time between the first generation and the fifth generation in a human family may be 80 to 100 years. Thus, the study of human heredity takes a great deal of time.

The small number of children in human families also limits the study of human genetics. Genetic probabilities are difficult to calculate when there are relatively few offspring.

To determine the effect of a single factor, geneticists try to control as many factors as they can in an experiment. To do this, they breed organisms that are very much alike. Geneticists use true-breeding organisms in various genetic crosses to search for patterns of heredity. They also attempt

Highlight

The study of human genetics is difficult because the human lifetime is long, the number of offspring in human families is small, and environmental factors that affect human beings cannot be easily controlled.

to control the environments where the offspring grow. In human beings, many genetic and environmental factors cannot be controlled.

Some organisms have large chromosomes that are easy to study. Human chromosomes are small and difficult to prepare for microscopic study. Not until 1956 did biologists learn that a normal human body cell has 46 chromosomes. By the late 1960s, geneticists had identified each of the 23 pairs of human chromosomes and mapped the locations of many genes. Today, scientists are determining the codes for the production of various cell proteins.

The basic laws and mechanisms of heredity first discovered in plants and animals apply to human beings. The inheritance of physical traits, such as eye color, hair color, blood type, and the shape of the ear lobe, has been understood for years. The inheritance of some genetic diseases is now also understood. This knowledge is being applied to develop effective treatments for genetic diseases and to prevent them altogether.

The genetic study of a group of organisms, rather than individuals, is called **population genetics.** To determine the frequency of traits in a population, geneticists often use **population sampling.** Population sampling involves choosing a random number of organisms from a population. Information about the traits of the sample population can be applied to the entire population. Population sampling is important to the study of human genetics.

Multiple Alleles

The contrasting traits that Mendel studied in pea plants are controlled by two alleles or genes. For example, the color of pea seeds is controlled by alleles for yellow and green. Many human traits are controlled by more than two alleles, or by **multiple alleles.** Some geneticists think that eye color is controlled by multiple alleles. They know that human skin color is controlled by multiple alleles. Research findings indicate that three to six pairs of genes may control skin color. However, there appears to be no dominant skin color in human beings.

Blood type in human beings is determined by multiple alleles. There are three genes that control blood types. The different types of blood were classified in 1900 by Dr. Karl Landsteiner, a scientist in Vienna. He found that red blood cells from different people would often *agglutinate* (ə-GLOOT-'n-āt), or clump together, when mixed. Landsteiner found that agglutination occurred when different blood proteins were mixed.

At this point, you may want to have your students do the Laboratory Investigation at the end of this chapter.

Highlight

If more than two alleles determine a trait, they are called multiple alleles.

Landsteiner found two different proteins, A and B, in blood. These proteins are now used to classify, or type, blood. Blood that contains red blood cells with protein A is called type A. Type B blood has protein B. Blood cells that have both types of protein are type AB. Blood cells that do not have either protein A or B are type O.

The genes for blood types A and B are dominant. Type A blood is found only in offspring who have at least one parent with type A blood. Type B blood is found only in offspring who have at least one parent with type B blood. Type O blood is found in offspring of parents having either A, B, or O blood. The gene for type O may be carried by a heterozygous A or heterozygous B parent or a homozygous O parent. Blood type AB is an example of incomplete dominance. When the genes for A and B come together, neither is dominant.

The symbols used for the three multiple alleles for blood type are I^A, I^B, and i. The following genotypes and phenotypes are possible. Note that only two of the three alleles are present in any genotype.

$I^A I^A$, $I^A i$	type A blood
$I^B I^B$, $I^B i$	type B blood
$I^A I^B$	type AB blood
ii	type O blood

Inherited Diseases

Many diseases are caused by genetic mistakes. Disease can occur when a protein needed for a normal life function is not present because of a missing gene, or when an abnormal protein is present because of an abnormal gene. A health problem may occur when one gene takes the place of another. Some diseases are caused when two recessive alleles combine. Genetic diseases can be passed from one generation to another.

SICKLE-CELL DISEASE An inherited disease found in people of African origin and some Hispanics is **sickle-cell disease.** About 9.5% of black Americans carry the trait. Most of the red blood cells in people with this disease become sickle-shaped. The sickled red blood cells can clog small blood vessels, causing swelling and pain. Sometimes damage to body organs and tissues also occurs.

The substance that carries oxygen in red blood cells is called *hemoglobin.* Hemoglobin is a protein made of many amino acids. Sickle-cell hemoglobin is not normal. One type of amino acid called *valine* replaces another called *glutamic acid* at a specific place in the hemoglobin molecule. The

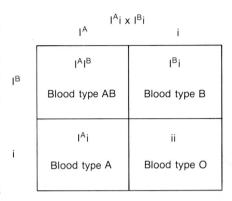

Figure 10–11 This cross shows that neither the gene for blood type A nor the gene for blood type B is dominant over the other. However, they are both dominant over the gene for O blood (i). Is it possible for a female with type A blood and a male with type B blood to have a child with type O blood? Explain your answer.

Yes. Both parents would have to carry a gene for type O blood, such as $I^A i \times I^B i$.

At this point, you may want to assign to several students the third of the Extensions and Applications at the end of this chapter.

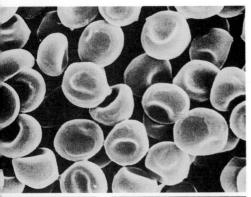
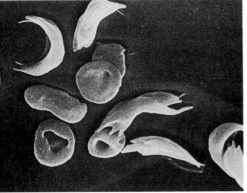

Figure 10-12 The normal donutlike shape of red blood cells becomes sickle-shaped in people who suffer from sickle-cell disease.

cause of this change can be traced to a defective gene on a DNA molecule. On this DNA molecule, a single base pair has been changed.

Sickle-cell hemoglobin is called hemoglobin S. It is caused by a recessive gene (Hb^S). The allele for normal hemoglobin is Hb^A. Only people who are homozygous (Hb^{S}Hb^S) for the trait develop sickle-cell disease. People who are heterozygous (Hb^{A}Hb^S) do not suffer from the disease. However, some of their red blood cells may become sickle-shaped.

People who think they may carry the trait for sickle-cell disease can be tested in hospitals or genetic research centers. Many hospitals also offer the services of a genetic counselor. The counselor can explain the nature of the disease to couples who have the trait so that they can understand what the probability is of their children getting the disease. Research is also being conducted to try to develop a drug that can restore the abnormal red blood cells to normality.

PHENYLKETONURIA An inherited disease called *phenylketonuria* (fen-il-kēt-ə-NYOOR-ē-a), or **PKU**, is caused by a recessive gene. PKU is found in infants. A child with PKU does not have the enzyme needed to change the amino acid *phenylalanine* (fen-il-AL-ə-nēn) to the amino acid *tyrosine.* Therefore, phenylalanine builds up in the blood and urine. Large amounts of this amino acid cause brain damage and often severe mental retardation.

Most states have laws that require all babies to be tested for PKU. The blood or urine of infants is used to detect the disease. If PKU is detected, the babies are fed a special mixture of proteins that has very little phenylalanine in it. This prevents the disease from developing. When brain growth has stopped at about age 5, the child can have a more normal diet.

Sex-Linked Traits in Human Beings

In human beings as well as fruit flies, the two sex chromosomes are called X and Y. The genotype of a female is XX. Males have the genotype XY. Some genes for traits in human beings are linked to the X chromosome, causing these traits to appear more often in males than females. Females called *carriers* often have the gene for the trait but do not show the trait. Because a female contains two X chromosomes, a recessive gene on one chromosome can be masked by a dominant gene for the same trait on the other chromosome. Because a male does not contain a homologous X chromosome, a recessive gene on the male's single X chromosome can cause a trait to show.

Only a few genes are linked to Y chromosomes. In human beings, the role of the Y chromosome is sex determination. However, hair on the rim of the ears of some males appears to be caused by a gene linked to the Y chromosome.

Hemophilia is an example of a condition caused by a gene mutation.

HEMOPHILIA If one of the proteins needed for blood to clot is missing or present in small amounts, the blood tends to clot slowly or not at all. This condition is called **hemophilia** (hē-mə-FIL-ē-ə). Hemophilia is a sex-linked recessive trait that is caused by a defective gene on the X chromosome. People with this disease bleed severely, even when they are only slightly injured. Their nose and mouth tissues bleed easily. Internal bleeding often occurs in the joints of their knees, ankles, and elbows. Too much bleeding around the brain or the loss of too much blood can cause death. Figure 10-13 shows a hereditary pattern for hemophilia.

Hemophilia was very common in the royal families of Europe. During the nineteenth century, Queen Victoria of England had a son and three grandsons with hemophilia. At least two of her daughters and four of her granddaughters were carriers. Hemophilia spread through the royal families in Europe as Victoria's descendents married other royalty.

COLORBLINDNESS Another recessive sex-linked trait is red-green *colorblindness*. People with this problem have trouble seeing the difference between red and green. Both colors look gray. Colorblindness appears more often in males than females. In fact, very few females are colorblind.

The genes involved in colorblindness are on the X chromosomes. The symbol C represents the dominant allele for normal color vision. Colorblindness is caused by the recessive allele represented by c. Following is a list of the possible genotypes and phenotypes of these genes.

$X^C Y$: a male with normal color vision

$X^c Y$: a colorblind male

$X^C X^C$: a female with normal color vision

$X^C X^c$: a carrier female with normal color vision

$X^c X^c$: a colorblind female

Nondisjunction in Human Chromosomes

Human gametes have 23 chromosomes. The male gamete, or sperm, carries either an X or Y chromosome along with 22 autosomes. The female gamete, or egg, carries an X chromosome along with 22 autosomes. Sometimes a

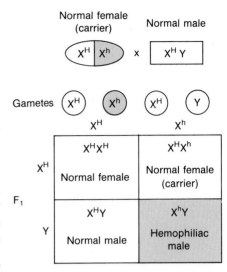

Figure 10-13 There is a 25% probability that a carrier female for hemophilia and a normal male will have a male child with hemophilia.

At this point, you may want to assign to several students the first and second of the Extensions and Applications at the end of this chapter.

Sidelight

Colorblindness affects about 6% of males and only about 1% of females. The most common form of colorblindness is red-green colorblindness. In this condition, red and green may appear gray, blue, or yellow.

homologous pair of chromosomes does not separate during meiosis. This nondisjunction results in some gametes with more than 23 chromosomes and some with less than 23. When a zygote has an extra chromosome, the condition is called **trisomy** (trī-SŌMĒ). When a zygote is missing a chromosome, the condition is called **monosomy** (MAHN-ə-sō-mē).

DOWN'S SYNDROME The homologous chromosome pairs in human beings are numbered 1 through 22. Sometimes an extra chromosome occurs on the twenty-first pair because of nondisjunction. This is one of the causes of **Down's syndrome,** or *trisomy-21,* a condition in which all body cells have three number 21 chromosomes. The extra genetic material interferes with the growth of the heart, brain, eyes, and hands. A child with Down's syndrome is mentally retarded.

The age of the mother affects the probability of a child being born with Down's syndrome. In mothers under 35 years old, the rate is about 1 in 1500 births. The rate is 1 in

CLOSE-UP: *Vivien Diaz*

One of the fastest changing fields in medical science today is human genetics. Knowledge of genetic disease has advanced rapidly in the past decade. Although much is still to be discovered, information already gained about genetic disorders, such as sickle-cell disease and Down's syndrome, is beginning to help people understand and deal with these problems.

Vivien Diaz is a genetic counselor at Queens Hospital Center in Jamaica, New York. Her job is to communicate genetic information to people who want to know more about a suspected or actual genetic disorder. Many are parents who are concerned that they might be carrying genes for a disease or trait that they could pass on to their children.

"While we have doctors who specialize in genetic disorders, they often don't have enough time to devote to every patient," Diaz says. Vivien Diaz has had special training so that she can discuss a particular genetic disease with patients. The major disease Diaz is dealing with now is sickle-cell disease. Sitting down, one-to-one, with patients, she is able to answer ques-

tions about the tests used to find genetic disorders. Diaz can also explain the statistical chance that a child will inherit a genetic disorder. She can also provide the latest medical information available on the disease.

Ten years ago, there were very few genetic counselors in the United States. "Now the field is opening up," says Diaz, who has a master's degree in human genetics. "There is a great need for genetic counselors," she says. "It's increasing every day. What we would like to see eventually is a genetic counselor at every hospital in the country."

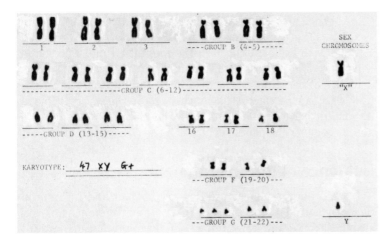

KARYOTYPE: ___47 XY G+___

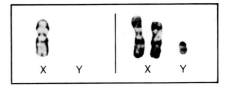

Figure 10-14 In Down's syndrome, there are three rather than the normal two chromosomes in the twenty-first set. Therefore, all the body cells of a person with Down's syndrome have 47 chromosomes.

300 births for mothers 35 to 40 years old. When the mother is more than 45 years old, the rate is 1 in 30 to 35 births.

Figure 10-15 Two genetic diseases, Turner's syndrome *(left)* and Klinefelter's syndrome *(right)*, are caused by nondisjunction in the sex chromosomes. There is an abnormal number of sex chromosomes in each case.

TURNER'S SYNDROME Nondisjunction may also occur in the sex chromosomes. Sometimes a gamete with no sex chromosome unites with a gamete with an X chromosome. The zygote has 44 autosomes and one X chromosome. The genotype is XO. This condition is called **Turner's syndrome.** These XO females are short. They have underdeveloped ovaries and do not mature sexually.

KLINEFELTER'S SYNDROME An XXY male has 47 chromosomes. This condition is called **Klinefelter's syndrome.** Nondisjunction results in an abnormal sperm cell with both X and Y chromosomes fertilizing a normal egg. Males with this condition are usually quite tall and below average in mental ability. They are also sterile because they do not produce sperm. Some men with this condition may have 48, 49, or 50 chromosomes. The genotypes may be XXXY, XXXXY, or XXXXXY.

Amniocentesis and Ultrasound

Some genetic disorders can now be discovered before a baby is born. A developing child, or *fetus*, is surrounded by *amniotic* (am-nē-AHT-ik) *fluid.* Amniotic fluid contains cells that have been lost by the fetus. The fluid is removed and the chromosomes in the cells studied. The fluid also contains waste materials with proteins that come from the fetus. The proteins can be analyzed to detect certain genetic disorders. The process of removing amniotic fluid through the abdomen of a pregnant woman is called **amniocentesis** (am-nē-ō-sen-TĒ-sis).

Another method used to detect genetic disorders before a baby is born involves *ultrasound tests.* In these tests, sound waves are sent through the amniotic fluid. The sound waves produce images on a screen. These images can provide evidence of certain genetic disorders. In addition, the age of the fetus can be estimated by the size of the image. This is important because the significance of chemical tests used to detect genetic disorders varies with the age of the fetus.

Influence of the Environment

Some human characteristics are shaped and influenced by both heredity and factors in the environment. For example, the average height of people in many nations has increased because of better diets, although inherited genes set a limit to height. Conversely, many people in the world do not have enough food to eat. Their height may be limited more by diet than by genetics.

The influence of the environment on a human being begins while it is developing inside its mother. Food, drugs, minerals, and other substances in a mother's blood may have an influence on the genes of an unborn child. Certain drugs can interfere with the normal development of an unborn child. Other substances, such as food, must be available for the normal development of the child.

The roles of heredity and environment are easier to evaluate in organisms that have the same or very similar heredity. To do this in human beings, geneticists often study *identical twins.* Identical twins develop from the same zygote. They are genetically identical. Therefore, most differences between identical twins are the result of environmental factors.

Recent studies of identical twins who were separated at birth or at an early age suggest that more of human behavior may be inherited than previously thought. Some of the twins that were studied were found to be very similar in their behavior. One pair of twins held the same kind of job, drove the same kind of car, and had similar health problems. Do you suppose the similarities were a matter of chance or shaped by heredity?

Figure 10–16 Studies of identical twins, who have identical sets of chromosomes, help genetists evaluate how heredity and environment affect development.

At this point, you may want to assign to several students the fourth of the Extensions and Applications at the end of this chapter.

SECTION REVIEW   Answers on page T–44.

1. What are multiple alleles?
2. How are human blood types determined?
3. What causes PKU?
4. What is hemophilia? What are its causes and symptoms?
5. Define trisomy and monosomy in human beings.

Observing Inherited Human Traits

Purpose The principles, rules, and laws of genetics in plants and animals can be applied to human genetics. Many human traits are caused by single gene pairs or by multiple alleles. Others are influenced by the environment. The purpose of this investigation is to examine some examples of inherited human traits.

Materials *(per 2 students)* ● Meter stick ● Bath scale

Procedure **1.** Copy Table 1. Provide a line in the table for each student in your class. **2.** Using the meter stick, measure your partner's height in centimeters. Have your partner measure your height. Using the bath scale, find out your weight. Record the data in your table. **3.** Fill in the remaining columns for you and your partner. The following information will help you determine which traits you have. **a.** *Hair color:* Indicate the color of your hair: brown, black, and so on. Then indicate whether the color is light or dark. **b.** *Tongue roller: sides:* Indicate whether you can roll your tongue into a U shape when it is extended from your mouth. **c.** *Tongue roller: back:* Indicate whether you can roll your tongue back in your mouth. **d.** *Ear lobe attachment:* Indicate whether your ear lobes hang free or are attached directly to the side of your head. **e.** *Widow's peak:* Indicate whether your hairline forms a distinct point in the center of your forehead. **4.** Complete the table for each person in your class. Then determine the frequency of each trait by dividing the number of individuals with a particular trait by the total number of individuals in the sample. Then multiply by 100 to get a percentage. To find the frequency for height, add the number of people in each of the ranges shown in Table 2. Use the total in each range as the number of individuals with the trait. Your teacher will help you devise a range table for weight.

Observations and Conclusions **1.** Do any members of your class have exactly the same set of characteristics? Explain your answer. **2.** What percentage of the class are males? Females? **3.** Which characteristic has the widest range of individual differences? How can you explain this? **4.** Based on the data in Table 2, is there a pattern to the distribution of body height? If so, describe it. **5.** How does the inheritance of body height differ from the inheritance of ear lobe attachment?

Table 2

Range of Heights (cm)	Number of Students
120–129	
130–139	
140–149	
150–159	
160–169	
170–179	
180–189	
190–200	

Table 1

Name	Sex	Height (cm)	Weight (kg)	Eye Color	Hair Color	Tongue Roller Side	Tongue Roller Back	Ear Lobe Attachment	Widow's Peak

CHAPTER SUMMARY

The Chromosome Theory In 1902, Walter S. Sutton suggested that Mendel's factors might be chromosomes or parts of chromosomes. After experimenting, Sutton concluded that chromosomes carried hereditary traits. He also stated that each chromosome carried factors for several traits.

The Nature of Genes Today, biologists think of genes as segments of DNA that carry hereditary messages. Work with pneumococcus led to the conclusion that DNA carried genetic information. Geneticists also discovered that DNA could transfer from one organism to another. This transfer changed the heredity of the other organism.

Cells have pairs of homologous chromosomes. Homologous chromosomes are identical in form, and usually carry the same kind of genes. However, sex chromosomes are not homologous. In humans, an XX is the female genotype and XY is the male genotype. Some traits are sex-linked and are carried on X chromosomes. Eye color in *Drosophila* and hemophilia and colorblindness in humans are sex-linked traits.

During mitosis or meiosis, homologous pairs of chromosomes do not always separate. This is called nondisjunction and results in cells having more or less than the normal number of chromosomes.

Genetic Changes Changes in segments of DNA or genes are mutations. Mutations may affect a short segment of a chromosome, large pieces of a chromosome, or the number of chromosomes. Some mutations may cause changes in the life functions and structures of organisms. Most mutations are harmful.

Human Genetics The basic laws of heredity apply to human beings. Many human traits such as blood type and skin color are controlled by multiple alleles. Conditions such as diabetes and sickle-cell disease are inherited. Nondisjunction of the twenty-first chromosome pair causes Down's syndrome in human beings. Nondisjunction of the sex chromosomes causes Turner's or Klinefelter's syndrome.

Some human traits are shaped and influenced by the environment. Geneticists often study identical twins to try to discover the roles of heredity and environment in human development.

CHAPTER VOCABULARY

albinism	Klinefelter's syndrome	population sampling
amniocentesis	monosomy	sex chromosome
autosome	multiple allele	sex-linked trait
crossing-over	mutation	sickle-cell disease
Down's syndrome	nondisjunction	test cross
hemophilia	PKU	trisomy
homologous	population genetics	Turner's syndrome

REVIEW of FACTS and CONCEPTS Answers on pages T–44 to T–45.

On a separate sheet of paper, answer each of the following as completely as possible.

1. Why did Sutton conclude that one chromosome carried the factors for several traits?
2. What conclusions about DNA were reached by conducting experiments in bacterial transformation?
3. What is meant by homologous chromosomes? Draw a hypothetical chromosome map for homologous chromosomes that carry 10 traits that you exhibit.

4. Which of the following genotypes show sex-linked traits: $I^A I^B$, $X^R X^R$, $X^r Y$, $Hb^A Hb^A$, $X^C X^C$?
5. Eye color is a sex-linked trait in *Drosophila*. Red eyes (R) are dominant over white eyes (r). Use a Punnett square to determine the possible genotypes and phenotypes of a cross between a white-eyed female and a red-eyed male.
6. Black fur (B) is dominant over white fur (b) in guinea pigs. Fur color is *not* a sex-linked trait. In

Punnett squares, show how you would determine if a guinea pig were homozygous or heterozygous for the dominant trait.

7. Define nondisjunction.

8. How is a gene mutation different from a chromosomal mutation?

9. Describe the different types of chromosomal mutations that can occur.

10. Suppose parents had a child with type O blood. What are all of the possible genotypes of the parents?

11. Use a Punnett square to show a cross between a male and female who are heterozygous (Hb^AHb^S) for the sickle-cell disease trait. What are the possible genotypes and phenotypes of their offspring?

12. Why are more males colorblind than females?

13. What is the difference between monosomic cells and trisomic cells?

14. What chromosomal differences cause Down's syndrome, Turner's syndrome, and Klinefelter's syndrome?

EXTENSIONS and APPLICATIONS For additional information, see page T–45.

1. Use reference materials to research the presence of hemophilia in the descendants of Queen Victoria of England. Prepare a genetic family tree that traces the spread of hemophilia through the royal families of Europe.

2. In books, find several different charts that are used to test for colorblindness. Conduct a survey in your school using the charts. Be sure to test an equal number of males and females. Prepare a written report on your findings.

3. Prepare a written report on the connection between sickle-cell disease and malaria.

4. If there is a pair of identical twins in your area, prepare a questionnaire to help you determine if they have the same or similar likes, dislikes, and personality traits. Have each of the twins complete the questionnaire separately. Have two brothers or two sisters who are unidentical complete the questionnaire. Compare the responses of both groups. Which pair is more similar?

SUGGESTED READINGS

Scheinfeld, A., *Why You Are You.* (2nd ed.) New York: Association Press.
This book presents simple basic answers to questions about human heredity.

Scheinfeld, A., *Heredity in Humans.* Philadelphia: J.B. Lippincott.
A thorough examination of the inheritance of physical and mental traits is presented in this book.

Singer, S., *Human Genetics.* San Francisco, Calif.: W.H. Freeman.
The principles of human heredity are presented in this illustrated introductory book.

Sullivan, N., *The Message of the Genes.* New York: Basic Books.
An account of the processes of genes and their chemical code is discussed in this book. How biologists broke this code is also explained.

11 Applications of Genetics

New varieties of corn can be grown through plant breeding.

Chapter Objectives *After completing this chapter, you will be able to:*

a ▦ Explain the importance of applied genetics. p. 186

b ▦ Define genetic breeding. p. 187

c ▦ Describe five methods of genetic breeding. p. 187

d ▦ Define genetic engineering and cloning. p. 191

e ▦ Summarize the techniques used to produce recombinant DNA. p. 192

f ▦ Discuss the practical applications of genetic engineering. p. 193

For teaching aids for this chapter, including a chapter overview and teaching strategies, see pages T–45 to T–46. The page number next to each chapter objective refers to the text page where the information needed to fulfill the objective begins.

A company selling hybrid vegetable seeds claims that they are bred for "increased yield, more vigor, disease resistance, and exceptional flavor." The search for plants that can fulfill the claims of an advertisement such as this has been long and hard. Before the science of genetics developed, much of the search was based on trial and error. Today, **applied genetics,** or the use of genetic knowledge, has made possible the development of many plants and animals with improved characteristics.

Through the use of new techniques, scientists have found a way to transplant genes from the cells of one species into the cells of other species. By doing this, relatively simple organisms, such as bacteria and yeasts, can be made to form proteins that once could be made only by other cells. Some of these substances help human beings in the fight against many diseases including cancer and diabetes.

Plant and Animal Breeding

For thousands of years, people have tried to breed plants and animals with desired traits. Usually, a plant or animal with the desired trait was crossed with another that had the same trait. People hoped that the offspring would have the particular trait and produce an entire population with the trait. This method is called **genetic breeding.**

Through genetic breeding, many varieties of corn, wheat, and rice have been developed that produce more food than do the original varieties. These new plant varieties also have been bred to be resistant to certain diseases or to need less water and fertilizers.

You may want to have your students research other new and improved plants developed by Luther Burbank.

Luther Burbank, an American plant breeder, developed many new plants and improved several different types of existing plants in the latter part of the nineteenth century. His most well-known plant is the Russett Burbank potato. Another well-known plant that he developed is the Shasta daisy.

For breeding, Burbank chose plants that had desired characteristics, such as good flavor, large fruit, and resistance to disease. He grew thousands of plants to ensure that at least some would have the desired characteristics. Burbank could then cross these plants to produce a population of organisms with the desired trait.

Selection

The process of choosing organisms with desired traits is called **selection.** Selection has been used to improve more than 20,000 varieties of wheat. Some of these varieties contain more protein, produce more seeds, and have stronger stems. Also, some are better able to survive in relatively dry soil than similar plants. Through the careful selection of certain plants as parents, plant breeders have been able to develop wheat plants that are suitable to particular climates.

Today, most plants that are used for food have been improved through selection. Much of this selection took place years before the science of genetics was understood. For example, originally the carrot was a tough, bitter-tasting weed. During the fifteenth century, the Dutch improved the size, texture, flavor, and color of the carrot by selection.

Animal breeders use some of the same methods of selection as do plant breeders. Cattle have been bred for characteristics such as resistance to insects and increased production of beef and milk. Breeders of thoroughbred horses, such as Man o' War and Secretariat, use selection methods in an attempt to produce faster running animals.

Figure 11-1 To produce offspring with desired traits, animal breeders select parents with those traits. For example, animal breeders select and mate horses that are speedy or very strong. A thoroughbred stallion is an offspring of speedy horses. A Belgian work horse is the offspring of strong horses.

At this point, you may want to assign to several students the second of the Extensions and Applications at the end of this chapter.

Figure 11-2 A genetic mutation produced the seedless navel orange.

You may want to review the discussion of mutations in Chapter 10.

Mutation

Scientists have developed other ways of varying the characteristics of plants and animals since the middle of the twentieth century. They found that **mutations,** or changes in the structure of DNA, in a parent's sex cells could change the characteristics of its offspring. The structure of the DNA molecule can be changed through exposure to various kinds of radiation. X-rays and some chemical substances can cause mutations.

In 1975, the International Atomic Energy Agency listed 96 new varieties of crop plants that developed from mutations caused by radiation. However, only a very small percentage of these types of plants proved to be useful. Because of these poor results, less attention is being given to this type of research. Instead, geneticists are turning their attention to preservation of the *genetic variability,* or differences in genes already present in plants. An example is the navel orange, which has a desired characteristic of having no seeds. The trees that bore navel oranges originally were found in Brazil more than one hundred years ago. Of the 12 trees that were brought to the United States in 1873 only one survived. Branches from this tree were attached to the root systems of other types of orange trees. These branches grew and produced seedless oranges.

Hybridization

The crossing of two genetically different but related species or organisms is called **hybridization** (hī-brəd-i-zĀ-shən). Hybridization is used to develop offspring with desired qualities from different parent species.

Usually, the offspring that are produced by hybridization grow faster than either parent and are more fit for cer-

Figure 11-3 A mule is the product of hybridization. The mule, a cross between a male donkey and a female horse, is stronger than a donkey and has more endurance than a horse.

tain conditions. This increased fitness of hybrids is called *hybrid vigor*. Mules are examples of hybrid vigor. They are the offspring of the cross of a male donkey with a female horse. Mules are more sure-footed and have more endurance than horses and are stronger than donkeys. The disadvantage of this type of cross is that the hybrid is usually *sterile*, or unable to reproduce.

Sometimes hybridization results in the production of new crops, such as the plant *triticale* (trit-ə-KĀ-lē). Triticale is a cross between a wheat plant and a rye plant. The triticale seeds possess more protein than those of wheat. They also produce a higher yield of plants than do some wheat varieties.

Many types of cattle have been bred using hybridization. For example, Brahman cattle, commonly found in India, are resistant to heat, insects, and many diseases. They have been bred with Shorthorn cattle to produce cattle called the Santa Gertrudis. The Brahman have also been crossed with Angus cattle to produce a breed called Brangus. Both the Santa Gertrudis and the Brangus are able to withstand heat, high humidity, and insects better than either the Shorthorn or Angus.

Figure 11-4 Hybridization is used to produce new and more productive crops, such as triticale. Triticale is a cross between a rye plant and a wheat plant.

Inbreeding

Another method that has helped breeders maintain desired traits is **inbreeding.** Inbreeding is the crossing of closely related plants or animals. In flowering plants, inbreeding involves *self-pollination*. Self-pollination occurs when pollen is transferred from the stamen of a flower to the pistil of the same flower. Therefore, genes from other plants are not introduced into the inbred plant. Inbreeding increases the chances of developing plants that are *homozygous*, or have identical pairs of genes for the desired trait. Inbreeding is the opposite of hybridization.

About 70% of the corn grown in the United States comes from six inbred varieties that are very closely related. This lack of genetic diversity concerns many scientists. They fear that most of the nation's corn crop could be destroyed by a disease to which these plants have no resistance. Diseases are also a threat to other inbred crops, such as rice.

Inbreeding also has some disadvantages. These disadvantages occur because the offspring have the same recessive genes as the parents. When these offspring are interbred, the probability of a recessive genotype increases. In some cases, the recessive genotype produces an undesirable trait.

At this point, you may want to have your students do the Laboratory Investigation at the end of this chapter.

You may want to review the concept of haploid and diploid numbers in Chapter 8.

Highlight

Plant and animal breeders use selection, mutation, hybridization, inbreeding, and polyploidy to produce desirable traits.

Polyploidy

The chromosomes in most organisms that reproduce sexually are in homologous pairs. Such organisms are said to contain the *diploid number* of chromosomes. Diploid means two sets of chromosomes. When reproductive cells are formed, the number of chromosomes is reduced to one-half the diploid number. These cells are now said to have the *haploid number* of chromosomes. The haploid number, the number of chromosomes in one set, is written as n. Therefore, the diploid equals 2n.

When an organism has more than two sets of chromosomes, **polyploidy** (PAHL-i-ploi-dē) results. Polyploidy occurs during the formation of gametes. Once a cell has become polyploid, cells that it produces during mitosis are also polyploid.

Polyploidy is much more common in plants than in animals. Variation in plants is increased through polyploidy.

CAREER: Animal Breeder

People who develop new and more productive breeds of animals are called animal breeders. Animal breeders may cross-breed a hen and a rooster of two different varieties to get a new kind of hen that lays more eggs than the hens of either parent variety. They may also cross two types of horses to produce a type that runs faster.

Animal breeders begin breeding programs by deciding what traits they wish to improve. Then, they choose animals that show the desired traits and cross-breed them. If the breeders are successful, the offspring have the desired traits.

Usually, animal breeders deal with more than one trait at a time. For example, they may wish to develop a chicken that grows quickly, produces more eggs, and is resistant to disease. Trying to improve several traits at the same time is much more complicated than improving only one trait at a time.

At least a bachelor's degree is needed to work in this field. Animal breeders must keep up to date on developments in their field and have a good knowledge of genetics, reproduction, and animal physiology. An understanding of statis-

tics is helpful, too, because many breeding programs involve maintaining records of large numbers of animals.

Many animal breeders work for agricultural colleges and veterinary schools where they do both research work and teaching. Other animal breeders work for the federal government or for private industry.

For further career information, write to American Society of Animal Sciences, 39 Sheridan Avenue, Albany, NY 12210.

The haploid number (n) of bananas is 11. Some types of bananas, such as the wild banana, are diploid and have 22 chromosomes (2n). Cultivated bananas are *triploid* and have 33 chromosomes (3n). These cultivated bananas grow faster and are more vigorous than the wild ones. Interestingly, plants that have odd numbers of chromosome sets, such as 3n, 5n, 7n, and so on are usually sterile. This characteristic often is desirable in some fruits because they do not have seeds. The cultivated banana is seedless and sterile.

Usually, polyploidy occurs naturally in plants. Chemicals such as *colchicine* (KAHL-chə-sēn) are used to increase the number of sets of chromosomes in plants. Colchicine interferes with mitosis, causing cells that contain more than two sets of chromosomes to develop. Colchicine has been used to develop several varieties of grains, fruits, and vegetables.

Sidelight

Baldwin and Gravenstein apples are triploid. They have 51 chromosomes.

Colchicine is obtained from the seeds and corms of the autumn crocus, a member of the lily family.

SECTION REVIEW   Answers on page T–45.

1. What is the importance of applied genetics?
2. What is genetic breeding?
3. Describe the relationship of selection and hybridization to genetic breeding.
4. If the diploid chromosome number of a plant is 20, how many chromosomes will there be in a triploid cell of that plant?
5. Of what use is colchicine?

You may want to review the structure of DNA in Chapter 8.

Genetic Engineering

In the last decade, much research has centered around **genetic engineering.** Genetic engineering involves the addition or removal of specific genes in an organism. Genes are made up of segments of DNA. A DNA molecule resembles a spiral ladder. The "rungs" of the DNA ladder are composed of pairs of the nitrogen bases adenine (*A*), guanine (*G*), cytosine (*C*), and thymine (*T*). Adenine forms a bond with thymine (*A-T*) while guanine joins with cytosine (*G-C*). The arrangement of the nitrogen bases in a segment of DNA forms a *genetic code*. Each genetic code provides the directions for the synthesis of a specific protein. Therefore, changing a code or putting a new code into a cell changes the instructions and the proteins made by the cell.

In its broadest meaning, genetic engineering includes any artificial process that affects the genetic material of an organism or its offspring. In this sense, **cloning** is considered genetic engineering. Cloning is the production of genetically identical organisms. Cloning usually results from

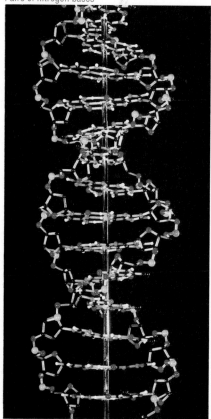

Figure 11-5 This photograph shows a model of a segment of a DNA molecule. What substances make up the "rungs" of the spiral ladder of DNA?
Pairs of nitrogen bases

asexual reproduction, in which a new organism develops from only one parent.

Plant breeders have used cloning techniques for centuries. When certain parts of a plant, such as stems and leaves, are removed and replaced in soil a new plant develops. This new plant is a *clone* and is genetically identical to its parent. In some areas, cloning has been used to redevelop new forests. Recently, techniques have been developed for cloning some vertebrates, such as frogs and mice. However, these methods are still in the experimental stage.

At this point, you may want to assign to several students the first of the Extensions and Applications at the end of this chapter.

Recombinant DNA

During the mid-1970s, scientists discovered how to transfer segments of DNA from one organism to another. The transferred segments of DNA were actually linked to the DNA of the receiving organism. The new strand of combined genetic material became known as **recombinant DNA.**

DNA can be transferred from complex organisms into simple ones such as bacteria. As the bacteria reproduce, copies of the recombinant DNA are passed from one generation to the next. Because bacteria divide about every 20 minutes, large numbers of bacteria that carry the recombinant DNA can be produced in a relatively short period of time. Consequently, these bacteria can manufacture great quantities of the protein coded for by the recombinant DNA. In recent years, bacteria have been genetically engineered to produce proteins normally made by other kinds of living things.

Figure 11-6 shows the steps that are involved in the formation of recombinant DNA. A segment of DNA is removed

Figure 11-6 During the formation of recombinant DNA, a plasmid, or circular form of DNA, from a bacterium is opened by special enzymes. These enzymes also remove a strand of DNA from a donor cell. When the ends of the donor DNA are spliced into the plasmid DNA, the ring of the plasmid is closed. The plasmid is then inserted back into the bacterium.

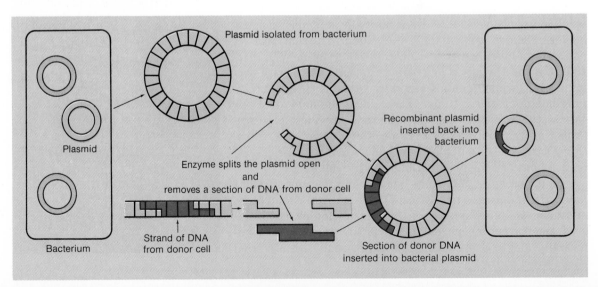

from, or "snipped off," the cell of an organism. The snipping is done with enzymes called *restriction endonucleases* (en-də-NOO-klē-ās-əz). More than 40 enzymes of this kind have been identified. Each is able to snip a different gene, or DNA segment, from a strand of DNA. Using such enzymes, researchers can choose which segments of DNA to transfer from one organism to another.

The common intestinal bacteria *Escherichia coli* generally is used to accept DNA segments. The segment of DNA is spliced into a circular form of DNA called a **plasmid.** The plasmid is first opened up using the same restriction enzyme that is used to remove a DNA strand from the donor cell. As a result, the exposed ends of the plasmid are "sticky," which means that the exposed bases on the donor strand are complementary to those on the plasmid. For example, the cytosine-adenine-thymine side of the donor strand will become attached to the side of the plasmid that has the guanine-thymine-adenine bases.

As the ends of the donor DNA are spliced to the plasmid DNA, the plasmid ring is closed and put back into the bacterial cell. The bacteria's spliced DNA passes new genetic information to its offspring and future generations.

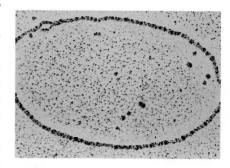

Figure 11-7 This photomicrograph shows a circular plasmid magnified 200,000X.

At this point, you may want to assign to several students the third of the Extensions and Applications at the end of this chapter.

"Protein Factories"

Scientists are using recombinant DNA to turn certain bacteria and yeasts into "protein factories." These organisms can *synthesize*, or make, proteins in large quantities. Bacteria have been engineered to produce substances that help fight disease. For example, in mid-1981, recombinant DNA techniques were used to develop a safe and effective vaccine against foot-and-mouth disease. Foot-and-mouth disease weakens livestock, such as cattle, sheep, and pigs, and reduces their agricultural value. Other practical applications of genetic engineering include the bacterial production of substances that are important to the human body.

HUMAN GROWTH HORMONE PRODUCTION The *human growth hormone*, or HGH, is a chemical messenger that controls growth in human beings. A lack of this hormone results in a condition called *dwarfism*, in which the human skeleton does not grow to a normal size. In the past, children who lacked HGH were given injections of the hormone and began to grow normally. However, only a limited supply of HGH was available for these injections. Recently, bacteria have been genetically engineered to make HGH. Soon, genetically engineered bacteria, which can be grown in large

Highlight

The transfer of segments of DNA from one organism to another is known as recombinant DNA technology.

Have some of your students bring in recent newspaper and magazine articles that discuss the uses of recombinant DNA.

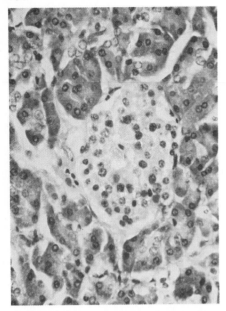

Figure 11-8 This photomicrograph (250X) shows pancreatic cells that secrete the hormone insulin. Insulin controls the level of sugar in the blood.

containers may be able to produce enough HGH to treat a larger number of children for this abnormality.

INSULIN PRODUCTION The human hormone *insulin* is secreted by the pancreas. Insulin controls the level of sugar in the blood by helping the simple sugar glucose move into the cells. Without this hormone, the glucose remains outside the cells, causing the blood sugar level to rise. This condition is called *diabetes mellitus.* The treatment for diabetes usually involves one or more injected doses of insulin daily.

For the past 60 years, the insulin that has been used to treat diabetes has come from the pancreases of animals. In some cases, diabetics have become allergic to the animal insulin, which is structurally different from human insulin. In addition, animal insulin is in short supply. Bacterially produced insulin is identical to the hormone produced in the human body and can be manufactured in large amounts. In 1980, a person suffering from diabetes was successfully injected with bacterial human insulin for the first time. Scientists predict that such insulin soon will be widely used.

INTERFERON PRODUCTION Another protein that has been produced by bacteria through recombinant DNA techniques is **interferon** (in-tər-FIR-ahn). The protein interferon is produced by the human body to fight viral diseases, such as the common cold, influenza, and hepatitis. There is also evidence that interferon has been effective against cancer in experimental animals.

How does interferon protect against viral infections? When a virus enters a cell, a gene in the cell causes the cell to produce interferon. Interferon leaves the infected cell and alerts the surrounding cells to produce their own antiviral chemicals. Most manufactured interferon is gathered from white blood cells that were infected with viruses in a laboratory. The small amount of interferon that is manufactured by this difficult process makes the cost of interferon very high. However, scientists are beginning to produce bacterial interferon through recombinant DNA techniques. They predict that the cost of genetically engineered interferon will be much lower.

SECTION REVIEW   Answers on page T–45.

1. What is genetic engineering?
2. Define cloning.
3. What is a restriction enzyme? A plasmid?
4. List and describe some of the practical applications of genetic engineering.

LABORATORY INVESTIGATION   **11** For additional information, see pages T–45 to T–46.

A Model for Animal Breeding

Purpose   Through the method of selection, animal breeders have developed a type of sheep that is able to produce more fleece and mutton than other sheep. The best fleece-producers have the genotype FFmm. The purpose of this investigation is to demonstrate the effect of selective breeding for increased fleece production in sheep.

Materials *(per group)*   ● 32 2-cm squares of white construction paper   ● 32 2-cm squares of colored construction paper   ● Penny

Procedure   Part A   1. Mark an "F" on 8 squares of white construction paper and an "f" on another 8 white squares. F represents the gene for heavy fleece production; f represents the gene for light fleece production. Mark an "M" on 8 squares of colored construction paper and an "m" on another 8 colored squares. M represents the gene for high mutton production; m represents the gene for low mutton production.   **2.** Randomly place all of the squares face down on a flat surface. These squares represent the genes of 8 wild sheep with the genotype FfMm.   **3.** Choose a set of 2 white squares and 2 colored squares.   **4.** Record the letters, which represent the genotype of the sheep.   **5.** Toss the penny to determine the sex of the sheep: heads = male; tails = female. Record the sex next to the sheep's genotype.   **6.** Repeat steps 3 to 5 until all 8 offspring are formed for the F_1 generation.
7. Examine the offspring to find the genotype FFmm for a male (ram) and a female (ewe) sheep.   **8.** If your group does not have a male-female pair of FFmm genotype sheep in the F_1 generation, place all the papers face down and repeat steps 3 to 7.   **9.** Record the number of generations that it takes to come up with a ram and a ewe that have the desired FFmm genotype. If a pair of sheep with this genotype is not found after 6 generations, go on to Part B.   **Part B
1.** Mark 4 of the remaining white squares with the individual letters for the genotype of a ram that is

heterozygous for both traits (FfMm).   **2.** Mark 3 more sets of 4 white squares each with the same genotype (FfMm).   **3.** Then, mark 4 of the remaining colored squares for the genotype of a ewe that is also heterozygous for both traits.   **4.** Mark 3 more sets of 4 colored squares each with the same genotype. The result is the desired genotypes for 4 rams and 4 ewes.
  5. Place these squares of paper face down and mix them. Select the genotype and sex of 8 sheep in the second generation.   **6.** Choose a ram and a ewe from the second generation. Continue this selection method until your group has produced a ram and a ewe that are purebred for high fleece production (FFmm).

Observations and Conclusions   1. In Part A, how many generations must be bred before obtaining a pair of sheep with the genotype FFmm?   **2.** In Part B, how many generations does it take to obtain a mating pair of FFmm sheep?   **3.** What is the difference between the procedure used in Part A and the one used in Part B?   **4.** What genotype would result in high mutton production?

CHAPTER SUMMARY

Plant and Animal Breeding   Applied genetics, or the use of genetic knowledge, has enabled breeders to develop many plants and animals with desired characteristics. In genetic breeding, plants and animals with desired traits are crossed with others that have the same trait. The process of choosing specific organisms is called selection.

Other processes that affect breeding are mutation, hybridization, inbreeding, and polyploidy. Mutations, or changes in the DNA structure of an organism, usually produce only a very small percentage of organisms with desired traits. These traits are more apt to appear when hybridization is used. The genetically different offspring that are produced by hybridization tend to be more fit and grow faster than either parent. This increased fitness is called hybrid vigor.

Inbreeding is useful when organisms, such as flowering plants, are homozygous for the same trait and are self-pollinated. Inbreeding keeps unwanted genes from being introduced by other plants. Polyploidy increases the variations in plants because the plants contain more than the normal two sets, or diploid number, of chromosomes. Usually polyploidy occurs naturally in plants, although some chemicals, such as colchicine, are used to cause an increase in the chromosome numbers.

Genetic Engineering   Today, scientists are producing genetically new organisms to perform specific and useful functions by the technique of recombinant DNA. Producing recombinant DNA involves removing a segment of DNA from a plant or animal cell and combining it with the DNA of another organism. As the organism reproduces, so does the recombined DNA, passing the new genetic information to its offspring.

Using recombinant DNA techniques, scientists have been able to get bacteria and yeasts to produce human proteins. Human growth hormone, insulin, and interferon are examples of proteins that are being produced in bacteria by recombinant DNA techniques.

CHAPTER VOCABULARY

applied genetics	hybridization	plasmid
cloning	inbreeding	polyploidy
genetic breeding	interferon	recombinant DNA
genetic engineering	mutation	selection

REVIEW of FACTS and CONCEPTS   Answers on page T–46.

On a separate sheet of paper, answer each of the following as completely as possible.

1. Why is a wide range of genetic variability important for plant and animal breeding programs?
2. Does selection always work the way a breeder might wish? Explain your answer.
3. In general, why do you think plant breeders have not used artifically induced mutations to improve plants?
4. What is triticale? How is it produced?
5. Why would a breeder decide to use hybridization or inbreeding?
6. Are there any disadvantages when most of the varieties of one kind of food crop are developed through inbreeding? Explain.
7. Why is polyploidy important in plant breeding?
8. The new plant that develops from a stem of another plant is considered a clone. Why?
9. Describe the steps involved in the technique of producing recombinant DNA.
10. Why are certain types of bacteria chosen to accept donor DNA?

EXTENSIONS and APPLICATIONS   For additional information, see page T–46.

1. Obtain an ivy plant and gently cut off three different growing stems about 10 cm from the tips. Make each cut just below the point where a leaf joins the stem. Remove the leaves from about half the length of each stem and any buds that might be present. Place the defoliated ends of the cut-

tings in water. When roots appear on the stems, fill three small beakers half full with clean soil. Transfer each cutting from the water into the soil to cover the roots. Gently add water to moisten the soil. Allow the cuttings to grow to about the same size as the original plant. Compare the three clones to the original. How are they alike? How are they different? Write a report summarizing your observations.

2. Complete a pedigree, or recorded history of ancestors, of a famous thoroughbred horse by using reference books. What desired genetic characteristics were passed on from previous generations?

3. Find out more information about the recent commercial uses of recombinant DNA technology. Write a report summarizing your findings. Include a colored clay model of the recombinant DNA technique mounted on posterboard.

SUGGESTED READINGS

Flacklam, M., and H. Flacklam, *From Cell to Clone: The Story of Genetic Engineering.* New York: Harcourt Brace Jovanovich.

The authors discuss how genetic engineering will provide more food and forests. Photographs and line drawings are also included.

Lear, J., *Recombinant DNA: The Untold Story.* New York: Crown.

This book examines the subject of gene splicing. It also discusses the advantages and disadvantages of this technique.

McKinnell, R.G., *Cloning: A Biologist Reports.* Minneapolis: University of Minnesota Press.

The author discusses the historical background of cloning. A description of procedures that have been used to clone frogs is included.

12 Variation Through Time

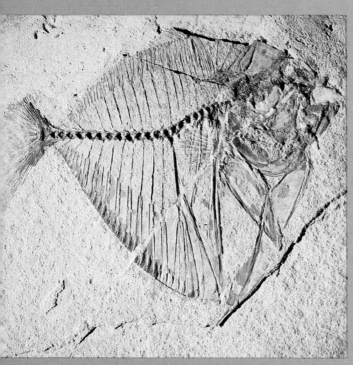

This fossilized fish is embedded in rock.

Chapter Objectives *After completing this chapter, you will be able to:*

a ■ Explain how organisms adapt to their environment. p. 199

b ■ Explain how fossils are used as evidence of change in living things. p. 200

c ■ Give examples of evidence of evolution. p. 200

d ■ Summarize Darwin's theory of evolution. p. 208

e ■ Compare the Lamarckian and Darwinian theories of evolution. p. 207

f ■ Explain why variations in living things are important for survival. p. 209

g ■ Summarize the processes of evolution. p. 211

h ■ State the difference between convergent and divergent evolution. p. 214

For teaching aids for this chapter, including a chapter overview and teaching strategies, see pages T–46 to T–48. The page number next to each chapter objective refers to the text page where the information needed to fulfill the objective begins.

Scientists estimate that the earth is about 4.6 billion years old. During its history, the surface of the earth has changed continuously. Today, volcanic eruptions, earthquakes, wind, and rain continue to change the surface of the earth.

There is evidence that life also has changed during the long history of the earth. Most of the plants and animals on the earth today are not the same as those that lived millions of years ago. However, some organisms, such as the cockroach and horseshoe crab, are considered living records of the past because they have changed very little.

Scientists have many questions about how and why living things have changed and why some organisms seem to have changed very little throughout the earth's history. New discoveries and techniques may help to answer some of these questions. As scientists try to piece together a more complete history of the earth and its organisms, new theories may also be developed.

198

Adaptations in Living Things

Take a look at your classmates. You will notice many similarities because all of you belong to the same **species.** A species is a group of organisms that interbreed. There are small differences among the members of each species. For example, you can easily see that no one in your class looks exactly like anyone else in your class. Differences exist in all species of organisms that reproduce sexually. Many of these differences, or *variations*, are neither helpful nor harmful to an organism. However, sometimes a variation helps an organism to be better suited to its environment.

The environment is constantly changing. Sometimes, the changes are gradual, as in changes in the climate. Other changes may be sudden, such as the eruption of Mount St. Helens in the state of Washington. This volcanic eruption destroyed the natural environment of many organisms. Sudden changes in the environment may also be caused by floods, violent storms, or earthquakes.

When an environment changes, some organisms die. Others move to a new environment. However, some organisms have a helpful variation that enables them to survive the change and reproduce. The helpful variation is inherited by some of their offspring. After many generations, most organisms in the species have the helpful variation.

There are many examples of variations that are helpful to an organism. Forty years ago, only a small percentage of mosquitoes were resistant to DDT. The mosquitoes with this variation were better suited to survive in an environment that contained DDT. They lived and produced offspring that DDT could not kill. As a result, the number of DDT-resistant mosquitoes has grown larger.

The process by which an organism becomes better suited to a change in environment is called **adaptation.** Each of the nearly 2 million known species of living things on the earth has special adaptations, or helpful variations that make them better suited to their environment. Organisms may have adaptations in body structure or function, coloration, or behavior. For example, horses have flat teeth and powerful jaw muscles for chewing and grinding grasses. Tigers have sharp, pointed teeth that are used for tearing flesh. The large tusks of walruses and elephants are used for defense.

Adaptations are sometimes more evident when you compare closely related species. In the hot, dry areas of the southwestern United States, a species of hare called a jack rabbit is very common. Jack rabbits have long, large ears and powerful hind legs. Their ears provide a large surface

Figure 12-1 Every living thing has adaptations that enable it to live successfully in its environment. What adaptations do the elephant and walking stick have?

Tusks enable the elephant to scrape bark from trees to obtain food and moisture. The walking stick's shape allows it to blend in with its environment.

Figure 12-2 Why would the color of the fur of the jack rabbit (*top*) and snowshoe hare (*bottom*) be a helpful adaptation in their different environments?

The colors of the animals closely match their environments. Predators would have more difficulty finding the animals.

area to allow excess body heat to escape. Powerful hind legs enable the jack rabbit to outrun its enemies.

In the northern plains and Canada, another species of hare is common. The snowshoe hare has small ears and broad feet. Unlike jack rabbits, snowshoe hares must keep in body heat during the cold winters. Their ears do not permit a large amount of heat loss. Their broad feet are well suited for running on top of snow. The special characteristics of these two species of hares enable them to live and reproduce in different environments.

SECTION REVIEW   Answers on page T–46.

1. Why are some variations in organisms helpful to their survival?
2. What is meant by an adaptation?

Evidence of Evolution

Many changes have occurred on the earth's surface during its long geologic history. Evidence indicates that organisms also have changed as the environment has changed. The evidence also indicates that species living today are not the same species that existed in the distant past. The diversity of living things appears to be greater today. The theory that describes changes in living things and links them to changes in the environment is called **evolution.** Evolution is change over a period of time. The theory of evolution is based on present scientific data.

Fossil Evidence

The remains or traces of organisms that lived in the past are called **fossils.** Fossils are most often found in *sedimentary rock.* Sedimentary rock is formed from layers of *sediments,* or deposited matter, such as sand, mud, and silt. These layers formed one on top of another. Great pressure on the bottom layers caused them to change to rock. Many organisms that were buried in these sediment layers became fossilized.

In order for a fossil to be formed, an organism must be buried soon after death by sediments. Quick burial slows down or stops *decay,* or the breaking down of the organism by bacteria. Quick burial also prevents other animals from eating the dead organism.

Some fossils are imprints of living things. *Imprint fossils* usually form from the soft body parts of a living thing,

Highlight

Fossils indicate that the climate of the earth has gradually changed over long periods of time.

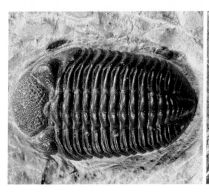

Figure 12-3 Fossils include molds, such as that of this trilobite *(left)*, and imprints, such as these made by fern leaves *(right)*.

Number of toes on each foot reduced to one, a hoof

Figure 12-4 Fossils indicate that the horse has changed in size during its evolution on the earth. How else has the horse changed?

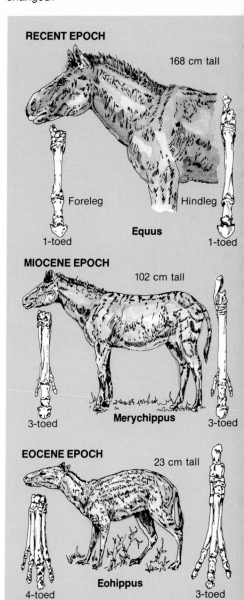

RECENT EPOCH

168 cm tall

Foreleg   Hindleg

Equus

1-toed   1-toed

MIOCENE EPOCH

102 cm tall

3-toed   **Merychippus**   3-toed

EOCENE EPOCH

23 cm tall

Eohippus

4-toed   3-toed

such as leaves. Hard body parts, such as bones, teeth, and shells, may form *fossil molds* or *fossil casts*. A fossil mold is a cavity in a rock that has taken on the shape of the trapped organism. A fossil cast is a filled mold. Other types of fossils are formed when the hard parts of an organism are replaced by minerals. These fossils are said to be *petrified*. The remains of some organisms were frozen. A whole mammoth was found frozen in the ground in Siberia. Some organisms are found preserved in volcanic ash, tar pits, and *amber*. Amber is hardened sticky plant resin. Insects are often found preserved in amber.

INTERPRETING FOSSILS   Fossils provide evidence that the surface and climate of the earth have gradually changed over a long period of time. *Paleontologists* (pā-lē-ahn-TAHL-ə-jists), scientists who look for and study fossils, have found fossils of ocean-dwelling animals preserved in inland rocks. Paleontologists reason that the land in these areas was once covered by an ocean.

Fossils of ancient corals have been found in the Arctic. Assuming that ancient corals lived in the same warm-water environment as corals do today, paleontologists reason that the arctic climate of the past was warmer than it is today. Fossils of palm tree leaves and ferns have been found in cold regions of the earth. Therefore, scientists can assume that these regions were once warm and humid.

Fossils are used as evidence that certain forms of life changed during the history of the earth. For example, scientists have found fossils of adult horses of different sizes. The fossils indicate that the size of horses and the form of their legs and feet have changed. The smallest horses were about the size of a small dog. They had four toes on each front leg and three toes on each hind leg. Today, horses are larger and have a single toe, or hoof, on each foot.

Fossils indicate that many different living things have existed on the earth at different times. However, many of

Sidelight

Dinosaurs were the dominant forms of life on earth for nearly 140 million years.

Figure 12-5 Carbon-14 has a half-life of 5730 years. What is the decay element of carbon-14? Nitrogen-14

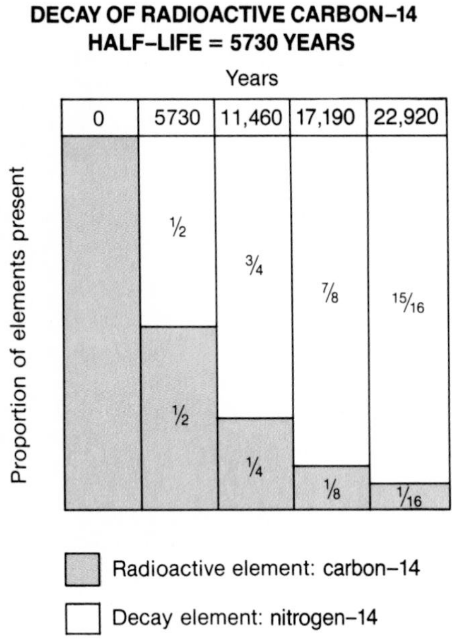

DECAY OF RADIOACTIVE CARBON–14
HALF–LIFE = 5730 YEARS

Years

0	5730	11,460	17,190	22,920

Proportion of elements present

½

¾

⅞

15/16

½

¼

⅛

1/16

■ Radioactive element: carbon–14

□ Decay element: nitrogen–14

At this point, you may want to assign to two groups of students the second and third of the Extensions and Applications at the end of this chapter.

these organisms became *extinct*. An extinct organism is one that no longer lives on the earth. Dinosaurs are well-known examples of extinct animals.

DATING FOSSILS Fossils are useful only if scientists can tell how long ago the organisms lived. Scientists use several techniques to date fossils. Scientists can tell the *relative age* of rocks and fossils by their position in sedimentary rock layers. In sedimentary rock, the layers of sediment are deposited at different times. The bottom layers are deposited before the top layers. Therefore, each layer of rock would be younger than the rocks below it and older than those above it. This is known as the *Law of Superposition.*

In the twentieth century, scientists discovered that radioactivity could be used to determine the *absolute age* of fossils. Absolute age is the measure of how many years ago an organism lived or an event occurred. One process of determining absolute age is called *radioactive dating.*

Many elements have radioactive forms. The nuclei, or centers, of radioactive atoms decay, or break apart, at a fixed rate. The rate at which an element decays is measured in terms of **half-life.** Half-life is the time it takes for one-half of any quantity of an element to decay.

The half-lives of different radioactive elements are not the same. For example, the half-life of carbon-14 is 5730 years. Carbon-14 decays into nitrogen-14. Because radioactive decay occurs at a fixed and known rate, the age of a fossil can be estimated. This is done by comparing the amount of the radioactive element with the amount of the *decay element*, or element formed as a result of radioactive decay. For example, suppose a rock containing a fossil had equal amounts of carbon-14 and its decay element, nitrogen-14. You could estimate that the rock was about 5730 years old. If the rock contained one-fourth carbon-14 and three-fourths nitrogen-14, you could estimate the age of the rock to be 11,460 years old. This is the amount of time it would take for three-fourths of the carbon-14 originally present to decay. Figure 12-5 illustrates the decay of carbon-14.

GEOLOGIC TIME Using information gained from different dating methods, scientists have been able to set up a geologic time scale of the history of the earth. The geologic time scale is divided into four large time spans called *eras.* The three most recent eras are subdivided into *periods.* Some of the periods are subdivided into *epochs.*

Many scientists estimate that the earth was formed about 4.6 billion years ago. The first four billion years of the earth's history is referred to as *Precambrian time.* Not much

Figure 12-6   Geologic Time Scale

ERA	PERIOD	EPOCH	BEGINNING (Millions of years ago)	DURATION (Millions of years ago)	MAJOR EVENTS
Cenozoic Era	Quaternary	Recent	Began 10,000 years ago		Civilization spreads. Human beings are the major form of life.
		Pleistocene	2.5	2.5	"The Ice Age." Modern human beings present. Mammoths and other animals become extinct.
	Tertiary	Pliocene	14	11.5	Fossil evidence of ancient human beings near the end of the epoch. Many birds, mammals, and sea life similar to modern types. Climate cools.
		Miocene	25	11	Many grazing animals. Flowering plants and trees similar to modern types.
		Oligocene	35	10	Fossil evidence of primitive apes. Elephants, camels, and horses develop. Climate generally mild.
		Eocene	55	20	Fossil evidence of a small horse. Grasslands and forests present. Many small mammals and larger mammals, such as primitive whales, rhinoceroses, and monkeys.
		Paleocene	70	15	Flowering plants and small mammals abundant. Many different climates exist.
Mesozoic Era	Cretaceous		135	65	First fossil evidence of flowering plants and trees. Many small mammals. Dinosaurs are extinct by the end of the period. Coal swamps develop.
	Jurassic		180	45	First fossil evidence of feathered birds and mammals. Many dinosaurs roam the earth.
	Triassic		230	50	Beginning of the "Age of Dinosaurs." Insects plentiful. Cone-bearing plants present.
Paleozoic Era	Permian		285	55	First evidence of seed plants. Fish, amphibians, and reptiles present.
	Carboniferous	Pennsylvanian Period	325	40	First evidence of reptiles. Many amphibians and giant insects present. Many large fern trees. Swamps cover many lowland areas.
		Mississippian Period	350	25	
	Devonian		410	60	"Age of Fish." First fossil evidence of amphibians and insects. Many different kinds of fish in the earth's waters. The first forests grow in swamps.
	Silurian		430	20	First evidence of land plants. Algae, trilobites, and armored fish plentiful. Coral reefs form.
	Ordovician		500	70	Fossil evidence of jawless fish. Algae and trilobites plentiful. Great floods cover most of North America.
	Cambrian		600	100	"Age of Invertebrates." Fossil evidence of trilobites, clams, snails, and seaweed. Seas spread across North America.
	Precambrian	Proterozoic Era	4.6 billion	Almost 4 billion	Fossil evidence of bacteria and algae. Earth forms.
		Archeozoic Era			

At this point, you may want to assign to the class the first of the Extensions and Applications at the end of this chapter.

Sidelight

The average life span of a species is less than 10 million years, although families and orders have lasted 100 million years or more.

is known about life on the earth during this era. Few fossils have been found that date from this time. The oldest record of life is fossil evidence discovered in Australia. Fossils of five different kinds of bacteria were found that scientists estimate lived 3.5 billion years ago.

The fossil evidence used to develop the geologic time scale indicates that other simple forms of life were present during the Cambrian period about 600 million years ago. Fossil evidence also indicates that there were not very many different kinds of living things during the Cambrian period. Some organisms found in the early eras or periods eventually disappeared. As time passed, the variety and complexity of life increased.

Anatomical Evidence

The study of the structure of living things is called *anatomy*. Scientists have compared the structures of many plants and animals and have found many similarities. They use these similarities as evidence of evolution.

HOMOLOGOUS ORGANS Body parts or organs that are similar in structure are said to be **homologous** (hō-MAHL-ə-gəs). For example, giraffes, elephants, mice, rabbits, and horses all have seven neck *vertebrae*. Vertebrae are the small bones that make up the entire backbone. The vertebrae of these different animals are homologous.

Suppose you were to look at the flipper of a whale, the wing of a bird, the arm of a human, and the foreleg of a frog. They would

Figure 12-7 The forelimbs of vertebrates are homologous structures. Notice that the structure, arrangement, and number of bones in each of these forelimbs are similar.

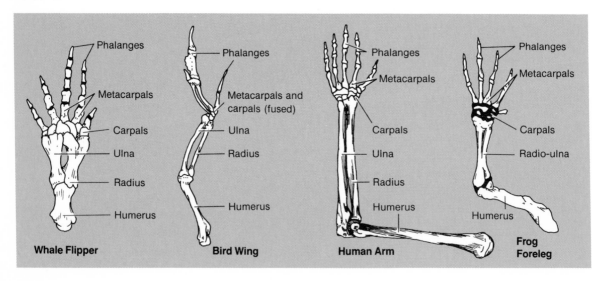

Whale Flipper — Phalanges, Metacarpals, Carpals, Ulna, Radius, Humerus

Bird Wing — Phalanges, Metacarpals and carpals (fused), Ulna, Radius, Humerus

Human Arm — Phalanges, Metacarpals, Carpals, Ulna, Radius, Humerus

Frog Foreleg — Phalanges, Metacarpals, Carpals, Radio-ulna, Humerus probably seem very different to you. However, the structure and arrangement of the bones and muscles are similar. These similarities cannot be explained by a common function of the limbs, since each of the limbs has a different function. However, the similarities can be explained by heredity. Scientists think that the arrangement of the bones in these animals was inherited from a common ancestor. The basic bone pattern of these organisms has remained the same, although adaptations have made each organism suited to its own special environment and to its own way of life.

VESTIGIAL ORGANS   According to some biologists, organs such as the human appendix or the remains of hind limbs on whales provide evidence of evolution. These structures are called **vestigial** (ves-TIJ-ē-əl) **organs.** Vestigial organs are reduced in size and appear to have no use. Most animals have some vestigial structures.

The appendix is a small pouch attached to the large intestine. In human beings, the appendix is a vestigial organ because it is small and has no obvious use. However, the appendix of a rabbit is well developed and is used in the digestion of *cellulose* (SEL-yoo-lōs), a plant fiber. The presence of the appendix in both rabbits and human beings cannot be explained by a similarity in function. Biologists maintain that the human appendix is an inherited structure that was well developed in the past.

Embryological Evidence

In the early stages of development, *vertebrates*, or animals with backbones, are very similar. Animals in these early stages are called *embryos*. Figure 12-8 illustrates three stages in the development of different vertebrates. Basing their theories on similarities of structure, scientists once thought that the different stages of development of an organism repeated its evolutionary history.

Today, scientists think that vertebrates have some common genetic material that makes their early development similar. However, as the embryo matures, other genetic material appears to change the form of the developing organism. For example, each of the embryos in Figure 12-8 have gill slits. The gill slits of fish eventually develop into breathing structures. However, in other vertebrates, the gill slits disappear or develop into different body parts. The existence of gill slits and several other embryological features in vertebrates seems to indicate that they have a common evolutionary origin.

Figure 12-8 The embryological development of vertebrates is similar in early stages. However, the embryos are very different in later stages.

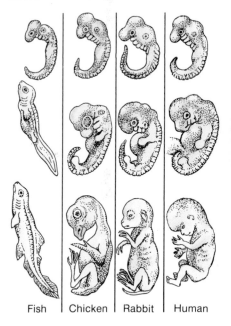

Fish | Chicken | Rabbit | Human

Biochemical Evidence

The most recent evidence used to support evolution comes from studies of the molecules that make up living things. Living things share many common substances that are made of *proteins*. Proteins are made up of smaller units called *amino acids*. Each kind of protein is made up of a specific combination of different amino acids.

Scientists recently discovered how the amino acids are arranged in some protein molecules. For example, *cytochrome c* is a simple protein made up of 104 amino acid units. Cytochrome c is an enzyme used to help cells obtain energy. It is found in the cells of most living things.

Research shows a pattern in the cytochrome c of various organisms. Scientists have discovered that living things with similar anatomical and embryological features have similar sequences of amino acids in their cytochrome c. For example, the arrangement of cytochrome c amino acids in moths is similar to the amino acid arrangement in screw worm flies. Living things with different anatomical and embryological features have many differences in the structure of their cytochrome c. Thus, the amino acid sequence in the cytochrome c of moths is very different from that in donkeys.

At this point, review with your students the evidence for evolution that includes fossil, anatomical, embryological, and biochemical data.

Highlight

Scientists use fossil, anatomical, embryological, and biochemical evidence to support the theory of evolution.

SECTION REVIEW   Answers on pages T–46 to T–47.

1. What do fossils suggest about the kinds of organisms that lived in the past?
2. List several examples of fossil evidence that reveal information about the history of the earth.
3. What anatomical evidence is used as evidence of evolution?
4. What has biochemical research suggested about similar organisms?

Theories of Evolution

Theories of evolution are used to explain how organisms either adapt to fit constantly changing environments or become extinct. The theories are also used to explain why plants and animals of today are different from related fossil forms and why different species share common characteristics.

Different theories were offered in the past to explain these observations about past and present life. One of the earliest theories of evolution was stated by Jean Baptiste de

Lamarck. Charles Darwin presented a second theory, which disagreed with Lamarck's. At the turn of the nineteenth century, yet another theory was developed by Hugo De Vries.

Lamarck's Theory

Jean Baptiste de Lamarck, a French biologist, was one of the first biologists to be convinced that all species evolved from other species. In the early 1800s, he devised a "scale of nature." He placed complex organisms at the top of the scale and simple organisms at the bottom. Lamarck developed one scale for plants and another for animals. Lamarck thought that organisms had an inner need to change. As the organisms changed, they moved up the scale of nature.

Lamarck based his scale of nature on the inner need to change and environmental needs. He thought that organisms changed to meet environmental needs. For example, Lamarck thought that the neck of the giraffe grew longer because giraffes with short necks had to stretch them to reach the tree leaves when there was a shortage of food. The longer necks were then passed on to the offspring.

Lamarck also thought that if organs were not used in early generations, they would become smaller and disappear. Organs that were used would become better developed in later generations. For example, Lamarck thought that the legs of horses became stronger after many generations of running. He also thought that if ducks were caged and could not fly, their wings would become small and weak after many generations. He believed that traits acquired in one generation could be inherited by the next generation.

Emphasize to your students that Lamarck's law of use and disuse implies that an organism can change body structures during its lifetime to meet its needs. Students should also be aware of the teleological aspect of Lamarckian theory, in other words, the assigning of a purpose for an evolutionary change.

Figure 12-9 According to French biologist Jean Baptiste de Lamarck, giraffes developed long necks during their lives because they had to stretch to reach the leaves in the trees. Lamarck believed that the giraffes passed on this acquired trait to their offspring.

Lamarck's theories were never accepted by many biologists. His observations that organisms can change during their lifetimes were correct. However, these **acquired traits** are not inherited. For example, if a person exercises and develops large muscles, the person's offspring does not inherit large muscles. Changes in the body cells of an organism are not passed on to its offspring. Only changes in the gametes, or sex cells, pass on to the next generation. Although Lamarck's theory was not correct, his ideas were important because they led other scientists to explore the idea of evolution.

Darwin's Theory

In 1859, Charles Darwin, a British naturalist, published a book entitled *On the Origin of Species by Means of Natural Selection*. His book contained four main hypotheses, which were based on years of careful observations of species around the world.

1. The world is not static but is changing.
2. Living things change through time.
3. Organisms with many common characteristics descended from a common ancestor.
4. Evolutionary change is a result of natural selection.

The first three of Darwin's hypotheses were not new. However, the fourth hypothesis, which attempted to explain how evolutionary change took place, was new and important. Darwin thought several factors were involved in **natural selection.** Natural selection is the process by which those organisms that are best suited to their environment survive and reproduce.

Overproduction Darwin noticed that all organisms had a tendency to produce more offspring than could survive. He assumed that the number of organisms would increase geometrically (1, 2, 4, 8, 16, 32, 64, 128, . . .) from generation to generation provided that all the offspring survived to reproduce. For example, a pair of elephants would have 19 million descendants in 750 years if all the young lived to reproduce.

Struggle for Existence Darwin noted that even with overproduction, the population of a given species generally stays about the same. He concluded that the reason populations do not increase is a "struggle for existence."

Highlight

The concept of natural selection was a major contribution of Darwin to the science of biology. Natural selection is the process by which those organisms that are best suited to their environment survive and reproduce.

Figure 12-10 According to British naturalist Charles Darwin, giraffes were born with different neck lengths. Those giraffes that had longer necks could reach the leaves in trees. These giraffes survived and passed the helpful variation to their offspring. Short-necked giraffes died before they could produce offspring.

He considered this struggle, or competition, among organisms to be a factor in what he called natural selection. Each individual and species must compete for food, water, light, and other things needed for life. When organisms compete for the same thing, some individuals are not successful and die. Those that are successful survive and produce offspring. Darwin concluded that individuals and species are "selected" by their environment.

Variations Another factor in the theory of natural selection is variations among individuals of a species. According to Darwin, no two individuals are exactly alike. Members of the same species show differences in size, color, behavior, and other features. Darwin was not able to explain what caused these variations in a species.

At this point, you may want to mention to your students that Darwin did not know that changes are transmitted by genes.

Natural Selection and the Origin of New Species Darwin thought that some variations were neutral or unimportant. Others were helpful to organisms, enabling them to adapt better to their environment. The organisms that were better suited to the environment survived and reproduced in greater numbers. The helpful variations were then passed on to the offspring. Over a long period of time, many small changes would occur, so that the populations as a whole would change. Eventually, they would become significantly different from

Remind your students that Darwin's most important contribution was to explain evolutionary change. His explanation suggested that organisms evolve gradually by the accumulation of small changes over very long periods of time.

past populations. Darwin thought that new species were formed in this way.

De Vries' Theory

In 1901, Hugo De Vries (də-VRĒS), a Dutch botanist, developed a theory to explain the sudden variations in organisms. He based his theory on observations of more than 53,000 primrose plants. During the ten years that he grew them, De Vries noticed several sudden differences among traits of parent and offspring plants. He found differences in the height of the plants, the shapes of the leaves, and the arrangement of the branches. De Vries called these sudden changes "mutations." De Vries claimed that new species arose in a single generation because of these mutations. Today, it is known that De Vries was actually observing the effects of genetic recombination rather than mutations. A mutation is a change in the genetic material of a cell. Mutations increase the genetic variability of a population.

Microevolution and Macroevolution

Today, scientists maintain that evolution has occurred in two ways. A small change in a species is referred to as **microevolution.** A large and sudden change that produces a new species is referred to as **macroevolution.** Some scientists think that fossils and genetic research show that organisms do not change significantly for a long time. Then, a major change suddenly occurs. The scientists do not agree as to whether the sudden change happens in a few generations or during many thousands of years. Some of the scientists also question whether the changes that occur make the new species better adapted to the environment.

Theories about evolution will continue to develop and change. New fossil discoveries and research in many areas of science will help scientists to give a more complete answer to the question of how life has changed.

SECTION REVIEW   Answers on page T–47.

1. Explain Lamarck's ideas of acquired traits and use and disuse.
2. What are the four main hypotheses in Darwin's book *On the Origin of Species by Means of Natural Selection?*
3. List the factors that Darwin thought were involved in evolution.
4. What did Hugo De Vries think caused the development of new species?

At this point, you may want to mention that microevolution is the process that accounts for the different varieties of Darwin's finches found in the Galapagos Islands.

Highlight

Microevolution refers to a small, gradual change in a species. Macroevolution refers to a large and sudden change that produces a new species.

Processes of Evolution

All of the genes of a given *population* are called a **gene pool.** A population is all members of a species living in a given area at the same time. Variations in the gene pool cause changes in the species. If there are no changes in the gene pool, there are no changes in the species.

The Hardy-Weinberg Law

In 1908, Godfrey Hardy, a British mathematician, and Wilhelm Weinberg, a German doctor, were doing independent studies on *gene frequency* and variations in the gene pool. Gene frequency is an indication of the relative number of individuals in a population that have a particular gene. Hardy and Weinberg discovered that the frequency of dominant and recessive genes in a population remains the same from generation to generation. This principle is known as the **Hardy-Weinberg Law.** However, this law only applies under the following conditions.

1. The population must be very large.
2. No new genes enter the gene pool.
3. Mating must be random.
4. Natural selection must not be operating.
5. Mutations must not occur.

The Hardy-Weinberg law can be used to study populations in which gene frequency has changed. If in such a situation the first four conditions of the law are met, an evolutionary change must have taken place in the population.

There are cases in which random changes in gene frequency occur. In such cases of **genetic drift,** the Hardy-Weinberg law may not apply. Despite these cases, the law continues to be useful because it enables geneticists to determine the processes involved in evolutionary change.

Gene Mutation

Genes are segments of the hereditary substance DNA. In some cases, the genetic message of DNA is changed through mutation. The changed gene then is passed on to the next generation. If the organism with the new gene survives and reproduces, the gene pool of the population changes slightly. Therefore, a change in the DNA can result in a change in the gene pool. Mutations in genes rarely oc-

Highlight

Variations in the gene pool of a population are caused by mutation, adaptive shifts through natural selection, genetic drift, migration, and isolation.

At this point, you may want to have your students do the Laboratory Investigation at the end of this chapter.

Sidelight

An interesting adaptation involves certain beetles that live in army ant colonies. The ants usually eat beetles. However the beetles have developed bodies that resemble those of ants, and so the ants do not eat the beetles.

Figure 12-11 The peppered moths of Manchester, England, could hardly be detected on the light-colored background of their environment. Black moths were less likely to avoid being eaten by predators. When the environment became covered with black soot, more black moths survived than peppered ones.

cur. In some organisms, a gene mutation may occur in only one of every million or billion sex cells.

The chances of mutations appearing in a population are increased not only because of the large number of genes but also because of the large numbers of individuals in a population. For example, since 1909 about 5000 sudden changes have been identified in the fruit fly, *Drosophila melanogaster*. As these mutations were passed on to offspring, the gene pool of the population changed considerably.

Adaptive Shifts

The recombination of genes that takes place during meiosis does not change the gene pool. The total number and kinds of alleles remain the same. However, if the environment changes and a certain combination of alleles helps an organism survive, the organism with those alleles has a greater chance of reproducing. Some of the offspring will have the alleles for the helpful trait. After several generations, the trait will show up more often.

When conditions in the environment favor one genetic trait over another, the gene pool of the population changes through natural selection. Changes in the frequency of occurence of certain genes as the environment changes are called **adaptive shifts**. An example of an adaptive shift is the change in the gene pool of the peppered moth in Manchester, England. Before 1845, peppered moths were light in color with dark specks. These moths were difficult for birds to see on the light-colored tree trunks. Therefore, the moths were less likely to be eaten. In 1845, only one black moth was observed in Manchester. By 1895, 99% of the moths in the city were black. What caused the light-colored population of moths to be replaced by a dark-colored population?

During the 1800s, Manchester became a center of industry. Pollution in the form of black, sooty smoke covered the bark of the trees and the outside of houses. Light-colored moths resting on the darkened tree trunks were easily seen by the birds that ate them. The dark-colored moths blended with the darkened tree bark. Therefore, their chance of survival increased. Soon, 99% of the moths were black. Recently, the percentage of dark-colored moths has decreased slightly as a result of a decrease in pollution.

Migration

Changes in the gene pool of a population may also be the result of **migration**, the movement of an organism into or out of a population. An organism moving into a population brings new genes to the gene pool of the group. Genes are removed from the gene pool when a member of the population leaves.

For example, dogs have traveled with human beings over a long period of time. Interbreeding among dogs has resulted in over 100 different breeds, such as bulldogs, collies, and greyhounds. The different breeds belong to one species, *Canis familiaris*, because they interbreed. However, migration has resulted in a gene pool that contains many variations.

Isolation

At this point, you may want to assign to two groups of students the second and third of the Extensions and Applications at the end of this chapter.

Sometimes a population of a certain species is separated from the other members of the same species. This separation is referred to as **isolation.** Isolation can be caused by a natural barrier such as a deep canyon, a river, or a mountain. Artificial barriers, such as canals or pipelines, can also cause a population of a species to become isolated.

If a population is isolated, it is possible for **speciation** to occur. That is, a new and distinct species can develop. Mutations and genetic recombination produce variations in the separated populations. Natural selection changes the two gene pools. Therefore, the organisms that live and reproduce in one environment become different from those in the other environment.

Geographic isolation is thought to have caused the development of two distinct species of squirrels in the Grand Canyon area. The north rim of the canyon is separated from the south rim by a river and a desert. Kaibab squirrels live on the north rim. These squirrels have white tails and black bellies. Abert squirrels live on the south rim. Abert squirrels have gray tails and white bellies. These two squirrels are considered to be different species since they do not interbreed. However, scientists think that the ancestors of these squirrels were once members of the same species. As variations occurred and the gene pools remained separated by the river and desert, the squirrels became different species.

The animal and plant populations found on some islands are very different from those found elsewhere in the world. For example, the most common *mammals,* or animals that feed milk to their young, found on the island-continent of Australia are the *marsupials* (mahr-soo-pē-əls). Marsupials are mammals that carry their young in pouches. Marsupials are not commonly found outside Australia. In North America, for example, the only species of marsupial is the opossum. There are 117 species of marsupials in Australia, including 45 different species of kangaroos.

Figure 12–12 Scientists think that geographic isolation led to the development of two species of similar squirrels in the Grand Canyon. One species is the Kaibab squirrel (*top*) and the other is the Abert squirrel (*bottom*). What barriers kept these squirrels isolated? River and desert

Figure 12-13 Wombats (*top*), Tasmanian devils (*center*), and kangaroos (*bottom*) are three of the many marsupials that live on the island-continent of Australia.

Why are so many marsupials found in Australia? Fossil records show that many kinds of mammals, including marsupials, lived in Australia 60 to 135 million years ago. Scientists theorize that Australia broke away from a large landmass during this time and became isolated. As the environments of Australia and the rest of the world changed, marsupials survived the changes in Australia but did not in other parts of the world. The isolated marsupials of Australia developed into diverse and unusual species.

Even after a long separation, some populations may still be able to interbreed. Their gametes can unite to form zygotes. However, the zygotes may never develop because of *genetic isolation,* or genetic differences. If offspring do develop, they are often born *sterile.* Sterile organisms are unable to reproduce. For example, a female horse and a male donkey can interbreed. The offspring is called a mule. Mules are usually sterile. As long as no fertile offspring are born, the populations show genetic isolation. Therefore, they remain separate species.

SECTION REVIEW   Answers on page T–47.

1. What is a gene mutation?
2. What is an adaptive shift? How does this influence the gene pool?
3. What are some causes of isolation? How may isolation affect a species?

Pathways of Evolution

Many organisms found in different parts of the world look alike and live in similar environments but are not closely related. Other organisms look very different but are closely related. The similarities and differences among these organisms resulted from the adaptations of species to their individual environments. There are two *pathways,* or processes, of evolutionary change that have led to these similarities and differences.

Divergent Evolution

Different species can develop from a common ancestor. As populations of species spread out and adapt to different environments, different variations are selected. The process whereby many different species develop from a common ancestor is called **divergent evolution.** "Divergent" means moving apart. This process is also known as *adaptive radiation*

because each species adapts to a special set of environmental conditions.

Biologists maintain that different species of birds developed from a common ancestor through divergent evolution. As a result of natural selection, each species became adapted to a certain environment and way of life. Examine the photographs of the two species of birds shown in Figure 12-14. Although penguins cannot fly, they have wings as their flying ancestors did. Their wings are adapted for swimming.

Figure 12-14 Penguins have wings and feet that are adapted for swimming. Vultures have wings for soaring and gliding and feet that are adapted for grasping.

CLOSE-UP: *Dr. Mary Dawson*

Every other summer, Dr. Mary Dawson goes camping in the Canadian Arctic. She flies to Ellesmere Island, which is located about 1600 kilometers north of Hudson Bay. For six weeks, she camps with a colleague in wilderness areas. The nearest point of civilization is a weather station 320 kilometers away.

Mary Dawson is Curator of Vertebrate Paleontology and Chairwoman of Earth Sciences at the Carnegie Museum in Pittsburgh, Pennsylvania. She is a paleontologist, and her arctic campout is a research field trip to look for fossils. She is interested in finding fossil bones of animals that lived 38 to 55 million years ago during the Eocene Epoch. Ellesmere Island is a good area in which to find fossils because it has outcroppings of thick sedimentary rock. These outcroppings have remained relatively undisturbed over millions of years.

"My colleague and I have developed the earliest known record of land vertebrate animals in the Canadian Arctic," Dawson explained. "The Eocene was a very dramatic age. It was the first age in which fossils of modern groups of animals we know today have been found." Bones of fish, lizards, turtles, and rhinoceroslike ani-

mals are some of the many fossils Dawson has recovered.

To an expert like Dawson, a single bone can reveal a great deal of information. For example, from a jaw bone, Dawson can reconstruct the type of animal to which the bone belonged and the kind of food the animal ate. She can also describe the environment in which the animal lived.

Dawson brings the fossils back to the museum and compares them with others the museum has acquired. Dawson and her staff members are making a significant contribution to present day biology by determining how animals have changed since Eocene times.

Vultures, on the other hand, have long wings that are used for gliding and soaring on rising currents of air. In both penguins and vultures, the wings have the same basic form. Yet each wing has a different function. As well as differences in wings, birds also have many other differences in individual body parts, such as feet and beaks.

Fossil evidence suggests that adaptive radiation occurred among mammals in the last 50 to 60 million years. Based on fossil records, some scientists think that the rate of adaptive radiation was greatest about 2 million years ago.

Convergent Evolution

Many unrelated plants and animals in different parts of the world look alike. According to biologists, these organisms developed similar adaptations because their environments were similar. The process of unrelated species developing similar characteristics is called **convergent evolution.** For example, jack rabbits are found in the western grasslands of the United States. In the grasslands of Argentina, there are animals called cavies, which look and behave like jack rabbits. The cavy has long hind legs and big ears. However, the cavy is a rodent and is related to the guinea pig. Biologists theorize that these two animals developed convergently.

Another striking example of convergent evolution can be seen in whales, porpoises, and dolphins. These organisms are mammals, yet they look like fishes. Scientists think that since these aquatic mammals had to survive in the same environment as the fishes, the mammals developed certain **analogous organs.** Analogous organs are similar in appearance and function but not in origin. The flippers of aquatic mammals are analogous to the fins of fishes.

Highlight

The process of divergent evolution refers to the development of many different species from a common ancestor. The process of convergent evolution refers to the development of similar characteristics in unrelated species.

The animals adapted to the same environment through the process of convergent evolution.

Figure 12-15 The dolphin is a mammal and the shark is a fish. How might a scientist explain the development of the similarity in appearance?

SECTION REVIEW   Answers on page T–47.

1. What is meant by divergent evolution? Give an example.
2. What is meant by convergent evolution? Give an example.

A Model for Natural Selection

Purpose In each population of living organisms, there are many variations. The variations of some organisms make them better adapted to the environmental conditions than other organisms. Because of natural selection, those organisms that are not as well adapted to the environment tend to have shorter life spans and produce fewer offspring. The purpose of the investigation is to simulate natural selection.

Materials *(per 3 students)* ● 1 large sheet of white construction paper ● 1 container with a lid or cover ● 100 white construction paper circles 2 cm in diameter ● 100 green construction paper circles 2 cm in diameter ● 1 blindfold

Procedure Part A 1. Copy the table on a sheet of paper. Leave a line for each team in your class under class data. **2.** Place the 100 white circles and 100 green circles in the container. Cover the container and shake it vigorously. **3.** Pour the circles onto the sheet of white construction paper. Spread the circles out on the paper so that none of them are touching or overlapping. **4.** Blindfold one team member. The blindfolded team member should pick up as many circles as possible in one minute and place them in the container. The circles must be picked up one at a time. **5.** Count and record the number of white and green circles remaining on the construction paper. These circles represent surviving organisms. **6.** Determine the frequency of white and green surviving organisms by dividing the number of each color organism by the total number of surviving organisms. Then multiply by 100 to find the percentage. Record each team's data in your table. **Part B 1.** Return all of the circles to the container. Repeat procedures 1 to 3 in Part A. **2.** Have one team member stand facing the table or desk upon which the sheet of construction paper has been placed. **Note:** *Do not blindfold the team member.* Have the person pick up as many circles as possible one at a time and place them in the container during a one-minute period. **3.** Repeat procedures 5 and 6 of Part A.

Observations and Conclusions 1. In Part A, which color of circle has the greater frequency of survivors? **2.** Is there much difference between the frequency of white and green organisms? Explain your answer. **3.** In Part B, which color of circle has the greater frequency of survivors? Explain your answer. **4.** If the circles represent two variations of a species, what does the removal of the circles represent? **5.** Which part of the investigation represents random selection? nonrandom or natural selection? Explain your answer. **6.** If the surviving "organisms" in each part produce only offspring of the same color, what would happen to the frequency of each color organism in each part?

	Number of White Organisms	Number of Green Organisms	Total Number of Organisms	Frequency of White Organisms	Frequency of Green Organisms
Team 1					
Team 2					
Class Data					

CHAPTER SUMMARY

Adaptations in Living Things Within a species, there are many variations. Many of these variations are neither helpful nor harmful. However, some variations may help an organism to be better adapted to its environment. The process by which organisms become better suited to a change in environment is called adaptation. The structures or functions of organisms that make them better able to survive in their environment are called adaptations.

Evidence of Evolution Fossils provide evidence that organisms and the surface of the earth have changed during the earth's history. Fossils also indicate that different forms of life have existed during different times of the earth's history. Homologous and vestigial organs, embryological development, and biochemical similarities are also evidence of the relationship of living things.

Theories of Evolution In the early 1800s, Jean Baptiste de Lamarck developed a theory of evolution based on the idea of inner needs and acquired traits. In 1859, Charles Darwin theorized that evolution occurred because all organisms did not have an equal chance to survive and reproduce. He observed that some organisms had variations that helped them to survive. These helpful variations were passed to the next generation. According to Darwin, gradual changes in form and function would accumulate in this way. Eventually, a new species could develop. In 1901, Hugo De Vries theorized that these changes re-

sulted from "mutations." Today, some scientists theorize that new species may result from microevolution and macroevolution.

Processes of Evolution Evolution results from changes in the gene pool of a population. Mutations change gene pools. Mutated genes and normal genes show up in many different combinations in the gametes of sexually reproducing organisms. This increases the variation in a population. If environmental factors favor one variation over another, the gene pool changes. Organisms with the favorable variation have a better chance of surviving and reproducing than others.

If a population is separated through geographic isolation, separate gene pools may develop. As a result of continued variation, environmental changes, and natural selection, the separate populations could become different. If the differences become great, the different groups are defined as separate species. Additional changes in the gene pools of the populations occur as members of the species migrate in and out of the population.

Pathways of Evolution Evolution seems to follow two pathways. Divergent evolution occurs when a number of species evolve from a common ancestor and become more different as they spread out and adapt to different environments. Convergent evolution occurs when organisms with similar characteristics evolve from unrelated or distantly related ancestors.

CHAPTER VOCABULARY

acquired trait	fossil	macroevolution
adaptation	gene pool	microevolution
adaptive shift	genetic drift	migration
analogous organ	half-life	natural selection
convergent evolution	Hardy-Weinberg Law	speciation
divergent evolution	homologous	species
evolution	isolation	vestigial organ

REVIEW of FACTS and CONCEPTS   Answers on page T–47 to T–48.

On a separate sheet of paper, answer each of the following as completely as possible.

1. What is a species? What is meant by variations in a species?

2. Name three kinds of animals. What adaptations do these animals have?

3. How can fossils be used as evidence that the surface, climate, and living things on the earth have changed?

4. What is radioactive decay? Why is it important to the study of fossils and evolution?

5. Why are the flippers of a whale and the arms of a human being considered homologous organs?

6. What evidence could you use to prove that Lamarck's theory of use and disuse is incorrect?

7. According to Darwin's theory of evolution, how does the process of natural selection work?

8. Explain the difference between the role of the environment in Lamarck's theory of evolution and Darwin's theory of evolution.

9. How is microevolution different from macroevolution?

10. What determines the value of a gene mutation? Develop a hypothetical situation that would support your answer.

11. How does genetic recombination increase the variation in a population?

12. Why is variation important to a population in a changing environment? How can you explain the existence of harmful variations in populations of organisms?

13. How does migration cause a change in the gene pool of a population?

14. Describe the role of geographic isolation in the development of new species.

15. What is the difference between convergent evolution and divergent evolution? Give an example of each.

EXTENSIONS and APPLICATIONS   For additional information, see page T–48.

1. Using reference materials in the library, find out how the surface of the earth and climate where you live have changed throughout geologic time. Also, look around your area for any evidence of change. Write a report to summarize your findings.

2. Scientists have proposed several explanations of how dinosaurs became extinct. Prepare a chart that summarizes and compares some of these explanations.

3. Prepare a chart that summarizes the fossil history of a mammal such as the horse, camel, or elephant. Use drawings or pictures to illustrate the changes that fossil evidence indicates have taken place.

4. Observe several different types of birds in your neighborhood. What are their feeding habits? Describe the type of beak each bird has. How is each bird adapted to its particular environment and habitat?

SUGGESTED READINGS

Desmond, A.J., *The Hot-Blooded Dinosaurs*. New York: Dial Press.
    One of the most recent upheavals in the science of paleontology is discussed in this book. The author presents evidence supporting the idea that dinosaurs were warmblooded animals, and not true reptiles.

Koestler, A., *The Case of the Midwife Toad*. New York: Random House.
    This book unravels one of the strangest stories in science. It explains the work of Paul Kammerer, a scientist who claimed to have proved Lamarck's theory of acquired traits.

Moore, R., and the Editors of *Life, Evolution*. New York: Time-Life Books.
    This interesting and descriptive book is filled with many color photographs and paintings that help make evolution and genetics easy to understand.

13 Human History

An artist's conception of Cro-Magnon people painting pictures.

Chapter Objectives *After completing this chapter, you will be able to:*

a ■ List several common features of primates. p. 221
b ■ Explain the differences between human beings and other primates. p. 222
c ■ Describe several early hominids. p. 225
d ■ Compare different theories about the biological history of human beings. p. 225
e ■ Compare the cultures of the Neanderthals and the Cro-Magnons. p. 229

For teaching aids for this chapter, including a chapter overview and teaching strategies, see pages T–48 to T–50. The page number next to each chapter objective refers to the text page where the information needed to fulfill the objective begins.

Within the last century, charred bones, human fossils, tools, and works of art have been discovered in caves or in buried rock layers around the world. These discoveries raise many questions. Who were the people whose remains and works have been discovered? When did they live? How were they different from people of today? The study of **anthropology** attempts to answer such questions. The scientists who study these topics are called *anthropologists.*

Anthropologists learn about people of the past and their culture by studying *artifacts*, objects made by people. They also study present-day primitive people to learn about their ways of life and to draw conclusions about how people may have lived in the past.

Progress in anthropology has led to a better understanding of modern human beings as well as people of the past. Anthropologists have shown that there are many variations among modern and prehistoric human beings. Yet, research also shows that human beings are basically similar in most respects.

Primate Characteristics

The order *Primates* contains more than 200 living species, ranging from primitive insect-eating tree shrews to human beings, the most advanced member of the order. Scientists think that the primates separated into different lines of development during the early *Cenozoic Era* of the earth's history.

Fossil evidence indicates that the primates had an **arboreal** (ahr-BAWR-ē-əl) **heritage.** That is, they lived among trees and in forests. Many of the features of the primates are related to their arboreal life. One characteristic that is common to nearly all primates is hands that are adapted for grasping. On their hands, primates usually have **opposable thumbs.** That is, the thumb is long and flexible enough to touch the tips of each finger. The fingers of primates have flat nails instead of claws.

Well-developed eyes that can see fine detail even in dim light are characteristic of primates. Primates have *stereoscopic vision,* meaning that they can see in three dimensions and can judge depth and distance. They can also distinguish between colors. Unlike other organisms, the eyes of the primates are located on the front of the head, not on the sides. These physical features suit primates for a tree-dwelling life. In fact, most primates, except human beings, live in trees, although many of them also spend much time on the ground.

Primates have similar skeletal features, which enable them to hold their bodies upright either during feeding or while moving. Primates have four types of teeth. These types of teeth are *incisors, canines, premolars,* and *molars.* Each type of tooth is adapted to different functions, such as grinding and tearing. Most primates are **omnivores,** organisms that eat plants and animals.

SECTION REVIEW   Answers on page T-49.

1. What adaptations do primate hands have for grasping?
2. What special adaptations do the eyes of primates have?

You may want to inform your students that other animals are classified as carnivores and herbivores.

Human Characteristics

Human beings, which are members of the family *Hominidae,* or the family of hominids, are classified as primates. However, there are differences between human beings and other primates, such as monkeys, apes, gorillas, and gibbons, which are members of the family *Pongidae* or the family of

Figure 13-1 The gibbon, a member of the primate family, uses its hands for grasping. What other primate characteristics do the hands of this animal have?

Opposable thumbs and flat nails on the fingers

pongids. These are differences in the degree of development of primate features. Several other characteristics also make human beings unique.

Anatomical Characteristics

Human beings can move from place to place in many ways and at different speeds. They can walk, run, jump, swim, and climb. They can carry heavy loads for long distances. No other organism can travel in an upright position for long periods of time or move in the variety of ways that people can.

An upright position gives human beings better use of their sharp, three-dimensional, color vision. The upright position expands their line of vision. This is important because as much as 90% of the information stored in the human brain is picked up through the eyes. Other structural characteristics, involving the thumbs, teeth, jaw, and brain, are also distinctive in people.

POSTURE Several *anatomical*, or structural, adaptations of the human skeleton permit human beings to stand erect. The shape of the foot is adapted to walking upright. The arch of the foot is a unique human feature adapted to support the pressure of the body. The large toe in the human foot is not opposable as it is in most other primates. Instead, the large toe is in line with the other toes and is adapted for walking rather than grasping.

In human beings, the *pelvis*, a combination of bones above the legs, is very wide. When standing upright, this bone structure gives better support to the body's internal organs and upper body mass. The pelvis also permits even distribution of the body's mass onto the legs.

TYPE OF THUMB Being **bipedal,** or able to walk on two limbs, has freed the arms and hands of human beings for other tasks, such as making and using tools. The human thumb is opposable and adapted for refined movements. In addition, the human hand can be rotated. The rotation of the hands and the opposable thumb enable people to grasp and hold a variety of objects in many different ways.

TYPE OF TEETH AND JAWS The teeth and jaws of human beings are different from those of the pongids and other primates. The pongids and other primates have large canine and premolar teeth that are adapted for cutting and slashing. Human teeth are much smaller. The canine teeth of human beings are about the same size as their incisors and are

Highlight

Erect posture, opposable thumbs, bow-shaped jaws with teeth arranged in a curved row, and a highly developed brain are some of the anatomical characteristics of human beings.

At this point, you may want to have your students do the Laboratory Investigation at the end of this chapter.

Figure 13-2 Structural Differences Between Human Beings and Apes

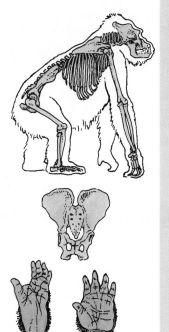

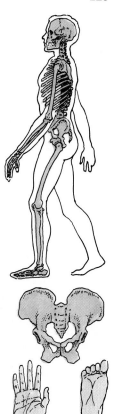

Head: The human head is balanced on the top of the backbone. The ape head hangs from the top of the backbone.

Backbone: The human backbone is S-shaped, providing support, strength, and balance. The ape has a curved, bow-shaped backbone with a straight lower portion.

Pelvis: Human beings have a wide pelvis that supports the body and helps keep the backbone erect. Apes have a long, narrow pelvis that pushes the backbone forward, causing a stooped posture.

Arms and Legs: Human beings have shorter arms than legs. Apes have longer arms than legs, and both are used for support.

Hands: Human beings and apes have opposable thumbs used for grasping. However, the human thumb can be used with the other fingers with greater flexibility.

Feet: Human feet have arches for support. The large toe is parallel to the other toes. The human foot is adapted for walking erect. Ape feet have opposable large toes used for grasping.

used to grip, hold, and tear. Human premolars are small and flat and are used for grinding and crushing.

The jaws of human beings are bow-shaped. The teeth are arranged in a curved row that is widest at the back. The jaws of pongids are rectangular in shape. The teeth are arranged in nearly parallel lines along the sides of the jaw.

Figure 13-3 The arrangement and type of teeth in pongids is different from that in human beings. In pongids, the teeth are found in parallel lines along the sides of the jaws and the canines and premolars are very large. In human beings, the teeth are arranged in a curved row and the canines and premolars are small.

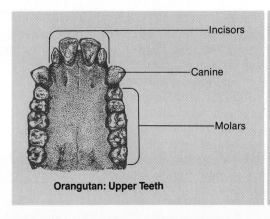

Incisors

Canine

Molars

Orangutan: Upper Teeth

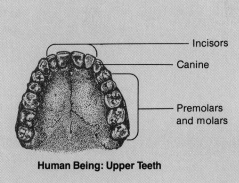

Incisors

Canine

Premolars and molars

Human Being: Upper Teeth

224

Sidelight

The average brain size of a modern human being is about 1500 cubic centimeters.

You may want to review the structure of DNA in Chapter 8.

BRAIN CAPACITY Human beings have very complex, highly developed brains. Much of the difference in intelligence between human beings and other organisms, especially the pongids, is related to the size and complexity of the brain. The internal anatomy of the human brain is responsible for a highly developed memory center and the ability to speak. The human brain gives human beings a level of intelligence that is not matched by any other organism.

Physiological Characteristics

The **physiology,** or bodily processes and functions, of human beings and other primates are very similar. One of the main physiological differences between human beings and other primates is that human beings do not have a definite breeding season and other primates do.

Human beings also develop and age more slowly and have a longer life span than do other primates. Scientists do not know very much about the causes of aging, although they think that it is caused by damage to DNA. The body can repair some damaged DNA, but the rate of repair is not the same in all living things.

Some scientists think that the rate of repair of DNA is directly related to an organism's life span. For example, one species of monkey has a low rate of DNA repair and lives only about 12 years. Human beings have a very high rate of DNA repair and, in most industrialized nations, live about 70 years. The life span of human beings is also influenced by many other factors, such as diet, disease control, and living conditions and habits.

Behavioral Characteristics

The large brain capacity of human beings gives them an enormous ability to learn. Human beings can solve problems, develop ideas, make judgments, and reach decisions. The two classical behavioral characteristics that distinguish human beings from other primates are making and using tools and using symbols to form languages. Recent experiments have shown that chimpanzees can be trained to use tools, but they cannot make them. Chimpanzees can also be trained to use sign language or abstract symbols to communicate to a limited degree with human beings and other chimpanzees. Although communication by sounds is found in other organisms, human beings are the only living things with a complex spoken and written language. They are unique in the degree to which they use language to pass knowledge from one individual to another.

Figure 13-4 Chimpanzees can be trained to use symbols like these to communicate with human beings.

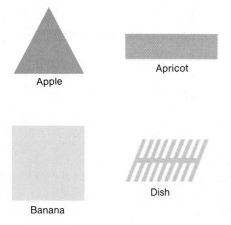

Apple

Apricot

Banana

Dish

SECTION REVIEW Answers on page T–49.

1. What special adaptations permit humans to stand erect?
2. What is meant by "bipedal?"
3. How do human teeth and jaws differ from those of the pongids?
4. What two physiological characteristics are unique to human beings?
5. What are the two classic examples of human behavioral characteristics?

Biological History of Human Beings

In 1859, Charles Darwin published *On the Origin of Species by Means of Natural Selection.* In this book, Darwin presented evidence to support his hypothesis that species change through time by means of natural selection. He

---

CLOSE-UP: *Dr. James Harris*

What do studies of human heredity patterns have to do with the ancient Nubians, a people who have lived in the upper Nile Valley for some 10,000 years? Plenty, according to Dr. James Harris. Harris is a University of Michigan orthodontist who has been X-raying the mummies and skeletal remains of ancient Nubians. Orthodontics is a branch of modern dentistry.

In recent years, the project took Dr. Harris and a team of specialists on a series of trips to Egypt. In Egypt, they gathered new information about the Nubian people, including information about their way of life, diet, and diseases. X-rays revealed that certain physical traits, especially the bone structure of the face and skull, were passed from generation to generation.

The study was of genetic interest because Harris confirmed a theory that the size of the human face has grown smaller over thousands of years. The human jaws of today are smaller than the jaws of ancient Egyptians. However, because teeth have remained relatively the same size, tooth crowding is a problem for most people today.

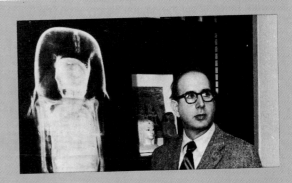

Harris used the concept of "relaxed selection" to explain his findings. According to Harris, the usual selection forces, or natural selection, have been changed by technology. In ancient times, people with crowded teeth usually did not survive because they could not bite and chew their food well. As technology made food easier to chew, people with the genes for crowded teeth did survive. They then passed the genetic trait of crowding to their children. Modern dental techniques are used to correct problems created by crowded teeth.

At this point, you may want to assign to several students the third of the Extensions and Applications at the end of this chapter.

the Leakeys argue that *Homo habilis* lived at the same time as the australopithecines. Therefore, the australopithecines could not have been the ancestors of *H. habilis*.

In 1891, the first fossils of *Homo erectus*, or Java man, were found on the island of Java. Other fossils of *Homo erectus* were found in Peking, China, in 1929. In 1975, Richard Leakey discovered another fossil of *Homo erectus* in Africa. These fossils have been dated from 1.6 million to 500,000 years ago. According to the Leakeys, *Homo erectus* also lived at the same time as the australopithecines.

The skeleton of *Homo erectus* is similar to that of modern *Homo sapiens*. However, *Homo erectus* was shorter than modern *Homo sapiens* and had thicker and heavier bones. The structure of the skull was also different. The forehead was sloped, the jaw was large, and the chin was very small.

Figure 13-7 Throughout human biological development, the shapes of the skulls of homonids have changed.

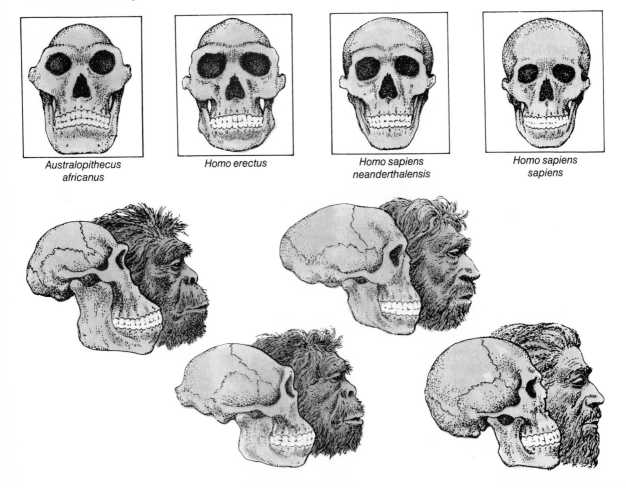

Australopithecus africanus

Homo erectus

Homo sapiens neanderthalensis

Homo sapiens sapiens

THE NEANDERTHALS   Neanderthals lived in Europe and parts of Asia from about 100,000 years ago to 35,000 years ago. They are classified as *Homo sapiens neanderthalensis.* A variety of hominid fossils have been classified in this group. Some Neanderthal fossils look more like those of modern human beings than do others in this grouping. In general, Neanderthals had erect postures. They had heavier and thicker bones than those of modern human beings. Their average height was 150 centimeters. The skulls of Neanderthals were large, with heavy jaws and teeth. Most of the fossils indicate that the Neanderthals were almost chinless. Some fossils have sloped foreheads.

Many stone tools have been found among Neanderthal fossils. As well as using tools, Neanderthals used fire. They hunted many different kinds of animals, such as bison and hairy mammoths. The Neanderthals lived in many different kinds of shelters, including caves. They cared for their old and sick and buried their dead.

THE CRO-MAGNONS   In 1868, fossils that have the same bone structure as modern human beings were discovered in rock layers and other materials that are estimated to be 40,000 years old. The name Cro-Magnon is taken from the cave in southwestern France in which the fossils were found.

Since their discovery, more than 100 Cro-Magnon fossils have been found. These fossils show that the Cro-Magnons, like present-day human beings, had high foreheads, small even teeth, and large brain cavities. The skeletons indicate that the Cro-Magnons were about 173 centimeters tall. Like the Neanderthals and present-day human beings, they are classified as *Homo sapiens.*

The tools, weapons, and other implements found with Cro-Magnon fossils indicate that these people had a complex culture. They made pottery, carved bones, and drew cave paintings. Their tools and weapons indicate that they were good hunters. The Cro-Magnons lived in many different places, and their culture adapted to different climates.

Figure 13-8   Neanderthals made tools and weapons out of stone and wood.

Figure 13-9   Like modern human beings, Cro-Magnons had high foreheads and large brain capacities. They developed various forms of art and produced cave drawings.

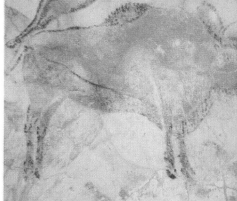

SECTION REVIEW   Answers on page T–49.

1. Describe the skull of *A. africanus.*
2. How do the skulls of the australopithecines differ from the skulls of *Homo habilis*?
3. Describe Johanson and White's fossil of *A. afarensis.*
4. In what respects were the skeletons of early hominids similar to those of modern humans?
5. What are some characteristics of the Cro-Magnon culture?

At this point, you may want to assign to several students the first of the Extensions and Applications at the end of this chapter.

Studying the Hands of Primates

Purpose One of the differences between human beings and other primates is the structure of the hand. The human hand has a totally opposable thumb adapted for refined movements. The purpose of this investigation is to compare the hands of several primates and to examine the usefulness of a totally opposable thumb.

Materials *(per 2 students)* ● Masking tape ● Comb ● Bottle with screw-on cap ● Clock or watch with second indicator

Procedure **1.** Do each of the following activities and have your partner time how long it takes to do each of them. **a.** Remove one shoe. **b.** Put your shoe on again, and tie the lace. **c.** Comb your hair. **d.** Unbutton several buttons and button them again. **e.** Unscrew a bottle cap. **f.** Open a door. **g.** Write your

name and address. **h.** Do four other everyday activities. **2.** Using masking tape, have your partner tape each of your thumbs to its adjacent index finger. **3.** After your thumbs are securely taped, try each of the activities again. Have your partner time how long it takes to do each. If an activity takes longer than 5 minutes, record the word "unsuccessful." **4.** Study the figure, which illustrates the hands of various primates.

Observation and Conclusions **1.** Based on the activities that you tried and timed with your thumbs free and taped down, summarize your conclusions about the movements of your hand and the usefulness of your thumbs. **2.** Study the figure and answer the following questions. **a.** List two features that all of the hands have in common. **b.** List one feature that is unique to each hand. **c.** What traits are different as you compare the hands in order from 1 to 6?

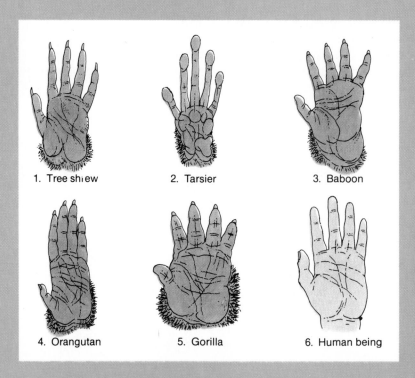

1. Tree shrew   2. Tarsier   3. Baboon

4. Orangutan   5. Gorilla   6. Human being

CHAPTER SUMMARY

Primate Characteristics   The primates are a diverse group of organisms. The basic characteristics of primates are hands that are useful for grasping and that have opposable thumbs and flat nails; stereoscopic vision with eyes on the front of the head; four types of teeth; and the ability to hold the body upright.

Human Characteristics   Human beings have many of the same characteristics as the other primates. Basically, these characteristics are more developed in people than in the other primates. However, several anatomical, physiological, and behavioral characteristics are unique to human beings. Because of the structure of the skeleton, people have an erect posture. They also have completely opposable thumbs, and their hands are adapted for refined movements. Human teeth are smaller than those of most other primates and are arranged in a curved row in a bow-shaped jaw. The most distinctive human characteristic is a complex, highly developed brain.

Physiologically, human beings are similar to the other primates. However, unlike other primates, people do not have a definite breeding season. People have a longer life span than other primates and develop more slowly.

The two classical behavioral characteristics that separate human beings from other primates are making and using tools and using symbols to form a complex spoken and written language.

Biological History of Human Beings   In 1859, Darwin presented evidence for the hypothesis that species had changed through time. Since Darwin's time, many different hominid fossils have been found and used to develop theories about the biological history of humans. Many of the fossils of the various australopithecines, *Homo habilis,* and *Homo erectus* were found in Africa.

The first fossils to be classified as *Homo sapiens,* the genus of modern human beings, were the Neanderthals. The Neanderthals lived between 100,000 and 35,000 years ago. They had a simple culture. Cro-Magnon fossils seem to show the same physical features as do modern humans. The Cro-Magnons, also *Homo sapiens,* lived as long as 40,000 years ago. They developed a complex culture.

CHAPTER VOCABULARY

anthropology	**omnivore**
arboreal heritage	**opposable thumb**
bipedal	**physiology**

REVIEW of FACTS and CONCEPTS   Answers on pages T–49 to T–50.

On a separate sheet of paper, answer each of the following as completely as possible.

1. List the characteristics of primates that are related to their arboreal heritage.
2. What are the major differences that set human beings apart from the other primates, especially the pongids?
3. What makes the human brain unique?
4. What can anthropologists determine from the position of the hole through which a spinal cord enters a skull? What can they determine by studying the teeth of early hominids?
5. What differences between *A. africanus* and *A. robustus* do fossils reveal?
6. Describe the appearance of *Homo habilis.*
7. How do the Leakeys' ideas about the biological history of human beings differ from the ideas of Johanson and White?
8. What were some of the physical characteristics of the Neanderthals? Of the Cro-Magnons?
9. How were the cultures of the Neanderthals and Cro-Magnons alike? Different?

EXTENSIONS and APPLICATIONS   For additional information, see page T–50.

1. Prepare a presentation that shows some objects that represent the culture of where you live. Present objects that would help an anthropologist 10,000 years from now understand the important aspects of your culture.

2. A skull that represented the Piltdown man turned out to be a hoax. Using library resources, prepare a report on this anthropological hoax.

3. Collect several comic strips, advertisements, or other media forms that show early human beings. Develop some general ideas about how early human beings are popularly presented.

4. Use library resources to write a report about the discovery and importance of one of the early hominids. Include scientists' ideas about the culture, intelligence, and so on of these hominids.

SUGGESTED READINGS

Johanson, D., and M. Edey, *Lucy: The Beginnings of Humankind.* New York: Simon and Schuster.
   A personal account by paleoanthropologist Johanson of the discovery of the oldest reasonably complete human skeleton to date.
Leakey, R.E., and R. Lewin, *Origins.* New York: Dutton.
   Written by one of the world's most famous anthropologists, this book traces human history from the early hominids to the beginnings of agriculture and civilization.
Singer, A. (ed.), *Atlas of Man.* New York: St. Martin's Press.
   The development of the many cultures of the world is discussed in this book. A representative group of the different societies of the world is presented.
Tullar, R.M., *The Human Species: Its Nature, Evolution, and Ecology.* New York: McGraw-Hill.
   A thorough discussion of the human species and its place in the history of life on the earth is presented.

Sudden or Gradual Changes in Living Things

Most scientists agree that species change either when mutations occur in genes or, more commonly, when genes recombine during meiosis. Through natural selection, new organisms in the species that are best adapted to the environment survive to pass along the new genes.

Scientists disagree, however, on the rate at which new species develop and on the processes of this development. As theorized by Charles Darwin and other gradualists, new species are the result of many small genetic changes that have taken place over hundreds of millions of years. Such small changes are known as microevolution.

Critics of the gradualist view have proposed a theory in which macroevolution, or the appearance of new species, occurs suddenly. Species are thought to have resulted from sudden or tremendous changes in the environment, which have occurred many times in the earth's past. Organisms that were able to survive in the drastically changed environment tended to be very different from those that had adapted to the earlier environment.

The transitional, or in-between, forms of most organisms are missing from the fossil record. Darwin explained this absence by saying that scientists had not done enough exploring to find the missing fossils. Critics of Darwin's gradualist view see these fossil "gaps" not as the result of insufficient exploration, but as proof of more dramatic jumps in the evolution of species. These critics feel that the new species arose so quickly that there is only a small probability that transitional forms exist in the fossil record.

The fossil record does seem to indicate eras in the earth's past in which the pace of evolution appears to have quickened and new life forms developed at an incredible rate, while others just as suddenly died out. For example, the end of the dinosaur era was also the time of the rise of mammals. The disappearance of the dinosaurs is thought to have occurred because of their inability to adapt to a sudden environmental change, such as the disappearance of their food.

Supporters of sudden evolutionary change feel that without these bursts of evolutionary activity, the higher forms of plants and animals would never have evolved. These scientists find support for their views in the fact that many species that live in a rather unchanging environment, such as the ocean, have shown little change over long stretches of time. Sharks and marine turtles, for example, have kept the same general form for millions of years. Supporters of sudden changes in species feel that these animals would no longer have the same appearance today that they had millions of years ago if new species had been evolving through microevolution all the while.

Viewpoints

1. Gather information on the theories of evolutionary change and debate how each of the theories accounts for, or does not account for, the extinction of dinosaurs over a relatively brief geological time span.

2. Collect recent newspaper and magazine articles concerning the theories of evolutionary change. Using this information, set up a panel discussion in your class in order to compare these theories.

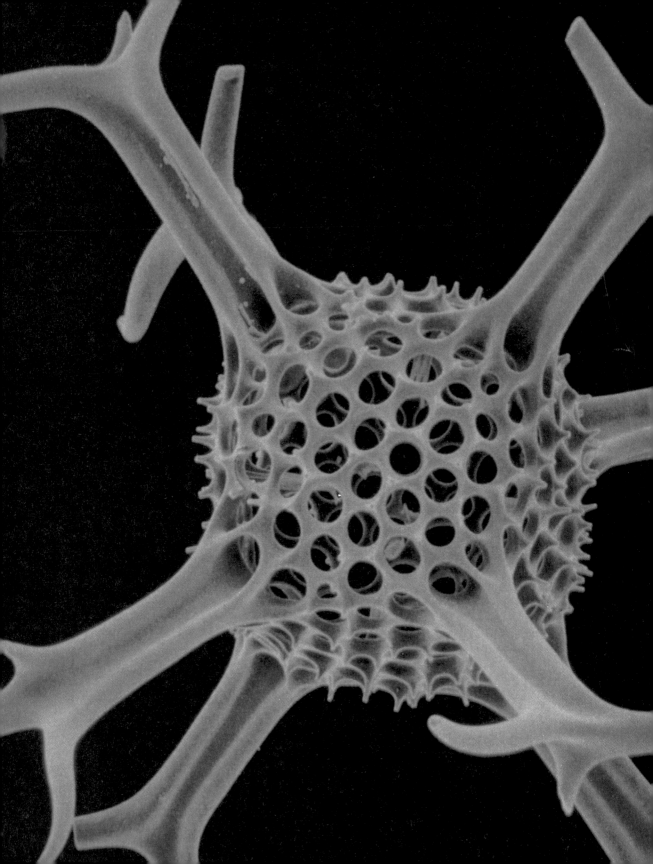

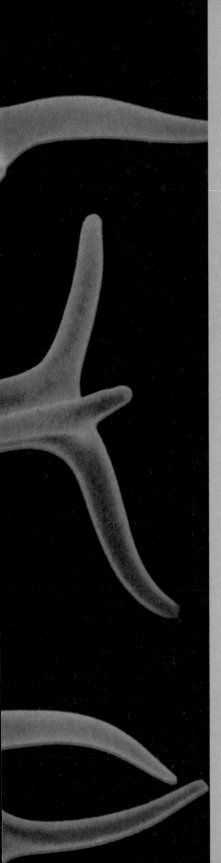

UNIT FOUR

Microbes

For an overview of this unit, including field trip suggestions, a bibliography, and a list of audio-visual materials, see pages T-51 to T-58. You may want to check the Laboratory Investigations in this unit so that materials may be ordered, gathered, or prepared in advance.

Many living things are so small that they cannot be seen with the unaided eye. These microscopic organisms are called microbes. A special branch of biology called microbiology is devoted to the study of these organisms.

Microbes are found everywhere—on your hands, in your body, and on this page. Some microbes are even found in hot springs and in volcanoes! Many microbes are an important part of the environment. Others are used in the preparation of foods and medicines, as well as in various industries. However, some microbes are harmful and cause disease in plants and animals. In this unit, you will discover some of these interesting organisms.

14 Viruses

15 Monerans

16 Protozoans

17 Human Microbial Disease and Immunity

This radolarian shell, magnified 2000 times, was photographed through a scanning electron microscope.

14 Viruses

The tulip-breaking virus caused the stripes on these tulips.

For teaching aids for this chapter, including a chapter overview and teaching strategies, see pages T–51 to T–52. The page number next to each chapter objective refers to the text page where the information needed to fulfill the objective begins.

One of the newest and most interesting fields of study in biology is **virology** (vi-RAHL-ə-jē), the study of **viruses.** Viruses are tiny particles that contain hereditary material, which enables them to reproduce. Some viruses cause the common cold. Other viruses produce colorful patterns on tulips.

Unlike other organisms, viruses cannot carry on any life processes unless they are within a living cell. For this reason, many scientists do not consider viruses to be living organisms. Other scientists think that viruses are living organisms on the level of *molecules*, extremely small particles of matter. If this is correct, viruses are the simplest form of life known.

Viruses are too tiny to be seen with an ordinary light microscope. However, scientists can photograph and study viruses by using the electron microscope and special preparation techniques.

Discovery of Viruses

In 1892, a Russian scientist, Dimitri Iwanowski, was studying a disease of tobacco plants. The disease is called tobacco mosaic because of a pattern of bleached spots that appear on the leaves. Iwanowski discovered that the disease was caused by a virus that was **filterable,** or small enough to pass through filters. The openings in the filter were so small that *bacteria* could not pass through them. Bacteria are unicellular microscopic organisms that were once thought to be the smallest disease-causing agents.

In 1898, the filterability of viruses was also observed by a Dutch scientist, Martinus Beijerinck. Beijerinck discovered that by squeezing the sap from tobacco plants with tobacco mosaic disease onto healthy plants, he could transmit the disease to the healthy plants. Even after he removed all of the bacteria from the sap by filtering it, the disease was still transmitted to the healthy plants. Beijerinck also found that the disease-causing agent was able to reproduce only in a living tobacco plant. Although Beijerinck was not able to identify the agent, he gave it a name. He named it "virus," from the Latin word meaning poison.

In 1935, Wendell M. Stanley, an American scientist, isolated the disease-causing agent and identified it as the *tobacco mosaic virus* (TMV). This was the first virus to be isolated. Since then, scientists have isolated and studied many viruses, enabling scientists to learn a great deal about viral chemistry and structure.

In the last decade, scientists have discovered disease-causing agents called *viroids* (vī-roids), which are simpler than viruses. Viroids consist of a short strand of *ribonucleic acid* (RNA), a substance that transmits hereditary information. Viroids have been identified as the cause of some plant diseases. One type of viroid has destroyed millions of coconut trees in the Philippines.

Figure 14-1 The tobacco mosaic disease causes healthy tobacco plant leaves (*top*) to develop characteristic patterns of light-colored spots (*bottom*).

SECTION REVIEW   Answers on page T–51.

1. What was the first virus to be isolated and identified?
2. What is a viroid?   At this point, you may want to assign to several students the third of the Extensions and Applications at the end of this chapter.

Viral Anatomy

With the invention of the electron microscope, scientists could observe viruses and study their overall size and shape. In addition, scientists have been able to observe the internal structure of viruses.

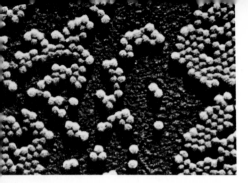

Figure 14-2 A shadow-casting method was used to take this electron micrograph of a T$_2$ virus (72,000X).

At this point, you may want to assign to several students the first of the Extensions and Applications at the end of this chapter.

Special electron microscope techniques are used to study the structure of viruses. One such technique is called **shadow casting,** or *electron-shadow micrography* (mī-KRAHG-rə-fē). A thin layer of metal, such as chromium or gold, is deposited at an angle onto the viruses. This causes the viruses to cast a shadow when observed with an electron microscope. Photographs of the viruses look three-dimensional. Figure 14-2 illustrates shadow casting.

Structure of Viruses

Most viruses are made of a core of hereditary material surrounded by a layer of protein. The layer of protein is called the **capsid** (KAP-sid). The capsid is made up of repeating protein units. Each protein unit is called a **capsomere** (KAPS-ə-mir). Some viruses may also have a *membranous envelope* that surrounds the protein coat. This envelope is made up of fats, proteins, and carbohydrates.

The capsid gives the virus its shape. It protects the core of the virus from physical or chemical damage. The capsid also has special sites where the virus can attach itself to a living cell.

The hereditary material is called the **nucleic acid core.** The hereditary material in a viral core may be either RNA or *DNA* (deoxyribonucleic acid), another substance that carries genetic information. Unlike cells, viruses have only one type of nucleic acid, but not both. All viruses that attack plants contain RNA. Viruses that infect animals may contain either RNA or DNA.

In cells, RNA and DNA have different functions. In viruses, however, their functions are the same. Either DNA or

Highlight

Viruses are made up of a capsid and a nucleic acid core. The nucleic acid core contains either RNA or DNA.

Figure 14-3 The tobacco mosaic virus is made up of a coil of RNA surrounded by a cylindrical coat made up of protein units called capsomeres.

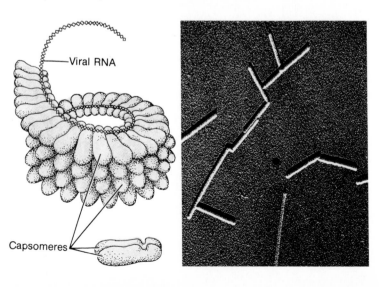

Viral RNA

Capsomeres

RNA is used to code the production of a new viral nucleic acid. DNA or RNA also controls the making of the viral protein coat. The structure of the nucleic acids in viruses may differ from that in cells. In cells, DNA is always a double-stranded molecule and RNA is a single-stranded molecule. In viruses, however, DNA or RNA can be double- or single-stranded.

You may wish to have your students refer to the information on the structure of DNA and RNA in Chapter 8.

Shape and Size

Techniques such as shadow casting have shown that viruses have many different shapes. Some viruses are spherical or oval. Others are long, narrow, and cylindrical. Still others are shaped somewhat like tadpoles. Some examples of viruses are shown in Figure 14-4. Notice how their sizes compare with the size of a yeast cell.

Viruses vary in size from approximately 25 to 250 **nanometers.** A nanometer is equal to one millionth of a millimeter! Some of the smallest viruses are those that cause poliomyelitis and yellow fever. One of the largest viruses is the smallpox virus.

Classifying Viruses

At one time, viruses were grouped in several ways. One classification method was based on the **host,** or organism the virus infected. Viruses were also grouped according to the type of tissues they attacked. Another method of classifying viruses was based on how the virus was transmitted to the host and what disease symptoms were produced. These classification methods often proved unsatisfactory because viruses that were not alike in other respects were grouped together.

Today, a viral classification system generally accepted by biologists is based on structural and chemical composition. The separation of viruses into either RNA or DNA types usually provides the first classification group, known as a *division.* Each division is further subdivided by chemical and structural characteristics particular to the virus being classified. The final subdivisions correspond to genus and species.

SECTION REVIEW
Answers on page T–51.

1. What is a capsid? A capsomere?
2. What unit is used to measure the size of viruses?
3. How were viruses classified in the past?
4. What is the first viral classification grouping used today?

Classification problems are not unique to viruses. You may wish to refer to the information on different taxonomic systems in Chapter 3.

Sidelight

Some viruses are so small that a billion of them, laid end to end, would form a line only one meter long.

Figure 14-4 Viruses vary significantly in size and shape. Viruses at left are compared in size with a yeast cell.

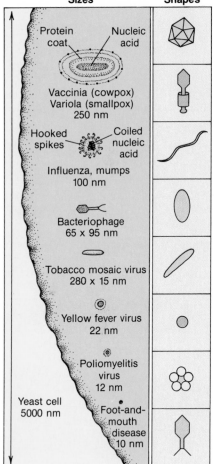

COMPARING VIRUSES

Stress the fact that when outside the cell, viruses do not carry on the functions of living things. For this reason, some scientists do not consider viruses to be living things.

Viral Replication and the Lytic Cycle

Viruses cannot carry out the functions of a living cell. They do not have specialized cell parts, such as a nucleus and cytoplasm. Viruses do not grow, make their own proteins, or generate their own energy. **Replication,** or reproduction, of a virus occurs only inside a living cell, or host cell. Viruses must penetrate a cell and use the ribosomes and enzymes of the cell to produce new virus particles. Ribosomes contain large amounts of the RNA a virus needs for replication.

Scientists have gathered the most complete information concerning viral replication from extensive research on **bacteriophages** (bak-TIR-ē-ə-faj-əz). Bacteriophages, or *phages,* as scientists often refer to them, are viruses that infect bacterial cells. Bacteriophages were first described in 1915. They were more fully studied two years later by Félix d'Herelle, a French scientist, who gave them their name. The name comes from the Greek word *phagein* meaning to eat. Originally, scientists thought that the bacteriophage "ate" the bacterium from within.

Highlight

Viruses can replicate only inside living cells. The process of infection and replication is the lytic cycle. The steps of the lytic cycle are adsorption, host cell penetration, eclipse, formation of new phages, and host cell rupture.

Figure 14-5 The drawing of the bacteriophage shows the structure of a virus that attacks bacterial cells. The photograph is of the same virus.

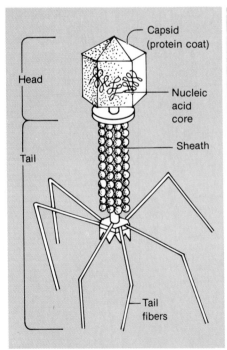

Capsid (protein coat)

Head

Nucleic acid core

Sheath

Tail

Tail fibers

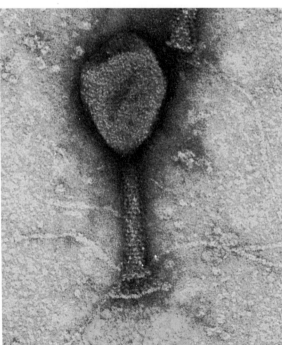

At this point, you may want to have your students do the Laboratory Investigation at the end of this chapter.

241

Bacteriophages have round, oval, or many-sided heads and hollow tails. Usually, the tail has fibers at its tip. Most of the T phages have a head and tail fibers. The letter "T" stands for "type." These phages are referred to as T_1, T_2, T_3, and so on.

Today, scientists have a much better understanding of the process that occurs when a cell is infected by a virus. This process is called the **lytic** (LIT-ik) **cycle.** The time it takes for a complete lytic cycle to occur varies with the virus and the host cell. In order to study the lytic cycle, scientists have observed the infection of bacteria by bacteriophages. The bacteria most often used in studying the lytic cycle are *Escherichia coli* (esh-uh-RIK-ē-uh KŌ-lī), common intestinal bacteria. These bacteria grow rapidly under laboratory conditions, reproducing every 20 to 30 minutes. The lytic cycle is broken down into the following series of steps.

Adsorption   The bacteriophage first attaches itself to a cell by means of its tail fibers. This process of attachment is called **adsorption.** The tail of the bacteriophage contains specific *adsorption sites.* The bacteriophage tail can attach itself to the cell only if the phage's adsorption sites correspond to the *receptor sites* on the surface of the cell. In this way, only certain viruses are able to infect specific bacteria.

Host Cell Penetration   Once adsorption has taken place, an enzyme in the tip of the tail of the bacteriophage makes an opening in the cell wall of the bacterium. The nucleic acid of the bacteriophage moves through the tubelike tail into the opening in the bacterial cell. The contraction of the *sheath,* or outer covering of the tail, helps inject the nucleic acid into the cell. The capsid and tail of the bacteriophage remain outside the cell.

Eclipse   During the third stage of the cycle, the nucleic acid of the bacteriophage seems to disappear inside the bacterium. If the host cell were broken open at this time, no complete viruses could be found. At this stage, the phage is said to be in **eclipse** (ē-KLIPS). During the eclipse stage, the nucleic acid of the bacteriophage causes the cell to form new viral parts, including proteins, viral nucleic acid, and capsomeres.

Formation of New Phages   After the eclipse stage, the viral parts assemble to form complete bacteriophages. This assembly of parts continues for some time after the end of the eclipse period. Usually, 100 to 300 new viruses are formed within a single host bacterium.

At this point, you may want to assign to several students the second of the Extensions and Applications at the end of this chapter.

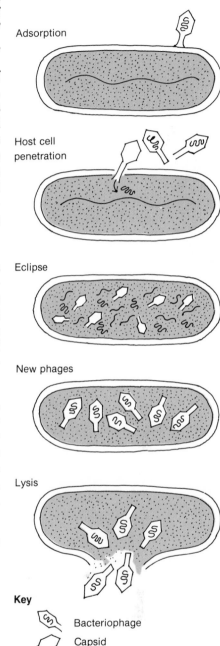

Adsorption

Host cell penetration

Eclipse

New phages

Lysis

Key

🦠 Bacteriophage

Capsid

Bacterial nucleic acid

ᰟ Viral nucleic acid

Figure 14-6   The process that occurs when a bacteriophage infects a cell is called the lytic cycle. The cycle is made up of five basic stages.

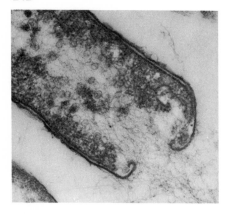

Figure 14-7 The enzymes produced by bacteriophages shown within this bacterial cell have caused the cell to rupture.

Host Cell Rupture At the end of the cycle, **cell lysis** occurs. Cell lysis is the bursting of the host cell. During this step, the concentration of a viral enzyme known as **lysozyme** (LĪ-sə-zīm) steadily increases. This enzyme destroys the chemical bonds of the bacterial cell wall, causing the cell wall to become thinner. Eventually, the cell wall ruptures, releasing new phages that are able to infect other cells. The lytic cycle can begin again. Within several hours, there may be enough phages to destroy billions of bacteria.

SECTION REVIEW Answers on page T–51.

1. What is a bacteriophage?
2. What is the lytic cycle?
3. What is cell lysis?

Viruses and Disease

Viral infections in people are discussed in Chapter 17.

The presence of a harmful virus in a plant or animal host can cause disease. Only specific viruses can infect certain types of cells. For example, a plant virus cannot infect an animal cell. Some viruses attack only certain species of organisms. The virus that causes distemper in dogs is an example of this type. Other viruses may infect a wider variety of organisms. Pox viruses, for example, infect people, cows, and rabbits and cause diseases such as cowpox and chickenpox.

Plant Viruses

A large number of plants are subject to viral infections. Tomato bushy stunt disease and southern bean mosaic disease are examples of viral infections that affect plants. When a plant is invaded by a virus, various tissues of the plant may become discolored or deformed. Plants sometimes develop **tumors,** or collections of cells that grow and multiply more quickly than do the surrounding normal cells. Viral infections do not always kill the affected plant, but they often make it unuseable as food for other organisms. Viruses may also make the plant weak and unable to obtain proper nutrients and water necessary for growth and metabolism.

Figure 14-8 The large tumor at the base of this pine tree was caused by a virus infection.

Animal Viruses

Both *vertebrates*, animals with a backbone, and some *invertebrates*, animals without a backbone, act as hosts to harmful viruses. Sometimes the same virus may travel between vertebrate and invertebrate hosts. The virus may affect only one or the other.

The only invertebrates that have been found to be hosts to viruses are the *arthropods*. Arthropods are animals with jointed legs and outside skeletons, for example mosquitoes, flies, and ticks. A few *arboviruses*, or viruses that are transmitted by arthropods, replicate only in arthropod hosts. Most arboviruses, however, must multiply in the tissues of both vertebrates and arthropods. These viruses multiply in the arthropod without damaging it. The arthropod is said to act as a **vector**, or transmittor, of the virus, to vertebrates such as birds, horses, rabbits, and people.

Sometimes the arthropod vector transmits a virus from one vertebrate host to another vertebrate host. A virus transmitted in this way is called a **dual-host virus**. The

Highlight

Harmful viruses attack plants and animals. Plant viruses do not infect animals, and animal viruses do not infect plants. However, a certain virus may attack many different kinds of animals or plants.

At this point, you may want to assign to several students the fourth of the Extensions and Applications at the end of this chapter.

CAREER: Virologist

A virologist studies viruses and viral diseases. Virologists study how viruses grow and reproduce. They are especially interested in finding out exactly how different viruses attach themselves to cells and then enter the cells. Virologists also study how viruses are able to change host cells so that they make new viral parts.

Much of a virologist's work is done in the laboratory. A virologist designs experiments and testing programs. Supervising laboratory technicians and other workers who carry out experiments and tests is also a responsibility of a virologist.

Recent studies carried out by virologists have produced many uses for viruses, such as in insect control. Virologists are trying to find ways of using certain viruses as natural insecticides to attack insect pests. Virus studies have also helped virologists gain a better understanding of genes and DNA.

One of the most important areas of virology is the study of viral diseases. Virologists study viruses that attack plants and animals. They are interested in finding out how viruses are passed from one host to another and how they affect host cells. Virologists also try to determine what factors limit the growth and spread of viruses. In some cases, they have been able to develop vac-

cines to prevent viral diseases. Virologists have developed several drugs that help fight viral infections as well.

A bachelor's degree is needed to work in virology, although a doctorate in a specialized area is preferred. A good understanding of biochemistry, chemistry, genetics, and mathematics is also necessary.

Some virologists work for colleges, universities, and medical schools. They divide their time between research work and teaching. Other virologists work for government organizations such as health and agricultural departments. Some virologists work for pharmaceutical companies or other private industries.

For further career information, write to American Institute of Biological Sciences, 1401 Wilson Boulevard, Arlington, VA 22209.

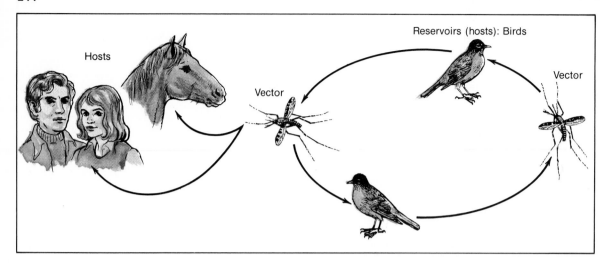

Figure 14-9 Equine encephalitis is caused by a dual-host virus. The virus grows in birds, which are the reservoir hosts. Mosquitoes pick up the virus from birds and transmit it to other birds or to second hosts, which can be people or horses.

Sidelight

In 1885, Louis Pasteur developed the first vaccine for rabies. Pasteur showed that the "germ" for rabies could be attenuated, or made less deadly, by passing it through different species of animals. The first person to be given Pasteur's rabies vaccine was Joseph Meister, a young boy who had been bitten by a dog that had rabies. The boy did not develop the disease.

equine encephalitis virus is an example of a dual-host virus. This virus is one of many that can cause encephalitis in people and in horses. Each type is transmitted by a particular species of mosquito. Generally, the virus is not transmitted to the mosquito when it bites people or horses. The major **viral reservoir,** or source of the virus, is birds. The mosquito becomes infected while taking blood from a bird carrying the virus. The virus replicates in the tissues of the mosquito and can then be transmitted back to a bird, or to a person, or to a horse. The virus then replicates in the internal organs of the infected vertebrate, eventually reaching the central nervous system and causing damage to the nervous system or possibly death.

Many types of vertebrates are hosts for viruses. A few species of viruses attack *coldblooded animals.* Coldblooded animals have a body temperature that changes with the temperature of the environment. Viruses cause diseases such as cancer in leopard frogs and blood poisoning in rainbow trout. *Warmblooded animals* are also attacked by viruses. Warmblooded animals have a relatively constant body temperature. Two viral diseases found in warmblooded animals are *rabies* and *foot-and-mouth disease.* Rabies can infect all kinds of mammals and, in some cases, birds. Domestic mammals such as dogs, cats, and cattle are particularly susceptible to this infection. Foot-and-mouth disease affects cattle, sheep, and pigs.

SECTION REVIEW   Answers on page T–51.

1. What may happen when a plant is infected with a virus?
2. What is a vector? A viral reservoir?
3. List three viral diseases found in animals.

Constructing a Bacteriophage Model

Purpose A bacteriophage is a virus that attacks bacteria. The purpose of this investigation is to construct a model of a bacteriophage and to study its parts.

Materials *(per student)* ● ¼ × 1½-inch round-headed stove bolt or machine screw ● ¼-inch nut ● ¼-inch acorn nut ● ⁵⁄₁₆-inch flat metal washer ● 2 ¼-inch flat metal washers ● 4 8-cm lengths of floral wire ● needle-nose pliers ● ruler ● 15-cm-long pipe cleaner ● screwdriver

Procedure **1.** With the stove bolt head down, slip a ¼-inch washer onto the bolt. **2.** Bend each piece of wire about 5 mm from one end to form a small hook. Secure the hooked end of each piece of wire tightly around the ⁵⁄₁₆-inch washer in the positions shown in the figure. **3.** Place the ⁵⁄₁₆-inch flat washer with the attached wires over the bolt. The short, hooked ends of the wires should face away from the head of the stove bolt. **4.** Place the other ¼-inch flat washer on top of the washer with the wires. **5.** Screw the ¼-inch nut onto the bolt and tighten it. **Note:** *Be sure that the wires remain at right angles to each other as the nut is tightened.* **6.** Coil the pipe cleaner around the remaining length of the bolt. **7.** Place the acorn nut on the end of the bolt and tighten it against the coiled pipe cleaner. **8.** Bend each length of wire in half to form a standing model of a bacteriophage.

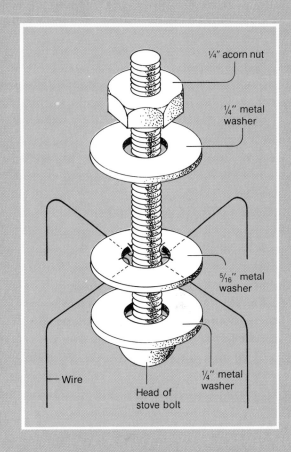

¼″ acorn nut

¼″ metal washer

⁵⁄₁₆″ metal washer

¼″ metal washer

Wire

Head of stove bolt

Observations and Conclusions **1.** Compare your model of a bacteriophage with Figure 14-5 on page 240. Make a drawing of your model. Label the parts of your drawing with the names of corresponding bacteriophage parts. **2.** Which part of your model would contain the nucleic acid of the bacteriophage?

3. Which part of your model would represent the sheath of a T₄ phage? **4.** What structures on your model would the phage use to attach itself to a bacterial cell?

CHAPTER SUMMARY

Discovery of Viruses   The filterability of tobacco mosaic virus was observed by Dimitri Iwanowski and Martinus Beijerinck. Beijerinck discovered that the disease could be transmitted from diseased to healthy tobacco plants. In 1935, Wendell M. Stanley isolated and identified the tobacco mosaic virus. This was the first virus to be isolated.

Viral Anatomy   A virus is a tiny particle that contains a core of either DNA or RNA surrounded by a capsid. Viruses cannot carry out any life processes unless they are within a host cell. Viruses have many different shapes and vary in size from 25 to 250 nanometers. Viruses have been classified according to the host they infect, the type of tissues they attack, and the way the virus was transmitted to the host and what disease symptoms were produced. Today, viruses are classified according to structural and chemical composition.

Viral Replication and the Lytic Cycle   Viral replication occurs only when a virus comes into direct contact with a living cell. Bacteriophages, or viruses that attack bacteria, are usually used to study viral replication. The process of infection and destruction of the host bacterial cell by a bacteriophage is called the lytic cycle. The cycle begins when a bacteriophage attaches itself to a bacterium and ends with the destruction of the host cell.

Viruses and Disease   Both plants and animals are subject to diseases caused by viral infections. Viruses requiring two hosts are called dual-host viruses. The equine encephalitis virus is a dual-host virus.

CHAPTER VOCABULARY

adsorption	filterability	shadow casting
bacteriophage	host	tumor
capsid	lysozyme	vector
capsomere	lytic cycle	viral reservoir
cell lysis	nanometer	virology
dual-host virus	nucleic acid core	virus
eclipse	replication	

REVIEW of FACTS and CONCEPTS   Answers on page T–52.

On a separate sheet of paper, answer each of the following as completely as possible.

1. What is the study of viruses called?
2. What were the contributions of Dimitri Iwanowski and Martinus Beijerinck to viral studies?
3. What is shadow casting?
4. Name the structures of a virus. Give the function of each part.
5. Explain the differences between viruses and cells.
6. How are viruses classified today?
7. Describe the structure of a bacteriophage.
8. Name and briefly explain the five stages in the lytic cycle of a bacteriophage.
9. What is a dual-host virus?

EXTENSIONS and APPLICATIONS   For additional information, see page T–52.

1. Using library materials, find more information on how the electron microscope has contributed to the study of viruses. Prepare a written report.
2. Construct a model of the lytic cycle of a virus. Cut out five large ovals from black construction paper to represent bacterial cells. Next, cut out some tadpole-shaped phages from construction paper of another color. Use coiled pipe cleaners as tha viral nucleic acids. Mount the models on posterboard with glue in the proper order. Label each

stage. Include labels for each structure. Compare your model of the lytic cycle with Figure 14-6 on page 241.

3. Find more information on the experiments of Martinus Beijerinck and Wendell Stanley. How did their experiments aid in the development of virology?

4. Make a survey of local veterinarians to find out more about viral diseases that affect household pets. Summarize your survey in a written report.

SUGGESTED READINGS

Curtis, H., *The Viruses*. New York: The Natural History Press.
    This book discusses the simplest of microbes, the viruses. It begins with the history of their discovery and then explains their structure, reproduction, and control.
Locke, D.M., *Viruses: The Smallest Enemy*. New York: Crown.
    This comprehensive summary of viruses also includes recent research on gene manipulation in viruses.
Williams, G., *Virus Hunters*. New York: Knopf.
    This book discusses the history of the study of viruses, with special emphasis on how scientists have developed ways to stop the spread of the smallpox and polio viruses.

15 Monerans

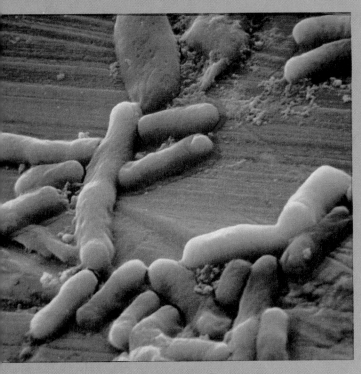

The bacterium Clostridium perfringens *causes food poisoning.*

Chapter Objectives *After completing this chapter, you will be able to:*

a ■ Explain why bacteria are important to the environment and to people. p. 248

b ■ List and describe the three basic shapes of bacteria. p. 250

c ■ Describe the structure and size of a bacterial cell. p. 249

d ■ Explain the difference between autotrophic and heterotrophic bacteria. p. 252

e ■ Explain respiration in different types of bacteria. p. 253

f ■ Describe some ways to slow down or stop bacterial growth. p. 254

g ■ Describe reproduction and methods of DNA transfer in bacteria. p. 254

h ■ Describe the structure of blue-green algae. p. 258

For teaching aids for this chapter, including a chapter overview and teaching strategies, see pages T–52 to T–54. The page number next to each chapter objective refers to the text page where the information needed to fulfill the objective begins.

Life on earth would be impossible without the presence of two groups of microscopic organisms. These two groups of organisms are the **bacteria** and **cyanophytes,** or blue-green algae. They are members of the kingdom *Monera.*

Monerans can be found almost everywhere on the earth. Not only are monerans so numerous and so widespread, they have also been around for a long time. Both the bacteria and blue-green algae appear in the fossil record long before any other kind of organism. In fact, scientists have found evidence of bacteria in rocks over 3.5 billion years old! Blue-green algae are somewhat younger, only about 2.5 billion years old.

Substances such as carbon dioxide, which is needed by green plants to make food, would eventually be used up if bacteria did not recycle them. All living things depend upon plants either directly or indirectly for food and energy. Therefore, all living things would eventually die if it were not for bacteria.

Characteristics of Bacteria

Bacteria are among the simplest forms of living things. They are one-celled **prokaryotic** (PRŌ-kar-ē-ah-tik) organisms. A prokaryotic cell does not have a nuclear membrane surrounding its nuclear material. Instead, the nuclear material is spread throughout the cell. Prokaryotes also contain only a few *organelles,* or specialized cell structures.

Size of Bacteria

Under the highest power of most light microscopes, about 1000X, the general shape of some bacteria can be seen. Biologists use electron microscopes to view the internal structures of bacteria. Electron microscopes can magnify an object more than 100,000 times.

Bacteria are measured in units called *micrometers* (MĪ-krōmē-tərs), or *microns* (μ). One micrometer is equal to one-thousandth of a millimeter. Most bacteria vary in width from 0.1 micrometer to more than 2 micrometers. They vary in length from 0.1 micrometer to more than 5 micrometers. Some bacteria, such as the *rickettsia* (ri-KET-sē-ah), are as small as some of the largest viruses.

Figure 15–1 Bacteria can be classified according to their shape and the kinds of groups they form.

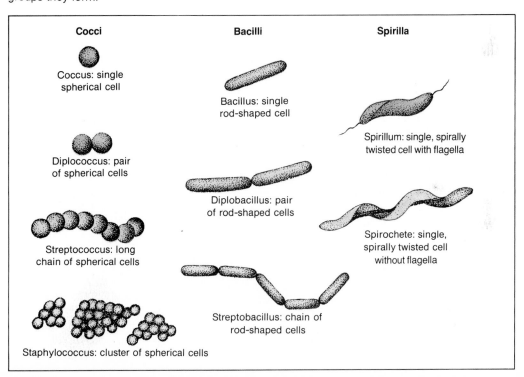

Cocci

Coccus: single spherical cell

Diplococcus: pair of spherical cells

Streptococcus: long chain of spherical cells

Staphylococcus: cluster of spherical cells

Bacilli

Bacillus: single rod-shaped cell

Diplobacillus: pair of rod-shaped cells

Streptobacillus: chain of rod-shaped cells

Spirilla

Spirillum: single, spirally twisted cell with flagella

Spirochete: single, spirally twisted cell without flagella

Bacteria are classified by shape. The shapes are spherical (cocci), rod (bacilli), and spiral (spirilla).

Classification of Bacteria

About 2000 bacterial species have been identified and classified. In the five-kingdom classification system, all bacteria are classified in the kingdom *Monera*. Traditionally, bacteria are further classified according to their shapes. Spherical bacteria are called **cocci** (KAHK-sī; singular: coccus). Rod-shaped bacteria are called **bacilli** (bə-SIL-ī; singular: bacillus). Spiral-shaped bacteria are called **spirilla** (spī-RIL-ə; singular: spirillum).

Bacteriologists also describe bacteria by using different prefixes. These prefixes are used with the names for the basic shapes. The prefixes are *diplo-*, meaning two, *staphylo-*, meaning cluster, and *strepto-*, meaning chain. These prefixes reflect the way bacterial cells group. Figure 15-1 on page 249 illustrates these groupings.

Today, bacteriologists use other factors in identifying and classifying bacteria. These factors include size, staining properties, conditions needed for growth, and appearance of *colonies*. A colony is a large group of bacteria appearing on a culture medium. The colony arises from a single bacterium.

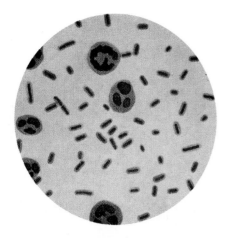

Figure 15-2 These pneumonia-causing bacteria (small rods) are surrounded by a capsule. The large objects are white blood cells. What is the function of the capsule?

The capsule protects the baterial cell from viral infections, environmental changes, and various chemicals.

Figure 15-3 Typical Structure of a Bacterium. What is the importance of ribosomes?

Ribosomes are involved in the manufacture of proteins.

Structure of Bacteria

The outermost boundary of a bacterial cell is the *cell wall*. The cell wall maintains the shape of the bacterium. In most bacteria, the cell wall is very rigid and strong. Other bacteria have a less rigid wall, and some bacteria, called *mycoplasmas*, do not have a cell wall at all and can change their shape.

Many bacteria produce a substance or coating on the outside of the cell wall. If the coating has a definite boundary, it is called a **capsule.** A coating that is more diffuse and

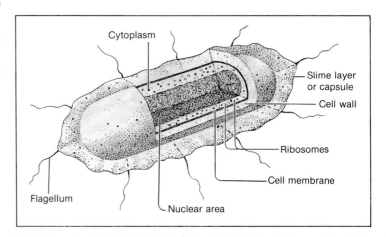

with no boundary is called a **slime layer.** Bacteriologists think that these coatings protect the bacteria against viral infections, changes in the environment, and the natural body defenses of organisms that the bacteria invade.

All bacteria have a *cell membrane* on the inner surface of the cell wall. The main function of the cell membrane is to control the substances that enter and leave the bacteria. The cell membrane surrounds the cytoplasm of bacteria.

The cytoplasm of bacteria is about 80% water and contains many *ribosomes.* The ribosomes are involved in the manufacture of proteins. Other structures found in the cytoplasm include small *vacuoles* that store water and **granules** that store food.

A nuclear area is also present in the cytoplasm. In some bacteria, the DNA in the nuclear area is located on a very long single chromosome. In other bacteria, the nuclear area is a mass of DNA. The DNA in some bacteria may also occur in small, separate segments called **plasmids.**

Movement of Bacteria

Many types of bacteria are **motile,** or capable of moving. Other types are incapable of moving, and are said to be *non-motile.* Some motile types of bacteria have long, thin, hair-like structures called **flagella.** By rotating, the flagella move the bacterial cell. Some bacteria have a single flagellum, whereas others have a band of flagella on either end of the cell. Flagella completely cover the surface of some bacteria. The spiral, or coiled, bacteria called **spirochetes** (SPĪ-rə-kēts) move without flagella. Spirochetes move by rotating with a spiral, or corkscrew, motion.

SECTION REVIEW   Answers on page T–53.

1. Under what power of the microscope can the general shape of some bacteria be seen?
2. What three shapes do bacteria have?
3. What is the function of the bacterial cell wall?
4. What are granules and plasmids?
5. How do spirochetes move?

Life Functions in Bacteria

All living things must carry out functions that are necessary to their survival. Even though bacterial cells have a very simple structure, they perform many functions.

At this point, you may want to assign to the class the third of the Extensions and Applications at the end of this chapter.

Figure 15–4 Some bacteria move by the action of flagella *(top).* Others move by rotating like a corkscrew *(bottom).*

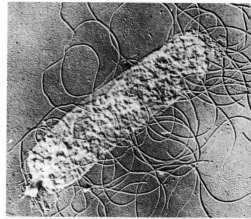

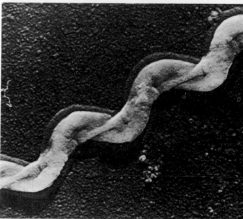

Nutrition and Digestion in Bacteria

Some bacteria are **autotrophs** (AWT-ə-trahfs). That is, they make their own food from inorganic substances. However, most bacteria are **heterotrophs** (HET-ər-ə-trahfs) and must obtain organic matter from their environment for food.

Autotrophic bacteria need water, carbon dioxide, nitrogen, and other substances for cell growth and reproduction. Some autotrophs, such as green and purple bacteria, contain chlorophyll and use the sun's energy to make food. These bacteria are called *photosynthetic autotrophs*. Other autotrophs make their own food by using energy from chemical reactions involving sulfur, iron, and nitrogen. This process is called **chemosynthesis** (kem-ō-SIN-thə-sis). These types of bacteria are called *chemosynthetic autotrophs*.

Review with your students the meaning of photosynthetic autotrophs, chemosynthetic autotrophs, saprophytic heterotrophs, and parasitic heterotrophs.

CAREER: Bacteriologist

The type of medication used to treat a bacterial infection is often determined by the work of a bacteriologist. A sample of the bacteria is taken from the infected organism and placed in a culture. Bacterial cultures are grown in the presence of several kinds of antibiotics to find out which slows or stops the growth of the bacteria.

Other bacteriologists are involved in research. They usually specialize in plant, animal, or human bacterial diseases. They study how diseases are transmitted, how the host is affected, and how the disease can be controlled. Some bacteriologists limit their research to bacteria found in the soil. Still other bacteriologists research the effects of bacteria on the production and preservation of foods.

One of the newest areas of bacteriological research is gene splicing, or recombinant DNA technology. In this area of research, genes from one organism are put into the DNA of a different species of bacteria. For example, one experiment that has been done is to place the human gene for insulin production into a common bacterium. The bacterium then is able to make human insulin. Bacteriologists are hoping that these studies will be helpful to people who have diabetes and need insulin.

A bachelor's degree is needed to begin work as a bacteriologist. However, an advanced degree in a particular area of bacteriology is preferred.

Many bacteriologists work in various industries, such as the dairy, pharmaceutical, and food industries. Some bacteriologists work in hospital laboratories and for government health agencies. Other bacteriologists are employed by colleges and universities where they combine teaching and research.

For further career information, write to American Society of Microbiology, 1913 I Street, N.W., Washington, DC 20006.

Heterotrophic bacteria feed on food molecules made by other organisms. Enzymes are secreted through the cell membrane by the bacterial cell. These enzymes break down, or digest, the food molecules outside the cell. The digested smaller molecules can then pass into the cell. The rotting of fruit is the effect of digestion by bacterial enzymes.

Some heterotrophic bacteria are **saprophytes** (SAP-rə-fīts). That is, they feed on dead organic matter. Many of these bacteria live in the intestines of human beings and other organisms and feed on undigested food material in the organisms. Other saprophytes live in the soil and break down the remains of dead organisms.

Some heterotrophic bacteria feed on other living things. These bacteria are called **parasites.** Some parasitic bacteria are capable of causing disease. The bacterialike organisms called *rickettsia,* for example, cause diseases such as Rocky Mountain spotted fever and Q fever.

Respiration in Bacteria

During *respiration,* food molecules are broken down to release energy that is necessary for the bacterial cell to carry out life functions. When cells use oxygen to break down substances, the process is called *aerobic* (er-ō-bik) *respiration.* When oxygen is not used, the process is called *anaerobic* (an-er-ō-bik) *respiration.* Bacteria differ in their need for oxygen during respiration.

OBLIGATE ANAEROBES   Bacteria that undergo anaerobic respiration and cannot live in the presence of oxygen are called **obligate anaerobes.** Some obligate anaerobes use nitrates, sulfates, or carbon dioxide in place of oxygen. Others chemically break down food molecules into an alcohol or an acid by a process called *fermentation.* One of the best-known obligate anaerobes is *Clostridium botulinum,* which causes *botulism,* a very serious kind of food poisoning.

OBLIGATE AEROBES   Bacteria that need and use oxygen to undergo respiration are called **obligate aerobes.** These bacteria can produce 19 times more energy than obligate anaerobes. Aerobic bacteria are found in environments that have a great deal of oxygen. They are often found in the air, in well-aerated water and soil, and on the surface of objects, including the human body. A common nonharmful aerobe found on the human skin is *Staphylococcus epidermidis.*

FACULTATIVE BACTERIA   Bacteria that can live with or without oxygen are called **facultative bacteria.** Facultative

Sidelight

The bacterium that causes anthrax in human beings and animals was first observed in 1850, but it was not until 1876 that it was found to cause anthrax. Soon after, Louis Pasteur discovered that if he heated these bacteria, he destroyed their ability to cause anthrax. Yet he found that the heat-killed bacteria were still capable of bringing about an immune response in animals. In 1881, Pasteur inoculated some sheep with heat-killed anthrax bacteria. Another group of sheep were not inoculated. After a time, Pasteur exposed all the sheep to live anthrax bacteria. Only the sheep that previously had been inoculated with the heat-killed bacteria lived. They had become immune to the disease.

Highlight

Obligate aerobes require oxygen. Obligate anaerobes require the absence of oxygen. Facultative bacteria can live with or without oxygen.

bacteria use oxygen or other substances to carry out respiration or fermentation. They have the ability to use either form of respiration depending on the presence or absence of oxygen. The common intestinal bacterium *E. coli* is an example of a facultative bacterium.

Bacterial Growth

Most often, *bacterial growth* refers to an increase in the number of bacterial cells in a colony. Bacterial growth can also refer to the increase in size of a single bacterium. In order for either type of growth to occur, specific nutritional and physical conditions are needed by different types of bacteria.

All bacteria need an adequate food and water supply. Obligate anaerobic bacteria must live in an oxygen-free environment. Obligate aerobic bacteria need oxygen. Many environmental factors affect the growth of bacteria.

Temperature Most bacteria are able to live only within a certain temperature range. Some bacteria grow better at moderately low temperatures. Other bacteria grow better at moderately high temperatures. However, most bacteria grow best within a range of 27 °C to 38 °C. Most bacterial growth can be slowed down by **refrigeration** and can be stopped by freezing. Heating above the boiling point of water also destroys most bacteria.

Moisture If their environment is kept dry for long periods of time, bacteria become inactive and do not grow. Many foods are preserved by drying.

Exposure to Sunlight Bacterial growth slows down or stops in direct sunlight. The sun's heat tends to dry out the bacteria. The sun's ultraviolet rays destroy most bacteria by causing harmful mutations in their DNA.

Chemicals Certain chemicals destroy the bacterial cell membrane or the slime layer or the capsule. They may also directly disrupt the life functions of bacteria.

Reproduction in Bacteria

Bacteria usually reproduce asexually by a process called **binary fission.** A single bacterium undergoing binary fission usually grows to twice its size and then splits in two. Each new bacterial cell receives a full amount of cytoplasm and genetic material.

Under ideal growth conditions, bacteria can double their size and divide very quickly. As a result, a colony grows at an

---

Sidelight

In human beings, one of the body's defenses against bacterial infection is fever. A high body temperature kills certain infectious bacteria.

At this point, you may want to have your students do the Laboratory Investigation at the end of this chapter.

amazing rate. If a bacterium reproduces every 20 minutes, a colony made up of more than 2 million bacteria could be produced from a single cell in about 7 hours. In practice, however, the reproduction rate slows down as the colony grows. Less food becomes available, while the accumulation of wastes usually makes the environment less favorable to growth and reproduction.

Spore Formation

Most kinds of bacteria die and break apart if their food supply is used up or their environment becomes unfavorable. However, during unfavorable conditions some bacteria form **endospores,** or small, spherical structures, in their cytoplasm. When the bacterium breaks apart, the endospore is released. An endospore has a thick outer coat that protects the DNA and other structures that are present in its core.

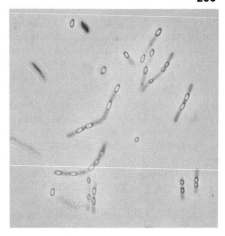

Figure 15–5 A bacillus forms endospores that enable it to survive unfavorable environmental conditions.

Endospores are *dormant,* or inactive. They do not carry out any life functions and can survive extreme environmental conditions, such as high temperatures and harmful chemicals. When endospores are in a favorable environment, they develop into active bacterial cells. The development of bacterial endospores is not a form of reproduction. Bacterial endospores only enable bacteria to survive unfavorable changes in their environment. Endospores have been known to survive in the dormant state for 50 years or more.

DNA Transfer in Bacteria

In some cases, the genetic material, or DNA, of one bacterium can be transferred to another bacterium. This transfer process is called *genetic recombination.* DNA transfer is not a method of reproduction because the number of organisms in the population does not increase. However, the DNA transfer increases the variation among species of bacteria. Variation helps species survive changes in the environment.

Highlight

Bacteria reproduce by binary fission. During unfavorable conditions, some types of bacteria form endospores.

Emphasize to your students the adaptive significance of DNA transfer in bacteria.

CONJUGATION   One way in which DNA is transferred is by **conjugation.** During conjugation, a bridge of cytoplasm forms between two bacteria, and plasmids, or small segments of DNA, are transferred. The plasmids are also called *F factors* or *fertility factors.*

Conjugation takes place only in certain species of bacteria. The species must contain both bacteria that have plasmids, F^+ *bacteria*, and bacteria that do not have plasmids, F^- *bacteria.* During conjugation, an F^+ bacterium transfers a plasmid to the F^- bacterium. After transfer of the F^+ factor, the F^- bacterium is changed to an F^+ bacterium because

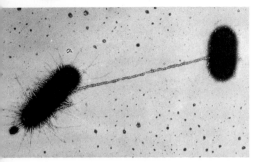

it now contains a plasmid that it can pass to its offspring. An entire population of F⁻ bacteria can rapidly be changed into F⁺ organisms. This can be especially significant if the plasmid provides drug resistance to a bacterium. For example, a population of bacteria normally sensitive to penicillin may become resistant to the antibiotic.

TRANSFORMATION In the process of **transformation,** part of the DNA from a dead or broken apart bacterium is taken in by a live bacterium. In the laboratory, scientists can remove a segment of DNA from a dead bacterium and insert it in a live bacterium. Transformation occurs only if the DNA segment adheres to the cell wall, enters the cell, and joins with the nuclear material of the cell.

TRANSDUCTION During **transduction,** a virus transfers DNA from one bacterium to another. The virus first infects a bacterium and destroys it. When the bacterium breaks and the virus is released, it may carry a piece of the bacterium's DNA. If the virus goes on to attack another bacterium, the piece of DNA is transferred to the new bacterium.

SECTION REVIEW   Answers on page T–53.

1. How do photosynthetic bacteria obtain food?
2. What is the difference between a saprophytic bacterium and a parasitic bacterium?
3. Briefly explain aerobic and anaerobic respiration. Give examples of bacteria that use each type of respiration.
4. What are the ideal growth conditions for a bacterium?
5. By what process do bacteria reproduce?
6. What is the difference between an F⁺ and an F⁻ bacterium?

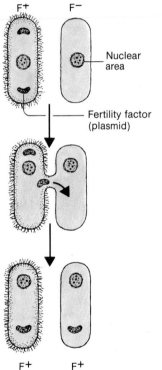

Figure 15–6 During conjugation, a fertility factor, or plasmid, is transferred by a bridge of cytoplasm from the F⁺ bacterium to the F⁻ bacterium. In this case, the F⁺ bacterium has hairlike projections.

You may want to mention certain diseases caused by bacteria, such as tuberculosis, tetanus, bubonic plague, diphtheria, and whooping cough.

Importance of Bacteria

Bacteria are found almost everywhere in the environment. Some bacteria are harmful and can spoil food, contaminate water, and cause disease. Some bacteria, however, are useful to people. These bacteria are used in processing food, in controlling disease, in tanning leather, and in agriculture.

Food industry Many food products, especially dairy products, are produced with the help of bacteria. Bacteria are needed to make cheeses, butter, yogurt, and sour cream. When cheeses are made, bacteria from a *starter culture* are added to milk. The bacteria change *lactose,* or milk sugar, into *lactic acid.* The lactic acid

causes milk solids to come together in curds. Different species of bacteria are added to the curds to form different cheese flavors and textures. Other food products in which bacteria are used include pickles and olives.

Figure 15–7 Bacteria are used to curdle milk in the production of cheese.

Medicine Some bacteria are used to fight the diseases that they cause. Biologists can prepare *vaccines* from killed or weakened strains of these bacteria. When these vaccines are injected into an organism, the organism can develop a resistance to an infection of the same bacteria.

Other uses of bacteria in medicine involve transformation techniques. Using these techniques, biologists have made certain bacteria into factories for the production of vital human chemicals, such as *insulin*. Insulin is a hormone that controls the rate at which the human body breaks down sugar. Its absence or shortage causes a disease called diabetes.

Leather tanning Some species of bacteria are used to tan leather. Tanning is a process used to change animal hides into leather. Animal hides are soaked in solutions that contain these bacteria. The bacteria secrete substances that soften the hide so that it can be used to make leather goods.

Figure 15–8 Nitrogen-fixing bacteria in lumpy root nodules convert free nitrogen to nitrogen compounds needed by plants for growth.

Agriculture Most living things need nitrogen to make proteins. About 78% of the air is made up of free nitrogen. However, most living things can use only nitrogen that is in the form of a compound. Some bacteria, called *nitrogen-fixing bacteria*, make nitrogen compounds from free nitrogen. Nitrogen compounds can be used by other organisms, such as plants. The nitrogen-fixing bacteria also replenish nitrogen compounds in soil.

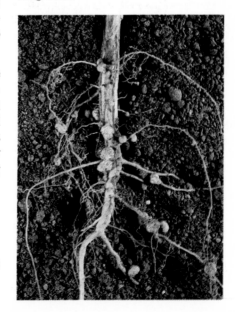

Explain to your students the importance of nitrogen-fixing bacteria in the nitrogen cycle.

SECTION REVIEW   Answers on page T–53.

1. What are three ways in which bacteria are harmful?
2. What change caused by bacteria is important to cheese making?
3. Why are nitrogen-fixing bacteria important?

Cyanophytes

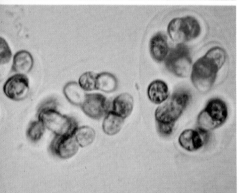

Courtesy Carolina Biological Supply Company

Figure 15–9 *Oscillatoria* (*top*) and *Gloecapsa* (*bottom*) are examples of blue-green filamentous algae.

Cyanophytes, or blue-green algae, belong to the phylum of *Monera* called *Cyanophyta* (sī-ə-NAH-fə-tə). The phylum name is derived from the name of the blue pigment *phycocyanin* (fīk-ō-SĪ-ə-nin) that these algae contain. Some blue-green algae also have a red pigment. One species of these organisms lives in the Red Sea, giving the sea its name.

Like bacteria, blue-green algae are *prokaryotes* (PRŌ-kar-ē-ōts). Unlike bacteria, blue-green algae contain chlorophyll, which enables these organisms to perform photosynthesis.

Most blue-green algae are *filamentous*. Their cells look like a string of beads surrounded by a jellylike sheath. Some examples of filamentous algae are *Gloeocapsa* (glē-ō-KAP-sə) and *Oscillatoria* (ah-səh-luh-TOR-ē-ə), shown in Figure 15-9. *Gloeocapsa* can exist as an individual cell or a group of cells. When seen under a microscope, *Oscillatoria* look like tiny green worms. The name *Oscillatoria* refers to the way these algae move with a swinging, or oscillating, motion.

Blue-green algae remove nitrogen from the air or water and *fix* it, or change it into nitrates. These algae are used as fertilizer for soil crops because of their nitrogen-fixing ability. Nitrogen is essential to plant growth.

Figure 15–10 Blue-green algae are found in many different environments on the earth, such as in a hot spring in Yellowstone National Park.

SECTION REVIEW   Answers on page T–53.

1. How are blue-green algae like bacteria?
2. What blue pigment is contained in blue-green algae?

Examining Bacterial Growth

Purpose   Bacteria exist almost everywhere on the earth. The objects that you are touching now have bacteria on them. Even your skin has bacteria on it. The purpose of this investigation is to show the presence of and to try to grow and examine some bacterial colonies.

Materials *(per group)*   ● 4 sterile cotton swabs ● 4 sterile nutrient agar plates ● 4 clean microscope slides ● 4 toothpicks ● Microscope ● Bunsen burner or other flame source ● Test tube holder ● Grease pencil ● Medicine dropper ● Methylene blue stain ● Safety goggles

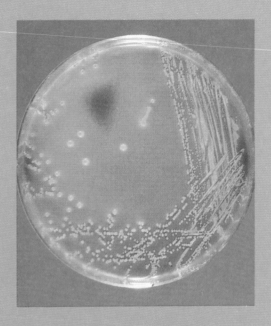

Procedure   1. CAUTION: *You should handle this laboratory investigation as if any bacteria collected are harmful.* Choose four places around your classroom that you think are the *least likely* places for bacteria to grow.   **2.** Draw a sterile cotton swab across the surface of one of these places.   **3.** Then, raise one side of the cover of the agar plate and slip the swab beneath the cover. Wipe the surface of the plate with the cotton swab to make a pattern, such as an S-shape. Cover the plate.   **4.** Using the grease pencil, label the bottom of the agar plate with the date and place that you took the sample.   **5.** Incubate the plate at room temperature for 2 to 5 days.   **6.** Repeat procedures 2 through 5 for each of the other places that you choose.   **7.** Observe the plates over the 2 to 5 days of incubation. **Note:** *Do not remove the covers.* Carefully note any growth, including color and general appearance of individual colonies.   **8. CAUTION:** *Be very careful when using a heat source. Wear safety goggles.* On the final day of observation, transfer a small amount of material from various colonies onto different microscope slides. To do this, lightly touch the tip of a toothpick to the colony. Then, rub it gently on the slide.   **9.** Using the test tube holder, heat-fix each slide by rapidly passing it once or twice through a Bunsen burner flame. Stain the smear with methylene blue stain or another simple stain. After 3 minutes,

gently rinse any excess stain from the slide. **10.** Then, observe each of the samples under the high power of the microscope. **Note:** *You do not need a cover slip.* Prepare laboratory drawings for each of the samples.   **11. CAUTION:** *Dispose of each plate properly at the conclusion of the investigation. Follow your teacher's instructions.*

Observations and Conclusions   1. Based on color and general appearance, how many different types of bacteria appear to be growing on each agar plate? **2.** On which day did growth, if any, first appear on each of the plates?   **3.** Which plate had the most bacterial growth? The least?   **4.** What are some of the types of bacteria that you are able to observe under the microscope?   **5.** What kinds of conditions appear to influence where bacteria are found?

CHAPTER SUMMARY

Characteristics of Bacteria Bacteria are one-celled prokaryotic organisms. As bacteria are microscopic organisms, they can be seen clearly only under high magnification. Bacterial cells are called cocci, bacilli, and spirilla, depending on their shape.

The structure of bacterial cells is simple. A cell membrane and a cell wall surround the cytoplasm. The cell walls of many bacteria are covered with a slime layer or capsule. The nuclear area of a bacterial cell is not surrounded by a membrane. Many motile bacteria have one or more flagella. Other motile bacteria called spirochetes move by rotating like a corkscrew.

Life Functions in Bacteria Autotrophic bacteria use the sun's energy or use energy from chemical reactions to make their food. Heterotrophic bacteria must obtain food molecules that are made by other organisms. Some heterotrophs are saprophytes, which feed on dead organic matter. Others are parasites, which live and feed on other living things.

Bacteria use enzymes to break down food molecules to release energy for life functions by aerobic or anaerobic respiration. Obligate anaerobic bacteria cannot use oxygen. Obligate aerobic bacteria require oxygen for respiration. Facultative bacteria can use either aerobic or anaerobic respiration.

Bacterial growth refers to an increase either in the number of cells in a colony or in the size of a single bacterium. Growth can be affected by temperature, moisture, exposure to sunlight, and chemicals. Bacteria reproduce by binary fission.

Sometimes the genetic material of one bacterium can be transferred to another bacterium in a process called genetic recombination, or DNA transfer. Genetic recombination can occur in three ways: conjugation, transformation, and transduction. DNA transfer is not a method of reproduction because the number of organisms in the population does not increase.

Importance of Bacteria Bacteria are all around us. Some bacteria are harmful and cause food spoilage, water contamination, and disease. However, many bacteria are helpful and have specialized uses in the food industry, in medicine, in tanning leather, and in agriculture.

Cyanophytes Like bacteria, blue-green algae are prokaryotes. Unlike bacteria, blue-green algae contain chlorophyll.

CHAPTER VOCABULARY

autotroph	endospore	parasite
bacillus	facultative bacteria	plasmid
bacteria	flagella	prokaryotic
binary fission	granule	saprophyte
capsule	heterotroph	slime layer
chemosynthesis	motile	spirillum
cyanophyte	moneran	spirochete
coccus	obligate aerobe	transduction
conjugation	obligate anaerobe	transformation

REVIEW of FACTS and CONCEPTS   Answers on pages T–53 to T–54.

On a separate sheet of paper, answer each of the following as completely as possible.

1. In what two ways are bacteria important to the environment?
2. Describe each of these groupings of bacteria: streptococcus, diplobacillus, staphylococcus, and streptobacillus.
3. Draw and label the parts of a typical bacterial cell.
4. What are the two ways in which motile bacteria move?
5. What is the difference between autotrophic and heterotrophic bacteria?
6. Distinguish between obligate anaerobes, obligate aerobes, and facultative bacteria. What conditions are necessary for each of these types of bacteria to carry out respiration?
7. Explain the following statement. "Old bacteria cannot exist in an actively growing culture."

8. List several ways to slow down bacterial growth.
9. What is the function of a bacterial endospore?
10. How are the processes of conjugation and transduction similar? How are they different?
11. In what way does transformation differ from conjugation and transduction?
12. List three specific ways in which bacteria are useful to people.

EXTENSIONS and APPLICATIONS   For additional information, see page T–54.

1. Bacteriology is a rapidly growing branch of biology. In the library, find information about the history of bacteriology. Prepare a timeline that shows the development of bacteriology. What role did Anton van Leeuwenhoek, Louis Pasteur, and Robert Koch play in the development of bacteriology?
2. Arrange to visit a bacteriology laboratory in a local hospital. Find out what role the laboratory plays in the functioning of the hospital. Report your findings to the class.
3. Obtain prepared slides of several different types of bacteria. Examine each slide under the high-power magnification of a microscope. Make laboratory drawings of what you see on large sheets of construction paper that can be displayed. Be sure to label the parts of the bacteria on the drawings.

SUGGESTED READINGS

Dixon, B., *Magnificent Microbes*. New York: Atheneum.
   The uses of microbes by scientists and in industry are described in this illustrated book. Examples of the applications of microbes in food production, pollution and insect control, and energy are discussed.
Dubos, R., *The Unseen World*. New York: Rockefeller Institute Press.
   This book is an introduction to the history and scope of microbiology. Special emphasis is given to bacteria.
Rosebury, T., *Life on Man*. New York: Viking Press.
   This book presents a humorous and informative look at microbes on the human body and the human compulsion to get rid of these "germs."

16 Protozoans

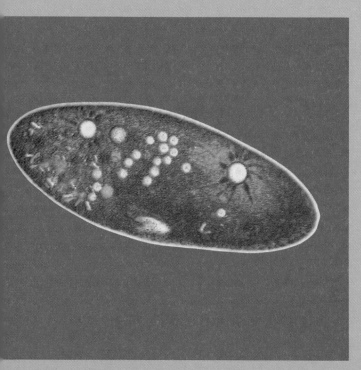

The protozoan Paramecium caudatum *shown is magnified 107 times.*

For teaching aids for this chapter, including a chapter overview and teaching strategies, see pages T–54 to T–55. The page number next to each chapter objective refers to the text page where the information needed to fulfill the objective begins.

The **protozoans** are classified in the kingdom *Protista*. Protozoans are simple animal-like protists. In fact, the word "protozoan" means *first animal.*

Typical protozoans are microscopic, unicellular organisms that do not have cell walls. Some protozoans are visible without a microscope, appearing as small specks to the unaided eye. Some protozoans live in *identical colonies*. In an identical colony, the cells are not specialized. The individual organisms in the colony are identical to one another in structure and function.

Protozoans are *eukaryotes* (YOO-kar-ē-ōts) and have a nucleus with a membrane and many cell organelles. Most protozoans have the ability to move from place to place. In fact, they are classified according to their method of movement.

The Sarcodines

The protozoans classified in the phylum *Sarcodina* move by extending projections of their cytoplasm and cell membrane. These projections are called **pseudopodia** (soo-də-PŌ-dē-ə). Pseudopodia (singular: pseudopodium) means "false feet."

Some sarcodines, such as *Foraminifera*, have a chambered outer shell made up of calcium carbonate, or limestone. Their pseudopodia poke through holes in their shells. Other sarcodines, such as *Radiolaria*, have internal silicon shells that form a latticework that has projecting spines. Their shells are covered with cytoplasm. Their pseudopodia extend from the cytoplasm. Most shelled sarcodines live in salt water.

The organisms in the genus *Amoeba* are sarcodines. Many forms of amoeba live in fresh water, on the leaves of water plants, and in the mud at the bottom of freshwater ponds and lakes. Some amoebas are parasites and live in other organisms. The most familiar amoeba is *Amoeba proteus*, an unshelled organism that lives in fresh water.

Structure of Amoebas

Under a microscope, a typical amoeba such as *Amoeba proteus*, appears as a shapeless, jellylike mass of cytoplasm surrounded by a cell membrane. An amoeba has two types of cytoplasm. One type called the **ectoplasm** appears close to the cell membrane and is relatively thin and clear. A thicker, grainy material called the **endoplasm** makes up the inner part of the cytoplasm.

The endoplasm of the amoeba contains one or more nuclei. The endoplasm may also contain *food vacuoles* and *con-*

Figure 16-1 These protozoans are classified in the phylum *Sarcodina*. How is the structure of an amoeba different from that of a radiolarian, a forminiferan, and a heliozoan?

The amoeba is an unshelled, shapeless mass of cytoplasm. The radiolarian, forminiferan, and heliozoan are shelled.

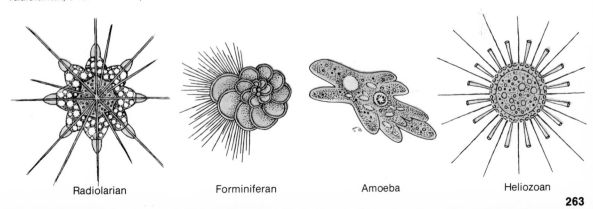

| Radiolarian | Forminiferan | Amoeba | Heliozoan |

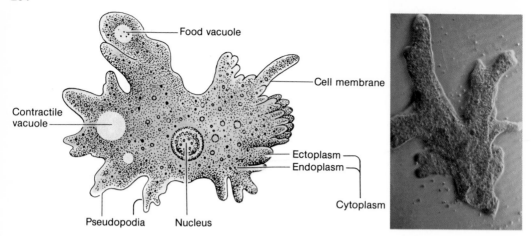

Food vacuole

Cell membrane

Contractile vacuole

Ectoplasm
Endoplasm

Cytoplasm

Pseudopodia   Nucleus

Figure 16-2 The protoplasm of the simple protozoan *Amoeba proteus* is organized into a clear, watery ectoplasm and a thicker, grainy endoplasm. Organelles, including the nucleus, are located in the endoplasm.

You may want to explain to your students that the process by which the amoeba obtains its food is called phagocytosis.

tractile vacuoles. Food vacuoles are used for digestion and storage. Contractile vacuoles pump excess water out of the amoeba. Other organelles that may be present in the endoplasm include ribosomes and mitochondria.

Food-Getting and Digestion in Amoebas

The amoeba eats small algae, other protists, and even some microscopic multicellular animals. An amoeba uses its pseudopodia to obtain food. The food is simply engulfed, or surrounded, by a pseudopod. A vacuole then forms around the piece of food.

To digest the food, enzymes in the cytoplasm enter the food vacuole and break down the food into small molecules. These molecules then pass into the cytoplasm. The food vacuole becomes smaller and smaller as digestion continues.

Some types of sarcodines called *Heliozoa* have rigid pseudopodia that extend in all directions. These pseudopodia shorten or lengthen very slowly. Although they are not used to engulf food, they do aid in obtaining food. A sticky substance covers the surface of each pseudopod. Food particles stick on the pseudopodia, and are partially digested by enzymes in the sticky substance. Eventually, the partly digested food is taken into the cell in a food vacuole.

Gas Exchange in Amoebas

Waste materials and undigested particles are moved from the food vacuole to the cell membrane and then eliminated. The amoeba uses oxygen for respiration. Dissolved oxygen in the water of the amoeba's environment enters the amoeba through its cell membrane. Carbon dioxide passes

Highlight

The sarcodines move by extending projections of cytoplasm called pseudopodia. The amoeba is one of the simplest sarcodines. It is a one-celled organism that carries out all life functions.

Emphasize that respiration in the amoeba is a passive process and does not require an expenditure of energy. Food-getting, digestion, and removal of excess water require energy and are active processes.

out of the amoeba in the same way. This exchange of gases occurs by *diffusion*. Diffusion is the movement of materials from areas of higher concentration to areas of lower concentration.

Response in Amoebas

Although the amoeba is a very simple organism, it still responds to changes in its environment. The amoeba responds to food by means of *chemotaxis* (kēm-ə-TAK-sis), a response to chemicals. The amoeba is also sensitive to light, and will move away from bright light into areas of dim light. This response is called *negative phototaxis*.

Some amoebas become inactive if their environment becomes unfavorable. They form a round **cyst.** The thick membrane of the cyst protects the amoeba. When environmental conditions improve, the amoeba will become active again.

Reproduction in Amoebas

The amoeba reproduces asexually by *binary fission.* A parent cell divides into two identical daughter cells. The daughter cells contain a full amount of identical hereditary material and about the same amount of cytoplasm and number of organelles. The entire reproduction process takes about one hour.

If an amoeba forms a cyst, it may reproduce by *multiple fission.* Within the cyst, the amoeba forms many nuclei with equal amounts of cytoplasm surrounding each nucleus. When the environment becomes favorable, the cyst breaks apart and many small amoebas are released.

SECTION REVIEW   Answers on page T–54.

1. What is a pseudopod?
2. On what organisms does the amoeba feed?
3. What is chemotaxis?
4. By what processes do amoebas reproduce?

The Ciliates

The largest protozoan phylum is *Ciliophora*. The ciliates have short, hairlike projections called **cilia.** Ciliates use cilia to move, to obtain food, and to sense and respond to their environment.

Cilia may cover the entire surface of a ciliate or may be concentrated in certain areas. For example, the ciliate

You may want to point out that cilia are made up of microtubules. Microtubules are also components of centrioles, asters, spindles, and other cell structures. You may want to refer your students to the discussion of microtubules and microfilaments in Chapter 5.

Sidelight

In ideal conditions, an amoeba will double its size and divide in 24 hours.

Paramecium is motile. Vorticella and Stentor are sessile.

Figure 16-3   All protozoans of the phylum *Ciliophora* have cilia. In what way does *Paramecium* differ from *Vorticella* and *Stentor*?

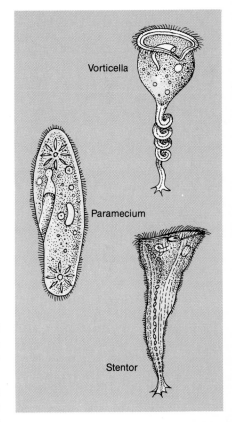

Highlight

The ciliates, such as the paramecium, move by using small, hairlike cilia. The paramecium is a complex cell with many organelles that help carry out its life functions.

Paramecium has rows of cilia along its body. These cilia beat forward or backward like oars, causing the paramecium to move in a spiraling motion.

Other ciliates, such as *Vorticella* and *Stentor*, have only a small number of cilia around their oral openings for sweeping food into their mouths. Unlike *Paramecium*, *Vorticella* and *Stentor* are *sessile organisms*. That is, they are stationary and attach themselves to objects. *Vorticella* has a cup-shaped body attached to a long stalk. *Stentor* has a trumpet-shaped body.

Structure of Paramecia

Compared to the amoeba, the paramecium is a complex cell. The function of the organelles in a paramecium can be compared to the functions of organs in more complex organisms.

CAREER: Microbiologist

There are thousands of different kinds of microscopic organisms. Microbiologists study the growth, structure, and development of microscopic organisms, including viruses, protozoa, some types of algae, and bacteria.

Many microbiologists specialize in the study of specific types of organisms. Medical microbiologists study the microorganisms that cause diseases. They may develop medicines to prevent or fight these diseases. Medical microbiologists may also work in hospital laboratories. They grow and identify cultures from patients who may be infected with a particular microorganism.

Veterinary microbiologists study the cause, prevention, and control of infectious microbial diseases in pets and farm animals. Agricultural microbiologists study the effects of microorganisms on farm crops. They often help develop chemicals that can be used to control microbial diseases in plants. Food microbiologists study microbes that develop in foods.

Some microbiologists work for water and waste-water treatment plants that use microbes to break wastes down into harmless substances. Microbiologists test the efficiency of the treatment processes. They make sure that the water that leaves the treatment plants is safe.

A microbiologist needs to have a bachelor's degree. However, an advanced degree with a specialization in one area of microbiology is preferred. A microbiology lab technician usually attends a special two-year training program.

Many microbiologists are employed by food, drug, and other industrial firms. Government health agencies also employ microbiologists. Other microbiologists are employed by colleges and medical schools.

For further career information, write to American Society of Microbiology, 1913 I Street, N.W., Washington, DC 20006.

The paramecium is a slipper-shaped organism with a distinct *anterior*, or front, end and *posterior*, or back, end. The outer surface of the paramecium is covered with a hard membrane called a **pellicle.** The pellicle gives the paramecium its distinct shape. Beneath the pellicle is a cell membrane.

The cytoplasm of the paramecium is made up of endoplasm and ectoplasm. Within the endoplasm, there are two nuclei. A small nucleus called the **micronucleus** controls reproduction. A large nucleus called the **macronucleus** controls all other metabolic functions. Other organelles in the endoplasm include food vacuoles and contractile vacuoles. Branched structures called *radiating canals* extend from the contractile vacuoles. These structures collect excess water from the cytoplasm.

Food-Getting and Digestion in Paramecia

The paramecium uses cilia to obtain food. The cilia surround an **oral groove,** an indentation that runs from the anterior end to the posterior end of the paramecium. Food particles are swept into the oral groove by the cilia, and are then directed toward the **mouth pore.** The mouth pore is an opening that leads into a funnel-shaped **gullet,** which extends into the cytoplasm. Food vacuoles form at the end of the gullet. When a food vacuole reaches a certain size, it breaks free of the gullet and floats in the cytoplasm. Enzymes in the cytoplasm diffuse into the food vacuole, and act on the food particles. Digested food is released from the food vacuole into the cytoplasm.

Excretion and Gas Exchange in Paramecia

Undigested food particles pass out through the **anal pore,** a small opening at the posterior end of the paramecium. Excess water collected by the radiating canals is directed into the contractile vacuoles located at each end of the paramecium. These vacuoles pump the excess water out of the paramecium through small pores in the pellicle. Oxygen and carbon dioxide gas diffuse into and out of the paramecium through the cell membrane and pellicle.

Response in Paramecia

Small structures called **trichocysts** (TRIK-ə-sists) are found in the pellicle of the paramecium. Trichocysts are poisonous dartlike threads of protoplasm used to capture food and to anchor and defend the organism. When the tricho-

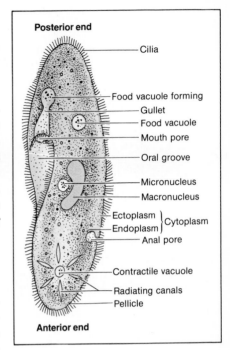

Figure 16-4 Unlike the amoeba, the paramecium has a distinct anterior end and posterior end. The paramecium also has many organelles, including a macronucleus and a micronucleus that control all cell functions.

At this point, you may want to assign to several students the second of the Extensions and Applications at the end of this chapter.

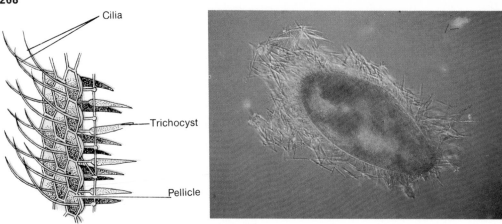

Figure 16-5 The hard pellicle of the paramecium contains trichocysts. With these dartlike poisonous threads of cytoplasm, the paramecium captures food and defends itself. When the trichocysts are ejected, the pellicle appears fuzzy.

Figure 16-6 The paramecium reproduces asexually by binary fission. The resulting two daughter cells are exactly alike in genetic composition.

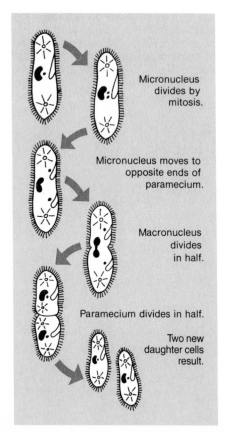

Micronucleus divides by mitosis.

Micronucleus moves to opposite ends of paramecium.

Macronucleus divides in half.

Parameteium divides in half.

Two new daughter cells result.

cysts are exposed, the pellicle of the paramecium has a fuzzy appearance.

The paramecium also has an *avoidance reaction* to objects. If a paramecium bumps into an object, it moves backward by reversing the beat of its cilia. Then, it turns slightly left or right and moves forward again. The avoidance reaction will be repeated until the paramecium passes the object.

Reproduction in Paramecia

The paramecium and other ciliates reproduce both sexually and asexually. Asexual reproduction is by binary fission. During binary fission, the micronucleus divides by mitosis to produce two micronuclei. Each micronucleus has the same number of chromosomes as the original. The micronuclei move to opposite ends of the paramecium. A second gullet and two more contractile vacuoles form. The paramecium then splits at the center to form two daughter cells.

Sexual reproduction in paramecia occurs through a process called **conjugation.** During conjugation, two paramecia join together at their oral grooves. The micronuclei of both organisms divide several times to form two *haploid micronuclei* in each paramecium. These micronuclei have half the original number of chromosomes. One of the micronuclei from each pair passes into the *conjugation tube* that joins the organisms. Here the micronuclei undergo mitotic division. The paramecia then exchange the micronuclei that result from this mitosis. Each paramecium receives two micronuclei, which fuse to form a single *diploid micronucleus.* The

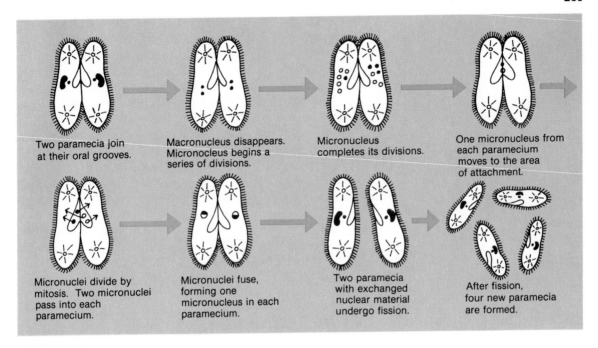

Figure 16-7   The paramecium reproduces sexually by the process of conjugation. Sexual reproduction produces variation in the species.

resulting micronucleus has the original number of chromosomes. The two paramecia undergo mitotic division after they separate. Conjugation produces variations within the species. These variations may be helpful to survival in a changing environment.

SECTION REVIEW   Answers on page T–54.

1. What is a pellicle?
2. What are the two functions of cilia?
3. What are trichocysts?
4. By what two processes do paramecia reproduce?

The Flagellates

The phylum *Mastigophora* (mas-tə-GAHF-ə-rə) is made up of flagellates, protozoans that have **flagella.** Flagella are long, whiplike structures that are used for movement. Most flagellates are unicellular organisms. However, several types form colonies.

There are two groups of flagellates. One group has *chloroplasts.* These flagellates are *autotrophs,* organisms

Highlight

The protozoans classified in the phylum *Mastigophora* move by means of whiplike structures called flagella.

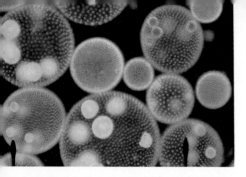

Figure 16-8 *Volvox* is an autotrophic flagellate. Autotrophs are capable of producing their own food through photosynthesis. In this way, they are similar to plants.

that make their own food. The chloroplasts contain the pigment *chlorophyll*, and are centers of photosynthesis. Some biologists consider these organisms to be plants because of their ability to carry out photosynthesis. Other biologists consider them to be animal-like because they move and do not have cell walls. Examples of flagellates include *Euglena* and *Volvox*.

The second group of flagellates do not have chloroplasts and are *heterotrophs*. These flagellates obtain their food from their environment. Most of these flagellates are parasitic and cause disease in other living things. For example, the flagellate *Trypanosoma* causes African sleeping sickness in human beings.

An example of a flagellate is the unicellular *Euglena gracilis*. The oval-shaped euglena has a pointed posterior end and a rounded anterior end. The cell is surrounded by a thin, flexible pellicle. The cell membrane is located directly beneath the pellicle.

The anterior end of the euglena has an inward pocket that forms a small gullet, which opens into a larger area called the **reservoir**. A flagellum is attached to the inside of the reservoir. A contractile vacuole empties excess water into the reservoir.

The cytoplasm of the euglena contains mitochondria, ribosomes, and a large nucleus. The nucleus contains a small dark body called the *nucleolus*. Other specialized organelles include food-storage bodies, chloroplasts, and an **eyespot**. The eyespot is a light-sensitive reddish area located near the reservoir.

The life functions of a euglena are similar to those of other protozoans. However, the euglena is different in some ways.

Nutrition and Digestion Unlike most other protozoans, the euglena is both autotrophic and heterotrophic. In the presence of sunlight, the euglena makes its own food through the process of photosynthesis. However, the euglena can also absorb food through its cell membrane when it is in areas without light. The food is then broken down by enzymes in the cytoplasm.

Response Unlike other protozoans, the euglena moves toward areas of bright light. Its eyespot is sensitive to the amount of light in the environment. The eyespot helps a euglena to find an environment that provides enough light for photosynthesis.

Reproduction The euglena reproduces asexually by *longitudinal binary fission*, that is, by splitting lengthwise.

Figure 16-9 *Euglena* is a plantlike protist. The reddish eyespot permits *Euglena* to respond to light from different directions.

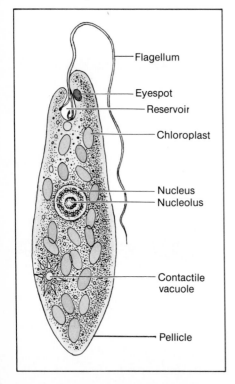

— Flagellum

— Eyespot
— Reservoir

— Chloroplast

— Nucleus
— Nucleolus

— Contactile vacuole

— Pellicle

This type of division produces two daughter cells that are mirror images of each other. Under ideal conditions, the euglena reproduces about once a day.

SECTION REVIEW   Answers on page T–54.

1. What is a flagellum?
2. Describe the eyespot in a euglena.
3. How does a euglena reproduce?

The Sporozoans

The organisms in the phylum *Sporozoa* have no means of *locomotion*, the ability to move from one place to another. They are parasitic and live within the cells or body fluids of animals. The sporozoans have complex life cycles that usually consist of two or three stages.

During reproduction, sporozoans produce *spores*. The nucleus of a mature sporozoan divides many times, forming small nuclei. Each nucleus, together with a small amount of cytoplasm surrounding it, forms a spore. When the mature sporozoan breaks apart, the spores are released. Each spore can develop into a mature sporozoan.

One of the most familiar of the sporozoans is *Plasmodium*. At least four different species of *Plasmodium* are known to cause malaria. The *Plasmodium* that causes malaria is transmitted by a small *Anopheles* mosquito. One stage of the life cycle of *Plasmodium* takes place in *Anopheles* mosquitoes and the other stage takes place in human beings.

Life Cycle of Plasmodium in the Mosquito   The cycle begins when a female *Anopheles* mosquito bites a person who is infected with the malaria parasite. In the process, the mosquito takes in some *Plasmodium* cells. Some of these cells are male, and others are female. In the stomach of the mosquito, the male and female cells develop into *gametes*, sperm and egg cells. This is the sexual phase of *Plasmodium* reproduction. Fertilization occurs and the resulting zygotes develop into spores. The spores are eventually carried to the salivary glands of the mosquito.

Life Cycle of Plasmodium in Human Beings   The asexual stage of reproduction occurs in people. When an infected mosquito bites a healthy person, the *Plasmodium* spores in the mosquito's saliva are injected into the person's bloodstream. These spores eventually pass into the

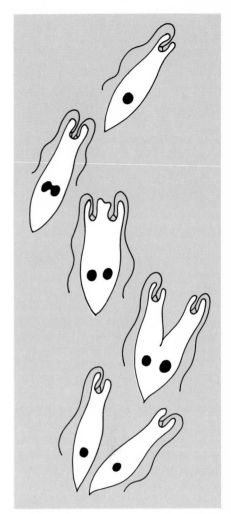

Figure 16-10   Under ideal conditions, *Euglena* reproduces asexually by longitudinal binary fission about once a day.

Highlight

The sporozoans have no means of locomotion and are parasitic. One example is the sporozoan *Plasmodium*, which causes malaria in people.

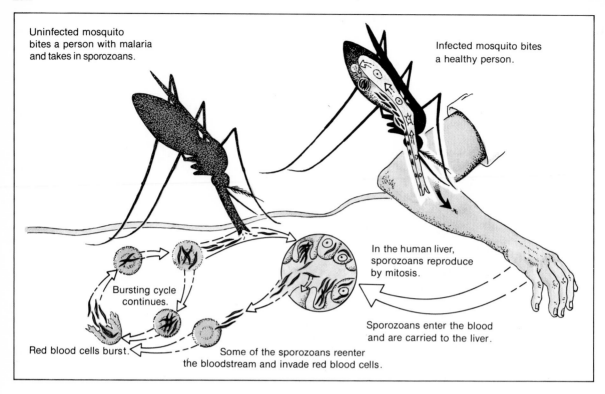

Uninfected mosquito bites a person with malaria and takes in sporozoans.

Infected mosquito bites a healthy person.

In the human liver, sporozoans reproduce by mitosis.

Bursting cycle continues.

Sporozoans enter the blood and are carried to the liver.

Red blood cells burst.

Some of the sporozoans reenter the bloodstream and invade red blood cells.

Figure 16–11 The life cycle of *Plasmodium* involves a sexual phase in the mosquito host and an asexual phase in the human host.

Sidelight

The number of malaria cases is increasing because anopheles mosquitoes are becoming resistant to insecticides.

You may want to point out that the sickle-cell trait is an adaptation that gives its carrier a resistance to malaria.

liver, where they grow and reproduce asexually. The *Plasmodium* cells produced then infect red blood cells.

Within each infected human red blood cell, the *Plasmodium* cells divide by mitosis many times and also produce poisonous substances. Eventually, the infected red blood cell breaks apart and is destroyed. New *Plasmodium* spores that can infect other red blood cells are released into the blood. When numerous spores and poisons are released, the person suffers from chills and fever. The cycle of infection and destruction of red blood cells repeats itself over regular periods. As many as 40% of a person's red blood cells may become infected during the course of malaria.

SECTION REVIEW   Answers on page T–54.

1. How do the sporozoans differ from the other organisms in the protozoan phyla?
2. What organism causes malaria in human beings? How is malaria transmitted?

Observing Examples of Living Protozoans

Purpose Protozoans are unicellular organisms that live in many different freshwater and saltwater habitats. Protozoans can be found in ponds, streams, lakes, and water-filled ditches. The purpose of this investigation is to observe representative living specimens from three protozoan phyla.

Materials *(per 2 students)* ● Microscope ● 3 medicine droppers ● Depression microscope slides ● Cotton ● Methyl cellulose ● Cover slips ● Cultures of *Amoeba, Paramecium,* and *Euglena*

Procedure **Part A** **1.** Copy the table shown in this investigation. After you examine each organism under the microscope, check off those structures for each organism that are visible. **2.** Using a *clean* medicine dropper, obtain a sample from the *Amoeba* culture. Take the sample from the bottom of the culture. Place the sample in the center of a clean microscope slide. Then, place a cover slip on the sample. **3.** Examine an amoeba under low power and under high power of the microscope. **4.** Prepare a laboratory drawing of one amoeba as it appears under high power. Label the visible parts. **Part B** **1.** Using a *clean* medicine dropper, obtain a sample from the *Paramecium* culture. Place the sample in the center of a clean microscope slide. Place a few cotton fibers on the slide and a drop of methyl cellulose. Then, place a cover slip on the sample. **2.** Examine the sample under the low power and high power of the microscope. **3.** Prepare a laboratory drawing of one paramecium as it appears under high power. **Part C** **1.** Using a *clean* medicine dropper, obtain a sample from the *Euglena* culture. Prepare a slide of the sample. **2.** Examine the sample under the low power and high power of the microscope. **3.** Prepare a laboratory drawing of one euglena as it appears under high power.

Observations and Conclusions **1.** What do you notice about the movement of cytoplasm in the amoeba? **2.** What do you notice about the position of the nucleus in the amoeba? **3.** Draw a diagram that shows the avoidance reaction of the paramecium as it encounters a cotton fiber. **4.** Describe the swimming movements of the paramecium. Do the cilia appear to beat individually at random or in coordinated movement? **5.** What color is the euglena? **6.** Describe the shape of the euglena. **7.** Do the movements of the euglena suggest a rigid or a flexible pellicle? Explain your answer.

	Amoeba	Paramecium	Euglena
Cell wall			
Pellicle			
Cell membrane			
Nucleus			
Cytoplasm			
Endoplasm			
Ectoplasm			
Food vacuole			
Contractile vacuole			
Peudopodia			
Cilia			
Flagella			
Chloroplasts			

CHAPTER SUMMARY

The Sarcodines Amoebas and other organisms that use pseudopodia for movement and obtaining food are classified in the phylum *Sarcodina*. A typical sarcodine is *Amoeba proteus*. Amoebas are irregularly shaped, simple organisms. They obtain food by surrounding it with pseudopodia and forming a vacuole. Digestion occurs in the vacuole. Wastes and undigested material are excreted through the cell membrane. Amoebas reproduce asexually by binary fission.

The Ciliates The organisms in the phylum *Ciliophora* have short, hairlike cilia that are used for movement and obtaining food. Compared to the amoeba, these organisms are very complex. A typical ciliate is *Paramecium*. The paramecium obtains food by using its cilia to sweep food particles into its oral groove. Particles are directed to the mouth pore and then into the gullet, where a vacuole forms. Digestion occurs within the vacuole. Undigested material is excreted through the anal pore. Paramecia reproduce asexually by binary fission and sexually by conjugation.

The Flagellates The organisms in the phylum *Mastigophora* use flagella to move. The flagellates are divided into two groups. The members of one group have chloroplasts and make their own food by photosynthesis. The members of the other group do not contain chloroplasts and obtain food from their environment. *Euglena gracilis* is an example of a flagellate that is both heterotrophic and autotrophic. The euglena has a light-sensitive eyespot and moves toward areas of bright light. It reproduces asexually by longitudinal binary fission.

The Sporozoans The organisms in the phylum *Sporozoa* have no means of locomotion. All sporozoans are parasites and have complex life cycles. They reproduce asexually by means of spores. A common sporozoan is *Plasmodium*. It has a two-stage life cycle and causes malaria in human beings.

CHAPTER VOCABULARY

anal pore	eyespot	oral groove
cilia	flagella	pellicle
conjugation	gullet	protozoan
cyst	macronucleus	pseudopodia
ectoplasm	micronucleus	reservoir
endoplasm	mouth pore	trichocysts

REVIEW of FACTS and CONCEPTS Answers on page T–55.

On a separate sheet of paper, answer each of the following as completely as possible.

1. List the characteristics of protozoans.
2. How are the protozoans classified?
3. What is the difference between ectoplasm and endoplasm?
4. How does an amoeba obtain its food?
5. Why is cyst formation important for some forms of amoebas?
6. How does the paramecium move?
7. What is the function of the contractile vacuole in amoebas and paramecia?
8. Explain conjugation in paramecia.
9. Why is *Paramecium* considered a more complex organism than *Amoeba proteus?*
10. How do euglenas move?
11. Why do the euglenas move toward light? What structure do biologists think is light-sensitive?
12. What is the difference between binary fission in euglenas and binary fission in amoebas or paramecia?
13. Explain the life cycle of *Plasmodium.*
14. What are the four major phyla of protozoans? Give an example of an organism in each phylum.

EXTENSIONS and APPLICATIONS   For additional information, see page T–55.

1. Collect leaves and small stones from around your school, near a pond, or near your home. Loosely pack the material into a large glass jar. Then, add tap water to the jar so that the leaves and stones are barely covered. Set the jar near a window, but not in direct sunlight. Over the next 10 to 12 days, take and examine water samples from the jar with a microscope. Take a sample from close to the top, from the middle, and from the bottom. Keep a record of the types of protozoans that you find in each sample. Also, devise a way to count the number of protozoans that you see with the microscope. Plot the growth of protozoans on a graph. Note any changes in the numbers of protozoans over the observation period. Explain your results.

2. Prepare a wet-mount slide from a *Paramecium* culture. Test the reaction of the paramecia to various substances such as salt, sugar, and vinegar. Prepare a different slide for each substance. View each slide with a microscope. How do the paramecia react to each substance? Explain your results.

3. Prepare a series of drawings that compare food-getting, movement, reproduction, and various responses in *Amoeba, Paramecium,* and *Euglena.*

SUGGESTED READINGS

Curtis, H., *The Marvelous Animals: An Introduction to the Protozoa.* Garden City, New York: The Natural History Press.
This book presents an illustrated introduction to the protozoans. Also included are descriptions of the anatomy of these organisms.

Farmer, J.N., *The Protozoa: Introduction to Protozoology.* St. Louis: C. V. Mosby Co.
This volume presents discussions of the structure and reproductive processes of the protozoans and their role in aquatic environments. The book also contains classification guides and experiments.

Harrison, G., *Mosquitoes, Malaria and Man—A History of the Hostilities Since 1880.* New York: Dutton.
The plasmodia have been a problem to human beings. This book traces the history of malaria in human beings.

Schwartz, G.E., *Life in a Drop of Water.* Garden City, New York: The Natural History Press.
Ponds are exciting environments to explore microscopically. Several chapters in this book examine the protozoans that are found in ponds.

17 Human Microbial Disease and Immunity

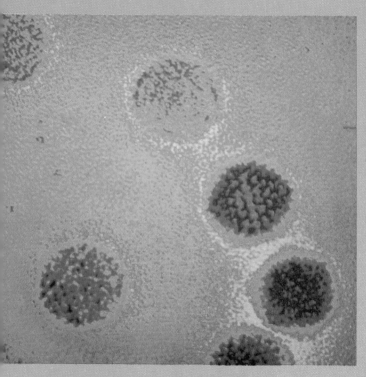

Chapter Objectives *After completing this chapter you will be able to:*

a ■ Explain the human body's natural defenses against disease. p. 277

b ■ List several ways in which microbes may enter the human body. p. 279

c ■ Describe some viral, bacterial, and protozoan diseases. p. 281

d ■ Explain some preventative measures used in disease control. p. 285

e ■ Compare inborn and acquired immunity. p. 286

f ■ Describe some therapeutic ways to control disease. p. 288

For teaching aids for this chapter, including a chapter overview and teaching strategies, see pages T–55 to T–57. The page number next to each chapter objective refers to the text page where the information needed to fulfill the objective begins.

Some adenoviruses cause respiratory illnesses.

Any harmful change other than an injury that interferes with the normal functions of the body is referred to as *disease*. Some diseases occur as a result of aging. Other diseases may occur when there is a breakdown of normal body functions. Still others are caused by harmful microbes, which are called **pathogens.**

Most human diseases that are caused by microbes are *communicable*. That is, they can be spread from objects or living things to people. The common cold is an example of a communicable disease. You probably got your last cold from someone else. You then exposed your friends, classmates, or family to the virus. However, these people may not all have caught your cold if their health was very good or their natural resistance was high.

Natural Defenses of the Body

Biologists have learned that the human body can fight disease in three ways. The human body has structures that prevent pathogenic microbes from entering the body. It also has special cells that attack pathogens should they enter the body. These two defenses are *nonspecific*. That is, they offer protection against all microbes. The third way the body fights diseases is to produce substances that fight certain diseases. Some of these substances are *specific* in that they fight only one kind of microbe.

Structural Defenses

In the human body, the main barrier of defense is the skin. Most microbes cannot get through unbroken skin. The perspiration and oil secreted, or released, by the skin also help prevent microbes from entering. The *fatty acids* and salts present in perspiration are **bacteriostats**, substances that help prevent the growth of microbes on the skin.

Tears secreted from the tear ducts in the eyes keep microbes from entering the body. Tears contain an enzyme that kills bacteria. However, bacterial infections may still occur in the eyes. A common infection of the clear membrane that covers the outside of the eye is called *pink eye*. Pink eye is caused by a bacillus, or rod-shaped bacterium.

Enzymes in the *mucus* and digestive juices of the stomach also can kill or slow the growth of pathogens. Mucus is a clear, sticky substance produced by special cell linings in the mouth, nose, and other parts of the body. These linings are called *mucous membranes*.

Cilia in the nose, throat, and tubes leading from the lungs also help keep pathogens out of the body. The mucus and trapped pathogens on these structures are removed by sneezing or coughing. If the mucus is swallowed, the acids in the stomach juices destroy the microbes.

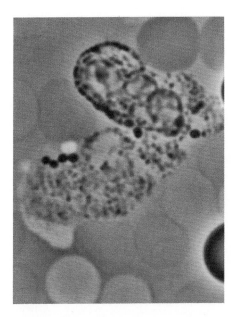

Figure 17-1 A phagocyte ingests staphylococcus bacteria (small, dark spheres).

Cellular Activity

The human body has specialized white blood cells called **phagocytes** (FAG-ə-sītes) that help fight disease. Phagocytes are amoebalike and have pseudopodia. Phagocytes surround microbes and then destroy them.

During infection, certain phagocytes called *leucocytes* leave the bloodstream and move to the site of the infection. While destroying microbes at the infected area, some of these leucocytes are also destroyed. A thick, yellow fluid

277

called *pus* forms. Pus is made up of dead microbes, dead leucocytes, and *blood serum*, or the liquid portion of the blood.

Spongy tissues in the body called *lymph nodes* act as filters for the blood. A fluid in the blood called *lymph* passes through the lymph nodes and then returns to the bloodstream. The lymph nodes filter out microorganisms that have gotten into the bloodstream. The phagocytes digest these microorganisms as well as dead microbes and dead white blood cells.

Chemical Defenses

The body possesses a number of chemical defenses against disease. One of these is based on the body's ability to recognize and then neutralize foreign proteins such as those of bacteria and viruses. These foreign proteins are called **antigens** and include parts of bacteria and viruses, *bacterial toxins*, or poisons, and other proteins found in living things, such as those in the pollen grains of plants.

When an antigen enters the tissues of the body, the body responds by producing special proteins called **antibodies**. Antibodies are produced by white blood cells called **lymphocytes** (LIM-fə-sītz). Each antigen causes the lympho-

Figure 17-2 Antibodies, produced by lymphocytes, cause pathogens to clump together. Macrophages then destroy the clumps. Some antibodies can directly destroy pathogens.

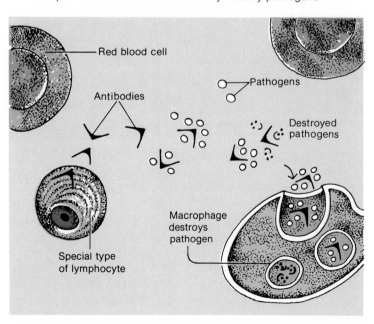

cytes to produce a specific antibody. For example, the antibody for the measles virus will not attack a mumps virus.

Antibodies and antigens interact to prevent disease. In bacteria, antibodies may destroy bacterial cell membranes or may force individual bacteria to clump together. Then the clumps can be surrounded and destroyed by large white blood cells called **macrophages.** If bacterial toxins are produced in the body, special antibodies called **antitoxins** make the toxins harmless. The body does not produce antitoxins to attack nonprotein poisons such as carbon monoxide gas, which is found in the exhaust fumes of automobiles.

During viral infections, antibodies may adhere to the viruses so that the virus cannot penetrate the host cells. The body can also protect itself against the attack of viruses by producing a substance called **interferon.** Interferon is produced by body cells that are invaded by viruses. Unlike antibodies, interferon does not attack a specific kind of virus. Interferon is effective against viruses in general. In addition, interferon produced by one kind of organism cannot be used by another kind of organism. Therefore, the only type of interferon that will protect a human being from viral infections is human interferon.

The body's response to a foreign protein sometimes is harmful. This is true in instances when the body reacts to proteins in plant pollens. The reaction, called an *allergic reaction,* can produce sneezing, rashes, irritated eyes, and difficulty in breathing.

SECTION REVIEW   Answers on page T–56.

1. What is a bacteriostat?
2. What is a phagocyte?
3. What is the relationship between an antibody and an antigen?
4. What is interferon?

Causes and Spread of Disease

Certain viruses, bacteria, rickettsias, and protozoans are pathogenic organisms. When these organisms enter the body and cause disease, they are said to be *infectious.* When an infectious disease can be passed from a sick person to another person, the disease is said to be *contagious.*

Pathogenic microbes can enter the human body through broken skin, the mucous membranes, and the respiratory tract, which is made up of the body structures that take in air. Infectious microbes are most commonly spread from

Sidelight

Scientists are now able to force bacteria to manufacture human interferon. The technique is called genetic engineering, recombinant DNA, or gene splicing.

Highlight

Infectious diseases can be spread by microbes in the air, by microbes in food and water, and by microbes on objects.

At this point, you may want to assign to the class the first of the Extensions and Applications at the end of this chapter.

person to person through the taking in of air, water, or food that contains the microbe, and through contact with an infected person or contaminated object.

Airborne diseases Many different microbial diseases are spread through the air. When you breathe, microbes, such as those that cause the common cold, enter your body on droplets of moisture and dust particles in the air. Contaminated droplets may be sprayed into the air by coughing, sneezing, or talking. Because airborne microbes enter the respiratory tract, the nose, throat, and lungs are often the first parts of the body that become infected by them.

Figure 17-3 Infectious diseases may be spread by water or food, by direct contact with disease-carrying organisms or contaminated objects, or through the air.

Food- and waterborne diseases Many diseases are spread through contaminated food and water. Food may become contaminated if it is handled by an infected person or is improperly processed or stored. Water may be contaminated if untreated sewage gets into a water supply or if an area has poor sanitation methods. When people eat or drink contaminated food or water, the pathogenic organisms enter the digestive tract. Food poisoning is an example of a disease caused by food- and waterborne microbes.

Contact diseases If a disease is spread by a contaminated object, an insect, or other living thing to a person, the method of transmission is referred to as *indirect contact*. If the disease is spread directly from one person to another, the method of transmission is referred to as *direct contact*. Direct contact includes transmission of pathogens by airborne droplets from sneezing, coughing, and so on or by touching an infected person.

At this point, you may want to have your students do the Laboratory Investigation at the end of this chapter.

Two infectious diseases that are spread by direct contact are syphilis and gonorrhea. Syphilis is caused by a spirochete called *Treponema pallidum*. The spirochete lives in the bloodstream and can invade the nervous system and heart. Gonorrhea is caused by a spherical bacterium called *Neisseria gonorrhoeae*. The bacterium infects the mucous membranes. Both syphilis and gonorrhea are serious infectious diseases that are transmitted through sexual contact.

Viral Diseases

Viruses are the smallest pathogens. Many familiar diseases, such as chicken pox, German measles, hepatitis, and polio, are caused by viruses. Several viral diseases are discussed later in this section.

Fever, headache, vomiting, and body aches are symptoms of many viral infections. However, each viral disease also has its own specific symptoms. Some viruses cause more severe symptoms than do other viruses. The measure of a virus' or other pathogen's ability to cause disease is called *virulence* (VIR-yoo-ləns). The virulence of a virus depends on three factors.

Highlight

Virulence is the measure of a pathogen's ability to cause disease in an organism.

The ability of a virus to adsorb and to penetrate a cell.

The ability of a virus to multiply and to spread in the organism.

The number of viral particles infecting the organism.

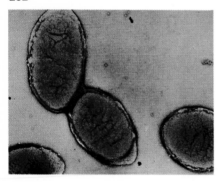

Figure 17-4 These tiny viruses (10,800X) cause influenza.

Sidelight

Biologists have identified more than 100 different viruses that can cause the common cold.

INFLUENZA AND THE COMMON COLD Influenza, or the "flu," and the common cold are both infections of the respiratory tract. The common cold is a much less serious infection than influenza. Both diseases are spread by direct contact with contaminated droplets in the air. The symptoms of both may include fever, chills, headache, coughing, and congestion.

VIRAL HEPATITIS Damage to the liver is caused by viral hepatitis. Two different viruses cause viral hepatitis. One virus, called hepatitis A virus, causes *infectious hepatitis*. Infectious hepatitis is spread by direct contact with an infected person or indirect contact with infected food or objects. The other virus, called hepatitis B virus, causes *serum hepatitis*. Hepatitis B viruses are found in the blood serum of an infected person. The virus can be spread from one person to another by contaminated hypodermic needles, which are used for injections. Some of the symptoms for both types of hepatitis include fever, vomiting, fatigue, loss of appetite, and **jaundice**. Jaundice is a condition in which the skin, eyeballs, and urine become deep yellow.

GERMAN MEASLES German measles is also called *rubella*. It is a childhood viral disease that causes mild respiratory symptoms and a body rash. However, it is dangerous for a pregnant woman and may cause birth defects in her unborn child. The virus is spread through direct contact with airborne secretions from an infected person or indirect contact with contaminated objects. The virus usually enters the body through the respiratory tract and quickly enters the bloodstream by way of the lungs.

Bacterial Diseases

Billions of bacteria exist in air, soil, and water, and within and on the surface of your body. Most of these bacteria are harmless, although some are pathogenic. The virulence of a pathogenic bacterium depends on two factors.

The ability of the bacterium to multiply and spread in the infected organism.

The number of bacteria infecting the organism.

Pathogenic bacteria grow rapidly in the human body because its temperature is ideal for their growth. Their rapid growth disrupts the normal metabolic functions of the body's host cells. The bacteria also use food molecules that are needed by the cells, causing the body to become weak.

Bacterial toxins can destroy cells or disrupt metabolic functions. The toxins often produce the symptoms of bacterial infection, such as fever and weakness. Some toxins produce specific symptoms. For example, the tetanus bacterium stops nerve impulses that control movement, causing muscle spasms and paralysis.

FOOD POISONING   Food poisoning is caused by bacteria and their toxins that are present in contaminated food or drinks. One type of food poisoning is called **botulism.** Botulism is caused by a rod-shaped bacterium found in improperly canned foods. The symptoms of botulism are caused by a powerful **exotoxin** secreted by the bacterium. An exotoxin is a poisonous substance produced and secreted by the bacterium as it grows. The exotoxin from the botulism bacterium affects the body's nervous system, causing dizziness, double vision, and difficulty in breathing. Death can occur as a result of respiratory and heart failure.

Two less serious forms of food poisoning are caused by *Staphylococcus* and *Salmonella* bacteria. Improperly stored fish, meats, and dairy products may contain *Staphylococcus* bacteria. The exotoxin produced by these bacteria acts on the body's digestive system, causing vomiting and cramps. Recovery usually takes place within 24 hours.

Eggs, sausages, ground meats, and custards may contain *Salmonella* bacteria. Usually, infected food handlers cause the contamination. The symptoms of this type of food poisoning include cramps, vomiting, and diarrhea. Biologists think that the symptoms of *Salmonella* food poisoning are produced by an **endotoxin.** The endotoxin is released only when the bacterium dies and breaks apart. Endotoxins usually produce aches and fever.

Your students may be interested in knowing that the bacterium that causes botulism is an anaerobe. Botulism toxin is usually found in foods that are improperly canned at home. It is rarely found in commercially canned food products.

Highlight

Bacterial diseases are often caused by the endotoxins or exotoxins produced by bacteria.

Figure 17-5   Each of these bacteria can cause serious illnesses in human beings.

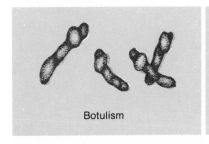

Botulism

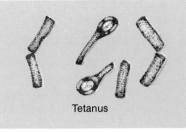

Tetanus

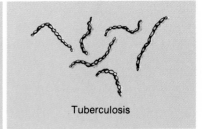

Tuberculosis

TUBERCULOSIS Tuberculosis is caused by the *tubercle* bacillus. Tuberculosis is a long-lasting disease that usually infects the lungs. However, it can also infect other body parts. The bacterium infects and destroys lung tissue and other body tissues. Some of the symptoms of tuberculosis are coughing, chest pains, and loss of weight. The bacillus is usually transmitted by airborne droplets that are sprayed into the air by an infected person.

Protozoan Diseases

Certain members of all four protozoan phyla can cause human diseases. Pathogenic protozoans are often transmitted to human beings by an insect or other arthropod carrier. Protozoans, such as *Plasmodium* and *Trypanosoma*, are carried in the stomach and salivary glands of certain arthropods.

AFRICAN SLEEPING SICKNESS A species of *Trypanosoma* causes African sleeping sickness. An infected tsetse fly injects the protozoan into a person through biting. The protozoan reproduces in a person's blood and infects the nervous system. The infected person becomes increasingly sleepy, and, in the final stages of the disease, cannot be awakened. Death often occurs, due to heart failure.

AMOEBIC DYSENTERY An amoeba called *Endamoeba histolytica* causes amoebic dysentery. The symptoms include cramps and long periods of diarrhea. The amoeba is trans-

Highlight

African sleeping sickness and amoebic dysentery are two diseases caused by protozoans.

Figure 17-6 The protozoan *Trypanosoma*, which causes African sleeping sickness, follows a simple path from the tsetse fly to the human nervous system.

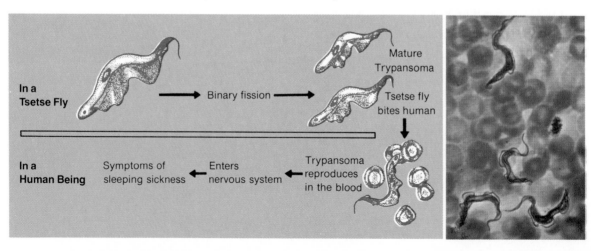

mitted to people by food or water contaminated with in-fected *feces*, the solid wastes eliminated from the body. Usu-ally, such contamination occurs in areas with poor sanitation facilities and poor control of sewage disposal.

The infected feces contain amoebas encased in pro-tective cysts. In the body, the cyst protects the amoeba as it travels through the digestive system. In the small intestine, the cyst develops into an actively reproducing amoeba. The amoebas feed on the tissues of the intestines and on red blood cells. Some amoebas may reenter the cyst stage and are passed from the body in the feces.

SECTION REVIEW   Answers on page T–56.

1. List three of the ways in which infectious microbes can be spread.
2. Name three viral diseases.
3. What types of organisms cause food poisoning?
4. How are pathogenic protozoans usually transmitted to people?

Control of Disease

There are two general ways to control disease. One way is to decrease the virulence of the disease-causing agent. The sec-ond way is to increase the defenses of the host. These two methods can be used either before or after a person becomes infected. If methods are used before infection, they are re-ferred to as *preventative*. If they are used after infection, they are referred to as *therapeutic*.

Prevention

One or more of the following measures may be taken to prevent disease.

Destroy the disease-causing agent.

Interrupt the route of transmission.

Increase the ability of the host to defend itself.

DISINFECTANTS   A **disinfectant** is a chemical substance that is used to kill microorganisms present on nonliving things. Most disinfectants are poisonous and cannot be used on or in the human body. However, some substances contain-ing chlorine are used in small amounts to control bacterial growth in drinking water, swimming pools, and laundry. If

Highlight

Preventive methods are used to con-trol diseases before an organism is in-fected by a pathogen.

Figure 17-7 To produce vaccines, viruses are grown in chick embryos. The viruses are then harvested and weakened or killed. The weakened or killed viruses make up the vaccine.

At this point, you may want to assign to the class the second and third of the Extensions and Applications at the end of this chapter.

the use of disinfectants is impractical, high temperature or radiation may be used to kill the disease-causing micro-organisms.

QUARANTINES The separation of infected individuals from noninfected ones is called **quarantine.** Quarantines are effective because they interrupt the routes of disease transmission. This same principle of interrupting transmission can be applied in other ways. For example, certain insects that transmit diseases may be destroyed in order to prevent the spread of the disease.

VACCINES A very effective way to prevent disease is to increase the ability of the host to defend itself. **Vaccines** can be used to do this. A vaccine is a substance that is injected into the body in order to increase resistance. Vaccines either contain chemical substances, dead or weakened pathogenic organisms, or their parts. Different vaccines cause the body to produce specific antibodies. Vaccines against smallpox, polio, measles, and other microbial diseases have been developed.

In 1798, the first safe *vaccination* against smallpox was performed by an English country doctor named Edward Jenner. Jenner developed the smallpox vaccine from cows infected with cowpox virus, a virus very similar to the smallpox virus. Cowpox only causes a mild disease in cattle and people. Today, smallpox has been totally eliminated throughout the world because of smallpox vaccinations.

Two types of vaccines have been developed that prevent *poliomyelitis* (pō-lē-ō-mī-ə-LĪ-təs), a crippling viral disease. In 1953, the Salk vaccine was developed by an American scientist, Jonas Salk. The Salk vaccine contains inactive strains of the three polio viruses.

Between 1955 and 1957, the Sabin vaccine was introduced. It was developed by another American, Albert Sabin. The Sabin vaccine contains live strains of the three polio viruses. However, the virulence of the viruses that are used in the vaccine has been decreased. The Sabin vaccine is given orally rather than injected. Today, the Sabin vaccine, or *OPV* (oral polio vaccine), is used more often than the Salk vaccine because it is easier to administer and because it provides longer-lasting protection than the Salk vaccine.

Highlight

Immunity is an organism's ability to resist or fight infection by a pathogen.

Immunity

Human beings have two types of **immunity,** or resistance to disease. One type of immunity, called *inborn immunity,* refers to the body's natural defenses against disease. People are born with immunity to many diseases that infect other organisms. For example, people cannot contract tobacco mosaic disease. The second type of immunity, called *acquired immunity*, refers to resistance that is produced during a person's life. There are two types of acquired immunity.

PASSIVE IMMUNITY   In order to bring about **passive immunity,** antibodies are introduced into the body. This type of immunity is said to be passive because the person receives the antibodies rather than making them. Passive immunity may be acquired either naturally or artificially. For example, a baby in its mother's *uterus*, or womb, may acquire antibodies naturally from its mother. A person also may acquire antibodies artificially by injection. For example, a person exposed to hepatitis can be given an injection of *gamma globulin*. Gamma globulin is a part of the blood that contains antibodies. Gamma globulin is collected from the blood of

CLOSE-UP: *Dr. Marjorie Pollack*

Dr. Marjorie Pollack's job, like that of most medical doctors, is to control or prevent disease. However, Dr. Pollack does not have a permanent office, nor do her patients come to call. Instead, her office can be wherever disease strikes in the world. Her patients are entire populations of people. Dr. Pollack is an *epidemiologist* (ep-ə-dē-mē-AHL-ə-jist). She works to stamp out diseases such as polio, diphtheria, and tuberculosis.

Much of Dr. Pollack's work is done in nations in which health care is less advanced than it is in the United States or Europe. For example, Dr. Pollack helped evaluate Brazil's polio control program. She worked with public health officials on methods of immunizing more people with polio vaccines. She worked with the Ministry of Health in India on a survey to identify areas that were hardest hit by polio and *neonatal tetanus,* a disease that strikes newborn babies.

Fighting diseases after they strike is only one part of Dr. Pollack's job. Another is preventing diseases from striking, especially in children.

"The objective is that by 1990, immunization should be available to all children," she says.

Dr. Pollack works for different health organizations in various parts of the world. However, many programs are run by the World Health Organization, which operates under the United Nations Charter. By working together, nations can wipe out preventable diseases everywhere on earth.

"Smallpox," she adds, "is one disease that has been completely eradicated by the united efforts of world health organizations."

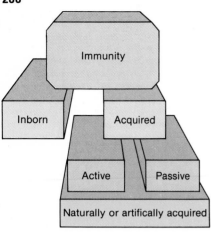

Figure 17-8 A person can become immune to a disease in a number of ways.

many donors. Since hepatitis is a common disease, gamma globulin from a large group of people will contain antibodies to the disease. These antibodies can prevent an exposed person from getting hepatitis. Both artificially and naturally acquired passive immunity are temporary, lasting from a few weeks to a few years.

ACTIVE IMMUNITY A person acquires **active immunity** to a disease when the individual's body is made to produce antibodies. Active immunity can be acquired artificially by means of vaccines. Active immunity can also occur naturally when the body recovers from an infection and produces specific antibodies. The natural active immunity may last from several months to many years and sometimes is permanent. Permanent immunity occurs when certain lymphocytes develop into *memory cells.* These memory cells can produce many antibodies very quickly if the antigen to which they are sensitive reenters the body. Scarlet fever, mumps, and measles are some diseases that often result in a permanent natural active immunity. Other diseases, such as pneumonia, do not result in permanent immunity, and can be contracted again and again.

Therapy

Various methods of therapy, or treatment, are used to help cure or control diseases. Some types of therapy are effective only against certain disease-causing agents. For example, medications that help fight bacterial infections do not help fight viral infections. These medications do not stop viruses because they work on cell structures and processes that viruses do not have.

CHEMOTHERAPY The use of specific chemical compounds in the treatment of disease is called **chemotherapy** (kem-ō-THER-ə-pē). These compounds are usually made in a laboratory. A German scientist, Paul Ehrlich, was the first scientist to do major research in chemotherapy. Ehrlich studied substances used to stain tissues. From his studies, he knew that certain stains only reacted, or stained, certain types of tissues. He theorized that there could also be chemical compounds that would only react with certain bacteria and not harm the host cells. Ehrlich worked with poisonous arsenic compounds. His work led to the synthesis of a chemical substance that was effective against the bacterial disease syphilis.

In 1935, another German scientist named Gerhard Domagk (DŌ-mahk) discovered a red stain called *prontosil* that was effective against *Streptococcus* infections in mice. Other investigators discovered that the red stain was chemically changed in living things to an antimicrobial sulfa drug called *sulfanilamide* (sul-fə-NIL-ə-mīd). Sulfa drugs stop bacterial growth by interfering with a bacterium's ability to make a particular vitamin.

Most work in chemotherapy has been directed against bacterial and protozoan infections. It is very difficult to develop substances that kill viruses but that do not harm the host. However, some developments have taken place. One substance, called *idoxuridine*, is useful in fighting a viral disease of the eye that causes blindness. However, idoxuridine has some serious side effects. Another substance, called *amantadine*, prevents viruses from penetrating the host cell. It appears to be effective against one type of influenza.

ANTIBIOTICS   An **antibiotic** is a chemical substance produced by a mold or bacterium that slows down or stops the growth of microorganisms. Antibiotics were first discovered in 1929, when a Scottish scientist named Alexander Fleming observed a mold on a culture of *Staphylococcus* bacteria that seemed to stop the growth of the bacteria. The mold was later named *Penicillium notatum*, and the substance it produced was called *penicillin*. Fleming discovered that penicillin killed many different kinds of bacteria.

The clear areas around the red, yellow, and orange disks indicate antibacterial action.

Figure 17–9 White growth of bacteria is affected differently by various antibiotics (colored disks). Which disks show antibacterial action?

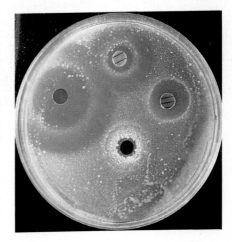

Penicillin was first used against bacterial infections during World War II. Since the discovery of penicillin, many other antibiotics have been isolated. Some commonly used and highly effective antibiotics are *terramycin, tetracycline,* and *erythromycin.*

Antibiotics, as well as other medicines, should only be used when prescribed by a doctor because some antibiotics cause side effects. Side effects may range from allergic skin rashes and upset stomachs to severe reactions that can cause death.

Antibiotics also should be used cautiously because bacteria mutate, or change quickly. Therefore, some bacteria may become resistant to an antibiotic and will no longer be destroyed by the antibiotic. For example, one species of bacteria now digests penicillin.

SECTION REVIEW   Answers on page T–56.

1. How does a quarantine help control disease?
2. What is a vaccine?
3. What are the different types of immunity?
4. How do substances made for chemotherapy differ from antibiotics?

A Model for Disease Transmission

Purpose   The study of the distribution and transmission of disease is called epidemiology. Pathogenic microbes do not move from one person to another on their own. Instead, the microbes are transmitted through contact with an infected person or a contaminated object or substance. The purpose of this investigation is to study how easily a harmless microscopic organism is transmitted from person to person.

Materials *(per group)* ● 4 nutrient agar plates with covers ● 4 grease pencils ● 8 wire loops ● Sterile cotton swabs ● Sterile water ● Yeast culture ● Alcohol burner ● Safety goggles

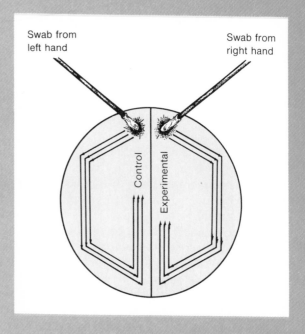

Procedure   **1.** Assign a number from 1 to 4 to each team member.   **2.** Using a grease pencil, each team member should draw a line on the bottom of an agar plate to divide it in half. Then, each person should label one side "control" and the other side "experimental." Each person should also mark his or her number on the bottom of the plate.   **3.** The team members should swab their left hand, with a sterile cotton swab moistened in sterile water. Then, they should swab one corner of the control side of the agar using the same swab.   **4. CAUTION:** *Be very careful when using a heat source. Wear safety goggles.* Each team member should sterilize a wire loop by passing it through the flame of the alcohol burner until the entire length of wire has been heated to a red glow.   **5.** The team members should streak their plate with the sterilized wire loops, as shown in the figure. **Note:** *Sterilize the wire loop after use by heating as before.*   **6.** The right hand of team member 1 is swabbed with a culture of yeast by the teacher.   **7.** Team member 1 should then shake hands with team member 2. Team member 2 then shakes hands with team member 3. Finally, team member 3 shakes hands with team member 4.   **8.** The team members should swab their right hands with a sterile cotton swab moistened with sterile water. Then, using the same swab, they should swab one corner of the experimental side of their agar plate and repeat procedures 4 and 5. Wash hands thoroughly.   **9.** Replace cover and incubate all of the plates in an inverted position at room temperature for 48 hours. Then examine the plates and compare them to the yeast culture.

Observations and Conclusions   **1.** In a brief paragraph, compare the experimental and control sides of the plates.   **2.** In another paragraph, compare your plates with the yeast culture prepared by your teacher.   **3.** Why is it necessary to compare your plates with the yeast culture?   **4.** Do your results indicate a pattern of transmission? If so, what was the method of transmission? Explain your answer.
5. How would population density influence disease transmission?

CHAPTER SUMMARY

Natural Defenses of the Body Within the human body are defenses to prevent pathogens from entering. The human body has structures and specialized cells that help fight disease. The main barrier of defense is the skin. Within the blood, specialized white blood cells called phagocytes surround and destroy pathogenic microbes. Special proteins called antibodies are produced by lymphocytes in response to foreign proteins called antigens. If bacterial poisons are present, antitoxins that make the poison harmless are produced. Interferon is another body substance that helps fight viral infections.

Causes and Spread of Disease Infectious microbes can enter the human body through broken skin, the respiratory tract, and the mucous membranes. Microbes are spread from person to person through the air, in food and water, and by contact with a contaminated object or person.

Many diseases, such as influenza, the common cold, hepatitis, and German measles, are caused by viruses. Food poisoning and tuberculosis are examples of bacterial diseases. Bacteria that cause diseases grow rapidly in the body and may produce exotoxins or endotoxins that destroy cells or disrupt metabolic functions.

Diseases caused by protozoans are often transmitted by insects or other arthropods. African sleeping sickness and amoebic dysentery are two diseases caused by pathogenic protozoans.

Control of Disease Diseases can be controlled by lowering the virulence of the disease-causing agent or increasing the host's defenses. One of the most effective ways to prevent some diseases is by the use of vaccines. Immunity, or resistance to disease, may be inborn or acquired. Acquired immunity is passive or active depending on whether the antibodies involved are formed by the body or introduced into the body.

Several different kinds of therapy are used to control diseases. Chemotherapy is the use of chemical compounds made in a laboratory to control disease. Antibiotics such as penicillin are chemical substances naturally produced by molds or bacteria that are also used to control diseases.

CHAPTER VOCABULARY

active immunity	**chemotherapy**	**lymphocyte**
antibiotic	**disinfectant**	**macrophage**
antibody	**endotoxin**	**passive immunity**
antigen	**exotoxin**	**pathogen**
antitoxin	**immunity**	**phagocyte**
bacteriostat	**interferon**	**quarantine**
botulism	**jaundice**	**vaccine**

REVIEW of FACTS and CONCEPTS   Answers on pages T–56 to T–57.

On a separate sheet of paper, answer each of the following as completely as possible.

1. List the structural defenses of the body.
2. How do phagocytes help fight disease?
3. Explain how antibodies and macrophages work together during an antibody-antigen reaction.
4. What is the difference between direct contact and indirect contact?
5. List the three factors that affect the virulence of a virus.
6. Compare and contrast the two types of hepatitis.
7. What is the difference between an endotoxin and an exotoxin?
8. How is the protozoan that causes amoebic dysentery transmitted? The protozoan that causes sleeping sickness?
9. Explain the difference between preventative and therapeutic measures for disease control.
10. What are three measures that can be taken to prevent disease?

11. Distinguish between the Salk vaccine and OPV.

12. How does passive immunity differ from active immunity? Name a disease that can be prevented by each type of immunity.

13. What is an antibiotic?

14. Why is chemotherapy more effective in treating bacterial and protozoan infections than in treating viral infections?

15. List two reasons why antibiotics should only be used under a doctor's supervision.

EXTENSIONS and APPLICATIONS For additional information, see page T–57.

1. Carry out an experiment to show that microbes are sprayed into the air by talking and laughing. Talk for 30 seconds facing a sterile nutrient agar plate held 15 cm from your mouth. Repeat this procedure with a second agar plate held at arm's length from your mouth. Repeat the same procedure for two more agar plates but this time cough onto each. Repeat the procedure for two more agar plates but this time laugh in the direction of each plate. Cover each plate and incubate all of the plates at room temperature for 24 to 48 hours. Observe the amount of microbial growth on each plate. Write a brief report explaining your results.

2. Using reference materials found in the library, make a list of diseases that have been successfully treated and controlled by the use of vaccines. Also, find out when each vaccine was developed.

3. Prepare a checklist of various vaccinations that are administered today. Take a poll of students in your school to find out which vaccinations the students have had. Summarize your findings in a written report.

SUGGESTED READINGS

Baldry, P., *The Battle Against Bacteria: A Fresh Look* (2nd ed.). New York: Cambridge University Press.

The author describes the history of human progress against pathogenic bacteria from early times to the discovery of modern chemical weapons.

Schmeck, Jr., H.M., *Immunology: The Many-Edged Sword.* New York: George Braziller.

Immunology as an advancing area of medical research is presented in this book. This book also explains what is known about the body's defenses against disease.

Zinsser, H., *Rats, Lice and History.* New York: Bantam Books.

This book discusses the impact upon human history of the bacterium that causes typhus.

A New Technology: Genetic Engineering

During the last few years, a new technology known as genetic engineering has been developed. Recombinant DNA techniques are a product of genetic engineering. Scientists use these techniques to take genes from one organism and place them in other organisms, such as *E. coli* bacteria. When biologists move genes from one organism to another, they produce new strains, or forms, of the organism.

A simple procedure is used to form new strains of an *E. coli* bacterium. The outer membrane of a bacterium is dissolved using a detergentlike liquid. Strands of DNA, which are located in the nucleus of the bacterium, are released into the solution and isolated from the bacterium. Isolated strands of DNA are transferred to another solution containing an enzyme that breaks the DNA strands at specific points, leaving segments with "sticky," or exposed, ends.

Genes from the DNA of a plant, animal, virus, or other bacterium are then added to this solution. Another enzyme is added to the solution that cements the genes to the exposed ends of the DNA strand of the host organism. The new recombined DNA strands are then implanted in normal bacteria. When these bacteria reproduce, their offspring will contain the new DNA strands. These offspring are new strains of bacteria.

The products of recombinant DNA techniques have many benefits. In 1981, recombinant DNA techniques were used to develop a vaccine against foot-and-mouth disease, which affects cattle, sheep, and pigs. Bacteria have also been used to produce vital human substances such as insulin. Insulin is a hormone that is used to treat people who have diabetes. Scientists have also developed bacteria that can produce substances to fight other human diseases.

Despite the many advantages of recombinant DNA techniques, some people feel there are risks associated with the research. New forms of bacteria might be produced that might be dangerous to human beings if accidentally set loose in the environment. For example, many people are concerned that there might be an accidental spread of bacteria that are resistant to antibiotics. Others think that growing large cultures of new bacteria might be harmful to the people working with them.

Most biologists, however, feel that there is little or no danger. They argue that for a number of reasons the research is relatively safe. For example, they point out that many recombinant bacterial strains cannot live very long outside laboratory conditions. In addition, recombinant DNA research is regulated by the National Institutes of Health, which has issued safety guidelines for such work. Most research must be done in sterile laboratories. Before materials from these laboratories are thrown out, the materials must be decontaminated. In some laboratories, the workers must wear special clothes while working. When they leave, they must change clothes and shower. These measures are taken to ensure that recombinant bacterial strains are not released into the environment.

Viewpoints

1. Many newspaper and magazine articles have been written about recombinant DNA technology in bacteria. Obtain copies of several articles and list the positive and negative points raised in each article. Conduct a survey of 50 people. Ask each person whether he or she agrees or disagrees with each positive and negative point. Organize your data and report your findings to the class.

2. Conduct a debate in the classroom on the pros and cons of recombinant DNA technology. The students on each side of the issue should investigate recombinant DNA technology thoroughly before the debate.

3. Prepare a list of guidelines that you think are necessary for a recombinant DNA research laboratory. In a report, explain the reason that you think each guideline is necessary.

UNIT FIVE

Plants and Fungi

For an overview of this unit, including field trip suggestions, a bibliography, and a list of audio-visual materials, see pages T–58 to T–70. You may want to check the Laboratory Investigations in this unit so that materials may be ordered, gathered, or prepared in advance.

Plants can be found on land, in the water, in the air, and even in other organisms. Have you ever wondered what the earth would look like without them? Imagine fields without grass, mountains without trees, and gardens without flowers. The earth without its nearly 400,000 kinds of plants would be plain and lifeless.

All life on earth is directly or indirectly dependent on plants. In the presence of sunlight, green plants use water and carbon dioxide to produce food and oxygen, which are necessary for the survival of animals.

A blade of grass gives off water through a process called transpiration.

295

18 Algae and Fungi

Mushrooms, a type of fungi, are found in moist areas.

Chapter Objectives   *After completing this chapter, you will be able to:*

a ■ Distinguish between algae and fungi. p. 296
b ■ List some examples of algae and fungi. p. 296
c ■ Explain how algae and fungi are classified. p. 296
d ■ Summarize the methods of reproduction in algae and fungi. p. 297
e ■ List several uses of algae and fungi. p. 297
f ■ Discuss the symbiotic relationship in lichens. p. 309
g ■ Describe the life cycle of slime molds. p. 310

For teaching aids for this chapter, including a chapter overview and teaching strategies, see pages T–58 to T–60. The page number next to each chapter objective refers to the text page where the information needed to fulfill the objective begins.

One of the most fascinating organisms treated in **botany,** the study of plants, is a group of simple plants. This group is made up of plants called **algae** (AL-jē). A single plant is called an *alga*. Algae perform about 90% of the world's *photosynthesis*, thereby providing most of the earth's atmospheric oxygen.

Another group of interesting organisms are placed in a kingdom all their own. This kingdom is called **Fungi** (FUHN-jī). One of these organisms is called a *fungus*. Toadstools and mushrooms are among the most common fungi. Fungi are called *decomposers* because they break down organic materials and return them to the environment.

Algae are classified in a group of plants called **thallophytes** (THAL-ə-fīts). Thallophytes are simple plants that lack true roots, stems, and leaves. The body of an alga is called a **thallus** (plural: thalli).

Algae

Most algae live in water environments such as ponds, lakes, and oceans. Others are found on moist rocks, in soil, and on the trunks of trees. Scientists have found tiny algae in hot springs, deserts, snowfields, and very salty water. Algae have even been found in the atmosphere as high as 15,000 meters above sea level.

Some algae are *unicellular*, or one-celled, and can only be seen with a microscope. In many species of algae, these cells may group together to form colonies. These colonies may be attached in a chainlike form called a *filament*. Other colonies may be shaped like spheres or sheets. Still other algae are *multicellular*, or many-celled. Seaweed and kelp are examples of multicellular algae.

All algae are **autotrophs**, organisms that undergo photosynthesis. Algae contain *chlorophyll*, the green pigment that makes photosynthesis possible. In some algae, other pigments mask the chlorophyll and give the algae various characteristic colors. One way that algae are classified and named is according to their color. For example, the common names given to the divisions, or groups, of algae include blue-green, green, golden, red, brown, and fire algae.

Algae have simple reproductive structures. Some algae reproduce sexually. Single-celled algae function as **gametes**, or sex cells. Multicellular algae form structures called *gametangia* (gam-ə-TAN-jē-ə), which produce the gametes. When two gametes unite, they form a fertilized cell, or **zygote**, that develops into a mature alga.

Other algae reproduce asexually. During asexual reproduction, algae produce and release single reproductive cells, called **zoospores**. When conditions are favorable, these zoospores germinate, or grow, into new algae. Many algae reproduce by *fission*, or cell division, forming two new cells. In colonial species, the colony as a whole may break apart, thereby increasing the number of colonies but not the number of cells. This method of asexual reproduction is called *fragmentation*.

When phosphates and other chemicals are dumped into ponds and lakes, the algae population greatly increases. These chemicals are used in cell growth and reproduction. A rapid increase of any algae that live in water is called an *algal bloom*. Algal blooms cut down the amount of oxygen available in the water, which can cause many fish to die. Deeper layers of algae are shaded from the sun by algae above, causing the shaded algae to die and decay. Oxygen in the water is consumed in the process of decay.

Figure 18-1 *Anabaena*, like all algae, is an autotroph. It contains chlorophyll and carries out photosynthesis.

297

Green Algae

Botanists have classified about 7000 different species of green algae. The chlorophyll in these organisms gives this division its name, *Chlorophyta* (klǝ-RAH-fǝ-tǝ). Most green algae are found in fresh water. However, several species live in the sea and in moist places on the land. Some green algae are unicellular and others are multicellular.

Green algae are *eukaryotes* (YOO-kar-ē-ōts). The cells of eukaryotic organisms contain a clearly defined nucleus. Green algae can reproduce sexually or asexually. In sexual reproduction, some green algae form *isogametes*, or gametes that are identical to one another in appearance. Others form *heterogametes*, or different male and female sex cells. In asexual reproduction, green algae form spores or undergo fission.

Green algae have been used in sewage and water purification systems because they remove poisonous materials from water. Certain forms, such as *Chlorella*, are used as a source of antibiotics. Some large green algae found in the ocean are used as food in many parts of the world.

PROTOCOCCUS *Protococcus* is a simple, unicellular green alga. Its oval-shaped cells often clump to form dense

Highlight

Eukaryotes are organisms with cells that have clearly defined nuclei. Prokaryotes are organisms that do not have distinct nuclei.

Figure 18–2 The green patches floating on the surface of this lake are colonies of threadlike green algae.

masses. The green, slippery film on moist rocks or on the damp trunks of hardwood trees is made up of layers of *Protococcus*. Reproduction in *Protococcus* is asexual through fission.

SPIROGYRA   A filamentous green alga commonly used in laboratory experimental work is *Spirogyra*. It is found in stagnant fresh water. The cells of *Spirogyra* contain spiral *chloroplasts*. These chloroplasts contain chlorophyll and look like twisted green ribbons. On each chloroplast is a tiny protein body called a **pyrenoid** (pī-RĒ-noid), which is a storage area for the cell. The pyrenoid is surrounded by layers of starch, a product of photosynthesis. *Spirogyra* uses this starch as food.

Spirogyra can reproduce asexually or sexually. During asexual reproduction, the filaments of *Spirogyra* break apart and undergo fission. In sexual reproduction, the contents of two cells exchange material in a process called **conjugation.** During conjugation, two adjacent filaments of *Spirogyra* form connecting tubes. The entire contents of one cell moves through a tube into the adjacent cell. A zygote is formed when the contents of both cells are joined. Each zygote develops a thick wall and becomes a *zygospore*. Under favorable conditions, the zygospore develops into a new *Spirogyra* cell. New cells then form new filaments of *Spirogyra*.

Figure 18-3   The filmy green covering on this tree trunk is *Protococcus*, a green alga.

Figure 18-4   The filamentous green alga *Spirogyra* can reproduce sexually through a process called conjugation. The adjacent filaments of *Spirogyra* form connecting tubes. The contents of the connected cells unite to form a zygote, which in turn develops into a zygospore.

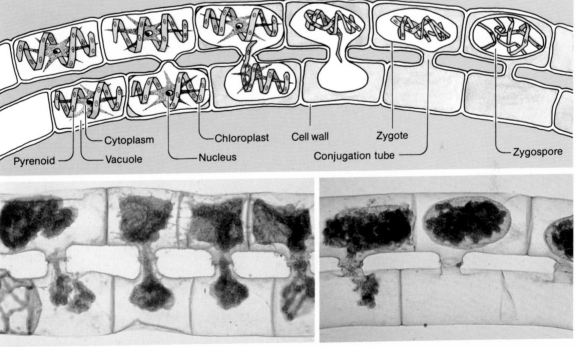

Pyrenoid — Cytoplasm — Vacuole — Chloroplast — Nucleus — Cell wall — Conjugation tube — Zygote — Zygospore

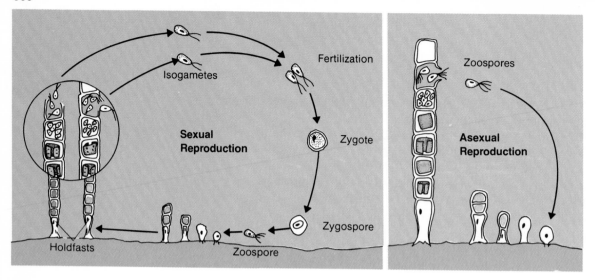

Figure 18-5 The green alga *Ulothrix* can reproduce sexually by forming isogametes that join to form a zygote. The zygote develops into a zygospore, which then becomes a zoospore.

ULOTHRIX   *Ulothrix* is an alga usually found in fresh water. Its cells contain ringlike chloroplasts and are arranged in filaments.

Ulothrix reproduces asexually in one generation and sexually in the next. This process is called **alternation of generations.** As shown in Figure 18-5, asexual reproduction occurs by means of zoospores. Each zoospore has four flagella, or whiplike structures, that enable the spore to move through the water. When conditions are favorable, the zoospore grows into a special cell called a **holdfast.** A holdfast attaches itself to an object and produces a new filament.

During sexual reproduction, an isogamete is produced instead of a zoospore. The isogametes of *Ulothrix* are smaller than zoospores and have two flagella. When two isogametes join, a zygote forms. Eventually, the zygote becomes a zygospore. The zygospore then develops into a zoospore and undergoes asexual reproduction.

OEDOGONIUM   Another example of filamentous green algae is *Oedogonium.* Reproduction of *Oedogonium* can be asexual or sexual. Asexual reproduction in *Oedogonium* is similar to that in *Ulothrix.* Zoospores, each containing several flagella, form. Under suitable conditions, each zoospore develops into a holdfast that becomes a new filament.

Alternation of generations occurs in *Oedogonium.* As a filament matures, it forms reproductive cells and *vegetative,* or nonreproductive, cells. The reproductive cells develop into enlarged female cells that form egg cells. Each of the smaller, specialized male cells form two sperm cells. During sexual reproduction, the sperm cells enter the egg cells through pores. Sperm cells unite with egg cells to form zygotes. The zygotes thicken into zygospores. Later, each zygospore develops into four zoospores through the process of meiosis. Each of these zoospores can grow into a holdfast and form a new filament of *Oedogonium*.

DESMIDS   The vast **plankton** communities in seas and lakes are made up of algae called *desmids*. Plankton are tiny organisms that float or drift near the surface of the water. Plankton are generally classified into one of two groups. Those that carry on photosynthesis are called *phytoplankton*. Those that do not undergo photosynthesis consist mainly of protozoans and small animals and are called *zooplankton*.

Desmids are usually made up of two identical half cells, which are joined by a bridge containing the nucleus. Desmids undergo both sexual and asexual reproduction. In sexual reproduction, cell contents are exchanged directly between cells rather than through a conjugation tube. During asexual reproduction, the half cells separate and each divides to produce another half cell.

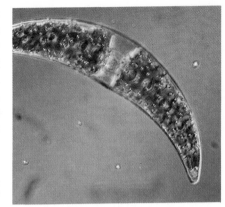

Figure 18-6 The desmid *Cosmarium* is a green alga. Desmids make up vast plankton communities in seas and lakes.

Sidelight

Green algae are used as food by some people who live on the Pacific islands and on the Pacific coast of Asia.

Golden Algae

The 6000 living species of golden algae are grouped in the division *Chrysophyta* (kri-SAH-fə-tə). The golden algae vary in size and shape. While some golden algae are multicellular, most are unicellular organisms. Golden algae are found in both fresh and salt water.

The golden colors of *Chrysophyta* are caused by various pigments, including orange *carotenes*, yellow *xanthophylls* (ZANTH-ō-fils), and brown *fucoxanthins* (fyoo-kō-ZAN-thinz). The green color of the chlorophyll in golden algae can be seen when the algae are gently heated.

The most numerous of the golden algae are the **diatoms.** Diatoms have cell walls made of *silica*, which is a major component of glass. When diatoms die, the silica of their outer walls remains. Over time, the silica accumulates in layers known as *diatomaceous* (dī-ət-ə-MĀ-shəs) *earth.*

The walls of the diatom form two overlapping halves. During asexual reproduction, the halves of the diatom separate and each half develops a new half. Diatoms also reproduce sexually by the formation and union of isogametes.

Figure 18-7 The cell walls of the golden algae known as diatoms are made of silica. After the diatoms die, the silica accumulates in layers called diatomaceous earth.

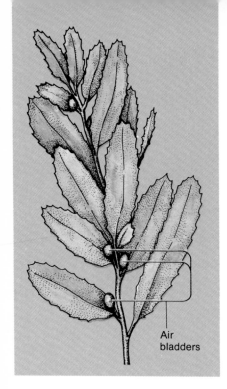

Figure 18-8 The brown alga *Sargassum* has air bladders along the branches of its thalli.

Figure 18-9 The red alga *Polysiphonia* has a branched thallus. Each filament of *Polysiphonia* contains one large central cell.

Brown Algae

Brown algae, commonly known as seaweed or kelp, are the largest forms of algae. The giant kelps can grow as long as 30 meters. More than 1000 species of brown algae make up the division *Phaeophyta* (fē-AH-fə-tə). These algae contain fucoxanthin. Most brown algae are found in the cold regions of the sea. Whereas some are free-floating, others grow on the sea floor. The free ends of the thallus of submerged brown algae are held up by *air bladders.* Air bladders help to keep the plants floating near the water's surface to enable the plants to use sunlight for photosynthesis.

A common brown alga is *Fucus* (FYOO-kəs), or rockweed. It lives on the rocks of coastal shores, where it can be observed after the tide has gone out. *Fucus* usually reproduces sexually. The reproductive organs are in the tips of the thalli. Special male and female structures in the reproductive organs produce gametes. The gametes unite to form a zygote that grows into a new *Fucus.*

Another brown alga is *Sargassum. Sargassum* is unusual in that it has air bladders along the branches of the thalli rather than at the ends. The Sargasso Sea, southeast of Bermuda in the North Atlantic, gets its name because of the large number of *Sargassum* found there.

Brown algae have many commercial uses. They are used in foods as a major source of iodine. *Algin,* an extract of brown algae, is used in many products, including ice cream, pudding, chocolate milk, and toothpaste. Algin is also found in more than 300 other commercial items, including lotions and paints. At this point, you may want to assign to several students the first of the Extensions and Applications at the end of this chapter.

Red Algae

All 2500 species of red algae are classified in the division *Rhodophyta* (rō-DAH-fə-tə). A red pigment called *phycoerythrin* helps these plants carry out photosynthesis in the deep parts of the sea where they live. Red algae range in size from single cells to multicellular plants. The multicellular plants have stemlike and leaflike structures similar to those of brown algae. However, red algae are smaller and more fragile. Red algae have a complex reproductive cycle, which involves special male and female sex organs and sexual and asexual reproduction.

Common types of red algae are *Nemalion* (ne-MAL-ē-'n) and *Polysiphonia* (pahl-ē-sī-FŌN-ē-ə). *Nemalion* is a simple type of red algae. *Polysiphonia* is a more complex form, having a branched thallus. Each of the fine filaments of *Polysiphonia* contains a large central cell.

Fire Algae

Fire algae belong to the division *Pyrrophyta* (pī-RAH-fə-tə). There are only about 1000 species of algae in this division. Fire algae are unicellular phytoplankton whose cells range in color from yellow-green to orange-brown.

Most fire algae are *dinoflagellates* (dī-nō-FLAJ-ə-lātz). Dinoflagellates have cell walls that look like interlocking armorlike plates. Each dinoflagellate has two flagella used for movement. One flagellum circles the middle of the cell and the other extends behind the cell like a tail.

Some species of dinoflagellate, such as *Gymnodinium*, can be harmful. When these red organisms become concentrated in sea water, they produce "red tides" that are poisonous to fish. Other species of dinoflagellates contaminate other types of seafood, such as mussels. If eaten by people, the contaminated seafood can cause serious illness.

Certain species of dinoflagellates are capable of *bioluminescence* (bī-ō-loo-mə-NES-'ns), or glowing. This bioluminescence is seen at night, especially if the sea is disturbed. The glow that is produced is similar to that produced by "lightning bugs."

Figure 18-10 When concentrated in large numbers in sea water, the fire alga *Gymnodinium* causes "red tides" that are poisonous to fish and harmful to swimmers.

SECTION REVIEW   Answers on page T–59.

1. What are algae?
2. What is plankton?
3. List the different divisions of algae. Give an example of an organism in each division.
4. What is bioluminescence?

Fungi

Fungi are eukaryotic and mostly multicellular. They grow in warm and cold climates, on land and in fresh and salt water. Fungi, like algae, have cell walls. Unlike algae, fungi do not contain chlorophyll. They are **heterotrophs,** organisms that do not produce food through photosynthesis and must obtain their food from other sources. Together with bacteria, the fungi are the main organisms of decay. They break down important substances and return them to the soil to be used by plants. As a result, fungi play an important part in the nutrition of green plants.

Some fungi are **saprophytes,** organisms that feed on dead or decaying matter. Other fungi are **parasites,** organisms that feed on the tissues of living organisms. Parasitic fungi often cause destruction of crops and other plants.

Highlight

Fungi lack true roots, stems, and leaves. They are heterotrophs, organisms that do not produce food through photosynthesis.

The autotroph-heterotroph distinction is an important one. Stress that all animals are heterotrophs, but only plants that can carry out photosynthesis are autotrophs.

Other fungi infect animals and human beings. Athlete's foot is an example of a fungus infection.

Fungi do not ingest their food directly, as do animals. Instead, they release *enzymes* into the living or decaying remains of plants and animals on which the fungus lives. The enzymes help to speed up the process of food digestion. The fungus then absorbs the digested food.

True fungi are members of the subkingdom *Eumycophyta* (yoo-mī-KAH-fə-tə). The true fungi have branching filaments called **hyphae** (HĪ-fē). The hyphae of most true fungi develop into masses called **mycelia** (mī-SĒ-lē-ə; singular: mycelium).

Fungi reproduce asexually and sexually. For example, a large mushroom produces billions of spores within hours of beginning its three-day existence. The spores germinate easily in moist areas such as a forest floor. Fungi are classified according to the kinds of spores they produce and the *fruiting bodies* they form. Fruiting bodies are the solid structures, such as mushrooms, that form from the closely packed hyphae. The fruiting bodies contain the spore-producing organs.

Conjugating Molds

The phylum of fungi that reproduces by conjugation is called *Zygomycetes* (zī-gə-MĪ-set-ēz). These fungi are named after the zygospore, which is the result of sexual reproduction in this phylum. Bread molds are *Zygomycetes*. Although some forms of *Zygomycetes* are saprophytes, many are parasites and cause diseases of plants and animals.

At this point, you may want to have your students do the Laboratory Investigation at the end of this chapter.

Highlight

Molds obtain their food through structures called rhizoids.

Figure 18–11 Bread mold, such as *Rhizopus stolonifer*, can reproduce by means of spores released by structures called sporangia.

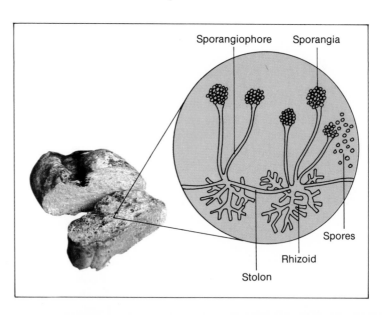

Sporangiophore   Sporangia

Spores

Rhizoid

Stolon

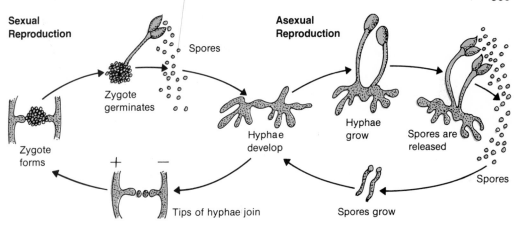

Sexual Reproduction

Zygote forms

Zygote germinates

Spores

Tips of hyphae join

+ −

Hyphae develop

Asexual Reproduction

Hyphae grow

Spores are released

Spores

Spores grow

The bread mold *Rhizopus stolonifer* is in this group of fungi. This bread mold forms many different types of hyphae. Those that spread over the surface of bread are called *stolons* (STŌ-lənz). The stolons give bread molds a cottony appearance. Clusters of short hyphae form on the stolons and are called **rhizoids** (RĪ-zoidz). Molds obtain their food through these structures, which resemble tiny roots. The rhizoids secrete enzymes into food and then absorb the digested food.

After several days, black, rounded **sporangia** (spaw-RAN-jē-ə) appear on bread molds, such as *Rhizopus*. Sporangia are asexual reproductive structures that produce and store spores. *Rhizopus* can also undergo sexual reproduction similar to conjugation, involving two different hyphae. The hyphae are referred to as *plus* and *minus*. The tip of each hypha acts as a gamete. When the tips of a plus and minus hypha come into contact with each other, a zygote forms. Eventually, the zygote thickens into a zygospore. The zygospore then germinates, as shown in Figure 18-12.

Sac Fungi

Sac fungi belong to the phylum *Ascomycetes* (as-kō-MĪ-set-ēz), which contains more than 30,000 species. Although there are many differences among the species, they all develop a saclike container called an **ascus** (plural: asci). Each ascus usually contains eight spores, known as *ascospores*, which are formed by sexual reproduction. The sac fungi range in size from single-celled yeasts to the multicellular morels, cup fungi, and powdery mildews.

YEASTS Yeasts are single-celled fungi that form chains of cells instead of mycelia. Each yeast cell produces an ascus containing four or eight spores.

Figure 18-12 Bread molds can reproduce either sexually or asexually. During sexual reproduction, plus and minus hyphae join to form a zygote. During asexual reproduction, hyphae develop from spores.

At this point, you may want to have some students attempt to grow molds. Tell the students to dampen a piece of bread and leave it in a dark place for several days. They should use a bread that does not contain preservatives. Using a hand lens, they should examine the molds and draw and describe what they observe.

Figure 18-13 Yeasts are able to reproduce by budding. The cells that result can form new colonies.

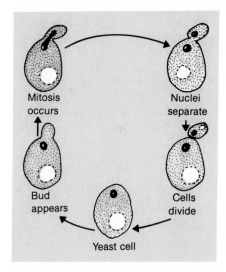

Mitosis occurs

Nuclei separate

Bud appears

Cells divide

Yeast cell

Yeasts also can reproduce asexually either by fission or by **budding.** Budding occurs when some of the yeast material pushes out of the cell wall, forming a *bud.* Several cells may grow from this bud and then separate from the parent cell to form a new colony of yeasts. In some species of yeast, a cell may simply divide to produce two new yeast cells.

In 1857, the French scientist Charles de Latour discovered that yeasts caused *fermentation.* Fermentation is a process by which enzymes change sugars to ethyl alcohol and carbon dioxide. During the baking process, the alcohol produced by fermentation evaporates. The bubbles of carbon dioxide cause the dough to rise. Today, the common yeast *Saccaromyces* is used in the fermenting process in bakeries.

Figure 18-14 Morels are sac fungi that are used as food by some people.

MORELS AND CUP FUNGI Among the most colorful fungi are the morels and cup fungi, which can be red, orange, yellow, or black. The fungi have a cup-shaped body containing many asci. Each ascus contains eight ascospores. Morels and cup fungi are found under logs and leaves, and on the forest floor. Some people eat morels and another sac fungus called a truffle.

CAREER: Mushroom Grower

Wild mushrooms grow under a variety of conditions. In order to grow mushrooms commercially, special conditions are required. The mushrooms must be grown in buildings in which the temperature, humidity, and ventilation are carefully controlled.

Growers can choose to cultivate many strains of mushrooms. The size of the mushroom crop must be decided upon as well as choosing the best soil conditions for the crop. In addition, growers must know how to identify and treat diseases of mushrooms.

Usually, mushroom growers hire helpers to care for the mushrooms. These people are trained in the proper care and maintenance of the crops. Some of these trained workers eventually begin their own mushroom farms.

Mushroom growers sell their crops to large canning companies or supermarkets. Some sell directly to consumers.

A college degree is not necessary to become a mushroom grower. However, people who are

interested in this career should study mushroom cultivation and botany. Courses in business management and marketing are also helpful.

For further career information, write to Mushroom Growers Association, 18 South Water Market, Chicago, IL 60608.

POWDERY MILDEWS   The powdery mildews get their name from the white, dusty spores they form on the leaves of apples, roses, and other plants. The hyphae of these fungi can penetrate and destroy entire crops.

Club Fungi

The *Basidiomycetes* (bə-sid-ē-ō-MĪ-set-ēz) derive their name from a club-shaped reproductive structure known as a **basidium** (bə-SID-ē-uhm; plural: basidia). Asexual reproduction is rare in club fungi, which usually reproduce by means of spores called *basidiospores*. These spores are formed outside the basidia as a result of sexual reproduction. Usually, four basidiospores are produced on the end of each basidium.

The more advanced club fungi form fruiting bodies, structures that protect basidiospores. Fruiting bodies are the most recognizable structures of mushrooms, puffballs, and bracket fungi.

MUSHROOMS   One of the most familiar fungi is the mushroom. The fruiting body of the mushroom is above ground, and the mycelia are underground, as shown in Figure 18-15. The umbrella-shaped structure is called the *cap*. The cap grows on a stalk that has a ring near its top. Depending on the species of the mushroom, the cap can be any of a variety of colors. On the underside of the cap are fine ridges called *gills*. Spores are produced on the surfaces of the gills.

Sidelight

A single giant puffball mushroom produces so many spores that if groups of 20 spores were placed in individual square meters, an area the size of Pennsylvania would be needed to contain all the spores.

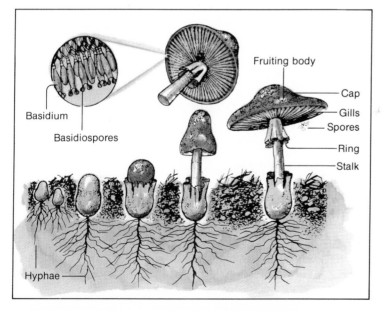

Figure 18-15   As a mushroom develops, the fruiting body emerges from underground and releases spores. These spores then develop into new mushrooms.

A common edible mushroom is the field mushroom, *Agaricus campestris*, which is often found in open fields or meadows. Rain brings about the germination of its spores. The spores develop into buttons that look like small knobs and rapidly grow umbrellalike caps. Within three days, spores may be observed on the gills of the caps.

At this point, you may want to assign to several students the third of the Extensions and Applications at the end of this chapter.

Different kinds of mushrooms have different growth requirements. For example, the honey mushroom requires shade and often grows under leaves and on dead wood and trees. The puffball mushroom usually grows on decaying logs and may reach up to 60 centimeters in length. The bracket mushroom is a shelflike fungus found on the trunks of trees.

Some mushrooms are poisonous. Perhaps the most deadly of all mushrooms is *Amanita*, or the death angel. It secretes enzymes that can cause paralysis and death in human beings. Most people cannot tell the difference between poisonous and edible mushrooms. Therefore, wild mushrooms should never be picked or eaten.

RUSTS AND SMUTS *Rusts* and *smuts* are parasitic fungi. They do not form fruiting bodies but do produce basidiospores. Rust spores appear as rusty-looking spots on the leaves or stems of plants. The various types of rusts include *black stem rust* and *wheat rust*. The wheat rust has a very complicated life cycle, requiring two hosts, wheat and barberry plants, and producing five kinds of spores.

Figure 18-16 This brightly colored parasitic rust fungus is growing on a cone-bearing plant.

Smuts form a dusty, black mass of spores on the plants they attack. *Corn smut*, which attacks the ears and tassels of corn plants, produces spores that are carried in the air. When the spores germinate, they develop hyphae that produce basidia, which, in turn, produce basidiospores. Upon germination of the basidiospores on suitable young corn tissue, hyphae are produced. These hyphae fuse and produce a thick, ball-like structure that gives a black, bloated appearance to the stems and leaves of the corn plants. Other smuts attack cereal plants, including oats, barley, and wheat.

Imperfect Fungi

Highlight

Imperfect fungi do not reproduce sexually.

The imperfect fungi belong to the phylum *Deuteromycetes* (doot-ər-ō-MĪ-set-ēz). These fungi are classified as imperfect because they do not reproduce sexually. Many imperfect fungi, such as *Penicillium*, are saprophytic. Other imperfect fungi are parasitic and can cause diseases in living things. In human beings, such fungal infections include ringworm and certain lung diseases.

At this point, you may want to assign to several students the second of the Extensions and Applications at the end of this chapter.

309

Usually, the blue or green molds that grow on the surface of oranges or open jars of jelly are *Penicillium* molds. Billions of bluish or greenish spores that are called *conidia* (kə-NID-ē-ə) give these molds their color. *Penicillium* is used to flavor cheeses because of special enzymes it produces. The most beneficial product of *Penicillium* molds is the antibiotic penicillin.

Another common imperfect fungus is the black mold *Aspergillus*. This fungus can appear on cured meats and fabrics. The citric acid produced by some species of *Aspergillus* is often used as a substitute for lemon juice. Some species of *Aspergillus* are harmful, causing certain human ear infections.

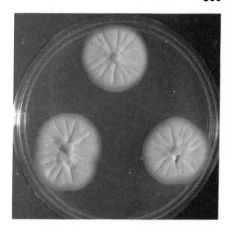

Figure 18-17 The *Penicillium* mold is an example of an imperfect fungus.

SECTION REVIEW   Answers on page T-59.

1. Name the four phyla of fungi.
2. What is the distinguishing characteristic of imperfect fungi?
3. List some diseases caused by fungi.

Lichens

There are more than 10,000 species of **lichens** (LĪ-kənz), ranging in color from green to red. Lichens are combined fungi and algae. They exhibit **symbiosis** (sim-bī-ō-sis), a

Highlight

Lichens are combinations of algae and fungi that live symbiotically.

Figure 18-18 The reindeer moss and other lichens are combinations of algae and fungi. Lichens such as these are able to grow in areas of permanent frost. They provide food for various animals.

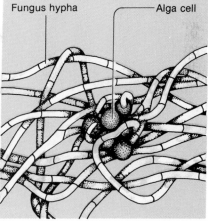

Fungus hypha — Alga cell

mutually beneficial relationship between two members of different species. The fungus is usually an *Ascomycetes*, and it combines with a blue-green or green alga. The fungus provides a means of attachment for the lichen and also absorbs water and minerals from the environment. The alga uses these materials during photosynthesis to provide food for itself and for the fungus.

Lichens are found on moist soil, rocks, and trunks of trees. In areas where permanent frost covers the ground, lichens such as reindeer moss serve as food for caribou and other animals.

SECTION REVIEW   Answers on page T–59.

1. What is a lichen?
2. Define symbiosis.

Highlight

Slime molds alternate between animal-like and funguslike stages during their life cycle.

Figure 18–19 Slime molds belong to the subkingdom *Gymnomycota*. They alternate between animal-like and funguslike stages.

Courtesy Carolina Biological Supply Company

Slime Molds

The slime molds belong to the subkingdom *Gymnomycota* (jim-nə-mī-KAH-fə-tə). Slime molds alternate between animallike and funguslike stages during their life cycle. For this reason, they are difficult to classify.

Slime molds grow in moist areas on dead leaves, rotting logs, and other types of decaying material. They are yellow, red, or white. Although slime molds contain many nuclei, they have no cell walls. The entire slime mold mass is called a **plasmodium** (plaz-MŌ-dē-əm). The plasmodium may dry up temporarily when food and water are unavailable. As the plasmodium moves along the forest floor taking in food, it resembles an amoeba. A slime mold in the plasmodium stage is considered animal-like.

Under certain conditions, slime molds go through a funguslike stage. The plasmodium stops moving and develops fruiting bodies. The fruiting bodies produce spores in much the same way a fungus does. The spores produce gametes that have flagella. When two gametes join, a zygote forms. The zygote then develops into a new plasmodium, and the cycle begins again.

At this point, you may want to have several students prepare a report on slime molds. Have them include information on the problems involved in classifying these organisms.

SECTION REVIEW

1. Where are slime molds found?   Answers on page T–59.
2. Describe the life cycle of the slime mold.

LABORATORY INVESTIGATION 18

For additional information, see page T–59.

Investigating Algae and Fungi

Purpose Although algae and fungi are in two different kingdoms, they do have some similarities. The purpose of this investigation is to examine and observe the structures of algae and fungi.

Materials *(per group)* ● Cultures of living *Spirogyra* and Rhizopus ● Lugol's iodine solution ● 2 medicine droppers ● Forceps ● 2 microscope slides ● 2 cover slips ● Compound microscope ● Paper towel ● Hand lens

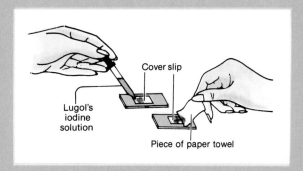

Procedure   Part A: Algae   1. Place several filaments of *Spirogyra* on a clean microscope slide. Add a drop of water from the *Spirogyra* culture to the slide. Gently place a cover slip over the drop of water containing the *Spirogyra.* **2.** Examine the filaments under low power. Find a filament that shows no sign of shrinkage. Look for the cell walls that divide the filament into many cells. Note the spiral-shaped, ribbonlike chloroplasts. **3.** Adjust the microscope to a higher power and locate the pyrenoids. In order to make the pyrenoids more easily visible, add a drop of Lugol's iodine solution to one edge of the cover slip. Use a small piece of paper towel to absorb the stain at the opposite edge, as shown in the figure. **4.** Make a sketch of your observations and label all parts. **Part B: Fungi   1.** Obtain a specimen of the bread mold *Rhizopus* and observe it with a hand lens. Locate the mycelium and hyphae. **2.** Carefully remove a few

strands of the bread mold with the forceps. Place the strands on a clean microscope slide containing a drop of water. Gently place a cover slip over the drop of water. **3.** Examine the strands under low power. Locate the stolons, sporangia, and rhizoids. **4.** Make a sketch of your observations and label all parts.

Observations and Conclusions   1. How many chloroplasts are in each cell of *Spirogyra?* What is their function? **2.** What is the function of the pyrenoids in *Spirogyra?* **3.** Where are the walls located in the filaments of bread mold? **4.** Are the hyphae in the bread mold colored? **5.** Do fungi have chloroplasts? **6.** List three ways that algae and fungi differ.

CHAPTER SUMMARY

Algae Algae are simple plants that lack true roots, stems, and leaves. Algae contain chlorophyll, a green pigment that is needed for photosynthesis. Algae perform approximately 90% of all photosynthesis in the world.

One of the ways that algae are classified is according to the type of pigment they contain. They are grouped as green, golden, brown, red, and fire algae. All algae are eukaryotes, with clearly-defined nuclei in each cell.

Most algae reproduce both asexually and sexually. During asexual reproduction, spores are produced. In sexual reproduction, either isogametes or heterogametes are formed. The life cycles of some algae alternate between asexual and sexual reproduction in a process called alternation of generations.

Fungi Fungi are multicellular organisms. They do not contain chlorophyll. Fungi are heterotrophs because they do not perform photosynthesis. Some fungi are saprophytes, organisms that feed on dead or decaying matter. Others are parasites and feed on the living cells or tissues of other organisms.

Fungi are classified according to the kind of spores they produce and the fruiting bodies they form. The classes of fungi include the conjugating molds, the sac fungi, the club fungi, and the imperfect fungi. With the exception of the imperfect fungi, which reproduce only asexually, all fungi reproduce both asexually and sexually. All methods of reproduction in fungi result in the production of a single reproductive cell called a spore.

Lichens Lichens are a combination of fungi and algae. Each species benefits the other in a relationship called symbiosis.

Slime Molds During their life cycle, the slime molds alternate between a funguslike stage and an animal-like stage. The animal-like mass of cells is called a plasmodium.

CHAPTER VOCABULARY

alga	**gamete**	**pyrenoid**
alternation of generations	**heterotroph**	**rhizoid**
ascus	**holdfast**	**saprophyte**
autotroph	**hypha**	**sporangium**
basidium	**lichen**	**symbiosis**
botany	**mycelium**	**thallophyte**
budding	**parasite**	**thallus**
conjugation	**plankton**	**zoospore**
diatom	**plasmodium**	**zygote**
fungus		

REVIEW of FACTS and CONCEPTS   Answers on pages T–59 to T–60.

On a separate sheet of paper, answer each of the following as completely as possible.

1. Compare and contrast the general characteristics of algae and fungi.
2. Name the various divisions of algae. Describe the characteristics of each division.
3. Describe conjugation in *Spirogyra*.
4. Discuss alternation of generations in *Ulothrix*.
5. Why are the fungi called heterotrophs?
6. How do fungi ingest their food?
7. Name the phyla of fungi. Give an example of an organism in each phylum.
8. Describe the structure of true fungi.
9. Briefly explain how sexual reproduction occurs in the bread mold *Rhizopus stolonifer*.
10. How does reproduction occur in yeast cells?

11. What is fermentation? Why are yeast cells used in this process?

12. Describe the reproductive structure of the mushroom. What is the function of each part?

13. How do lichens illustrate symbiosis?

14. Describe the life cycle of slime molds.

15. Distinguish between the following pairs of terms: isogamete and heterogamete and saprophyte and parasite.

EXTENSIONS and APPLICATIONS   For additional information, see page T–60.

1. Use materials in the library to obtain information on food chains. Use photographs or drawings to construct a food chain that links algae with human beings. Label all the organisms involved. In what way or ways are these living things interrelated?

2. Collect five different algae and five different fungi from around your neighborhood. On separate sheets of paper, list the characteristics that you observe for each organism. Using reference materials, include the name of the division or class.

Also include a description of the habitat, or location, where each organism was found.

3. Make spore prints of three different kinds of mushrooms. Cut off the stalk of a mushroom near the cap and place the cap, gills down, on white or light-colored paper. To collect as many spores as possible, allow the cap to remain on the paper overnight. Remove the cap the next day and compare the spore prints. To preserve the spore prints, lightly spray them with hair spray or shellac.

SUGGESTED READINGS

Kavaler, L., *Mushrooms, Molds, and Miracles*. New York: John Day.
This book provides a look at fungi as food, as sources of antibiotics, and as causes of disease.

Shuttleworth, F.S., and H.S. Zim, *Non-Flowering Plants*. New York: Golden Press.
A great deal of this book is devoted to algae and fungi. Many colorful drawings are included to help identify these organisms.

Tiffany, L.H., *Algae, the Grass of Many Waters*. Springfield, Ill.: Charles C Thomas.
This book discusses the reproduction, distribution, and economic value of algae.

19 Mosses and Ferns

Mosses and ferns thrive in damp soil and in shaded areas.

Chapter Objectives *After completing this chapter, you will be able to:*

a ■ Differentiate between bryophytes and tracheophytes. p. 315

b ■ Describe the characteristics of mosses, liverworts, ferns, and horsetails. p. 315

c ■ Compare the life cycles of mosses and ferns. p. 316

For teaching aids for this chapter, including a chapter overview and teaching strategies, see pages T-60 to T-62. The page number next to each chapter objective refers to the text page where the information needed to fulfill the objective begins.

Scientists think that the *terrestrial* or land plants developed from algalike plants that were abundant in the sea millions of years ago. These terrestrial plants that moved from water to land are thought to have developed into two different groups.

One group contains no specialized conducting or supporting tissues. Mosses and liverworts are examples found today of these early plants. Because of the absence of conducting tissues, materials could not be transported very far in these plants. This, together with the absence of supporting tissues, limited their size.

The other group of early terrestrial plants possessed conducting and supporting tissues and were able to grow to a considerable size. Psilopsids, ferns, club mosses, and horsetails are some examples found today of this second group of plants.

Bryophytes

Plants such as mosses and liverworts do not have specialized conducting and supporting tissues. These plants are classified in the division *Bryophyta* (brī-AH-fə-tə), and are called **bryophytes.** There are about 23,000 species of bryophytes. Because bryophytes lack true roots, stems, and leaves, they can only grow a few centimeters above the ground. Like algae and fungi, bryophytes lack **vascular tissue,** an interior network of conducting tubes through which materials travel in some plants. The lack of vascular tissue restricts bryophytes to moist, shady environments. They grow particularly well in slightly acidic soil and on the banks of rivers and lakes and are abundant in tropical rain forests.

Bryophytes reproduce by undergoing *alternation of generations.* This process, which is similar to that found in certain algae, involves two distinct stages. The sexual stage is called the *gametophyte generation,* or the gamete-producing generation. Zygotes, or fertilized cells, produced during this generation develop into simple plants called *embryos.* The asexual stage is the *sporophyte generation,* or the spore-forming generation. Bryophytes are like algae and fungi, in that they produce spores.

You may wish to point out that alternation of generations is not limited to bryophytes but is also characteristic of tracheophytes.

Mosses

Most mosses grow in damp soil, or on the shaded surfaces of rocks or tree trunks. Approximately 14,000 species of plants belong to the class of mosses. They may be classified into three closely related orders. The most common mosses belong to the *true mosses. Polytrichum,* or "haircap moss," is a true moss that has a leafy, stemlike structure that branches out into thick, soft masses. Unlike other mosses, *Polytrichum* contains separate male and female reproductive parts. *Sphagnum* is a familiar *peat moss.* It grows in thick, soft masses, covering large areas. *Sphagnum* is found in wet boggy areas. *Andreaea,* the only *rock moss,* is dark in color and small in size. It grows mostly in colder regions.

Moss plants play an important environmental role in nature. The *rhizoids* of mosses break off small pieces of rock which contain minerals needed to keep soil fertile. Rhizoids are hairlike filaments that function as roots. Because of their ability to absorb moisture, mosses also keep the soil damp, allowing other plants to grow. The absorbing property of mosses also helps prevent flooding in certain areas.

Mosses often grow so close to one another that they form cushions or dense tufts. Each moss plant has a tiny

Figure 19-1 In this cross section of the stem of a moss, no specialized vascular tissue is present.

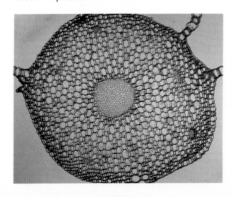

Figure 19-2 The true moss *Polytrichum* is also known as the haircap moss. Unlike other mosses, it contains separate male and female reproductive parts.

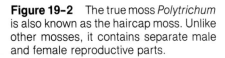

Highlight

During the gametophyte generation, the antheridium produces sperm cells. The archegonium produces egg cells. These sex cells are haploid. When they unite, they form a diploid zygote. The zygote develops into the sporophyte generation.

You may wish to refer to information on chromosomes in Chapter 8.

stemlike structure that is surrounded by equally tiny leaf-like parts. At the bottom of each stemlike structure are rhizoids. The rhizoids absorb water from the soil, rocks, or surrounding area.

A moss begins its life cycle with the germination of a spore, as shown in Figure 19-3. As the spore grows, it develops a tiny, green threadlike structure called a **protonema** (prōt-ə-NĒ-mə). The protonema is the beginning of the gametophyte generation. Eventually, the protonema branches and spreads over the soil or rock surface. Rhizoids and green, leafy structures containing chlorophyll grow on these branches.

The tips of the leafy structures bear numerous reproductive organs. Like all bryophytes, the mosses contain a male reproductive organ called the **antheridium** (an-thə-RID-ē-əm; plural: antheridia). The female reproductive organ is known as the **archegonium** (ahr-kə-GŌ-nē-əm; plural: archegonia).

In some species of moss, both kinds of reproductive organs grow on the same plant. Other plants only possess one kind of reproductive organ. Coiled male gametes, called *sperm* cells, are produced by the antheridia. Female gametes, or *egg* cells, are produced by the archegonia. The nucleus of each egg and sperm contains half the usual number of *chromosomes* for that species. Chromosomes are structures that carry hereditary information. These cells are *haploid*. Each sperm has two *flagella*. When moisture from rain or dew is present, mature sperm cells swim toward the archegonium. A sperm cell and an egg cell unite to form a *diploid* zygote. A diploid cell has the usual number of chromosomes.

The sporophyte generation begins with the zygote. The zygote develops into an embryo plant, which eventually becomes a sporophyte, or spore-bearing plant. The mature sporophyte is smaller than its parents and differs from them in

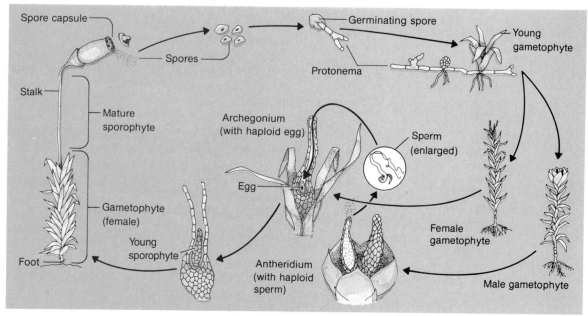

Spore capsule

Spores

Germinating spore

Young gametophyte

Protonema

Stalk

Mature sporophyte

Archegonium (with haploid egg)

Sperm (enlarged)

Egg

Gametophyte (female)

Young sporophyte

Female gametophyte

Foot

Antheridium (with haploid sperm)

Male gametophyte

Figure 19–3 The life cycle of mosses involves alternation of generations. A sporophyte, or spore-producing, stage alternates with a gametophyte, or gamete-producing, stage.

appearance and function. Although it grows out of the female gametophyte, it is neither female nor male. Instead of sperm and egg cells, the sporophyte contains many spores in a *capsule*. The stemlike *stalk* of the sporophyte is attached to the gametophyte by a *foot*. Both the stalk and the capsule contain chlorophyll, so that the sporophyte can make its own food. However, the sporophyte depends on the gametophyte for water, minerals, and some food.

The sporophyte produces spores through meiosis. Mature spores are released into the air. Under favorable conditions, these spores will germinate into a new protonema. This begins a new gametophyte generation.

Liverworts

There are about 6000 species of plants that belong to the class of liverworts. These tiny green plants look like flattened, branched leaves. The *thallus*, or body of the liverwort, has *lobes*, or rounded divisions. Liverworts are found in very moist places, such as stream banks.

Liverworts usually reproduce through alternation of generations, similar to mosses. In the gametophyte generation, liverworts produce antheridia that contain sperm cells, and archegonia that contain egg cells. The haploid sperm and egg unite to form a zygote that is diploid. The zygote develops into an embryo plant within the archegonium. The embryo plant is the beginning of the sporophyte generation.

Figure 19–4 Liverworts, such as this *Conocephalum*, make up an order of bryophytes.

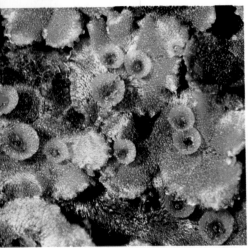

Courtesy Carolina Biological Supply Company

Figure 19-5 The thallus of the liverwort *Marchantia* produces specialized structures called gemmae cups.

Highlight

Tracheophytes are plants that contain vascular tissue called xylem and phloem.

Figure 19-6 This cross section of a fern sporophyte clearly shows bundles of vascular tissue characteristic of tracheophytes. Compare this cross section with the moss stem cross section in Figure 19–1.

Courtesy Carolina Biological Supply Company

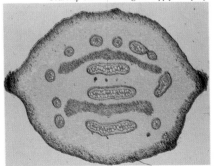

The sporophyte is made up of a foot, a stemlike stalk, and a capsule. Each capsule contains spores.

The structure of liverworts resembles that of mosses except that liverworts have *elaters*. These spindle-shaped structures respond to humidity changes in the environment and trigger the release of the spores into the air. Under moist conditions, the spores germinate into new gametophyte plants.

In addition to sexual reproduction, many species of liverworts reproduce *vegetatively*. This type of asexual reproduction occurs when new plants grow from parts of the parent plant. In *Marchantia*, shown in Figure 19-5, the older structures of the plant die away as the plant grows. Younger parts that are no longer attached to the plant develop into new individual plants. Several liverworts, such as *Marchantia*, also produce specialized structures on the thallus called **gemmae** (JEM-ē; singular: gemma) **cups**. Gemmae cups are notched, cup-shaped outgrowths that contain chlorophyll and are attached to the gametophyte by a short stem. Within these structures are *gemmae*, or tiny asexual bodies. Gemmae may separate from the thallus and grow into new plants. You may wish to ask students to prepare a chart of the forms of asexual reproduction they have studied thus far.

SECTION REVIEW   Answers on page T–61.

1. What are bryophytes?
2. Briefly describe the characteristics of mosses and liverworts.

Tracheophytes

Plants that contain vascular tissue are classified in division *Tracheophyta* (trā-kē-AH-fə-tə) and are called **tracheophytes.** Vascular tissues, which bryophytes do not possess, allow tracheophytes to live in drier environments than bryophytes can tolerate.

There are approximately 300,000 species of tracheophytes. Tracheophytes are classified into five subdivisions that include the *psilopsids, ferns, club mosses, horsetails,* and *seed-bearing plants.* Discussions of the first four subdivisions follow in this chapter. The seed-bearing plants are examined in Chapter 20.

Psilopsids

The oldest tracheophytes belong to the subdivision *Psilopsida* (sī-LAHP-si-də). Some of the oldest fossilized vascular plants are members of this subdivision. Scientists think that

Stress the importance of xylem and phloem in the psilopsids and ferns, and mention that these structures are also characteristic of seed-bearing plants.

319

some fossilized psilopsids are more than 400 million years old. There is only one order of psilopsids still living.

The living psilopsids of today look much like their ancestors. They have simple bodies and no true roots or leaves, making them similar to the bryophytes. The body of a psilopsid has two conducting vessels made of vascular tissue. The inner vascular tissue is known as **xylem** (ZĪ-ləm) and conducts water throughout the plant. The other vascular tissue, the **phloem** (FLŌ-əm), conducts nutrients throughout the plant.

One of two primitive genera of psilopsids living today is *Psilotum*. *Psilotum* grows on the ground or on the trunks of trees in tropical environments. The gametophyte of *Psilotum* is very small. It looks like a tiny forked tube with many branching rhizoids. The antheridia and archegonia grow on different parts of the gametophyte body. The sporophyte stage looks like an upright, forking stalk with no leaves. *Sporangia*, cases containing spores, develop at the tips of some of the forking stalks.

Figure 19-7 This *Psilotum* is an example of the primitive subdivision of tracheophytes called *Psilopsida*.

Ferns

Ferns belong to the subdivision *Pteropsida* (ter-AHP-si-də), which contains about 15,000 species. Most ferns are found in warm, moist, and shady woods and on mountain cliffs. Unlike bryophytes, ferns have conducting tissues and true roots, stems, and leaves.

Ferns are among the oldest plants on the earth, having appeared shortly after the psilopsids. These plants dominated the earth's landscape during the *Carboniferous Period*, between 300 and 345 million years ago. Fossil evidence indicates that many ferns were huge. Species of ferns the size of trees can still be found in tropical rain forests.

You may wish to refer students to the discussion of geological periods in Chapter 12.

Figure 19-8 Large ferns dominated the earth's landscape during the Carboniferous Period, as shown in this reconstruction.

Highlight

A fern has a stem, called a rhizome, that is usually located underground. The leaves of a fern are called fronds.

The ferns contain more specialized structures than the psilopsids. The stem of the fern is usually underground and is known as a **rhizome** (RĪ-zōm). A rhizome grows many **fronds,** or leaves. The fronds are large in comparison to the stem. They are made up of a *blade* and a *stipe*, or stalk. The blade is the extended leaf. The tip of a growing frond is a coiled structure called the *fiddlehead*. As the frond grows, the fiddlehead uncoils slowly and straightens out. The underside of the frond is dotted with reddish-brown **sori** (SŌ-rī; singular: sorus). These tiny, round structures contain clusters of sporangia, saclike structures that produce haploid spores. The sporangia break open and release the spores. They are carried from place to place by the wind.

A spore germinates and grows into a tiny, heart-shaped green plant. The new plant is called the **prothallus** (prō-THAL-əs) and contains chlorophyll, which enables the plant to perform photosynthesis. The prothallus represents the beginning of the haploid gametophyte generation. The mature prothallus is no more than two centimeters wide. Rhizoids

At this point, you may want to assign to several students the first of the Extensions and Applications at the end of this chapter.

CLOSE-UP: *Dr. Helen Stafford*

Botanist Helen Stafford has been studying plants for more than 30 years. She is Professor of Biology at Reed College in Portland, Oregon. Apart from teaching, she says that she spends 99% of her working time in the lab. "Going on field trips is my fun, but the lab is where my work is done," she says.

One hundred years ago, botanists had to actually go to forests and fields to study plant species. However, many twentieth-century botanists, such as Dr. Stafford, grow and study plant life in modern laboratories. Modern biologists are concerned with the biological systems and chemical processes of plants.

Over the years, Dr. Stafford has investigated many different areas of botany, and published many papers on various botanical subjects. One project that she has been working on for a number of years is a study of plant defense systems. "Plants have no immunological defense as human beings do, but they do produce a chemical defense against fungi, bacteria, and animals," she says. For example, woody plants produce a substance that causes their leaves to taste bitter to people and animals. Some plants, she added,

produce subtle poisons which, over time, may kill animals that continue to eat them.

Through research, Stafford is seeking to discover why plants use so much energy to make defense substances. She also wants to know how these defense substances are made. Most of the plant tissues that she studies are grown in her laboratory. In her work, she separates cellular parts into various fractions for biochemical analyses. Then, she is able to isolate and study individual processes occurring inside plant cells. "I take cells apart to see what makes them tick," explains Stafford.

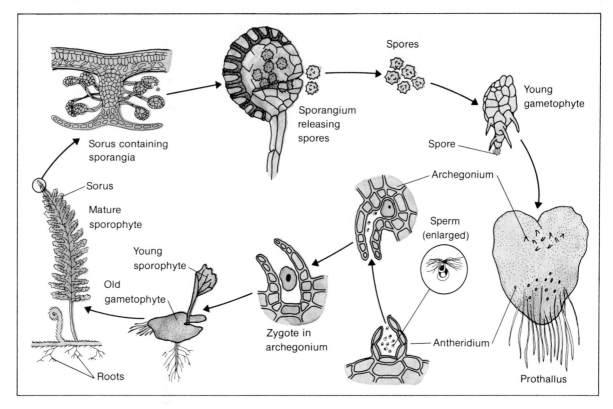

Figure 19–9 The life cycle of the fern, like that of the moss, involves alternation of generations. The fern's sporophyte generation is much larger than its gametophyte generation.

are found on the underside of the prothallus and attach it to moist soil.

The antheridia and archegonia are also located on the underside of the prothallus. The antheridia, which are dome-shaped structures found among the rhizoids, contain sperm. When water is present in the soil due to rain or dew, the antheridia absorb water and swell, finally releasing the sperm. These sperm swim toward the center of the prothallus, where the archegonia are located. These flask-shaped female organs each contain a large egg cell. When the archegonia absorb moisture, they often take in nearby sperm. The union of a sperm cell and an egg cell results in a zygote. The development of the zygote is the beginning of the diploid sporophyte generation. At this point, you may want to have your students do the Laboratory Investigation at the end of this chapter.

Club Mosses

Club mosses, which belong to the subdivision *Lycopsida* (lī-KAHP-si-də), include about 1000 species. Although ancient species of club mosses were quite large, present-day forms are tiny. Like ferns, club mosses are found in largest numbers in subtropical and tropical forests. They are also found in temperate regions.

Sidelight

Because ferns dominated the natural landscape during the Carboniferous Period, this geological period is often referred to as the Age of Ferns.

Be careful to point out that club mosses are not really mosses at all but tracheophytes.

Figure 19-10 The spore-bearing leaves of the club moss *Selaginella* are clusters at the tips of the stems.

At this point, you may want to assign to several students the second of the Extensions and Applications at the end of this chapter.

Figure 19-11 The stems of horsetails have nodes, or joints, and contain silica, making them tough.

The stems of club mosses have many tiny fan-shaped green leaves that spread out from each stem. Both the stem and roots contain vascular tissues that are arranged in irregular lobes. Commonly, club mosses such as *Lycopodium* are called "ground pines" or "trailing evergreens" because they resemble a tiny evergreen.

Club mosses reproduce by alternation of generations. The sporophytes of club mosses have tiny roots and leaves, which grow from the rhizomes. The sporangia are formed on special spore-bearing leaves. In some species, such as *Selaginella*, these leaves cluster at the tips of the stems, forming conelike structures. The sporangia produce two types of spores. The smaller *microspores* develop into the male gametophytes. The larger *megaspores* develop into the female gametophytes. These gametophytes develop antheridia and archegonia, respectively. Fertilization occurs when moisture is present and allows the sperm to swim to the egg cell in the archegonium.

Horsetails

Horsetails belong to the subdivision *Sphenopsida* (sfen-AHP-si-də). Members of this subdivision, now mostly extinct, once grew in great numbers. Fossils from the Carboniferous Period indicate that horsetails once grew as tall as 30 meters. Today *Equisetum* is the only living genus of horsetails. This genus name means horse bristle in Latin. The shoots of horsetail sporophytes look like the tails of horses. Horsetails usually are found in moist environments. However, a few may be found growing in dry areas.

Like the club mosses, horsetails have true roots, stems, and leaves. However, horsetails have their vascular tissue arranged in a ring of small bundles. Horsetail stems also contain glasslike silica, which makes the horsetail stronger. The stems of horsetail plants also have *nodes*, the knobs or joints along the stem from which leaves grow.

Along the leaves are many sporangia. Horsetail spores are unique because they contain chlorophyll. In a moist environment, the spores germinate into tiny, ribbonlike plants. These new plants later form antheridia and archegonia. Reproduction is similar to that of ferns and club mosses.

SECTION REVIEW   Answers on page T-61.

1. Name five subdivisions of tracheophytes.
2. List the structures of a fern and give their functions.
3. What is a sorus? A sporangium?
4. How do horsetails differ from club mosses?

LABORATORY INVESTIGATION 19 For additional information, see page T-61.

Investigating Mosses and Ferns

Purpose Mosses are bryophytes because they lack true roots, stems, and leaves. Ferns are tracheophytes because they have true roots, stems, and leaves. Like bryophytes, tracheophytes reproduce by alternation of generations, alternating between a gametophyte and a sporophyte. The purpose of this investigation is to examine mosses and ferns in order to compare their reproductive structures.

Materials *(per student)* ● Microscope ● Magnifying glass ● 2 slides ● 2 cover slips ● Forceps ● Scissors ● Specimens of mosses and ferns (both sporophyte and gametophyte generations)

Procedure **Part A: Mosses** **1.** Examine the moss specimens containing sporophytes and male and female gametophytes. Observe these plants with the magnifying glass. **2.** Locate the archegonia and antheridia. Sketch and label these structures, identifying the sporangia and capsule in the sporophyte plant. **3.** With the forceps and scissors, carefully remove a mature capsule and put it on a clean slide. **4.** To make a wet-mount slide, add a drop of water to the capsule. Place a cover slip over the water and capsule and gently press down on the cover slip to crush the capsule. **5.** Examine the capsule under low and high power. **Part B: Ferns** **1.** Obtain fern specimens containing sporophytes and male and female gametophytes. **2.** Examine the sporophyte plant. **3.** Locate the rhizomes, roots, stipe, and blade. Sketch and label these structures. **4.** With the magnifying glass, examine the underside of the fronds. **5.** Carefully remove a sorus from the underside of the frond and make a wet-mount slide. **6.** Examine the sorus under low and high power. **7.** Sketch what you see.

Observations and Conclusions **1.** How are the reproductive structures of mosses and ferns different? Similar? **2.** Why are mosses classified as bryophytes rather than as tracheophytes? **3.** Describe the appearance of the spores of the moss and the fern.

CHAPTER SUMMARY

Bryophytes Plants in the division *Bryophyta,* or bryophytes, were among the first terrestrial plants. Bryophytes have no true roots, stems, and leaves. These plants lack vascular tissue, an interior network of tubes through which food and water travel. Bryophytes undergo alternation of generations.

In mosses, a class of bryophyte, the gametophyte generation begins with the germination of a spore into a green threadlike structure called a protonema. The protonema grows into a small plant with rootlike structures called rhizoids. Male reproductive organs called antheridia produce sperm. Female reproductive organs called archegonia produce eggs. These reproductive cells are haploid, containing half the usual number of chromosomes. When an egg and sperm unite, fertilization occurs. This union is the beginning of the sporophyte generation. The diploid zygote, or fertilized egg, develops into a sporophyte. A diploid cell has the usual number of chromosomes. When the spores mature, they are released into the air. Under favorable conditions they germinate into new protonema. Mosses improve soil texture and trap moisture in the soil.

Another class of bryophytes, the liverworts, also undergoes alternation of generations. The thallus, or body of the liverwort, produces separate male and female plants. Some liverworts contain structures called gemmae that are notched discs attached to the thallus by a short stem. When a gemma separates from the gametophyte, it begins to grow into a new plant.

Tracheophytes Tracheophytes belong to the division *Tracheophyta.* These plants contain vascular tissue and have true roots, stems, and leaves. Tracheophytes are divided into five subdivisions. These subdivisions are psilopsids, tracheophytes, ferns, club mosses, horsetails, and seed-bearing plants.

The early tracheophytes, or psilopsids, can only be studied through their fossil remains. The living psilopsids contain two conducting vessels made of vascular tissue. The xylem conducts water throughout the plant while the phloem conducts nutrients.

Ferns and fernlike plants were once abundant on the earth millions of years ago. Ferns have true roots, stems, and leaves. The underground stems of ferns are called rhizomes. Each rhizome grows many fronds, or leaves. The undersides of these fronds are dotted with reddish-brown spots, called sori, that produce sporangia. The sporangia contain spores. Sporangia break open and release spores. Spores are carried from place to place by the wind. When a spore germinates, it grows into a heart-shaped structure called a prothallus. This begins the gametophyte stage. Each prothallus has antheridia and archegonia. When the archegonia absorb moisture, they take in nearby sperm. The eggs and sperm join and the sporophyte generation begins again.

Club mosses resemble tiny evergreens. They are different from the other tracheophytes in that they form two types of spores, microspores and megaspores. These spores produce the antheridia and archegonia, respectively.

Horsetails have several more advanced structures than club mosses. The horsetail stem has clearly formed nodes, or knobs, and contain glass silica. Also the spores of horsetails contain chlorophyll.

CHAPTER VOCABULARY

antheridium	phloem	tracheophyte
archegonium	prothallus	vascular tissue
bryophyte	protonema	xylem
frond	rhizome	
gemma cup	sorus	

REVIEW of FACTS and CONCEPTS   Answers on pages T–61 to T–62.

On a separate sheet of paper, answer each of the following as completely as possible.

1. What are the two major classes of bryophytes? Give an example for each class.
2. Why was the development of vascular tissue so important to the development of land plants?
3. List the common names of the three orders of mosses.
4. How is the reproductive method of bryophytes different from that of algae? How is it similar?
5. Summarize the life cycle of a moss.
6. What is the importance of mosses in the environment?
7. What is the function of gemmae in liverworts?
8. What place do the psilopsids have in the history of plants?
9. Diagram the life cycle of a fern. Label all structures.
10. Explain the differences between mosses and club mosses.
11. Why are the spores of horsetails unique?
12. Explain the difference between the following pairs of terms: haploid and diploid; rhizoid and rhizome; and protonema and prothallus.

EXTENSIONS and APPLICATIONS   For additional information, see page T–62.

1. In a wooded area, find mosses, ferns, and other kinds of plants that have been discussed in this chapter. Use a trowel to remove a few of these plants. Be sure to remove some of the surrounding soil along with each plant. Place each plant in a plastic bag until you get home. When you have finished collecting the plants, consult a reference book to find out how to make a terrarium. A terrarium is a mini-environment that duplicates the growing conditions of organisms. After planting, gently spray-mist the plants. Be sure to use a glass lid to trap the moisture within the container. Why are mosses and ferns ideal for a terrarium? Why should they be kept away from direct sunlight?
2. Look for a horsetail in a moist, swampy area. Carefully remove a thin section of the outer portion of the plant. Notice how it feels. Mount it on a slide and view it under a microscope. Look for the glasslike silica material in the plant. Draw and label what you see.

SUGGESTED READINGS

Bland, J., *Forests of Lilliput: The Realm of Mosses and Lichens.* Englewood Cliffs, N.J.: Prentice-Hall.
   The structure, physiology, and reproduction of mosses and lichens are discussed.
Mikel, J.T., *How to Know the Ferns and Fern Allies.* Dubuque, Iowa: William C. Brown.
   This book is an illustrated guide to the identification of ferns and some fern allies, or club mosses, in North America.
Perl, P., and the Editors of Time-Life Books, *Ferns.* Alexandria, Va.: Time-Life Books.
   This illustrated volume explores the natural history, diversity, and reproduction of ferns.

20 Seed-Bearing Plants

For teaching aids for this chapter, including a chapter overview and teaching strategies, see pages T–62 to T–63. The page number next to each chapter objective refers to the text page where the information needed to fulfill the objective begins.

Wind disperses the seeds of these dandelions.

A **seed** is a reproductive structure that contains a young plant, stored food, and a protective seed coat. The seed is produced by the joining of a male and a female gamete. When placed in warm, moist soil, the seed grows by using its stored food and absorbing water from the soil.

The first plants to bear seeds, called seed ferns, are thought to have lived more than 300 million years ago during the Carboniferous Period. Today, seed-bearing plants are among the most numerous of the tracheophytes, or vascular plants. Some botanists think that these plants are the descendants of the now-extinct seed ferns.

A reason for the success of seed-bearing plants is that their vascular, or conducting, tissues enable them to adapt to dry land environments. Another advantage is that they do not need water for fertilization to occur. Instead, the *pollen*, which contains the male gamete, is carried to the female gametes by other means, such as wind.

Characteristics of Seed-Bearing Plants

You may find it useful at this point to have students compare the types of reproduction characteristic of each division of plants studied so far.

At this point, you may want to assign to several students the first of the Extensions and Applications at the end of this chapter.

Figure 20-1 The seeds of gymnosperms do not develop within a protective structure. In many cases, the seeds are carried on the scales of structures called cones. The seeds of angiosperms develop within the protective walls of fruits.

The seed-bearing plants make up the fifth subdivision, *Spermopsida* (sper-MOP-sə-də), of tracheophytes. This subdivision is itself divided into two classes, based on the appearance of the seeds. In **gymnosperms** (JIM-nə-spermz), the seeds do not develop within a protective wall. Most of the seeds of gymnosperms develop in structures called **cones**. In **angiosperms** (AN-jē-ə-spermz), the seeds develop within a protective structure called a **fruit.** Angiosperms also produce **flowers,** or organs with a reproductive function.

Seed-bearing plants undergo *alternation of generations.* In this type of reproduction, an asexual stage alternates with a sexual stage. In the asexual stage, the sporophyte, or spore-producing plant, has diploid cells, or cells that contain the normal number of chromosomes.

Two types of spores are formed from the sporophyte, the *megaspore* and the *microspore*. These spores become the gametophytes, or gamete-producing plants, that contribute to the sexual phase. The megaspore develops into the *ovule,* which contains the egg, or female gamete. The microspore grows into the *pollen grain,* which holds the sperm, or male gamete. The microscopic gametophytes are found within the sporophyte plant. These plants rely on the larger plant for their nutrition and protection. Each type of gamete, the egg and the sperm, is said to be haploid. They each contain half the normal number of chromosomes.

When fertilization occurs, a diploid zygote results. The zygote develops into the sporophyte embryo plant, which is held in a seed. When conditions are favorable, the seed begins to *germinate,* or grow, into the sporophyte plant, and the plant's cycle begins again.

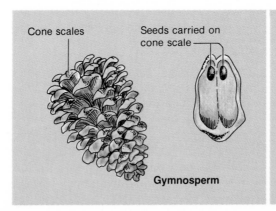

Cone scales

Seeds carried on cone scale

Gymnosperm

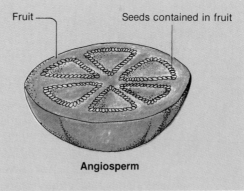

Fruit

Seeds contained in fruit

Angiosperm

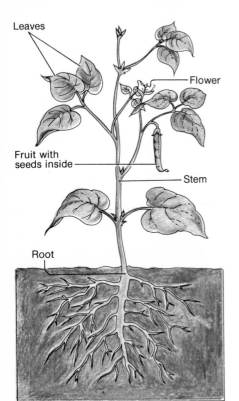

Leaves

Flower

Fruit with seeds inside

Stem

Root

Figure 20-2 Roots, stems, and leaves are the vegetative organs of seed-bearing plants. Angiosperms develop reproductive organs called flowers.

If you do not have enough time to cover the following three chapters in detail, you may wish at this point to summarize the information presented there or to assign specific readings in those chapters.

Stress that respiration is an energy-releasing chemical process usually involving oxygen. Many students incorrectly associate respiration with breathing.

Figure 20-3 Plants such as this Chinese bitter melon develop coiling supportive structures called tendrils.

You may want to have several students attempt to grow plants by means of vegetative propagation.

External Features

Most seed-bearing plants have three external features. These features are the **roots**, the **stems**, and the **leaves**. Together these structures are the **vegetative organs** of the plant and perform all the life processes except sexual reproduction. In some seed-bearing plants, the vegetative organs can grow into new plants through a process called *vegetative propagation*. For example, new strawberry plants can develop from runners, or horizontal stems, that touch the soil. Dahlias and columbines can be grown vegetatively from leaves or from pieces of leaves. Angiosperms have a fourth external feature, called the *flower*, which plays a role in reproduction.

ROOTS Roots have several functions. They anchor the plant in the soil, absorb minerals and water from the soil, and conduct these substances up to the stem. In some cases, roots also store the food made by the plant. Roots that grow in water, such as those of the water hyacinth, are called *aquatic roots*. Roots that grow above the soil, such as those of certain orchids, are called *aerial roots*. Roots that store food, such as beets and carrots, are called *fleshy roots*.

STEMS Stems serve several purposes. One purpose is to support the plant and produce the leaves. Another function is to carry water and minerals from the roots to the leaves. At the same time, stems conduct the food that was made in the leaves down to the roots. In some plants the stems act as storage areas for food, and in other plants green stems are able to make their own food.

Stems may be either *herbaceous* or *woody*. Herbaceous stems are soft, green, and fleshy. Plants with herbaceous stems are supported by the pressure of the water in the stem. For this reason, plants with herbaceous stems, such as most flowers and vegetables, droop when they do not have enough water. Woody stems are hard. Plants with woody stems, such as trees and shrubs, do not droop when they lack water.

LEAVES Three important functions take place in leaves. In *photosynthesis*, the plant makes food for itself. In *respiration*, the plant breaks down the food to produce energy. Both photosynthesis and respiration produce gases as byproducts. These gases pass through the leaves into the air surrounding the plant. Also passing into the air is any excess water that has been absorbed through the roots and up into the stem. The process of releasing water vapor from the leaves is called *transpiration*.

The leaves of certain plants develop long and slender structures called *tendrils*. Tendrils coil around the plant and sometimes around nearby objects as well. The coiling aids in the support of the plant. The garden pea and greenbriar are examples of plants with tendrils.

Another type of leaf is called a *spine*. Spines are leaves that have lost their green color during their early development. They are slender, hard, and conelike. Spines are found in such plants as cacti.

FLOWERS   The organ of sexual reproduction in angiosperms is the flower. It contains the male and female gametes that unite during fertilization. After fertilization, part of the flower develops into *fruit*. The fruit encloses the seeds that contain embryo plants.

Flowers differ in the number and arrangement of their *petals* and *sepals*. Petals are brightly colored and leaflike. Sepals are green and leaflike, and they surround the flower when it is a bud. Although petals and sepals are usually arranged in concentric rings, the number of them in each ring depends upon the species of flower.

Specialized Tissues

Over the millions of years that seed-bearing plants have been on earth, they have developed complex structures. These structures are made up of specialized plant *tissues*. Tissues are groups of cells that are similar in structure and function. Groups of tissues, in turn, form the various organs in plants.

Tissues are divided into six groups. Except for their cell structure, these tissue types are very similar in both gymnosperms and angiosperms. In both classes of seed-bearing plants, each type of specialized tissue has a specific function, such as the growth, development, or repair of plant parts.

EPIDERMAL TISSUE   The outermost layer of cells on the roots, stems, and leaves is **epidermal tissue.** In most plants, the epidermal tissue is only one cell thick, but it protects and covers the tissues beneath it. The epidermal tissue on stems and leaves contains a waxy substance that cuts down on the amount of water lost by the plant.

MERISTEMATIC TISSUE   At the tips of stems and roots are areas of rapid cell division called *meristems*. Within these areas, **meristematic** (mer-ə-stə-MAT-ik) **tissue** is found. As meristematic tissue grows, it increases the length of these structures.

Figure 20-4   Flowers, such as the lily (*top*) and bird cherry blossom (*bottom*), differ considerably in color, size, and form.

Students sometimes confuse the types of specialized tissues with particular areas or structures, such as cambium, that contain such tissues. It may be useful to write the types of specialized tissues on the chalkboard and fill in functions and examples as you proceed.

Figure 20-5 Specialized Plant Tissues

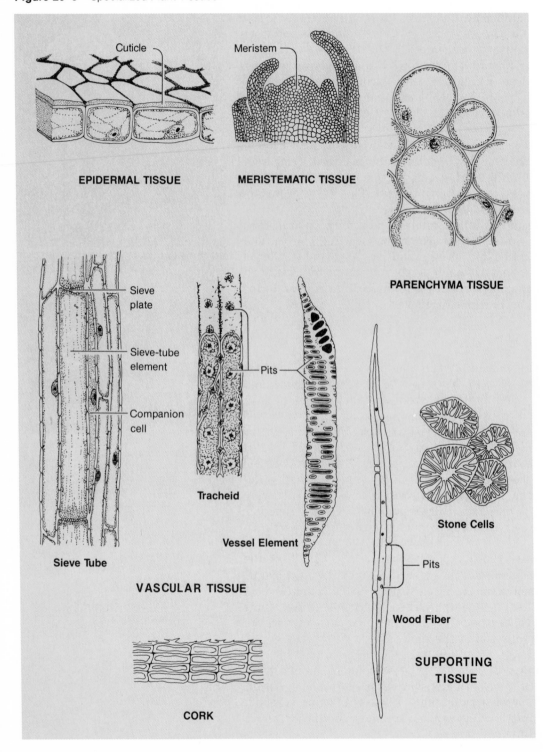

Another area that contains meristematic tissue is the **cambium** (KAM-bē-əm). The cambium is a cylinder of tissue that is found in stems and roots. This tissue is only one cell thick. As the cells in the cambium reproduce by cell division, the roots and stems increase in diameter.

Meristematic tissue *differentiates*, or develops, into specialized tissues. These tissues develop into organs, such as leaves and flowers. Meristematic tissue also differentiates to enable it to carry materials throughout the plant.

PARENCHYMA TISSUE   The organisms in which **parenchyma** (pə-REN-ki-mə) **tissue** is found are mainly herbaceous plants and the leaves, the flowers, and sometimes the fruits of woody plants. The cells in the parenchyma tissue are large and contain large vacuoles. This tissue is able to store food and water very well.

Photosynthesis takes place in parenchyma cells that contain the green pigment chlorophyll. These cells, sometimes called **chlorenchyma** (klor-EN-ki-mə), are found under the epidermal layer on leaves and on some flower parts and stems.

VASCULAR TISSUE   Materials are conducted throughout the plant by *vascular tissue*. Like the other tracheophytes, seed-bearing plants have two kinds of conducting tissues. While the *phloem* conducts food throughout the plant, the *xylem* carries water and minerals and helps to support the plant. In herbaceous plants, the phloem almost entirely surrounds the xylem. In woody shrubs and trees, the xylem forms the trunk, and the phloem is found in the *bark*, the outside covering of the stem.

In gymnosperms, the xylem tissue is made up primarily of **tracheids** (TRĀ-kē-idz). Tracheids are long, pointed cells that have thick walls. Usually in the walls are tiny holes, called *pits*, that enable one tracheid to attach to another. By connecting in this way tracheids form columns that support the plant. Tracheids also form tubes through which water flows. The wood of gymnosperms is composed mainly of dead tracheids. Although some tracheids are also present in angiosperms, their xylem is made up mainly of cells called **vessel elements.** Vessel elements are joined into **vessels.** Vessels are tubes up to 1 meter long. Like tracheids, most vessel elements are dead and contain pits.

The phloem of angiosperms is made up of **sieve-tube elements.** These elements get their name from the sievelike holes in the end walls of their cells. These end walls are called *sieve plates*. The cells of the sieve-tube elements join end to end to form **sieve tubes.** Sieve tubes conduct food

Highlight

The tissues of seed-bearing plants are divided into six groups. These groups are epidermal tissue, meristematic tissue, parenchyma tissue, vascular tissue, supporting tissue, and cork.

down the stem. Although the phloem of gymnosperms is similar to that of angiosperms, the sieve tubes of gymnosperms do not contain sieve plates.

A unique feature of the cells of sieve-tube elements is that their nuclei usually disintegrate during cell development. Although cells usually live only a few days or so without their nuclei, sieve-tube element cells may live for several years after the loss of theirs. Scientists think that the nuclei of other adjacent phloem cells, or **companion cells,** help the sieve-tube elements carry out their life functions.

SUPPORTING TISSUE   Tissue called **sclerenchyma** (skli-REN-ki-mə) strengthens and supports parts of plants. Two types of cells are found in sclerenchyma tissue. *Fiber cells,* the first type, are long and slender. They occur in clusters, and they support and give hardness to the plant. These cells form the fibers that are used commercially to make ropes and threads. The Philippine abaca plant, for example contains fiber cells. It produces Manila hemp, which is used to make rope.

CAREER: Forester

Forests cover about one-third of the land area of the United States. Foresters plan and care for these wooded areas in numerous ways. They recommend ways in which forests can best be used for both economic and recreational purposes. They map and survey woodlands to learn how much timber is available and how fast it will grow. They then decide which trees can be cut.

Foresters must be aware not only of diseases that affect different types of trees, but also of insect pests and how to control them. Perhaps the most important aspect of foresting is conducting fire prevention programs. During forest fires, foresters must supervise hundreds of fire fighters. Another responsibility of foresters is to rescue people who have gotten lost in the forest.

Foresters deal with a wide variety of people, such as landowners, loggers, wildlife conservationists, and tourists. Foresters also work with architects who design campsites and with specialists in tree diseases, flood control, and erosion.

Many foresters also do research. They try to find ways to cut timber in order to limit damage to the environment and to ensure a continuous production of timber. They develop ways to pro-

tect forests from fire and study ways to process wood for various uses.

A bachelor's degree is needed to become a forester. People who have high school diplomas may begin as forestry assistants. Forestry assistants trim trees, cut down dead trees, and remove stumps. They also remove fallen branches, logs, and other debris from the forest.

Many foresters work for lumber companies. Others work for federal and state governments.

For further career information, write to Society of American Foresters, 1010 Sixteenth Street N.W., Washington, DC 20036.

At this point, you may want to assign to several students the second of the Extensions and Applications at the end of this chapter.

333

The second type of cells in sclerenchyma are the *stone cells*. These branched cells of different shapes add rigidity to the plant. They are found in roots and stems, in the pulps of fruits and the shells of nuts. Stone cells give pears their gritty texture.

CORK   The waxy outer tissue of woody stems and roots is called **cork.** Cork cells, which are short-lived, contain a waterproof substance that helps to prevent water loss. Usually box-shaped and flat, cork cells fit together tightly.

Growth Cycles

You may want to ask students to bring in actual examples or photographs of annuals, biennials, and perennials.

One method biologists use to group seed-bearing plants is according to the length of their growth cycle. According to this method, seed-bearing plants are classified in three groups.

An **annual** is a plant whose entire life cycle, from germination to seed production, takes place within one growing season. The new seeds produced at the end of one cycle begin another cycle at the start of the next growing season. Most annuals are herbaceous. Cereal plants, peas, beans, and tobacco are examples of annuals.

A **biennial** (bī-EN-ē-əl) lives for two growing seasons. During the first season, it grows roots, short stems, and a rosette of leaves. Most biennials then require a period of colder temperatures, after which they develop flowers, fruits, and seeds. Biennials may be either herbaceous or woody. Many garden food plants, such as beets, celery, cabbage, and carrots, are biennials.

A **perennial** (pə-REN-ē-əl) is a plant that lives for more than two growing seasons. Perennials are either woody or herbaceous. In temperate climates, the above-ground plant structures of perennials die at the end of each growing season, but their underground roots or stems remain alive. Asparagus, rhubarb, peony, and dahlia are examples of herbaceous perennial plants. Trees, shrubs, and vines are examples of woody perennial plants.

Figure 20-6   Seed-bearing plants can be grouped on the basis of the number of growing seasons for which they live. The tobacco plant (*top*) is an annual. The flowering cabbage (*center*) is a biennial. The tree peony (*bottom*) is a perennial.

SECTION REVIEW   Answers on page T–62.

1. Define gymnosperm and angiosperm.
2. List the characteristics of seed-bearing plants.
3. What are the functions of roots, stems, leaves, and flowers?
4. Name and give the functions of the specialized tissues in seed-bearing plants.
5. Define annuals, biennials, and perennials.

Gymnosperms

Highlight

Cycads, gingkos, and conifers make up the three orders of gymnosperms.

Gymnosperms are thought to have existed more than 300 million years ago during the Carboniferous Period. Many of the early gymnosperms, now extinct, are known only from fossil records. Today, more than 700 species make up the three major orders of gymnosperms: *Cycadophyta* (sī-kə-dō-FĪ-tə), or cycads (SI-kadz); *Gingkophyta* (gin-kə-FĪ-tə), or gingkoes; and *Coniferophyta* (kohn-i-fer-ō-FĪ-tə), or conifers.

Cycads

Cycads were the most numerous land plants during the Mesozoic Era, more than 125 million years ago. Present-day cycads are found mostly in tropical regions. They are generally small trees that look like ferns or palm trees, although some have been known to reach a height of 18 meters. An example of a cycad is *Zamia*, which is found in Florida, Mexico, and Central America. Growing at the top of its trunk, which is underground, its leaves resemble a feathery crown.

Figure 20-7 This *Zamia* grows in tropical regions and is an example of a cycad.

Gingkoes

The gingko, or maidenhair tree, which was first identified in China, can grow up to 30 meters tall. The only living species of the gingko is *Gingko biloba*. The species name, *biloba*, comes from its double-lobed, fan-shaped leaves.

In the gingko, the male and female cones, or reproductive structures, are found on separate plants. The cones of the male plant, which contain the pollen, resemble cat tails.

Figure 20-8 Decorative gingko trees (*left*) are sometimes grown along city streets. Female gingkoes develop fleshy seeds (*right*) that are about the size of cherries.

The cones of the female plant, which contain the ovules, are found in pairs at the end of long stalks. After fertilization, the ovules develop into yellowish seeds that are about the size of cherries and have an unpleasant odor. In fact, the odor is so unpleasant that male rather than female gingko trees are usually cultivated on streets and in parks and gardens.

Conifers

The largest order of gymnosperms consists of the conifers, whose name means *cone-bearing*. Thought to have first appeared during the Carboniferous Period, conifers are now found in temperate or colder climates throughout the world.

Conifers are woody plants that produce cones with either pollen or ovules that eventually develop into seeds. *Pollen cones* are found in clusters at the tips of branches in the spring. *Ovulate*, or seed, *cones*, which are larger and woodier than pollen cones, produce seeds on the upper parts of shelf-like cone scales. The shapes and sizes of seed cones are used to identify various species of conifers.

Most conifers, such as the pines, cedars, cypresses, firs, hemlocks, and spruces, are evergreen. In other words, their leaves or needles stay green year round and may remain on the plant for 2 to 12 years. In contrast, two other kinds of conifers, larches and bald cypresses, tend to shed their leaves regularly.

Most conifers are trees, even though some, such as the junipers, are shrubs or small woody plants. Some types of conifer trees may get to be very large or very old. In California, one redwood, which represents the tallest type of conifer, is 112 meters tall. The bristlecone pine trees in eastern Nevada are thought to be more than 4000 years old.

SECTION REVIEW   Answers on pages T-62 to T-63.

1. What are the names of the three major orders of gymnosperms? Give an example of each order.
2. Describe the pollen cones and seed cones of conifers.

Angiosperms

With 250,000 species, the angiosperms, or flowering plants, are the most numerous of land plants. Angiosperms are also the most recently developed of these plants. They are thought to have appeared about 100 million years ago, during the Cretaceous (krēTĀ-shəs) Period. Fossil evidence has

Figure 20-9   Firs, spruces, and other conifers grow in forests in many cool areas of the world.

At this point, you may want to have your students do the Laboratory Investigation at the end of this chapter.

Figure 20-10   These wildflowers contain male and female sexual reproductive structures typical of angiosperms.

Figure 20-11 The orchid (*top*) is an example of a monocot, an angiosperm whose seeds have one cotyledon. The saguaro cactus (*bottom*) is an example of a dicot, an angiosperm whose seeds have two cotyledons.

Highlight

Monocots are angiosperms with one cotyledon. Dicots are angiosperms with two cotyledons.

At this point, you may want to assign to several students the third of the Extensions and Applications at the end of this chapter.

shown that the angiosperms developed specialized parts at a faster rate than the other vascular plants did. Such specialized parts as flowers, seeds within fruits, large leaves, and complex vascular tissue make angiosperms a highly successful group of plants.

Angiosperms have many features in common with gymnosperms, from which they probably developed. The two types of seed-bearing plants differ, however, in several ways. Perhaps the most obvious of these differences is the presence of a flower, or reproductive organ in angiosperms. In most angiosperms, the flower contains both the male and female structures necessary to produce the pollen and the ovules. Enclosing the ovules is a structure called the *ovary.* After fertilization, the ovary enlarges, ripens, and becomes a fruit, enclosing and protecting the seed. Another difference is that the xylem and phloem are more specialized in angiosperms than in gymnosperms. Also, whereas gymnosperms are usually woody, angiosperms include many herbaceous plants.

Another feature of angiosperms is the number of their **cotyledons** (kaht-'l-ĒD-'nz), or first leaves developed by the embryo plant. In most angiosperms, the cotyledons provide the food for the growing plant. The flowering plants are divided into two subclasses according to whether they have one or two cotyledons.

Monocots   The types of angiosperms that have one cotyledon are called **monocots,** and they are placed in the subclass *Monocotyledonae* (mahn-ə-kaht-'l-Ē-dən-ē). There are more than 65,000 species of monocots, including for example, grasses, orchids, irises, lilies, and palms.

Dicots   Angiosperms that have two cotyledons are called **dicots,** and they are placed in the subclass *Dicotyledonae* (dī-kaht-'l-Ē-dən-ē). Cacti, beeches, roses, maples, walnuts, peas, and beans are only a few examples of the more than 170,000 species of dicots.

SECTION REVIEW   Answers on page T–63.

1. What specialized parts of angiosperms enable them to be a highly successful group of plants?
2. What are some differences between gymnosperms and angiosperms?
3. Name and briefly describe the two subclasses of angiosperms.

LABORATORY INVESTIGATION 20 For additional information, see page T-63.

Investigating Gymnosperms

Purpose   In conifers, which are gymnosperms, seeds are found in structures called cones. Some familiar conifers are pines, spruces, cedars, and firs. The purpose of this investigation is to examine the structures and life cycle of a representative gymnosperm, the pine.

Materials *(per group)*   ● Several species of pine branches with needles   ● Pine branch bearing male cones   ● Pine branch bearing female cones ● Two-year-old female cone   ● Pine seeds ● Hand lens   ● Microscope   ● 2 glass slides ● Cover slips   ● Knife   ● White paper

Procedure   1. Examine the branch of each species of pine. Count and record the number of needles in the bundles of each branch. Sketch each branch and label all the structures.   **2.** Choose a branch bearing male cones. **CAUTION:** *Be very careful when using a knife.* With the knife, cut a cone in two lengthwise. Remove one of the cone scales and examine the two sacs of pollen with a hand lens.   **3.** Gently crush one of these sacs, and place some of the pollen grains in a drop of water on a glass slide.   **4.** Add a cover slip and examine the pollen with the microscope under low and high powers. Sketch and label all the structures under each magnification.   **5.** Examine a branch bearing a two-year-old female or seed cone. Note the arrangement of the scales on the cone. Sketch and label the parts of the female cone.   **6.** Look for a scale that bears two winged seeds on its upper surface, near the point at which it was attached to the cone. Remove a small number of these seeds, and place them on a sheet of white paper.   **7.** Examine the seeds with the hand lens and sketch what you see. **8.** Soak a pine seed in water overnight. Then carefully remove the seed coat. Sketch and label all the structures of the seed.

Observations and Conclusions   1. How many needles occur in the bundle of each pine tree species? Do all pine tree species have the same number of needles?   **2.** How are different species of pine recognized?   **3.** How are the male cones arranged on pine branches? How do male and female cones differ? **4.** Did you observe any differences in structure between pollen grains and seeds? Any similarities?

CHAPTER SUMMARY

Characteristics of Seed-Bearing Plants Seed-bearing plants, the most numerous land plants, have special adaptive structures that enable them to survive in dry land environments. Their seeds contain a young plant, stored food, and a protective seed coat.

The two classes of seed-bearing plants are the gymnosperms and the angiosperms. Gymnosperms contain seeds that do not develop within a protective wall and are found in cones. The seeds of angiosperms develop within a protective wall called a fruit. All the flowering plants are angiosperms.

The external features of seed-bearing plants are roots, stems, and leaves. These structures are the vegetative organs of the plant. Angiosperms contain another external feature called flowers, which are reproductive organs.

Seed-bearing plants are made up of many types of cells and tissues. Epidermal tissue covers the roots, stems, and leaves of the plant. Meristematic tissue continuously forms new cells. Parenchyma tissue is involved in food-making and storage. Vascular, or conducting, tissues include xylem and phloem. The supporting tissue is made up of sclerenchyma cells. Cork is waterproof tissue that surrounds woody stems and roots.

Seed-bearing plants may be classified as annuals, biennials, or perennials, according to the lengths of their growth cycles. Annuals have a growth cycle of about a year, while biennials live for about two years and perennials persist for an indefinite period of time.

Gymnosperms Cycads, gingkos, and conifers are the three major orders of gymnosperms. Conifers, gymnosperms that produce pollen and seed cones, make up the largest order.

Angiosperms Angiosperms are the most numerous of seed-bearing plants. The two major subclasses of angiosperms are dicots and monocots. Monocots have one cotyledon, or seed leaf, while dicots have two cotyledons.

CHAPTER VOCABULARY

angiosperm	epidermal tissue	sclerenchyma
annual	flower	seed
biennial	fruit	sieve tube
cambium	gymnosperm	sieve-tube element
chlorenchyma	leaf	stem
companion cell	meristematic tissue	tracheid
cone	monocot	vegetative organ
cork	parenchyma tissue	vessel
cotyledon	perennial	vessel element
dicot	root	

REVIEW of FACTS and CONCEPTS   Answers on page T–63.

On a separate sheet of paper, answer each of the following as completely as possible.

1. What is a seed?
2. Why have the seed-bearing plants been successful for millions of years?
3. Briefly describe alternation of generations in seed-bearing plants.
4. Name and briefly describe the different types of roots, stems, and leaves.
5. Sketch and label each of the specialized tissues in seed-bearing plants.
6. How is meristematic tissue different from other kinds of plant tissue?
7. How do the vascular tissues in gymnosperms and angiosperms differ? How are they similar?
8. Describe the male and female cones in conifers.
9. What is a cotyledon?
10. Distinguish between the following pairs of terms: vegetative and reproductive organs; herbaceous and woody stems; and xylem and phloem.

EXTENSIONS and APPLICATIONS For additional information, see page T–63.

1. Obtain three different types of flowers. Gently remove some pollen grains from each of them. Place the pollen grains on separate glass slides. Using a stereomicroscope or a hand lens, examine and diagram each of the different types of pollen grains. What are some of the structural adaptations that you see?

2. From old magazines, cut out photographs of angiosperms and gymnosperms. Arrange the pictures on posterboard, and classify them as angiosperms or gymnosperms. Use reference materials to identify each plant. Next to each photograph, draw the seed-bearing structure for the plant.

3. Obtain a very ripe pear. Carefully remove the skin, and then slice off a thin section of the pulp with a knife. Using a compound microscope, look for the stone cells. Why do these cells give a gritty texture to some fruits?

SUGGESTED READINGS

Galston, A.W., P.J. Davies, and R.L. Satter, *The Life of the Green Plant.* Englewood Cliffs, N.J.: Prentice-Hall.
This book provides a comprehensive look at the physiology of a green plant. It also serves as a source of ideas for high-school projects.

Greulach, V., and J.E. Adams, *Plants: An Introduction to Modern Botany.* New York: John Wiley.
In this text, the authors emphasize the concepts and principles of modern botany. In addition, they include the historical background of such topics as photosynthesis, mineral nutrition, and genetics.

Went, F.W., and the Editors of Life, *The Plants.* New York: Time-Life Books.
In this basic botany book, emphasis is placed on the seed-bearing plants. Many colorful photographs of angiosperms and gymnosperms are included.

21 Roots and Stems

Banyan tree roots grow down from the branches into the soil.

For teaching aids for this chapter, including a chapter overview and teaching strategies, see pages T–63 to T–65. The page number next to each chapter objective refers to the text page where the information needed to fulfill the objective begins.

The vegetation of the earth is made up mainly of seed-bearing plants. Over millions of years, these plants have developed not only rigid cell structures, but also certain organs that enable them to survive in relatively dry environments.

The development of special structures such as *roots* and *stems* has allowed certain plants to grow extremely tall. Roots anchor plants in the soil, while they absorb water and minerals. Certain roots also store food materials. Stems conduct material throughout plants and provide support for them.

Roots

Observing the growth of a corn or bean root on a sheet of moistened filter paper or sponge can be very revealing. As the plant starts to grow, an *embryonic root* appears. The first root to develop from the embryonic root is the **primary root.** Smaller **secondary roots** grow from the primary root.

If the primary root continues to be the main root as the plant grows, it is called a **taproot.** Sometimes the taproot becomes much bigger than the stem to which it is attached. Taproots that store food are called *fleshy roots.* Such plants as beets, carrots, and radishes are fleshy roots.

The secondary roots of some plants develop into threadlike, highly branched **fibrous roots,** which are made up of many roots of nearly equal size. They do not grow as deeply underground as taproots do, but they help to hold soil particles together. In this way, fibrous roots help to prevent *erosion,* or the wearing away of the soil. As an example, the roots found in rye and other grasses are fibrous.

Some roots are highly specialized. For example, the roots of the willow tree are longer than those of other trees. They are able to grow toward the source of underground water in dry climates. Many desert plants have an extensive root system that takes in and stores water. Such plants can survive in an environment in which the soil is dry for most of the year.

The composition of the soil around roots affects the growth of the entire plant. The **topsoil,** typically the uppermost layer in plant soil, contains **humus,** a mixture of roots and decayed organic materials. Humus is valuable to farmers because it is rich in minerals that plants need.

Figure 21-1 The primary root appears first in a young seedling. Secondary roots then branch off from the primary root. The primary root of the dandelion (*center*) is a taproot. The secondary roots of the African violet (*right*) are fibrous roots.

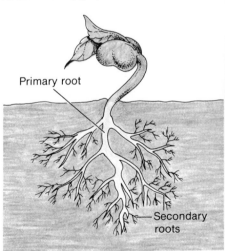

Primary root

Secondary roots

At this point, you may want to have your students do Part A of the Laboratory Investigation at the end of this chapter.

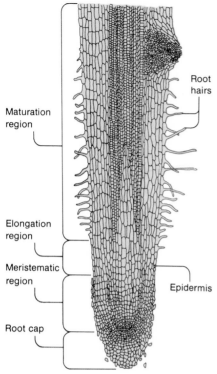

Figure 21-2 Structure of a Root Tip

Structure of Roots

The end of the root absorbs water and minerals for the plant and is called the *root tip*. Several layers of cells protect the root tip, and they are called the **root cap.** In the root cap, new cells often replace older ones as the root pushes its way into the soil.

The root tip is made up of the root cap and three other parts. The **meristematic region** gives rise to all new cells. Above the meristematic region is the **elongation region.** In this region, newly formed cells, by increasing in length, push the meristematic region and the root cap deeper into the soil. In the **maturation region,** cells mature and become *differentiated*, or specialized in their functions. Some of the cells in the outer layer of this region develop **root hairs.** A root hair is a microscopic projection of an individual cell at the surface of the root. Through the thin membrane of the root hair, the cell easily absorbs water. The large numbers of root hairs all along the root greatly increases the surface area of the root, enabling it to absorb a maximum amount of water and dissolved minerals.

As a root grows, it develops different kinds of tissues. The first group of cells that form in a young root make up the **primary tissues** of the root. After a root's primary tissues have matured, tissues that then develop are called **secondary tissues.**

PRIMARY TISSUES   The best way to examine primary tissues is to look at a thin cross section of a young root. Primary tissue is made up of three regions.

The **epidermis** is the outermost tissue of the root. The epidermis usually is made up of a single layer of cells and many root hairs. The root hair and the epidermal cell from which it grows make up a single cell.

The **cortex** lies just inside the epidermis. The cortex is several cell layers thick, and it is made up of *parenchyma cells,* or storage cells. These cells have thin walls with spaces between them. The cortex is surrounded on its inner side by an *endodermis,* or inner skin. The endodermis, which is only one cell thick, is also composed of parenchyma cells. Scientists think that the endodermis controls the movement of water between the cortex and the center of the root. Within the endodermis is a cell layer called the *pericycle,* which is made up of a single layer of parenchyma cells. These cells are meristematic because they give rise to other cells, such as the secondary roots, during the growth process.

The **vascular cylinder,** found below the pericycle, carries water and other essential substances throughout the plant.

At this point, you may want to assign to your students the second of the Extensions and Applications at the end of this chapter.

Within the vascular cylinder are three kinds of tissues. The *xylem* conducts water and minerals from the roots up through the plant. The *phloem* transports food from the leaves to the roots and to other parts of the plant. The vascular cylinder also contains the **vascular cambium,** which is made up of meristematic cells that are found between the xylem and phloem.

SECONDARY TISSUES The differentiated cells of the vascular cambium develop into two other types of cells. The cells of one type remain part of the cambium. Cells of the other type give rise to secondary tissues, as do the cells of the pericycle, which continue to divide. The cells of the cambium produce both secondary xylem and phloem tissue.

Due to the enlarging and dividing of the cells during the growth process, these tissues increase the diameter of the root rather than its length. In the cross-sectional view of a mature dicot root, the xylem has the shape of a star with arms that extend into the pericycle. This star-shaped arrangement is common in most kinds of dicot roots. The vascular cambium grows between the arms of xylem, as shown in Figure 21-3. The secondary xylem grows just inside the vascular cambium, and the secondary phloem grows just outside it.

In the later stages of the secondary growth in many roots, another kind of secondary tissue is eventually formed.

Highlight

The root tip is made up of the root cap, the meristematic region, the elongation region, and the maturation region. The primary tissues are the first group of cells to develop in a root. The secondary tissues develop after the primary tissues mature.

The major difference is the arrangement of the primary xylem.

Figure 21-3 Cross Sections of Monocot and Dicot Roots. What is the major difference between the two?

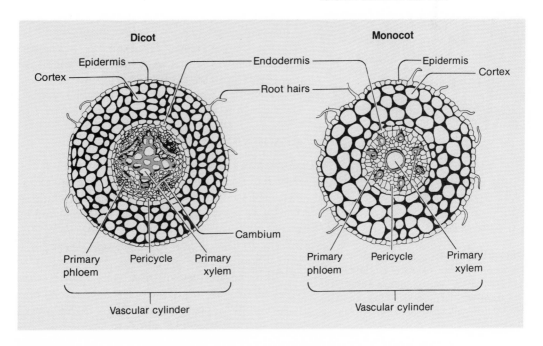

Figure 21-4 Roots are adapted to their environment. For example, aquatic roots are adapted to lakes or ponds. Aerial roots are adapted to treetop environments. Brace roots are adapted to certain soil conditions.

The pericycle begins to divide and to form the **cork cambium,** which is only one cell thick. New layers of cells grow inward and outward from the cork cambium, but the cells that grow outward form a tissue known as *cork.* As the corky layer matures, the root loses its ability to absorb nutrients from the soil.

Root Adaptations

At this point, you may want to assign to your students the initial part of the first of the Extensions and Applications at the end of this chapter.

Roots generally grow in a downward direction and anchor the plant in soil. However, certain roots are specialized in their functions. These roots are adapted to special features of their environment.

Water hyacinths and water lilies have **aquatic roots.** Large air spaces in these roots carry needed oxygen to the parts of the plant that are anchored in the soil at the bottom of a body of water. Thus aquatic roots make these plants specially suited for growth in water.

Special roots that are suspended in air are called **aerial roots.** In tropical rain forests, plants such as orchids have roots that are completely above ground level. Such plants, called *epiphytes* (EP-ə-fītz), are supported by the branches of trees or by rocks. Their roots have special tissues that easily absorb moisture from the air. In many cases, aerial roots contain *chlorophyll,* the green pigment that uses the sun's energy to make food for the plant.

Roots that sprout from other parts of a plant, such as from the stem or leaves, are called **adventitious** (ad-vən-TISH-əs) **roots.** When adventitious roots help to support the plant, they are also called *brace roots* or *prop roots.* Corn plants and tropical banyan trees, for example, have prop roots that grow from the stems. Adventitious roots that enable the stem to cling to tree trunks or walls are called *climbing roots.* Many climbing plants, such as poison ivy and English ivy, have climbing roots.

Absorption of Materials

Plants need a large supply of water and raw materials, and they absorb these substances through their roots. Plant roots thus perform an important and complicated function. The roots let water and certain other needed materials permeate, or pass through, their surfaces. Yet the roots do not let any of the plant's food pass out through their surfaces into the soil.

The membranes of root cells have many microscopic pores that allow small particles, such as water molecules, to pass through. They do not allow large molecules, such as those of fats, proteins, and complex sugars, to escape from the root into the soil. The cell membranes "select," in a sense, what may or may not pass through, and so they are said to be *selectively permeable.*

On either side of the root cell membrane, inside or outside the root's surface, is water. Sometimes the concentration of water outside the cell membrane is greater than the concentration inside. Sometimes the opposite is true, that is, the concentration of water inside is greater than the concentration outside. In either case, water molecules diffuse, or pass, through the membrane from the side with the higher concentration to the side with the lower concentration. The diffusion of water through a selectively permeable membrane is called *osmosis.* The pressure created by this movement of water is called *osmotic pressure.*

As water enters the epidermis of the root hairs, **root pressure** builds up as a result of osmosis and of pressure in the cortex cells. Root pressure causes water molecules to move into the vascular cylinder. As water moves into this region, more water is absorbed from the surrounding soil by osmosis. Leaves use the water for *photosynthesis,* or *food-making.*

The movement of water by osmosis is called **active absorption.** The movement of water through the stem due to *transpiration,* or the loss of water through the leaves, is called **passive absorption.** The reduced pressure in the leaves, causes water to be pushed upward from the roots, where the pressure is greater.

Besides water, plants need to absorb minerals, such as compounds of nitrogen, magnesium, calcium, phosphorus, and sulfur. Scientists have observed that dissolved minerals enter the cells of the root hairs even if the concentration of mineral *ions,* or charged particles, is higher in the cells than it is in the surroundings. If the mineral ions were to act like water molecules in osmosis, they could not pass from a lower concentration outside to a higher concentration inside. Yet minerals do just that. This movement of minerals occurs not by osmosis, but by *active transport.* In active transport, the plant uses energy, not pressure, to move mineral ions.

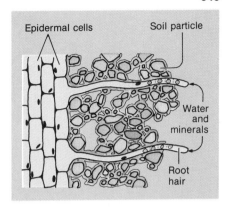

Figure 21-5 The structure of roots permits water and dissolved minerals to pass from the soil into the plant. At the same time, the root structure prevents food from leaving the plant.

Highlight

Water passes into the root by osmosis. Minerals move into the cells of the root by active transport.

At this point, you may want to assign to your students the third of the Extensions and Applications at the end of this chapter.

SECTION REVIEW   Answers on page T-64.

1. What are the functions of the root?
2. Describe a taproot and a fibrous root.
3. Which types of tissues make up the primary tissue in roots? Which make up the secondary tissue?
4. Name three adaptations of roots.
5. How does the root absorb minerals?
6. What is active absorption? Passive absorption?

Sidelight

The stem, or trunk, of the California redwood tree can grow to 3.7 meters in diameter and more than 107 meters tall.

Highlight

Herbaceous stems are not rigid. Herbaceous stems are able to support the plant and retain their shape due to the turgidity caused by water pressure inside the stem.

Figure 21-6 Water loss during a hot afternoon causes plants with herbaceous stems, such as this begonia, to become temporarily wilted. By the next morning, the plants usually absorb enough water to appear healthy again.

Stems

In the seventeenth century, an Italian scientist, Marcello Malpighi (mahl-PĒ-gē), studied the stems of plants. He described the stem as a bundle of tubes in the form of a single cylinder. He also pointed out that the plant tubes connect the roots, stem, and leaves. Today, botanists call this set of conducting tubes the *vascular bundle*. This structure transports materials back and forth between the roots and the other parts of the plant.

The stem serves a number of purposes. It plays a role as part of the **shoot,** which also includes the leaves, flowers, and fruits. The stem produces new cells for the growth and development of the shoot system. The stem also supports the shoot, raising the leaves into the air and exposing them to sunlight. It also supports the flower. Stems can be classified in two groups according to their hardness.

Structure of Herbaceous Stems

A *herbaceous stem* is soft and fleshy, protected only by a single layer of epidermal cells. Most herbaceous plants are thus supported not by hard tissue, but by the water pressure in the cells of the stems. As water diffuses into the plant cells, pressure builds up inside them. The cellular contents begin to swell until they push against the cell walls. This pressure, called **turgor pressure,** causes the condition known as **turgidity** (ter-JID-i-tē). Thus turgidity in plant cells not only maintains the shape of the soft tissues of plants, but also provides support for most herbaceous stems.

When the plant does not get enough water, herbaceous stems wilt or droop. Sometimes on a hot day, **temporary wilting** occurs because the rate of transpiration is greater than the rate of absorption. Plants usually recover from this condition at night. After sunset, the temperature decreases and the humidity increases. As a result, the rate of transpiration decreases while the rate of absorption increases. Less water is leaving the plant through transpiration than is coming in through absorption. During long periods of drought, **permanent wilting** occurs. This type of wilting, which causes the plant to die, occurs when the plant's roots are destroyed or damaged.

Most annuals and biennials, as well as many perennial plants, have herbaceous stems. The structure of these plants' stems is related to whether they are monocots or dicots. Herbaceous monocots include, for example, cereal plants, such as corn, rice, oats, and wheat. A cross section of a herbaceous monocot stem shows that the vascular bundles are scattered

At this point, you may want to have your students do Part B of the Laboratory Investigation at the end of this chapter.

347

throughout the **pith.** The pith is found at the center of the stem and is used for food storage. The stem does not have a separate cortex or vascular cambium. The absence of a vascular cambium prevents the secondary growth of the xylem or phloem. As a result, herbaceous monocot stems grow to only limited diameters.

The vascular tissues of herbaceous dicots, such as tomatoes, eggplants, and sunflowers, are arranged in a definite ring pattern. Cortex surrounds the phloem. The xylem, found inside the phloem ring, is separated from it by a thin layer of vascular cambium.

Structure of Woody Stems

Other stems are erect, rigid structures. They contain special cells called *fibers, vessel elements,* and *tracheids.* Stems that have these cells are called *woody stems.* The fibers, vessel elements, and tracheids make up the woody portion of the stem. Woody stems have **nodes** and **internodes.** The node serves as a connecting link between the stem and leaves. The gap between two nodes is called an internode.

The vascular bundles that lead to the leaves in woody stems are called *leaf traces.* When leaves fall, the broken ends of the vascular bundles produce marks on the stem known as **bundle scars.** Because these scars are different for various kinds of trees, they are sometimes used to identify trees during the winter, when they have no leaves.

Woody stems also have tiny openings, called **lenticels,** that are often raised and can be seen easily on young woody stems. Because oxygen enters through the lenticels, they serve as "breathing" organs for young woody stems.

Stems grow from buds. Some buds remain active during the entire life of the plant. Others are dormant, or inactive, but become active and give rise to new growth when the end of a twig is cut off. The buds on trees and shrubs that are located at the ends of twigs or branches are known as *terminal buds.* They remain active and give rise to leaves and branches. The smaller buds that grow from the sides of woody stems, usually just above the point where a leaf joins a stem, are called *lateral buds,* or *axillary* (AK-sə-ler-ē) *buds.* Although some lateral buds produce leaves, flowers, or branches, they are usually dormant. Some plants, such as the peach tree, have *accessory buds,* which are located above or on either side of lateral buds.

In the growth of woody stems from buds, the first stem seen in a growing seedling is known as the *plumule* (PLOOM-yool). As the young stem elongates, it may acquire several internodes and buds. Different tissues grow from different

Highlight

Woody stems, such as the trunk or branches of an oak tree, are able to maintain their shape and support tremendous weights without the presence of water. This ability enables woody-stemmed plants to grow many times larger than the largest herbaceous-stemmed plants.

Figure 21-7 External Structure of a Woody Stem

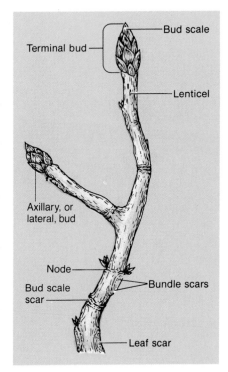

Figure 21-8 The shoot apex is the new tissue at the tip of the stem. As the cells of the shoot apex divide, the stem grows longer.

The palm tree is an example of columnar branching. The oak tree is an example of deliquescent branching. The pine tree is an example of excurrent branching.

Figure 21-9 What are the three kinds of branching exhibited by the palm, the oak, and the pine?

kinds of buds. The new tissue at the tip of the bud is called the **shoot apex.** Cells in the shoot apex increase the length of the stem by cell division and give rise to the lateral buds and leaves.

As the stem matures, the internodes begin to lengthen, while the lateral buds and leaves become differentiated. Some of the lateral buds develop into branches, into other lateral buds, and into leaves. Yet other lateral buds remain inactive due to **apical dominance.** This inactivity occurs because a substance produced in the terminal bud suppresses the growth of certain lateral buds.

Because of apical dominance, woody stems exhibit several different patterns of branching. The *columnar* stems on some large trees bear branches, leaves, flowers, and fruits near the top of the tree. Coconut trees and other palm trees have this kind of stem. In other trees, such as oaks and maples, the main stem or trunk rises for a few meters and then divides into smaller and smaller branches. As the branches spread out, the main trunk seems to deliquesce, or melt away. This type of stem is therefore described as *deliquescent* (del-ə-KWES-'nt). In the kind of woody stem referred to as *excurrent*, several branches grow outward in rings around the main trunk. The hemlock and many of the cone-bearing trees have excurrent branching.

As all these kinds of woody stems increase in length and diameter, they produce two basic types of tissue. The increase in the length of woody stems is called *primary growth*. Within the shoot apex of woody stems is an area of new cell growth that makes up the *apical meristem*. The api-

cal meristem, located at the tip of the shoot, is similar to the meristem found at the tip of a root. The apical meristem is made up mainly of parenchyma cells with large nuclei and thick cytoplasm.

The parenchyma cells differentiate into three types of primary tissues. The first tissue develops into the epidermis, or outermost layer, of the stems, and it protects the other primary tissues beneath it. The second tissue gives rise to the primary xylem and phloem. The third type of tissue develops into the cortex and the pith.

The increase in the diameter of woody stems is called *secondary growth*, and it may begin even before the primary tissues have completely developed. In woody stems, the two

Ask your students whether they have ever seen initials carved into a tree trunk and how high up they were. Explain that even carvings made twenty, thirty, or more years ago will still be at or near eye level because primary growth occurs from the shoot apex at the tip of the stem or trunk. Something carved at eye level will remain at that height for the age of the tree.

CAREER: Floral Designer

Shops in which flowers and plants are sold are called florist shops. People who work in these shops are called floral designers or florists. They put together interesting and attractive arrangements of flowers and plants. These arrangements are usually designed to express a particular quality or feeling.

To make attractive and suitable displays, floral designers must be creative and perceptive. Floral designers must also be familiar with all types of flowers and plants. In other words, they must know the names of flowering plants and the lasting qualities of the flowers they produce.

Florists must also be good business people. By knowing which flowers and plants are available during the different seasons, they can estimate costs. By keeping records of what they sell and buy, they can plan future purchases. Planning is very important due to the short life spans of flowers.

Floral designers also explain to customers how to care properly for plants and flowers. They must know the types of diseases and insects that affect each type of plant, and they must be able to control these problems.

Some floral designers conduct classes or demonstrations at local high schools or civic centers. During peak periods, floral designers may employ extra help on a part-time basis. In this way, they provide valuable on-the-job train-

ing for those who are interested in this type of work.

A high school diploma is desirable, although not essential, to enter this field. Many floral designers attend junior colleges that have programs in floriculture. In addition, special schools teach people how to design floral arrangements. Other programs give training in flower arrangement. Still other programs give training in flower marketing and shop management for floral designers who wish to operate their own businesses. Some floral designers receive their training on the job by working under the supervision of an experienced floral designer. Usually a person can become a qualified floral designer in two years of on-the-job experience.

For further career information, write to The Society of American Florists, 901 North Washington Street, Alexandria, VA 22314.

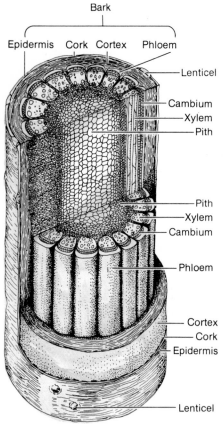

Epidermis   Cork Cortex   Phloem

Bark

— Lenticel

— Cambium
— Xylem
— Pith

— Pith
— Xylem
— Cambium

— Phloem

— Cortex
— Cork
— Epidermis

— Lenticel

Figure 21-10 Stems have an orderly, layered structure beginning with the pith in the center and extending out to the bark.

Figure 21-11 The age of a tree can be determined by counting the number of rings. Each ring represents one year's growth.

major types of secondary tissues are the secondary xylem and secondary phloem.

BARK   The primary and secondary tissues develop into the various parts of the mature woody stem, which include the **bark.** Bark is composed of a series of layers of living and dead tissues that cover and protect the stem. A true, mature bark consists only of phloem and cork. In fact, the term phloem is derived from the Greek word meaning bark.

Because the bark contains the phloem, it is involved in the transport of food and other materials from the leaves to the roots. If the bark is completely removed from a section of the trunk, the living tissues below this section eventually die. Bark removal of this sort is known as **girdling** (GER-d'l-ing). Beavers and other gnawing animals have destroyed trees in this way.

Bark is divided into inner and outer sections. The outer bark consists mostly of the epidermis, cork, and cork cambium. Within the cork cambium are meristematic cells that divide constantly, thus building up more material on the outer side of the stem. These cells soon die and form the cork tissue. Cork tissue contains a waxy waterproof substance that helps to protect the inner tissues from drying out. Cork tissue also prevents insects, other parasites, and sudden changes in temperature from harming the inner tissues. The inner bark consists mostly of living tissues, including the cortex and the phloem.

VASCULAR CAMBIUM   Another part of the mature woody stem is the vascular cambium, a single layer of cells found between the xylem and phloem. The secondary phloem is on the outer side of the vascular cambium, and the secondary xylem is on the inner side. Because the vascular cambium is mainly meristematic, it adds new secondary tissues to the phloem and xylem as its cells divide.

WOOD   The **wood** in a woody stem is made up of xylem tissue. Depending on the species of tree, different forms of xylem tissues, called vessels and tracheids, are formed. After maturing, the living materials of these tissues die, and their thick cell walls pile up one on top of another. The vessels and tracheids form ducts, or long tubes. Water and minerals are transported through the ducts in the outermost layer only. The other ducts are used as food storage areas for the plant.

Each year, another layer of secondary xylem grows out of and eventually wraps around the layer before it. Since each layer represents one year's growth of xylem cells, these layers are called **annual rings.** Because each ring normally represents one layer, or one year, of growth, the age of a tree can be determined by counting the number of its annual rings.

PITH The pith, located at the center of the stem, is made up mainly of parenchyma cells. Because these cells are large and have many air spaces between them, the pith serves as a storage tissue in some plants. As the stem grows, the pith does not undergo any major changes in size. In mature stems, the pith loses its function and dies.

Stem Adaptations

Although most stems grow vertically and above the ground, certain types of stems, like roots, have become adapted to special circumstances in their environments. In some plants, the stems grow horizontally and under the surface of the ground, and they have modified structures and functions. These stems, called **rhizomes** (RĪ-zōmz), look like roots, but they are really stems because they have nodes, internodes, buds, and scalelike leaves. Examples of plants that have rhizomes are ginger, iris, Solomon's seal, and lily of the valley.

The stems of other plants grow horizontally like rhizomes, but they are found either under or above ground. They are also longer and narrower than rhizomes. These stems are called **stolons,** or *runners.* Strawberries and many grasses, for example, have stolons.

Another modified stem is the **tuber.** A tuber is an enlarged part of an underground stolon. The potato, for example, is a tuber that stores carbohydrates and other plant materials. The "eyes" of a potato are actually buds that form at the nodes, each of which is capable of developing into a new potato plant. Other tubers include the Jerusalem artichoke and the caladium.

Gladiolus and crocus are examples of plants that have another type of stem, called a **corm.** Corms are underground stems that grow vertically and that are enclosed by several thin, scalelike leaves. In the gladiolus, a corm grows only one shoot in its entire lifetime. In other plants, corms grow new shoots every growing season.

Certain spring plants, such as onions, tulips, and hyacinths, produce another type of stem called a **bulb.** Bulbs are short stems that are thicker than corms and have scalelike leaves. The thick leaves of a bulb contain food for the plant.

At this point, you may want to assign to your students the latter part of the first of the Extensions and Applications at the end of this chapter.

Figure 21–12 The stolons of strawberries (*top*) and the bulbs of daffodils (*bottom*) are modified stems. The stem modifications increase the chances of each plant's survival in its environment.

Highlight

Most stems grow vertically and above the ground. Rhizomes and stolons are modified stems that grow horizontally and sometimes below the ground. Tubers, corms, and bulbs are stems that grow below the ground.

Highlight

Translocation is the process by which food, water, and dissolved minerals travel from place to place within a plant.

Figure 21-13 During the winter, sugar maple trees are tapped with spouts. Buckets are used to collect the escaping sap. The sap is boiled down to produce maple syrup.

Translocation of Materials

The most important function of the stem is the transportation of water, minerals, and food back and forth between the roots and the other parts of the plant. The movement of these materials within the plant is called **translocation.**

Scientists do not all agree on how translocation takes place. They know that osmotic root pressure and gravity are a partial cause. They are also fairly certain that **capillarity** contributes to translocation. Capillarity is the tendency of water to rise when forced into a vessel that is shaped like a narrow column. In a stem, the narrow columns take the form of the tiny tubelike vessels and tracheids in the xylem. As liquid molecules enter the stem, they are attracted to sides of these tubelike ducts and thus cause the column of liquid to rise.

Most scientists doubt that root pressure and capillarity can explain how liquid can be conducted all the way to the tops of such tall plants as trees. To explain translocation in even the tallest trees, they therefore offer the **transpiration-cohesion theory.** This theory assumes that, when a plant loses water through evaporation, the top of the plant exerts a kind of pull on the bottom. This pull is transmitted downward through the tree through *cohesion,* which is the attraction of like molecules of a substance for each other. Thus, water is continuously pulled upwards.

The rapid transport of food in plants takes place mainly in the sieve tubes of the phloem. These structures are large and well developed in such plants as the watermelon, pumpkin, and squash.

When the twigs of plants are broken, the translocated water and materials flow out in the form of *sap.* While proteins and other substances are found in small amounts in sap, sap consists mostly of sugar. The sap from maple trees, for example, contains such large amounts of sugar that it is used to make maple syrup.

SECTION REVIEW   Answers on pages T-64.

1. What are the functions of the stem?
2. Define turgidity.
3. Name three branching patterns of stems due to apical dominance.
4. Name and describe five stem adaptations.
5. Define translocation.
6. Briefly explain the transpiration-cohesion theory of water translocation.

LABORATORY INVESTIGATION

Observing the Structure of Roots and Stems

Purpose Besides anchoring plants, roots absorb and store materials. Stems conduct these and other materials through plants and provide plants with support. In this investigation, you will observe the structure of roots and stems.

Materials *(per group)* ● Germinating radish (dicot) seedlings ● Hand lens ● Germinating grass (monocot) seedlings ● Single-edged razor blade ● Microscope ● 4 glass slides ● 4 cover slips ● Bean plant ● Corn plant ● Forceps ● Scissors ● 250-mL beaker ● Red ink ● Graduated cylinder

Procedure Part A 1. Obtain a germinating radish seedling and a germinating grass seedling. Through a hand lens, examine the roots and root hairs of each seedling. Sketch each seedling. **2. CAUTION:** *Always use a razor blade with care.* Carefully use the razor blade to cut a thin cross section from each seedling's root tip. **3.** Using the forceps, place each section in a drop of water on a glass slide and put a cover slip over it. **4.** Examine the slide under the low power of a microscope. Make a sketch of each

section. Label the parts. **Part B 1.** Pour 125 mL of water into the beaker. Add about 20 drops of red ink to the water and stir. **2.** Obtain a bean plant and a corn plant from your teacher. Cut the roots off the plants, and place the cut ends of the stems into the red ink solution. Allow the stems to remain in the solution for 24 hours. **3.** Observe the stems. **4.** Remove the stems, and carefully cut off a very thin section of each stem near the root end. **5.** Place each stem section in a drop of water on a glass slide and put a cover slip over it. **6.** Observe the stems under the low power of the microscope. Sketch and label what you see.

Observations and Conclusions 1. What part of the seedlings contains the longest root hairs? **2.** Compare the sections of the root tips of the radish and the grass seedling. List the differences you observe. **3.** How do root hairs increase the rate of absorption of water? **4.** Did the red ink spread throughout the tissues of the stem or did it remain concentrated in certain tissues? Why? **5.** By observing the stems of the bean and corn, how can you tell whether they are dicots or monocots?

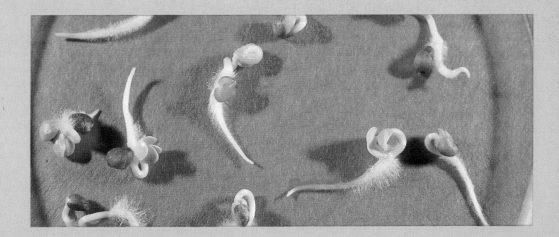

CHAPTER SUMMARY

Roots Roots anchor plants in the soil, absorb water and minerals, and store food. The first root that grows in a plant is called the primary root. The smaller roots that branch from the primary root are called secondary roots. The secondary roots of some plants develop into threadlike, highly branched fibrous roots.

The root tip actively absorbs water and minerals. The root tip is made up of the root cap and the meristematic, elongation, and maturation regions. The meristematic region gives rise to all new cells. The elongation region increases the length of a root. In the maturation region, the cells become specialized in function. Some of these cells develop root hairs, structures that absorb water through their thin membranes.

As a plant begins to grow, the first group of cells that form in the root are the primary tissues. The primary tissues are the epidermis, cortex, and vascular cylinder. The epidermis, which is the outermost root tissue, contains the many root hairs. Inside the epidermis is the cortex that stores food for the plant. The vascular cylinder is the region that carries water and other essential substances throughout the plant.

Secondary root tissues are produced from the cambium. These tissues increase the diameter of the root.

Water is absorbed by roots by the process of osmosis. The movement of water from the soil into the root hairs is called active absorption. Once water enters the root hairs, root pressure causes the water to move into the vascular cylinder. Passive absorption is the movement of water through the stem due to the loss of water from the leaves by the process of transpiration.

Stems Stems give support to a plant. They also serve as a passageway for materials the plant needs. They transport water and minerals from the roots to the leaves, and they conduct food from the leaves to other parts of the plant.

Herbaceous stems are soft, while woody stems are rigid. Like herbaceous stems, woody stems consist of vascular cambium and pith. Woody stems also have bark and wood. Some structures, such as rhizomes, stolons, tubers, corms, and bulbs, are modified stems.

Stems perform translocation, or the movement of materials within the plant. In most plants, translocation is thought to occur through the processes of root pressure, gravity, and capillarity. In tall trees, the transpiration–cohesion theory may account for translocation.

CHAPTER VOCABULARY

active absorption	girdling	secondary root
adventitious root	humus	secondary tissue
aerial root	internode	shoot
annual ring	lenticel	shoot apex
apical dominance	maturation region	stolon
aquatic root	meristematic region	taproot
bark	node	temporary wilting
bulb	passive absorption	topsoil
bundle scar	permanent wilting	translocation
capillarity	pith	transpiration–cohesion theory
cork cambium	primary root	tuber
corm	primary tissue	turgidity
cortex	rhizome	turgor pressure
elongation region	root cap	vascular cambium
epidermis	root hair	vascular cylinder
fibrous root	root pressure	wood

REVIEW of FACTS and CONCEPTS   Answers on page T–65.

On a separate sheet of paper, answer each of the following as completely as possible.

1. Distinguish between primary and secondary roots.
2. Name the four regions of the root tip and give the activities that occur in them.
3. What is the difference between primary and secondary tissue growth in roots?
4. What causes water to be absorbed by the roots?
5. When do plants permanently wilt? Temporarily wilt?
6. Name and describe the parts of a woody stem.
7. Distinguish between terminal and lateral buds.
8. Describe primary and secondary growth in stems.
9. Distinguish between woody and herbaceous stems.
10. Why does a nail that is hammered into the trunk of a tree eventually become buried in it?
11. What causes translocation of water in a stem?
12. Some giant sequoia trees that have had an automobile tunnel cut through them continue to grow. Why?

EXTENSIONS and APPLICATIONS   For additional information, see page T–65.

1. Visit the nearest botanical garden or observe some of the plants in a nearby field or park. Look for different types of roots and stems. Classify the roots as aquatic, aerial, or adventitious, and the adventitious roots as prop or climbing. Classify the stems according to type, such as rhizome, stolon, tuber, corm, or bulb. On posterboard, sketch the plants you observe, and label the plants and their root and stem structures.
2. Obtain three pea or bean seeds. Soak them overnight in water. The next day, remove them from the water, and place then on a paper towel that has been moistened with water. Put the moistened paper towel and seeds into a covered dish. Observe the seeds every day until the primary roots reach a length of 2 cm. Gently remove the seeds from the paper towel. Starting from the root tips, mark off 10 intervals 1 mm apart with thin thread that has been dipped in India ink. Carefully pull the thread tight and gently press down on the root to make short thin lines. Sketch the germinating seeds along with the ink marks. Return the seeds to the moistened paper towel and cover the dish. Observe the germinating seeds again in 24 hours. Sketch what you see. Where did most of the growth in the root occur? Explain.
3. Visit the library to obtain information on hydroponics. Prepare a written or oral report describing the procedure and explaining its importance. Try growing some plants hydroponically.

SUGGESTED READINGS

Bold, H.C., *The Plant Kingdom*. Englewood Cliffs, N.J.: Prentice-Hall.
  This book provides a discussion of the structure of the vegetative organs of vascular plants. In addition to this topic, basic facts concerning organization, reproduction, and classification of these plants are presented.
Elliot, D.B., *Roots: An Underground Botany and Forager's Guide*. Old Greenwich, Conn.: The Chatham Press.
  This book offers a unique approach to the study of the roots of common plants. The author emphasizes the practical uses of roots.
Wilson, C.M., *Roots: Miracles Below*. Garden City, N.Y.: Doubleday.
  The roots of plants are discussed, as well as their uses as foods and drugs. The relationship between roots and soil is also explored.

22 Leaves

In autumn, the leaves of Virginia creeper turn brilliant red.

Chapter Objectives *After completing this chapter, you will be able to:*

a ■ Explain leaf color change and leaf shedding in autumn. p. 357
b ■ Describe the structure and functions of a leaf. p. 358
c ■ Distinguish between simple and compound leaves. p. 358
d ■ Describe the different types of venation. p. 359
e ■ Name and give the functions of the three layers of tissues in a leaf. p. 360
f ■ Explain the function of leaf stomata. p. 360
g ■ List some types of leaf adaptations. p. 361
h ■ Describe photosynthesis, respiration, transpiration, and guttation in plants. p. 362

For teaching aids for this chapter, including a chapter overview and teaching strategies, see pages T–65 to T–67. The page number next to each chapter objective refers to the text page where the information needed to fulfill the objective begins.

The most varied organs of seed plants are **leaves.** They are important not only to the plants that possess them but to all living things on the earth. Leaves produce materials that are used by animals, by other plants, and by microorganisms. Leaves also help to maintain a balance of water in the atmosphere.

The relatively large surface area of leaves permits them to absorb great amounts of energy from the sun and carbon dioxide from the air. At the same time, the roots of the plant absorb water from the soil. The leaves use the energy from the sun, the carbon dioxide from the air, and the water from the soil to make food for the plant. In the process of making food, leaves release oxygen into the air.

Leaves also return water, in the form of a gas, to the air. Sometimes the plant absorbs more water from the soil than the leaves need to make food. The water escapes through openings in leaves and returns to the atmosphere.

Leaf Characteristics

Although plants that bear leaves vary greatly in appearance, most of them can be placed into three groups. *Broad-leafed* plants, such as maple trees, are the most numerous. Most of the trees in the temperate regions of the earth shed their broad leaves in the autumn and grow new leaves in the spring. These broad-leafed trees are *deciduous*. *Narrow-leafed* plants, such as grass, have leaves that usually die in the winter and are replaced by new leaves in the spring. Most *needle-leafed* trees, such as firs, pines, and other evergreens, are *coniferous*. They shed their old leaves and grow new ones continuously throughout the year.

All three types of leaves contain *chlorophyll*, a pigment that gives leaves their green color. Not all leaves are exactly the same shade of green. The leaves of some species of plants also contain a yellow pigment, called *xanthophyll*, along with an orange pigment, called *carotene*. The various shades of green in leaves are due to the different mixtures of these pigments with chlorophyll.

Chlorophyll, a very unstable pigment, breaks down during periods of cooler temperatures, such as in autumn. This breakdown unmasks the more stable yellow and orange pigments. Xanthophyll and carotene account for the bright colors of autumn leaves. Some of these leaves eventually turn red or purple. A red pigment called *anthocyanin*, which is usually formed during the autumn months, produces these colors of leaves.

The shedding of a leaf or other plant organ is known as **abscission** (ab-SIZH-'n). Special plant cells form an *abscission layer* at the point where the leaf grows out of the stem.

Figure 22-1 Pigments such as xanthophyll and carotene account for the brilliant colors of autumn foliage.

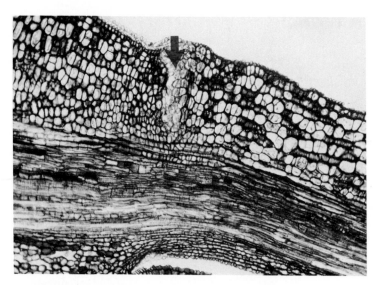

Figure 22-2 Leaves separate from stems along the abscission layer (*arrow*).

Figure 22-3 The external structures of leaves include the blade, the petiole, and, in some cases, outgrowths called stipules.

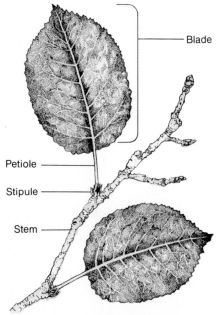

Blade

Petiole

Stipule

Stem

When an abscission layer forms, the leaf separates from the plant. Abscission occurs not only during the autumn, but also at other times of the year as a normal result of aging or other conditions, such as a drought.

Since 1953, scientists have known that a substance called *auxin* controls the falling of leaves. Experiments indicate that, as long as a leaf has more auxin than the stem to which it is attached, abscission does not take place. During the active growing months of spring and summer, the leaf produces enough of its own auxin to stay attached to the plant. Growth slows down during the cold weather, which also slows down auxin production. Reduced auxin production causes the leaf to separate from the stem at the abscission layer.

Leaf Structure

Most leaves have two major parts. The **petiole** (PET-ē-ōl) is the stalk of the leaf. The petiole connects the stem to the **blade**. The blade, which contains most of the green, photosynthetic cells, is the thin, flat part of the leaf. Leaves that do not have petioles are called **sessile** (SES-il). The blades of sessile leaves grow directly out of the stem.

At the base of some leaves are small outgrowths, called **stipules** (STIP-yoolz). Stipules look like tiny leaves or scales. In some species of plants, the stipules fall off when the main leaf is fully developed. The functions of stipules include supporting the stem of climbing plants and protecting the leaf.

DIVISION OF LEAVES Leaves are classified into two types. A *simple leaf* is one whose blade is not divided into

sections. Maple, dogwood, sycamore, and apple trees, for example, all have simple leaves. *Compound leaves* are divided into two or more **leaflets,** or bladelike sections. Poison ivy, Virginia creeper, buckeye, and black locust are examples of plants with compound leaves.

Compound leaves are classified into two subgroups. **Palmate** leaves have several extensions merging from a single point located at the petiole. An example is the buckeye leaf. The second subgroup of compound leaves is **pinnate** leaves. These leaves are arranged along the sides of a single extension that is connected to the petiole.

VENATION OF LEAVES Leaves contain long tubelike structures called *veins*. The petiole connects the veins to the vascular tissue of the stem. The arrangement of the veins in leaves, called **venation,** helps to support the leaf blade.

Venation is used to help identify plant types. Generally, monocots have *parallel venation*, in that the veins run parallel to the edge of the leaf and to each other. A corn leaf is an example of parallel venation. Dicot leaves have *net venation*, in which the veins spread out in a netlike pattern. *Pinnate*

Highlight

Leaves are divided into two basic types, simple and compound. Compound leaves may be palmate or pinnate. Leaves may have parallel or net venation.

venation is a type of net venation that is found, for example, in the leaves of the ash tree. In a leaf with pinnate venation, small veins branch out from a *midrib*, or large central vein.

Leaf Tissues

The leaf is a living food factory that is adapted to produce and to store chemical energy. To perform this function, the leaf relies on three groups of tissue.

EPIDERMIS   The outermost leaf tissue, the **epidermis**, is actually a continuation of the epidermis of the stem. The epidermis covers the entire leaf and protects all the tissues within it. The epidermis usually is made up of only a single layer of cells on the upper and lower surfaces of the leaf.

The epidermis keeps the leaf from drying out. Within the epidermis are cells that secrete a waxy substance. This substance hardens and forms a film over the epidermis, called the **cuticle.** The cuticle prevents water from escaping from the leaf. **Epidermal hairs,** if present, also serve the same purpose by slowing down the evaporation of water from the leaf surface. Epidermal hairs make some leaves feel fuzzy or "hairy."

To allow water vapor and other gases to pass into or out of the leaf when necessary, the lower epidermis contains **guard cells.** A pair of guard cells looks like two sausages that are tied end-to-end. The opening between the two cells is called a **stoma** (plural: stomata). When the two guard cells

Highlight

The outermost tissues of leaves are the epidermis. The middle layer is the mesophyll. The third group of leaf tissues is the fibrovascular bundles.

Figure 22-5   This cross section reveals the tissues and structures present in the various layers of a leaf.

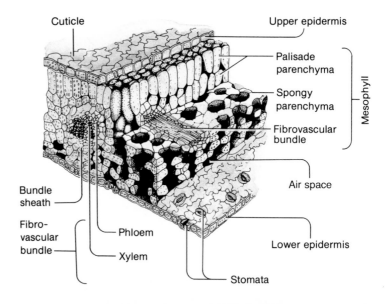

are pressed closed, the stoma is shut. No water can pass through it. When the guard cells are not pressed together, water vapor can pass into or out of the leaf through the stoma.

MESOPHYLL   The middle leaf tissue is the **mesophyll.** This tissue is made up of special *parenchyma*, or unspecialized cells, called *chlorenchyma cells.* In these cells are many *chloroplasts*, or food-making organelles, where photosynthesis actually takes place.

The mesophyll has two layers of cells. The first, located just below the upper epidermis, is the **palisade mesophyll,** as shown in Figure 22-5. The palisade mesophyll is usually made up of one row of elongated cells. The second layer, called the **spongy mesophyll,** lies beneath the palisade mesophyll and extends toward the lower epidermis. The cells in the spongy mesophyll are irregularly shaped, and have many air spaces between them. These air spaces enable the cells to take in oxygen and carbon dioxide. The spongy cells do not have as many chloroplasts as the palisade cells do.

FIBROVASCULAR BUNDLES   The **fibrovascular bundles,** or veins, make up the third leaf tissue. These bundles contain the *xylem* and *phloem.* By connecting the many types of tissues in the leaf, the veins provide structural support for it. The veins also provide a passageway for the *translocation*, or movement, of substances. The xylem transports water and minerals to the leaf. The phloem transports food and other materials to different parts of the plant. The midrib and other large veins contain several kinds of cells. These are the *xylem vessels, tracheids, phloem sieve tubes*, and *companion cells.* The companion cells help to control the flow of materials throughout the sieve tubes.

The conducting tissues are often enclosed by supporting structures, called **bundle sheaths** and **sclerenchyma fibers.** Bundle sheaths enclose smaller veins. In larger veins, sclerenchyma fibers strengthen the vascular bundles and extend into the epidermis. At this point, you may want to have your students do the Laboratory Investigation at the end of this chapter.

Leaf Adaptations

Although photosynthesis is the primary function of leaves, some leaves have adaptations for other functions. For example, the modified leaves, or scales, of the onion store food. The modified leaves of many desert cacti have developed into sharp structures, called **spines,** for protection. Thick fleshy tissues, called **succulent leaves,** are adapted to store large quantities of water in dry environments. The

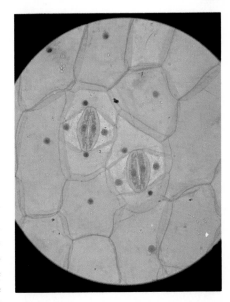

Figure 22-6 Sausage-shaped guard cells control the sizes of the stomata in leaves.

Sidelight

If all the fibrovascular bundles in a single elm leaf were placed end to end, they would form a line more than 200 meters long.

You may want to ask your students to do library research on certain adaptations of leaves and to bring in examples of these specially adapted leaves.

362

Figure 22-7 The leaves of some plants are adapted in unusual ways. The leaves of the golden ball cactus (*top*) are modified into protective spines. Those of the Venus' flytrap (*bottom*) are modified to trap and digest insects.

Figure 22-8 The leaves of this impatiens plant change carbon dioxide and water into oxygen and glucose by the process called photosynthesis. Light triggers the first stages of this process.

At this point, you may want to assign to several students the third of the Extensions and Applications at the end of this chapter.

century and ice plants are examples of plants with this type of leaf. The terminal leaflets of some compound-leafed plants, such as a garden pea plant, produce **tendrils,** which coil around the plant to give added support.

Plants with leaves that are adapted for catching tiny animals, particularly insects, are called **insectivorous** (in-sek-TIV-ər-əs) **plants.** The leaves of these plants are equipped with chemical and mechanical traps. Once trapped inside the plant, insects are digested by secretions that contain enzymes. The Venus' flytrap, the pitcher plant, and the sundew are examples of insectivorous plants.

SECTION REVIEW   Answers on page T–66.

1. What is abscission?
2. Distinguish between simple and compound leaves.
3. Define venation.
4. Name two types of leaf adaptations.

Leaf Processes

The cells and tissues of a leaf carry out several important processes. Through *photosynthesis*, the leaf produces food. During *respiration*, the leaf makes use of the energy stored in the food. **Transpiration** and **guttation** enable the leaf to eliminate water.

Photosynthesis and Respiration

During photosynthesis, the leaf changes carbon dioxide and water into oxygen and the food glucose. The carbon dioxide enters through the stomata of the leaf, and the water rises from the roots. After photosynthesis, oxygen diffuses through the stomata of the leaf and the glucose is kept as food. Through this process, the leaf produces a variety of food materials, some of which the leaf uses for itself.

Photosynthesis involves a string of complex chemical reactions that occur very quickly. These reactions can be broken down into two stages. The reactions of the first stage are the light reactions. Light is required to trigger this stage of photosynthesis. In this stage, the chlorophyll in the chloroplasts of green plants becomes energized by the light. The reactions of the second stage are called the dark reactions because they do not require light. One of the products formed during this stage is glucose, some of which the leaf uses for its own activities. Enzymes act on the rest of the glucose to change it into starch, which is stored in the mesophyll.

At this point, you may want to assign to several students the first of the Extensions and Applications at the end of this chapter.

Like other living things, plants use food and oxygen to obtain energy. Respiration involves the breaking down of glucose and other food molecules to make use of their chemical energy. When the plant requires food, certain enzymes change the starch back into glucose. The glucose is then transported as a solution through the phloem sieve tubes to various parts of the plant. The breakdown of the glucose yields water, carbon dioxide, and ATP, an energy-rich substance. Respiration is the reverse process of photosynthesis. Unlike photosynthesis and transpiration, respiration not only occurs in the leaf but throughout the entire plant. Chapter 7 presents a more detailed explanation of photosynthesis and respiration.

Transpiration and Guttation

Both photosynthesis and respiration produce water as a byproduct. This water is eliminated from the plant by means of transpiration. The main organs of transpiration are

Highlight

During photosynthesis, leaves change carbon dioxide and water into oxygen and glucose. During respiration, oxygen and food molecules are converted into water, carbon dioxide, and ATP.

CAREER: Botanist

People who study plants are called botanists. Botanists may study different aspects of plant life, including reproduction, growth, and behavior, or specialize in certain areas. For example, plant taxonomists identify and classify plants. Plant physiologists study how the parts of a plant function, while paleobotanists study plants that lived long ago. Some botanists specialize in the study of one kind of plant. For example, pteridologists study ferns, mycologists study fungi, and phycologists study algae.

Many botanists search for solutions to such problems as food shortages. They develop methods to produce higher-yield crops, ways to monitor pollution, and techniques to prevent erosion.

Often, botanists work with specialists in other fields. For example, by working with economists and sociologists, botanists help find ways to improve agriculture in developing countries. Paleobotanists work with geologists to discover new oil deposits.

To work in botany, a bachelor's degree with a broad background in the biological sciences is essential. The study of physical sciences and

mathematics is also important, as is the study of computer science.

Many botanists combine research with teaching. They work in colleges, universities, and agricultural schools. Some botanists work for private companies, such as those whose business is to produce fertilizers, herbicides, seeds, or lumber. Others work for federal and state agencies, such as various departments of agriculture and forestry. The United Nations also employs botanists.

For further career information, write to Botanical Society of America, School of Biological Sciences, University of Kentucky, Lexington, KY 40506.

At this point, you may want to assign to several students the second of the Extensions and Applications at the end of this chapter.

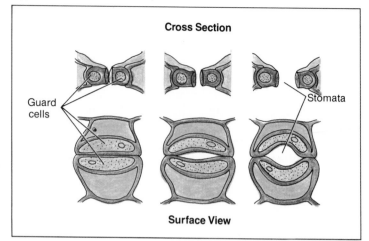

Figure 22-9 When guard cells are turgid, or full of water, the stomata open, allowing water vapor to transpire through the leaf. When the guard cells are not turgid, the stomata are closed, and transpiration of water vapor does not occur.

Highlight

Plants eliminate excess water vapor by means of transpiration. They release liquid water by means of guttation.

Figure 22-10 The leaves of this rosebush have released droplets of liquid water through the process of guttation.

leaves. When the air around the leaf is relatively dry, water vapor diffuses from the leaf into the air. As the air becomes drier, transpiration takes place at a faster rate. The rate of transpiration is controlled by guard cells in the leaf. When the guard cells are full of water, or turgid, the stomata open. When the guard cells are not full, the stomata close. By opening and closing in this way, the stomata limit water loss through transpiration and enable the plant to survive. In the summer months, transpiration helps leaves to stay cool. As water evaporates from the surfaces of leaves, it draws off heat, as perspiration does for humans.

If a tomato plant is observed early on a summer morning, droplets of water may be found near the edges of the leaves. This water has been released by the plant. Guttation is the loss of water in liquid form by a plant.

Guttation occurs when soil water is abundant and when the atmosphere is saturated with water vapor. Under these conditions, pressure in the root and stem forces droplets of water out of the ends of the xylem of the leaf veins. The pressure also causes water to move through special pores near the leaf edges. Guttation is exhibited by many plants, such as potatoes, cabbages, strawberries, and grasses.

The water produced by guttation should not be confused with *dew*. Dew is the condensation that occurs when water vapor in the air comes into contact with a colder object. Dew usually appears as a film that covers the leaf, rather than as droplets.

SECTION REVIEW   Answers on page T-66.

1. Define photosynthesis and respiration.
2. What is transpiration? Guttation?

The Structure of Leaves

Purpose Although leaves vary in shape and size, their internal anatomy is similar. The purposes of this investigation are to observe the internal anatomy of a leaf and to relate the various structures to their functions.

Materials *(per student)* ● 5 different types of green leaves ● Cover slip ● Prepared slide of monocot and dicot leaf cross sections ● Microscope ● Forceps ● Glass slide ● Medicine dropper

Procedure   **1.** Obtain 5 different leaves from your teacher. Observe their similarities and differences. **2.** Sketch and label the external structures of each of the 5 leaves.   **3.** Obtain the prepared slide of the leaf cross sections of a monocot and dicot. Examine it under low and high powers.   **4.** Sketch and label the different types of tissue for each leaf.   **5.** Choose one of the 5 leaves. Gently rip the leaf in half, to make a ragged edge.   **6.** With the forceps, peel away a piece of the epidermal tissue from the lower side of the leaf along the ragged edge, as shown in the figure. **7.** Make a wet-mount slide of the epidermal tissue. Cover it with a cover slip.   **8.** Observe the tissue under low and high powers.   **9.** Sketch and label all structures.

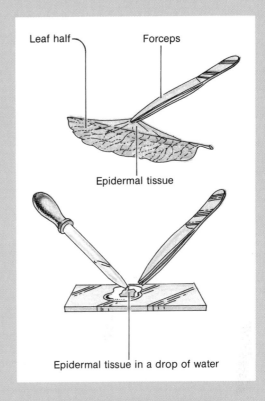

Leaf half — Forceps

Epidermal tissue

Epidermal tissue in a drop of water

Observations and Conclusions   **1.** Describe the appearance of the upper and lower surfaces of the 5 leaves, as seen with the unaided eye. Which of the surfaces would be expected to have more photosynthetic cells? Why?   **2.** Describe the appearance of the two layers of mesophyll tissue in the prepared slides of the monocot and dicot leaves. **3.** Do any of the cells in the lower epidermis contain chloroplasts? Which ones?   **4.** Which microscopic structures can you see in the lower epidermal tissue?

CHAPTER SUMMARY

Leaf Characteristics The primary function of the leaf is photosynthesis. Transpiration, or the process by which plants lose excess water, is another function of the leaf.

As the weather turns colder, most green leaves change color. The green chlorophyll begins to break down. At the same time, the red and yellow pigments, which are ordinarily masked by chlorophyll, begin to show. Plants may also shed their leaves in cold weather. The shedding of leaves is called abscission.

Most leaves have two parts. They are the petiole and the blade. The petiole is the stalk of the leaf, and the blade is the thin, flat part. Sessile leaves do not have petioles. Veins containing xylem and phloem provide leaf blades with support. Some leaves have stipules, or small outgrowths that look like tiny leaves. Stipules help to support the stems of tiny plants and to protect the buds.

Leaves may be simple or compound. Simple leaves have blades that do not contain sections. Compound leaves are divided into two or more leaflets or blade-like sections. The arrangement of the veins in leaves, called venation, is used to identify plants.

Three groups of tissues make up the leaf. They are the epidermis, the mesophyll, and the fibrovascular bundles. The epidermis, which is the outermost group, protects the tissue inside it. The cuticle, a waxy film, covers the upper epidermis. The lower epidermis contains pairs of cells called guard cells. Each pair of guard cells controls the size of the stoma, or opening between them. Water vapor and other gases pass into and out of the leaf through the stomata. The middle group, the mesophyll, contains the chloroplasts. Within the mesophyll are two types of cells, the palisade mesophyll and the spongy mesophyll. The fibrovascular bundles make up the third group of leaf tissue. Within this group are the veins containing the xylem and phloem. These structures transport food, water, and minerals throughout the plant.

To carry out certain other functions, some leaves have become adapted, or modified. Spines and tendrils are examples of such adaptations. Other plants, called insectivorous plants, have leaves that are modified to trap and to digest insects.

Leaf Processes Photosynthesis, respiration, transpiration, and guttation are important processes that occur within the leaf. During photosynthesis, the plant changes carbon dioxide and water into oxygen and glucose. During respiration, the glucose combines with oxygen to produce carbon dioxide and ATP.

In transpiration, excess water is removed from the plant. In guttation, water is forced out of small pores near the leaf edges by pressure in the root and stem.

CHAPTER VOCABULARY

abscission	insectivorous plant	sessile leaf
blade	leaf	spine
bundle sheath	leaflet	spongy mesophyll
cuticle	mesophyll	stipule
epidermal hair	palisade mesophyll	stoma
epidermis	palmate leaf	succulent leaf
fibrovascular bundle	petiole	tendril
guard cell	pinnate leaf	transpiration
guttation	sclerenchyma fiber	venation

REVIEW of FACTS and CONCEPTS   Answers on pages T–66 to T–67.

On a separate sheet of paper, answer each of the following as completely as possible.

1. How are leaves grouped according to appearance?
2. What causes the leaves of green plants to change color in autumn?
3. Explain what causes leaves to fall.
4. Name the external structures of a leaf and give their functions.

5. Give some examples of plants that have simple and compound leaves.
6. Discuss the different types of venation.
7. Describe the three groups of tissues in the leaf.
8. Describe the two types of cell layers in the mesophyll of a leaf.

9. Why are insectivorous plants not truly dependent upon insects for their food?
10. Briefly describe the processes of photosynthesis and respiration.
11. Briefly explain the action of the stomata during transpiration.

EXTENSIONS and APPLICATIONS   For additional information, see page T–67.

1. Cut out any two of the following shapes from a sheet of black construction paper: circle, triangle, square, star, and diamond. Attach the two cutouts to the top surface of a leaf on a plant that has broad leaves. The cutouts must be significantly smaller than the leaf. Use small paper clips to hold the paper against the leaves. Place the plant in sunlight for several days, giving it water as needed. Then remove the paper from the leaves. Explain the reason for what you observe.

2. To obtain stomate impressions of a leaf, remove a green leaf from a tree on a warm sunny day. Gently tear away a piece of the leaf about the size of a half-dollar piece. Place a drop of xylene on a plastic cover slip. Place the leaf on top of the cover slip. Position the leaf so that the waxy side faces up and the dull underside is in direct contact with the cover slip. Be sure to work on a hard flat surface, such as a table. After gently pressing down on the leaf and cover slip, remove the cover slip from the leaf. View the cover slip under the low power of a microscope. Sketch what you see. Go through the same steps with another leaf from the same kind of plant that you have kept in the dark for a few hours. What similarities or differences do you observe between the stomate impressions made by the two leaves?

3. Visit the library to gather information on insectivorous plants. Discuss how each type of plant captures its prey. Give an oral report to the class.

SUGGESTED READINGS

Kramer, J. and D. Worth, *Cacti and Other Succulents*. New York: Abrams.
   This book gives an account of the structure, organization, and history of succulent plants. Many color photographs and illustrations are included.
Slack, A., *Carnivorous Plants*. Cambridge, Mass.: MIT Press.
   In this book, the author examines fifty species of carnivorous plants. Photographs and drawings are included, as well as information on the cultivation of these plants.
Wohlrabe, R.A., *Exploring the World of Leaves*. New York: Thomas Y. Crowell.
   The anatomy and physiology of many different leaf types are discussed. Directions on how to collect and mount leaves are also included.

23 Reproduction in Flowering Plants

Bees pollinate many flowering plants.

Chapter Objectives *After completing this chapter, you will be able to:*

a ■ Distinguish between vegetative propagation and sexual reproduction. p. 368

b ■ Give examples of natural vegetative propagation. p. 369

c ■ Describe some methods used in artificial propagation. p. 369

d ■ List the parts of a flower and describe the function of each part. p. 371

e ■ Explain ovule and pollen formation. p. 374

f ■ Describe pollination and fertilization in a flower. p. 375

g ■ Discuss fruit and seed development. p. 377

h ■ Distinguish between monocot and dicot seeds. p. 377

i ■ Describe seed germination. p. 379

For teaching aids for this chapter, including a chapter overview and teaching strategies, see pages T–67 to T–68. The page number next to each chapter objective refers to the text page where the information needed to fulfill the objective begins.

About a quarter of a million flowering plants beautify the earth with all kinds of vivid colors. The flowers on these plants are all different sizes. The world's largest flower measures up to 91 centimeters across. Others are hardly larger than the head of a pin. Regardless of their size, shape, or form, all flowers are vital to the reproductive process of a plant.

The life cycle of flowering plants is divided into two stages. During the *vegetative stage*, which is a form of *asexual reproduction*, the plant grows roots, stems, and leaves. During the *reproductive stage*, the plant develops flowers and seeds. This stage is a form of *sexual reproduction*.

Vegetative Propagation

During the vegetative stage, many flowering plants are capable of reproducing asexually through **vegetative propagation** (prahp-ə-GĀ-shən). In this type of reproduction, certain organs of the plant grow into new plants, which are identical to the parent plants but smaller. Vegetative propagation can occur naturally or artificially.

Figure 23-1 The devil's backbone reproduces naturally by vegetative propagation.

At this point, you may want to assign to the class the first of the Extensions and Applications at the end of this chapter.

Natural Vegetative Propagation

Vegetative propagation takes place naturally in many plants. In these plants, the parenchyma tissue in the vascular bundle produces axillary buds and roots. From these buds and roots grow *stolons* and *runners*, which are modified types of stems that were discussed in Chapter 21. At the ends of the stolons and runners are *adventitious roots* and *adventitious buds*. The strawberry plant reproduces in this way.

Asexual reproduction occurs naturally in other ways. For instance, the leaf of the *Bryophyllum* can produce more than a dozen *plantlets*, or tiny plants. Each plantlet is capable of developing into a new plant. Some roots, such as those of the dandelion and sweet potato, build up reserve food in their tissues. When separated from the plant, these roots can develop into new individual plants.

Artificial Vegetative Propagation

For centuries, people have experimented and developed methods for growing more desirable types of plants. In one method, called *artificial propagation*, plant growers grow a new plant from a vegetative organ of a parent plant. Commercial flowering and fruiting plants, such as roses, carnations, irises, apples, and pears, are grown in this way. Plant growers can bring about vegetative propagation artificially in several ways.

CUTTINGS   Among the most common methods of artificial propagation is the **cutting.** In this method, the vegetative part of a plant is removed, or cut, from the parent plant and then rooted in water or in moist soil. Cuttings can be taken from stems, roots, and leaves. To hasten the formation of roots, substances that promote growth are applied to the base of the cutting. Roses, sugar cane, grapes, and ornamental shrubs are examples of plants that can develop from cuttings.

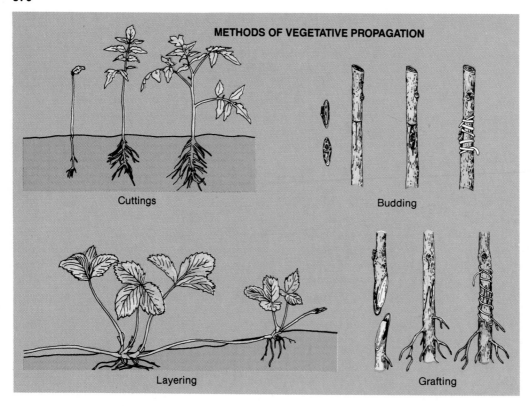

METHODS OF VEGETATIVE PROPAGATION

Cuttings

Budding

Layering

Grafting

Figure 23-2 Cuttings, budding, layering, and grafting are all methods of commercially used artificial vegetative propagation.

LAYERING In some plants, such as azaleas, honey-suckles, roses, grapes, and blackberries, **layering** can be used. To layer such plants, moist soil is used to cover their stems. Adventitious roots then grow from the stems. Layering differs from cutting in that adventitious roots form before the vegetative parts are separated from the plant.

GRAFTING A cutting from the parent plant is also made in **grafting,** but in this case the cutting is called a **scion** (sī-ən). Instead of being rooted, the cutting is attached to a **stock** or stem of another plant. The stock may be of the same species or genus as the scion, but it is usually of a different variety. The stock stem and the scion are cut so that their layers of *vascular cambium* will be in close contact when grafted. The vascular cambium contains unspecialized cells and helps to form quick growth between the stem and scion. After the graft, both the stock and the scion continue to have all the characteristics of the plants from which they came. Cherries, apples, and roses are examples of plants that are propagated by grafting.

Highlight

Vegetative propagation is a form of asexual reproduction. Vegetative propagation may occur naturally or artificially.

BUDDING A specialized form of grafting in which a bud is used as the scion is called **budding.** In budding, a piece of bark that contains the bud and some of the cambium is cut from the parent plant. A V-shaped cut is made in the bark of the stock. Then the bud, containing the bark of the parent plant, is placed into the cut stem. Once it is in place, the scion is tied or taped. The growth of the scion begins the following spring. Many fruit trees, such as those bearing peaches, apples, and pears, are grown with this method of artificial vegetative propagation.

SECTION REVIEW Answers on page T–67.

1. Distinguish between the vegetative stage and the reproductive stage in the life cycle of flowering plants.
2. Name two examples of natural vegetative propagation.
3. Name four methods of artificial vegetative propagation.

Sexual Reproduction

In *angiosperms,* or flowering plants, such as strawberries, apples, peaches, and roses, reproduction occurs both vegetatively and sexually. During sexual reproduction, *gametes,* or sex cells, form in the flower. Most flowers produce both male and female gametes. These gametes are called the sperm and egg cells, respectively. The gametes of the parent plants join to form a *zygote,* or fertilized egg. This zygote eventually becomes a *seed.* The seed contains a young plant, or *embryo,* stored food, and a protective seed coat. The structure that contains the stored food is called the *cotyledon,* or seed leaf. Plants that produce seeds with one cotyledon are called *monocotyledons,* or monocots. Plants that have two cotyledons are called *dicotyledons,* or dicots. A seed transmits genetic information from both gametes.

Structure of Flowers

J.W. von Goethe, an eighteenth-century German poet and scientist, was one of the first naturalists to describe the flower as a special shoot with modified leaves. This description is still accepted by botanists. Figure 23-4 shows the structures of a typical flower. Notice some of the structures resemble those of leaves. Two of these structures give support to the flower. One of these structures, the **pedicel** (PED-i-s'l), serves as the stalk on which the flower rests. At the tip of the pedicel is an enlarged second structure called

Highlight

In sexual reproduction, plants reproduced by means of meiosis.

At this point, you may want to assign to the class the second of the Extensions and Applications at the end of this chapter.

Figure 23-3 These wildflowers reproduce sexually. Male and female gametes are produced and then unite to form a zygote.

the **receptacle.** In the young flower, the receptacle looks like a shoot apex of a stem. Instead of developing leaves, however, the receptacle produces four other types of flower structures.

Beginning from the base of the flower, the first structures to develop from the receptacle are the **sepals** (SĒ-p'lz). Looking like tiny leaves, the sepals enclose the flower when it is a bud. The sepals of some flowers, such as lilies and tulips, are brightly colored. All of the sepals on the receptacle, taken together, make up the **calyx** (KĀ-liks).

The **petals** are the second structures to develop from the receptacle. They are perhaps the most attractive structures of the flower. These are often brightly colored and usually arranged in a circular pattern. All of the petals on a receptacle, taken together, make up the **corolla** (kə-RŌL-ə). The corolla is usually the most noticeable and beautiful part of the flower. Together, the calyx and the corolla make up the *perianth* (PER-ē-anth).

Within the perianth, or just above the petals, are the third type of structures formed by the receptacle. These structures are called the **stamens** (STĀ-mənz), which are the male organs of the flower. Each stamen is usually made up of two parts. The stalklike part is called the **filament.** At the top of the filament is the **anther,** which contains pollen.

The fourth type of flower structure, the **pistil** (PIS-t'l), is located at the center of the flower. The pistil is the female organ. It usually looks like a tiny flask with an enlarged base. The base, which is attached to the receptacle, is called the **ovary.** Inside the ovary are structures called **ovules,** which develop into seeds. The *style* is a slender stalk that extends from the ovary. At the top of the style is the *stigma*. The surface of the stigma is sticky, which enables pollen to adhere to it.

At this point, you may want to have your students do the Laboratory Investigation at the end of this chapter.

Highlight

The mature flower has four basic parts. The sepals and petals are leaf-like structures that surround the flower's reproductive organs, the stamens and the pistils.

Figure 23-4 This cross section of a typical flower reveals the structures that enable the flower to carry out its primary function, reproduction.

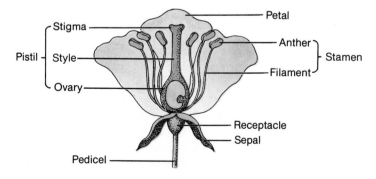

Modifications of Flowers

Flowers show a wide variety of modifications. For example, while most flowers have both pistils and stamens, other flowers, such as corn, contain only the pistil or the stamen. In corn, the tassels at the top are the stamen-containing flowers, and the ears are the pistil-containing flowers. Some plants, such as holly and willow, have stamens and pistils on separate male and female plants.

In addition to the presence or absence of stamens and pistils, flower structures may differ in other ways. For example, the flower parts of monocots, such as the daffodil, appear in threes or in multiples of threes. In dicots, these parts occur in multiples of four or five, such as in the marsh marigold.

Some blossoms are actually made up of different types of flowers. For instance, in the black-eyed Susan, the outer

CAREER: Plant Nursery Operator

In plant nurseries, young trees or other plants are planted, cultivated, and harvested for experimentation or for selling. Some plant nurseries grow flowers, bedding plants, and house plants. These plants may grow outdoors, in greenhouses, or in other buildings where environmental conditions can be controlled. Some nurseries grow only trees, and they may even specialize in one kind of tree.

Plant nursery operators decide which kinds of plants are to be grown in the nursery. The operators must know the best conditions for propagating the plants that they choose to grow. They determine how much space, light, fertilizer, and water that each plant needs. They must also be sure that the plant is grown at the proper temperature.

Each year, plant breeders develop new varieties of plants. Nursery operators must not only keep records of these new varieties, but they must also determine which varieties will grow and will sell well in their areas.

Nursery operators hire and supervise plant nursery workers. They assign duties and train the workers in gardening techniques, planting, watering, weeding, and fertilizing. The workers also sort, pot, and pack plants that are ready to be sold.

Many plant nursery operators begin their careers as workers in the nursery. As they become more skilled and better informed about the propagation and care of plants, they assume more responsibilities. Their on-the-job training is supplemented with courses in the biological sciences, chemistry, and business management. Many colleges offer two-year or four-year courses in horticulture, the science of plant growing.

For further career information, write to American Society of Horticulture Science, 701 North Saint Asaph St., Alexandria, VA 22314.

Figure 23-5 The daffodil (*top*) is a monocot. Its flower parts are found in multiples of three. The marsh marigold (*bottom*) is a dicot. Its flower parts are found in multiples of either four or five.

yellow portion is made up of flowers that attract insects but that are not involved in reproduction. The inner cluster contains the reproductive flowers.

Flowers also differ in the number of ovules contained in their ovaries. While only one ovule is found in the ovaries of some flowers, such as those of the avocado, several are contained in the ovaries of other flowers. Some ovaries, such as those of the tomato flower, hold many ovules.

Formation of Egg Cells and Pollen

In all flowers, each of the ovules contains a mother cell called a **megaspore**. Because this megaspore contains two sets of chromosomes, it is *diploid*. The diploid megaspore undergoes two meiotic divisions, to form four megaspores. Each of these megaspores, which contains one set of chromosomes, is said to be *haploid*. Only one of the megaspores survives to grow and to develop into a structure that contains the plant embryo. This structure is called the *embryo sac*.

During the development of the embryo sac, the nucleus of the surviving megaspore divides three times by mitosis. This series of divisions results in eight haploid cells. Four of the cells move as a group toward the **micropyle** (MĪ-krə-pīl), which is a tiny opening in the sac. The other four move as

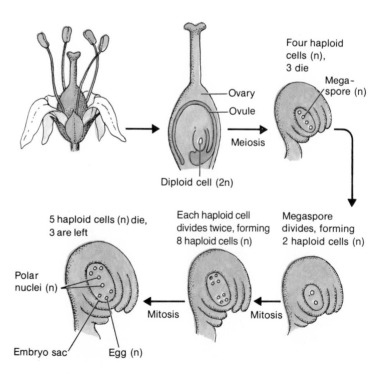

Figure 23-6 Development of Female Gamete in Ovary

another group to the opposite end. In each group, one cell develops what is called the *polar nucleus.* The two cells with the polar nuclei move to the center of the embryo sac, leaving three cells in each group. One of the six cells remaining near the micropyle develops into the egg. The other five cells die.

While the egg is forming in the ovule of the flower, changes occur in the anther. The anther consists of four chambers, each of which has a *pollen sac.* Each pollen sac contains a cluster of cells with large nuclei. As the anther grows, each cell undergoes two meiotic divisions, producing a group of four **microspore** cells.

In each microspore, the nucleus divides by mitosis to form the **tube nucleus** and the **generative nucleus**, both of which play a role in reproduction. The microspores then develop into pollen grains. The outer surface of the thick walls on pollen grains are covered with spines and ridges that are characteristic of the given species.

Pollination and Fertilization

When the anthers are mature, they open and release pollen. The pollen may then be transferred to the stigma, in a process called **pollination.** In *self-pollination,* pollen is transferred to the stigma of the same flower. When pollen is transferred to the stigma of another flower of the same species, *cross-pollination* occurs.

For cross-pollination to occur, the pollen must be carried by *pollinating agents,* which include wind and insects. Plants such as corn, oak, and ragweed, for example, are pollinated by wind. Many fruit plants, such as apple and pear trees, are pollinated by insects. Most insect-pollinated flowers have brightly colored petals and a sweet odor to attract insects, especially bees. When the insect is drawn inside the flower, pollen sticks to it. When the same insect travels to another flower, some of the pollen may fall off of the insect and onto the stigma of that flower. Pollination is complete when the pollen has been transferred from an anther to a stigma.

The pollen grain begins to form an outgrowth, called the **pollen tube.** The growth of this tube is thought to be controlled by the tube nucleus. The pollen tube grows down the stigma and style into the ovary. The generative nucleus moves into the pollen tube, where it divides into two **sperm nuclei.** Enzymes produced by the pollen tube digest a small part of the wall of the embryo sac. The pollen tube then enters the embryo sac through the micropyle.

Inside the embryo sac, the two sperm nuclei function differently. One sperm nucleus unites with the egg nucleus

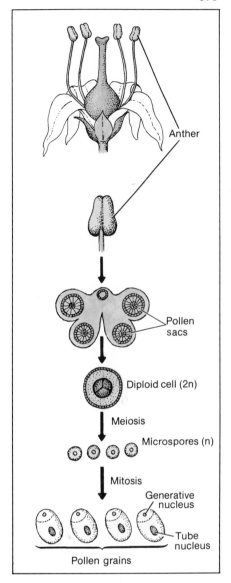

Figure 23-7 Development of Male Gamete in Anther

Highlight

Pollination is the process by which pollen travels from the anther of the stamen to the stigma of the pistil.

Figure 23-8 Pollinating agents include animals and the wind. Pollen is carried from one fusia flower to another on the hummingbird's beak, wings, or feet. Powdery pollen is blown from one oak flower to another by the wind.

and *fertilization* occurs. Fertilization produces a diploid zygote that develops into the embryo plant. The second sperm nucleus joins with the two polar nuclei in the center of the embryo sac, forming the primary **endosperm nucleus.** This nucleus develops into the **endosperm.** The endosperm

Figure 23-9 After pollination, a pollen tube begins to grow from the grain of pollen into the style to the ovary. Double fertilization occurs in the ovule when one sperm unites with an egg and the other sperm unites with the polar nuclei.

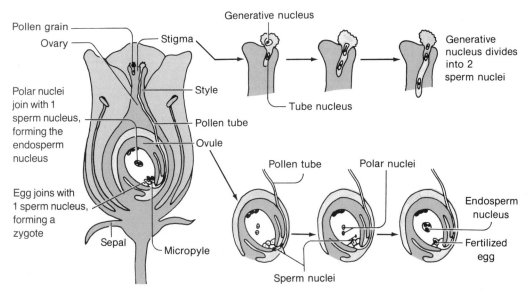

contains tissues that are capable of storing proteins and other food materials. When the functions of the two sperm nuclei are complete, the embryo that is contained in the seed, or in the ripened ovule, uses the stored food for growth. The petals and sepals of the flower then dry up and fall off the plant.

Fruit Development

One of the organs that remains on the plant after pollination and fertilization is the ovary. Within the ovary, the developing embryo produces special chemical substances that stimulate the young ovary. These substances also signal the start of the formation of the *fruit*, which is a mature ovary. During fruit formation, the ovary increases in size, while ripening or maturing.

There are many types of fruits. Some fruits are *fleshy*, such as the apple, and some are *dry*, like the bean. A *simple fruit*, such as the pea pod, has only one ovary. Another type of fruit is the *aggregate fruit*. An aggregate fruit consists of a group of ripened ovaries that appear on a common receptacle. Examples of aggregate fruits are blackberries and raspberries, which develop from a single flower with many pistils. *Multiple fruits* are made up of all the ripened ovaries of several flowers that have fused together. The mulberry and the pineapple, for example, are multiple fruits.

Seed Structure

The seeds that develop within the fruit are made up of a seed coat, stored food, and an embryo. Some seeds, such as those of corn plants, also have an endosperm. The food for the embryo, or young plant, is stored in the endosperm. The endosperm takes up a large portion of the seed. The outer part of the seed coat is called the **testa.**

In the embryos of angiosperms, food is also stored in one or more cotyledons. Figure 23-11 shows a monocot and a dicot seed. Above the cotyledon in plant embryos, there is the **epicotyl** (ep-ə-KAHT-'l). The epicotyl is made up of embryonic leaves. The epicotyl and its young leaves form the **plumule** (PLOOM-yool). Below the cotyledon is the **hypocotyl** (hī-pə-KAHT-'l), or the embryonic stem. The **radicle**, or embryonic root, is slightly below the hypocotyl.

In addition to one cotyledon, monocots share many other characteristics. These include parallel veins in leaves, flower parts in multiples of threes, and scattered vascular bundles in the stem. Monocots include not only members of the grass family, such as rice, oats, wheat, sugar cane, and bamboo,

Many students are confused by the terms "fruit" and "vegetable," because the common definitions differ greatly from scientific ones. "Vegetable" is scientifically synonymous with the word "plant." A "fruit" is that part of a seed-bearing plant that contains the seed or seeds.

Figure 23-10 Mature ovaries develop into fruits. They may contain one or more seeds.

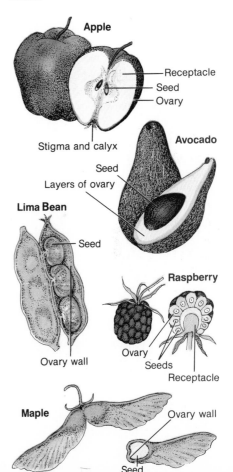

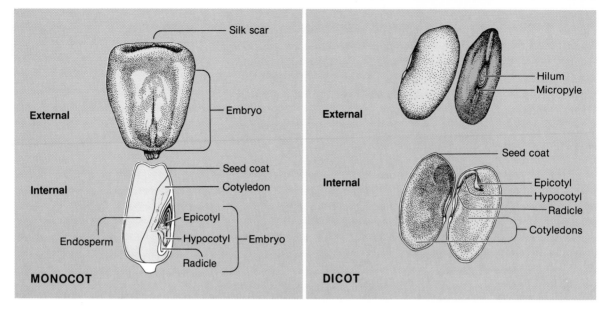

Figure 23-11 Monocot seeds have one cotyledon and dicot seeds have two. In monocots, the food for the embryo plant is stored in the endosperm. In most dicots, food for the embryo is stored in the two cotyledons. The seed coat protects the seed.

Figure 23-12 Milkweed seeds are dispersed by the wind. Light breezes lift the seeds and their parachutelike structures out of the fruit and carry them wherever the wind happens to be blowing.

but also many spring plants, like onions, lilies, and daffodils. Corn is a typical monocot, as each kernel is a complete fruit with only one seed. A tiny pointed structure, called a *silk scar*, is located near the micropyle at the top of the kernel. The silk scar is where the seed broke away from the style.

The bean is an example of a dicot seed. Although a bean has two cotyledons, it lacks the endosperm. The food for the embryo is therefore stored entirely in the cotyledons. Like other members of the bean or pea family, bean seeds are enclosed in a pod. Each seed is attached to the pod by a stalk. When this stalk breaks off, it leaves a scar called the **hilum** (HĪ-ləm). The plumule, located at the top of the bean seed, develops into two distinct leaves.

Seed Dispersal

The process by which seeds are taken from one place to another by wind, water, or animals is called **seed dispersal.** Milkweed and dandelion seeds, for example, are carried on the wind with the help of special "parachute" structures. Maple, pine, and elm seeds also travel on the wind with the help of their "wings." Coconuts, which are the seeds of the coconut palm, float on water because air is trapped inside them. Coconut seeds are therefore dispersed by the movement of ocean currents that carry the seeds from one land mass to another. Many seeds, such as those of burdock, have spines that stick to animal fur and people's clothing. Such seeds are dispersed by the movement of animals and people. Birds and squirrels also carry seeds to other areas. Other seeds, such as those of the dwarf mistletoe, are expelled forcefully into the air from the fruit. This plant can propel its seed up to a distance of 15 meters.

Seed Germination and Growth

After the seed is mature and dispersed, it often passes through a period of *dormancy*, or inactivity. The length of this period varies with the type of plant. Seeds of the perennials may remain dormant during the winter, while the dormancy of other seeds may last for many years. At the end of the dormant period, seeds *germinate*, or begin to grow. When seeds are kept cool and dry during dormancy, their ability to germinate, or their **viability** (vī-ə-BIL-ə-tē), is improved.

Favorable environmental conditions trigger germination. Such conditions include sufficient moisture and oxygen, and an appropriate temperature. The moisture softens the seed coat and causes the seed to swell. Oxygen is needed for the seedling's respiration. Finally, a period of low temperatures is often needed to stimulate the growth of dormant seeds.

During the germination of most seeds, the radicle is the first structure to emerge from the seed coat. Growing through the micropyle, the radicle produces the primary root. This root in turn develops root hairs and secondary roots. Adventitious roots may also appear. All these roots anchor the plant in the soil and absorb water.

When a monocot, such as corn, germinates, the food stored in the endosperm begins to break down, providing nutrients for the growing parts of the seed. The **coleoptile** (kō-lē-AHP-t'l) protects and covers the plumule as it pushes upward through the soil. When the base of the coleoptile reaches the soil surface, its edges spread apart at the tip. The first leaves of the plumule emerge from this point, and the stem continues to grow upward. The seed or kernel, which contains the cotyledon and endosperm, remains underground. As the embryonic leaves unfold, photosynthesis begins. Soon the plant becomes established and no longer depends on the endosperm for nourishment.

In dicot seeds, such as those of beans, the hypocotyl becomes long, eventually bending or hooking over after the radicle emerges from the seed. The hypocotyl straightens out when it reaches the surface of the soil, pulling the cotyledons and plumule out of the soil. As the young leaves

Highlight

Germination is the stage in a plant's development when the seed begins to grow into a seedling.

At this point, you may want to assign to the class the third of the Extensions and Applications at the end of this chapter.

Sidelight

There are more than 250,000 known species of seed-producing, flowering plants. About 190,000 of these species are dicots. Fewer than 60,000 species are monocots.

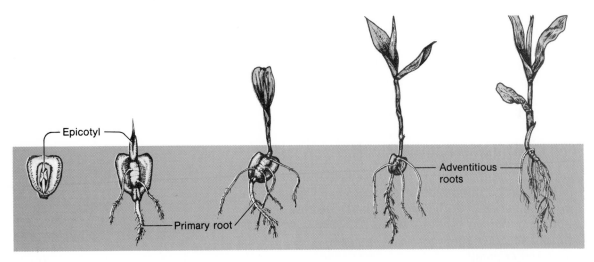

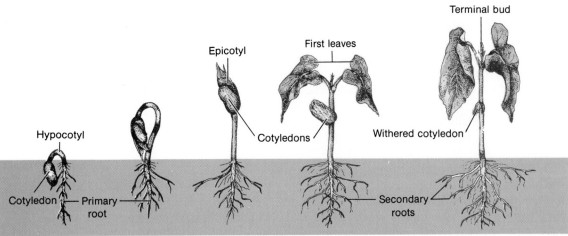

Figure 23–13 During the germination of a monocot (*top*), the seed remains in the ground. In a dicot, the seed is pushed above the ground by the growing hypocotyl. Eventually, the food stored in the seed of both kinds of plants becomes depleted and the plant makes its own food by photosynthesis.

emerge, the plant is able to perform photosynthesis. At the same time, the starch stored in the cotyledons is converted into sugar, which is carried to the growing parts of the young plant. Eventually, the cotyledons decrease in size, wither, and drop off.

SECTION REVIEW
Answers on page T–67.

1. What is a flower?
2. Name the structures that develop from a flower receptacle.
3. Define pollination. What are some pollinating agents?
4. What is a fruit? A seed?
5. What conditions are needed for seed germination?

Flower Anatomy

Purpose Despite differences in size, color, and form, all flowers contain the sexual reproductive parts of the plant. The purpose of this investigation is to observe and to identify the basic structures in a flower.

Materials *(per student)* ● 2 flowers of different kinds ● Single-edged razor blade ● Microscope ● Forceps ● 4 cover slips ● 4 glass slides ● Medicine dropper

Courtesy Carolina Biological Supply Company

Procedure   Part A   1. Obtain 2 flowers from your teacher. Examine each flower carefully.   **2.** Identify the external parts of each.   **3.** Gently remove the sepals and then the petals from each.   **4.** Locate the stamens of the flowers and carefully break open one of the anthers of each. Tap some pollen grains from each anther onto two different glass slides.   **5.** With the medicine dropper, add a drop of water to the pollen grains. Gently cover them with cover slips, and view them under low and high powers.   **6.** Sketch the pollen grains.   **Part B   1.** Look for the flasklike ovary at the base of the pistil in each flower.   **2. CAUTION:** *Be very careful when using a razor blade.* Cut the ovary of each lengthwise with the razor blade. **3.** Examine the tiny ovules inside.   **4.** Make wet mounts of the ovules, and observe them under low and high power.   **5.** Sketch the opened ovaries and the ovules.

Observations and Conclusions   1. How many petals, sepals, pistils, and stamens does each flower have? **2.** In what ways are the flowers similar? Different? **3.** Did the flowers come from dicot or monocot plants? Explain.   **4.** How are the pollen grains similar? Different?   **5.** How many chambers does the ovary of each flower contain?

Courtesy Carolina Biological Supply Company

CHAPTER SUMMARY

Vegetative Propagation Vegetative propagation is a type of asexual reproduction in which new plants develop from parts of older plants. Natural vegetative propagation includes the development of new plants from runners and stolons.

Plant growers use artificial vegetative propagation methods to reproduce plants vegetatively. These methods include cutting, layering, grafting, and budding. In cuttings, the vegetative parts of a parent plant are removed and rooted. In layering, new plants develop from the stems of parent plants that have been covered with moist soil. Grafting is the attachment of a cut stem, or scion, to a rooted stem, or stock. In budding, a piece of bark containing a bud and some cambium is used as the scion.

Sexual Reproduction During sexual reproduction, gametes are formed within the flower, the reproductive structure of angiosperms. These gametes join to form a seed, containing the young embryo plant, stored food, and a protective seed coat. At the tip of the stalklike pedicel in the flower is the receptacle, which produces four types of flower structures. These structures are sepals, petals, stamens, and pistils. The sepals are tiny green leaflike structures that enclose the flower when it is a bud. A ring of sepals is called a calyx. The brightly colored petals are responsible for attracting insects and other animals. The collection of petals is called the corolla. The remaining two struc-tures, the stamens and pistils, are the reproductive organs. The stamens, or male organs of the flower, are inside the petals. They contain a stalklike filament and pollen-producing anther. The pollen contains the generative nucleus and tube nucleus. Within the center of the flower is the pistil, or female organ. The top portion of the pistil, the stigma, is supported by a slender stalk, called the style. At the base of the pistil is an enlarged structure, called the ovary, which contains the ovules.

When pollen grains from the anther of a flower are transferred to the stigma of the same flower, self-pollination occurs. When the anther and the stigma are on different flowers of the same species, cross-pollination occurs. The pollen grain forms a pollen tube that grows through the stigma and style into the ovary. The male cells fertilize the female cells, and a seed develops within the ovary. The ovary then increases in size and ripens to form a fruit.

Monocot seeds have one cotyledon, or seed leaf, while dicot seeds have two cotyledons. In a seed, the epicotyl gives rise to the embryonic shoot, and the plumule forms the young leaves. From the hypocotyl grow the embryonic stem and the radicle.

For a seed to germinate or grow, it needs sufficient moisture, enough oxygen, and a favorable temperature. The ability of a seed to germinate is called viability.

CHAPTER VOCABULARY

anther	hypocotyl	radicle
budding	layering	receptacle
calyx	megaspore	scion
coleoptile	micropyle	seed dispersal
corolla	microspore	sepal
cutting	ovary	sperm nucleus
endosperm	ovule	stamen
endosperm nucleus	pedicel	stock
epicotyl	petal	testa
filament	pistil	tube nucleus
generative nucleus	plumule	vegetative propagation
grafting	pollen tube	viability
hilum	pollination	

REVIEW of FACTS and CONCEPTS   Answers on page T–68.

On a separate sheet of paper, answer each of the following as completely as possible.

1. Briefly describe four methods of artificial vegetative propagation.
2. If a pear branch is grafted onto an apple tree, what type of fruit will the pear branch bear? Explain.
3. Distinguish between grafting and budding.
4. Name the parts of a flower and give their functions.
5. Briefly describe egg cell and pollen formation.
6. What is the function of the micropyle?
7. Describe pollination and fertilization.
8. Differentiate between a monocot and a dicot seed.
9. Name three methods of seed dispersal.
10. Describe the germination of a monocot and a dicot seed.
11. What is viability?
12. Distinguish between the following pairs of terms: scion and stock; calyx and corolla; megaspore and microspore; cross-pollination and self-pollination; epicotyl and hypocotyl; and plumule and radicle.

EXTENSIONS and APPLICATIONS   For additional information, see page T–68.

1. Visit a nearby orchard, plant nursery, or farm, and conduct an interview with the owner. Your questions should include, ''What type of plants are artificially propagated? What methods of propagation are used?''
2. Collect 10 different types of seeds. Classify each as a monocot or dicot. Using a hand lens, examine each seed. On posterboard, sketch and label each seed.
3. Place 12 bean seeds in water and let them soak overnight to soften the seed coats. Remove the seeds from the water. Place a piece of blotter (2.5 cm x 5 cm) in each of 12 test tubes. For each test tube, place a seed between the blotter and the test tube wall. Moisten the blotters in six of the test tubes with water. Use a small piece of cotton to plug each test tube. Place 2 moist and 2 dry test tubes in a cold, dark refrigerator. Place 2 other moist and 2 dry test tubes in a warm, dark place. Place the remaining 2 moist and 2 dry test tubes under a constant source of light. After 3 days, which seeds germinated? Explain.

SUGGESTED READINGS

Evans, C.M., *New Plants from Old.* New York: Random House.
   This book shows how to produce plants by artificial propagation. Line drawings and step-by-step instructions are included.
Free, M., *Plant Propagation in Pictures.* Garden City, N.Y.: Doubleday.
   Information is given on how to increase the number of house and garden plants by grafting, layering, cuttings, and seed planting.
Langer, R.W., *The After-Dinner Gardening Book.* New York: Collier Books.
   The author explains how to grow plants from seeds collected from foods. Also included is information on types of soil, cultivation, germination, and potting plants.

24 Plant Growth and Behavior

The winged seed of a maple tree germinates in the soil.

Chapter Objectives *After completing this chapter, you will be able to:*

a ■ Define growth in plants. p. 384
b ■ Summarize the factors influencing the growth of plants. p. 385
c ■ Give the function of auxins, gibberellins, and other plant hormones. p. 385
d ■ Explain the importance of light in plant growth and development. p. 388
e ■ Define photoperiodism. p. 388
f ■ Name and describe the different kinds of tropisms. p. 392
g ■ Differentiate between nastic movements and tropisms. p. 393

For teaching aids for this chapter, including a chapter overview and teaching strategies, see pages T–68 to T–70. The page number next to each chapter objective refers to the text page where the information needed to fulfill the objective begins.

An increase in the number or size of cells due to cell division or enlargement is *growth. Behavior* consists of the responses to stimuli. Both growth and behavior in plants are controlled by two types of influence. One results from the processes that go on inside the plant, such as the various chemical substances produced by the plant. The other influence arises from external conditions. These conditions include *environmental influences*, such as light, temperature, moisture, and physical contact.

The Nature of Plant Growth

Much of a plant's growth takes place in its *meristematic regions*. These regions are located at the tips of the roots and shoots. Cells in these regions divide and enlarge continuously. They develop into specialized tissues, such as stems, roots, and leaves. This progressive specialization is known as *development*. Growth and development are irreversible processes. In other words, newly formed stem, root, or leaf cells do not change back to their meristematic forms.

Growth is the result of balanced *metabolism*. Metabolism is the total of all the building-up and breaking-down activities within the cell. In younger plants, the rate of building up is greater than the rate of breaking down. As a result, seedlings tend to grow faster than do older plants. When the opposing metabolic rates are equal, growth continues, but all it does is maintain or repair plant organs. When the breaking-down process occurs faster than the building-up process, the plant dies.

Highlight

Plant growth occurs in the meristematic regions when cells either elongate or multiply.

SECTION REVIEW   Answers on page T–69.

1. Define plant growth and behavior.
2. Where in a plant does most of the growth occur?

Internal Factors Affecting Growth

Within the same plant, the growth of some structures affects the growth of others. For example, the growth of leaves influences the growth of flowers. The development of terminal buds affects the development of lateral buds. Such interrelationships are controlled for the most part by *hormones*, or growth-regulating chemical substances. These substances are found in very small amounts in plants and animals. A particular hormone may either stimulate or inhibit growth. For example, if the growing tip of a stem is cut and a certain type of hormone is absent, lateral buds grow. When the hormone is present, lateral buds do not grow.

The first plant hormones to be discovered were the **auxins** (AWK-sinz), whose name comes from a Greek word that means to excite. Auxins are found in apical meristems, cambium, leaves, fruits, seeds, and pollen. Together with other hormones, auxins play an important role in plant metabolism.

The particular role of auxins in the metabolism of a plant is to regulate cell growth and development. Auxins

Highlight

Hormones produced in the cells of a plant control and direct the growth and development of the plant.

At this point, you may want to assign to the class the third of the Extensions and Applications at the end of this chapter.

generally stimulate stem growth but inhibit root growth. They inhibit *abscission*, or the shedding of plant parts. In this role, auxins prevent trees from shedding their fruits before they are ripe. Auxins also stimulate the development of vascular tissues. Their most important function, however, seems to be bringing about elongation or cell enlargement.

As early as the 1880s, scientists had suspected the presence in plants of growth substances that are now called auxins. In 1910, scientists began experiments on oat seedlings that eventually proved the existence of auxins. Normally, as an oat seedling grows, the primary shoot pierces the tip of the *coleoptile*, the protective sheath enclosing the primary shoot. If the tip of the coleoptile is removed, the shoot stops elongating, as shown in Figure 24-1a. When the tip is replaced, as shown in Figure 24-1b, growth begins again. This observation led scientists to the conclusion that growth-stimulating auxins are secreted by the tip of the coleoptile. The auxins travel down to the growing cells, causing them to elongate.

At this point, you may want to assign to the class the first of the Extensions and Applications at the end of this chapter.

Figure 24-1 Early experiments not only proved the existence of plant auxins but demonstrated how auxins affect a plant's growth. Auxins are produced in the coleoptile and can pass into and through agar.

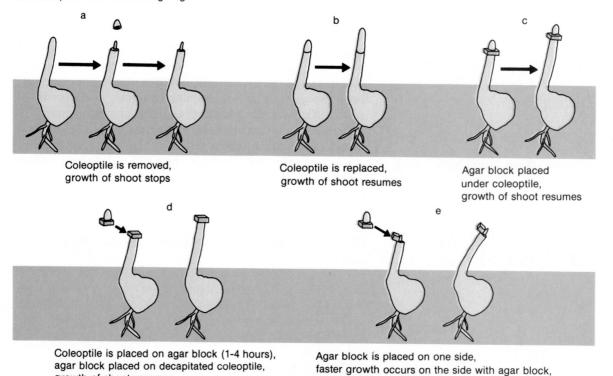

Coleoptile is removed, growth of shoot stops

Coleoptile is replaced, growth of shoot resumes

Agar block placed under coleoptile, growth of shoot resumes

Coleoptile is placed on agar block (1-4 hours), agar block placed on decapitated coleoptile, growth of shoot resumes

Agar block is placed on one side, faster growth occurs on the side with agar block, causing shoot to bend

In another group of experiments, shown in Figure 24-1c through 24-1e, an agar block was placed under the removed coleoptile tip. In the experiment shown in Figure 24-1c, the block and tip were immediately placed on the shoot from which the tip had been removed. The shoot grew, showing that auxins from the tip are able to diffuse through the block into the shoot. In the experiment shown in Figure 24-1d, the tip was left on the block for 1 to 4 hours. Then only the block was placed on the shoot from which the tip had been removed. Once again, the shoot grew. This finding indicated that the block absorbed the auxin, which then diffused into the shoot. The last experiment is shown in Figure 24-1e. An agar block, prepared as in Figure 24-1d, was placed on one half of the cut surface of a coleoptile. The auxins from the agar block caused faster growth directly beneath the coleoptile than the growth in the uncovered part of the shoot. The two unequal growth rates caused the shoot to bend.

Certain types of auxin have been synthesized in the laboratory. One such auxin is *indoleacetic* (IN-dōl-ə-sēt-ik) *acid*, or *IAA*. Another is 2,4-dichlorophenoxyacetic acid, or 2,4-D, a powerful weed killer. When absorbed by a plant, such as a dandelion, 2,4-D stimulates such rapid growth that the plant cannot take in enough food and carbon dioxide to keep up with its growth. In a sense, the weed starves to death.

Another group of growth hormones, called **gibberellins** (jib-ə-REL-inz), are produced by the *Gibberella* fungus. In the 1930s, Japanese scientists chemically isolated and identified the growth-stimulating substance, naming it gibberellin. Not until the 1950s did scientists isolate gibberellins from plants other than a fungus. The gibberellin most often used by plant experimenters is *gibberellic acid*, or *GA*.

The gibberellins have remarkable effects on stem elongation. When applied to plants, extracts from the *Gibberella* fungus promote stem growth. For example, if gibberellins are added to dwarf corn and pea plants, the plants grow to unusual heights.

The **cytokinins** (sī-tə-KĪ-ninz) make up another group of hormones whose main function is to stimulate cell division in plants. Cytokinins occur in large amounts in endosperm tissues and in young fruits. An example of a cytokinin is *kinetin*, which promotes budding.

Not all plant hormones stimulate growth. In recent years, scientists have discovered quite a few that inhibit growth. One such hormone, *abscisic acid*, inhibits cell elongation and seed germination. Another inhibitor is *maleic hydrazine* (mə-LĒ-ik HI-drə-zēn). This hormone extends the period of dormancy in perennial plants by delaying the

Sidelight

Auxins have many commercial uses. Tomato plants, when sprayed with an auxin, will produce fruit even though fertilization has not occurred. Another auxin can be sprayed on potatoes or onions to prevent them from sprouting.

Figure 24-2 The birdsnest fern on the right was treated with gibberellic acid; the one on the left was not. Based on the results of this experiment, does gibberellic acid promote or inhibit plant growth?

The plant on the right is obviously much more developed than the plant on the left. Gibberellic acid therefore promotes plant growth.

Figure 24-3 Ethylene affects the flowering of a plant. The plant on the left was exposed to a small amount of ethylene. The plant on the right received none. At the start of the experiment, both plants looked like the one on the right. This photograph was taken only 6 hours after the ethylene treatment.

Highlight

Environmental factors, such as light, temperature, and water, affect the way plants grow and develop.

Figure 24-4 The leaves of the coleus plant grown in an environment with sufficient light are large and have a distinctive pinkish color. The leaves of the coleus plant grown without sufficient light appear small and faintly colored.

growth of buds. As a result, the buds may be protected from freezing during an unusually cold spring.

Like the auxins, some substances are both growth inhibitors and growth stimulators. One such substance is the gas *ethylene*. Although ethylene was known to promote fruit ripening, scientists also found that it inhibits cell elongation. Plant investigators think that ethylene is produced by plants to balance an excess of auxin. In this way, the plant maintains a normal growth pattern. Ethylene can also cause some flowering plants to flower.

SECTION REVIEW   <small>Answers on page T–69.</small>

1. What effect do hormones have on plant growth?
2. Name the three groups of plant hormones. Describe how each affects plant growth.

External Factors Affecting Growth

The growth and behavior of plants depend greatly on environmental factors, such as the amount of light, the level of the temperature, and the availability of water. Temperature, for example, affects the rates of photosynthesis, transpiration, and reproduction.

Light

<small>At this point, you may want to refer your students to Chapter 7 for a short review of the role of light in the process of photosynthesis.</small>

Light is the primary source of energy for green plants. Without light, photosynthesis and plant growth would stop. In that event, plant life would end, and all organisms that depend directly or indirectly on green plants would die also.

Various plants have different requirements for light. Some plants require light of low *intensity*, or brightness. Many houseplants fall into this category. Other plants, such as corn and tomatoes, need high-intensity light, like direct sunlight.

The duration of exposure to light also affects the growth and reproduction of plants. **Photoperiodism** is the response of a plant to lengths of light and dark periods. Biologists have found that the length of the *photoperiod*, or the duration of exposure to light, is extremely important to flowering in plants. Plants may be divided into three groups according to their photoperiods.

To flower, *short-day plants* must be exposed to dark periods that are longer than the light periods. Short-day plants

Figure 24-5 To flower, short-day plants, like the Japanese primrose (*left*), require more hours of dark than of light. Long-day plants, like the iris (*center*), require more hours of light than of dark to flower. The flowering of day-neutral plants, like the snapdragon (*right*), is not affected by the ratio of light to dark hours.

tend to flower in the early spring or in the fall, when the days have fewer hours of daylight. Examples of short-day plants are poinsettias, chrysanthemums, strawberries, and primroses.

Plants that need longer periods of light to flower are called *long-day plants*. Such plants tend to flower in late spring or in summer, when the sun is out most of the day. Spinach, irises, lettuce, and some varieties of wheat are examples of long-day plants.

The flowering of *day-neutral plants* is not affected by the duration of the daylight. Tomatoes, roses, snapdragons, carnations, and marigolds are day-neutral plants.

For all three groups, the maximum or minimum period of uninterrupted darkness that a particular plant needs to bloom is called its *critical dark period*. Short-day plants bloom only if they are in a period of darkness that is longer than their critical dark period. Long-day plants bloom only if they are in a period of darkness that is shorter than their critical dark period. Plants can be forced to bloom artificially by exposing them to varied periods of light and dark. Artificial conditions can also force plants not to bloom. For example, many short-day trees that grow near streetlights do not flower.

Flowering can also be controlled by a combination of temperature and photoperiodic conditions called *vernalization* (ver-n'l-i-zā-shən). In this situation, the appropriate

Sidelight

Not all living communities require light as a basic source of energy. Scientists have found several communities at the bottom of the ocean that live in total darkness. The energy source of these communities is chemosynthesis rather than photosynthesis. Chemosynthesis releases energy through the breakdown of chemicals.

Figure 24-6 Temperature affects the growth of plants. The cotton plant on the left was damaged by cold temperatures. The cotton plant on the right was grown at temperatures closer to the plant's optimum temperatures.

Figure 24-7 Cacti are adapted to life in the desert. They have structures that enable them to store great quantities of water. In addition, cacti have spinelike leaves whose small surface area reduces loss of water due to transpiration.

photoperiod stimulates flowering only after a plant has been exposed to near-freezing temperatures.

Temperature and Dormancy

Temperature is another important factor that affects plant growth and flowering, by influencing photosynthesis, respiration, transpiration, digestion, and absorption. At the **optimum temperatures** of a plant, these processes occur the most rapidly and efficiently. At optimum temperatures, the growth rate is therefore the greatest. At temperatures that are significantly higher or lower than optimum, the plant fails to grow. Although plants have different optimum temperatures for various growth processes, most plants grow best between 10° C and 38° C.

When temperatures fall very low, some plants undergo a period of rest, called *dormancy*. Although this reaction occurs particularly in woody plants during winter, herbaceous plants also respond to cold. They do so by developing dormant structures, such as tubers, bulbs, and rhizomes. These structures, like deciduous twigs, can tolerate very low temperatures without injury. The ability of a plant to withstand such conditions is sometimes referred to as plant *hardiness*.

Moisture

The growth of every living cell is influenced by the amount of water available. In plants, for example, photosynthesis, which is essential to the growth of green plants, is effective only when a proper supply of water is present. Growth occurs mainly in plant cells that are *turgid*, or swollen with water.

Water is so valuable that many plants are adapted for surviving in extremely dry conditions by conserving the little water available. Desert cacti store water in succulent structures. Covered with a heavy waxy cuticle, these structures reduce the loss of water because they have few stomata. In addition, cacti have spinelike leaves that lose very little water through transpiration. Plants that grow in water are also adapted to their environment by tending to develop structures with many air spaces. These spaces allow gases, such as oxygen, to diffuse downward through the plant.

Plants are sometimes classified on the basis of the amount of water in their habitats. For example, **xerophytes** are mesquite shrubs and cactus plants, which are adapted to dry climates and deserts. Water lilies and water hyacinths, which are called **hydrophytes**, thrive in ponds, lakes, and other watery places. **Mesophytes,** such as the philodendron, grow under moderately moist conditions.

SECTION REVIEW   Answers on page T–69.

1. Name three external factors that affect plant growth.
2. What is photoperiodism? The critical dark period?
3. What is vernalization?

Responses to Stimuli

A plant's environment plays an important role in its growth and behavior. Environmental factors affecting a plant include habitat, light, availability of water, air, inorganic substances, and temperature. These factors affect plants by

CAREER: Landscape Architect

Landscape architects often design outdoor land areas, such as parks, gardens, and forest campsites. The grounds along highways and around schools, offices, and other buildings are also designed by landscape architects.

Landscape architects first discuss with their clients how a particular piece of land is to be used. Together, the landscape architect and the client determine where sidewalks, play areas, and similar structures should be located. Then the landscape architect studies the physical site. Such factors as the slope of the land, the kinds of trees and soil present, and the amount of sunlight on each part of the site must be determined.

Once all the information is collected, the landscape architect prepares plans that show how the site is to be developed, along with the kinds of plants to be used in each area of the site. This planning requires extensive knowledge of plants. Landscape architects must know which plants will grow in different soils and climates. Landscape architects who work in large cities must also know which plants are likely to resist the damage of air pollution.

The landscape architect then discusses the plans with the client and with other people who are working on buildings on the site. This communication helps to ensure that the finished land will be a pleasing and appropriate setting for the buildings.

Once a plan is approved, the landscape architect prepares detailed instructions for the contractor. The landscape architect will then oversee the work of the contractor to make sure that the plans are followed.

Landscape architects must have a bachelor's degree in landscape architecture. In all states, they must be licensed before they can practice. To receive a license, they must pass an exam, and they must show that they have received on-the-job training under the supervision of a licensed landscape architect.

For career information, write to The American Society of Landscape Architects, 1900 M Street, N.W., Suite 750, Washington, DC 20009.

392

Highlight

Tropisms are a plant's responses to various stimuli from the environment. A plant's tropic response is either toward (positive) or away from (negative) the stimulus. Nastic movements are a form of response to environmental stimuli. In a nastic movement, the plant's response is rapid and reversible.

exerting a stimulus on the plant, which causes a growth response. Stimuli may be in the form of light, water, chemicals, touch, or pressure.

Tropisms

A plant's growth response to environmental stimuli is called a **tropism.** Plant responses may be positive or negative. A positive tropism is a growth movement toward the stimulus, such as the downward growth of a root into the soil in response to gravity. A negative tropism is a growth movement away from the stimulus. Stem growth, for example, is a negative tropism in response to gravity.

Tropisms are classified according to the type of stimulus to which they respond.

Phototropism　The growth response of a plant to light is called **phototropism.** Positive phototropism usually causes stems to bend in the direction of the light source. Experiments seem to indicate that auxins become concentrated on the side of the stem that faces away from the light. The large supply of auxins on this dark side results in cell elongation. Therefore, the growth on the auxin-concentrated side of the stem is faster than on the lighted side. The darkness indirectly causes the plant stem to bend toward the source of light.

Geotropism　The growth, or response, of plant parts to gravity is called **geotropism.** Geotropism is easily demonstrated by placing a young potted plant in a horizontal position. Within a few days, the shoot bends upward and the roots grow downward. In response to the pull of

Figure 24-8　Phototropism keeps this plant facing toward the sunlight.

Figure 24-9　Roots exhibit positive geotropism, that is, they grow toward a source of gravity. Stems, however, exhibit negative geotropism by growing away from a source of gravity.

gravity, auxins become concentrated on the lower side of the stem. As a result, cell elongation becomes greater on the lower side, and the stem turns upward. In the roots, the concentration of auxins inhibits growth on the lower side of the root. The upper side continues to grow, however, forcing the tip of the root to bend downward.

Hydrotropism   The growth response of plants to water is called **hydrotropism.** Root systems usually show a positive response to water, because their growth movements are directed toward the source of water. For example, the roots of sycamore and willow trees grow toward stream banks and drainage systems.

Thigmotropism   Another growth response is **thigmotropism** (thig-MAHT-rə-piz'm), which is the twisting or coiling movement in response to contact or touch. The tendrils of squash and grape plants show positive thigmotropism, since they coil around objects, such as wooden stakes or trellises.

Chemotropism   The growth response to certain chemicals is called **chemotropism.** Roots usually show a positive response to inorganic chemicals within the soil.

Nastic Movements

At this point, you may want to have your students do Part B of the Laboratory Investigation at the end of this chapter.

Plant movements that are independent of the direction of the stimulus are not classified as tropisms. Instead, they are called **nastic movements.** They can involve the movements of leaves and petals, as well as other parts of a plant. For example, dandelion flowers open during the day and close at night. The flowers of the fragrant night-blooming cereus, on the other hand, open in the evening and close during the day. While tropisms take a long time to occur and are generally not reversible, nastic movements occur rapidly and are reversible.

Plants show various forms of nastic movement. As a dramatic example, when the leaves of the sensitive *Mimosa pudica* are touched or warmed, they quickly close, as shown in Figure 24-10. Both contact and heat cause water to rush out of cells at the base of these leaves, causing them to close.

At this point, you may want to have your students do Part A of the Laboratory Investigation at the end of this chapter.

SECTION REVIEW   Answers on page T-69.

1. Name five tropisms and include the environmental stimulus for each.
2. Define the term nastic movement.

Figure 24-10 A nastic movement, a movement independent of the direction of a stimulus, is exhibited by this mimosa. Mimosa leaves respond to touch by closing up.

Responses to Stimuli

Purpose   One of the basic characteristics of living things is their ability to respond to environmental changes. Plants respond to such changes in two ways. A tropism is a response in which plants grow toward or away from a stimulus. A nastic movement is a movement that is independent of the direction of the stimulus. The purpose of this investigation is to observe these movements, along with the stimuli that cause them.

Materials *(per group)*   ● Oxalis plant ● Corn seeds, soaked in water for 24 hours ● Shoe box ● Paper towels ● Petri dish ● Masking tape ● 2 colored pencils ● Grease pencil

Procedure   Part A   1. Obtain an oxalis plant from your teacher. Examine the angle between the leaves and the stem.   **2.** Using one of the colored pencils, draw a straight vertical line about 10 cm long on a sheet of paper. Then draw a second, shorter line that intersects with the vertical line at the same angle that the oxalis leaves intersect with the stem.   **3.** Label the diagram, "Oxalis in the Light."   **4.** Place a shoe box over the plant and leave it undisturbed for 30 minutes. **5.** Remove the box and observe the angle of the leaves relative to the stem.   **6.** Using the other colored pencil, make a second sketch indicating the angle between the leaves and the stem. Label this sketch, "Oxalis in the Dark."   **Part B   1.** Obtain 4 corn seeds that have been soaked in water for 24 hours. Arrange the seeds with the embryo side down on the top half of a petri dish as shown in the figure. Keep the pointed ends of the corn seeds toward the center of the dish.   **2.** Place a paper towel against the seeds. **3.** Pack the petri dish with crumpled paper towels so that when the top of the dish is put on, the seeds are held in place.   **4.** Dampen the paper towels, and cover the petri dish.   **5.** Seal the top of the petri dish to the bottom with a strip of masking tape.   **6.** Stand the dish on its edge so that one seed is at the 12-o'clock position. Mark the top of the petri dish with a

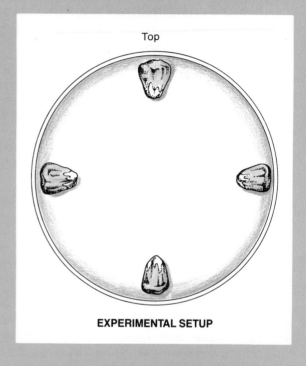

Top

EXPERIMENTAL SETUP

grease pencil.   **7.** Place your petri dish with the dishes of other class members in a place indicated by your teacher. Make sure that the dish remains on edge and in the right position.   **8.** Examine the germinating corn seeds every day for a week. Draw a sketch of them each day.

Observations and Conclusions   1. From your line drawings in Part A, what type of movement is shown by the oxalis plant when it is placed in the dark?   **2.** In Part B, in which direction did the young corn roots grow? The stems? Explain.   **3.** What is the specific name of the growth response of the corn stem and root?

CHAPTER SUMMARY

The Nature of Plant Growth Growth is an increase in the number or size of cells. The growth of plants and of other organisms is influenced by both internal and external factors.

Internal Factors Affecting Growth Plant hormones are growth regulators that plants produce in minute quantities. Examples of growth-regulating plant hormones are auxins, gibberellins, and cytokinins. Auxins and gibberellins stimulate cell elongation. Cytokinins stimulate cell division. In contrast, other hormones, such as abscisic acid and maleic hydrazine, inhibit growth.

External Factors Affecting Growth The external, or environmental, factors include light, temperature, water, chemicals, and physical contact. Light is the principal source of energy for green plants. Plants are influenced by the intensity and duration of light. The response to the duration of light and dark conditions is called photoperiodism, which controls flowering in plants. Plant growth and behavior is also significantly affected by temperature and water conditions.

Responses to Stimuli Environmental factors affect plants by exerting a stimulus on the plant, which causes a response. A tropism is a growth response to environmental stimuli. For example, phototropism is a response to light, geotropism is a response to gravity, and hydrotropism is a response to water.

Nastic movements differ from tropisms in several ways. Nastic movements are not only independent of the direction of the stimulus, but they also happen rapidly and are reversible. Tropisms occur more slowly than nastic movements, and they are generally irreversible.

CHAPTER VOCABULARY

auxin	**hydrophyte**	**photoperiodism**
chemotropism	**hydrotropism**	**phototropism**
cytokinin	**mesophyte**	**thigmotropism**
geotropism	**nastic movement**	**tropism**
gibberellin	**optimum temperature**	**xerophyte**

REVIEW of FACTS and CONCEPTS   Answers on pages T–69 to T–70.

On a separate sheet of paper, answer each of the following as completely as possible.

1. Why are growth and development considered irreversible processes?
2. Describe one experiment that demonstrates the role of auxins.
3. Name three specific plant hormones, and explain their effects on plants.
4. Name some environmental factors that affect plant growth and behavior.
5. Explain the importance of light in plant growth and development.
6. Name and describe three groups of plants according to their photoperiods. Give examples of each.
7. What is meant by optimum temperature in plants?
8. What are xerophytes, hydrophytes, and mesophytes?
9. Define tropism. What is a positive tropism? A negative tropism?
10. Differentiate between nastic movements and tropisms.

EXTENSIONS and APPLICATIONS   For additional information, see page T–70.

1. Add soil to 4 small flower pots until they are three-quarters full. Plant 3 oat or grass seeds in each pot, and moisten the soil. Keep the soil moist and the pots away from direct heat. Take a cardboard box, and cut out a window (4 cm x 4 cm) on one side. When the seedlings reach a height of about 2

cm, place the box over one of the pots. Be sure that the pot is placed against the side opposite the cut-out window. Then place the box with its cut-out window facing a window that receives adequate sunlight. With a single-edged razor blade, *carefully* cut 4 mm from the top of each of the seedlings in a second pot. Position this pot under a second box with the same type of cut-out window, as you did before. Also, put this box in a sunny window. Place a third pot in sunlight. Cut 4 mm from the top of each of the seedlings in the fourth pot, and place this pot in sunlight. After 2 to 3 days, compare the seedlings in the 4 pots. Explain your results, using the terms "experimental setup" and "control setup."

2. Obtain a potted plant. Take a piece of cardboard, and make a collar around the plant so that no soil will fall out. Place the plant in a horizontal position. After several days, observe the growth of the stem. To what kind of stimulus has the plant responded? Think up other methods of investigating the responses of plants to various stimuli.

3. Visit the library to obtain more information on the experiments that led to the discoveries of plant hormones. Present your findings in an oral report to the class.

SUGGESTED READINGS

Elbert, V.F., and A. George, *Grow Odd and Curious House Plants.* New York: Crown.
   The author explains how to grow some of the more unusual types of plants, including the mimosa and the sundew plant.

Paturi, F., *Nature, Mother of Invention—The Engineering of Plant Life.* New York: Harper and Row.
   In this book, the author explains how people can learn about survival of plants from their growth patterns and behavior. Also included is a discussion of the evolutionary adaptations of plants.

Prime, C.T., and A.E. Klein, *Seedlings and Soil: Botany for Young Experimenters.* Garden City, N.Y.: Doubleday.
   This is a sourcebook of experiments on plant growth and reproduction. Inexpensive and simple materials are used in these experiments.

Chemical Versus Organic Farming

The number of farms is decreasing in the United States. However, the average size of farms is increasing. Agriculture has become a corporate business today. To increase profit and food yields, farmers have greatly increased their use of various chemicals. These include insecticides, fertilizers, antibiotics, and hormones. The insecticides are used to kill or control insect pests. The fertilizers increase the yield of crops. Germ-killing antibiotics are mixed with poultry feed to speed the growth rate of chickens. Steroid hormones are added to the food of cattle, which then become heavier.

Many people think that such practices dangerously contaminate food products. They cite evidence that the build-up of such chemicals in the human body is a cause of major health problems. For example, one of the hormones used to fatten cattle has been implicated as a cause of certain human cancers. In addition, the runoff of chemical substances used in fertilizers has been shown to be a major cause of water pollution.

There is an alternative to the use of chemicals in farming. Proponents of *organic farming* suggest the use of natural materials in farming. One suggestion these people make is that crops should be grown on farmland fertilized with compost or manure instead of chemical fertilizers. Compost consists of decomposed plant materials and manure. Compost and manure do not pollute bodies of water and, thus, do not poison aquatic life.

Organic farming proponents also discourage the use of chemical insecticides. These people suggest that insect pests be controlled by the use of the pests' natural enemies. The process may be more costly and work more slowly, but it does not harm the environment or the living things in it. People who favor organic farming are also opposed to the use of antibiotics or hormones in the animal-raising process. These substances can remain in the tissues of the animals. When eaten by human beings, the substances can have harmful effects.

Consumers with a preference for organically grown food often have difficulty finding it or in paying the high prices that are sometimes charged for these foods. However, consumers have been finding solutions to these problems in enterprising ways. A growing number of people prefer to grow their own fruits and vegetables organically in backyard or community gardens. Others have formed cooperative foodstores, or co-ops, in which the quality of food, and not business profit, is most important. These organizations are financed and run by members. They buy organically grown foodstuffs directly from farmers.

The agricultural industry, as well as some scientific advisors for the government, contends that organic farming is not profitable on a large scale. These people also feel that large-scale organic farming is unnecessary. They claim that there is no evidence that foods grown exclusively with organic fertilizer have a greater nutrient content or are any healthier to eat than are other foods.

Viewpoints

1. Design and perform an experiment to determine any differences between the effects of inorganic fertilizers and those of organic fertilizers. Commercial chemical fertilizers versus dried store-bought manure can be used. Bean plants grown from seed can serve as subjects. The experiment can be conducted out-of-doors in warm weather. Trays set indoors on the window sill can also be used. Be sure to keep other factors, such as water, temperature, and light the same in the two groups. Record growth rate, height, leaf size, color, and other data for comparisons. Draw conclusions to support or oppose some of the arguments presented in this Perspective.

2. Many arid regions of the world have poor soil-fertility conditions. Several countries, particularly Israel, are experimenting with an approach to crop growing known as hydroponics in which select crops are grown in a chemically controlled environment, without soil. Do research and prepare a report on the recent progress and history of this completely inorganic approach to farming. What are the advantages? What are the problems? How do the crops produced compare with those produced by organic methods?

Invertebrates

For an overview of this unit, including field trip suggestions, a bibliography, and a list of audio-visual materials, see pages T–70 to T–80. You may want to check the Laboratory Investigations in this unit so that materials may be ordered, gathered, or prepared in advance.

Of all the species of animals living on the earth today, more than 90% have no backbones. Animals without backbones are called invertebrates. Although people use many of these animals, such as shrimp, clams, and lobsters, as food, some invertebrates are harmful. Many of them, such as beetles and locusts, destroy crops and trees. Others, such as tapeworms and ticks, cause diseases. Biologists classify invertebrates in many phyla. In this unit, you will read not only about various invertebrates, but also about the various kinds of specialized cells and groups of cells found in them.

Many marine worms, such as this yellow-red, tipped corla worm, grow on coral.

399

25 Sponges and Coelenterates

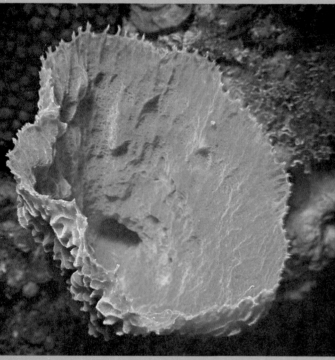

All sponges, like this chalice sponge, live in water.

Chapter Objectives *After completing this chapter, you will be able to:*

a ▪ Describe the structure of a sponge. p. 401
b ▪ Explain how sponges obtain food. p. 402
c ▪ List and describe the methods of reproduction in sponges. p. 404
d ▪ List the three classes of coelenterates. p. 405
e ▪ Describe the structure of the coelenterates. p. 405
f ▪ Describe food-getting, response, and reproduction in the hydra. p. 406
g ▪ Outline the life cycle of the jellyfish. p. 408
h ▪ Describe the three types of coral reefs. p. 410

For teaching aids for this chapter, including a chapter overview and teaching strategies, see pages T–71 to T–72. The page number next to each chapter objective refers to the text page where the information needed to fulfill the objective begins.

Sponges and coelenterates (sē-LEN-tə-rāts) are *multicellular*, or many-celled, organisms. All multicellular organisms are called **metazoans.** Unlike the *unicellular*, or one-celled, organisms in which one cell carries out all life functions, the metazoans have specialized cells. Certain cells carry out different life functions that benefit all the cells of the entire organism. This is called **division of labor.** In a division of labor, each cell is dependent on other cells for survival. This is called *interdependence*.

In simple metazoans, such as the sponges and coelenterates, there are only several different types of cells. Many of these organisms are organized only at the *tissue* level of organization. A tissue is a group of cells that works together. Simple metazoans do not have *organs*, which are groups of tissues that work together. However, the more complex metazoans are organized at higher levels of organization. These organisms have many different specialized cells and groups of cells, tissues, and organs.

Sponges

Sponges live in shallow water and in the deepest parts of the oceans. Although a few kinds of sponges live in fresh water, most live in salt water. Wherever they live, adult sponges are **sessile** (SES-'l). That is, they attach their bases to rocks and other objects. They do not move from place to place.

Sponges have many shapes, colors, and sizes. Some sponges are irregularly shaped, and others look like a basket or vase. They live singly or in large colonies. Their colors vary from gray to green, yellow, red, or purple. They range in diameter from under 1 centimeter to over 2 meters.

Biologists classify sponges in the phylum *Porifera* (pə-RIF-ə-rə). The name *Porifera* means pore-bearing and refers to the many pores, or openings, in the bodies of these animals. Because poriferans, the simplest multicellular organisms, have masses of interdependent cells, they may be called multicellular. They do not, however, have tissues, organs, and organ systems.

A simple sponge has a hollow body covered with many **ostia,** or *incurrent pores*, which allow water to enter the sponge. A large opening called the **osculum,** or *excurrent pore*, allows water and wastes to leave the sponge. The body wall of the sponge is made up of two cell layers that are separated by a layer of jellylike material.

The outer cell layer is called the **epidermis.** It is made up of flat cells called *epithelial cells*. Some of these cells, called **porocytes,** form the ostia. The porocytes control the opening and closing of the ostia. They react to touch and to irritating chemical substances by closing the ostia.

The middle layer of the body wall is made up of a jellylike substance that contains amoebalike cells called **amoebocytes.** These cells carry out several functions, such as bringing food and oxygen to other cells. In addition to their other functions, amoebocytes secrete the substances that form the skeleton of the sponge. The skeleton helps to protect the sponge, support its body, and give the sponge its shape. In many sponges, the skeleton is made up of sharp, pointed, noncellular projections called **spicules** (SPIK-yoolz), which support the sponge body. Although the skeleton itself is found in the middle cell layer, the spicules often stick out through the epidermis.

Scientists group sponges according to the chemical makeup of the sponge's skeleton. In one group of sponges, the spicules are made from lime, or calcium carbonate. These sponges are able to take lime from ocean water to build their skeletons. The spicules of another group of sponges, called

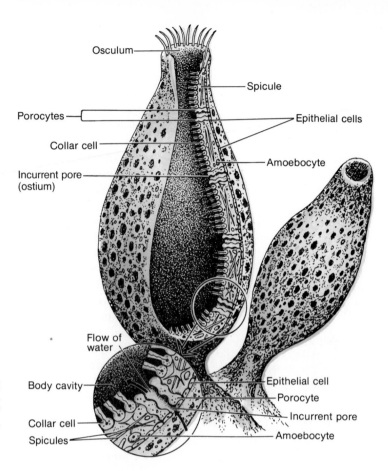

Osculum

Spicule

Porocytes

Epithelial cells

Collar cell

Incurrent pore
(ostium)

Amoebocyte

Flow of
water

Body cavity

Epithelial cell

Porocyte

Collar cell

Incurrent pore

Spicules

Amoebocyte

Figure 25-1 Different types of cells and structures are characteristic of the different layers of a sponge. A function of one of these structures, the incurrent pore, is to take water into the sponge.

At this point, you may want to assign to several students the fourth of the Extensions and Applications at the end of this chapter.

Figure 25-2 The skeletons of some sponges are made up of sharp projections called spicules.

glass sponges, are made of silica. As ocean water filters through these sponges, silica is extracted from sand suspended in the water. A third group of sponges has a tough skeleton made up not of spicules but of crossed fibers of a protein material called **spongin** (SPUHN-jin). The skeletons of some sponges contain both spicules and spongin.

The inner cell layer of the sponge's body wall is made up of specialized **collar cells,** or *choanocytes* (KŌ-ə-nə-sīts). Each vase-shaped collar cell has a *flagellum,* or long, whiplike projection. The collar of the cell is made up of many small hairlike projections.

Food-Getting in Sponges

Sponges are sessile organisms. They cannot move about to get their food. Sponges rely on the flow of water into their ostia for food and oxygen. They depend on the same flow of water to eliminate body wastes through their osculum.

The sponge must control the water passing through its body. By opening and closing, the osculum controls not only the amount of water going through the sponge, but the rate of the water's flow as well. Inside the sponge, the beating flagella of the collar cells form water currents. As the water flows through the sponge the many hairlike projections that form the collar of each collar cell filter out microscopic food particles, such as bacteria, protozoans, and one-celled algae. The food is then taken into the collar cells and enclosed in structures called *vacuoles*.

All of the digestive processes are carried out within individual cells. Enzymes in the collar cells begin to digest the food. The partly digested food is then passed to the amoebocytes through diffusion. The amoebocytes complete the digestive process and transport the digested food to other cells. The amoebocytes also remove wastes and carbon dioxide from the other cells. These wastes pass out of the sponge through the osculum, along with undigested material.

Sidelight

A sponge 10 centimeters tall and 1 centimeter in diameter may have more than 2 million collar cells and may filter more than 22 liters of water each day.

The lack of special digestive organs is characteristic of the simplest phyla of animals.

CAREER: Marine Biologist

Marine biologists study the plants and animals that live in the oceans, from the smallest marine bacteria and algae to the giant whales. These scientists may study how seals communicate, how fish behave, and why certain animals migrate. Their work includes studies of life in tidal pools and in the open sea.

Many people in this field devote their studies to only one kind of animal, such as sponges, crabs, or whales. Other marine biologists may study a specific aspect of ocean life. For example, some marine biologists study the biochemical processes, the genetic relationships, or the diseases of marine organisms. Marine ecologists study the relationships between organisms and their ocean environment. They may investigate how chemical and physical changes in the ocean affect marine life. Marine physiologists are interested in the internal structures and functions of marine organisms. They may study the respiratory systems of invertebrates or the light-producing structures of deep sea fish.

The work conducted by marine biologists is often useful to the fishing and food production industries. An understanding of the migration patterns of fish can result in improved fishing yields. Knowledge of the growth and reproduction of such organisms as the small shrimplike krill may provide a way to farm these organisms as a protein source.

For a career as a marine biologist, a bachelor's degree, along with a broad background in the biological sciences and chemistry, is necessary. Many marine biologists also have an advanced degree in oceanography.

Marine biologists often work for colleges, universities, and oceanographic institutions, where they combine teaching and research work. Government environmental and fishery agencies also employ marine biologists. Some industries, such as those that assess the environmental impact of ocean oil drilling and harbor drilling, also need marine biologists.

For career information, write to Virginia Institute of Marine Science, Gloucester Point, VA 23062.

Sponges reproduce asexually by budding and by forming gemmules. Sponges can also reproduce sexually by producing male and female gametes.

Use the chalkboard to list and compare the forms of asexual reproduction characteristic of the organisms studied so far.

Reproduction in Sponges

Asexual reproduction in sponges can occur in two ways. In **budding,** a group of cells, called a *bud,* enlarges and then breaks off from the parent sponge to form a new sponge. Another method of asexual reproduction occurs when environmental conditions become unfavorable. The sponges then form **gemmules** (JEM-yoolz), groups of amoebocytes that are surrounded by a hard protective coat. If the sponge dies due to unfavorable conditions, such as the cold of winter, the sponge breaks apart. However, the gemmules survive because they are able to withstand the unfavorable conditions. When conditions again become favorable, as in the spring, each gemmule can then develop into a sponge. Gemmule formation usually does not occur in saltwater sponges because environmental conditions in the oceans do not change very much.

A related form of asexual reproduction is **regeneration,** or the ability to grow back missing parts and replace old parts. When a part of a sponge is broken off, the sponge can replace the missing part. Sponges are grown commercially

Figure 25-3 In order to reproduce sexually, a sponge produces egg and sperm cells that unite during fertilization. The resulting larva gives rise to a new sponge.

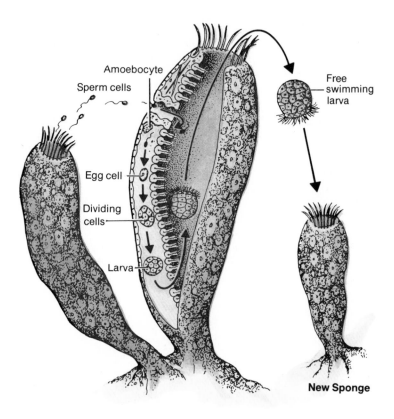

Amoebocyte

Sperm cells

Egg cell

Dividing cells

Larva

Free swimming larva

New Sponge

through the regeneration method. The sponges are cut up into many pieces, and the pieces are attached to cement blocks under water. Each piece develops into a new sponge and is then harvested.

Sponges also reproduce sexually. Most sponges are *hermaphrodites* (hər-MAF-rə-dīts), or organisms that can produce both male and female reproductive cells, which are called *gametes*. Male gametes, or *sperm cells*, are produced by the collar cells, and the female gametes, or eggs, are formed by amoebocytes. Hermaphroditic sponges usually produce sperm cells or eggs at different times. A single sponge, therefore, cannot fertilize itself.

During sexual reproduction, the collar cells release the sperm cells into the body cavity. The sperm leave the sponge through the osculum and enter another sponge through its ostia. In the second sponge, the sperm are captured by collar cells and transferred to amoebocytes, which carry the sperm to the egg cells. When a sperm cell unites with an egg cell, a *zygote*, or fertilized egg, results. The zygote develops into a free-living *larva* (plural: larvae). The larva is an immature form of a sponge that looks very different from the adult. Each larva has many *cilia*, or hairlike structures, that enable it to move through the water. After a short, free-swimming life, the larva attaches itself to the floor of the ocean or other body of water, where it grows into a sessile adult sponge.

SECTION REVIEW   Answers on page T–71.

1. In which phylum are sponges classified?
2. What is the function of collar cells?
3. What are spicules?
4. What are gemmules?
5. What does regeneration mean?

Coelenterates

Biologists classify coelenterates in the phylum *Coelenterata*, meaning hollow intestine. Jellyfish, hydras, sea anemones, and corals are examples of such animals. All coelenterates live in water. Most of them are *marine*, or live in the ocean. Some species, such as the hydra, live in fresh water.

Coelenterates have two different body forms. Coelenterates that have tubelike bodies are called **polyps,** and they are sessile. Coelenterates that have bell- or cup-shaped bodies are called **medusas,** and they can move from place to

Highlight

Coelenterates have polyp and medusa forms, exhibit radial symmetry, and have a body wall made up of an ectoderm, a mesoglea, and a gastrodermis.

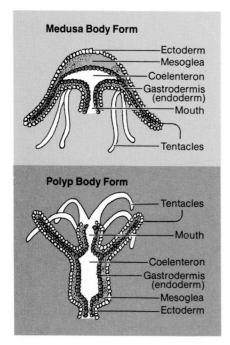

Medusa Body Form

- Ectoderm
- Mesoglea
- Coelenteron
- Gastrodermis (endoderm)
- Mouth
- Tentacles

Polyp Body Form

- Tentacles
- Mouth
- Coelenteron
- Gastrodermis (endoderm)
- Mesoglea
- Ectoderm

Figure 25-4 Coelenterates have two different body forms, the medusa form and the polyp form. Some kinds of coelenterates may pass through both a polyp and a medusa stage.

Organisms that exhibit radial symmetry are generally less complex than those that exhibit bilateral symmetry, although there are important exceptions.

Figure 25-5 The Portuguese man-of-war, a colonial coelenterate, is made up of individual polyps that perform different functions.

place. Most coelenterates pass through both a polyp form and a medusa form during their life cycles.

The coelenterates are grouped into three classes according to the body form they have during most of their lives.

Class *Hydrozoa* The polyp is the usual body form. The hydra is an example.

Class *Scyphozoa* The medusa is the usual body form, as in the jellyfish *Aurelia*.

Class *Anthozoa* The polyp is the only body form. Examples include sea anemones and corals.

Many coelenterates live as individual organisms. Some live as part of a colony. *Physalia*, or Portuguese man-of-war, is a colonial coelenterate made up of individual polyps. In the colony, each type of polyp performs a different function, such as digestion or sex cell formation. Some of the individual organisms of *Physalia* form a bright blue sac that is filled with air and that keeps the colony afloat. Other individual organisms form long, stinging tentacles that can extend 9 to 12 meters below the water's surface.

Coelenterates have certain structural features in common. One such feature is **radial symmetry,** or the regular circular arrangement of body parts around a central area. A good example of radial symmetry is the arrangement of spokes around the hub of a bicycle wheel. All coelenterates also have a single digestive cavity called a **coelenteron** (si-LEN-tə-rahn). The digestive cavity has one opening, or *mouth,* that is surrounded with tentacles. The tentacles contain stinging cells called **cnidoblasts** (NĪ-də-blasts). Within the cnidoblasts are spearlike threads, called **nematocysts** (NEM-ə-tō-sists). Nematocysts may be sticky, barbed, or poisonous.

The coelenterates have three types of tissues. The outer layer of cells, called the **ectoderm** or epidermis, serves as a protective covering. The inner cell layer is called the **gastrodermis,** or *endoderm.* Between the outer and inner layers is a jellylike layer called the **mesoglea** (mes-ō-GLĒ-a). The mesoglea supports the organism and holds the cells together. The mesoglea is thin in polyp organisms, such as the hydra, and makes up most of the body in medusa organisms, such as the jellyfish.

At this point, you may want to assign to several students the third of the Extensions and Applications at the end of this chapter.

Hydras

The hydra, a common freshwater coelenterate, is a vase-shaped polyp with a single opening that is surrounded by

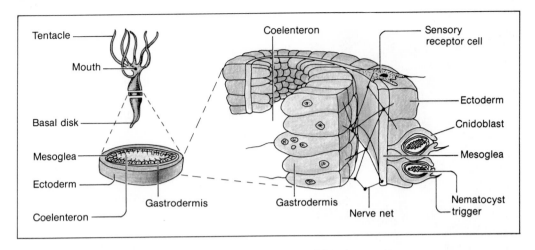

Tentacle

Mouth

Basal disk

Mesoglea

Ectoderm

Coelenteron

Gastrodermis

Coelenteron

Gastrodermis

Nerve net

Sensory
receptor cell

Ectoderm

Cnidoblast

Mesoglea

Nematocyst
trigger

Figure 25–6 The hydra has a three-walled tubelike body, a simple nervous system, and specialized cells.

tentacles. It is a small organism, ranging in size from about 1 to 4 centimeters. It may be gray, green, tan, or brown.

Usually, hydras attach themselves to leaves or rocks with a sticky substance produced in their **basal disks.** By contracting the cells in both the ectoderm and the gastrodermis, however, hydras can extend, stretch, shorten, and bend themselves. Although hydras are sessile, they are capable of some movement. They can move quickly from one place of attachment to another by means of a tumbling motion or move slowly by gliding on their basal disks. Hydras can also form an air bubble at their bases and float upside down.

At this point, you may want to have your students do the Laboratory Investigation at the end of this chapter.

FOOD-GETTING IN HYDRAS The hydra feeds on many small organisms, such as freshwater shrimps and water fleas. To lure its prey, a hydra extends and waves its tentacles. When an organism touches one of the tentacles, nematocysts are released that sting and paralyze the prey. The wounded prey releases a chemical substance, called *gluta-thione* (gloo-tə-thī-ōN), causing the tentacles of the hydra to contract and its mouth to open. If the glutathione is not released, the hydra does not complete its feeding action. With the release of the glutathione, however, the tentacles pull the prey into the mouth of the hydra.

Once the prey is pushed into the coelenteron, the cells of the gastrodermis release enzymes that begin the digestive process. The partly digested food is then taken into the cells of the gastrodermis, which complete the digestive process. The products of digestion diffuse to other cells, and undigested materials are released through the mouth.

RESPONSE IN HYDRAS The simple nervous system of the hydra is made up of nerve cells that are arranged in an irregular network called a **nerve net.** Located in the

Figure 25–7 A hydra stings and paralyzes its prey by releasing spearlike nematocysts from cnidoblasts, or special stinging cells.

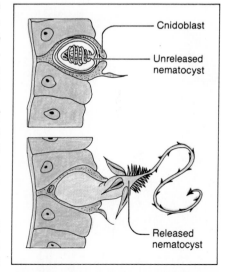

Cnidoblast

Unreleased
nematocyst

Released
nematocyst

Figure 25-8 This hydra is undergoing asexual reproduction by developing a bud. The bud eventually will separate from the parent hydra.

Figure 25-9 Jellyfishes move with a jet-like motion by rhythmically contracting muscle cells that enable the jellyfish to take in and force out water.

mesoglea, the nerve net is able to conduct nerve impulses in all directions throughout the organism. For example, if one tentacle of a hydra is touched, the entire hydra responds by contracting. The nerve net coordinates the feeding reaction.

The hydra also has *sensory receptor cells.* These cells are special structures that are sensitive to chemicals, touch, and light. Sensory receptor cells are located in the ectoderm and gastrodermis.

REPRODUCTION IN HYDRAS Hydras reproduce asexually by budding, the most common form of reproduction during the warm weather. A bud develops as a small knoblike projection on the body wall. The projection includes a part of the parent's digestive cavity. As the bud grows, it develops a mouth and tentacles, and then it separates from the parent.

Sexual reproduction occurs mainly in the autumn. Hydras reproduce sexually by forming eggs and sperm. The male reproductive structures, or *testes,* produce the sperm cells. Each of the female reproductive structures, or *ovaries,* produces only one egg. Most hydras are **dioecious** (dī-Ē-shəs), that is, an individual hydra contains either the male or the female reproductive structure, not both.

Sperm from a male hydra are released into the water and swim to an egg on a female hydra. The fertilized egg begins to divide. A hard protective shell forms around the dividing egg. Once the shell forms, the developing egg falls off the parent and remains in the shell through the winter. In the spring, the shell softens, and a young hydra emerges.

Jellyfishes

The jellyfishes are medusa organisms with long, trailing tentacles. Jellyfishes range in diameter from less than 2 centimeters to more than 2 meters. They have an ectoderm, endoderm, and mesoglea. Their mesoglea is so firm that a freshly beached jellyfish will not burst even if an average-sized person stands on it.

Unlike hydras, jellyfishes have true muscle cells. By contracting rhythmically, these cells enable jellyfishes to take water in and force it out. The jetlike motion of the water propels jellyfishes freely from one place to another.

RESPONSE IN JELLYFISHES The jellyfishes have a nerve net that is concentrated in two rings around their bodies. The nerve net is connected to the tentacles, to muscle cells, and to sense organs. The jellyfishes also have sensory receptor cells that respond to chemicals and touch. In addition, these coelenterates have two specialized groups of sense cells. One group of cells, called the **statolith** (STAT-ə-lith), helps to orient jellyfishes with respect to gravity. The other group of cells, called the **ocelli** (ō-SEL-ī), responds to light.

REPRODUCTION IN JELLYFISHES Jellyfishes pass through both a polyp and a medusa stage in their life cycles. They reproduce asexually as polyps and sexually as medusas. The *Aurelia,* a common jellyfish, goes through a typical life cycle. The adult male *Aurelia* medusa releases mature sperm cells into its digestive cavity. The female medusa releases eggs into the surrounding water. These eggs usually become lodged in the tentacles of the female. When the male releases sperm into the water through its mouth, the eggs are fertilized within the female's tentacles.

Once the egg is fertilized, it divides to form a hollow ball of cells, or **blastula** (BLAS-tyoo-lə). The blastula develops into a free-swimming, ciliated larva called a **planula.** After the planula attaches itself to a rock, water plant, or other object in the water, it eventually develops into a polyp called a **scyphistoma** (sī-FIS-tə-mə), which has a mouth and tentacles.

Sidelight

The giant jellyfish *Cyanea artica* is one of the largest known invertebrates. Its body is 2 meters in diameter and its tentacles can be 36 meters long. A single specimen can weigh up to 900 kilograms.

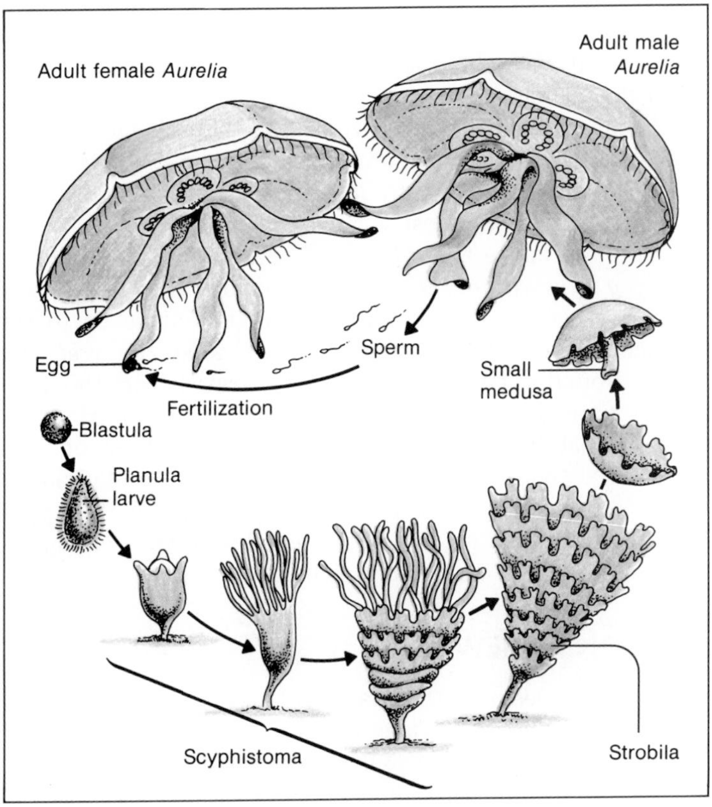

Figure 25-10 The life cycle of the jellyfish *Aurelia* involves production of egg and sperm cells and formation of a polyp scyphistoma. This structure develops into a stacklike strobila, from which individual medusas are released.

Figure 25-11 Sea anemones (*top*) and corals (*bottom*) are examples of polyp coelenterates of the class *Anthozoa*.

Figure 25-12 The skeletons of dead corals can build up over a period of years to form various types of reefs.

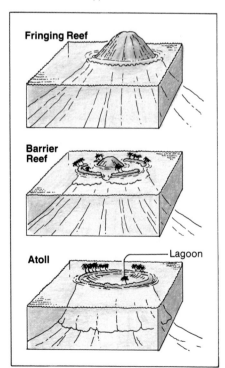

During the summer and fall, the scyphistoma grows and changes into a *strobila*. In a process called **strobilation,** the strobila produces small medusas that stack like saucers. One by one, the small medusas are released and grow into full-sized jellyfishes.

Sea Anemones and Corals

The sea anemones and corals are flowerlike, brightly colored polyp organisms. Sea anemones range in size from 1 to 5 centimeters in length, with diameters between 2.5 and 5 centimeters. These organisms live singly by attaching themselves to objects by the basal disks at the bottom of their body tubes. Although anemones are basically sessile, they can move by gradually gliding on their basal disks or by "walking" on their tentacles. Sea anemones reproduce sexually by forming eggs and sperm. They are also able to reproduce asexually by budding and by dividing in half.

Most corals live in colonies located in warm, shallow waters. The size of a colony increases when the corals reproduce by budding. New colonies are usually formed when the corals reproduce sexually by means of eggs and sperm. Within the colony, individual polyps grow skeletons. The ectoderm cells form these skeletons by secreting calcium carbonate, or lime. Eventually, these skeletons become cemented to each other in one mass.

When corals die, they leave behind their skeletons. Over the years, the skeletons pile up, creating a *coral reef.* These reefs are made up of many layers of skeletons, with living corals only on the topmost surface.

Corals produce three types of reefs. One type, called a *fringing* or *marginal reef,* forms in shallow waters. It closely borders the coast of a landmass, and it is attached to the landmass. A second type of reef, called a *barrier reef,* also forms around a landmass, but it is separated from the landmass by a wide area of water. An example of a barrier reef is the Great Barrier Reef off the northeast coast of Australia. It is about 2000 kilometers long and up to 145 kilometers wide. In some places it is 120 meters high. A third type of reef, called an *atoll,* is a ring of coral with an open *lagoon,* or shallow body of water, in the middle.

SECTION REVIEW   Answers on page T–71.

1. List the three different classes of coelenterates.
2. What are cnidoblasts and nematocysts?
3. By what two methods do hydras reproduce?
4. What is strobilation?

At this point, you may want to assign to several students the first of the Extensions and Applications at the end of this chapter.

LABORATORY INVESTIGATION 25

For additional information, see page T-71.

Observing a Hydra

Purpose The hydra, a small coelenterate, attaches itself to leaves, twigs, and rocks in freshwater streams, lakes, and ponds. The purpose of this investigation is to observe the structure and behavior of a hydra.

Materials *(per 2 students)* ● *Hydra* culture ● Depression slides ● Cover slips ● Brine shrimp culture ● Toothpicks ● 5% acetic acid solution ● Microscope ● Medicine droppers

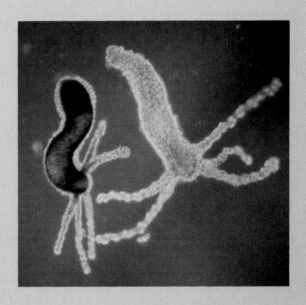

Procedure **1.** Obtain a hydra from the culture, and place it on the depression slide. **2.** Observe the hydra under low power of the microscope. Count the number of tentacles on your specimen. Make a sketch of the hydra, and label the visible parts. **3.** While observing the hydra under low power, use a toothpick as a probe to touch one of the tentacles. After a minute or two, touch a spot on the tubular body. **4.** Obtain a drop of brine shrimp from the culture, and add it to the slide. Observe and record any responses from the hydra. **5.** Place a cover slip over the depression on the slide. Observe the hydra under high power of your microscope. Make a drawing of the hydra. Show the details of the body wall and the coelenteron. **6.** Obtain a second hydra, and prepare a slide of it. Under high power, focus the microscope on the tentacles of the hydra. Add a drop of acetic acid solution at the edge of the cover slip. Note any changes that you observe.

Observations and Conclusions **1.** How many tentacles does your hydra specimen have? Find out how many tentacles are present on the other hydras that were observed in your class. What is the average number of tentacles? **2.** How does the hydra react when you touch one tentacle? When you touch the tubular body? **3.** In a brief paragraph, describe the responses of the hydra to the brine shrimp. **4.** What parts of the body wall of the hydra are visible? Where is the coelenteron located? Does the coelenteron appear to extend into the tentacles? **5.** What changes in the tentacles occur when the acetic acid solution is added to the specimen? Do the nematocysts appear to be equally distributed over the entire body and over the tentacles of the hydra?

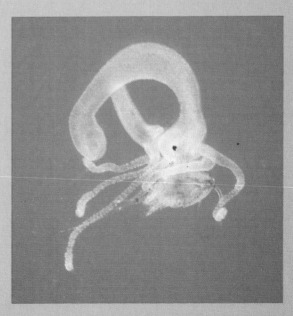

CHAPTER SUMMARY

Sponges Sponges are classified in the phylum *Porifera,* because their hollow bodies are covered with many pores, called ostia. The large pore at one end is called the osculum. The body wall is made up of an epidermis, a middle jellylike layer, and an inner layer of collar cells.

A sponge obtains its food by filtering food particles from the water. Water is moved through the sponge in currents formed by the flagella of the collar cells. Digestion takes place within both the collar cells and the amoebocytes. Undigested material, wastes, and carbon dioxide are removed through the osculum by water currents.

Sponges reproduce asexually by means of budding, gemmules, and regeneration. In budding, a projection grows out of the side of the parent sponge. Eventually, the bud drops off the parent and becomes a new sponge. By the second method, the sponge forms gemmules when the temperature becomes too low for it to live. Each gemmule is made up of a group of amoebocytes surrounded by a protective coat. The gemmule is capable of developing into a new sponge. Finally, sponges can also regenerate missing parts or old parts.

Sponges can reproduce sexually by producing sperm and eggs. Fertilized eggs develop into free-living larvae that eventually grow into sessile adult sponges.

Coelenterates The coelenterates, classified in the phylum *Coelenterata,* have hollow, saclike bodies. Their body form may be either a polyp or a medusa. Coelenterates, all of which live in water, are grouped into three classes. These classes are *Hydrozoa, Scyphozoa,* and *Anthozoa.*

The coelenterates have three basic features in common. They are a single digestive cavity, tentacles with nematocysts, and bodies with radial symmetry.

A common freshwater coelenterate is the hydra, a polyp organism. The hydra feeds by first attracting and then stinging its prey with its tentacles. The tentacles then move the prey to the mouth of the hydra. The hydra has a simple nervous system, called a nerve net. Hydras can reproduce asexually by budding, and sexually by producing eggs and sperms.

Adult jellyfishes are medusa organisms with long tentacles. They have true muscles and a nerve net. Jellyfishes have a complex life cycle, including both a polyp and a medusa form. During the polyp stage, jellyfishes reproduce asexually. During the medusa stage, they reproduce sexually.

The sea anemones and corals are polyp organisms. Sea anemones live singly, whereas corals live in colonies. Unlike the other coelenterates, corals have calcium carbonate skeletons. These skeletons become cemented to one another to form colonies called fringing reefs, barrier reefs, and atolls.

CHAPTER VOCABULARY

amoebocyte	gastrodermis	polyp
basal disk	gemmule	porocyte
blastula	medusa	radial symmetry
budding	mesoglea	regeneration
cnidoblast	metazoan	scyphistoma
coelenteron	nematocyst	sessile
collar cell	nerve net	spicule
dioecious	ocelli	spongin
division of labor	osculum	statolith
ectoderm	ostia	strobilation
epidermis	planula	

REVIEW of FACTS and CONCEPTS   Answers on page T–72.

On a separate sheet of paper, answer each of the following as completely as possible.

1. Describe the structure of a sponge.
2. What are the functions of the skeleton of a sponge?
3. Explain how sponges are grouped.
4. How do sponges obtain food?
5. Name two methods of asexual reproduction by which sponges reproduce.
6. Describe the functions of the amoebocytes, as well as the functions of the cells of the epidermis and the inner cell layer.
7. In which phylum are coelenterates classified? How does this classification reflect their body plan?
8. Describe the two body forms found among the coelenterates.
9. How do hydras obtain food?
10. What is a nerve net?
11. Explain sexual reproduction in *Hydra.*
12. How are hydras and jellyfishes alike? How are they different?
13. Describe the life cycle of a typical jellyfish such as *Aurelia.*
14. How are coral reefs formed? Describe three types of coral reefs.
15. List the differences between the sponges and coelenterates.

EXTENSIONS and APPLICATIONS   For additional information, see page T–72.

1. Many interrelationships exist between coelenterates and other animals. Using reference books in the library, prepare a report on the relationships between sea anemones and clownfish, between sea anemones and hermit crabs, and between coral and snapping shrimp.
2. Observe the spicules of a sponge. Dissolve a piece of a preserved sponge in a dish of household bleach. **CAUTION:** *Keep the bleach from touching your clothes or skin.* After 15 minutes, swirl the dish to concentrate the spicules in the center of the dish. Place a drop of the liquid from the center of the dish on a slide. Observe the slide under low and high powers of a microscope. Prepare drawings of your observations.
3. The stinging cells of coelenterates can be harmful to people. Using reference books in the library, prepare a written report about such stinging animals as the Portuguese man-of-war, the sea wasp, the fire coral, and the sea anemone.
4. Obtain a natural sponge, or visit a local pharmacy or health food store where you can observe a natural sponge. Compare a natural sponge to a commonly used synthetic sponge. Note any similarities and differences. Present your findings to the class in a chart.

SUGGESTED READINGS

Faulkner, D., and R. Chester, *Living Corals.* New York: Clarkson N. Potter.
This book contains color photographs of living corals from around the world. It also explains the biology of coral animals.
Grzimek, B., ed., *Animal Life Encyclopedia, Volume I: Lower Animals.* New York: Van Nostrand Reinhold.
In this reference volume, an extended section describes the sponges and coelenterates.
Wells, M., *Lower Animals.* New York: McGraw-Hill, World University Library.
This book is an introduction to the biology of the invertebrates, with sections describing the sponges and coelenterates.

26 Worms

The feathery tentacles of marine worms aid in food-getting.

For teaching aids for this chapter, including a chapter overview and teaching strategies, see pages T–72 to T–74. The page number next to each chapter objective refers to the text page where the information needed to fulfill the objective begins.

Biologists classify worms into three phyla. The worms in all three phyla are more complex than the animals studied so far. Whereas the sponges and coelenterates have only two layers of cells, worms have three. Worms have true organs and organ systems that simpler organisms do not have. Also in comparison to simpler animals, worms have more complex nervous systems.

Like the bodies of most higher animals, including human beings, the bodies of worms exhibit **bilateral symmetry.** That is, they have definite left and right sides that are mirror images of each other. Worms also have definite *anterior,* or front, and *posterior,* or rear, ends.

Although the number of species of worms is rather small, the total number of worms is very large. Biologists have classified about 20,000 different species of worms. Some of these species are microscopic, while others are several meters long. Some worms, such as the marine worms, are very colorful and have feathery extensions that give them unusual shapes.

Flatworms

Biologists classify the least complex worms in the phylum *Platyhelminthes* (pla-tē-hel-MINTH-ēz). The phylum name is derived from the Greek words *platy*, meaning flat, and *helminth*, meaning worm. The worms in this phylum have flat bodies and do not have a body cavity. Organisms that lack body cavities are called **acoelomates** (ā-SĒ-lō-māts). Like all worms, the flatworms have three cell layers. The inner cell layer is called the **endoderm**, and the outer cell layer is called the **ectoderm.** Between the two is the middle cell layer, or **mesoderm.**

Flatworms also have definite upper and lower surfaces. The upper surface is called the **dorsal surface**, and the underside, or lower surface, is called the **ventral surface.** Most flatworms are **parasites,** or organisms that live on or in other living things. Some flatworms, however, are free-living organisms. Most free-living flatworms live in the oceans, although some live in fresh water or in soil. Biologists group the flatworms in three classes.

Planarians

Free-living flatworms are grouped in the class *Turbellaria*. The most common example of these free-living flatworms is *Planaria*. Although most planarians are black, brown, or gray, some species are brightly colored. Planarians range in size from less than 1 centimeter long up to 60 centimeters long. They live in the oceans, in freshwater ponds and lakes, and in damp soil. A few of the large planarians live on land in tropical forests.

A planarian moves by secreting mucus from gland cells on its ventral surface. Cilia on this surface beat back and forth, moving the organism on a smooth track of mucus. Muscle contractions help the larger planarians move.

A planarian has a simple digestive system. The *mouth* is located in the middle of the body on the ventral surface. A long tube, called the **pharynx** (FAR-ingks), can be extended from the mouth to draw in microscopic organisms. The food moves from the pharynx into the *intestine*, a branched sac that is lined with special cells. These cells produce enzymes that digest the food. The digested food materials then diffuse to other parts of the body. Undigested food passes out of the planarian through its mouth.

The excretory system of the planarian regulates the amount of water in the worm. The system is made up of a series of tubes that lead to *pores*, or openings, on the surface

The presence of absence of a coelom is a major distinguishing feature among different phyla of animals.

Highlight

Flatworms are classified in the phylum *Platyhelminthes*. Like all worms, they have three cell layers and are bilaterally symmetrical.

At this point, you may want to assign to several students the fifth of the Extensions and Applications at the end of this chapter.

416

of the planarian's body. At the internal end of each tube is a single cell called a **flame bulb.** The flame bulbs have long cilia that beat back and forth, sending water and wastes from tissues through the tube and out of the pores.

The nervous system of a planarian consists of a *nerve net.* At the anterior end of the worm, there is a mass of nerve tissue that is commonly referred to as the brain. Two nerve cords extend from the brain to the posterior end of the planarian. Many smaller nerves branch out along the length of these nerve cords.

The planarian's main sense organs are its two **eyespots** and its **sensory lobes.** The eyespots are *photosensitive,* that is, they respond to light. Two small nerves connect the eyespots to the brain of the planarian. The sensory lobes detect chemicals and respond to touch. Both sets of sense organs are located at the anterior end of the worm. The localization of sense organs in the head area of an organism is called **cephalization** (sef-'l-ə-zĀ-shən).

Planarians reproduce sexually. They are hermaphrodites, with each organism having both male and female reproductive organs. Planarians, however, do not usually

Figure 26-1   The digestive and nervous systems of the flatworm *Planaria* are simple in structure. In the photograph, the intestine is visible as a dark branched structure that almost fills the entire planarian. Like all worms, planarians exhibit bilateral symmetry.

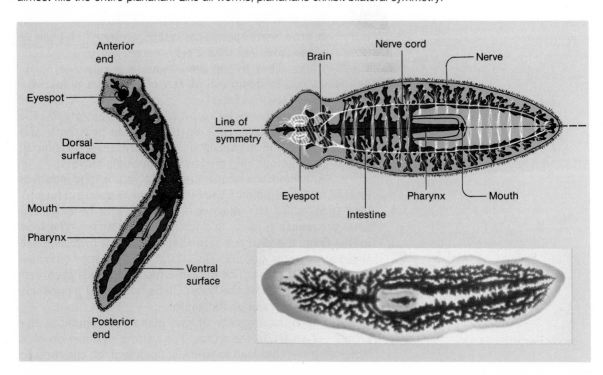

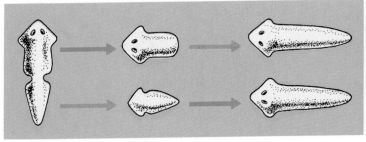

Figure 26-2 The divided halves of a planarian are able to regenerate the missing parts, resulting in two complete planarians. The planarian in the photograph has been incompletely divided along its line of symmetry and has grown two heads.

fertilize themselves. Instead, a pair of planarians *cross-fertilize* each other. In a two-way exchange of sperm, the two worms fertilize each other's egg cells. The fertilized eggs in each of the two worms are then shed in capsules that contain 10 or fewer eggs. Tiny planarians hatch in several weeks.

Planarians also reproduce asexually by means of **fragmentation.** During fragmentation, a portion of the posterior end of the body is pinched off. Each of the two parts then regenerates, or grows back, the missing parts. The anterior grows a new posterior, and the posterior develops a new anterior.

At this point, you may want to have your students do the Laboratory Investigation at the end of this chapter.

Flukes

Biologists group the flukes in the class *Trematoda.* The organisms in this class are parasitic flatworms. Flukes live on and in human beings and many different animals. They often live in the intestines, lungs, liver, and blood of these organisms. Because flukes are parasitic, there are many differences in their structure when compared to planarians. The flukes have a thick, outer layer of cells called a **tegument.** The tegument protects flukes from being digested by their *hosts.* Hosts are the organisms from which parasites obtain their food. The flukes do not have muscles or cilia for movement. Instead, they have *suckers* that are used to attach themselves to their hosts. Flukes also lack specialized sense organs.

In other ways, however, flukes are similar to planarians. Flukes have excretory systems that are like those of planarians. Flukes are also hermaphrodites with well-developed reproductive systems. They produce a large number of eggs that are stored in a long, coiled tube called the **uterus** (plural: uteri).

Highlight

Flukes are parasitic flatworms in the class *Trematoda.* They have complicated life cycles that may involve more than one host.

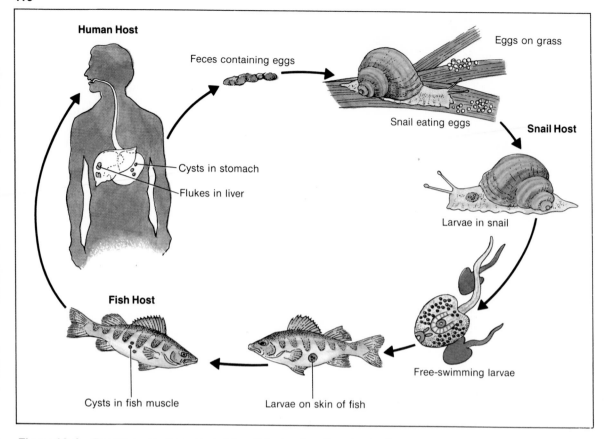

Figure 26-3 The life cycle of one kind of liver fluke involves three hosts. These hosts are a human being, a snail, and a fish.

Flukes have complicated life cycles. A certain kind of liver fluke found in China, Korea, Japan, and other Asian countries, for example, lives part of its life in a snail and another part of its life cycle in one or more other hosts. At the beginning of the life cycle of the liver fluke, eggs pass out of the host with its *feces*, or solid wastes. If the eggs fall into fresh water, they become attached to plants, where a certain kind of snail eats them. Inside the snail, the eggs hatch and reproduce asexually.

After a time, the swimming fluke larvae leave the snail. After attaching themselves to the skin of certain kinds of fish, the larvae lose their tails and bore into the muscle tissue of the fish. Inside the fish, they form protective **cysts.** When a human being eats undercooked or raw fish, a cyst may enter the stomach. In the human stomach, digestive juices break down the wall of the cyst and release the fluke into the small intestine. The fluke then travels to the liver through the *bile duct.* In the liver, the fluke matures and lays

It is important to stress that meat and fish should be thoroughly cooked in order to destroy any parasites that might be present.

eggs. The eggs pass from the liver into the gallbladder and then into the intestines. When the eggs pass out of the human host with the feces, the cycle can begin again. Mature flukes in the liver can cause serious damage.

Tapeworms

Biologists group tapeworms in the class *Cestoda.* Cestodes are parasitic, living as adults in the intestine of *vertebrate animals,* or animals with backbones. Tapeworms are ribbonlike flatworms that may grow to a length of 18 meters.

The body of a tapeworm has three parts. The knob-shaped head area, or **scolex,** may have a ring of hooks or suckers that enable the tapeworm to attach itself to its host. The scolex has no mouth, and the worm has no digestive system. Once attached to the host's digestive system, the tapeworm absorbs nutrients directly from its host. The nutrients are absorbed through the tapeworm's body wall.

Behind the scolex is a narrow *neck.* The rest of the tapeworm's body is made up of nearly square sections called **proglottids** (prō-GLAHT-idz). New proglottids grow from the neck. Therefore, the youngest segments are close to the neck and the oldest segments are farther away.

Tapeworms spread from one host to another by means of the proglottids. Each proglottid contains both male and female reproductive structures and can fertilize either its own eggs or those of another proglottid. The older proglottids containing mature fertilized eggs break off the tapeworm and pass out of the host in the feces. These proglottids may then be eaten by cows, pigs, or fish. Inside these hosts, the eggs in the proglottids hatch into larvae. The larvae then burrow into the host's muscle tissues and form cysts. Each cyst contains a fully developed scolex.

Human beings may get tapeworms by eating raw or undercooked beef, pork, or fish. When a cyst in these meats enters the human intestine and breaks open, the scolex attaches itself to the intestinal wall. It then develops proglottids, beginning another cycle. To prevent infections in human beings, meat is inspected for tapeworm cysts. However, meats should always be cooked thoroughly to destroy any cysts that may be present.

SECTION REVIEW

At this point, you may want to assign to several students the second of the Extensions and Applications at the end of this chapter.

1. In which class are the planarians grouped?
2. What is the function of the pharynx?
3. What is cephalization?
4. List the body parts of the tapeworm.   Answers on page T-73.

Highlight

Tapeworms are grouped in the class *Cestoda.* The three parts of the body of the tapeworm, a parasitic flatworm, are the scolex, the neck, and the proglottid segments.

Figure 26-4 The tapeworm, a parasitic flatworm, is made up of a scolex, a neck, and many segments called proglottids. Each proglottid contains male and female reproductive structures.

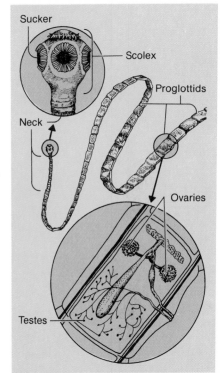

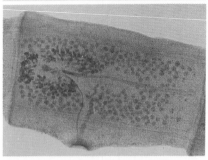

The presence of a separate opening for ingestion and elimination is an important adaptation of roundworms. Point out that separate openings provide a more efficient digestive tract than that found in planarians, which have a single opening for ingestion and excretion.

Exclusively sexual reproduction is a feature of the more complex animals. A combination of sexual and asexual means of reproduction, including regeneration, is a characteristic of simpler animals.

Roundworms

Biologists classify the roundworms, or *nematodes*, in the phylum *Nematoda*. The worms in this phylum have long, slender bodies that taper to points at both ends. There are more species of roundworm than of any other kind of worm. Roundworms live in nearly every kind of environment, including deserts, arctic regions, hot springs, and oceans. Many nematodes are parasites, and live in different animals and plants.

The nematode is more complex than the flatworm. At its anterior end it has a mouth, and at its posterior end it has another opening called the **anus**. The two openings are connected by a digestive tube. Food is taken in through the mouth, and nutrients are absorbed in the digestive tube. Undigested wastes leave the body through the anus. To rid itself of extra water, the nematode has a canal system, not flame bulbs. To move, the roundworm has long muscles that extend along its body wall. When these muscles contract, they create a snakelike, gliding movement. The nematode does not have either a circulatory or a respiratory system. Oxygen and carbon dioxide pass directly into and out of the worm through its body wall.

Roundworms reproduce sexually. The male and female sex organs of nematodes usually occur in different individuals. Male and female worms differ in size, shape, and color. In addition, their living habits can be very unusual. For example, in the case of a parasitic roundworm of rats, the tiny male worm lives inside the reproductive structure of the female worm.

The female reproductive structures of roundworms include two *ovaries*, or egg-producing organs. The ovaries

Figure 26–5 Roundworms are classified in the phylum *Nematoda*. This parasitic roundworm is living among blue-green algae.

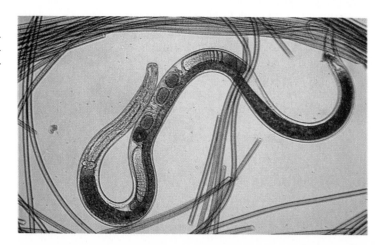

widen into *oviducts*, passages that lead into the *uteri*, or egg-storage organs. Each uterus opens into a tube, called a *vagina*, that leads to the outside of the body.

A male roundworm has a single *testis* (plural: testes), or sperm-producing organ. Sperm passes from the testis into a *sperm duct*. This duct leads to the **cloaca** (klō-Ā-kə). The cloaca is a chamber into which the digestive, excretory, and reproductive systems empty. During mating, sperm leaves the cloaca and enters the female through the vagina. Fertilization occurs in the uterus.

Ascaris

The roundworm *Ascaris lumbricoides* is a parasitic organism that lives in the intestines of pigs, horses, and sometimes human beings. The female *Ascaris* is larger than the male. During mating, the male *Ascaris* uses a pair of spines at its posterior end to grasp the female.

In human beings, the life cycle of *Ascaris* begins when its eggs enter the digestive system with contaminated food or water. In the intestine, the eggs hatch into larvae. The larvae burrow through the intestinal wall and enter the bloodstream. After they reach the lungs, they travel through the air passages into the throat. They are then swallowed and return to the small intestine, where they mature and reproduce. A tough coating, called a **cuticle**, keeps *Ascaris* from being digested by enzymes of the host. Inside the host's intestine, the female *Ascaris* may produce up to 200,000 eggs every day. After fertilization, the eggs develop a tough thick shell. When these fertilized eggs pass out of the host in the feces, the cycle is repeated.

Hookworms

The hookworm is a parasitic roundworm that commonly infects dogs, cats, and human beings in tropical and subtropical regions. The hookworm attaches itself to the intestinal wall of its host by means of *cutting plates*, or teeth, on its anterior end.

The life cycle of the hookworm begins when fertilized eggs pass out of a host with its feces. In the soil, the eggs hatch into larvae. The larvae enter a host by attaching themselves to a part of the host's body, usually a foot. Burrowing through the skin of the host, the larvae sooner or later reach a blood vessel. Once in the bloodstream, the life cycle is the same as the life cycle of *Ascaris*. However, hookworm larvae attach themselves to the intestinal wall of the host and grow into mature worms, using the blood of the host for food.

Figure 26-6 *Ascaris*, a roundworm, has better-developed organ systems than the planarian. Compare the organ systems in this figure with those in Figure 26-1.

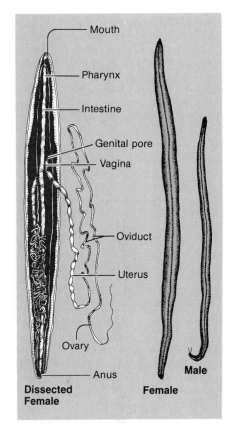

422

Biologists estimate that over 600 million people have hookworm infections. Infection by hookworms can lead to a number of medical problems. A serious infection can cause a great deal of tissue damage and blood loss, making the host sluggish and weak. Uncontrolled hookworm infections in young children can cause mental and physical retardation. Hookworm infections can be controlled if proper sanitation methods are followed and if shoes are worn to prevent hookworms from entering through the skin of the feet.

Trichina

The *Trichinella spiralis*, or trichina worm, is found in a cyst in the muscles of pigs, dogs, cats, and rats. When human beings eat undercooked and infested pork, they get a disease called **trichinosis**. Encysted larvae of the trichina worm enter the intestine of the host with the eaten pork. In the intestine, mature larvae are freed from the cysts and reproduce. Newly formed larvae then pass into the bloodstream and enter the muscles of the host, where they form cysts.

At least 30 million people in the United States are infected with these larvae. Unfortunately, there is no medical treatment for trichinosis. To avoid getting the disease, pork should be cooked well to kill any larvae that might be present. In the United States, meat scraps are sterilized before they are fed to hogs, to prevent the hogs from eating food that contains active *Trichinella* larvae.

Figure 26-7 Trichinosis is caused by the trichina, a parasitic roundworm that infects the muscles of certain animals such as pigs. When human beings eat infested pork that is incompletely cooked, the trichina cysts release larvae. These larvae eventually make their way to muscles and become encysted.

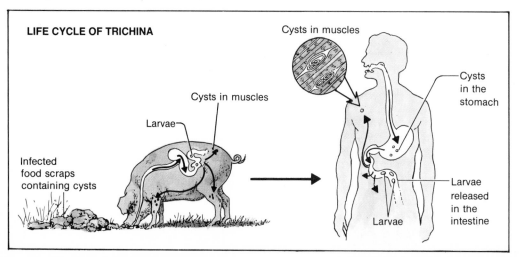

At this point, you may want to assign to several students the first of the Extensions and Applications at the end of this chapter.

At this point, you may want to assign to several students the third of the Extensions and Applications at the end of this chapter.

SECTION REVIEW   Answers on page T–73.

1. In which phylum are the roundworms classified?
2. What is the cloaca?
3. Describe the life cycle of the hookworm.

Segmented Worms

The segmented worms in the phylum *Annelida* include earthworms and leeches. Although many of the annelids live in the oceans, some species live in fresh water. Other species, such as the common earthworm, live in soil.

The annelids are the most complex worms. Like other worms, they are bilaterally symmetrical. Their body plan, however, differs from that of other worms. The body of a segmented worm is divided into many small ringlike segments. Most of the segments appear to be almost exact duplicates of the ones in front of them. Unlike other worms, the segmented worms have a **coelom** (sĒ-lum), a space filled with fluid. The coelom gives the segmented worm a tube-within-a-tube body plan. Because this worm has a coelom, it is known as a **eucoelomate** (yoo-sĒ-lō-māt). In comparison to other worms, the segmented worm also has better-developed nervous and circulatory systems.

Earthworms

The body of the earthworm, perhaps the best known segmented worm, is dark on its dorsal surface and light on its ventral surface. The *epidermis*, or skin, secretes a substance that forms a thin protective wall, or *cuticle*, around the entire body. A small lip located at the anterior end is

Highlight

The phylum *Annelida* is made up of segmented worms that have a coelom, or inner space filled with fluid.

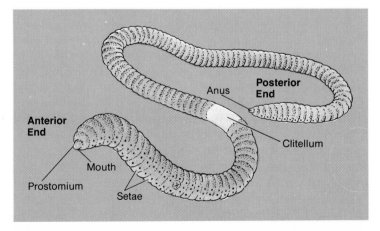

Figure 26–8   External Anatomy of Earthworm

called the **prostomium** (prō-STŌ-me-əm). Also toward the anterior end is a swollen area, called the **clitellum**, that is involved in reproduction. The *anus* is located at the posterior end.

To move, the earthworm uses a combination of hairlike bristles and two sets of muscles. On each of the 100 or so segments of the worm are four pairs of bristles called **setae** (SĒ-tē). The setae appear on the two sides and on the ventral surface of the segment. The earthworm first anchors the setae of the posterior segments on the ground. A layer of muscles, called the *circular muscles*, contracts, pushing the front end of the worm forward. The anterior setae anchor the front end, and the rear setae let go. The *longitudinal muscles* contract all along the length of the earthworm and pull the posterior end forward.

Earthworms are able to eat soil as they burrow through it. The burrows they leave behind not only permit air and water to enter the soil, but also break up the soil. In this way, earthworms make the soil more fertile for growing plants, and thus earthworms are beneficial to farmers.

The interior anatomy of the earthworm is much more complex than that of other worms. Its body contains well developed nervous, digestive, circulatory, respiratory, excretory, and reproductive systems.

NERVOUS SYSTEM Close to the anterior end of the earthworm, two nerves encircle the pharynx. These two branches join to form the *ventral nerve cord*, which runs through the ventral part of the worm along its entire length. In each of the segments, this ventral nerve cord is enlarged. These bulblike enlargements are called **ganglia** (singular: ganglion). Several pairs of nerves extend from each ganglion.

The nervous system coordinates all the movements and reactions of the earthworm by carrying impulses over definite nerve pathways. The earthworm can detect different kinds of stimuli, including touch, light, chemical substances, and temperature changes. This annelid moves away from strong light, from irritating chemicals, and from areas that become too cold or too hot.

DIGESTIVE SYSTEM The earthworm draws food through its mouth by means of a muscular pharynx that narrows to form a tubelike **esophagus** (i-SAHF-ə-gəs). Food passes through the esophagus, and enters a thin-walled storage chamber called a **crop.** The food is then forced into a thick-walled muscular chamber, called the **gizzard.** The food is ground up by the contraction and expansion of the gizzard.

At this point, you may want to assign to several students the fourth of the Extensions and Applications at the end of this chapter.

Highlight

The earthworm's nervous system includes a ventral nerve cord and ganglia.

Highlight

The earthworm's digestive system includes a pharynx, esophagus, crop, gizzard, intestine, and anus.

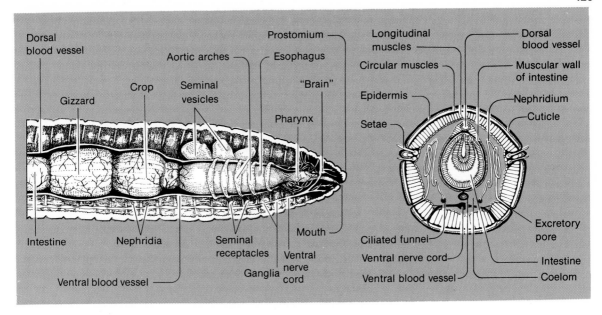

Dorsal blood vessel
Aortic arches
Prostomium
Esophagus
Gizzard
Crop
Seminal vesicles
"Brain"
Pharynx
Intestine
Nephridia
Seminal receptacles
Ventral nerve cord
Mouth
Ventral blood vessel
Ganglia

Longitudinal muscles
Circular muscles
Epidermis
Setae
Dorsal blood vessel
Muscular wall of intestine
Nephridium
Cuticle
Ciliated funnel
Ventral nerve cord
Ventral blood vessel
Excretory pore
Intestine
Coelom

Figure 26-9 The internal anatomy of the earthworm is much more complex than that of the flatworms or roundworms. This cross section (*right*) is of a typical earthworm segment.

The remainder of the digestive system is a long tube, called the *intestine*, which is the actual site of digestion. While nutrients are absorbed into the body through the intestine, undigested food is excreted through the anus and often left on the ground in the form of *castings.*

CIRCULATORY SYSTEM The earthworm has a *closed circulatory system*. That is, the blood constantly moves through a closed system of blood vessels. Within this system, two large blood vessels run the length of the earthworm's body. The *dorsal blood vessel* extends along the dorsal surface of the earthworm, carrying blood toward the anterior end. The *ventral blood vessel* carries blood along the ventral surface toward the posterior end. Small paired vessels connect these two blood vessels along their entire lengths. At the anterior end, five pairs of large muscular blood vessels, called **aortic arches,** connect the dorsal and ventral blood vessels. Alternately contracting and relaxing, these arches help to move the blood.

RESPIRATORY SYSTEM The earthworm takes in oxygen and gives off carbon dioxide through its thin skin. If the earthworm dries out in the sun, it dies, because this exchange of gases cannot take place without the mucus. The epidermis keeps the skin moist by secreting mucus.

EXCRETORY SYSTEM Every segment in the earthworm, except the first three and the last one, contains a pair of excretory organs, called **nephridia** (nə-FRID-ē-ə; singular: nephridium). Each nephridium is made of a small funnel and a long, coiled tube that leads to a bladderlike sac in the coelom. Inside the funnel, the wavelike motion of cilia pushes wastes through the coiled tube. Useable materials from the wastes diffuse out of the tube and into the *capillaries*, or the thin blood vessels, that surround the tube. Waste products, such as ammonia and *urea*, a nitrogen-containing substance, are excreted from the bladderlike sac through a small pore on the outside of the earthworm.

REPRODUCTIVE SYSTEM The earthworm is a hermaphrodite that produces both sperm and egg cells in various segments of its body. Two pairs of testes in segments 10 and 11 produce sperm. The segments are numbered from the anterior to posterior end of the worm. The testes are surrounded by saclike bodies, called **seminal vesicles,** that store sperm. On the same worm, a pair of small ovaries in segment 13 produce eggs. The eggs are stored in a small sac.

Although it produces sperm and eggs, an earthworm cannot fertilize its own eggs. Instead, it must go through a two-way cross-fertilization with another worm. When two

Highlight

The earthworm's excretory system includes organs called nephridia.

CLOSE-UP: *Saul Zackson*

Studying leeches is a fascinating experience to Saul Zackson. Saul Zackson is a young graduate student in the Department of Molecular Biology at the University of California at Berkeley. Like most students, he wears blue jeans and carries his notes in a knapsack on his back. What makes him different from the other students is the special work he does in his campus laboratory. Zackson studies leeches to see what makes them grow the way they do.

In Saul Zackson's laboratory, leeches live in an aquarium and eat snails. Leeches, which are also called bloodsuckers, have segmented bodies. The number of segments in a leech's body never varies. Except for the tail and the head, the segments are essentially the same. Zackson wants to find out why a leech embryo grows in such a predictable way.

"If we can understand what goes on in the leech, we might be able to know better what

goes on in other more complicated animals," he says. "The leech is a simple form of animal life so it's easier to study its system."

Another exciting aspect of Zackson's project is that it is producing original research. "As far as I know, nobody else in the world is working on a project like this," says Zackson. Saul Zackson likes the idea that his research may contribute new and important information to the ongoing study of animal life.

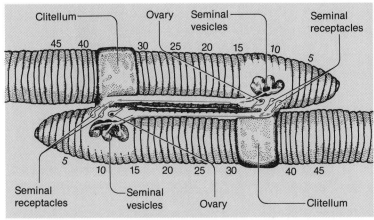

Figure 26-10 Earthworms are hermaphrodites, containing both male and female reproductive structures. When earthworms mate, they exchange sperm (*arrows*). The exchanged sperm is stored in seminal receptacles. A few days after mating, the earthworms' eggs are fertilized in a mucous ring secreted by the clitellum.

earthworms mate, they are held together by mucus secreted by the clitellum of each worm. During reproduction, sperm are carried by the sperm ducts to the male genital pore on segment 15. The two earthworms then exchange sperm cells. Traveling a short distance down a groove in the body, the sperm of each earthworm enter the *seminal receptacle* on segments 9 and 10 of the other worm.

A few days after the earthworms separate, the clitellum of each worm secretes a mucus ring that covers the anterior end and the clitellum. Eggs are passed through the oviduct to the *female genital pore* on segment 14. From there, the eggs move into the mucus ring, and the stored sperm is discharged. The mucus ring slips off the anterior end of the earthworm and seals itself, forming a **cocoon.** Each cocoon contains between 1 and 20 eggs that hatch into small earthworms.

Other Segmented Worms

The segmented sandworm *Nereis* lives and burrows in the sandy areas of the ocean. Unlike the earthworm, the sandworm has two large paddlelike appendages on each of its segments. These appendages are called **parapodia** (par-ə-PŌD-ē-ə; singular: parapodium). These appendages are used for swimming and burrowing. Clusters of setae are also located at the end of each parapod. To seize its prey, the *Nereis* has a pair of large jaws attached to a *proboscis* that can be pushed out of the mouth.

Highlight

Earthworms are hermaphroditic and undergo cross-fertilization during mating.

Figure 26-11 The sandworm (*left*) and the leech (*right*) are examples of segmented worms that spend most or all of their time in water.

Another segmented worm is the leech. Most leeches usually feed on the blood of other animals. A few species of leeches eat their prey whole. Leeches live in freshwater streams, in ponds, or in very moist forests.

The leech has 33 or 34 body segments and is an annelid. Unlike that of the earthworm, the coelom of the leech is not divided into internal segments. The leech also differs from other segmented worms in that it does not have setae.

At its anterior end, the leech has a pair of eyes and a small sucker. It also has a large sucker on the underside of the posterior end. These suckers help the leech hold on to its host while feeding. With three razor-sharp teeth, the leech bites its host and injects an *anesthetic* so that the host does not feel the bite. The pharynx then draws the blood of the host into the stomach of the leech. *Hirudin*, a substance secreted by the saliva glands of the leech, prevents the host's blood from clotting.

During feeding, a leech takes in an amount of blood that is three to five times its body weight. Gorged on blood, a leech can then go six to eight weeks between feedings. Within this time, the blood is slowly digested in the intestine of the leech by enzymes that come entirely from intestinal bacteria.

SECTION REVIEW   Answers on page T-73.

1. What is the coelom?
2. What is the clitellum?
3. What is the function of the nervous system in the earthworm?
4. What is the function of the parapodia in *Nereis?*

Observing a Planarian

Purpose The phylum *Platyhelminthes* is subdivided into several classes. Two classes, *Trematoda,* or flukes, and *Cestoda,* or tapeworms, are made up of parasitic flatworms. Another class, *Turbellaria,* is made up of free-living flatworms, of which planarians are the most common. The purpose of this investigation is to observe the structure of a planarian, its responses to some stimuli, and its ability to regenerate.

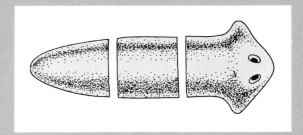

Materials *(per group)* ● Living planarian ● Medicine dropper ● Small piece of beef liver ● Microscope ● Hand lens ● Microscope slides and cover slips ● Depression slides ● Toothpicks ● Single-edged razor blade or scalpel ● Several ice cubes ● 3 petri dishes ● Small square of construction paper ● Aquarium water ● Wax pencil

Procedure **1.** Using a medicine dropper, obtain a specimen of *Planaria.* Place the specimen on a depression slide. **2.** Examine the planarian under the hand lens. Locate the anterior and posterior ends, the ventral and dorsal surfaces, the eyespots, and the sensory lobes. **3.** Place a small piece of construction paper over half the hand lens. Observe how the planarian responds. **4.** Remove the paper. After several seconds, touch the sensory lobes of the planarian with the tip of a toothpick. Observe how the planarian responds. After several more seconds, touch the body of the worm with the tip of a toothpick. Observe the response. **5.** After several more seconds, add a very small piece of liver to the depression slide. Observe the behavior of the planarian. **6.** Using the medicine dropper, rinse the depression with aquarium water. **NOTE:** *Be sure you do this carefully so that the planarian is not washed off the slide.* Carefully lower a cover slip over the depression. **7.** Mount the slide on the microscope.

Observe the planarian under low power. Sketch the planarian. Label any visible internal structures in the sketch. **8.** Remove the cover slip. Using the flat end of a toothpick, transfer the planarian to a flat microscope slide. Hold the slide over a cube of ice to chill the worm. **9. CAUTION:** *Be very careful when using a razor blade or scalpel.* When the worm is outstretched and immobile, carefully cut it into three pieces. Use the pattern shown in the figure. **10.** Using the wax pencil, mark one petri dish HEAD, the second petri dish MIDDLE, and the third TAIL. Place each section of the planarian in the proper petri dish. Fill half of each petri dish with aquarium water. Cover the dishes, and place them in a dark place. **11.** Examine the sections three times a week for three weeks. Keep a record of your observations.

Observations and Conclusions **1.** On your sketch, label the structures of the planarian that you are able to observe under the hand lens and at low power of the microscope. **2.** In what way does the planarian respond when part of the field of the hand lens is covered? **3.** What happens when you touch the sensory lobe of the planarian with the tip of the toothpick? When the body is touched? **4.** In a brief paragraph, describe how the planarian responds to the piece of liver. **5.** In a table, summarize your observations of the regeneration of the three planarian sections.

CHAPTER SUMMARY

Flatworms   The flatworms are classified in the phylum *Platyhelminthes*. Flatworms can be either parasitic or free-living. Like all worms, they have three cell layers, an anterior and a posterior end, and a dorsal and a ventral surface. They also exhibit cephalization. In the class *Turbellaria,* planarians are typical free-living flatworms that live in fresh water or in the sea. Food, taken in through the mouth, passes through the pharynx, and undigested materials pass back out through the mouth. The planarian excretory system includes flame bulbs that eliminate excess water from the planarian's body. Planaria have a nerve net and various sensory structures. Each planarian contains both male and female sex organs and reproduces sexually by means of cross-fertilization. Asexual reproduction can also occur by fragmentation and regeneration in a planarian.

Flukes, parasitic flatworms in the class *Trematoda,* have suckers and a well-developed reproductive system. Tapeworms of the class *Cestoda* are also adapted to a parasitic way of life. Although they have hooks or suckers on the head region, or scolex, tapeworms have no digestive, respiratory, or circulatory system. Both flukes and tapeworms have complicated life cycles involving several hosts.

Roundworms   These worms are also called nematodes, and may be either parasitic or free-living. Their digestive system includes both a mouth and an anus. Roundworms obtain oxygen through their skin and remove wastes through a system of canals. Parasitic roundworms, such as the *Ascaris,* the hookworm, and the trichina worm, can infect animals and people, causing illness. Roundworms are either male or female, not hermaphroditic.

Segmented Worms   Annelids include earthworms and many freshwater and marine worms. The body of the earthworm, a typical annelid, is divided into segments. Outside each segment are bristles, called setae, that assist in movement. Annelids have a well-developed nervous system, with a two-branched "brain" and a ventral nerve cord. They have a coelom, a closed circulatory system with five pairs of aortic arches, and a one-way digestive system. Gases are exchanged through the skin, and wastes are excreted through organs called nephridia. Each worm, although it is hermaphroditic, does not fertilize its own eggs.

The roundworm *Nereis* is a marine worm that feeds on small invertebrates and that has a well-developed sensory system to locate prey. Leeches are annelids that suck blood from various hosts.

CHAPTER VOCABULARY

acoelomate	ectoderm	pharynx
anus	endoderm	proglottid
aortic arch	esophagus	prostomium
bilateral symmetry	eucoelomate	scolex
cephalization	eyespot	seminal vesicle
clitellum	flame bulb	sensory lobe
cloaca	fragmentation	setae
cocoon	ganglia	tegument
coelom	gizzard	trichinosis
crop	mesoderm	uterus
cuticle	nephridia	ventral surface
cyst	parapod	
dorsal surface	parasite	

REVIEW of FACTS and CONCEPTS   Answers on pages T–73 to T–74.

On a separate sheet of paper answer each of the following as completely as possible.

1. Give evidence to show that worms are more complex organisms than the sponges and the coelenterates.
2. Define bilateral symmetry, using the flatworm as an example.
3. How does the flatworm take in and digest food?
4. Describe the excretory structures of a flatworm, and explain their functions.
5. How do planaria reproduce?
6. Diagram the life cycle of a liver fluke.
7. Describe the structure of the tapeworm.
8. The tapeworm is not considered a segmented worm. Explain this statement.
9. How do nematodes get oxygen?
10. Describe the life cycle of *Ascaris*.
11. Why do you think nematodes rarely reach a length of 1 meter, whereas annelids can grow up to 3 meters long?
12. Describe the life cycle of the hookworm.
13. How do humans contract trichinosis?
14. How does the body plan of annelids differ those of flatworms and roundworms?
15. How do earthworms take in and digest food?
16. Describe the circulatory system of the earthworm.
17. How are nerve messages sent in the body of the earthworm?
18. How do earthworms reproduce?

EXTENSIONS and APPLICATIONS   For additional information, see page T–74.

1. Call local veterinarians. Ask them what the incidence of various flatworm and roundworm infections is in your area. Present your findings to the class.
2. On a sheet of paper or posterboard, diagram the life cycles of the liver fluke and the tapeworm.
3. Prepare a report on one or more diseases. Make your selection or selections from elephantiasis, onchocerciasis, schistosomiasis. Present your findings to the class.
4. Obtain an earthworm. Place the worm on a moist paper towel, and allow it to crawl around on it. Observe how the worm moves. Can you tell the anterior from the posterior end? Place the worm on a smooth desk top or a glass plate. What role does friction play in the movement?
5. You can collect planarians by tying a piece of string around a piece of liver and lowering it into a pond or lake. In a few hours, raise the string. You should find planarians attached to the liver.

SUGGESTED READINGS

Darwin, C., *The Formation of Vegetable Mould Through the Action of Worms.* New York: AMS Press.
    This easy-to-read book explains the importance of earthworms to soil fertility.
Kenk, R., *Freshwater Planarians of North America.* Cincinnati: U.S. Environmental Protection Agency.
    This reference book identifies and discusses many freshwater planarians.
Rudloe, J., *The Exotic Ocean.* New York: World Publishing Co.
    This book contains a section on the collection, identification, and preservation of common and unusual-looking marine worms.

27 Mollusks and Echinoderms

Chapter Objectives *After completing this chapter, you will be able to:*

a ■ Describe the larval form in mollusks. p. 433
b ■ Describe the structure of a mollusk shell. p. 433
c ■ Name and describe three classes of mollusks. p. 433
d ■ Contrast the characteristics of mollusks and echinoderms. p. 439
e ■ Discuss the water-vascular system in echinoderms. p. 440
f ■ Name five examples of echinoderms. p. 439
g ■ Describe the structures of a starfish. p. 439

For teaching aids for this chapter, including a chapter overview and teaching strategies, see pages T~74 to T~76. The page number next to each chapter objective refers to the text page where the information needed to fulfill the objective begins.

A starfish, which is an echinoderm, feeds on a clam, which is a mollusk.

The phylum *Mollusca* (mahl-UHS-kə) has many species, including clams, snails, slugs, octopuses, and squids. In fact, only the phylum that includes the insects has a greater number of species. The many different types of mollusks may swim freely, float, or burrow into the sand or mud. Although most mollusks are *marine*, or sea-living, some mollusks live in fresh water, and others are *terrestrial*, or land-living. For thousands of years, people have eaten many types of mollusks, such as clams, scallops, oysters, and squids. Other kinds of mollusks have been used to make buttons, ornaments, tools, money, and dyes.

Unlike mollusks, animals in the phylum *Echinodermata* (ē-kī-nō-dər-MAH-tə) live only in the sea, and they have spiny skins. Most echinoderms, such as starfishes and sea urchins, either attach themselves permanently to the ocean bottom or move very slowly over it. In some areas of the world, the eggs of echinoderms are used for food. Some echinoderms that are common along seashores are also used for fertilizer.

Mollusks

Some of your students might be interested in doing research into the fossil record left by early mollusks.

Studying fossil records is one way for scientists to find relationships among organisms and to classify them. Perhaps no group of animals has left a more complete fossil record than the mollusks. They are known to have existed since the Paleozoic Era.

Another way to find relationships among organisms is to look for structural similarities. One such similarity exists in the larval stage of the mollusk. This larval form is called the **trochophore** (TRAHK-ə-fawr). The trochophore is shaped like a top with a ring of cilia around its middle. The cilia help the larva to move freely and also transport food into the larva's mouth. This form is one of the structures that scientists look for to identify organisms as mollusks. In addition, some of the segmented worms in the phylum *Annelida* are similar in their larval form to mollusk trochophores. As a result, some biologists think that a close relationship exists between these two phyla.

Also like the annelids, the mollusks have a *coelom* (SĒ-ləm), or body cavity. It is considered a true coelom because it is formed from the mesoderm layer of cells. In mollusks, the coelom surrounds the excretory organs, the heart, and the *gonads*, or reproductive organs.

The body of an adult mollusk is soft and contains three regions. The first region, the *head*, holds the mouth and sensory organs. The **visceral mass**, containing the gonads, the digestive system, the excretory organs, and the heart, makes up the second region. Covering the visceral mass is a thin membrane, called the **mantle**. It secretes the material that forms the mollusk shell. The mantle hangs down over the body, forming a mantle cavity. Within this cavity are the **gills**, or respiratory organs. The third region, the muscular **foot**, is located below the mantle. The foot is used for locomotion and, in some mollusks, for burrowing into sand or mud. Most mollusks also have a tonguelike structure, called a **radula**. The radula scrapes food from the ocean bottom and carries the food toward the digestive organs.

Among the characteristics used to classify mollusks are the presence or absence of a shell, the type of shell, and the type of foot. Although there are six classes in the phylum *Mollusca*, only three classes are discussed in this chapter.

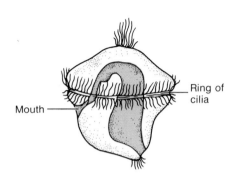

Figure 27–1 The trochophore is the larval stage of all mollusks.

Mouth — Ring of cilia

Highlight

The more than 80,000 species of animals that make up the phylum *Mollusca* are often called shellfish, even though many have no shells and many live out of the water.

Two-Shelled Mollusks

Mussels, clams, scallops, oysters, and shipworms are all two-shelled mollusks. The mollusks in the class *Pelecypoda* (pel-ə-SĪP-ə-də) are *bilaterally symmetrical*, or have identical

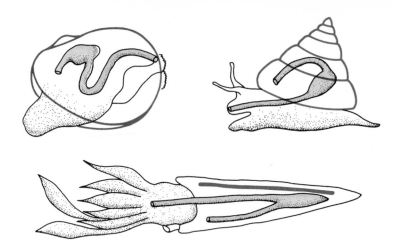

Figure 27-2 Mollusks are classified by their kind of shell (red), digestive tract (blue), and type of foot (shaded).

halves. Their bodies are contained in a shell that has two parts. For this reason, they are also called **bivalves.** A hinge joins the two valves, or shell parts, together, Two large muscles, called *adductor muscles,* hold them shut.

A bivalve typically uses its hatchet-shaped foot for burrowing into soft sand or mud. Occasionally, a bivalve like the sea mussel attaches itself to solid objects by threads secreted from glands in the foot.

The blood of pelecypods is not contained in blood vessels. The blood travels freely to and from the heart, small body cavities, tissues, organs, and gills. Therefore, these mollusks are said to have an *open circulatory system.*

The nervous system of these mollusks is made of three pairs of ganglia. The sensory organs in the head region at the end of the mantle respond to light and touch.

Most individual two-shelled mollusks have either male or female reproductive organs. During reproduction, the male releases sperm, and the female releases eggs. Fertilization occurs in the surrounding water, and the fertilized egg develops into a trochophore. After swimming freely for a while, the larva sinks to the bottom and develops into a tiny bivalve.

At this point, you may want your students to do the Laboratory Investigation at the end of this chapter.

Figure 27-3 The clam is a typical bivalve mollusk. Its shell is made of three layers.

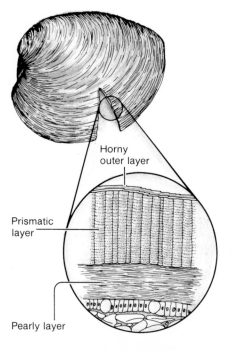

Horny outer layer

Prismatic layer

Pearly layer

CLAMS   As a typical bivalve, a clam does not attach itself permanently to objects. The hard shell of a clam is made of three layers, each of which is secreted by the mantle. The **horny outer layer** protects the parts that lie beneath it. The middle layer, called the **prismatic** (priz-MAT-ik) **layer,** contains crystals of calcium carbonate. The inner layer, or **pearly layer,** is made of thin layers of calcium carbonate.

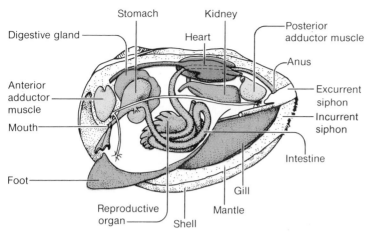

Figure 27-4 All of the clam's structures are housed within its hard, protective shell.

Within the mantle cavity are the gills, containing cilia. As water enters the mantle cavity through an **incurrent siphon,** or incoming tube, the cilia push the water over the gills. The gills then filter the water, taking out oxygen and replacing it with carbon dioxide. The mucus in the gills also traps microorganisms carried in the water. The cilia then move this food-carrying mucus toward two thin, fleshy folds. These folds guide the microorganisms into the mouth. Bivalves obtain food by filtering. They do not have radula. Undigested food passes out through the anus, and the water leaves the clam through a tube called the **excurrent siphon.**

OYSTERS AND SCALLOPS An oyster is a marine bivalve animal that has a body structure similar to that of the clam. Like a clam, the oyster feeds by filtering water through its gills. Unlike a clam, which moves from place to place, an oyster attaches itself permanently to objects by cementing one valve to the surface of an object.

Oysters are used as food and are also valued for their pearls. Pearls are formed when an irritation, such as a grain of sand, is caught between the mantle and the shell. A piece of the mantle surrounds the sand and secretes pearly layers of calcium carbonate. In a few years, a pearl is formed. Cultured pearls are produced when small particles are placed into the mantle by hand.

Scallops, which are found in grassy areas on the ocean bottom, swim by opening and closing their valves. This action causes a jet of water to shoot out at the hinge, propelling the scallop in the opposite direction. A scallop has a row of steel-blue eyes located along the edge of its mantle.

Sidelight

Giant clams living in the warm waters of the southern Pacific Ocean can measure up to 2 meters across.

Figure 27-5 The blue dots on this bay scallop are its eyes. Scallops use their eyes to detect changes in the intensity of light.

Highlight

Mollusks made of two shells held together by adductor muscles are called bivalves. One-shelled mollusks are called univalves or gastropods.

The function of these eyes is to detect sudden changes in light intensity.

One-Shelled Mollusks

The class *Gastropoda* (gas-TRAHP-ə-də) includes snails, slugs, conchs, and whelks. This class is the largest class of mollusks. Because most of those mollusks have single shells, they are called **univalves.** Others have reduced or internal shells, or no shells. The body of a gastropod is unlike that of other mollusks. During its development, the body becomes twisted. As a result, the rear mantle cavity of the adult gastropod is located just behind its head. Gastropods are found in the sea, in fresh water, and on land.

CAREER: Physical Oceanographer

Physical oceanographers study the physical properties of the oceans, which cover about 75% of the earth's surface. Some of these oceanographers study waves, tides, and currents. Others study ocean temperature, heat transfer in the ocean, and the ability of ocean water to transmit sound and light.

Some physical oceanographers examine the relationships between the oceans, land masses, and the atmosphere. For example, they may study why certain beaches are losing sand. This work is important in planning erosion control programs and in developing seaside resorts. Studies of the relationships between the oceans and the atmosphere provide information about the formation of weather systems. This work may increase the accuracy of weather predictions.

Physical oceanographers often work with specialists in other scientific fields. For example, a specialist in waves may consult with a meteorologist, or weather scientist, to determine wind speeds. The wave specialist can then predict the height and other characteristics of the waves that result from the winds. Such information is useful to offshore oil drillers and shipping companies.

Knowledge of currents is important to the shipping and fishing industries. For example, the speed and direction of currents in the North At-

lantic Ocean affect the drifting of icebergs and the movements of fish.

A bachelor's degree is needed to work in this field. Most physical oceanographers, however, have advanced degrees. They also have a broad educational background in oceanography, the physical sciences, and mathematics.

Many physical oceanographers work in colleges, universities, and oceanographic institutions. They usually teach and do research work. Some physical oceanographers work for government agencies and private industries.

For further career information, write to Scripps Institute of Oceanography, P.O. Box 109, La Jolla, CA 92037.

At this point, you may want to assign to your students the second of the Extensions and Applications at the end of this chapter.

437

SNAILS Snails are typical univalves and may be aquatic or land-living. While aquatic snails have one pair of tentacles, the land forms have two pairs. Also, an aquatic snail has a single coiled shell, and it breathes through its gills. A land snail, on the other hand, must have a *lung*, or network of blood vessels. These blood vessels are found on the outer wall of the mantle in the mantle cavity. The lining of this cavity must be kept moist, so that the diffusion of oxygen can take place.

A land snail's need for moisture affects its day and night activities. The land snail is most active during the night or early morning, when the air is filled with moisture. During the day, the land snail can be found beneath objects on the ground, with its soft head and foot drawn into its shell. In dry weather, its glands secrete mucus. The mucus forms a seal over the shell opening. This covering keeps the animal from drying out.

Most snails are plant eaters and use their radula to scrape small bits of food from plants. When present in large numbers, land snails can do severe damage to garden plants and even to trees.

SLUGS Slugs live in salt water, in fresh water, and on land. Most of these mollusks have a reduced or internal shell, and some have no shell at all. They do, however, have other gastropod features. All slugs have one pair of tentacles. Like land snails, land slugs lack gills and use the mantle cavity as a breathing organ. Some sea slugs, called *nudibranchs* (NOO-də-brankz), do not have mantle cavities and breathe by means of gills. They feed on sponges and hydrozoans.

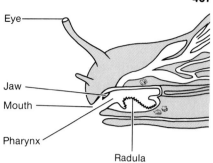

Figure 27-6 The snail possesses a number of organs associated with food-getting. Radula are used to scrape food from the surface of plants.

Figure 27-7 Slugs and snails live on land or in water. Snails have shells while slugs do not. The photograph on the left shows a land snail and a land slug. The photograph on the right shows a sea slug.

438

Highlight

Cephalopods, the most structurally advanced mollusks, have definite heads surrounded by tentacles, or armlike structures.

"Head-Footed" Mollusks

The class *Cephalopoda* (sef-'l-AHP-ə-də) includes octopuses, squids, cuttlefishes, and chambered nautiluses. These mollusks are bilaterally symmetrical. They may have external shells, internal shells, or, in some cases, no shell at all.

Cephalopods are clearly the most highly organized mollusks. The brain and sense organs are well developed. The foot has adapted into a ring of tentacles with suckers.

In addition, cephalopods have a *closed circulatory system*, unlike the other classes of mollusks. Food moves through their digestive systems by means of muscle contraction, not the cilia movement that characterizes other mollusks.

OCTOPUSES An octopus lacks an external or internal shell and moves in two ways. It can pull itself over ocean rocks with its eight suckered tentacles, or it can jet through the water by forcing water out of its mantle cavity.

An octopus has a very advanced nervous system. This system links touch receptors on the tentacles with the animal's eyes. Octopus eyes, which are similar to those of vertebrates, can adapt to changes in light intensity, form sharp images, and possibly detect colors.

An octopus can protect itself in a number of ways. First, it can blend in with its surroundings by making use of its special pigment cells. These cells contain black, brown, red, and yellow pigments. When the octopus is disturbed, the pigment cells contract, causing the octopus to change color. Second, when attacked an octopus can release a cloud of ink that forms an aquatic "smoke screen." This enables the octopus to escape from its predators.

When feeding on prey, such as fishes and crabs, an octopus uses its strong beaklike jaws. The secretions from the octopus' salivary glands paralyze the prey.

Figure 27-8 The octopus has no shell. It uses eight tentacles, or armlike structures, to move and to capture its prey.

SQUIDS A squid has an internal shell and ten tentacles. Although the tentacles have suckers on them, the squid does not use them to pull itself along slowly. Instead, a squid swims by jet propulsion and steers itself with a pair of fins. In fact, squids are the fastest swimming marine invertebrates. One species, the giant squid, is also the largest invertebrate. It can reach a length of 16 meters and it can weigh more than 1800 kilograms. The eyes of this giant squid are about the size of basketballs!

Sidelight

Many ancient stories about mermaids and sea serpents are now believed to have been based on sightings of giant squids.

NAUTILUSES Unlike some of the other cephalopods, a nautilus has an external, coiled shell. By taking in and releasing gas from chambers in this shell, a nautilus is able to change its buoyancy. It can, therefore, live at any level from the ocean's surface down to 600 meters. The body of the nautilus is divided into two sections. The *head* is covered by the hood, a tough tissue that acts as a shield. Tentacles, which can number more than ninety, are located in the head. Unlike those of other cephalopods, the tentacles lack suckers. Instead, they are covered with a sticky substance that helps to hold prey. In addition, the head contains eyes that do not have any lenses. The second section, the *body*, has a large sac that contains the nautilus' organs. The sac is enclosed by the mantle. Between the mantle and the sac is a space that contains four large gills. At this point, you may want to assign to your students the first of the Extensions and Applications at the end of this chapter.

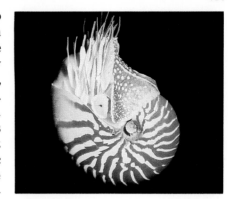

Figure 27-9 The chambered nautilus can change the depth at which it floats by taking in or releasing gas from chambers inside its shell.

SECTION REVIEW   Answers on page T–75.

1. In what ways are the structures of mollusks and annelids similar?
2. What are the regions of the mollusk's soft body?
3. Name three features of mollusks that are used to classify them.
4. What are bivalves? Univalves?
5. Why are cephalopods considered the most highly organized mollusks?

Echinoderms

Starfishes, sea urchins, brittle stars, sand dollars, and sea cucumbers are members of the phylum *Echinodermata*. Like mollusks, the echinoderms, with their hard body parts, have left fossil records that date back to the Paleozoic Era.

Echinoderms are easily identified by the presence of spines, which are made up of small calcium plates. These plates are covered with a thin epidermal, or outer, layer. As a result, echinoderms have an **endoskeleton,** or inner skeleton. Unlike mollusks, echinoderms lack a well-defined head region, blood vessels, and excretory system. Their bodies usually have five parts and are said to be *pentaradial* (pen-tə-RA-dē-əl). The prefix *pent-* means five. In addition, the bodies of most echinoderms are *radially symmetrical*.

Starfishes

Starfishes are found along most seacoasts, especially on rocky shores and wharf pilings. They range in size from 1 centimeter to 1 meter in diameter. The body of a starfish

Highlight

Echinoderms are spiny-skinned animals that live in a marine habitat.

consists of a central disk and five tapering *rays*, or arms. The upper surface of a starfish is called the **aboral** (ā-BOR-'l) **surface.** This surface contains the spines that form a starfish endoskeleton.

The aboral surface also has tiny projections that cover the epidermis. These are projections of the coelom, and they are formed from the mesoderm. They serve as respiratory and excretory organs. Waste products are excreted and gases are exchanged through these projections by diffusion.

A starfish's nervous system contains a *nerve ring* around the mouth. Nerves travel from the nerve ring into each of the starfish's five rays. At the tip of each ray is a light-sensitive *eye spot.*

In echinoderms, the coelom gives rise to a **water-vascular system** and to a cavity that surrounds the internal organs. In

Figure 27-10 Starfishes exhibit the water-vascular system and other advanced organ systems found in the echinoderms.

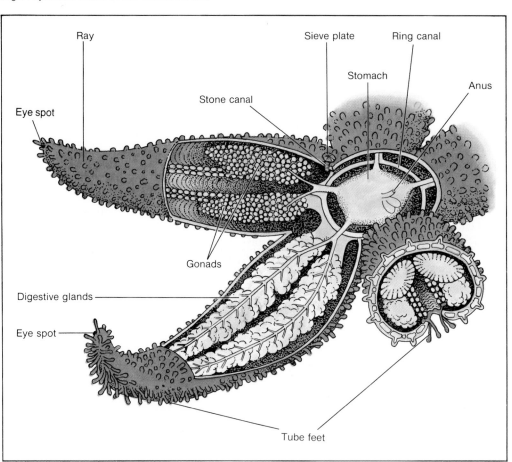

starfishes, the water-vascular system is used for locomotion and for food-getting. As water enters a starfish through a sievelike structure on the aboral side, it passes through a *stone canal*. The stone canal connects the sievelike structure to the *ring canal*, which is located around the mouth. This second canal leads to the five **radial canals**, one in each ray. Connected to each radial canal are the **tube feet**, which make up the external part of the water-vascular system.

Located on the tube feet of most starfishes are suckers that adhere to vertical surfaces and rocks. These suckers enable a starfish to draw itself over these types of surfaces.

Starfishes eat mollusks, especially clams and oysters. Pressing against the shell of the mollusk, the tube feet of a starfish exert a steady pull on the shell. In half an hour or so, the adductor muscles of the mollusk tire and relax. The shell opens slightly, and the starfish turns its stomach inside out through the mouth. Then the starfish's stomach passes through the opening between the valves of the clam. As enzymes are secreted by the starfish's stomach, the clam or oyster is digested in its own shell.

Starfishes can be troublesome predators in certain marine communities. They have damaged coral reefs, as well as oyster, clam, and mussel beds. At one time, owners of such beds would destroy starfishes by cutting them into pieces and throwing them back into the water. This practice, however, only caused the starfishes to multiply by *regeneration*. Regeneration is the development of a whole new animal from each of its parts. Regeneration occurs in starfishes as long as the detached ray of a starfish is still connected to part of the central disk.

Starfishes normally reproduce sexually. Although each ray of a starfish contains a pair of gonads, individual starfishes are either male or female. Fertilization occurs externally when the eggs and sperm are deposited into the water. The larvae that develop are free-swimming, self-feeding, and ciliated. These larvae are called **bipinnarias**. Within a few weeks, they settle to the ocean bottom and develop into adult starfish.

Other Echinoderms

The brittle star is another type of echinoderm. As shown in Figure 27-12, brittle stars have five very flexible rays that enable the animal to move rapidly. If seized by a predator, the brittle star can shed an arm, escape, and regenerate its missing part.

Sea urchins and sand dollars are echinoderms that do not have arms. Instead, sea urchins are covered with movable

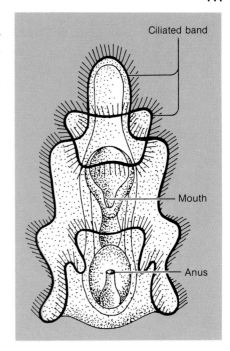

Ciliated band

Mouth

Anus

Figure 27-11 Unlike their parents, starfish larvae, called bipinnarias, can swim. They move by waving the many tiny cilia on their surface.

You might want to have some of your students prepare a chart comparing the process of regeneration in animals with the process of vegetative propagation in plants, as discussed in Chapter 23.

Sidelight

The female starfish can lay as many as 100,000,000 eggs during a single season.

Figure 27-12 Brittle stars (*top left*), sea urchins (*top right*), sand dollars (*bottom left*), and sea cucumbers (*bottom right*) are all echinoderms.

spines, which are long enough to be used for locomotion, attachment, and defense. Sand dollars resemble flattened sea urchins with very small spines. Both of these echinoderms are plant eaters.

Sea cucumbers are so named because they are shaped like cucumbers. At one end of the body is a mouth that is surrounded by a ring of tentacles. At the other end is the anus. Sea cucumbers are very slow-moving animals.

SECTION REVIEW   Answers on page T–75.

1. Define pentaradial.
2. What is the function of the water-vascular system?
3. What is regeneration?
4. In addition to the starfish, name four other echinoderms.

Observing a Mollusk

Purpose   Although some mollusks live in fresh water, most live in salt water. One class of mollusks, the bivalves, have their bodies contained in a shell. This shell has two parts. Other classes of mollusks have external or internal shells. Some have no shells at all. The purpose of this investigation is to examine the external and internal structures of a bivalve.

Materials *(per student)*   ● Empty clam shell
● Fresh clam   ● Scalpel   ● Hand lens   ● 2 glass slides   ● Microscope   ● Dissecting tray
● Screwdriver   ● Forceps   ● Methylene blue
● 2 cover slips

Procedure Part A   **1.** Place the clam and the empty clam shell in a dissecting tray.   **2.** Carefully break a small piece off the empty clam shell.   **3.** Using the hand lens, examine an edge of the shell.   **4.** Observe the three layers of the clam shell.   **5.** With the screwdriver, carefully pry apart the two valves of the fresh clam.   **6. Caution:** *Be very careful when using a scalpel.* Use the scalpel to cut the two large adductor muscles that hold the valves together.
7. Open the clam completely.   **8.** With the scalpel, carefully remove part of the mantle to observe the organs in the mantle cavity. The mantle is a white membrane that lines each shell.   **9.** Locate the heart near the hinge.   **10.** Observe the dark kidneys. They are found posterior to the heart and in front of the posterior adductor muscle.   **11.** Cut away the muscle of the foot to find the digestive gland.   **12.** Use Figure 27-4 on page 435 to identify the internal structures of the clam.   **13.** Sketch and label all structures.
Part B   **1.** With the forceps, peel a thin section from the edge of the mantle and the edge of the gills.

2. Make a wet mount of each of these sections.
3. Before placing the cover slip over each, add a drop of methylene blue to the slide.   **4.** Examine each slide under high power.   **5.** Locate the cilia in the gills.
6. Sketch what you see.

Observations and Conclusions   **1.** Describe the appearance of the three layers of the clam shell.
2. What is the position of the incurrent siphon in relation to the excurrent siphons?   **3.** What other structures are located in the gills? What are their functions?   **4.** Which of the adductor muscles is the larger?

CHAPTER SUMMARY

Mollusks   Animals in the phylum *Mollusca* have a soft body that is divided into the head, the visceral mass, and the foot. The head contains the mouth and sensory organs. The visceral mass holds the reproductive, digestive, and excretory organs. The muscular foot is used in locomotion and burrowing.

A thin membrane, called the mantle, covers the visceral mass. In most mollusks, the mantle secretes the material that forms the shell. Within the mantle cavity are the gills, or respiratory organs. Most mollusks also have a tonguelike structure, called a radula. Three classes of mollusks are *Pelecypoda, Gastropoda,* and *Cephalopoda.*

In pelecypods, or bivalves, the shells are divided into two parts held together by the hinge. The hard shell of typical bivalves have three layers. They are a thin horny outer layer, a prismatic middle layer, and an inner pearly layer. Water enters the clam through the incurrent siphon, and it leaves through the excurrent siphon. As the water passes over the gills, oxygen and food are removed from it. Clams have an open circulatory system. A clam's nervous system has three pairs of ganglia. The sexes of clams are separate, and most fertilization is external. The fertilized egg develops into a trochopore larva. Other examples of pelecypods are oysters and scallops.

Gastropods often have only one-part shells. One-shelled gastropods, such as the snails, whelks, and conchs, are called univalves. The shells of other gastropods may be reduced, internal, or totally missing. Slugs, for example, have internal or reduced shells.

Cephalopods may have internal shells, external shells, or no shells at all. Unlike the other classes of mollusks, cephalopods have a closed circulatory system. They are the most highly organized mollusks, with a well-developed brain and sense organs, and feet that have become adapted into tentacles that may contain suckers.

Echinoderms   Starfishes, sea urchins, brittle stars, sand dollars, and sea cucumbers are members of the phylum *Echinodermata.* These radially symmetrical animals have no well-defined head region, blood vessels, or excretory system. Their chief feature is the presence of spines covered with an epidermis. Echinoderms also have an endoskeleton, or inner skeleton. In echinoderms, the coelom gives rise to the water-vascular system.

Starfishes, are typical echinoderms. In these animals the water-vascular system is used for locomotion and food-getting. Along the underside of each ray, or arm, are many slender projections, called the tube feet. These are the external parts of the water-vascular system. Suckers, located on the end of their tube feet, enable starfishes to draw themselves over rocks and vertical surfaces. Starfishes use their tube feet to open clams and oysters. Then, by forcing their stomachs out through their mouths and into the bivalve, starfishes digest their prey. Although starfishes normally reproduce sexually, they may also regenerate, or grow new parts. Other types of echinoderms include the brittle stars, sea urchins, sand dollars, and sea cucumbers.

CHAPTER VOCABULARY

aboral surface	horny outer layer	trochophore
bipinnaria	incurrent siphon	tube foot
bivalve	mantle	univalve
endoskeleton	pearly layer	visceral mass
excurrent siphon	prismatic layer	water-vascular system
foot	radial canal	
gill	radula	

REVIEW of FACTS and CONCEPTS   Answers on pages T–75 to T–76.

On a separate sheet of paper, answer each of the following as completely as possible.

1. Name and describe the larval stage of mollusks.
2. What are the three layers of the clam's shell called?
3. Describe the respiratory, circulatory, nervous, and reproductive systems in bivalves.
4. How do oysters and scallops differ from clams?

5. How are pearls formed?
6. How do cephalopods differ from other mollusks?
7. Name and briefly describe three classes of mollusks. Give examples of each class.
8. What type of skeleton do echinoderms have? Explain.
9. Compare the coelom of mollusks and echinoderms.

10. Explain how starfishes get their food.
11. Briefly describe the respiratory, nervous, and reproductive systems in starfishes.
12. Why are some mollusks and echinoderms destructive? Explain.
13. Distinguish between the following pairs of terms: bivalve and univalve; bilateral symmetry and radial symmetry; and trochophore and bipinnaria.

EXTENSIONS and APPLICATIONS For additional information, see page T–76.

1. Visit the library and gather more information on the buoyancy system of chambered nautiluses. Write a report on the way these mollusks fill sections of their shells with gas.
2. Collect some snails from around your neighborhood. On your collection trip, bring two average-sized jars with lids to hold the snails. Land snails are often found attached to stones or logs, or they may be found in leaf mold on the ground. Aquatic snails are found attached to rocks or to the stems of plants that are growing in ponds or streams. Place about 5 land snails in one jar and 5 aquatic snails in the other jar. Include some of the leaf mold or water from the place where they were found. After collecting the snails, do not place the jars in the sun or leave the lids on the jars longer than necessary. Set up a small terrarium with leaf mold for the land snails. Place the aquatic snails in an aquarium. Observe both types of snails. Describe their methods of locomotion. What structures enable the snails to remove algae from the glass? Explain.
3. If you live near or visit the seashore, observe some mollusks or echinoderms in their natural habitat. You may wish to start a collection of shells that have been washed up on shore. Use a guide book of shell collecting, which can be found in the library, to identify the different species. Arrange the shells on cardboard or posterboard, and glue them into place. Identify each shell by writing its name under it. State where it was found and the date it was found.

SUGGESTED READINGS

Cousteau, J., and P. Diole, *Octopus and Squid: The Soft Intelligence.* Garden City, N.Y.: Doubleday.
  The authors, both experienced divers, provide a personal account of these unusual marine mollusks. Many illustrations are included.
Lane, F. W., *Kingdom of the Octopus.* New York: Sheridan House.
  This book provides a wealth of information on the cephalopods, with a special section on the giant squid. The author discusses why these mollusks are believed to be quite intelligent.
Stix, H., and M. and R. Tucker-Abbott, *The Shell.* New York: Abrams.
  In addition to a description of the shells of mollusks, the authors have included many interesting photographs of shells from around the world.

28 Crustaceans and Myriapods

A hermit crab peers out from its borrowed shell.

Chapter Objectives *After completing this chapter, you will be able to:*

a ■ List the characteristics of arthropods. p. 446
b ■ Name five main classes of arthropods. p. 446
c ■ Identify and give the functions of the parts of a crayfish. p. 448
d ■ List some of the differences between annelids and crustaceans. p. 447
e ■ Describe the characteristics of centipedes and millipedes. p. 453

For teaching aids for this chapter, including a chapter overview and teaching strategies, see pages T–76 to T–77. The page number next to each chapter objective refers to the text page where the information needed to fulfill the objective begins.

About 75% of all animal species belong to the phylum *Arthropoda* (ahr-THRAHP-ə-də), whose name means *jointed leg*. All the members of this phylum have bodies with jointed *appendages*, or outgrowths. Like annelids, arthropods have segmented bodies.

Arthropods are found in all types of environments, from ocean depths of 9750 meters to altitudes of 6000 meters. Different species of arthropods are adapted for life on land, in soil, in the air, and in fresh and salt water. Some kinds of arthropods destroy large quantities of food crops and stored food. Others spread diseases. However, some arthropods are important sources of food. Others produce silk, as well as substances that can be used as dyes.

The arthropod phylum consists of five main classes. These are *Crustacea* (kruhs-TĀ-shə), *Chilopoda* (kē-LAHP-ə-də), *Diplopoda* (di-PLAHP-ə-də), *Arachnida* (ə-RAK-nə-də), and *Insecta*. In this book, the two classes *Chilopoda* and *Diplopoda* are grouped together as *myriapods* (MĔR-ē-ə-pahdz).

Characteristics of Arthropods

The body of an arthropod is protected by a hard **exoskeleton,** or outer skeleton. The exoskeleton is made of a substance called **chitin** (KĪT-'n). Because this skeleton does not grow, the arthropod must periodically shed its exoskeleton and grow a new one. The shedding of the exoskeleton is called **molting.**

Attached to the exoskeleton are muscles, which are arranged in bands. Due to this band arrangement, most arthropods can crawl, swim, or fly at high speeds. In land-dwelling arthropods, the exoskeleton limits the amount of water lost from the body.

Another function of the exoskeleton is to protect the delicate inner organs of the arthropod. In contrast to annelids, arthropods have a small *coelom,* or body cavity. The coelom is divided into separate spaces. One of these spaces contains the excretory organs, and another encloses the reproductive organs. A third, larger space, called the **hemocoel** (HEM-ə-sēl), contains blood and surrounds the digestive system.

SECTION REVIEW   Answers on page T–76.

1. What are some of the characteristics of arthropods?
2. What is molting?
3. What is a hemocoel?

Crustaceans

At this point, you may want to assign to your students the third of the Extensions and Applications at the end of this chapter.

Animals in the class *Crustacea* include crabs, lobsters, crayfishes, and shrimps. These crustaceans are familiar as food sources for people. Most crustaceans are aquatic, and their gills make them different from the other classes of arthropods. Although crustaceans are usually free-living, some are sessile, or permanently attached to a surface.

In addition to the familiar crab, lobster, or shrimp, there are other species in the class *Crustacea.* A few crustaceans, such as the *isopods,* live on the land, even though they have gills. The gills of these animals can function only when wet. For this reason, isopods are found in damp places, such as moist soil. The pill bug and the sow bug are isopods. Among the aquatic crustaceans are the *copepods.* Copepods are small and numerous and are important food sources for fishes. The tiny *ostracods* are also aquatic crustaceans. Enclosed by small bivalve shells, these animals look like tiny clams. The *Daphnia,* or water flea, is a typical ostracod.

Figure 28-1   Isopods, such as this pill bug, must live in moist areas so that their gills can function.

447

448

Figure 28-2 The crayfish exhibits the segmented body and jointed legs of all arthropods.

Crayfishes

Crayfishes are usually bottom dwellers that avoid predators by burrowing into sand or mud. They resemble lobsters, with some minor differences. One difference is that crayfishes have two fewer body segments than lobsters. Another difference is that, whereas lobsters live in salt water, crayfishes are found in freshwater streams, swamps, and ponds. These sources of fresh water often contain large amounts of lime. This lime is absorbed by crayfishes and toughens their chitinous exoskeletons.

As in all crustaceans, a crayfish's body is divided into two main parts. The first part, the **cephalothorax,** consists of the *head* and the *thorax,* or middle section. Containing thirteen segments in all, the cephalothorax is covered and protected by a part of the exoskeleton called the **carapace** (KAR-ə-pās). The second main part of a crayfish's body, the **abdomen,** is behind the cephalothorax and has six segments.

Each segment of the cephalothorax and abdomen contains a pair of appendages, as shown in Figure 28-2. The most anterior segment of the cephalothorax contains the **antennules.** These appendages not only help crayfishes maintain their *equilibrium,* or balance, but they are also sense organs for touch and taste. Behind the antennules are longer appendages, called **antennae,** which are also organs of touch and taste. The **mandibles,** or true jaws, are found be-

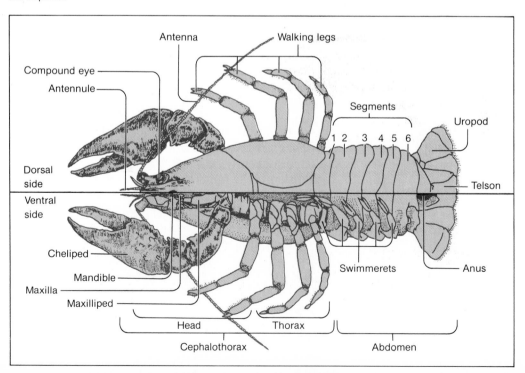

hind the antennae. These structures crush food with the help of two pairs of **maxillae** (mak-SIL-ē; singular: maxilla). The first pair of maxillae holds the food during feeding. The second pair draws water over the gills.

Located on the thorax portion of the cephalothorax are three pairs of **maxillipeds** (mak-SIL-i-pedz). Maxillipeds are structures that taste and hold the food while crayfishes chew. The next pair of appendages, called **chelipeds** (KĒ-lə-pedz), are large claws that are used for food-getting and for protection. Behind the chelipeds are the last four segments of the cephalothorax. Each of these segments contains a pair of **walking legs.**

On the abdomen, each of the first five segments contains a pair of appendages called **swimmerets.** Swimmerets are used for swimming, and aid in respiration. In the female, the last three pairs of swimmerets also carry the eggs. The last abdominal segment contains a pair of appendages called the **uropod** (YOOR-ə-pahd), or flipper. In the middle of the uropod is a triangular structure called the **telson.** By moving the telson and uropod, crayfishes are able to make quick backward movements.

DIGESTIVE SYSTEM Crayfishes feed on living or dead plants and animals. They seize their food with their chelipeds and pass it to the maxillae and maxillipeds. These structures tear the food into small pieces and pass it to the mandible, where it is crushed.

Once in small pieces, the food is moved into the mouth and down a short *esophagus*, or food tube, to the stomach. As the pieces of food enter the anterior portion of the stomach, chitinous teeth chew them up into fine particles. The next portion of the stomach contains tiny hairlike structures that allow only fine particles to enter. Digestive glands in the stomach break down the food. In the stomach, the digested food is absorbed into the blood. Undigested food moves down the intestine and out of the body through the anus.

CIRCULATORY SYSTEM Unlike the annelids, crayfishes and some of the other crustaceans have an open circulatory system. In crayfishes, an irregularly shaped heart is found in a cavity called the *pericardial sinus*. From this sinus, the blood enters the heart through three pairs of openings, called **ostia** (AHS-tē-ə; singular: ostium). After it is filled, the heart contracts and pumps the blood through large vessels, called *arteries*. The blood is stopped from flowing back into the pericardial sinus by valves in the arteries. These large arteries lead to narrower arteries. They empty into small sinuses between body organs. The blood from these sinuses

Sidelight

Unique animals are still being discovered. Recently, several new kinds of crustaceans were found living at the bottom of the Pacific Ocean.

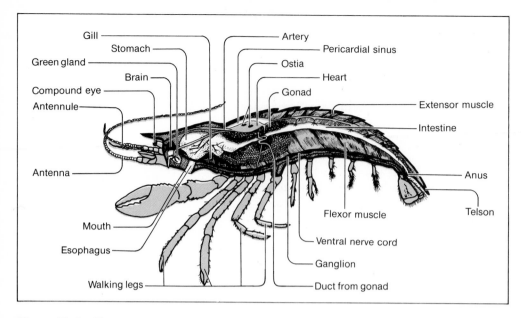

Labels on figure:
Gill · Stomach · Green gland · Brain · Compound eye · Antennule · Antenna · Mouth · Esophagus · Walking legs · Artery · Pericardial sinus · Ostia · Heart · Gonad · Extensor muscle · Intestine · Anus · Telson · Flexor muscle · Ventral nerve cord · Ganglion · Duct from gonad

Figure 28-3 The internal organs of the crayfish are grouped into systems for digestion, circulation, respiration, and reproduction.

then collects in the *sternal sinus*, another large cavity. From there the blood is carried by other vessels to the gills, where respiration occurs. The blood is then carried back to the pericardial sinus through still other vessels.

RESPIRATORY AND EXCRETORY SYSTEMS   The respiratory system is made up of the gills. The gills are featherlike projections of the body wall. Their function is to remove oxygen from the water. The gills are found in the *gill chambers.* Gill chambers are small spaces between the thorax and the carapace. As crayfishes move through the water, water passes over the gills. When the crayfishes are not moving, the *gill bailer*, a small structure on the second pair of maxillae, draws water in and passes it over the gills.

The excretory organs of most crustaceans are the **green glands.** The green glands remove excess water and wastes from the blood. These glands are tubular structures in front of the esophagus near the base of the antennae.

NERVOUS SYSTEM   The nervous systems of crayfishes and annelids have much in common. The nervous system of a crayfish, however, is larger than that of an annelid. In addition, the crayfish's nervous system has more fused *ganglia,* or groups of nerve cells.

The "brain" of a crayfish contains a pair of ganglia that branch into nerves to the eyes, antennules, and antennae. Two other large nerves leading from the brain run around the esophagus and join the *ventral nerve cord.* This cord then extends to the posterior end of the body. In each segment of a crayfish's body, the nerve cord contains a pair of joined ganglia. From these ganglia, nerves lead to the appendages, muscles, and organs.

The sense organs are also better developed in crustaceans than they are in annelids. The most sensitive of the crustacean organs are the antennae and antennules, which are used for taste, touch, and smell. Located near the base of each antennule, a saclike structure, called a **statocyst,** controls balance. Within the statocyst is a ridge containing fine sensory hairs. Tiny grains of sand become attached to these hairs. Whenever a crayfish changes its position, these sand grains also change their position. The movement of the grains stimulates the sensory hairs and sends messages to the brain. The statocyst enables the crayfish to maintain its balance or to right itself when tilted.

A crayfish has a pair of **compound eyes,** which are eyes with more than one lens. In fact, each compound eye of a crayfish has about 2500 lenses. Although the images formed are not sharp, these eyes can detect movement very well. Due to their location on short movable stalks, the eyes also provide a wide field of vision. This feature helps crayfishes search for food and avoid predators.

CLOSE-UP: *Dr. Eduardo Macagno*

Eduardo Macagno is a biologist who works in a modern lab at Columbia University in New York City. He is a professor in the Department of Biological Sciences. Macagno is studying the nervous systems of invertebrates, and he uses a computer. In particular, Macagno is studying the nervous system of *Daphnia,* which are tiny, freshwater animals, also called water fleas. *Daphnia* have a very simple nervous system. If Macagno can understand how *Daphnia* function, he will know more about the nervous systems of more complex animals.

Daphnia are so small that they are hard to study. Most are only 4 or 5 millimeters long. Moreover, to study their nervous system, Macagno must look at the individual nerve cells that make up the system. By using a microscope hooked up to a computer, Macagno is able to examine these cells.

"Before the computer, we had to make plastic models to help us understand the function and structure of the nerve cells." Macagno says. "It

took a very long time to make a model of a cell. Now we use a computer to draw the features of the cells."

After scanning sections of *Daphnia* tissue, the computer can instantly display information that took biologists weeks to uncover in the past. The computer that Macagno uses is one that he helped to develop at Columbia. It is only a few years old. With the computer, Macagno's research, as well as the research of other biologists, is moving ahead at new and impressive speeds.

Figure 28-4 A crustacean's exoskeleton does not grow. Thus, a growing crustacean, such as the crayfish, periodically molts or sheds its exoskeleton. The shed exoskeleton is replaced by a new, larger one.

Figure 28-5 Crayfishes can regenerate limbs that break off at certain breakage points.

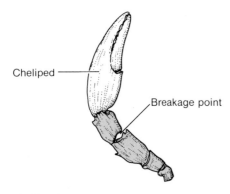

Cheliped

Breakage point

At this point, you may want your students to do the Laboratory Investigation at the end of this chapter.

At this point, you may want to assign to your students the first of the Extensions and Applications at the end of this chapter.

REPRODUCTION AND GROWTH Crayfishes mate in the spring or early fall. At this time, the male deposits the sperm in small receptacles in the female's body. A few weeks later, the female produces 200 to 300 eggs. Then, the female uses the stored sperm to fertilize the eggs.

After fertilization, the eggs are attached to the swimmerets of the female. The eggs remain there for the five or six weeks of their development, after which they hatch. The hatched, young crayfishes stay attached to the female for several more weeks.

The young crayfishes begin molting while they are still on the swimmerets of the female. They also molt several more times soon after leaving the female. Adult crayfishes usually molt twice a year, in late spring and in summer.

Molting occurs in several stages. First, the epidermis digests the inner surface of the old exoskeleton, leaving a little space between the skeleton and the body. The epidermis also removes inorganic salts, such as calcium carbonate, from the exoskeleton. At the same time, the new exoskeleton is beginning to form. The old exoskeleton cracks open, and the crayfish backs out of it. The body of the crayfish then swells to its new size by absorbing water. Finally the epidermis adds salts to the newly forming exoskeleton, hardening it. Before the new exoskeleton hardens, however, the crayfish is defenseless, and it has to hide from its predators.

In addition to molting, crayfishes can replace appendages that are lost during fighting or during escape from a predator. The appendage breaks off at a certain breakage point, and a special membrane tightens to prevent blood loss. When the animal molts, a new appendage begins to grow. This process of replacing lost parts is called *regeneration*.

Other Crustaceans

Other familiar crustaceans are crabs, shrimps, lobsters, and barnacles. Compared to crayfishes and lobsters, crabs have a small abdomen that turns up on the underside of the thorax. Crabs are also different in that their cephalothorax is as wide as, or sometimes wider than, it is long. These features give crabs their characteristic shape.

Most crabs walk sideways. The five legs on one side of the body pull the crab, while the five legs on the other side push. Although some crabs move slowly, others, like the ghost crab, can move up to 30 meters in one minute. Some crabs have flattened legs that they use as paddles to propel themselves while swimming. In addition to these adaptations, some crabs can change color to match their environments and to

Figure 28-6 The blue crab (*left*) shows the familiar shape and structures of all crabs. The snapping shrimp (*center*) has the flattened body and large swimmerets common to all shrimp. Barnacles (*right*) are unlike other crustaceans in that they cement themselves to solid, underwater objects.

hide from predators. Hormones in the stalk of the eye regulate this color change.

Shrimps are crustaceans that have flattened bodies and large feathery swimmerets for swimming. Found in both salt and fresh water, most shrimps either are bottom dwellers or live in holes in rocks and coral.

Barnacles are classified as crustaceans, despite their attachment to one place for all of their adult lives. The free-swimming, shrimplike larvae of barnacles cement themselves not only to ships, rocks, or wooden pilings, but also to other organisms, such as fishes and whales. Barnacles are found only in salt water.

When feeding, barnacles extend feathery appendages out of the hard plates that cover their entire bodies. As water flows over these appendages, they filter out food.

SECTION REVIEW   Answers on page T–76.

1. How do crayfishes differ from lobsters?
2. What are the divisions of a crayfish's body called?
3. What are maxillipeds? Chelipeds?
4. What is the function of the green glands in the crayfish?
5. How do crabs differ from crayfishes?

Sidelight

For centuries, sailors had to scrape barnacles off the bottoms of boats. Today, special machines produce ultrasonic vibrations that keep these crustaceans from attaching themselves to the bottoms of sea-going vessels.

At this point, you may want to assign to your students the second of the Extensions and Applications at the end of this chapter.

Myriapods

To distinguish between the two kinds of myriapods, you might find it helpful to construct a chart comparing and contrasting the structures of centipedes and millipedes.

The name myriapod means many legs and is a common name for a group of several classes of many-legged arthropods. Two of these classes are *Chilopoda*, which contains the centipedes and *Diplopoda*, or the millipedes. The animals in both of these classes live on land, typically beneath stones and in the soil. Their long, segmented bodies are made up of a head and thorax with many pairs of legs. On the head are two simple eyes, which have only one lens each. The head also contains two antennae and mandibles. To carry the gases of respiration directly to and from the body cells, the myriapods have **tracheae** (TRĀ-kē-ē; singular: trachea), or air tubes.

Highlight

Myriapods are arthropods with many jointed legs. The two classes of myriapods are the centipedes and the millipedes.

Figure 28-7 Centipedes do not have 100 legs as their name implies. They have two legs on each body segment.

Figure 28-8 Millipedes have four legs on each body segment.

Centipedes

Centipedes live in moist places, usually under logs and stones. Although most species are harmless to people, some can inflict painful bites. Some tropical centipedes, which may grow to a length of 30 centimeters, feed on small *vertebrates*. Vertebrates are animals with backbones. While some centipedes lay eggs, others produce live young. In both cases, the young centipedes resemble the adults.

The name centipede means 100 legs. Contrary to what its name says, the centipede does not have 100 legs. The common house centipede, for example, has only 30 legs. A centipede has a pair of appendages for each segment of its body, except for the segment following the head and the last two segments. The heads of all types of centipedes contain a pair of antennae, a pair of mandibles, one or two pairs of maxillae, and simple eyes. The segment after the head contains appendages that are poison claws used to capture and kill prey.

Within the body of the centipede is a straight tube that makes up the digestive system. Salivary glands empty into this tube at the anterior end. Like most arthropods, centipedes have two pairs of **Malpighian** (mal-PIG-ē-'n) **tubules.** Malpighian tubules are tiny tubes that remove wastes from the body cavity. The centipede's elongated heart has a pair of arteries that extend to each segment.

Millipedes

Although the word "millipede" means one thousand legs, millipedes do not have that many legs. Actually, they have between one hundred and four hundred legs. The head of the millipede contains a pair of simple eyes, a pair of antennae, mandibles, and maxillae.

Millipedes have two pairs of appendages on every segment, whereas centipedes have only one pair on each. Compared to centipedes, millipedes are less active, they move more slowly, and their bodies are more cylindrical. Like centipedes, millipedes prefer dark moist places. When disturbed, they roll up into balls. Some orders of millipedes have "stink glands" that spray an unpleasant smelling fluid to repel predators.

Sidelight

Although modern millipedes are fairly small in size, extinct species grew as long as 2 meters.

SECTION REVIEW Answers on page T–77.

1. What is the meaning of myriapod?
2. What are the functions of the tracheae and of the Malpighian tubules in myriapods?

Observing a Crustacean

Purpose Crustaceans make up one class of the invertebrate phylum called *Arthropoda*. The animals in this phylum are characterized by the presence of jointed legs, segmented bodies, and chitinous exoskeletons. The purpose of this investigation is to identify the structures and observe some characteristics of a crustacean.

Materials *(per group)* ● *Daphnia* culture
● *Chlorella* culture ● Hand lens ● Microscope
● 3 glass slides ● 3 cover slips ● Drinking straw
● Scissors   1 or 2 ice cubes ● 100-mL beaker
● Tripod ● Bunsen burner ● Wire gauze
● Forceps ● Petroleum jelly ● 2 medicine droppers ● Flat toothpick ● Safety goggles

Procedure   Part A 1. Examine the *Daphnia* culture with a hand lens.   **2.** Cut off the tip of the drinking straw about 1 mm from the end. Use this 1-mm ring as a chamber for examining *Daphnia*.   **3.** With the flat toothpick, apply some petroleum jelly along one rim to the outside surface of the ring, to seal it and to attach it to the slide.   **4.** Place the ring, jelly side down, on the slide.   **5.** Add a drop of *Daphnia* culture to the chamber.   **6.** Place a cover slip over the chamber and

locate a *Daphnia* under low power.   **7.** Identify the *Daphnia* structures shown in Figure 2.   **Part B 1.** Have one member of the group keep track of exactly 60 seconds. Have another member count the number of heartbeats of *Daphnia* per minute. Record this number.   **2.** To determine the effects of a change in temperature on the heartbeat of *Daphnia,* cool a glass slide by placing it on an ice cube.   **3.** Remove the glass slide and repeat steps 2 to 6 from Part A.   **4.** Count the number of *Daphnia* heartbeats per minute, and record this information.   **5. CAUTION:** *Be very careful when using a heat source. Wear safety goggles.* Set up a hot-water bath, and place a clean slide in the water bath for about 5 minutes.   **6.** With the forceps, carefully remove the slide, and repeat steps 2 to 6 from Part A.   **7.** Count the number of *Daphnia* heartbeats per minute, and record this information.   **Part C 1.** Using the first slide containing *Daphnia,* add a drop from the *Chlorella* culture to the chamber.   **2.** Observe *Daphnia* under low power, and record any changes.

Observations and Conclusions   1. Why is a chamber necessary to hold *Daphnia*?   **2.** How does temperature affect the heartbeat in *Daphnia*?   **3.** Draw a *Daphnia,* and trace the path of *Chlorella* through a *Daphnia's* digestive system.   **4.** Why is *Chlorella* chosen for this purpose?

Figure 1

Figure 2

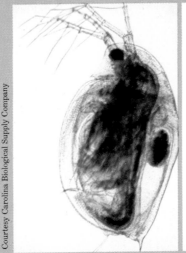

Courtesy Carolina Biological Supply Company

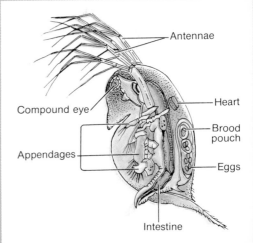

Antennae

Compound eye

Appendages

Heart

Brood pouch

Eggs

Intestine

CHAPTER SUMMARY

Characteristics of Arthropods Arthropods are animals with jointed legs, hard exoskeletons, hemocoels, and muscles arranged in bands. The arthropod phylum includes five main classes. These classes are *Crustacea, Chilopoda, Diplopoda, Insecta,* and *Arachnida.*

Crustaceans Crustaceans are aquatic arthropods with gills. Examples of freshwater crustaceans are the crayfishes. The body of a crayfish is divided into a cephalothorax and an abdomen. The cephalothorax is a combined head and thorax. The part of the exoskeleton that covers and protects the cephalothorax is called the carapace. Each segment of the cephalothorax and abdomen contains a pair of appendages. The most anterior of the appendages in the cephalothorax are the antennules, which are used for equilibrium, touch, and taste. Behind these structures are the antennae, which are also used for touch and taste. Behind the antennae, the mandibles, or true jaws, are used to crush food, with the help of two pairs of maxillae. Maxillipeds are appendages that touch, taste, and hold food while a crayfish chews. Chelipeds are large claws that are used for food-getting and for protection. Located behind the chelipeds are the walking legs.

The abdomen contains swimmerets that aid in swimming. The last abdominal segment contains the uropod, or flipper. In the middle of this structure is the telson, which, along with the uropod, enables crayfishes to move backward quickly.

Unlike annelids, crayfishes and some other crustaceans have open circulatory systems. Blood from the pericardial sinus, or the cavity surrounding the heart, enters a crayfish's heart through ostia, or openings. Blood is then pumped into arteries, and it collects in other sinuses.

Oxygen is obtained from water as it moves over the gills. Green glands at the base of the antennae remove excess water and wastes.

The brain of a crayfish has a pair of ganglia, located in the head region. A central nerve cord runs from the brain to each body segment. Antennae, statocysts, and compound eyes are used for touch, taste, sight, and balance.

The crayfishes have separate sexes. Sperm from the male is stored in the female until the eggs are released. The female then carries the eggs until they hatch and young crayfishes for a little while after they hatch. Like most arthropods, crayfishes molt, or shed their exoskeleton.

Lobsters are crustaceans that are very similar to crayfishes, except that lobsters live in salt water and are larger. Other crustaceans, such as crabs, have flatter bodies, and they can move both by swimming and by walking. Examples of still other crustaceans are shrimps and barnacles.

Myriapods Two classes of arthropods, *Chilopoda* and *Diplopoda,* contain the centipedes and millipedes, respectively. Jointly, the organisms in these two classes are commonly called myriapods. The centipedes have one pair of appendages per segment, while the millipedes have two pairs.

The myriapods use tracheae, or air tubes, to carry oxygen and carbon dioxide to and from the body. Like most arthropods, these invertebrates contain Malpighian tubules to remove waste from the body cavity.

CHAPTER VOCABULARY

abdomen	exoskeleton	ostium
antenna	green gland	statocyst
antennule	hemocoel	swimmeret
carapace	Malpighian tubule	telson
cephalothorax	mandible	trachea
cheliped	maxilla	uropod
chitin	maxilliped	walking leg
compound eye	molting	

REVIEW of FACTS and CONCEPTS   Answers on page T–77.

On a separate sheet of paper, answer each of the following as completely as possible.

1. Name five main classes of arthropods.
2. Why do arthropods undergo molting?
3. What are isopods, copepods, and ostracods?
4. List the outer body parts of the crayfish. Briefly state the function of each part.
5. How is the crayfish equipped for movement?
6. Compare the circulatory system of the crayfish with that of the annelids.
7. Briefly describe the nervous system of the crayfish. Include an explanation of the function of the statocysts.
8. Describe the molting process in the crayfish.
9. List some differences between annelids and crustaceans.
10. Briefly summarize the characteristics of four other crustaceans.
11. How do centipedes differ from millipedes?
12. How do millipedes protect themselves from predators?
13. Distinguish between the following pairs of terms: antennae and antennules; mandible and maxilla; and gill chamber and gill bailer.

EXTENSIONS and APPLICATIONS   For additional information, see page T–77.

1. Obtain a fiddler crab from a pet store. Place the crab in the middle of a shoe box that contains a layer of sand 5 cm deep, as well as some small and medium-sized stones. Where does the crab go? Why is this reaction of value to the crab?

   Next, place the crab in a small aquarium filled with water to a depth of 10 cm. Gently touch the feelers of the crab with a pencil. Use a net to remove the crab from the water. Compare the behavior of the crab in water with its behavior on land. Make an oral presentation to your class.

2. Visit the library to find out what krill are. What part do these animals play in ocean food chains? Submit a written report to your teacher, or make an oral presentation to the class.
3. Prepare a presentation to the class illustrating the different subclasses and orders of crustaceans. Assemble your information in the form of a chart. For each order, include a photograph or a drawing of a typical crustacean. Also, briefly summarize the characteristics of each order next to its illustration.

SUGGESTED READINGS

Cloudly-Thompson, J. L., *Spiders, Scorpions, Centipedes, and Mites.* New York: Pergamon Press.
   The characteristics of these arthropods are discussed. Many illustrations are also included.
Huxley, T. H., *The Crayfish.* Cambridge, Mass.: MIT Press.
   This book, which serves as an introduction to zoology, examines a crayfish, a crustacean. The author presents this information clearly and concisely.
Taylor, H., *The Lobster: Its Life Cycle.* New York: Sterling Publishing.
   The development of the American lobster is discussed in this book. Many illustrations are included.

29 Arachnids and Insects

A wasp, which is an insect, approaches its prey, a tarantula, which is an arachnid.

For teaching aids for this chapter, including a chapter overview and teaching strategies, see pages T–78 to T–79. The page number next to each chapter objective refers to the text page where the information needed to fulfill the objective begins.

Like all arthropods, animals that belong to the classes *Arachnida* and *Insecta* have an exoskeleton and jointed legs. These animals are found in many environments. Although most arachnids are terrestrial, one species lives in the water. Species of insects are found in tropical jungles and polar regions.

Although the animals in the two classes are often confused, arachnids are not the same as insects. Arachnids have four pairs of legs and no antennae. The bodies of arachnids are divided into only two regions. Spiders, scorpions, ticks, and mites, for example, are all arachnids. Insects have three pairs of legs and one pair of antennae. Their bodies are divided into three regions. Some examples of insects are grasshoppers, butterflies, beetles, ants, and bees.

Arachnids

All arachnids have certain common features, such as their four pairs of legs and the two regions of their bodies. One of these regions, called the *cephalothorax*, is composed of the head and thorax. The second region is called the *abdomen*.

In addition to the legs, two other pairs of appendages are attached to the cephalothorax of the arachnid. The first appendages are two clawlike fangs, which are called **chelicerae** (kə-LIS-ə-rē; singular: chelicera), with a poison gland at the base of each. The poison from this gland travels through the fangs and can paralyze the arachnid's prey. The other appendages, the **pedipalps** (PED-i-palpz), are used for chewing, but they also have sensory functions. Unlike the crustaceans and myriapods, arachnids do not have antennae or mandibles.

Most arachnids live on land. The majority of arachnids actually help people by destroying many insect pests. The bites of a few, such as that of the poisonous black widow spider, are harmful to people.

Spiders

All spiders share several features. For example, spiders have open circulatory systems and hearts with *ostia*, or openings. Wastes are removed from spiders by *Malpighian tubules* located on the posterior end of the abdomen. Glands on

Highlight

Arachnids are arthropods with two body sections, four pairs of jointed legs, and no antennae.

At this point, you may want to refer to Chapter 28 to review the general characteristics of all arthropods.

Figure 29-1 Spiders exhibit all of the characteristics of arthropods and a few unique to spiders, such as silk glands and spinnerets for making webs.

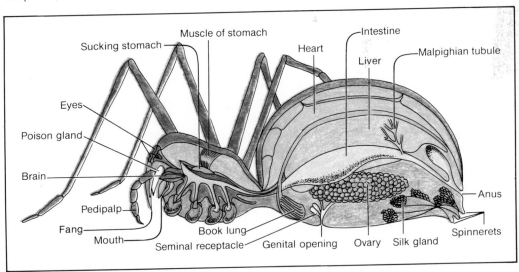

Figure 29-2 While under water, the diving spider breathes air it has stored in bubbles. The diving spider collects the bubbles from the surface of the water.

Figure 29-3 The fishing spider (*top*) and the trapdoor spider (*bottom*) do not spin webs to catch prey. These spiders hunt their prey.

the first and third pairs of walking legs also remove wastes from spiders.

Mature male spiders can usually be distinguished from female spiders by the male's smaller size. In some species, however, the sizes of both sexes are the same. In such cases, the sexes can be identified by comparing the pedipalps, which are more slender in female spiders.

In the mature male spider, sperm are produced in the gonads and are transferred to small sacs in the pedipalps. During mating, the male places the sperm in the *seminal receptacle* of the female. The sperm then fertilize the eggs of the female as the eggs pass through the female genital opening. The eggs are usually laid in a silken cocoon or in a nest.

Sometimes before mating, the male spider performs various types of courtship behavior, such as waving his appendages. After mating, the male quickly moves away from the female to avoid being eaten, because the females of many species use male spiders as food.

Some spiders are specially adapted to their environments. For example, the environment of the diving spider is the bottom of a pond. This spider forms air bubbles at the surface of the water, brings the bubbles down to the bottom of the pond, and stores them in a sac. The diving spider then breathes air from these bubbles. When the air bubbles are used up, the spider returns to the surface for more.

A familiar adaptation of most spiders is their ability to spin webs to trap their prey. The spinning organs of spiders are two or three pairs of **spinnerets**. Spinnerets are finger-like appendages found on the abdomen. These structures contain hundreds of microscopic tubes, through which fluid silk flows. Made in the *silk glands*, the fluid silk passes through the tubes to the outside and then hardens into silk thread. In addition to spinning webs, spiders use these threads to line their nests, to form cocoons, and, in some cases, to move from place to place. Some young spiders, for example, are blown from one place to another when the wind catches the threads to which they are clinging.

Not all spiders spin webs. The hunting spider and the fishing spider, for example, chase and catch their prey. Trapdoor spiders dig burrows that are covered by a camouflaged trapdoor. Holding the door slightly open, the spider watches for prey. When prey comes within reach, the spider snatches it and drags it into the burrow.

Spiders may have one of two types of systems for respiration. One system uses specially adapted structures, called **book lungs**. A book lung is made of leaflike plates that contain blood vessels. As air enters the body of the spider through slits in the abdomen and circulates between these plates, an exchange of gases occurs. Some spiders have another type of system that contains *tracheae,* or air tubes. The exchange of gases takes place in the tracheae. These tubes are connected to the outside of the spider's body through small openings in the abdomen, called **spiracles** (SPĪ-rə-k'lz).

Other Arachnids

The class *Arachnida* includes many other animals besides spiders. One familiar arachnid, the daddy-longlegs, lives in moist forests and in caves. Unlike spiders, it eats plants, as well as other animals.

SCORPIONS   The scorpion, another type of arachnid, is found mainly in tropical and subtropical areas. In the United States, it lives in the Southwest and along the Gulf of Mexico. Like spiders, scorpions live solitary lives, except during mating. They are most active at night. During the day, either they burrow into the ground, or they hide under wood or stones.

Scorpions capture and hold their prey with their pedipalps, which have teeth. They then stab the prey with their stingers, located at the tip of the abdomen. These stingers inject a poison that paralyzes the prey and that can kill small insects. Of the more than forty species of scorpions found in the United States, only two are considered to be harmful to people.

Highlight

In addition to spiders, arachnids include scorpions, mites, and ticks.

At this point, you may want to assign to your students the third of the Extensions and Applications at the end of this chapter.

Figure 29-4   Scorpions (*left*) and ticks (*right*) are examples of animals that belong to the class *Arachnida.*

TICKS AND MITES Ticks and mites, which are usually 1 millimeter or less in length, are found almost everywhere. They live in fresh and salt water, on the ground, and on plants. Many species of these arachnids are parasites. Some ticks and mites transmit disease from plant to plant, and they can also damage fruit.

SECTION REVIEW Answers on page T–78.

1. List the characteristics of arachnids.
2. What are chelicerae? Pedipalps?
3. What are spiracles?
4. Name three types of spiders.
5. Name two types of arachnids other than spiders.

Insect Anatomy

Insects have lived on the earth for almost 300 million years. They have not only adapted to every possible land habitat, but they are also found in freshwater and marine habitats. Scientists have identified more than 900,000 species belonging to the arthropod class *Insecta*. One reason for the successful survival of these animals is their ability to fly. By flying, they can escape predators and move to areas with more favorable living conditions.

Because flying is an important characteristic of insects, they are classified into orders according to the types of wings they have. Some of the orders include *Orthoptera*, which means straight wing, and *Isoptera*, or equal wings. *Hemiptera* stands for half wings, and *Hymenoptera* means membranous wings. Insects with two wings are in the order *Diptera*, and those with wings of uniform texture are included in the order *Homoptera*.

Insects differ from other arthropods in that they have only three pairs of jointed legs and three distinct body regions. The *head* region, unlike that of crustaceans, has one pair of antennae, in addition to the eyes and mouthparts. The middle region, or *thorax*, usually bears two pairs of wings and the typical three pairs of legs. The third region, the *abdomen*, has no more than 11 segments and no appendages.

Insects breathe through tracheae. They have an open circulatory system with no veins or capillaries and a reduced coelom. An insect may be male or female, but never both.

Like all arthropods, insects have a chitinous exoskeleton that protects against water loss. Although the exoskeleton forms a tough covering, it is flexible and light. Flexible

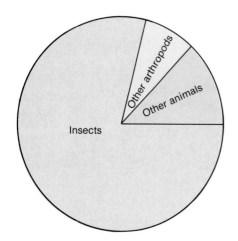

Figure 29-5 The more than 900,000 species of insects make up almost 80% of all animal species.

Highlight

Insects are arthropods with three body sections, three pairs of jointed legs, one pair of antennae, and usually one or two pairs of wings.

At this point, you may want to assign to your students the second of the Extensions and Applications at the end of this chapter.

463

hinge joints connect the plates of the exoskeleton to one another. Muscles between these plates enable the insect to move with precision.

The exoskeletons of many insects have another interesting feature. The color enables insects to blend in with their environment. This characteristic, called *camouflage*, helps insects to hide from their enemies.

The eating habits of insects depend on their mouthparts, which are used either for biting or for sucking. Biting mouthparts, such as those of grasshoppers, are adapted for grasping and crushing food. A sucking mouthpart is shaped like a tube that can pierce the tissues of plants and animals. The mosquito is an insect that has a sucking mouthpart. Butterflies and moths have a sucking tube for drawing nectar from flowers. The tube is usually coiled up when not in use.

Some insects are harmful. Not only can they transmit disease to people and to animals, but they can also damage or destroy crops. On the other hand, some insects are helpful. They pollinate fruit trees and other plants, destroy insect pests, and are food for animals.

Grasshoppers

Grasshoppers are found throughout the world and are relatively large in size. They belong to the order *Orthoptera*. The structure of grasshoppers is similar to that of insects in general.

Grasshoppers are plant-eaters. They live in open grasslands and in areas with leafy vegetation. In the western United States, the early settlers of the great plains often had to fight off large swarms of grasshoppers, called *locusts*. Locusts usually migrate from dry areas where food is scarce. They have been known to destroy all plant life for hundreds of square kilometers.

EXTERNAL FEATURES   The fairly large body of grasshoppers, like that of all arthropods, is covered with a chitinous exoskeleton. Also like other arthropods, grasshoppers have muscles attached to the inside of their exoskeletons. These very strong muscles, which are similar in structure to human muscles, allow grasshoppers to chew, to hop, and to fly.

The body of a grasshopper has three regions. They are the head, the thorax, and the abdomen. The first region, the head, contains one pair of antennae, the eyes, and the mouthparts.

The second region, the thorax, is further divided into three parts. The first part, the **prothorax**, is joined to the head, and it contains the first pair of legs. The next part,

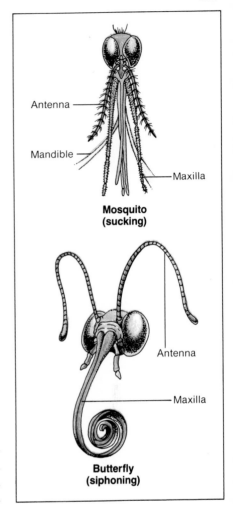

Antenna

Mandible

Maxilla

Mosquito (sucking)

Antenna

Maxilla

Butterfly (siphoning)

Figure 29-6   The structure of an insect's mouthparts determines how it takes in food.

Highlight

Grasshoppers belong to the order of insects that has straight wings.

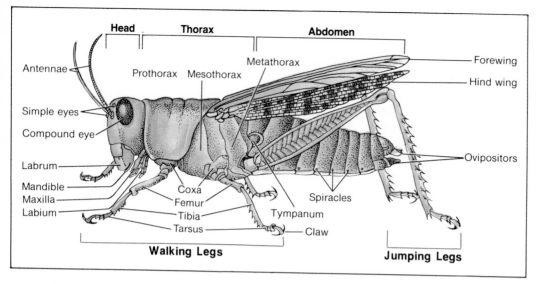

Figure 29-7   External Structure of a Grasshopper

called the **mesothorax,** contains the second pair of legs and the *forewings,* or the first pair of wings. The last part, the **metathorax,** contains the third pair of legs and the *hind wings,* or the second pair of wings. The third body region is the abdomen, which is modified for egg laying.

The legs of the grasshopper have different uses. The first and second pairs of legs are used for walking. The legs of the third pair are large and muscular, enabling grasshoppers to jump away from enemies, to launch themselves into flight, and to leap from place to place for food. On each leg, a *coxa* connects the top section of the leg, called the *femur,* to the grasshopper's body. A slender, spiny *tibia* connects the femur to the bottom part of the leg. This part is called the *tarsus.* Using the pads and claws on the tarsus, grasshoppers cling to and climb on plants.

The two sets of wings differ in several ways. The forewings on the mesothorax are narrow, colored, and slightly stiff. They protect the hind wings, which are made of broad membranes with many veins. Because the patterns of these veins vary from one species to another, they are used as one method of classification. When not in use, the wings fold up like a fan against a grasshopper's body. The hind wings lie beneath the forewings.

RESPIRATORY SYSTEM   The lower sides of the abdomen contain *spiracles* that connect to the respiratory system. Air enters these spiracles and moves into the tracheae. Fine branches of the tracheae, called *tracheoles,* then carry oxygen to and remove carbon dioxide from the cells.

Unlike some insects, the grasshopper has thin-walled air sacs in its abdomen. When the abdomen contracts and the wings beat, they cause these air sacs to pump air into and out of the tracheae. As air is drawn in, the first four pairs of spiracles are open, and the other six are closed. As air is pumped out, the first four pairs are closed, and the other six are open.

DIGESTIVE SYSTEM The mouthparts of the grasshopper are adapted for chewing on plants. Beneath the **labrum,** or upper lip, are two sets of jaws. The first set of jaws, or *mandibles,* are used for cutting, tearing, and crushing food. Posterior to the mandibles is another set of jaws, called *maxillae,* that hold and cut food. Directly behind the maxillae is the **labium,** or lower lip.

From the mouth of the grasshopper, food travels into a narrow tube, called the *esophagus.* The esophagus leads into a large, thin-walled structure called the **crop.** The crop is a storage area for the food. While it is stored in the crop, the food is moistened by secretions from small, branched **salivary glands.** The salivary glands are located below the crop. The moistened food then passes easily through the digestive system. At the end of the crop is the **gizzard.** The gizzard is thick and muscular and contains toothlike structures for grinding and straining food.

The food then travels into the *midgut,* or stomach. Within the midgut, finger-shaped glands, called **gastric caeca** (SĒ-kə), secrete enzymes that digest the food. The digested food is then absorbed into the bloodstream through the walls of the midgut. Undigested food moves into the *hindgut,* which contains the intestines and the *rectum.*

Highlight

During digestion, food passes from the grasshopper's mouth through the esophagus into the crop. The food then passes into the gizzard and midgut.

Figure 29-8 Internal Organs of a Grasshopper

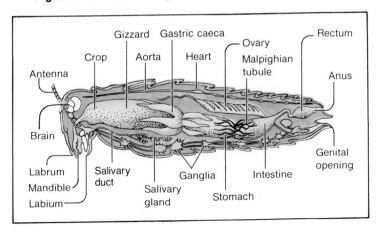

EXCRETORY SYSTEM The main organs of excretion in grasshoppers are the Malpighian tubules. These organs are found where the midgut meets the hindgut. Through the Malpighian tubules, wastes are removed from the blood and pass into the hindgut. These wastes then pass out of the body, along with the undigested wastes, through the anus.

CIRCULATORY SYSTEM Like all arthropods, grasshoppers have an open circulatory system. The tubelike heart is located on the dorsal side and toward the posterior end of the body. It is connected to a large artery, called the **aorta**, and leads to the head of the grasshopper. The colorless blood enters the heart through the ostia, and is then pumped forward through the aorta. Near the head, the blood empties into the body cavity. As the blood flows freely through the body cavity, it comes into contact with all the cells in the body of the grasshopper.

NERVOUS SYSTEM The nervous system of the grasshopper includes a brain, or paired ganglia, and a ventral nerve cord. The nerve cord forms a chain of ganglia that reach all parts of the body.

The head of the grasshopper contains both *simple* and *compound eyes*. The three simple eyes, each of which has only a single lens, can detect light and darkness. On the sides of the head are two compound eyes, which function somewhat like those of the crayfish. Within the compound eyes are many six-sided lenses. Because each lens in a compound eye sees a different portion of an object, the image becomes a blurred mosaic. The compound eye is especially well adapted for detecting movement.

In addition to simple and compound eyes, the grasshopper has another sensory organ called the **tympanum.** Located on the abdomen, the tympanum is a membrane that vibrates when sound waves strike it. These vibrations stimulate nerves. In this way, the grasshopper can hear sounds through the tympanum.

REPRODUCTIVE SYSTEM The sexes of the grasshopper occur separately. In the male, the *testes* produce sperm. In the female, the *ovaries* produce the eggs. During mating, the male deposits sperm in the seminal receptacle of the female, where they are stored until the eggs are ready to be fertilized.

In the female, the abdomen ends in a pair of pointed structures, called the **ovipositors** (ō-vi-PAHZ-i-tərz). In the fall of each year, the female uses the ovipositors to dig a hole

Highlight

The grasshopper is able to hear sounds through a membrane called the tympanum.

and then to deposit the fertilized eggs in the hole. The eggs hatch in the following spring.

Other Insects

At this point, you may want to assign to your students the first of the Extensions and Applications at the end of this chapter.

Grasshoppers have features that are common to many insects. Other insects, however, have certain special characteristics and adaptations. For example, the members of the order *Hemiptera*, such as the water bug and the southern green plant bug, are the only true bugs. They have mouthparts that are specially modified for piercing plant tissues and for sucking the juices. Bees and wasps belong to the order *Hymenoptera*, and have ovipositors that are modified into stingers. Some members of the order *Diptera*, such as houseflies, have legs with special pads that allow them to walk on walls and ceilings. The variations in other kinds of insects involve reproduction. For example, aphids, members of the order *Homoptera*, lay eggs that develop without fertilization. This type of egg development is called **parthenogenesis** (par-then-ō-JEN-ə-sis).

Figure 29-9 In incomplete metamorphosis, the insect progresses from an egg to a nymph to an adult.

SECTION REVIEW   Answers on page T–78.

1. Name the three regions in the body of the grasshopper.
2. What are the divisions of the thorax called?
3. What is the tympanum?
4. What is the function of the ovipositors in the female grasshopper?
5. Define parthenogenesis.

Insect Development

As most insects develop, they go through a series of changes in appearance, which is called *metamorphosis*. Insects undergo one of two types of metamorphosis.

Such insects as grasshoppers, termites, chinch bugs, and dragonflies go through **incomplete metamorphosis.** Incomplete metamorphosis occurs in three stages. The insect begins as an *egg* and then hatches and develops into a *nymph,* or immature insect. Although the nymph resembles the full-grown insect and has compound eyes, it lacks wings. As the nymph grows in size, it molts until it reaches the last stage, the *adult.*

In most other insects, such as moths, flies, butterflies, and beetles, **complete metamorphosis** occurs. During complete metamorphosis, the insect undergoes four stages of

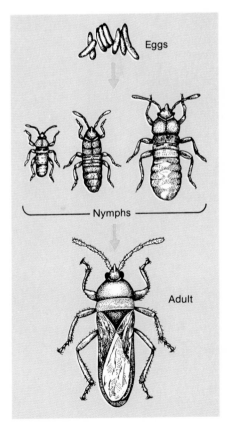

Eggs

Nymphs

Adult

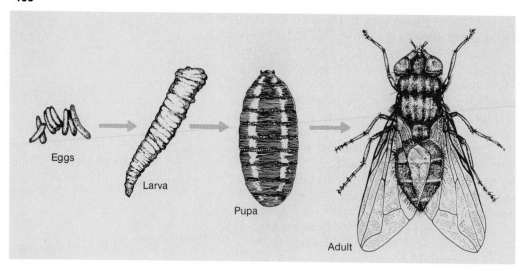

Figure 29-10 In complete metamorphosis, the insect progresses from an egg to a larva to a pupa to an adult.

Highlight

Most insects pass through a series of physical changes as they develop from an egg into an adult. These changes are called metamorphosis.

Sidelight

Recently, larvae of the gypsy moth destroyed more than 40,000 square kilometers of forest land in the northeastern United States.

development. The stages are the *egg*, the *larva*, the *pupa*, and the *adult*. The egg hatches into a segmented, wormlike larva. The larval stage form has a number of names. The larval forms of moths and butterflies, for instance, are called *caterpillars*. *Maggots* are the larvae of flies, and *grubs* are the second stage of some beetles. During the larval stage, the insect eats a great deal and increases in size. As the larva grows, it molts, or sheds its exoskeleton. Then, after the last molt, the insect stops eating and rests. During this resting period, the insect is called a pupa (plural: pupae). Pupae are sometimes covered by a case, called a *cocoon* or *chrysalis*. Within the cocoon, the pupa changes into an adult. The adult insect emerges from the cocoon fully grown and undergoes no further molting.

Metamorphosis is controlled and regulated by *hormones*. Hormones are chemicals secreted into the blood by a gland or an organ. During metamorphosis, a hormone from the brain of the insect causes a gland in the prothorax to release other hormones that control molting. At the same time, another gland produces what is called **juvenile hormone.** Juvenile hormone stimulates larval development and inhibits the development of the adult. As long as juvenile hormone is secreted, the molting hormone causes the larva to continue molting and growing. When juvenile hormone stops being secreted and only the molting hormone is present in the blood, the adult emerges.

Entomologists (en-tə-MAHL-ə-jists), or biologists who study insects, discovered how these hormones work through experiments. If the gland that produces the juvenile hormone is removed experimentally, the insect changes into an adult following the molt. If this same gland is transplanted from a young larva into an old larva, the old larva becomes a larger larva.

SECTION REVIEW Answers on page T–78.

1. Define metamorphosis.
2. Name the stages of incomplete and complete metamorphosis.
3. What is the function of juvenile hormone?

Insect Behavior

Insects spend most of their lives eating food and laying large numbers of eggs. These two activities have made insects very successful as a class of organisms. Their success is also due to their social instincts, their defense mechanisms, and their courtship behavior.

Social Instincts

At this point, you may want your students to do the Laboratory Investigation at the end of this chapter.

Some insects, such as ants, bees, termites, and wasps, live in highly organized societies. Each member of the society has a special job that is necessary for the survival of the colony. Such an arrangement is called **division of labor**.

ANTS An ant colony is started when a male and female ant fly away from an established colony and mate. After mating, the male ant dies, and the female, or *queen*, begins a colony. Usually, the female digs tunnels into the earth and begins laying eggs, which is her only function. The first eggs to hatch are wingless females, called *workers*. These worker ants are sterile, which means that they do not produce eggs. Instead, they care for the other immature ants, gather food, and build or repair the nest. In some ant societies, wingless female *soldier ants* protect the colony.

HONEYBEES The honeybee is one type of bee that shows a high level of social organization. In a honeybee colony, the queen bee lays eggs, while several thousand sterile female worker bees gather food and care for young bees. Whether a female larva develops into a worker or a queen depends on the kind of food that other workers feed it. If it is fed royal jelly, which is a high-protein substance secreted by the workers, the female larva becomes a queen rather

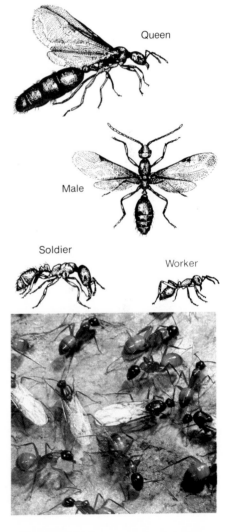

Figure 29-11 A colony of ants consists of four different kinds of ants, as shown in the drawing. The photograph shows winged male ants and wingless female soldier ants.

Queen

Male

Soldier

Worker

Sidelight

Bees make honey from the nectar they collect from flowers. The taste and color of the honey depends on the kind of flowers from which the nectar comes.

than a worker. Male bees, or *drones*, develop from unfertilized eggs, and they die after mating with the queen.

Wild honeybees usually build their hives in hollow trees or under the roofs of buildings. Each hive contains a wax *comb* with a layer of six-sided cells or chambers. Two or three combs may be built one on top of another. In the center of the comb are the cells for rearing the larvae. Near the top of the comb are the cells for storing the pollen and honey.

Bees communicate with one another by means of food-sharing and certain other behaviors. When worker bees return from gathering nectar, other workers meet them in the nest. If the food supply is small in the comb, the workers in the nest look for nectar stored in the returning bees' crops.

The most complicated form of communication takes place among food-searching bees. Whenever a honeybee dis-

CAREER: Beekeeper

Honeybees make honey from nectar that they gather from flowers. Beekeepers raise honeybees so that the honey the bees produce can be gathered and sold. In the process of gathering nectar, bees also pollinate flowers. Sometimes, therefore, beekeepers rent their bees to people who raise fruit trees, berries, and other plants that are pollinated by bees.

The bees are raised in hives. Beekeepers must regularly clean and inspect the hives to make sure the bees are not overcrowded or diseased. To ensure that the bees produce a great deal of honey, the beekeepers place the hives near plants that produce a great deal of nectar. In fact, many beekeepers move their hives to different orchards or fields during the growing season. In this way, beekeepers take advantage of the different blooming periods of flowers.

To harvest the honey, beekeepers remove the honeycombs from the hive. They take the honey out of the honeycombs with a special instrument called an extractor. Once impurities are removed from the honey, it is packaged and sold. New, empty honeycombs are put into the hive to replace those that were removed.

To prevent being stung by the bees while working around a hive, beekeepers usually wear

protective clothing. They also learn how to work on the hive without exciting the bees.

No special education is needed to become a beekeeper. Courses in beekeeping, agriculture, and business, however, can be very useful.

Most keepers work by themselves or with a few assistants. The assistants help with cleaning the hives, as well as with repairing or replacing damaged parts of the hive. They may also help with harvesting and processing the honey.

For further career information, write to American Beekeeping Federation, 13637 N.W. 39th Avenue, Gainesville, FL 32601.

covers a food source, it flies back to the hive. If the new source of food is within 100 meters of the hive, the bee does a sort of dance, turning in little circles. This dance causes other bees to search for food near the hive. To announce a food supply that is more than 100 meters away, the bee does a different dance, called a *waggle dance*. Other bees locate the food by the speed and direction of the dance, as well as by the number of times the bee waggles.

Bees also communicate information about the queen. The workers who care for the queen lick her with their tongues, taking in a liquid called queen substance. This substance inhibits the development of the ovaries in the workers and prevents them from becoming queens. Queen substance is transferred to other workers through close contact. When a hive gets too crowded, the queen substance does not reach all the bees, and, as a result, some workers become fertile. Part of the hive then swarms to another place and begins a new colony with another queen.

TERMITES In the United States, there are two main types of termites. Subterranean termites nest in moist ground, and they tunnel into houses, where they destroy the structural wood. The second type of termite, the dry wood termite, lives in wood above ground.

In the case of either kind of termite, a king and a queen start a new colony. Both the king, or the fertile male, and the queen shed their wings after mating. The eggs laid by the queen hatch into two types of nymphs. One kind develops into wingless workers, which build and repair the colony. The other nymphs become soldiers and defend the nest. Usually, if the original royal pair dies, a substitute pair becomes fertile.

Defense Mechanisms

Insects defend themselves in many ways. For example, the lacewing, a small pale-green insect, protects itself by releasing a foul-smelling liquid. Other insects, such as the blister beetle, bombardier beetle, and lady bug, give off a chemical substance that produces a burning sensation. Bees and wasps protect themselves by stinging, and ants use their powerful jaws for defense.

Some insects are protected from predators by **mimicry** (MIM-ik-rē), the imitation of other insects. For example, birds avoid eating the monarch butterfly due to its bad taste. Birds also avoid eating the viceroy butterfly, even though it does not taste bad, because it has the same orange coloration as the monarch.

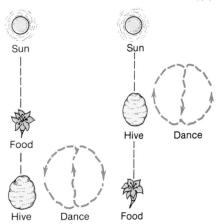

Figure 29-12 The various motions of a bee's dance indicate where a source of food is located. Bees use the sun as a reference point.

Figure 29-13 The viceroy butterfly (*above*) tends to escape bird predators because it looks like, or mimics, the bad-tasting monarch butterfly (*below*).

Courtship

Some insects go through complicated behavior patterns to attract mates. For example, the male firebrat, an insect similar to the silverfish, wags its head from side to side and touches the female. The male cricket chirps to attract the female. The male firefly responds to the flashing light of the female of its species.

SECTION REVIEW Answers on page T–78.

1. What is division of labor?
2. What is mimicry?

Insect Control

Insects can be very harmful. In addition to transmitting disease, they can destroy crops and forests. Losses due to insects in the United States are estimated at over 3 billion dollars each year. For example, spruce budworms have eaten their way through millions of hectares of forests in Maine and Canada. In one year, gypsy moth larvae ate through 1.4 million hectares of American forests. In Texas, a summer attack on peach trees by grasshoppers destroyed trees and many metric tons of fruit.

Insect control is, therefore, very important. In the past, people had to use mechanical means, such as fly swatters and screens, to fight harmful insects. Today, other methods, such as chemical and biological controls, are proving to be more efficient.

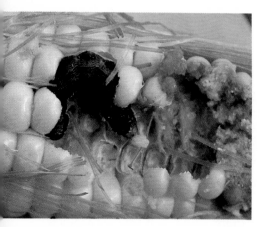

Figure 29-14 Insect larvae can destroy valuable food crops.

Chemical Control

Several types of commercially produced chemical substances are used to kill insects. Chlorinated hydrocarbons, such as *DDT*, *dieldrin*, and *chlordane*, act on the nervous systems of insects. These pesticides quickly kill insects, but they have drawbacks. One drawback is that the pesticides often take a long time to break down into harmless substances. Because these pesticides are fat-soluble, dangerous amounts of them can be stored in the fatty tissues of human beings and animals. Substances such as DDT have been shown to be poisonous to a number of animals, including hawks and other birds. As a result of drawbacks such as these, DDT has been banned in the United States.

Have some students prepare reports on various insecticides and their effects on the environment.

Biological Control

A more natural way of controlling insects is to let their natural enemies attack them. In Florida, for example, citrus growers are introducing a stingless Mexican wasp into orchards. These wasps kill flies that harm the citrus trees. In Michigan, parasitic wasps have also been used to reduce the fly population. These wasps eat their way into fly pupae and lay eggs. When the wasp larvae hatch, they eat the fly pupae. Unfortunately, in the absence of their own predators, some of these imported natural enemies may reproduce rapidly and become pests themselves. Therefore, entomologists must be very careful when choosing certain insects to control other insects.

Another way to control pests biologically is to sterilize the males of the species. In this method, large numbers of insects are grown in the laboratory. The males are sterilized with high-energy radiation. These sterile males are released in the infested area to mate with females. If a sterile male mates with a female, no offspring are produced. A drawback of this method is that, in some species, the sterile male is too weak to compete with normal males. Also, insect sterilization is an expensive process.

Still another type of biological control makes use of chemical attractants produced by the insects themselves. These chemicals, called **pheromones** (FER-ə-mōnz), are given off by insects, such as the gypsy moth. When pheromone from a female insect is placed inside a trap, the males are drawn into the trap, where they die from starvation. Juvenile hormones have also been used against some species of insects. By preventing the larvae from developing into their adult form, these substances cause the insects to die before they can reproduce.

Biological control methods offer several advantages over the use of synthetic chemicals. One advantage is that biological controls act only on the target pest. Also, the pests cannot become resistant, and there are no side effects on animals or on people. Biological control programs, however, are expensive, and they often take years to produce results.

Highlight

Harmful insects can be controlled by chemical and biological methods.

SECTION REVIEW   Answers on page T–78.

1. Give an advantage and a disadvantage of chemical insect control methods.
2. Give an advantage and a disadvantage of biological insect control methods.
3. What is a pheromone?

Observing an Insect Colony

Purpose   The class *Insecta* contains more species than any other class in the animal kingdom. Due to the incredible variety of physical and behavioral adaptations, insects have been successful in inhabiting even the remotest and harshest places on the earth. The purpose of this investigation is to observe the physical and behavioral adaptations of a common insect, the ant.

Materials *(per group)* ● 2-L colorless plastic soft drink bottle ● 207-mL (7-fl oz) soft drink bottle ● Sandy soil ● Tape ● Plastic wrap ● Black construction paper ● 10-cm cotton coil ● Colony of ants ● Hand lens ● Shallow pan or dish ● Pin

Procedure   1. Cut off 10 cm from the top of the 2-L plastic soft drink bottle. Be sure to leave the plastic cup attached to the bottom of the container, as shown in the figure.   **2.** Fill the 207-mL plastic soft drink bottle with water. Place the smaller bottle inside the first bottle.   **3.** Fill the space between the two bottles with moistened sandy soil. The level of the sandy soil should come to within 5 cm of the top of the smaller bottle. The larger bottle serves as an observation chamber.   **4.** Place a 10-cm length of cotton in the mouth of the small bottle to serve as a wick. Half of the length of the wick should hang over the side of the inner bottle just above the soil level. This device provides water for the ants. Be sure to replace water in the inner bottle as it evaporates.
5. Obtain about a dozen ants from your teacher. Place the ants in the observation chamber. At least two groups in the class should have a queen in their colonies.   **6.** To cover the outside of the observation chamber, make a sleeve out of black construction paper. The width of the construction paper should be 10 cm, and the sleeve should encircle the top 5 cm of the large plastic bottle. Use tape to attach the construction paper to the sides of the bottle.   **7.** With the pin, carefully make about 10 small holes in the plastic wrap. Place the plastic wrap over the top of the

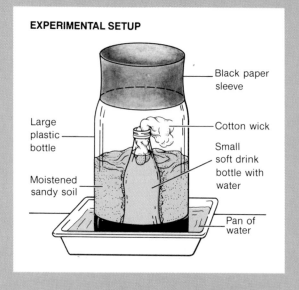

EXPERIMENTAL SETUP

Black paper sleeve

Large plastic bottle

Cotton wick

Small soft drink bottle with water

Moistened sandy soil

Pan of water

black paper sleeve. Use tape to hold the plastic wrap in place.   **8.** Place the observation chamber in a shallow pan of water to prevent the ants from escaping.   **9.** Place food on the surface of the soil three times a week. Small pieces of lettuce, carrots, and hard boiled egg yolks make good food, and so do potatoes with honey, syrup, or peanut butter. Remove any excess food to prevent the growth of mold.
10. Using the hand lens, observe the ants twice a week for one month. Keep a record of your observations.

Observations and Conclusions   1. Which characteristics of ants are common to all insects? Which characteristics set ants apart from other insect families?   **2.** Sketch the tunnels and nests that the ants build. How long did it take them to make these?
3. Describe the activity that goes on in each chamber.
4. Identify the members of the colony.   **5.** From your observations, why are ants called social insects?

CHAPTER SUMMARY

Arachnids   Arachnids are arthropods that have four pairs of legs and no antennae. The bodies of arachnids are divided into the cephalothorax and the abdomen. Attached to the cephalothorax are the chelicerae and the pedipalps. The remaining four pairs of appendages are used for walking.

Spiders spin webs with spinnerets. These structures contain silk glands that produce fluid silk. Outside the body of the spider, the fluid silk hardens into silk thread.

Spiders use book lungs or tracheae for respiration. The tracheae are connected to the outside of the body by means of spiracles. Spiders have open circulatory systems, and their wastes are removed by means of Malpighian tubules.

Insect Anatomy   The insects have three pairs of legs and three distinct body parts. These body parts are the head, the thorax, and the abdomen. The grasshopper is a typical insect. The thorax of the grasshopper is divided into the prothorax, the mesothorax, and the metathorax. In grasshoppers, the spiracles lead into tracheoles. Tracheoles carry oxygen to the cells and remove carbon dioxide from them.

The mouthparts of the grasshopper are adapted for chewing plants. These mouthparts consist of a labrum and a labium. Between these structures are the mandibles and maxillae. From the mouth, food travels to the esophagus and then to the crop. At the end of the crop is the gizzard. The food then travels from the gizzard to the stomach where the gastric caeca secrete enzymes that digest the food. Undigested food moves through the intestine and leaves the body of the grasshopper through the anus. Grasshoppers have an open circulatory system, with blood pumped toward the head through the aorta.

The nervous system of the grasshopper consists of paired ganglia and a ventral nerve cord. A grasshopper's simple eyes detect light and darkness. Its compound eyes detect movement. The tympanum is the grasshopper's hearing organ.

Grasshoppers have separate sexes. The female uses the ovipositors to dig a hole and deposit the fertilized eggs.

Insect Development   As they develop, insects undergo metamorphosis. There are two types of metamorphosis, incomplete and complete. In incomplete metamorphosis, the insect begins as an egg and develops into a nymph. The nymph then develops into an adult. Complete metamorphosis has four stages. These stages are the egg, larva, pupa, and adult. Juvenile hormone controls metamorphosis.

Insect Behavior   Some insects have highly organized societies. Each member has a particular job that is necessary for the survival of the colony. This arrangement of work is called division of labor.

In a bee colony, the queen lays eggs, and the workers care for the eggs. Drones develop from unfertilized eggs. Bees communicate information on the location of new food sources to each other by performing special dances.

Insects defend themselves by biting, stinging, and releasing offensive substances. Some insects are protected by mimicry.

Insect Control   Insects can be harmful to crops and to animals. Chemicals used to destroy insects may also be harmful to other organisms. The biological control of insects involves the use of the natural enemies of insects, sterilization, pheromones, or juvenile hormones.

CHAPTER VOCABULARY

aorta	incomplete metamorphosis	parthenogenesis
book lung	juvenile hormone	pedipalp
chelicera	labium	pheromone
complete metamorphosis	labrum	prothorax
crop	mesothorax	salivary gland
division of labor	metathorax	spinneret
gastric caeca	mimicry	spiracle
gizzard	ovipositor	tympanum

REVIEW of FACTS and CONCEPTS Answers on page T–79.

On a separate sheet of paper, answer each of the following as completely as possible.

1. List the parts of the spider. Give the function of each part.
2. How does a spider spin its web?
3. How are arachnids different from insects?
4. Name some adaptations of insects.
5. List the parts of the grasshopper. Give the function of each part.
6. In what ways is the grasshopper similar to the crayfish?
7. Summarize incomplete and complete metamorphosis.
8. Describe the division of labor in a honeybee society.
9. How do bees communicate with one another?
10. Name three defense mechanisms of insects.
11. Biological control of insects often involves using an organism from another country to control the pest. What is one disadvantage of doing so?

EXTENSIONS and APPLICATIONS For additional information, see page T–79.

1. Collect photographs or make drawings of 20 different kinds of insects. Using books in the library, group them according to their orders. Mount these photographs or drawings on posterboard, along with descriptions of their characteristics.
2. Collect some insects from fields or wooded areas in your neighborhood. Do not touch the insects directly. Keep a log that gives information on the habitat of the insects, the time collected, and so on. Place the insects in a terrarium and observe their behavior.
3. Horseshoe crabs are close relatives of the arachnids, although they look like crustaceans. Using the library, find out why horseshoe crabs are classified as they are. Summarize your findings in a short written report.

SUGGESTED READINGS

Gertsch, W.J., *American Spiders*. New York: Van Nostrand Reinhold.
   The author gives an illustrated natural history of North American spiders. Included in this book are topics on the complexity and uniqueness of these arachnids.
Hocking, B., *Six-Legged Science*. Cambridge, Mass.: Schenkman.
   This book offers a description of the anatomy, behavior, and reproduction of insects.
von Frisch, K., *The Dancing Bees*. New York: Harcourt Brace Jovanovich.
   The author describes the way in which honeybees ''dance'' to communicate where food is located.

Triage Among Endangered Species

Biologists are alarmed by the increasingly rapid rate of extinction of species of animals. In the past few hundred years, this rate has increased dramatically. Today, approximately one mammal species becomes extinct each year. This is especially alarming, since there are only about 4000 known species of mammals. A number of species of mollusks that might be of importance as food sources are also endangered. Some endangered arthropods play a role in the pollination of food crops.

Ecologists see the removal of species from the biosphere as a potentially disastrous occurrence. This belief is based on the fact that the interrelationships within an ecosystem are complex. The extinction of one species may adversely affect other species. Some ecologists feel, however, that not all of the endangered species can be saved from extinction. These ecologists believe that selected species should be saved through the use of a selection system called triage (trē-AHZH).

"Triage" is a French word meaning to sift or to pick. The earliest English usage of the word dates back to the 1700s. Wool dealers had to go through a sheep's fleece and pick out the highest-quality wool. This process was called triage. During the 1800s, triage was used frequently in the process of selecting the best coffee beans from the harvest. More recently, triage has been used to describe a medical practice that was developed on the battlefield. During the worst fighting of World War I, doctors were unable to treat all of the wounded immediately. Instead, they would check through the casualties and select from among those who had severe injuries those who had the best chance of survival. Those patients would be treated first. This medical usage of the term "triage" comes closest to its modern ecological usage.

Through the use of triage, adequate care, research, and funding could be given to those endangered species that are of most value to human beings or that, with help, have the greatest chance of survival. Critics of triage argue that its use would interfere with natural selection processes. These critics also feel that the criteria for using triage might be superficial. They wonder whether, for example, the panda would be chosen for survival over the Gila monster because the panda is more "appealing" to people.

The triage method is under considerable study by ecologists and conservationists around the world. They are attempting to devise a procedure for establishing how specific organisms are to be chosen for special protection. One proposal suggests that biological, economic, and cultural values be considered before any decision is made. These scientists claim that the impact that the organism has on its ecosystem also must be carefully considered.

Viewpoints

1. Contact the United States Office of Endangered Species and the World Wildlife Fund in Washington, D.C., and request information on the requirements for preserving endangered species. Set up a panel discussion involving different viewpoints on this issue.

2. Set up a display that shows photographs of endangered animal species. Also include some endangered plant species. Ask to have this display set up in a prominent place in your school. Ask fellow students and teachers to list the organisms in the order of their importance, that is, according to their order in a triage ranking. Also ask participants to give reasons why they chose the particular order. Report your findings to your class.

3. Set up a debate on whether people should continue to save endangered species by placing them in zoos and preserves.

477

Vertebrates

For an overview of this unit, including field trip suggestions, a bibliography, and a list of audio-visual materials, see pages T–80 to T–88. You may want to check the Laboratory Investigations in this unit so that materials may be ordered, gathered, or prepared in advance.

About 500 million years ago, a new group of animals evolved. Since that time, these animals, called the vertebrates, have learned to live in almost all the habitats of the world. Today, they are found in great numbers and in many different forms. The vertebrates include the fishes, the amphibians, the reptiles, the birds, and the mammals.

All vertebrates have one feature in common. That feature is a vertebral column, which is a nerve cord that is encased in a series of small, flexible, but strong bones, called vertebrae. The name, vertebrates, comes from the word for these bones.

30 Fishes

31 Amphibians

32 Reptiles

33 Birds

34 Mammals

Mammals, such as these Asian water buffaloes, are the most advanced group of vertebrates.

479

30 Fishes

Protective spines cover this porcupine fish.

Chapter Objectives *After completing this chapter, you will be able to:*

a ■ List the characteristics of the three classes of fishes. p. 481

b ■ Distinguish between cartilaginous and bony fishes. p. 482

c ■ List and give the functions of the parts of a perch. p. 486

d ■ Describe the special adaptations of fishes. p. 481

e ■ Describe the breeding habits of the perch. p. 492

For teaching aids for this chapter, including a chapter overview and teaching strategies, see pages T–80 to T–81. The page number next to each chapter objective refers to the text page where the information needed to fulfill the objective begins.

The fishes have been swimming the waters of the earth for about 500 million years. They first appeared in the Devonian Period, which is sometimes called the Age of Fishes. Today, with about 31,000 species, the fishes are the most numerous vertebrates.

For thousands of years, fishes have been important food sources for people. Today over a million metric tons of freshwater and marine fishes are caught annually and are used for food. Fishes are good sources of proteins and some vitamins. In fact, people are beginning to develop fish farms where fishes are cultivated for use as food. In the future, the fishes may become a major source of protein for the growing world population.

Classification of Fishes

Fishes are *cold-blooded*, meaning that no internal mechanism controls their body temperatures. Adapted for living in water, the fishes have **gills** that are used for breathing. Fishes have *fins* that aid in movement. The skin of most fishes is covered with scales. With these adaptations, the fishes have pushed their way into almost every marine and freshwater habitat. The fishes are grouped into three main classes.

At this point, you may want to refer to Chapter 3 to give your students a better understanding of how fishes are classified.

Class *Agnatha* Fishes in this class are jawless. The lampreys and hagfishes are examples of jawless fishes.

Class *Chondrichthyes* The skeletons of these fishes are cartilaginous, or have cartilage, a strong, flexible tissue. Examples of fishes in this class are skates, rays, and sharks.

Class *Osteichthyes* Fishes in this class have bony skeletons. The ray-finned and lobed-finned fishes and lungfishes are found in this class.

Jawless Fishes

The most primitive vertebrates were small, fishlike animals that lacked jaws and that had bodies encased in a hard, bony shell. Fossilized remains of these *ostracoderms* are found in rocks dating from the Ordovician Period, more than 500 million years ago. Although the original ostracoderms vanished 300 million years ago, two similar species of fish are alive today. They are lampreys and hagfishes. *Ichthyologists*, or scientists who study fishes, believe that these two jawless types of fish are close relatives of the extinct ostracoderms.

The bodies of lampreys and hagfishes look like those of eels. Their skeletons are made of cartilage. Lampreys and hagfishes lack pairs of fins, and they each have a single nostril in the center of the head. Their gill apparatus, unlike that of other fishes, looks like a series of holes rather than a set of movable plates.

Despite their similarity to their armored ancestors, however, modern lampreys and hagfishes differ in important ways. For example, the long, thin, scaleless bodies of lampreys and hagfishes are not encased in bony armor.

LAMPREYS Lampreys are both freshwater and marine fishes. As *parasites*, many lampreys live on, and gain nourishment from, the bodies of host organisms. As adaptations for its parasitic lifestyle, the lamprey has a wide, circular

Highlight

The most primitive class of fishes is *Agnatha,* the jawless fishes. Lampreys and hagfish are the only existing examples of fishes in this class.

481

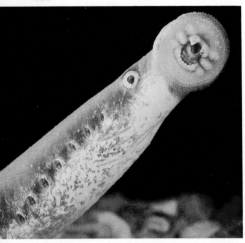

Figure 30-1 The lamprey has a mouth that is like a huge suction cup. The lamprey uses its mouth to attach itself to other fishes.

mouth, with sharp, file-shaped teeth and a muscular tongue. With its suckerlike mouth, the lamprey attaches itself tightly to the body wall of a living host fish. It then bores a hole through the protective scales of the fish with its teeth and tongue. The body fluids and blood obtained from the host fish make up the main diet of the lamprey.

In the Great Lakes, sea lampreys destroyed so many trout and other desirable game fishes that the lampreys became a serious threat. To kill the lampreys, scientists used chemical substances that are toxic to the sensitive, newly hatched lamprey larvae. After the larvae were destroyed, the lakes were restocked with desirable game fishes.

In the spring, adult sea lampreys migrate up freshwater streams to **spawn,** or lay their eggs. The eggs hatch into wormlike larvae that look very different from their parents. The larvae do not have the specialized mouthparts of the adult, and they are blind. Buried in the sand for three to seven years, they feed by straining microorganisms from the water. They then undergo *metamorphosis*, which is a change that turns them into free-swimming, sighted, parasitic adult lampreys. Certain freshwater lampreys stop feeding after metamorphosis, live only one season, spawn, and then die.

HAGFISHES   Living only in the sea, hagfishes are primarily *scavengers*, or animals that feed on dead and dying organisms. Hagfishes also eat worms and crustaceans, and sometimes they attack living fishes. Hagfishes look like lampreys, but the design of their mouths is different. The hagfish mouth is smaller and less suckerlike than that of a lamprey. In addition, six short, fleshy tentacles, called *barbels*, surround the mouth. These tentacles are used for sensing food, and they are particularly important because the hagfish is blind. The sharp, hard teeth are organized, as they are in lampreys, to tear the flesh from the prey of the hagfish. Unlike the lamprey, newly hatched hagfish larvae look like the adults, and they do not undergo metamorphosis.

Cartilaginous Fishes

The first fish with true hinged jaws, the *placoderm*, appeared about 350 million years ago, and it flourished during the Devonian Period. Like the lamprey and hagfish, the placoderm had an all-cartilaginous skeleton. Setting it apart from the agnathans, however, were its movable jaw and paired fins. The very mobile and ferocious placoderm gave rise to the two modern classes of the cartilaginous and bony fishes.

SKATES AND RAYS Of the modern cartilaginous fishes in the class *Chondrichthyes*, skates and rays make up a large number. Their bodies are very flat, and two large **pectoral fins** stick out from the sides. These fins look very much like wings. In fact, when rays swim by beating these winglike fins, they look like birds flying in slow motion. The various species can be as small as 15 centimeters or as large as 7 meters. Skates and rays live mainly in salt water, feeding on other fish and on bottom-dwelling invertebrates. The rays, for example, lie quietly on the bottom, buried in the sand, waiting to catch prey.

On top of the head of the ray, two large holes, called *spiracles*, allow water to enter and to bathe the gills. The gills open on the underside of the fish in a series of slits. Most rays have a tail that is long and thin. In some rays, this tail has a sharp poisonous spine for defense against large predators. Other species have organs that can stun small fishes with charges of electricity and therefore aid in the capture of prey.

Rays reproduce by means of **ovoviviparity** (ō-vō-vī-vi-PAR-ə-tē). Ovoviviparity means that the offspring are produced from eggs that hatch within the female's body. During mating, the male ray clasps the female with a specially modified pair of **pelvic fins**. These fins are attached to the ventral side, or underside. Fertilization of the eggs takes place inside the female. In most species, the female keeps the fertilized eggs in her body cavity until the young are born fully developed.

SHARKS Another group of cartilaginous fishes, the sharks, range in length from 15 centimeters to 20 meters. Their bodies are generally long and streamlined. Most sharks, such as the hammerhead and tiger shark, are *carnivores*, or meat-eaters. They feed on many animals, including other fishes, squids, and crustaceans. A few sharks, such as the whale shark and the basking shark, are *filter feeders*. They strain microscopic organisms from the sea water.

The skin of most sharks is rough and covered with **placoid scales**. Each of these scales is thin and disklike, with a hard, sharp point projecting from its center. These small points are responsible for the sandpapery feel of shark skin.

Sharks can reproduce in three ways. Like skates and rays, some sharks are ovoviviparous. Others, however, reproduce by means of **oviparity**. Oviparous female sharks release their fertilized eggs, which then hatch outside the parent. Still other sharks reproduce by **viviparity**. They bear live offspring. The paired pelvic fins of the male shark, like those of of skates and rays, serve as clasping organs during mating.

Figure 30-2 Rays swim by beating their huge pectoral fins much the same way a bird flaps its wings when flying.

At this point, you may want to assign to your students the first of the Extensions and Applications at the end of this chapter.

Sidelight

The whale shark is the largest living fish. It can grow up to 20 meters long and weigh up to 14 metric tons. The smallest fish is the pygmy goby, measuring less than 1.5 centimeters.

Figure 30-3 The external structures of a shark make this animal easy to recognize.

On both sides of the head of the shark, five to seven external gill slits are arranged in series. When the shark opens its mouth while swimming, water is forced into its *pharynx*, or muscular throat cavity. The water then moves over the gills, and exits through gill slits.

In addition to keen senses of sight and smell, sharks have very specialized taste and touch organs. A series of pits are arranged in lines along the body of the shark, either between or under its placoid scales. This series of pits is called the **lateral line.** These pits function mainly as touch receptors. Saclike structures on the head, called *ampullae of Lorenzini*, are very sensitive to touch and to electrical stimuli. They are believed to aid in the detection of prey.

At this point, you may want to assign to your students the second of the Extensions and Applications at the end of this chapter.

Bony Fishes

The bony fishes of the class *Osteichthyes* first appeared 350 million years ago in the Ordovician Period. Today, they are the most successful and numerous of modern fishes. They are divided into the ray-finned fishes, the lobe-finned fishes, and the lungfishes.

RAY-FINNED FISHES These fishes have an air-filled **swim bladder,** or air bladder. The swim bladder helps the ray-finned fishes to rise and sink in the water. Ray-finned fishes get their name from their paired fins with spiny rays of cartilage or bone. The ray-finned fishes live in all water habitats. They are found in shallow tidal waters and in the deepest parts of the oceans, as well as in mudholes, rivers, and deep lakes. As the most numerous of all vertebrates, they are a major source of food for human beings. The over 20,000 living species of modern ray-finned fishes include the trout, the eel, the minnow, and the perch. Other bony fishes, such as the sturgeon and gar, have skeletons that have been largely replaced by cartilage.

LOBE-FINNED FISHES With one exception, lobe-finned fishes all vanished long ago. Their name comes from the fleshy, paired fins that they had. Lobe-finned fishes are believed to be the ancestors of land-dwelling vertebrates. The only species living today is the *Latimeria*, or coelacanth. This species was thought to be extinct until it was discovered by fishermen off the coast of South Africa in 1938.

At this point, you may want to assign to your students the third of the Extensions and Applications at the end of this chapter.

CAREER: Fish Farmer

Fish farms are located throughout the United States, usually in rural areas. The many types of fishes raised on these farms may be either sold or used to stock lakes and streams where people go fishing.

Fish farmers begin the farming process by removing eggs from female fishes. The eggs are then fertilized with milt taken from male fishes. The fertilized eggs are placed into incubation troughs, in which the growing conditions are ideal. Fish farmers closely monitor the temperature, oxygen content, movement, and depth of the water. They also make sure that the water is free of wastes, harmful chemicals, and other unwanted materials.

When the eggs hatch, the young fishes are moved to special ponds, where they are fed high-protein foods, vitamins, and minerals. This special diet ensures rapid growth. When the fishes are large enough to be sold, they are removed from the pond and packed for shipment.

Some fish farmers raise only one kind of fish, such as trout. In fact, most of the trout eaten in the United States are raised on trout farms. In the southern states, catfish farms are common.

Other kinds of fish farms, such as carp farms, are common in Asia.

Fish farmers try to breed fishes that grow fast, taste good, and resist disease. These efforts are important because, as the world population grows and as ocean fish catches decline, more food will be needed from fish farms.

A person who wishes to become a fish farmer needs no special educational background. However, courses in fish behavior, physiology, and disease are very helpful. Business management courses are also a benefit.

For further career information, write to American Fisheries Society, 5400 Grosvenor Lane, Washington, DC 20014.

Sidelight

Some lungfish can live for several months buried in dry mud waiting for rains to come and free them. During this time they neither eat nor drink.

LUNGFISHES   These fishes are noted for their well-developed lungs and fleshy fins. During the dry season, lung-fishes are able to breathe air and walk from pool to pool in search of water. Although they were once a large group, only six living species exist today, in Africa, South America, and Australia.

SECTION REVIEW   Answers on pages T–80 to T–81.

1. List the three classes of fishes.
2. How does the lamprey attach itself to its host?
3. Describe the skin of most sharks.

The Perch: A Representative Bony Fish

At this point, or at any point during the examination of the perch, you may want to assign to your students the fourth of the Extensions and Applications at the end of this chapter.

The perch is a typical ray-finned bony fish that grows to about 30 centimeters in length. Found in many lakes and rivers in North America, the perch is a popular game fish. The perch is a freshwater fish that is used as food.

External Features

The perch has both paired and *median fins*, each of which has a special function. Two types of fins keep the perch from rolling while swimming. One type is the median

Figure 30-4   The perch is typical of the bony fishes. It has both paired and median fins, gills, and flat scales covering its body.

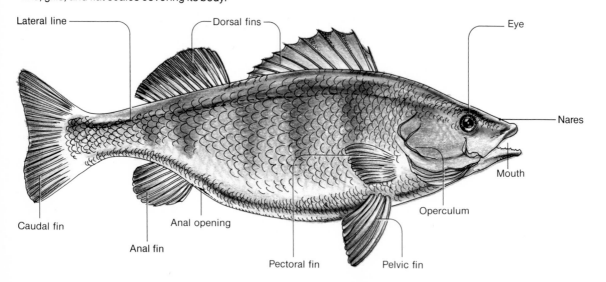

Lateral line

Dorsal fins

Eye

Nares

Mouth

Operculum

Caudal fin

Anal opening

Anal fin

Pectoral fin

Pelvic fin

dorsal fins, which are attached to the upper surface of the perch. The other is the median **anal fin** on the ventral surface. The fanlike **caudal fin,** attached to the tail, propels the perch through the water. Two pairs of fins enable the perch to steer and to brake. One of these sets, located behind the gill openings on both sides of the body, is the pair of pectoral fins. The other is the pair of pelvic fins on the ventral side, just in front of the anal fin.

At the anterior, or front, end of the fish is a pair of hinged jaws that are lined with teeth. Above the mouth, just in front of the eyes, are paired openings, called **nares.** The nares lead into the nasal cavity. On each side of the head, behind the eyes, are two gill chambers. Each chamber contains four pairs of gills that are covered externally by a hard movable flap called the **operculum** (ō-PER-kyoo-ləm).

The perch has two layers of skin that fit tightly over its muscles. Glands in the skin secrete the mucus that gives the fish its slimy feeling. The perch can change color to blend into its surroundings because both skin layers contain special cells, called **chromatophores.** These cells contain pigment granules of brown, yellow, or red that can spread out or concentrate, making different colors.

Covering the skin of the perch are scales that are quite different from the placoid scales of sharks. Perch scales are flat plates, and their outer surfaces are marked with circular, bony ridges. As the perch grows, new ridges are added, and the scales get bigger. The number of growth rings on the scales indicates the approximate age of the fish.

Movement and Muscles

The swim bladder of the perch has several functions. It can, for example, produce sounds, and it takes part in the hearing process. The main purpose of the swim bladder, however, is to let the fish change its depth in the water. The bladder removes oxygen, carbon dioxide, and nitrogen from the blood. As the fish changes depth, these gases are pumped either into or out of the bladder. At any depth, the pressure inside the bladder has to equal the pressure outside the body of the fish. If the two pressures are not equal, the fish can die. For example, if a fish is hooked very deep in the water and then quickly reeled to the surface, the pressure of the surrounding water becomes much lower than the pressure inside the fish. As a result, the swim bladder bursts. When collecting live deep-water fishes for zoos and aquariums, divers must therefore bring their specimens to the surface very slowly.

Figure 30-5 The pigment-containing cells of flounders enable them to change color and blend in with their environment.

Figure 30-6 The flat scales of the perch and other bony fishes are made of concentric ridges. The number of ridges indicates a fish's age.

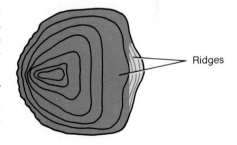

Ridges

Highlight

Most bony fishes swim forward and backward by use of muscles called myomeres. The fish's vertical movements are controlled by a swim bladder, or air-filled organ.

Along both sides of the body of the perch are large blocks of muscle, called *myomeres*. When the myomeres on one side contract, or shorten, the myomeres on the other side relax. As the fish swims, it contracts the myomeres first on one side and then the other. These contractions and relaxations result in the familiar motion of a swimming fish. The fish moves forward, instead of just wiggling in the water, because this motion makes the tail fin and the caudal fins beat from side to side. As these structures move, they push against the water behind the fish and propel the fish in a forward direction.

Internal Skeleton

The bony skeleton of the perch is very strong. The skull is made of bone and some cartilage. It not only encases the brain, but it also offers protection and support for the various sensory organs in the head. The skull is attached to the bony vertebral column, which protects the *spinal cord*, or ventral nerve cord. The vertebral column is made of small, spool-like bones called *vertebrae* (singular: vertebra).

In addition to flexibility, the skeletal structure of the perch provides attachment points for muscles. The muscles of the paired pelvic and pectoral fins are attached to the skeleton by means of groups of bones called *girdles*. The median fins are connected by muscles to the long bony processes of the vertebrae. The muscles for controlling movement are linked to the rays in the fins.

Figure 30–7   Skeletal System of a Perch

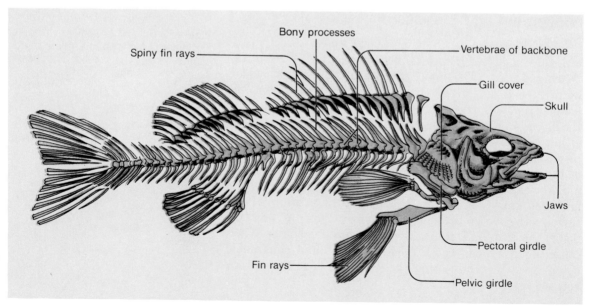

Organ Systems

The organ systems of the perch are characteristic of those of bony fishes in general. Several of the systems are similar to those of the vertebrates that will be treated in later chapters.

NERVOUS SYSTEM The nervous system of the perch includes the brain, the spinal cord, nerves, and sensory organs. Encased by the bony skull, the brain has five major regions. The **olfactory lobes,** the first region, get sensory information from the nasal cavities. The **cerebrum,** whose function in fishes is unclear, has two halves, called *lateral hemispheres.* The third major region of the brain consists of the **optic lobes.** The optic lobes process visual information from the eyes. The **cerebellum** coordinates movement and controls balance. The fifth region of the brain, the **medulla oblongata,** controls the heartbeat and other functions.

Connected to the medulla oblongata is the segmented spinal cord. Each segment sends out paired **spinal nerves** that signal organs and muscles to do work and that carry information back from the body. Pairs of nerves, called **cranial nerves,** leave the brain and connect with the head, neck, and sensory organs. Like the spinal nerves, they carry information to and from the body regions.

Fishes sense their environments with the help of **sensory receptors.** These receptors are nerve endings in the skin that detect pain, temperature, and pressure. Although the perch has good eyesight, it can also sense distant objects with its *lateral line system.* Along each side of the perch is a lateral line of pitted scales. Little tubes connect the pits to a canal underneath the scales that run the length of a fish. Within the canal, special cells with hairs are attached to the nervous system. Any water movement outside the fish causes these hairs to bend and to trigger the nerve cells. As a result, the fish gets a sensation from the direction of the movement in the water. For example, a moving object to the right and rear of the perch would cause water to strike the hairs on that part of the perch first.

The paired nares on the snout of the perch lead into a pair of pockets, or nasal cavities, which are lined with olfactory cells. Dissolved chemical substances stimulate these nerve cells, which relay sensory information to the brain. Although the perch has no eardrum or ear bones, a well-developed inner ear allows the fish to hear quite well.

DIGESTIVE SYSTEM The very sharp teeth and flexible jaws of the perch make this fish a successful predator. The

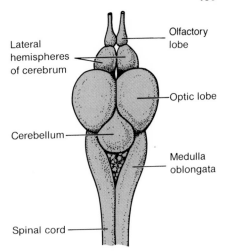

Figure 30-8 Brain of a Perch

Sidelight

A flatfish, like the flounder, is born with one eye on each side of its head. As the fish matures, however, one of the eyes migrates until both eyes are on the same side of the head.

perch feeds on other fishes, as well as on insects, worms, and small invertebrates. The mouth of the perch is connected to the stomach by a short tube called the *esophagus.* In the stomach, food is broken down, both physically and chemically, to release nutrients and to prepare the nutrients for absorption. At a later stage of digestion, the *liver* removes and concentrates the nutrients absorbed from the food. The liver also secretes *bile,* a chemical substance that breaks down fats. Bile is stored in the *gall bladder,* a small saclike structure that is connected both to the liver and to the stomach. This bladder releases bile to the stomach, where fats are broken down.

When food leaves the stomach, it enters a short intestine, where the last stages of digestion and absorption take place. The *enzymes,* which are substances needed to complete digestion, come from the *pancreas.* The pancreas is an organ that is connected to the intestine. To absorb fully digested food into the body, the intestine needs a large surface area. Pouches in the intestine, called **pyloric caeca** (singular: caecum), provide this increased surface area. When digested food enters these pouches, the food is absorbed into a capillary network in the wall of the pouches. The blood circulating through this network carries the nutrients to the liver, where toxic substances are removed and some excess sugars are stored. Undigested material is left in the intestine. This material leaves the body through an opening called the *anus.*

Figure 30-9   Internal Anatomy of a Perch

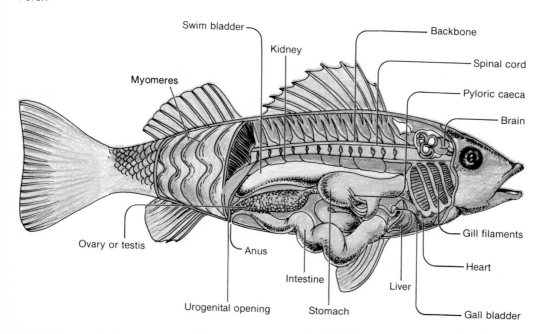

Swim bladder

Kidney

Backbone

Spinal cord

Pyloric caeca

Brain

Myomeres

Gill filaments

Ovary or testis

Anus

Heart

Intestine

Liver

Urogenital opening

Stomach

Gall bladder

EXCRETORY SYSTEM   In most vertebrates, the major organs of excretion are the paired **kidneys.** The blood carries nitrogen wastes from various organs to the kidneys. In the kidneys, these wastes are removed as the fluid called *urine.* In bony fishes, however, 50 to 90% of the nitrogen wastes are not released as urine. Instead, they are excreted by the gills as ammonia, which is a nitrogen-containing substance.

In fishes, the kidneys act mainly as *osmoregulators,* or structures that keep the water and salts properly balanced in the body. In fresh water, the body of a fish loses salts and takes in water. If the fish takes in too much water, the blood becomes too diluted for the fish to live. The kidneys of a freshwater fish, such as the perch, excrete excess water and prevent salt from leaving. In sea water, the body of a fish loses water and takes in salt. The kidneys of saltwater fishes work to keep water in the body. Special cells in the gills of saltwater fishes excrete the salt that is taken in with sea water.

RESPIRATORY SYSTEM.   The gills of the perch are contained in two large *gill chambers,* located immediately behind and on each side of the mouth. Covering each gill chamber is the operculum. When the perch "breathes," the operculum closes and the mouth opens, bringing water into the pharynx. When the mouth closes and the operculum reopens, water is forced over the gills and out through the operculum. As the water passes over the gills, the gas exchange occurs.

Inside each chamber, where the gas exchange takes place, are four gills. Each gill is made up of many **gill filaments,** which contain tiny, thin disks stacked like pennies. The gill is supported by a piece of bone that bears a row of short **gill rakers** on its inner side. The gill rakers stop food or dirt from clogging the filaments. The structure of the gill filaments provides a large surface for the gas exchange between the gill and the water. Inside the fingerlike gill filaments is a network of fine blood vessels, called *capillaries.* As blood circulates through these vessels, it absorbs oxygen from the water and gives off carbon dioxide.

CIRCULATORY SYSTEM   As in all vertebrates, the circulatory system of the perch carries oxygen, nutrients, and wastes throughout the body. The heart of the perch is simply a tube with two chambers. Oxygen-poor blood from the body enters the heart through a vessel called the *sinus venosus.* From the **atrium,** or first chamber of the heart, the blood flows into the **ventricle.** The ventricle does the actual pumping of the blood. From the ventricle, the blood passes into a

At this point, you may want your students to do the Laboratory Investigation at the end of this chapter.

Figure 30-10 The thousands of filaments in a fish's gills provide a large surface area for absorbing oxygen from the water.

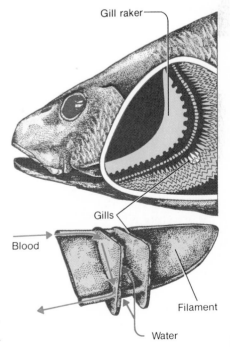

Gill raker

Gills

Blood

Filament

Water

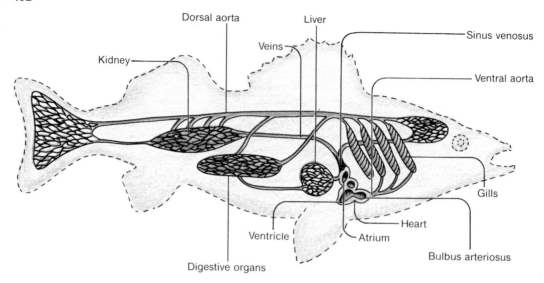

Figure 30-11 Circulatory System of a Perch

bulb, called the *bulbus arteriosis*, which joins the *ventral aorta*. Branches of the ventral aorta carry the oxygen-poor blood into the gill capillaries. Here carbon dioxide is replaced with oxygen. The *dorsal aorta* then carries the oxygen-rich blood to all parts of the body. After delivering its oxygen to various cells and organs, the blood returns to the heart through blood vessels called *veins*.

REPRODUCTIVE SYSTEM   Fertilization takes place outside the bodies of most bony fishes, including the perch. The sexes are separate. In both sexes, the reproductive organs are located just above the digestive organs against the dorsal body wall. In the male, the paired *testes* produce sperm. The sperm travels through the sperm ducts and out of the body through the *urogenital opening*. In the female, a single *ovary* produces eggs. When the eggs are mature, they are delivered out of the body through a duct system leading to the urogenital opening.

Breeding Habits and Development

At the age of two or three years, perch become sexually mature. In the spring, the adult fish leave the deeper water for the shallows. After pairing off with the males, the females start spawning, or laying their eggs. Each egg is about 2 millimeters in diameter. One female lays several

At this point, you may want to have some of your students set up a classroom aquarium. This activity lends itself to the observation of the habits and behavior of various fishes. Guppies can be used to observe breeding. Tetras can be used to observe schooling.

hundred thousand eggs in long strings that cling to plants and stones. The male then swims over the eggs, releasing **milt**, a fluid that contains the sperm.

The fertilized eggs hatch in about 18 days, releasing fish larvae about 6 millimeters long. Until the larvae are able to catch their own food, the **yolk** supplies the nutrients. The yolk is stored in the *yolk sac* that is attached to the larvae. To inflate their swim bladders, the larvae must swim to the surface and swallow air. Once the bladder is inflated, the larvae can swim well enough to catch microscopic organisms. They then grow quickly and join in the shallows to form schools.

Most young bony fishes do not survive to adulthood because they are exposed to many predators. For a species of bony fishes to survive, its members must lay many thousands of eggs. The parents must also protect their young in various ways. For example, salmon and trout bury their eggs in gravel. The male seahorse hides the eggs in a pouch under his tail until they hatch. The male stickleback builds a spawning nest for the eggs out of grass and weeds, and then

Sidelight

Some species of fish live together in schools, or groups. Tuna swim in schools of fewer than 25 fish. Herring, on the other hand, swim in schools with hundreds of thousands of fish.

Figure 30-12 Salmon larvae consume food stored in wing-shaped yolk sacs.

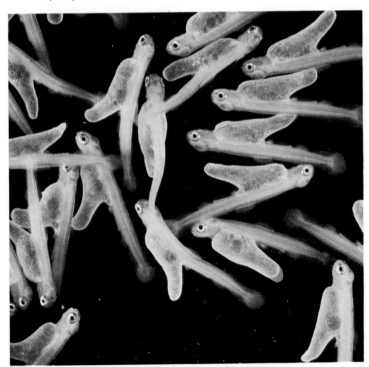

Figure 30-13 The male stickleback builds a nest for his mate's eggs. He then protects the eggs until the larvae are old enough to swim away on their own.

guards the larvae that hatch. Sticklebacks protect their young so well, that they survive as species despite the fact that they lay relatively few eggs.

How far a fish migrates to lay eggs depends on its species. Perch, for example, do not migrate very far. The Pacific salmon, in contrast, may swim as far as 3200 kilometers. This salmon spends a year or more in the subarctic Pacific, feeding and growing. When it matures, it leaves the deep sea for coastal waters. It then searches, mainly by smell, for the river where it was originally spawned and hatched. The salmon swims upstream, spawns, and dies. When the eggs hatch, the salmon larvae swim out to sea to begin this reproductive cycle again.

Not all bony fishes lay eggs. A few fishes such as guppies and swordtails give birth to live young. During mating, their eggs, like those of some sharks, are fertilized within the ovary. The fertilized eggs are then kept inside the body cavity of the female. The larvae develop there, fed by yolk until they hatch. They are then delivered alive and free-swimming.

SECTION REVIEW   Answers on page T–81.

1. What are chromatophores?
2. List and give the functions of the parts of the perch.
3. Describe the breeding habits of the perch.

Figure 30-14 Salmon swim thousands of kilometers from the sea to their birthplace in freshwater streams. Here they lay their eggs and fertilize them.

Respiration Rate in Fish

Purpose Fishes are cold-blooded vertebrates. They lack an internal mechanism for regulating their body temperatures. Their rate of respiration, as shown by operculum movements, therefore depends directly on the temperature of the water. Oxygen and carbon dioxide are exchanged in the gill filaments as water flows over them. The purpose of this investigation is to determine the effect of temperature on the respiration rate of a goldfish.

Materials *(per group)* ● 1000-mL glass beaker
● 250-mL glass beaker ● Glass or plastic funnel
● Thermometer (Celsius) ● Hot-water source (or hot plate) ● ice (crushed or cubed) ● Goldfish

Procedure **1.** Copy the table shown in this investigation into your notebook. As you perform the investigation, record your data in this table. **2.** Place a goldfish in a 250-mL beaker that contains enough aquarium water to cover the fish. **3.** Put the thermometer in the beaker with the fish, and secure it so that it can be read easily. **4.** Place the 250-mL beaker inside the 1000-mL beaker. Slowly add warm (not hot!) water to the larger beaker using the funnel. **5.** Once the temperature of the water in the beaker with the fish has stabilized at the first desired level, count the operculum movements of the goldfish for 1 minute. Record your data in the table. **6.** Continue changing the water temperature, as shown in the data table, by adding warmer water until you have reached the highest desired temperature. Record the operculum movements per minute for each temperature indicated. **7.** Add crushed or cubed ice to the water in the large beaker to cool it. Repeat the steps until the lowest temperature in the table is reached. Record your data in your table and in the class data table on the chalkboard. **8.** Using class data, make up a graph to illustrate the respiration rate for the fish. Also plot your data on the graph. After the experiment is completed, replace the goldfish in its original aquarium.

Observations and Conclusions **1.** How are oxygen and carbon dioxide exchanged in the gills? **2.** What relationship is demonstrated between operculum movements and respiration rate? **3.** Why should the water temperature be stabilized each time before counting operculum movements? **4.** At what temperature were the operculum movements the slowest? Fastest?

Data Table

Temperature °C	Operculum movements per minute	
	Group	Class
0		
4		
8		
12		
16		
20		
24		
28		
32		

Graph of Data

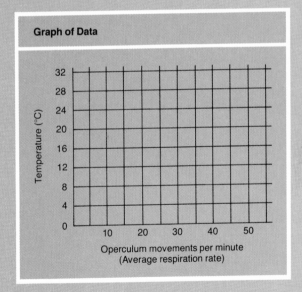

CHAPTER SUMMARY

Classification of Fishes The fishes are the simplest and most ancient of vertebrates. Fishes have gills for breathing and fins for movement. The jawless fishes of the class *Agnatha* are mostly extinct. The lampreys and hagfishes are modern fishes that lack jaws and scales and that have a cartilage skeleton. Most lampreys are parasitic. They attach themselves to their prey with a mouth that is like a suction cup. The lamprey has caused the destruction of trout in the Great Lakes. Hagfishes live in the sea and are scavengers.

Members of the class *Chondrichthyes* have jaws and paired fins. Sharks, skates, and rays have skeletons of cartilage, but they do not have swim bladders. Swim bladders help fish move to different depths in the water.

The class *Osteichthyes* includes most modern fishes. These fishes have skeletons of bone and scales on their bodies. The bony fishes are divided into three smaller groups, which are the ray-finned fishes, the lobe-finned fishes, and the lungfishes. Most bony fishes have a streamlined body, highly movable fins, and a swim bladder. These features allow the fishes to swim easily, and they partially explain the success of bony fishes in so many different habitats.

Perch: A Representative Bony Fish In a bony fish, such as a perch, breathing occurs through gills. Each gill is made up of many gill filaments. Water entering through the mouth bathes the gills and exits through the opened operculum. The water passes over the gills, and blood circulates in the capillary network of the gills. Oxygen from the water is then exchanged with carbon dioxide from the fish. The oxygen-rich blood is carried by the dorsal aorta to all parts of the body. The deoxygenated blood is returned to the gills through a two-chambered heart and the ventral aorta.

The perch has a brain with five major regions. The olfactory lobes take part in the sense of smell. The role of the cerebrum remains unclear in the fish, but the optic lobes take part in the sense of vision. The cerebellum controls balance and coordinates the muscles. The medulla oblongata regulates involuntary activities. Spinal nerves in the spinal cord, which is attached to the base of the medulla oblongata, carry messages between the brain and the body. Cranial nerves leave the brain directly.

The digestive system of the perch includes an esophagus, a stomach, and an intestine. Pyloric caeca add surface area where food is absorbed by the blood. The kidney filters nitrogen wastes from the blood, and both kidney and gills excrete these wastes to the environment as urine and ammonia.

The sexes are separate in perch. In most species, fertilization takes place outside the body of the female. In the act of spawning, the female releases the eggs into the water. The males then release milt, which contains sperm, to fertilize the eggs. In addition to external fertilization, the development of the young occurs outside the body of the parent. The eggs of a few fishes, such as the guppy, are fertilized internally and delivered as fully developed young. Some fishes, such as salmon, migrate great distances to spawn. Others guard their eggs, thus increasing the chance of survival for the larvae.

CHAPTER VOCABULARY

anal fin	kidney	pelvic fin
atrium	lateral line	placoid scale
caudal fin	medulla oblongata	pyloric caecum
cerebellum	milt	sensory receptor
cerebrum	nare	spawn
chromatophore	olfactory lobe	spinal nerve
cranial nerve	operculum	swim bladder
dorsal fin	optic lobe	ventricle
gill	oviparity	viviparity
gill filaments	ovoviviparity	yolk
gill rakers	pectoral fin	

REVIEW of FACTS and CONCEPTS   Answers on page T–81.

On a separate sheet of paper, answer each of the following as completely as possible.

1. Distinguish between jawless and bony fishes.
2. In what ways are the mouths of lampreys and hagfishes different?
3. What are the distinguishing characteristics of the class *Chondrichthyes?*
4. How are skates and rays adapted for bottom feeding?
5. Define ovoviviparity and oviparity.
6. What is the function of the lateral line in sharks?
7. What is the function of a swim bladder?
8. Are the scales of the perch similar to those of the shark? Explain.
9. Name and give the function of each of the five major regions of a bony fish's brain.
10. What is the function of the pyloric caeca?
11. What is an osmoregulator?
12. How do the kidneys function as osmoregulators in a freshwater fish? In a saltwater fish?
13. List the circulatory structures of a perch.   Start and end with the heart.

EXTENSIONS and APPLICATIONS   For additional information, see page T–81.

1. Sharks have a reputation for attacking people. Do research in the library to find out how often shark attacks occur, as well as which types of sharks are most dangerous to people. Make a report to the class.
2. Visit an aquarium or tropical fish store. Observe the different species of fish. How are the body shapes related to the habitats of the species of fish? What protective colors, structures, or behaviors do the species of fish have?
3. Find out what you can about *Latimeria,* a lobe-finned fish that is called a coelacanth. Write a report on its discovery.
4. Obtain a preserved shark or other cartilaginous fish. Dissect it and compare the internal and external structures with those of the perch.

SUGGESTED READINGS

Ellis, R., *The Book of Sharks.* New York: Grosset & Dunlap.
    The author examines the biology and habits of sharks, and provides helpful illustrations.

Ommanney, F.D., and the Editors of Life, *The Fishes.* New York: Time, Inc.
    This introductory volume describes the major groups of fishes.

Matthiessen, P., *Blue Meridian.* New York: Random House.
    This log was written by one of the crew members of an extensive expedition that set out to find and film the great white shark.

31 Amphibians

Chapter Objectives *After completing this chapter you will be able to:*

a ■ State the basic characteristics of each amphibian order. p. 499
b ■ Describe the process of development of the amphibian egg. p. 500
c ■ Identify the parts of a frog. p. 503
d ■ Summarize the steps in the development of a frog. p. 511

For teaching aids for this chapter, including a chapter over-view and teaching strategies, see pages T–82 to T–83. The page number next to each chapter objective refers to the text page where the information needed to fulfill the objective begins.

Frogs, such as these leopard frogs, vary in color and size.

If you compare an amphibian, such as a frog, with a fish, such as a perch, you find quite a difference in the way the two animals breathe and move. A frog, which lives partly on land and partly in water, has lungs rather than gills. Its backbone is stronger than that of the perch and it is adapted for movement on land. Its body resists drying out, a problem the aquatic perch does not have.

The changes that were required to produce the first amphibians took place gradually over a long period of time. The ancestors of the amphibians were probably ancient lobe-finned fishes. In the Devonian Period, 350 million years ago, droughts occurred. When a pool dried up during the droughts, the lobe-finned fishes moved to a new pool by using their fleshy fins like limbs. They had lungs for breathing air. Descendants of these fishes could eventually live on land for longer periods of time. One group of these ancient amphibians gave rise to modern amphibians. The members of another group were the ancestors of the reptiles and other land vertebrates.

Classification of Amphibians

The amphibians have several characteristics that distinguish them from other vertebrates. Amphibians live both on land and in water. In fact, the word "amphibian" means double life. During the life cycle of an amphibian, the organism goes through a *metamorphosis*, or series of changes. Young amphibians are adapted for an aquatic life. Adult amphibians live in moist areas on land. Most adult amphibians return to water to reproduce.

The amphibians are cold-blooded organisms. That is, their body temperature remains close to the temperature of their surroundings. Most amphibians have smooth, thin skin that is usually moist. The moist skin makes respiration more efficient. During the aquatic period in their life cycles, amphibians use gills for respiration. During the land period, amphibians use lungs for respiration. The amphibians are classified into three main orders.

Order *Apoda* The amphibians in this order are legless.

Order *Caudata* The amphibians in this order have tails throughout their lives. Examples are salamanders and newts.

Order *Anura* The amphibians in this order are tailless in the adult stage of their life cycle. Examples are frogs and toads.

Wormlike Amphibians

Wormlike, legless amphibians that belong to the order *Apoda* are found only in the tropics. These amphibians are commonly called *caecilians*. There are only about 75 species. Caecilians either live in water or burrow in the ground.

The caecilians look like large earthworms. They have no ears and very small eyes. In fact, most caecilians are blind. However, they have a pair of tentacles that help them sense their surroundings underground. They have a wide mouth and feed on earthworms and insects.

Amphibians with Tails

The salamanders are placed in the order *Caudata*, which means tailed. The tailed amphibians probably had the same ancestor as the caecilians. Salamanders are adapted to a moist environment and are found under damp logs and in streams and lakes.

Figure 31-1 The mudpuppy (*top*), American hellbender (*center*), and crimson spotted newt (*bottom*) are examples of amphibians with tails. Amphibians such as these belong to the order *Caudata*.

500

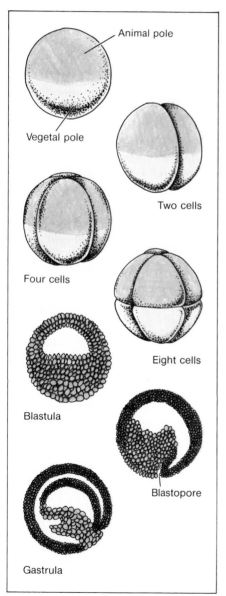

Figure 31-2 Development of an Amphibian Egg

Animal pole

Vegetal pole

Two cells

Four cells

Eight cells

Blastula

Blastopore

Gastrula

EXTERNAL FEATURES   In their external form, salamanders resemble the early amphibians that descended from fish. They have a long slender body with a muscular trunk and a long tail that helps them swim. They have four clawless limbs and they crawl very slowly. Salamanders may have either smooth or rough skin, but they never have scales.

INTERNAL FEATURES   Various internal features of the salamander are more developed than those of the fleshy, finned fish but less so than those of the land vertebrates. For example, the lung of the salamander is simple, with few subdivisions. It is similar to the lung of a lungfish. The heart of the salamander is more advanced than the heart of a fish. However, it is not as well organized as that of more complex animals. The kidney of the salamander is fishlike.

BREEDING HABITS AND DEVELOPMENT   Salamanders are *oviparous*, laying eggs that develop outside the female. The eggs of a few kinds of salamanders are fertilized outside the body of the female. The females lay eggs, and the male then deposits sperm on them. In most salamanders, however, fertilization occurs internally. The male salamander deposits a packet of sperm, a **spermatophore** (sper-MAT-ə-for), on the ground. He performs a special dance of courtship. The female then picks up the sperm packet with her **cloaca** (klō-Ā-kə), the structure into which the oviducts and intestine empty and through which wastes are passed to the outside. A special compartment of the oviduct protects the sperm until the female lays her eggs. As the eggs pass through this compartment, the sperm fertilizes them.

The female lays the fertilized eggs in water. The eggs are surrounded by a coat of jelly. The coat of jelly soaks up water so that the eggs will not dry out. The **animal pole**, or upper hemisphere, of each egg contains very little yolk. However, the **vegetal pole**, or lower hemisphere, contains a great deal. After being fertilized, the egg goes through a process called **cleavage**. The single egg cell divides into two halves. The two resulting cells, which will become the right and left sides of the body, remain attached. Each of these two cells divides again, producing four cells. Because of the concentration of yolk, the vegetal pole of the egg divides more slowly than does the animal pole. Many small cells form at the animal pole, and a few large yolky cells form at the vegetal pole.

After several hundred divisions, the salamander embryo resembles a hollow ball of cells and is called a **blastula** (BLAS-tyoo-lə). A hole called a **blastopore** develops at the vegetal pole. The cells from the animal pole of the blastula flow through this hole into the hollow interior. Soon the embryo looks like a double-layered sac, with cells on the inside and cells on the outside. At this stage it is called a **gastrula.** The outside layer of cells develops into the skin, and the inner layer develops into the gut lining, skeleton, and muscle.

The cells of the embryo gradually change into recognizable body structures. The larval salamander that hatches from the egg looks much like an adult except that it has feathery gills on the outside of its neck. Like the adult, it has teeth and is *carnivorous*, or meat-eating. After two to four months, the larval salamander changes into an adult. The salamander loses its gills and forms air-breathing lungs. Once this happens, the salamander can move from the water to a land habitat.

Some salamanders are able to grow a new tail or limbs if the original ones are lost or injured. This ability to grow new body parts is called *regeneration*. Salamanders can regenerate limbs throughout their life.

Your students have already learned about regeneration in worms and echinoderms. You might assign to some students the task of researching this topic as it applies to mammals, including human beings. Have students report on current scientific experiments.

Amphibians without Tails

Frogs and toads are the tailless amphibians. They have short bodies and muscular hind legs. They are adapted to habitats all over the world. About 2900 species of frogs and toads are known to live on the earth. Many toads and frogs are useful to people, eating insects that are harmful to crops.

TOADS   There are several hundred species of toads. The common American toad is classified in the genus *Bufo*. Toads live in all parts of the world except Australia and the polar regions. Typically, toads are found on land in moist soil. However, some species are found in dry areas.

Although toads are closely related to frogs, toads differ from frogs in some ways. Toads have dry, warty skin. They keep their skin moist by being active during rains and by moving about at night. By being active at night, toads can reduce water loss from their skin. During dry or cold weather, toads keep moist by digging into the ground. Unlike frogs, toads have skin glands behind their eyes that secrete a substance that is irritating or poisonous to other organisms. However, these substances do not seem to affect snakes, because snakes often feed on toads. Toads do not have teeth, and they have relatively shorter hind legs than do frogs.

Toads begin their life cycle in the water as fertilized eggs. The females of most species of toads lay jellylike strings of eggs up to 3.5 meters long. However, some species lay eggs one at a time. A single female may lay 20,000 eggs.

Highlight

The three main orders of amphibians are *Apoda, Caudata,* and *Anura.* The apodans are burrowing, legless amphibians. The tailed amphibians are classified in the order *Caudata.* Salamanders, newts, and mudpuppies are tailed amphibians. The tailless amphibians are classified in the order *Anura.* Frogs and toads are classified in this order.

Figure 31-3 The toad (*left*) and the frog (*right*) are examples of tailless amphibians.

Sidelight

Frogs vary greatly in size. Many species are as small as 1.5 centimeters in length. The largest frog, the Goliath frog, is 30 centimeters long.

The eggs hatch into small dark tadpoles, which develop into young toads.

FROGS Frogs are found throughout the world, except Antarctica. They live in ponds, lakes, marshes, and other wet habitats. Frogs are classified into about 18 family groupings. The true frogs are the most common and well-known family group. Other families include the tree frogs and the narrow-mouthed frogs. In North America, the most common frog species is the leopard frog, or *Rana pipiens*. Other species of frogs found in North America are the bull frog, green frog, and wood frog. In recent years, the numbers of frogs in some species have been reduced because ponds and marshes have been drained and filled in.

Frogs have some special behavior patterns that help them survive changes in their environment. Since the frog is cold-blooded, its blood decreases in temperature as air temperature falls. The frog, however, does not freeze during winter. It digs a hole in the mud at the bottom of a pond or in damp spots in the woods, below the frost line. The frog then enters the hole, where it spends the winter. During this period, the frog's body processes slow down, so that it needs very little oxygen. What little it does need is absorbed through its thin, moist skin. This state of winter rest is called **hibernation** (hī-bər-NĀ-shən). When the air begins to warm in the spring, the frog becomes active again.

In the summer, if the weather becomes too hot and dry, the frog will bury itself in the relatively cool mud to bring down its body temperature. This behavior, called **estivation** (es-tə-VĀ-shən), continues until the weather cools.

SECTION REVIEW   Answers on page T–82.

1. List three orders of amphibians.
2. What is a blastopore?
3. What is hibernation?

The Frog: A Representative Amphibian

The anatomy of the three types of amphibians varies considerably. However, the anatomy of the frog is representative of many of the general features, both external and internal, of most amphibians.

External Features

The frog has a short body with a pointed flat head and four limbs. The skin of the frog is smooth, thin, and moist, and serves as an important breathing organ. The skin contains pigment cells called *chromatophores*. Frogs appear green in light because the pigment cells absorb all but the green wavelengths of light.

The skin contains *mucus glands*. These glands are found mainly in two folds of skin running from behind each eye along the back to the base of the hind legs. The mucus glands keep the skin from drying out. The frog has no scales or other protective covering.

The frog has large, bulging eyes. Near the tip of the snout are *external nares*. The external nares are openings that lead into a *nasal cavity*. Behind each eye is a **tympanum,** or circular eardrum. A middle ear cavity is located behind each tympanum. Each middle ear is connected to the mouth cavity by an **Eustachian tube.** The Eustachian tubes have canals that allow air to enter the middle ear. Therefore, the air pressure on the outside and the inside of the tympanum remains equal. At the posterior end of the trunk is the *anus*, the external opening of the cloaca. The cloaca stores the digestive wastes of both sexes and the sperm of the males.

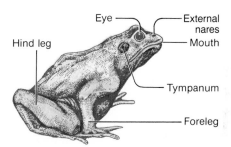

Figure 31-4   External Features of a Frog

Movement and Muscles

The hind legs of the frog are used for swimming and jumping. The hind feet have five toes with webbing between them. The hind feet act as paddles when the frog swims. The large hind legs allow the frog to leap, and thus escape predators. For example, some frogs can jump as far as 20 meters.

Sidelight

The old story that people can get warts from touching a frog's skin is not true. Warts are caused by viruses.

At this point, you may want to assign to your students the first of the Extensions and Applications at the end of this chapter.

The front legs have four toes and are shorter than the hind legs. They cushion the frog when it lands after jumping. The front legs are held motionless along the side of the body when the frog swims.

Skeleton

The spine of the frog is made up of nine *vertebrae*. A **cervical vertebra** allows the head some freedom of movement. A **sacral vertebra** helps to support each hind leg as the

Figure 31-5 Skeleton of a Frog

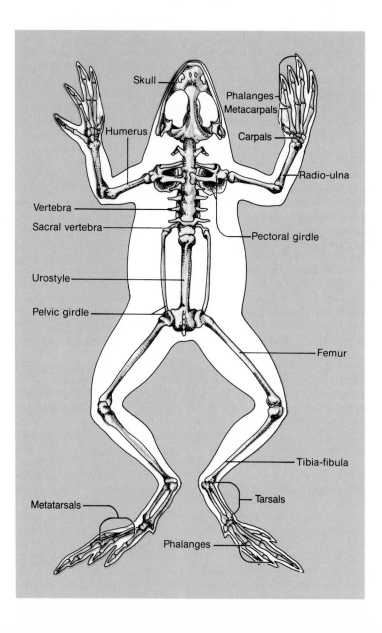

animal jumps. The other seven vertebrae are **trunk vertebrae.** Several fused vertebrae form a long **urostyle** at the posterior end of the spine.

The skull is made up of the bones of the braincase, face, and jaws. An opening in the skull allows the spinal cord to pass from the braincase into the spine, which joins the skull at its rear.

The *pectoral girdle* is made up of bones that attach to the front limbs. The pectoral girdle includes the breastbone, the collar bone, and the bones of the shoulder blade. The bones of the front limbs fit into sockets on the pectoral girdle, and the muscles of the limbs attach to the girdle itself.

Three pairs of fused bones make up the *pelvic girdle*, which is attached on each side of the spinal column to the sacral vertebra. The hind limbs fit into sockets in the pelvic girdle, and the muscles of the hind limbs attach to the sockets rather than to the girdle.

The front and hind limbs have a similar structure. The forelimb skeleton is made up of the bones of the upper arm, lower arm, wrist, hand, and fingers. The hind limb skeleton is made up of the bones of the thigh, shin, ankle, foot, and toes.

Organ Systems

The organs and organ systems of the frog are more complex than those of the fishes. They are also characteristic of those of many amphibians.

NERVOUS SYSTEM The brain of the frog is more highly developed than that of fishes. The *olfactory lobes* are not as large as they are in fishes, but the two halves of the *cerebrum* are longer than they are in fishes. The *optic lobes* are quite large. Behind the optic lobes is the *cerebellum*. The *medulla oblongata* is joined to the *spinal cord*. Although the frog's brain is larger than that of fishes of the same size, its spinal cord is shorter.

The eyes of the frog have an upper lid and a lower lid that do not move. The eyes are covered by a protective, transparent piece of skin called the **nictitating membrane.** The nictitating membrane also keeps the frog's eyes moist when the frog is on land. The outer surface of the frog's eye is flat, permitting it to see well when it is out of the water. Special muscles help the eye to focus. The frog's eye is, in general, more advanced than the eye of the fish.

As well as having a tympanum, frogs have an inner ear, as fishes do. In the frog, the inner ear serves as an organ of

Highlight

The frog is representative of all amphibians. The frog has organs and organ systems that are characteristic of many amphibians. Among these organs are a thin, smooth, moist skin and a three-chambered heart. Both the skin and the lungs are important to the functioning of the respiratory system.

Some of your students might be interested in finding out how the ear serves as an organ of balance.

balance as well as an organ of hearing. Unlike fishes, frogs have a middle ear bone that transmits sound waves to the inner ear.

The tongue of the frog has small bumps on it, which are taste buds. The skin of the frog, like that of fishes, is sensitive to touch and temperature. In the nasal cavity are olfactory cells similar to those in fishes.

DIGESTIVE SYSTEM   The frog is an insect-eating animal. It catches insects with its long, sticky tongue. The tongue is attached at the front of the mouth, and is flipped over and out. Instantly, the tongue is drawn back into the mouth with its prey. Then the frog closes its mouth and swallows the prey. Two teeth on the roof of the frog's mouth help hold the prey. These teeth are the **vomerine teeth.** The **maxillary teeth** line the edge of the upper jaw of the frog. These small cone-shaped teeth also help hold the prey. There are no teeth on the lower jaw. Glands in the mouth moisten the food, which is then passed down the esophagus to the stomach. Glands in the stomach secrete gastric fluids, which begin to break down the food. At the lower end of the stomach is an opening called the **pylorus.** The pylorus is controlled by a muscular valve. When this valve opens, the partly digested food is passed on to the small intestine. The small intestine contains several loops that are held in place in the abdomen by a clear membrane called the **mesentery.** The mesentery is attached to the body wall.

The part of the small intestine nearest the stomach is called the **duodenum** (doo-ə-DĒ-n'm). A yellowish gland called the *pancreas* releases three enzymes into the duodenum, which also receives *bile* from the liver. The bile, which breaks down fats, is stored in the *gall bladder* and travels through a *bile duct* into the intestine.

The next section of the small intestine is the **ileum.** The ileum is connected to the wider but shorter large intestine. The food that cannot be digested by the small intestine is stored for a time in the large intestine as wastes. The wastes pass into the cloaca and are excreted through the cloacal opening.

EXCRETORY SYSTEM   The frog , like the fish, has a *kidney* that is used in the excretion of nitrogen wastes. The kidney also is involved in maintaining water and salt balance in the animal's body. The waste products of the cells are released into the bloodstream in the form of carbon dioxide, water, and urea. The carbon dioxide leaves the body mostly through the skin. The other waste products are collected from the blood by the kidney. Wastes are carried in the form

Internal nares openings

Opening to esophagus

Vomerine teeth

Maxillary teeth

Glottis

Tongue

Figure 31-6   The structures of a frog's mouth and tongue are well adapted for catching insects.

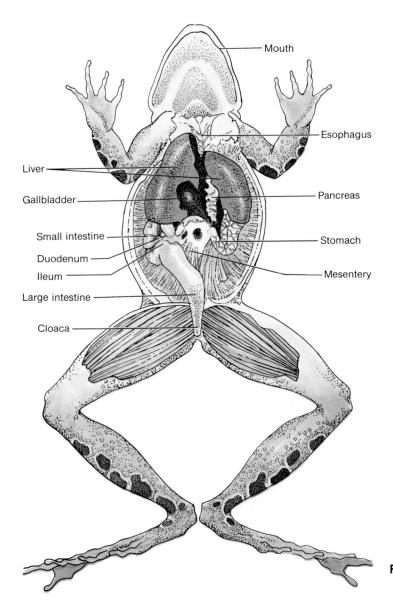

Mouth

Esophagus

Liver

Gallbladder

Pancreas

Small intestine

Duodenum

Stomach

Ileum

Mesentery

Large intestine

Cloaca

Figure 31-7 Digestive System of a Frog

of urine from the kidney to the *bladder* by tiny tubes called *urinary ducts*. In the male frog, the ducts carry sperm as well as urine. The urine is held in the bladder until a special valve opens, permitting the urine to flow into the cloaca and then out of the body. Frogs absorb a great deal of water through their skin and, as a result, must excrete a great deal of urine.

The frog also has another organ, the liver, that plays a role in nitrogen waste removal. Urea forms in the liver and is passed into the intestine and excreted with the feces.

RESPIRATORY SYSTEM   A frog respires in several ways. When a frog is hibernating or sitting still under water, it respires directly through its skin. Because the skin is thin and moist, oxygen and carbon dioxide pass through it to the blood vessels beneath.

When a frog is active, respiration through the skin does not provide enough oxygen. The frog then takes in air through the mouth. The lining of the mouth and pharynx has many blood vessels, providing a suitable place for gas exchange.

The frog also uses its lungs for breathing. When a frog brings air into its lungs, the mouth is tightly closed. Oxygen-rich air goes through the external nares into the pharynx. An opening called the **glottis** leads from the pharynx to the **larynx,** or voice box. From the larynx the air passes directly to the lungs through tubes called **bronchi.** The air then flows back from the lungs into the mouth. Immediately, the throat muscles contract and the air passes again to the lungs. After the air moves several times between the mouth and lungs, the glottis closes. The nostrils open and the oxygen-poor air moves out of the frog.

When the lungs of a male frog force air into the larynx, the vocal organ can be made to vibrate, causing a sound that attracts mates. The sound is made louder by vocal sacs in the mouth. In many male frogs, the vocal sacs come together to form a large throat sac that inflates when the frog is calling. Each species of frog makes a different calling sound.

CIRCULATORY SYSTEM   The frog's three-chambered heart is more highly developed than the two-chambered heart of the perch. A double circuit of blood passes through the frog's heart. One circuit carries blood between the heart and the lungs. The other carries blood between the heart and the rest of the body.

A membrane separates the *atrium* of the frog's heart into two chambers. When the frog is taking air into its lungs, the *pulmonary vein* carries oxygen-rich blood from the lungs to the left atrium. The right atrium receives oxygen-poor blood from the body. The third chamber of the heart, the *ventricle*, pumps the blood out of the heart.

When the ventricle contracts, the blood passes into the large *truncus arteriosus*, a vessel that divides into other main arteries. The *carotid arteries* carry the blood to the head. The right and left *systemic arches* come together below the liver to form the *dorsal aorta*. Branches of this artery take blood to the digestive system, kidneys, legs, and other parts of the body. The *pulmocutaneous* (pul-mō-kyoo-TĀN-ē-əs) *artery* carries blood to the skin and lungs.

Sidelight

The bullfrog has about 80 milliliters of blood for every kilogram of body weight. This ratio is almost twice as high as the ratio in human beings.

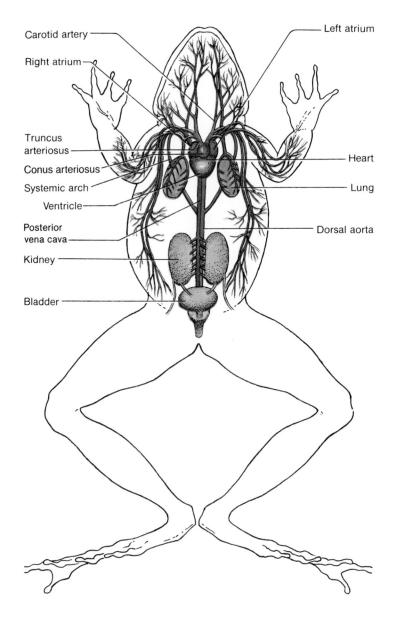

Carotid artery

Right atrium

Truncus arteriosus

Conus arteriosus

Systemic arch

Ventricle

Posterior vena cava

Kidney

Bladder

Left atrium

Heart

Lung

Dorsal aorta

Figure 31-8 Circulatory and Excretory Systems of a Frog

Veins return the blood from the organs to the heart. The *ventral abdominal vein* carries blood from the hind legs and kidney to the liver. Small veins from the intestine drain into the *hepatic portal vein*, a large vein that passes through the pancreas. This vein passes into the liver, where it breaks up into *capillaries*, or tiny blood vessels. Blood is taken from the liver by the *hepatic veins* to the heart. The oxygen-poor blood enters a collecting vessel called the *sinus venosus*. The sinus venosus empties into the right atrium. The blood goes from there into the ventricle.

REPRODUCTIVE SYSTEM   Looking at external characteristics only, it is difficult to tell a male frog from a female frog except during the mating season. At this time, the thumb pads of the male appear to be black and swollen. The internal reproductive organs of the two sexes, however, are completely different.

In the female frog, a pair of transparent *ovaries* is located next to the kidneys. Attached to each ovary is a yellow fat body. Underneath each ovary is a whitish coiled **oviduct.** At the opening of the oviduct are cells with whiplike cilia. Each ovary makes hundreds of black and white eggs that ripen all at once and are shed into the body cavity. The cilia propel the eggs into the funnel-like openings of the oviducts. These ducts secrete a jelly that coats the eggs. Each oviduct widens into a thin-walled **ovisac.** The eggs are stored here until they are laid. The two ovisacs join and lead into the cloaca.

In the male frog, a yellow *testis* is located at the anterior, or front, end of each kidney. Attached to the testis are

CLOSE-UP: *Dr. Janice Brothers*

There was never any doubt in Janice Brothers' mind that she would be a biologist. "The first time I looked at an egg developing under a microscope and saw the colors, the beauty of it, I was hooked," she says.

The first egg Dr. Brothers examined was a frog egg that she studied in a grade-school class. Today, Dr. Brothers is an amphibian embryologist at the University of California, Berkeley. Dr. Brothers received a Ph.D. in zoology from Indiana University. Though she has studied thousands of eggs since that first one, her excitement has never worn off. "You know, a good many scientists find they never lose their wonder of the world," she says.

At Berkeley, Dr. Brothers is an assistant professor in the Department of Zoology. During the school year, she teaches courses in vertebrate development and embryology. When summer comes, she is free to do research, and she spends hours in her university lab.

Dr. Brothers uses amphibian eggs in her research. She finds salamander, toad, and common pond frog eggs excellent for study because

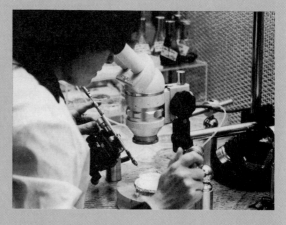

they develop outside the female's body and are large enough to handle easily. Dr. Brothers' chief interest is the study of how genes in an amphibian egg dictate precise growth patterns to cells. One of the questions she is studying is why certain cells combine to form muscle while others grow to become skin or bone. "The answer could shed light on human development," she says.

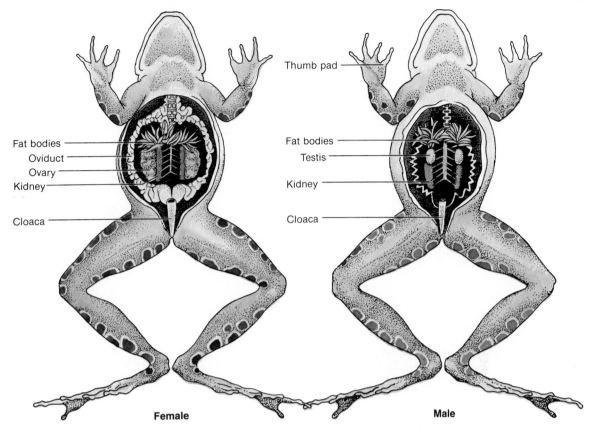

Figure 31-9 Reproductive Systems of Female and Male Frogs

the fingerlike strands of a fat body. Tiny white sperm ducts connect the testes to the kidneys. The sperm ducts transport sperm into the urinary ducts. The urinary ducts have enlarged structures called **seminal vesicles,** which store sperm. The urinary ducts carry the sperm to the cloaca, where it is released to the outside.

Breeding Habits and Development

The eggs of most frogs are fertilized externally. Using its enlarged thumb pads, the male clasps the female. As the male does so, the female releases the eggs. The male releases sperm, which fertilizes the eggs. The thick jelly coat that surrounds the fertilized eggs soaks up water and protects the eggs from drying out. The eggs usually have a brown or black pigment on the animal pole. The dark color absorbs heat, causing the eggs to develop faster.

Figure 31-10 During mating, the male clasps the female and releases sperm that fertilizes the eggs the female releases.

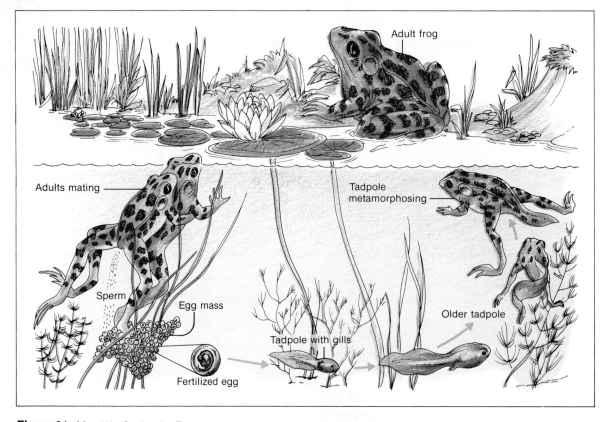

Figure 31-11   Life Cycle of a Frog

At this point, you may want to have your students do the Laboratory Investigation at the end of this chapter.

After 2 to 30 days, depending on the water temperature and the species of frog, the eggs hatch into tadpoles. The tadpoles have a short tail, lidless eyes, and a pair of suckers that permit them to hold on to objects. Three gills develop on the sides of the tadpole's head. A fold of skin then covers the gills. The suckers are eventually lost, and a pair of lips with horny teeth appear. The lips are used for feeding on algae. Hind legs appear first, and, later, forelegs break through the gill covers. The mouth widens, and it develops a tongue and strong jaws. The lungs complete their development, and the gills disappear. The tail is lost, and external nares form. When the metamorphosis is complete, the aquatic vegetarian tadpole has changed into a terrestrial carnivorous frog.

SECTION REVIEW   Answers on page T–82.

1. What is a tympanum?
2. Describe the brain of the frog.
3. What are the functions of the three chambers of the frog's heart?

LABORATORY INVESTIGATION 31 For additional information, see page T–82.

Observing Metamorphosis in Frogs

Purpose Metamorphosis in frogs is a dramatic illustration of animal development. Frog eggs may be found in ponds, ditches, lakes, swamps, and other bodies of water in the early spring. The eggs appear as clumps or irregular masses and sometimes are attached to twigs or other submerged debris. The purpose of this investigation is to observe the various stages of metamorphosis in frogs.

Materials *(per group)* ● Aquariums or large glass jars (liter- and 2-liter-sized) containing frog eggs and tadpoles in various stages of development in pond or lake water ● Baby-food jars ● Aquarium nets ● Magnifying glasses or dissecting microscopes ● Chart or book showing various stages of metamorphosis

Procedure **1.** Fill a baby-food jar with pond or lake water from the large containers. **2.** Using an aquarium net, remove some frog eggs from the large containers and place them in a baby-food jar. **3.** Observe the eggs in their jellylike coating with a magnifying glass or dissecting microscope. Notice the different-colored regions of the egg. Draw some eggs in your notebook. Use shading to show the different colored regions. Label the animal and vegetal poles of the egg. Then return the eggs to their original container. **4.** Refill the jar with water and tadpoles. Observe the swimming and feeding behavior of tadpoles in different stages of development. **5.** Draw. tadpoles in various stages of development. Use the drawings of tadpole development shown in this investigation to help you determine the approximate age of the stages that you observe. **6.** Identify the caudal fin, mouth, eyes, operculum, gills, nostrils, horny lip, hind legs and forelegs on the tadpoles. **7.** Observe the development of the eggs and tadpoles during the school term.

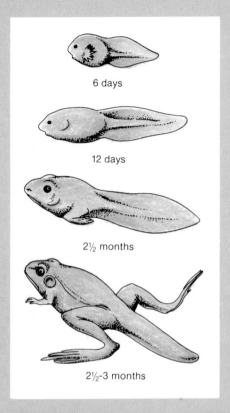

6 days

12 days

2½ months

2½–3 months

Observations and Conclusions **1.** What is the function of the jellylike coating surrounding the eggs? **2.** Describe the function of the caudal fin. Why does it disappear as the tadpole matures? **3.** How do the mouths of young and old tadpoles differ? **4.** How do the eyes of young and old tadpoles differ? **5.** How do tadpoles carry out respiration? **6.** Which pair of legs appears first? **7.** How long does it take for eggs to hatch into tadpoles? For tadpoles to develop into frogs?

CHAPTER SUMMARY

Classification of Amphibians Amphibians are animals that spend part of their lives in water and part of their lives on land. Members of this class include the caecilians, which are tropical amphibians without legs, salamanders, frogs, and toads.

The salamanders are in the order *Caudata.* They have a long slender body with a tail that helps them swim. They live under damp logs, in streams, or in lakes.

Salamander eggs are fertilized inside the female's body and then laid in water, where they develop. The egg goes through a process called cleavage in which the egg cell divides many times to produce a blastula. Migration of these cells produces a gastrula, which has several layers of cells. The layers develop gradually into different body structures. The salamander egg hatches, and in a process called metamorphosis, the larva changes into an adult salamander.

The frogs and toads make up the order *Anura.* They have a short body and long legs. Toads are rough-skinned; frogs are smooth-skinned. Frogs have evolved special patterns of behavior, such as hibernation, estivation, and regeneration, which make them able to live within a changing environment.

The Frog: A Representative Amphibian In the moist skin of the frog are pigment cells and mucus glands. The hind legs of the frog are used for jumping and swimming. The front legs cushion the frog's landing when it jumps.

The frog's skeleton has a spine with nine vertebrae. The brain is encased in a bony skull. The bones of the front and hind limbs of the frog attach to the pectoral and pelvic girdles.

The frog respires through the skin, the lining of the mouth, and the lungs. The brain of the frog is more developed than the fish brain. The frog possesses a tympanum and a middle ear bone. The frog tongue contains taste buds.

The frog eliminates nitrogen wastes during excretion. During the digestion process, food passes from the mouth through the esophagus to the stomach, where it is partly digested. The food is digested further in the small intestine. Undigested food passes through the large intestine to the cloaca, from which it is excreted.

The frog's three-chambered heart pumps blood in two circuits. Blood is pumped between the heart and body, and between the heart and lungs.

In frogs, fertilization occurs in water outside the female's body. The frog eggs hatch into tadpoles, which have gills and eat plant material. During metamorphosis, the tadpoles become four-legged, air-breathing carnivores.

CHAPTER VOCABULARY

animal pole	**gastrula**	**pylorus**
blastopore	**glottis**	**sacral vertebra**
blastula	**hibernation**	**seminal vesicle**
bronchi	**ileum**	**spermatophore**
cervical vertebra	**larynx**	**trunk vertebra**
cleavage	**mesentery**	**tympanum**
cloaca	**maxillary teeth**	**urostyle**
duodenum	**nictitating membrane**	**vegetal pole**
estivation	**oviduct**	**vomerine teeth**
Eustachian tube	**ovisac**	

REVIEW of FACTS and CONCEPTS   Answers on pages T–82 to T–83.

On a separate sheet of paper, answer each of the following as completely as possible.

1. List the characteristics of the members of the order *Apoda*.
2. List the characteristics of the members of the order *Caudata*.
3. Describe the cleavage process of the salamander egg.
4. List the characteristics of the members of the order *Anura*.
5. Distinguish between a frog and a toad.
6. In what regions of the world are toads not found?
7. What is the advantage of hibernation?
8. List the functions of the frog's limbs.
9. What types of vertebrae are present in the frog?
10. How does the frog respire?
11. What organs remove wastes from the frog?
12. How is the heart of the frog different from that of the perch?
13. Fat bodies in frogs change size during the year. They are largest in the summer. Why is this so?
14. What is the mating function of the thumb pads on the male frog?
15. Summarize metamorphosis in the frog.

EXTENSIONS and APPLICATIONS   For additional information, see page T–83.

1. Obtain a live frog. Put it into an aquarium and watch it swim. Place it on a table top and watch it jump. Which limbs does it use to swim? To jump? What structures are used in breathing? Place a live insect in the aquarium with the frog and observe how the frog feeds.
2. Collect frog or salamander eggs and place them in an aquarium. Each day, draw or write down any changes you observe.
3. Using reference materials, prepare a report on tree frogs and their use as sources of arrow poison by South American Indians.

SUGGESTED READINGS

Cochran, D. M., *Living Amphibians of the World*. Garden City, N.Y.: Doubleday.
This illustrated, large-format book describes all of the kinds of amphibians found on earth today.

Donaldson, G., *Frogs*. New York: Van Nostrand Reinhold.
This book explores frogs as subjects in literature, medicine, and science.

Noble, G. K., *The Biology of the Amphibia*. New York: Dover.
This book examines the anatomy and physiology of toads, frogs, and salamanders.

Rugh, R., *The Frog*. New York: McGraw-Hill.
This book provides descriptions and numerous illustrations of the reproduction process and the embryological development of frogs.

32 Reptiles

Chapter Objectives   *After completing this chapter, you will be able to:*

a ◼ Describe the general features of reptiles. p. 519
b ◼ Describe the historical development of reptiles. p. 517
c ◼ List the characteristics of reptiles in the different orders. p. 519
d ◼ Describe the organ systems of reptiles. p. 527
e ◼ Describe the breeding habits of reptiles. p. 531

For teaching aids for this chapter, including a chapter overview and teaching strategies, see pages T-83 to T-85. The page number next to each chapter objective refers to the text page where the information needed to fulfill the objective begins.

The casque-headed chameleon is a lizardlike reptile.

Fossil evidence indicates that the first primitive reptiles evolved about 300 million years ago. These early reptiles adapted very successfully to many different habitats in fresh water, in the sea, and on the land. There is evidence that some species have evolved into birds. Other reptiles may have been the ancestors of the mammals, now the dominant form of life.

Four groups of reptiles are living today. These are the lizardlike tuataras, the turtles, the snakes and lizards, and the crocodiles and alligators. Only a few species of reptiles are harmful to human beings, and many are useful. For example, snakes help control the rat population, and lizards eat insects. In addition, turtles are used as food by some people.

The History of Reptiles

Primitive reptiles, called *cotylosaurs* (kō-TIL-ə-sorz), left the water about 300 million years ago. Slowly, these terrestrial, or land-living, animals multiplied taking over more and more land. By the end of the Permian Period, about 230 million years ago, they had all but replaced the amphibians as the dominant vertebrate life form. The reptiles had become so widespread during the Permian Period that the Mesozoic Era, which followed, is often called the Age of Reptiles.

The reptiles owe their great success to three important adaptations. These adaptations are their scaly skin, internal fertilization, and hard-shelled egg. The scaly skin of reptiles prevented their body fluids from evaporating. Through internal fertilization of the hard-shelled **amniotic egg**, reptiles did not have to reproduce in water, as the amphibians did. An amniotic egg is an egg that has a membrane and a hard shell that enclose the developing organism. This membrane is called the *amnion.* The soft-shelled eggs of amphibians had to develop in a watery environment. In the hard-shelled amniotic egg, however, a reptile embryo could develop in a relatively safe, liquid-filled chamber. Reptiles could therefore reproduce on land.

Scientists think that the cotylosaurs gave rise to several major groups of specialized reptiles. Today's lizards, snakes, and tuataras are thought to be direct descendants of cotylosaurs. Mammal-like reptiles called *therapsids* (thər-AP-sidz) also may have descended from the cotylosaurs. Now extinct, the therapsids evolved into true mammals. The *Thecodonts* (THĒ-kō-dontz) probably sprang from the cotylosaur line too. Now almost all extinct, the thecodonts included the **dinosaurs,** the *pterosaurs* (TER-ə-sorz), or flying reptiles, and modern crocodiles.

The dinosaurs, whose name means terrible lizards, are probably the most familiar of all the early reptiles. It was long thought that the dinosaurs were cold-blooded. Recently, some scientists have proposed that dinosaurs may have been warm-blooded. By warm-blooded, scientists mean that the body temperature of dinosaurs remained stable, regardless of the temperature of the environment. The fossilized bones of dinosaurs show indications of extensive **capillary beds.** Capillary beds are groups of small blood vessels that are also found in modern warm-blooded animals. At least some of the dinosaurs may have had body coverings that conserved heat.

The dinosaurs were numerous during the Jurassic and Cretaceous Periods of the Mesozoic Era, but they are now

At this point, you may want to assign to your students the first of the Extensions and Applications at the end of this chapter.

extinct. By the end of the Cretaceous Period of the Mesozoic Era, most of them had disappeared. The reason the dinosaurs became extinct is still not known. Many scientists think that a sudden and drastic change in climate contributed to the extinction. The change in climate may have destroyed the foods of dinosaurs. Some scientists have found evidence suggesting that such a change in climate might have occurred when a comet or asteroid smashed into the earth.

Dinosaurs varied greatly, especially in size. Although most of them were small, some were very large. The large dinosaurs include *Brontosaurus, Triceratops, Tyrannosaurus,* and *Pterodactyl.*

Figure 32–1 *Tyrannosaurus* (top), *Pterodactyl* (center), *Triceratops* (bottom left), and *Brontosaurus* (bottom right) were among the large dinosaurs that lived during the Mesozoic Era.

Brontosaurus When people hear the word "dinosaur," they usually think of the huge *quadrupedal,* or four-footed, *Brontosaurus. Brontosaurus* and its close relative *Diplodocus* (di-PLAHD-ə-kus) were among the largest of all terrestrial vertebrates. Fossil records indicate that some individuals may have been up to 30 meters long, and they probably weighed as much as 32,000 kilograms. Fossil teeth indicate that these huge creatures were primarily **herbivores,** or plant-eaters. Although they had strong legs, these dinosaurs probably spent at least some of their time in water where their great weight was buoyed up.

Triceratops The *Triceratops,* also quadrupedal, grew to a maximum length of 8 meters. This dinosaur was covered with heavy armor. The posterior margin of the *Triceratops'* skull grew into a large bony frill, or collar, that protected its neck. Three huge horns on the front of the skull provided a defense from the larger and faster *bipedal,* or two-footed, dinosaurs that preyed on *Triceratops.*

Tyrannosaurus The *Tyrannosaurus* was probably the largest *carnivore* that ever lived on the earth. This bipedal dinosaur was a very successful predator. Nearly 20

Tyrannosaurus

Pterodactyl

Triceratops

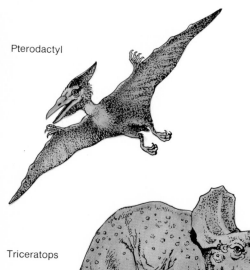

Brontosaurus

meters long, it stood 8 meters tall. Its hind limbs were strong and supported its body. Its very small forelimbs were used mainly for grasping and tearing. The huge jaws of *Tyrannosaurus* were moved by well-developed jaw muscles and filled with long, sharp teeth.

Pterodactyl The *Pterodactyl* (tər-ə-DAK-t'l) first appeared in the Jurassic Period. It was able to glide and perhaps even to fly. Several body features allowed *Pterodactyl* to do so. The skeleton of *Pterodactyl* was generally lighter than that of most reptiles. In addition, it had two 4-meter-long membranous wings. Each wing was attached to the long bones of both a forelimb and a fourth finger. The *Pterodactyl* fossils found in marine sediments suggest that these reptiles lived along seacoasts. If they did, then they might have been able to soar from high coastal cliffs on updrafts from the sea. The tooth-lined beak of *Pterodactyl* suggests that this reptile fed mostly on fish.

SECTION REVIEW   Answers on page T–83.

1. What is a cotylosaur?
2. What adaptations enabled land-dwelling reptiles to develop?
3. Name three types of dinosaurs.

Classification of Reptiles

Like amphibians, modern reptiles are cold-blooded. Their body temperatures depend directly on the temperature of their surroundings. As a result, most reptiles are found only in temperate or tropical climates. Even in temperate climates, some reptiles must hibernate in mud at the bottom of a pond or remain inactive in burrows throughout the cold months.

The organisms in the class *Reptilia* have horny scales or plates that cover their bodies. These scales are made from skin cells that are filled with a hard protein called *keratin*. The reptiles are also air-breathers, and their hearts have a partially divided ventricle.

About 6500 species of reptiles are living today. *Herpetologists*, or scientists who study reptiles and amphibians, divide the living reptiles into four orders.

Order *Rhynchocephalia* (rin-kə-sə-FAL-ya) The single species in this order is called *Sphenodon*, or tuatara. It is nearly extinct.

Highlight

All of the 6500 or so species of reptiles alive today are placed into one of four reptilian orders.

At this point, you may want to assign to your students the second and/or third of the Extensions and Applications at the end of this chapter.

Figure 32–2 The *Sphenodon*, or tuatara, is the only surviving member of the reptilian order *Rynchocephalia*.

Order *Chelonia* (kə-LŌN-ya) The organisms in this order have two bony shells. The turtles and tortoises make up this order of *Reptilia*.

Order *Squamata* The organisms in this order are covered with horny skin scales. The snakes and lizards are classified in this order.

Order *Crocodilia* The organisms in this order are large reptiles with long, narrow heads. The crocodiles and alligators are examples of animals in this order.

Tuataras

The tuatara, or *Sphenodon punctatum*, looks much like a lizard. The tuatara has dark olive skin and yellow spines on its back. The tuatara grows to a length of about 70 centimeters. It lives in a burrow, and it is carnivorous, feeding primarily on insects. The eggs of this reptile require more than a year to develop and hatch.

As the oldest surviving species of reptile, the tuatara is virtually no different from its Mesozoic ancestors. It is different from other reptiles in that it has a well-developed **parietal** (pə-RĪ-ə-t'l) **body,** or third eye, beneath the skin. The parietal body, located in the middle of the head, can detect light and darkness.

Turtles and Tortoises

Members of the order *Chelonia* are known by several names. Tortoises live only on land, and they have short,

Highlight

The order *Rhynchocephalia* includes only one species, the insect-eating tuatara. The order *Chelonia* includes many species of hard-shelled turtles and tortoises.

stumpy legs with claws. Turtles spend much of their time in water, and they have legs that serve as paddles. Turtles and tortoises have very long life spans. The longest-living species of *Chelonia* is the giant Galapagos tortoise that normally lives 100 to 200 years.

Turtles and tortoises differ from other reptiles in that they have hard shells. These shells offer very good protection, but they slow down movement. The **carapace**, or dorsal shell, is made of bone. The vertebrae are fused with the carapace. The underside, or **plastron**, of the shell is made from parts of the pectoral girdle that are fused together. Covering the shell are plates, called **scutes**, that look like scales. Although the scutes give protection, they restrict movement.

Turtles and tortoises do not have teeth. Instead, they have a hard beak similar to that of birds. Tortoises are usually herbivorous, but turtles are **omnivores**, eating both plants and meat. The snapping turtle can catch and crush young ducks and muskrats with its powerful jaws.

Snakes

The snakes and lizards make up the order *Squamata*, whose name means scaly. Snakes have long, thin bodies that are covered with scales. Snakes do not have limbs. There are about 3000 species of snakes. Some well-known species are rattlesnakes, garter snakes, and water snakes. Generally, snakes play an important and positive role in nature.

NONPOISONOUS SNAKES Most snakes are nonpoisonous. Some snakes kill their prey by holding it against the ground and swallowing it alive and whole. The indigo snake and the black racer, for example, are nonpoisonous snakes that obtain food in this way. To take in large prey, the jaws of many snakes are specially hinged to open more widely than usual.

Other nonpoisonous snakes are *constrictors*. The constrictors wrap themselves around their prey and suffocate it by squeezing with muscular force. The constrictors then swallow the dead prey whole. Rat snakes, king snakes, and boas take their victims this way. One of the largest of all snakes, the python, is a nonpoisonous constrictor. The python grows as long as 10 meters, and it can consume a small pig.

POISONOUS SNAKES Poisonous snakes kill their prey by injecting *venom*, or poison, through a pair of **fangs**. These fangs, located at the front of the mouth, are large, hollow

Figure 32-3 The desert tortoise (*top*), green sea turtle (*center*), and red-eared turtle (*bottom*) are typical members of the reptilian order *Chelonia*.

Highlight

The order *Squamata* includes lizards and snakes, some of which are poisonous.

522

At this point, you may want to assign to your students the fourth of the Extensions and Applications at the end of this chapter.

Figure 32–4 The yellow anaconda (*top*), Sonora mountain king snake (*center*), and rough green snake (*bottom*) are examples of nonpoisonous snakes.

curved teeth. The venom moves down through each fang from a gland on either side of the head. These glands make and release venom.

There are three families of poisonous snakes. The *venomous snakes* of two of the families have a pair of tube-like fangs that are always erect. The third family is *vipers*. Vipers have fangs that are attached to a movable bone. The fangs fold back against the roof of the mouth when not in use.

The first family includes many of the most venomous snakes, such as the cobra, the mamba, and the North American coral snake. The coral snake has a blunt head and a body with broad rings of red and black that are separated by narrow yellow bands. The coral snake is often confused with the harmless scarlet king snake, whose color patterns are similar. The order of the red, black, and yellow bands on the scarlet king snake, however, are different from those of the coral snake.

The sea snakes are members of the second family of venomous snakes with nonmovable fangs. These snakes live permanently in the ocean, preying on fish. These very venomous snakes are found in the Pacific Ocean off the coast of Australia. Many fishermen have been fatally bitten by sea snakes accidentally caught in the fish nets.

The *old world vipers* and the *pit vipers* make up the third family of poisonous snakes. The old world vipers include the poisonous snakes of Europe, Asia, and Africa, except the cobra. The puff adder belongs to this family, and is the most common poisonous snake in Africa. It is responsible for more snake bite cases than any other African species.

The pit vipers include the rattlesnake, the copperhead, and the water moccasin of North America. Their name

Figure 32–5 The copperhead (*left*), coral snake (*center*), and coral cobra (*right*) are examples of poisonous snakes.

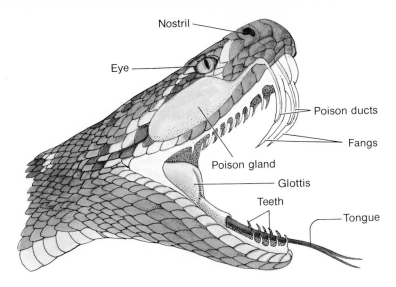

Nostril

Eye

Poison ducts

Fangs

Poison gland

Glottis

Teeth

Tongue

Figure 32-6 The mouth of a poisonous snake is adapted to kill its prey by injecting poisonous venom into its prey through a pair of fangs.

comes from the deep pits on the sides of their heads. These pits are heat-sensing organs that help pit vipers locate warm-blooded prey. The water moccasin eats fish, ducks, and frogs. Copperheads eat mice, other snakes, frogs, and toads. The rattlesnake feeds on mice, rats, rabbits, and the young of ground-nesting birds.

When a pit viper strikes, its fangs spring forward as the jaws open. The muscles of the poison gland force the venom through canals in the fangs and into the prey. The venom of most snakes is made up of two poisons. One is a **hemotoxin,** or a substance that destroys red blood cells and that alters blood clotting. The other is a **neurotoxin.** A neurotoxin interferes with the normal functions of the nervous system. The neurotoxin causes difficulty in breathing and swallowing. It can also interfere with the function of the heart. The sea snakes have a venom that affects muscles.

Lizards

Lizards are the other members of the order *Squamata.* They differ from snakes in a number of ways. Lizards have legs, movable eyelids, and external ear openings, none of which are possessed by snakes. Lizards live mainly in trees, on the ground, and in tunnels beneath the ground. These animals may be herbivores, omnivores, or carnivores. Most North American lizards are carnivores, preying on insects.

Sidelight

One of the world's smallest snakes is the Braminy blind snake. It is only about 15 centimeters long. Probably the most poisonous snake in the world is the bushmaster of southern Central America.

Sidelight

Geckoes, like cats and dogs, were once kept as house pets. At night, they would catch and eat household pests such as ants, roaches, and spiders.

Figure 32-7 The iguana (*top*), American anole (*center*), and komodo dragon lizard (*bottom*) are members of the reptilian order *Squamata*.

The anole, or American chameleon, is one type of lizard that is found in the southern United States. At rest, or on a dark background, the anole is brown or gray. When it becomes excited, or when it is placed on a green background, it turns a bright emerald green.

Another interesting lizard is the gecko. This medium-sized, nocturnal lizard lives in trees and hunts insects. The toes of the gecko are shaped like suction cups. They permit the lizard to climb. The special eyes of the gecko give it sharp sight, even in the dark. The slitlike pupil is unlike the eye of any other living reptile.

Although most lizards are quite small, some are large. The Komodo dragon of Malaysia, for example, is 4 meters long. The monitor lizard of Africa grows to a length of 2 meters. The largest lizard in the United States is the Gila (HĒ-lə) monster. It is one of only two poisonous lizards in the world. During the day, the Gila monster remains under rocks to avoid the heat of the desert, where it lives. At night, it hunts for mice and rabbits and kills them with its poisonous bite. It injects the venom through small teeth in the rear of the mouth, rather than through fangs. Gila monsters were once trapped and sold as curiosities to reptile collectors, and, as a result, they became very scarce. They are now protected by law.

Crocodiles and Alligators

Crocodiles and alligators are direct descendants of the crocodilians that existed during the Mesozoic Era. Crocodilians eat a mixed diet of birds, fish, mammals, turtles, and other animals. Attacks on human beings are rare. Crocodilians have many of the features of birds. For example, the heart of the alligator has four chambers, like that of a bird. Its brain is also very similar to that of a bird.

Modern crocodilians can be distinguished from one another by comparing the shapes of their heads. Alligators have a broad, round snout. The snout of the crocodile is tapered to a narrow point. Another way to identify a crocodilian is by a tooth that sticks out when the mouth is shut. When the mouth of the alligator is shut, its large fourth tooth fits into a cavity in the upper jaw. The tooth is hidden. When the mouth of the crocodile is closed, its fourth tooth protrudes over the upper jaw.

Both types of crocodilians spend their time swimming in the water and lying on the shore. The alligator is found only in the southeastern United States and in a small area of China. The crocodile is found throughout the tropics. In the United States, it is found only in the everglades of Florida.

Some of your students may be interested in tracing the evolution of crocodilians from the early cotylosaurs to the present crocodile and alligator.

Like other reptiles, crocodilians lay hard-shelled eggs on land. The female alligator, before laying her eggs, builds a large nest. She places torn vegetation in a pile, hollows out the center, and fills the hollow with mud. She then lays 10 to 100 eggs, covering the eggs with mud and vegetation. The heat from the decay of the vegetation causes the eggs to develop. The female guards the eggs for 2 to 3 months until the young hatch. As they hatch, the young make sounds that cause the female to rip open the top of the nest, permitting the young to crawl out.

The newly hatched alligators are about 20 centimeters long. If they are not eaten by bass, garfish, or other predators, they grow to a length of 1 meter by the time they are 3 years old. At 6 years, they are usually about 2 meters long. A fully grown male alligator is about 5.5 meters in length.

CAREER: Herpetologist

Herpetologists are scientists who study reptiles and amphibians. They study how these animals grow, behave, and reproduce. They try to describe the origins of the animals and how they spread across continents and around the world. New reptiles and amphibians are discovered, named, and classified each year. When new information is found, previously named reptiles and amphibians may also be reclassified.

Herpetologists pursue their studies in various ways. Some may concentrate on one aspect of herpetology. Those who carry out ecological work, for example, are interested in changes in populations and in the causes of these changes. Other herpetologists study reptile and amphibian fossils. They are interested in the structure, evolution, and distribution of animals that lived in the past. Some herpetologists specialize in behavior. They try to discover how members of the same species recognize one another. They try to determine which behavior patterns are learned and which are instinctive.

Herpetologists may travel widely. They may also use sophisticated biochemical equipment, electron microscopes, and computers. Often, they have student assistants or lab technicians as helpers on projects.

A bachelor's degree is needed to begin a career as a herpetologist and most herpetologists obtain doctoral degrees. A broad background in zoology and chemistry is necessary.

Many herpetologists work in museums as curators. Others are employed by colleges and universities, where they combine research and teaching. Some herpetologists work for government agencies, such as the United States Fish and Wildlife Service and state conservation departments.

For further career information, write to American Society of Ichthyologists and Herpetologists, Division of Reptiles, National Museum of Natural History, Washington, DC 20560.

Figure 32-8 Crocodiles and alligators are closely related reptiles. Notice that the crocodile (*left*) has a more tapered snout than the alligator (*right*). The crocodile also has teeth that visibly project from the lower jaw when the mouth is closed.

SECTION REVIEW   Answers on pages T–83 to T–84.

1. What is a herpetologist?
2. Describe several features of the tuatara.
3. What are the parts of the shell of a tortoise?
4. Contrast the features of snakes and lizards.

Anatomy of the Reptiles

The body of a reptile is divided into the head, the trunk, and the tail. Although most reptiles have four legs, snakes and a few lizards have no legs.

The tail has various functions in different reptiles. Some lizards can walk on their hind legs, balancing themselves with their long tails. The crocodilians use their long, powerful tail to propel themselves through the water and to defend themselves. The crocodile can also use its tail to knock prey into the water from the bank of a river. The tail of some lizards, such as the true chameleon, is prehensile. A **prehensile tail** is adapted for grasping, and it can be wrapped around tree limbs. Some small lizards can break free of their tails when they are seized by predators. The predator is distracted by the wriggling tail, and the lizard escapes. The growth of a new, and usually shorter, tail is called *regeneration*.

The horny scales of reptiles are formed from the outer layer of the skin, or the **epidermis.** These scales keep the bodies of reptiles from drying out. The scales of lizards and snakes overlap, like shingles on a roof. On turtles and croco-

Highlight

Even though some reptiles may look different from others, all reptiles share a basic body structure. Their bodies consist of a head, a trunk, and a tail.

At this point, you may want your students to do the Laboratory Investigation at the end of this chapter.

dilians, these scales lie flat, edge to edge, like bricks in a wall. In snakes, lizards, and tuataras, the scales dry and peel off periodically. Snakes can also shed their skins through a process called **molting.**

The toes of all reptiles with legs have claws. These structures help the animal to climb or to burrow. The claws also hold prey and help in defense. The cells that make up the claws are like those of the epidermis, but the cells of the claws include a waterproof material. When the outer cells break away or wear down, they are replaced by lower layers of cells.

Like fish and amphibians, reptiles get their color from *chromatophores* in the skin. Several types of color cells may be arranged in layers to produce the many different color patterns of reptiles. Some reptiles can change color. In the true chameleon, for example, the pigment granules in each of the chromatophores move in response to changes in light or behavior. Sometimes the pigments form a broken pattern of color that helps to camouflage the lizard. A change to a solid color may be an aggressive signal to other chameleons, warning them to keep away.

Figure 32-9 Snakes shed their skins through a process called molting.

Organ Systems

The internal anatomy of reptiles is quite complex. In addition to a number of well-developed organ systems, reptiles have a skeleton and muscles that are well adapted for movement. Although individual species of reptiles may have slight differences in internal structure, most reptiles have the same kinds of organ systems.

MOVEMENT AND MUSCLES The reptilian skeleton differs from the amphibian skeleton in several ways. Reptiles have more than one neck vertebra. This allows them to turn their heads by a circular movement of the neck. Reptiles also usually have two *sacral vertebrae* that provide a broad base of support for the hind limbs.

The limbs of amphibians cannot lift their bellies high off the ground, resulting in an awkward, sprawling gait. In contrast, the legs of reptiles are not only longer and stronger, but they also extend beneath the body. These limbs can easily support the weight of the reptile's body, permitting fast and easy locomotion.

Lizards have large sheets of muscles on their forelimbs and hind limbs that permit quick movement. The six-lined racerunner lizard, for example, may reach a speed of 29 kilometers per hour over short distances. Many lizards, such as the iguana, can actually run on their hind legs alone.

Highlight

In spite of the many environmental adaptations of reptiles, most have the same internal structures and organ systems.

Figure 32-10 Snakes move across surfaces such as sand in a series of curves, leaving tracks.

Snakes are limbless, and they move in four ways. The most common way that snakes move is *lateral undulation.* During lateral undulation, a snake's body forms a series of S-shaped curves. As muscle contractions move down the body in waves, the S-shape curves press against bumps and irregularities on the ground. Thus, the snake is able to push itself forward. Lateral undulation is used when a snake is crawling quickly or swimming.

Snakes move by another method called *rectilinear movement,* or caterpillar movement. This type of movement involves the large ventral scales of snakes. Muscles connected to the ribs move the ventral scales backward and forward. In this way, snakes grip the surface beneath them and pull themselves forward like caterpillars. This type of movement is useful only on rough surfaces that provide traction.

Snakes use *concertina movement* on flat, smooth surfaces and to climb through trees. During concertina movement, a snake anchors the front of its body. Then the snake moves its back end forward and coils it slightly. Anchoring its back end, the snake pushes the front of its body forward and coils it slightly.

Snakes that live in deserts use a fourth method of movement called *sidewinding.* During sidewinding, a snake twists its body into S-shaped loops, touching the ground at two points. Then the snake suddenly straightens out its body. A sidewinder rattlesnake moving in this way can travel at speeds approaching 3 kilometers per hour.

NERVOUS SYSTEM In comparison with the amphibians, the reptiles have a cerebrum with larger and more complex hemispheres. The reptiles also have better developed olfactory lobes. The optic lobes, the cerebellum, and the medulla are about equally developed in both types of vertebrates.

DIGESTIVE SYSTEM Reptiles get their food in a variety of ways. Some lizards have very fast-moving tongues for snatching prey. Other lizards grasp their prey with their jaws, and they either swallow it whole or chop it up with their teeth. The toothless turtles grind up plants, worms, or shellfish with their powerful jaws, after ripping these foods apart with their horny beaks.

The digestive system of reptiles is nearly identical to that of the frog. Food travels from the mouth through the esophagus, stomach, small intestine, and large intestine. The wastes are excreted from the cloaca. The cloaca also receives urinary wastes and sperm.

Figure 32-11 The unhinged jaws of a snake allow it to swallow its prey whole.

EXCRETORY SYSTEM The excretory system of the reptiles conserves water better than do the excretory systems of most animals. As a result, the kidneys of reptiles generally do not extract much water when they filter the blood. Thus, the fluid wastes of reptiles contain very little water. Turtles and crocodilians spend much of their time in water. Their bodies do not have to conserve as much water as do the bodies of land-living reptiles. Turtles and crocodilians, therefore, excrete up to 75% of their nitrogen wastes in the form of soluble ammonia. This type of ammonia has to be dissolved in water to be passed from the body. On the other hand, terrestrial lizards, snakes, and tortoises need to conserve water. They therefore excrete 80% to 98% of their nitrogen wastes as uric acid. This type of acid is largely insoluble, that is, it does not need water to be stored or passed by the body. It is also nontoxic. The body can store uric acid for some time without using up a lot of water and without causing harm to the animal.

Only tuataras, turtles, and lizards have urinary bladders. The other reptiles do not have a urinary bladder. In these animals, the wastes go directly into the cloaca and are mixed with digestive wastes. These wastes are released from the cloacal opening.

RESPIRATORY SYSTEM Respiratory systems vary among reptiles. The lungs of tuataras have few compartments, and they are similar to those of amphibians. The left lung of snakes is nonexistent or smaller than the right lung, which does all the work of respiration. The lungs of lizards have many small chambers that give them a spongy appearance and that provide additional surface area. In a few lizards, additional air sacs bulge from the lungs into the body cavity.

Sidelight

Crocodilians have a slitlike valve in their throat that closes to prevent them from swallowing water when they swim underwater with their mouths open.

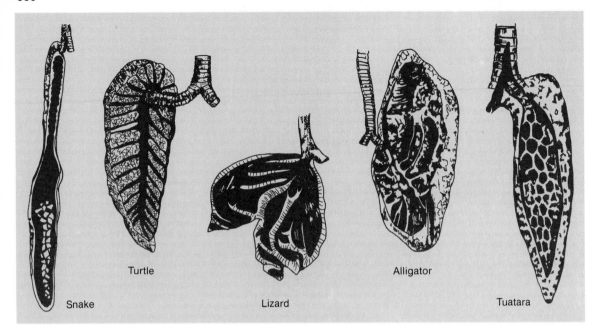

Turtle

Alligator

Snake

Lizard

Tuatara

Figure 32-12   The lungs of different reptiles vary considerably in shape.

These sacs provide more space for air, but they are not used for gas exchange. Unlike true lungs, the sacs have no blood vessels running through them.

The way reptiles breathe can vary. In most reptiles, the trunk muscles raise the rib cage, increasing the volume of the chest cavity and decreasing the air pressure inside the lungs. This difference in pressures causes air to flow into the lungs. In turtles, the rigid shell blocks rib movement. Special muscles in the abdomen allow turtles to inhale and exhale.

CIRCULATORY SYSTEM   The circulatory system of reptiles moves blood efficiently to and from the lungs. The hearts of most reptiles are much like that of the frog. The atrium is divided into two chambers. The right chamber receives oxygen-poor blood from the body, and the left chamber receives oxygen-rich blood from the lungs. There is a single ventricle, which is partially divided by a wall called the *septum*. The ventricle pumps oxygen-rich blood to the body. Unlike other reptiles, crocodilians have four-chambered hearts with two completely separate ventricles. There is no mixing of oxygen-rich and oxygen-poor blood.

REPRODUCTIVE SYSTEM   In the ovary of the female reptile, the unfertilized eggs mature, and yolk is formed. The male fertilizes the eggs inside the body of the female. To do

Sidelight

A high school student's heart beats about 85 times per minute. An alligator's heart beats about 40 times per minute, and a turtle's heart beats somewhere around 20 times per minute.

so, the male deposits sperm directly into the female. The sperm deposited in the cloaca swim up the oviduct to fertilize the mature eggs. Sperm can also be stored in the female cloaca for several months to several years without losing their fertilizing ability. As the fertilized eggs travel down the oviduct to the cloaca, they develop various protective membranes and a hard, outer shell. They are released from the body of the female through the cloaca.

Breeding Habits and Development

Most reptiles are *oviparous*. After mating, the female places her fertilized eggs either in a pit in the ground or in a pile of decaying vegetation that has been prepared for the eggs. The female then covers the eggs, and she may even guard them. The eggs develop in the nest for a period of weeks or months, after which the young hatch. During their development, the eggs are hidden and fairly safe from predators.

Reptile eggs survive on land due to several adaptations. The hard outer shell keeps moisture inside, but it allows oxygen and carbon dioxide to move freely into and out of the egg. The shell is lined with the **chorion.** The chorion is the outermost embryonic membrane. It also allows oxygen and carbon dioxide to diffuse in and out. A special membrane sac, the **allantois** (ə-LAN-tə-wis), stores the accumulating nitrogen wastes. The allantois also has many blood vessels and is used in respiration. Another adaptation is the large store

Highlight

Most reptiles lay hard-shelled eggs. Some reptiles, however, give birth to living young.

Figure 32-13 The eggs of reptiles have a hard outer shell and a large yolk. These Nile crocodiles are hatching from their shells.

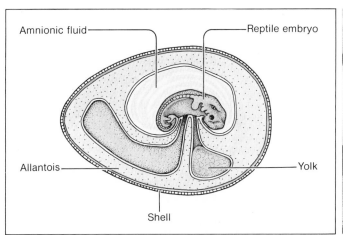

Figure 32-14 Some snakes, such as the garter snake (*left*), are ovoviviparous, producing young that are born alive. Other snakes, such as the hognose snake, are oviparous, laying eggs (*right*) that hatch outside the mother's body.

of **yolk** inside the egg. The yolk contains stored food, and enables the young reptile to grow more completely within the egg and to hatch at a later stage of development than do amphibian embryos. In fact, the yolk allows a complete but miniature adult to develop inside the egg before hatching. As a result, reptiles do not have to pass through different larval stages after they leave the egg.

Not all reptiles hatch from eggs that are outside the mother's body. A few reptiles are *ovoviviparous*. In these reptiles, the fertilized eggs are nourished by the yolk inside the body of the female. Hatching also occurs inside the mother, and the young snakes are born alive. The common water snake, the rattlesnake, and the garter snake are all ovoviviparous.

Some reptiles, such as the skinks and night lizards, are **viviparous.** In viviparous female reptiles, nutrients from the bloodstream of the mother are added to those from the yolk. Several species of European lizards are **parthenogenetic.** In these all-female reptiles, eggs can develop directly into adults without being fertilized by males.

Some of your students may be interested in doing research on the several species of European lizards that are parthenogenetic.

SECTION REVIEW   Answers on page T–84.

1. Describe the lungs in tuataras, snakes, and lizards.
2. Some reptiles excrete uric acid rather than ammonia. What function does this serve?
3. Describe the heart of most reptiles.
4. Give an example of an ovoviviparous and a viviparous reptile.

LABORATORY INVESTIGATION 32

For additional information, see page T-84.

Classifying and Comparing Reptiles

Purpose The class *Reptilia* is made up of a diverse group of animals. Turtles, snakes, tortoises, lizards, alligators, and crocodiles are all classified as reptiles. The purpose of this investigation is to classify different reptiles and to identify and compare the characteristics of reptiles.

Materials *(per group)* • Reference materials on reptiles • Pictures of reptiles of all the orders, cut from magazines, old texts, and so on • 4 8″ x 12″ sheets of white construction paper

Procedure **1.** Fold each piece of construction paper in half along its width. **2.** Tape together the sides of each folded piece of construction paper, forming an envelope. Leave the top of each envelope open. **3.** Label one envelope with the order name *Rhynchocephalia*. Label another *Chelonia*. Label the third envelope *Squamata* and the fourth *Crocodilia*. **4.** Study the pictures of reptiles provided by your teacher. **5.** Sort the animal pictures by order as well as you can and put them into the labeled envelopes. **6.** Copy Figure 1 on a sheet of paper. Place the identification code from each of the pictures in the proper space. **7.** In the second column of the chart, fill in the order in which you classified each of the animals. **8.** Fill in the characteristics of each of the animals based on your study of the pictures. **9.** Re-evaluate your classification of each pictured animal. Fill in the order in which you classify the animal based on the characteristics you listed. **10.** Copy Figure 2 on the same sheet of paper as Figure 1. Check with your teacher to find out the correct order and the name of each animal. Fill in this information in Figure 2.

Figure 2

Identification Code	Name of Organism	Correct Order

Observations and Conclusions **1.** How do the lizards differ from the snakes? **2.** What feature distinguishes the turtles and tortoises from other reptiles? **3.** List some differences among the turtles and tortoises in your pictures. **4.** Which animals appear the most similar? Explain your answer. **5.** List the characteristics that all of the reptiles have in common. **6.** Describe the feet of the reptiles that have feet.

Figure 1

Identification Code	Predicted Order	Characteristics	Re-evaluated Order

CHAPTER SUMMARY

The History of Reptiles Reptiles became adapted to a terrestrial existence 300 million years ago. Many reptile groups, such as dinosaurs, are extinct. Large dinosaurs included *Brontosaurus, Triceratops, Tyrannosaurus,* and *Pterodactyl.*

Classification of Reptiles The four living orders of reptiles are the tuataras, the turtles and tortoises, the snakes and lizards, and the alligators and crocodiles.

Several adaptations enable reptiles to live on land. These adaptations include a dry, scaly skin, internal fertilization, and the amniotic egg. Other adaptations limit water loss.

The tuatara is the only living species in the ancient order *Rhynchocephalia.* Although it looks like a modern lizard, it has changed little from its ancestors.

The turtles and tortoises are reptiles with shells outside their bodies. They do not have teeth, but they use a horny beak to rip their food. Turtles are mainly aquatic, whereas tortoises live on land.

The order *Squamata* is made up of the lizards and the snakes. Snakes have long bodies that are covered with scales and that have no limbs. The snakes move with the help of these scales. Most snakes are nonpoisonous.

Lizards usually have short legs, tails, movable eyelids, and external ear openings. They are a numerous and successful group of modern reptiles. They live in trees, as well as on and under the ground.

The order *Crocodilia* includes alligators and crocodiles. They are the most advanced reptile group. Crocodilians are also most closely related to the extinct cotylosaurs.

Anatomy of the Reptiles The bodies of most reptiles are encased in scales. These scales, formed from the epidermis, help reptiles to retain moisture. Reptiles also have claws that help them to climb or to burrow. Reptiles are cold-blooded. Their temperature varies directly with changes in air temperature. In extreme cold, reptiles tend to hibernate.

Nitrogenous wastes are excreted from reptiles either as ammonia or as uric acid. The circulatory system is adapted to move blood efficiently to and from the lungs. Reptiles reproduce by internal fertilization. This decreases the dependence of reptiles on water to complete the reproductive cycle.

CHAPTER VOCABULARY

allantois	**hemotoxin**	**prehensile tail**
amniotic egg	**herbivore**	**scutes**
capillary beds	**molting**	**viviparous**
carapace	**neurotoxin**	**yolk**
chorion	**omnivore**	
dinosaur	**parietal body**	
epidermis	**parthenogenetic**	
fang	**plastron**	

REVIEW of FACTS and CONCEPTS   Answers on page T–84.

On a separate sheet of paper, answer each of the following as completely as possible.

1. List the general characteristics of reptiles.
2. What three adaptations enabled reptiles to live so successfully on land?
3. Why is the tuatara sometimes called a living fossil?
4. What are the characteristics of turtles and tortoises?
5. How do lizards and snakes differ?
6. How do snakes move?
7. How can you tell an alligator from a crocodile?
8. Relate the means of locomotion of amphibians and reptiles to their skeletal structures.
9. Compare the brain of a reptile and an amphibian.
10. What features of the excretory system of reptiles enable them to live on land?
11. How are reptile eggs adapted to develop on land?
12. How does a large yolk supply affect the development of reptile embryos?

EXTENSIONS and APPLICATIONS   For additional information, see pages T–84 to T–85.

1. There are many theories to explain why the dinosaurs became extinct. Write a report discussing some of these theories.

2. Obtain some liquid-crystal temperature strips. Under the supervision of your teacher, hold the strips against the skin of reptiles. Record the temperature readings. Place the reptiles in the sun for 5 minutes and check the temperature again. Carry out the same procedure with birds and mammals, and compare the results.

3. Make a poster showing the different reptile groups. Use pictures or drawings to illustrate the poster.

4. Using reference materials, do research on the poisonous snakes of North America. Write a report including information on the snakes present in your area and on procedures to follow in case of snake bite.

SUGGESTED READINGS

Carr, A., *So Excellent a Fishe.* Garden City, N.Y.: The Natural History Press.
   This book is not about fish at all, but about the great marine turtles and their habits.

Hartley, W. and E., *The Alligator: King of the Wilderness.* New York: Thomas Nelson.
   This book describes the restoration of the population of the once-endangered American alligator.

Pope, C.H., *The Giant Snakes.* New York: Alfred A. Knopf.
   This book is a general introduction to snakes, highlighting the natural history of the boa constrictor, the anaconda, and the largest pythons.

Riedman, S.R., and R. Witham, *Turtles: Extinction or Survival?* New York: Abelard-Schuman.
   Many species of turtles are endangered. This book discusses them and how naturalists are trying to save them.

33 Birds

Feathers and wings enable these wild ducks to fly.

Chapter Objectives *After completing this chapter, you will be able to:*

a   Give evidence that suggests birds evolved from ancient reptiles. p. 537
b   Describe the structures of a bird that are involved in flight. p. 540
c   Describe the organ systems of a bird and their functions. p. 543
d   Describe the structure and development of a bird egg. p. 546

For teaching aids for this chapter, including a chapter over-view and teaching strategies, see pages T–85 to T–86. The page number next to each chapter objective refers to the text page where the information needed to fulfill the objective begins.

Birds are the most easily recognized of all vertebrates, and are very important to human beings. Although some species can be destructive, most birds help human beings by feeding on harmful insects. Many birds are sources of food for people.

Much evidence supports the concept that birds evolved from ancient reptiles. Like reptiles, birds lay eggs that allow the embryo to grow in a watery environment inside a protective shell. Birds have scales on their legs, similar to the scales of reptiles. The organ systems of birds and reptiles are also similar in a number of ways.

The History of Birds

The fossil remains of birds are rare because the bones of birds are very fragile. Scientists have found, however, well-preserved fossils of two birdlike dinosaurs. One flying reptile, called the *dawn lizard,* had flaps of skin attached to its long ribs. These flaps were useful in flying. The *pterodactyl,* another flying reptile, had wings made of skin stretched over long, fingerlike bones.

The *feathers* of the earliest birds adapted from scales. These scales developed into longer structures that were divided into parts. Feathers gave the early birds two advantages. First, feathers were lighter than other types of protective body covering, and so they did not hinder flying. Second, feathers controlled the exchange of heat between the bodies of birds and the air. A layer of air trapped between the feathers and the skin helped to keep in heat. As a result, birds could be active in all kinds of weather. Birds are *warm-blooded* because their body temperatures remain constant.

One of the earliest birds, called *Archaeopteryx,* lived about 150 million years ago. This pigeon-sized bird, like the reptiles, had teeth and a long tail. Like the later birds, however, it had feathers and feet adapted for perching. The size of its skull, its overall build, and its beak were all midway between those of reptiles and birds. *Archaeopteryx* lacked the large breastbone and well-developed chest muscles of modern birds. As a result, it did not flap its wings, as birds do today. Instead, *Archaeopteryx* probably used claws, located on the front edge of its wings, to climb up the branches of giant ferns. It then glided to the ground on its outstretched wings.

Primitive birds varied considerably in size. A bird called *Hesperornis,* which lived 64 million years ago, was about 1.5 meters long. *Diatryma,* a North American bird, was 2.5 meters long. Most primitive birds, however, were about the size of modern birds.

A number of species of modern birds have become extinct in fairly recent times. The moas of New Zealand and the American passenger pigeon, for example, have become extinct largely due to human activities. Two other examples of recently extinct birds are the dodo and the great auk.

The dodo lived on Mauritius, an island in the Indian Ocean. This large bird had a huge, hooked beak, and it could not fly. In the 1600s, explorers who visited Mauritius killed many of the dodos for food. They also brought pigs and goats to the island. These animals competed with the remaining dodos for food. In less than 100 years, the dodo became extinct.

Sidelight

Today the smallest bird is the hummingbird. It measures 5 centimeters long and weighs only 3 grams. The largest bird is the ostrich. It stands more than 2.5 meters tall and weighs more than 140 kilograms.

It might be helpful for some of your students to review Chapter 32, especially those sections dealing with the internal and external structures of reptiles.

Figure 33–1 The *Archaeopteryx,* one of the earliest birds, lived about 150 million years ago. This reptilelike bird had a long tail, sharp teeth, and claws at the tips of its wings.

At this point, you may want to assign to your students the first of the Extensions and Applications at the end of this chapter.

The great auk was a bird that stood 1 meter tall and that looked like a penguin in many ways. Its back and tail were black, and its breast and belly were white. It had very small wings that the bird used to swim under water instead of to fly. The great auks fed on fish and spent much of the year at sea. In the spring, they nested on small islands near Great Britain and Scandinavia. They were, however, slow and clumsy on land, and they could lay only one egg in a season. Sailors and merchants invaded the breeding grounds of these birds, herded the birds together, forced them into boats, and killed them. By 1850, the great auk was extinct.

SECTION REVIEW   Answers on page T–85.

1. Name two advantages that feathers gave to primitive birds.
2. What birdlike features did *Archaeopteryx* have? What reptilian features?
3. What factors caused the dodo to become extinct?

Figure 33-2 Birds such as rheas and penguins are flightless.

Characteristics of Birds

The 28 orders of modern birds can be divided into several major groups. These are *perching birds, water birds, birds of prey* and *flightless birds.* Perhaps the most familiar are the perching birds, such as robins, jays, and sparrows. Most of these land birds have feet that are adapted for holding onto branches. Some land birds, however, do not perch. Woodpeckers, for example, climb up the sides of trees. The position of their toes is an adaptation for this activity. Usually, woodpeckers have two toes pointing forward and two pointing backward. This allows woodpeckers to get a foothold on the sides of tree trunks.

Water birds are adapted to swim or wade. Swimming birds have paddlelike, webbed feet. Wading birds have long legs and long toes. Ducks and geese are examples of water birds. Examples of wading birds are herons and storks.

The birds of prey include eagles, hawks, and owls. These birds have hooked claws for seizing their food. They also have powerful hooked beaks for tearing flesh and a keen sense of sight used to locate prey.

Flightless birds live all over the world. These birds include the ostrich of Africa, the rhea of South America, the penguins of the southern seas, and the emu and cassowary of Australia. Flightless birds can see well, and those that live mostly on land have strong legs and feet that are made for running.

At this point, you may want to assign to your students the second of the Extensions and Applications at the end of this chapter.

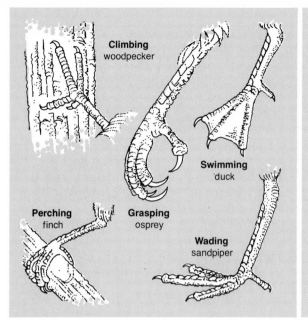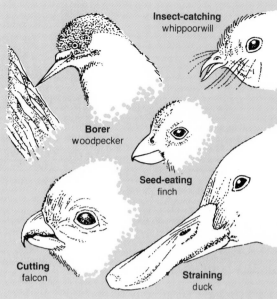

Figure 33-3 The feet and beaks of different kinds of birds are adapted to carry out various functions.

Birds can be classified by their behavior, as well as by their internal or external physical adaptations. For example, birds of prey swoop and seize their prey, using their **talons,** or sharp claws. The hunting behavior and the talons of these birds are features that scientists use to classify birds of prey. As another example, most birds classified as migratory birds nest and raise their young in northern latitudes during the spring and summer. When the days grow short, they fly south. To do so, these birds must have especially strong wings. The golden plover, for example, winters in Argentina and spends the summer in the Arctic. It must be able to fly for thousands of kilometers within a relatively short span of time.

The beak of a bird is a physical adaptation that fits its diet and habitat. The beak is especially important to birds for feeding because they have no teeth. Seed-eating birds, such as finches, have thick beaks. Birds that eat insects, like warblers and whippoorwills, have small, pointed beaks. The duck has a spoon-shaped beak that it uses to strain food from the water. The woodpecker has a beak adapted for drilling holes.

The color of the *plumage,* or a bird's feathers, may either camouflage a bird or make it stand out against its background. For example, the bright red male cardinal is easy to see in a woodland. The males of most bird species are more brightly colored than the females. This apparently plays a role in attracting females to males. In a similar setting, however, the olive-green warbler is nearly invisible. Several

Highlight

Modern birds can be grouped into the four broad categories perching birds, water birds, birds of prey, and flightless birds.

Figure 33-4 The male frigate bird inflates its brilliantly colored pouch to attract a mate.

factors are responsible for the coloration of a bird. The colors black, brown, yellow, and red come from pigments in the feathers. White and blue arise from the special reflections of light. Bird feathers contain no green pigments. The green plumage of parrots and parakeets is due to a combination of blue and yellow pigments.

The males of many bird species have special structures that females do not have. The comb, or fleshy outgrowth, on the head of the rooster, for instance, attracts hens. The rooster also uses the spurs on its legs to fight with other roosters. To attract a female, the male frigate bird inflates a bright red pouch that hangs below its neck.

By singing and calling, birds mark their territories, attract their mates, or warn of danger. Songs and calls are necessary for communication and are unique to each species of bird. The songs of birds of the same species may have local variations.

Unlike frogs and mammals, birds have no vocal cords. Their voices are produced by an organ, called the **syrinx**, that is located at the lower end of the windpipe. As air is expelled from the lungs, it passes over the membranes in the syrinx and causes them to vibrate. Muscles that control the membranes change the pitch of the sound. The quality of the sound depends on the structure of the syrinx.

SECTION REVIEW   Answers on page T–85.

1. What are talons?
2. How are the shapes of beaks related to diet?
3. How do birds produce their songs?

Anatomy of a Bird

Although birds are similar to reptiles in a number of ways, birds have certain features, adaptations, and structures that reptiles do not have. These differences are found in the external anatomy of the bird, such as the wings and feathers. Other differences involve internal anatomy, such as the skeleton and organ systems.

Structures Used in Flight

The body of a bird is divided into a head, a trunk, a tail, and limbs. Most birds use their forelimbs, or wings, to fly, and they use their two hind limbs to walk or to swim. The bones of the ankle and foot are fused, and they look like part of the leg. As a result, birds stand on their toes rather than flat on their feet.

Highlight

In most birds, the wings and muscles are adapted for flying. The largest and most powerful bird muscle is the pectoral muscle. Specialized feathers, such as the contour feathers, and hollow, light bones are also important adaptations that are necessary for flying.

The wing of a bird and the forelimb of other vertebrates appear to have had the same point of origin in evolutionary development. A bird wing is, therefore, said to be **homologous,** or similar in structure, to the forelimb of other vertebrates. The wings and muscles of nearly all birds are adapted for flight. The largest muscle in a bird is the *pectoral muscle.* This muscle attaches to the breastbone, or sternum, and to the wings. The sternum makes the chest cavity rigid, and it gives the pectoral muscles a large area of attachment. In birds that fly well, the breastbone is fairly large. In flightless birds, such as the ostrich, it does not appear at all. Birds that have small pectoral muscles are generally poor fliers. When a bird flaps its wings, its powerful pectoral muscles contract to pull the wings down and back. This phase of the flight action is called the *power stroke.* Other muscles then contract to pull the wings up and forward to their starting position.

The wings of all birds are not alike, and they are not all used in the same way. For example, long feathers stick out

CAREER: Game Warden

Every state has regulations and laws that are designed to protect and to save wildlife. The main job of a game warden is to enforce these laws and regulations. Wardens, however, have many other duties.

Game wardens are assigned specific natural areas to patrol. Wardens can warn violators, fine them, or even arrest them. For example, if the violators are found with animals that they have killed illegally, the wardens may confiscate the animals, as well as the guns or other equipment used to kill the animals. In addition to doing work as enforcement agents, game wardens must also keep records of the wildlife in their areas. They plan controlled hunts and issue hunting permits. They also conduct safety programs for hunters and take part in rescue operations.

Game wardens work outdoors all year round and in all kinds of weather. Frequently, they work on weekends and holidays. They are expected to have normal vision and hearing.

The educational requirements for game wardens vary from state to state. Usually, a college background is required. Game wardens should

be familiar with ecology, as well as with the habits and distribution of wildlife in their state. They should understand the principles of conservation.

State fish and wildlife departments are the main employers of game wardens. Federal agencies, such as the National Park Service, also employ wardens. People who are interested in this field may begin at an assistant level. To be promoted to higher positions, assistants may have to take some college courses and written state examinations.

For career information, write to United States Department of the Interior, National Park Service, Washington, DC 20240.

At this point, you may want your students to do the Laboratory Investigation at the end of this chapter.

from the large, broad wings of condors and vultures. Air flow over the wings lifts these birds, which can soar for hours without flapping their wings. In contrast, most perching birds must flap their wings almost constantly to remain in flight. The wings of the crow beat about 3 times per second, while those of a hummingbird beat 50 times per second. Sparrows must flap their short, round-tipped wings frequently, and can only fly a few feet at a time before having to stop. Limited to such short flights, sparrows tend to flutter from branch to branch.

Feathers not only enable birds to fly, but they also insulate the body of the bird. Some birds are always losing and replacing their feathers through a process called **molting.** When a bird loses a feather, a new one grows. Birds have several types of feathers.

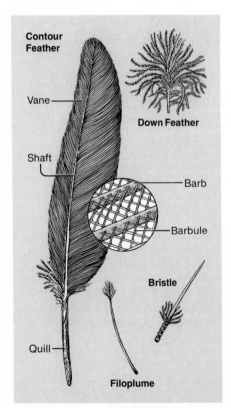

Figure 33-5 Birds have several different types of feathers, including contour feathers, down feathers, filoplumes, and bristles.

Contour Feather

Vane

Down Feather

Shaft

Barb

Barbule

Bristle

Quill

Filoplume

CONTOUR FEATHERS   The **contour feathers** are the largest and most familiar. The contour feathers give flying birds a smooth, streamlined shape that is useful in flying. The base, or point of attachment for contour feathers, is called the **quill.** The quill is a hollow cylinder filled with a jellylike substance. The quill lies in an opening in the skin, called a **follicle.** The **shaft** is the part of the feather that grows out of the quill. Extending outward from each side of the shaft are thin branches, called **barbs.** The barbs are hooked to one another by tiny **barbules.** Feathers with many barbule hooks are airtight, and they give the bird *lift*, or upward force, during flight. The feathers of birds that do not fly, such as ostriches, have few barbule hooks. The contour feathers of these birds are fluffy, plumelike structures.

DOWN FEATHERS   The simple feathers that cover the entire body of immature birds, such as chicks, are called **down feathers.** Down feathers have a quill and a reduced shaft. In adult birds, they cover the breast and abdomen beneath the contour feathers, and help to insulate the body.

FILOPLUMES   Very simple feathers that resemble fine hair are called **filoplumes,** or pinfeathers. Each has a single, hairlike shaft that ends in a few barbs. These feathers grow in groups near the follicles of some contour feathers. Filoplumes may function in controlling feather movements.

BRISTLES   Feathers that are hairlike and have a short quill are called **bristles.** Bristles have a thin shaft with a few or no barbs at the base. These feathers are found around the bird's nostrils, where they filter out dust.

Skeleton

The bones of birds are light and hollow. These two features make their skeletons well adapted for flying. The frigate bird, for example, has a 2-meter wingspan, but its skeleton weighs only 100 grams.

In addition, the skeleton of birds has more *cervical*, or neck, *vertebrae* than does any other group of animals. These cervical vertebrae move easily. As a result, that part of the spine is very elastic. With these added vertebrae, not only can birds turn their heads and necks to great angles, but they can also move their necks into many positions. In the neck of the owl, the bones allow an especially great freedom of movement. The owl can turn its head three-quarters around, or 270°.

Except for the neck vertebrae, the bones of the spinal column are fused together, making the trunk of the bird rigid. The bird therefore does not have to use muscular energy to keep its spinal column straight during flight. The fused *sacral vertebrae* connect the pelvic girdle rigidly to the spine. These fused vertebrae also help the bird to maintain its balance at rest. Small, fused tail vertebrae give skeletal support to the tail feathers.

Organ Systems

Like their wings and skeletons, the organ systems of birds make them well adapted for flight. For example, birds use their energy very efficiently, and their bodies are typically very lightweight for their size. Both of these features make birds more efficient fliers.

NERVOUS SYSTEM Compared to that of a reptile, the brain of a bird is large in relation to its body size. The *cerebellum* is larger than in reptiles. So is the *cerebrum*, which controls the movement of voluntary muscles and complex instinctive behaviors. The *optic lobe*, also quite large, gives the bird good eyesight. The *olfactory lobes* are small, however, resulting in a poor sense of smell. The *medulla oblongata*, the hindmost region of the brain, is joined to the spinal cord through an opening in the skull.

With the exception of the sense of smell, birds have generally keen senses. They have a hard tongue with taste buds that respond to substances in food. Their keen eyesight and acute hearing help birds to find food. Robins have hearing so acute that they can supposedly hear earthworms moving underground.

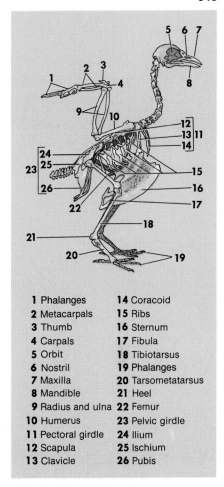

1 Phalanges	14 Coracoid
2 Metacarpals	15 Ribs
3 Thumb	16 Sternum
4 Carpals	17 Fibula
5 Orbit	18 Tibiotarsus
6 Nostril	19 Phalanges
7 Maxilla	20 Tarsometatarsus
8 Mandible	21 Heel
9 Radius and ulna	22 Femur
10 Humerus	23 Pelvic girdle
11 Pectoral girdle	24 Ilium
12 Scapula	25 Ischium
13 Clavicle	26 Pubis

Figure 33-6 Skeletal System of a Bird

DIGESTIVE SYSTEM With their high metabolic rates, birds break down food rapidly. Fruit that is fed to a growing cedar waxwing, for example, passes through its digestive tract in 27 minutes. Birds spend much of their time either looking for food or actually eating it. They select foods that are high in energy, such as seeds, fruit, worms, and insects. Most birds do not eat low-energy foods, such as leaves and grass.

Birds do not have teeth. As a result, they swallow most of their food whole. The food travels down the esophagus to a sac, called the **crop.** The crop is especially large in seed-eating birds. In the crop, food is moistened and passed on to the stomach.

The stomach has two divisions. In the first part, called the *proventriculus*, glands secrete digestive fluids. Food moves from the proventriculus to the second division of the stomach, called the **gizzard.** The gizzard has thick, muscular walls. The gizzard often contains small stones that the bird has ingested and that crush food when the gizzard muscles contract. The crushed food passes into the small intestine, and then into the *rectum*. The rectum is joined to the cloaca. Undigested food and nitrogen wastes leave the body through the cloaca.

EXCRETORY SYSTEM The high metabolic rate of birds produces a great deal of nitrogen wastes. These wastes are removed from the blood by a pair of kidneys. The wastes

Figure 33-7 Internal Systems of a Bird

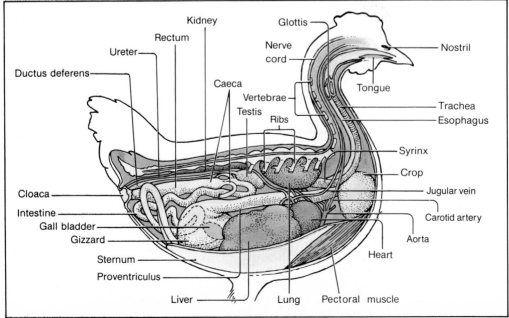

leave each kidney, through a tube called a *ureter*. These wastes are in the form of solid uric acid. They are excreted from the *cloaca*. Birds do not have urinary bladders because they do not produce liquid wastes.

RESPIRATORY SYSTEM Birds have the highest body temperatures of all warm-blooded animals. To maintain these temperatures, birds need large amounts of oxygen for cellular respiration. Birds have evolved a respiratory system that meets this need.

All gas exchange occurs in small, compact lungs that lie under the ribs in the lung cavities. Air enters the *pharynx* of the bird, through a slitlike *glottis*. From the pharynx, the air travels down into a *trachea*. The trachea branches into two *bronchi* (singular: bronchus) that lead to the lungs. Inside the lungs, these bronchi branch into *secondary bronchi* that contain branchings of their own. These tertiary branches are called **parabronchi**. Surrounding the parabronchi are tiny projections, called *air capillaries*, that lie close to tiny blood capillaries. Gas exchange takes place between these two sets of capillaries.

Birds have **air sacs** that make respiration more efficient in flying. The secondary bronchi lead from the lungs into these air sacs. When the bird inhales, air flows into the posterior air sacs. When the bird exhales, the oxygen-rich air stored in the posterior air sacs flows into the lungs. With the next inhalation, the oxygen-poor air from the lungs enters the anterior air sacs. Then this air flows out of the body through the trachea. This flow of air ensures a continuous supply of oxygen. This process produces a very high oxygen level in the blood, which permits many birds to fly at high altitudes, where oxygen is scarce.

CIRCULATORY SYSTEM The heart of a bird beats very rapidly. For example, the heart of the English sparrow beats 350 to 500 times per minute. A hummingbird heart beats 615 times per minute.

A bird heart has four chambers. The right and left *atria* are completely separated from each other, and so are the right and left *ventricles*. Oxygen-poor blood from the body enters the right atrium, and then it flows through a small valve into the right ventricle. The heart pumps this blood through the *pulmonary artery* to the lungs, where it picks up oxygen. The blood then returns through the *pulmonary veins* to the heart's left atrium. The blood then goes into the left ventricle and finally leaves the heart through the aorta. The aorta branches into smaller arteries that carry the blood

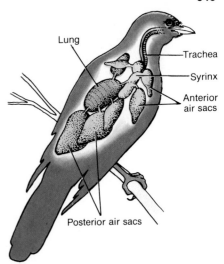

Figure 33-8 Respiratory System of a Bird

Sidelight

The highest flying bird is the bar-headed goose. It has been sighted at altitudes of more than 7.5 kilometers.

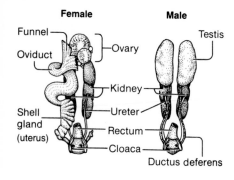

Female   Male

Funnel

Oviduct

Ovary

Testis

Kidney

Ureter

Shell gland (uterus)

Rectum

Cloaca

Ductus deferens

Figure 33-9 Reproductive Systems of Male and Female Birds

to the rest of the body. This double-circuit system is very efficient, and it ensures that the bird receives the oxygen it needs.

REPRODUCTIVE SYSTEM In birds, fertilization is internal. Female birds have only one *ovary*. During the nonbreeding season, this ovary is small. During the breeding season, the ovary gets bigger and releases eggs into the body cavity. After the eggs are fertilized, cilia draw the eggs into the *oviduct*. The oviduct is a tube through which eggs travel from the ovary to the cloaca. Special regions of the oviduct secrete nutrients, such as *albumin* that makes up the egg white. Another part of the oviduct secretes the substance that forms the shell.

The male reproductive system is like that of male amphibians, such as the frog. The *testis* produces sperm that travel through small tubes called the *ductus deferens*. These tubes lead from the testes to the cloaca. During mating, a male and a female place their cloacas close together, and the male passes sperm to the female.

Breeding Habits and Development

Before mating, birds usually go through a courtship dance or similar behavior. The male bowerbird of Australia, for example, makes an archway, or bower, of twigs. The male collects objects, which are usually blue, and places them into the bower. These objects attract a female to the bower. After the two birds mate, the male drives the female away. The female then makes a nest and raises the young alone.

The materials a bird uses to build a nest depend on where the bird lives. For example, few plants grow on rock islands. As a result, many sea birds that live on rock islands build nests of rocks. Penguins build nests of rocks. The oriole, a land bird, weaves a saclike nest using plant fibers, yarn, and bark. Flamingos build nests of mud. The female hummingbird builds a nest from lichens and plant-down that she fastens with spider silk.

After courtship, mating, and nest building, the female bird lays a **clutch**, or set, of eggs. While many large birds produce only one egg every two or three days, most small birds lay one egg daily. The rare California condor breeds only every other year and lays just one egg.

The color of bird eggs seems to be related in many cases to the location of the nest. Generally, eggs laid in holes or in burrows are white. Eggs in open nests or on the bare ground are colored, and they are often streaked and spotted. For example, the robin lays its blue egg in an open nest.

Figure 33-10 Birds such as the oriole (*top*) build nests in trees. The kingfisher (*bottom*) builds its nest in a riverbank.

Bird eggs must be **incubated,** or warmed, until they hatch. Some birds begin to incubate their eggs as soon as the first egg is laid. Others wait until all the eggs are laid. Birds warm their eggs for various lengths of time. For example, the female bluebird incubates her four to six eggs for 12 days. If the eggs are not warmed to 38 °C and turned regularly, they do not hatch. Chicken eggs are incubated for 21 days, and duck eggs for 28 days.

At this point, you may want to assign to your students the third of the Extensions and Applications at the end of this chapter.

Figure 33-11 Stages in the Development of a Chick

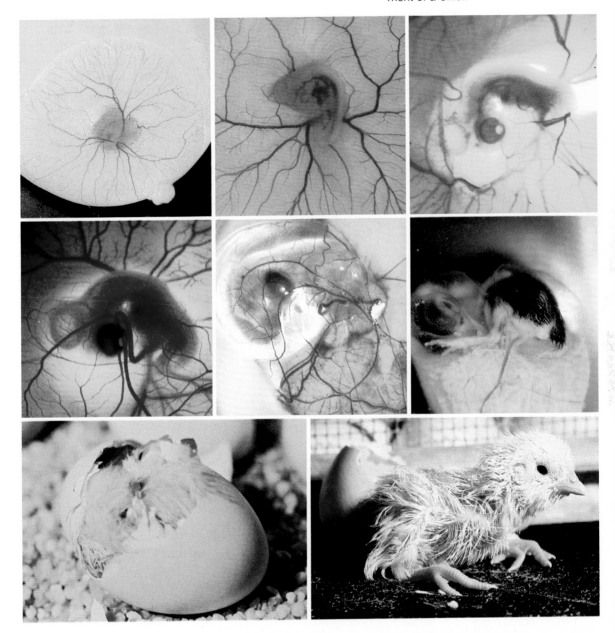

During incubation, the embryo develops in a sac called the **amnion.** The amnion is enclosed in the *amniotic membrane*. The embryo is attached to the *yolk sac* that contains nutrients for the developing bird. Both the embryo and the yolk sac are enclosed in a second membrane, called the **chorion.** The embryo is also attached to an organ called the *allantois*. The allantois carries out respiration and receives the waste products of the embryo. Blood vessels carry food from the yolk sac to the embryo as it grows.

When incubation is complete, the hatchling breaks out of its shell. The chick cracks the egg with a toothlike projection at the end of its beak. This hard projection drops off after a few days.

Depending on the species, the hatchlings may or may not be able to care of themselves. For example, when young waterfowl hatch, they are covered with protective down. Immediately after hatching, these young waterfowl are strong and active. They can follow the mother wherever she goes and look for their own food. These birds are said to be **precocial,** meaning well formed. Ducks and quail are examples of precocial birds. On the other hand, newly hatched baby songbirds are unable to see and depend totally on their parents. Songbirds, woodpeckers, and pigeons are **altricial.** Altricial birds are helpless and must be fed and cared for in the nest. For the first three or four days of life, hatchlings cannot control their body heat. As a result, the parents must shade the hatchlings from the sun and warm them at night. To feed their young, the parents bring food, including insects and berries to the nest. The parents predigest the food and then regurgitate it. They then push the regurgitated food into the throat of the hatchling. Soon the little bird grows feathers, opens its eyes, and learns to feed and fly. In some species such as robins, the male bird continues to feed the young after they leave the nest. The female stays in the nest, raising another brood.

Once they can fly, some birds go their separate ways. Other birds remain in family groups, even after the young mature. For example, Canada geese mate for life. Their young return to the place where they hatched in order to breed.

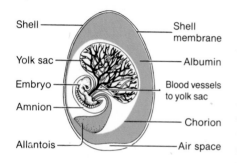

Shell
Yolk sac
Embryo
Amnion
Allantois

Shell membrane
Albumin
Blood vessels to yolk sac
Chorion
Air space

Figure 33-12 Structure of a Bird Egg

SECTION REVIEW   Answers on page T-85.

1. What are the parts of the contour feather?
2. Describe the process of incubation.
3. Distinguish between precocial and altricial birds.

LABORATORY INVESTIGATION

Examining Feathers

Purpose Birds are among the most successful vertebrates, and they display a wide variety of special adaptations. These adaptations allow them to live in different environments. The body of a bird is covered with structures called feathers. These feathers are actually modified scales. Each of the several kinds of feathers has a specific function. The purpose of this investigation is to examine some representative types of feathers and to learn their functions.

Materials *(per group)* ● 3 types of feathers
● Magnifying glass or dissecting microscope

Procedure **1.** Identify each type of feather as either down, contour, or filoplume. **2.** Examine the down feather using the magnifying glass or dissecting microscope. Notice the fluffy tufts at the end of the short quill. They lie close to the skin and act as insulation. **3.** Observe a contour feather with the unaided eye and with the magnifying glass or dissecting microscope. This kind of feather helps to protect and streamline the bird. The largest of these feathers come from the wings and tail. Identify the parts of the feather. **4.** Run your fingers through the contour feather, then examine it under magnification and identify its parts. **5.** Examine the filoplume with the unaided eye and with the magnifying glass or dissecting microscope. **6.** Draw and label each type of feather in your notebook. **7.** Copy the table and record a check mark next to the features that you observe.

Observations and Conclusions **1.** What characteristics of the down feather make it useful as a stuffing in pillows? **2.** Which type of feather is used mainly during flight? Where is this type of feather found on a flying bird's body? **3.** Why is the filoplume also known as a pinfeather?

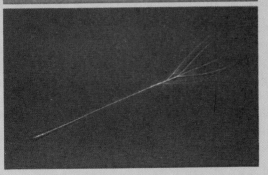

Identifying Number	Type of Feather	Quill	Shaft	Barbs	Barbules

CHAPTER SUMMARY

The History of Birds   Fossils show that birds probably evolved from ancient reptiles. The few fossil remains· of birds show that early birds, such as *Archaeopteryx,* had teeth and a long tail like a reptile. They also had feathers and feet for perching. Today, birds lay eggs and their legs have scales like reptiles.

Characteristics of Birds   Birds have many special characteristics that allow them to be placed in several different general groups. These groups include perching birds, water birds, birds of prey, and flightless birds. Some birds are territorial. Others migrate thousands of kilometers each year.

The beaks and feet of birds are adapted to their diets and habitats. The color of a bird aids in hiding from predators or in attracting a mate. Feather pigments produce a variety of colors in birds.

Internal features help birds to survive, and bird songs help members of a species to communicate. Voice production occurs in the syrinx.

Anatomy of a Bird   Nearly all birds have adaptations that enable them to fly. Feathers are the major adaptation for successful flight. The four types of feathers are the contour feather, the down feather, the filoplume, and the bristle. Birds lose and replace feathers by a process called molting. The large pectoral, or chest,

muscle of a bird moves the wings up and down. The hollow bones of the bird decrease its weight. Several bones called girdles are fused together, making them rigid structures for muscle attachment.

Birds have air sacs to store air during breathing. These air sacs ensure that a supply of oxygen-rich air is always moving through the lungs. Birds need a great deal of oxygen to maintain their high metabolic rates. The two atria and the two ventricles of the bird heart ensure that low-oxygen and high-oxygen blood do not mix.

To maintain their high metabolism, birds eat a great deal of food. They swallow most of their food whole. Food goes down through the esophagus to the crop, and then to a two-part stomach. The intestine absorbs nutrients from the food, and carries food wastes to the cloaca.

The male reproductive system is similar to that of the frog, and the female bird has only one ovary. Birds of both sexes usually exhibit an elaborate courtship behavior before mating. After mating, birds build nests. The materials and shapes of nests vary. The female then lays and incubates eggs. Precocial birds are young birds that are strong and active right after hatching. Altricial birds are helpless and depend on parents for care and food.

CHAPTER VOCABULARY

air sac	contour feather	molting
altricial	crop	parabronchi
amnion	down feather	precocial
barb	filoplume	quill
barbule	follicle	shaft
bristle	gizzard	syrinx
chorion	homologous	talon
clutch	incubate	

REVIEW of FACTS and CONCEPTS   Answers on page T–86.

On a separate sheet of paper, answer each of the following as completely as possible.

1. What evidence suggests that birds evolved from ancient reptiles?
2. In which respects was *Archaeopteryx* similar both to reptiles and to today's birds?
3. Name four major groups of birds. Give an example for each group.
4. In what way might the bright coloration of male birds contribute to the survival of the species?

5. How are singing and calling beneficial in birds?
6. What is meant by a homologous structure? Give an example.
7. Describe the four types of feathers.

8. Name the structures in the digestive system of a bird. Describe the function of each structure.
9. What is the function of air sacs in a bird?
10. Draw and label the inside of a fertilized bird egg.

EXTENSIONS and APPLICATIONS   For additional information, see page T–86.

1. Many birds have become extinct in recent years. Find out about the extinction of the passenger pigeon, the Hawaiian o'o, the Carolina parakeet, and the moa.
2. Observe birds around your home or school. Make a list of the birds you recognize. Obtain a key to North American birds and use it to identify the birds you do not recognize. Call the Audubon Society or other group, and ask for information on the birds in your area.
3. Obtain some fertilized chicken eggs. Incubate them at 39 °C for three days, turning the eggs daily. Break open an egg. Place the contents into a finger bowl filled with warm, slightly salty solution. Examine the embryo under a microscope or magnifying glass. Draw what you see.

SUGGESTED READINGS

Pasquier, R.F., *Watching Birds*. Boston: Houghton Mifflin.
    This book is an introduction to ornithology, the study of birds. The book explains the evolution, anatomy, flight, reproduction, migration, and communication of birds.
Riserer, L. *The American Robin: A Backyard Institution*. Chicago: Nelson-Hall.
    Robins are among the most common birds in America. This book tells about their natural history.
Stranger, M.A., *That Quail, Robert*. Greenwich, Conn.: Fawcett.
    This book is a true nature tale about an adopted baby quail that had a strong influence on the family with which it shared a home.
Walker, L.W., *The Book of Owls*. New York: Alfred A. Knopf.
    A guide that describes the major owl species found in North America.

34 Mammals

Tree kangaroos are found in New Guinea and Australia.

Chapter Objectives *After completing this chapter, you will be able to:*

a ■ List the major characteristics of mammals. p. 553

b ■ Describe the organ systems of a mammal. p. 554

c ■ Compare monotremes, marsupials, and placental mammals. p. 558

d ■ Describe migration, parental care, and hibernation in mammals. p. 557

e ■ Identify major orders of mammals. p. 558

For teaching aids for this chapter, including a chapter overview and teaching strategies, see pages T-86 to T-88. The page number next to each chapter objective refers to the text page where the information needed to fulfill the objective begins.

More than 4000 species of mammals live in almost all the habitats of the world. Many mammals inhabit saltwater and freshwater environments. Some mammals can fly, and others burrow into the ground. Some mammals dwell in the ice-bound polar regions, while others make their homes in steamy jungles. Together with the *arthropods*, or joint-legged animals, mammals dominate the world's terrestrial habitats.

Over the centuries, mammals have become important to human beings in positive and negative ways. Domesticated mammals have provided people with transportation, food, and clothing. Some types of wild species have been hunted both for food and for their fur, or hair. Other mammals, such as the gnawing mammals, have been responsible for damaging large amounts of crops. A few species of mammals also act as reservoirs, or sources, of disease.

The History of Mammals

The mammals probably descended from the *therapsids,* a group of ancient reptiles that lived and became extinct during the Mesozoic Era. The jaws of the therapsids opened and closed like those of reptiles. In most other ways, however, the therapsids resembled mammals. The limbs, teeth, and skull of therapsids were all like those of mammals. In addition, their brains gradually became very similar to mammalian brains.

The first mammals were very small. Similar in many respects to the tiny shrew of today, these mammals probably fed on worms and insects. Many of these early mammals died out. Several of the groups of mammals that exist today, however, descended from mammals that lived during the middle of the Cretaceous Period, about 100 million years ago.

About 65 million years ago, the Age of Mammals, or Cenozoic Era, began. The families of mammals that are familiar to us today developed during the Oligocene Epoch, between 40 million and about 26 million years ago. Some mammals became extinct during the Pleistocene Epoch, beginning about 1.75 million years ago. During this epoch, glaciers advanced over much of the land area of the world. This ice cover made survival very hard and even impossible for some mammals, such as the mammoth and the saber-toothed tiger.

Early human beings may have hunted some mammals to extinction. In recent times, human beings have destroyed forests and jungles areas. In so doing, they have removed habitats that many wild animals need to survive. As a result, some of these animals have become extinct.

SECTION REVIEW   Answers on page T–87.

1. From which ancient reptile did mammals probably descend?
2. When did the Cenozoic Era begin?

Characteristics of Mammals

Whether domesticated or wild, all mammals have certain characteristics in common. These characteristics, both in behavior and in structure, make mammals unique in many ways.

Mammals are vertebrates that feed their young with milk from the **mammary glands** of the mother. The class

Highlight

The Cenozoic Era, beginning about 65 million years ago, is called the Age of Mammals because at that time mammals became the dominant species of animal on the earth.

Highlight

The main characteristics of mammals are that they feed their young milk from the mammary glands of the mother, have hair, and provide the most parental care for their young of all the vertebrates.

At this point, you may want to assign to your students the fourth of the Extensions and Applications at the end of this chapter.

name, *Mammalia*, comes from the name for these glands. In addition to mammary glands, almost all mammals give birth to live young and are said to be *viviparous*. All mammals have varying amounts of hair on their bodies and are warm-blooded. Of all vertebrates, mammals provide the greatest parental care for their young.

The mammals have the most highly developed brain. The parts that are especially well developed are the **cerebrum** and **cerebellum.** The cerebrum controls all activity in the mammal's body, including the action of most muscles and the senses. The cerebellum coordinates movement of groups of muscles.

Mammals are also characterized by having a four-chambered heart and two pairs of limbs. These limbs are adapted for walking, climbing, burrowing, running, swimming, and flying. During their entire lifetime, mammals breathe by means of lungs. The lungs and the heart are separated from the abdominal cavity by a muscle called the **diaphragm.** Another mammalian characteristic is the division of the vertebral column into five distinct regions. In the *cervical*, or neck, region of most mammals, there are only seven cervical vertebrae.

Organ Systems

Mammalian organ systems are specially adapted to the way of life of each type of mammal. *Herbivorous*, or plant-eating, mammals have a longer intestine than do *carnivores*, or meat-eaters. This is a useful adaptation because the tough plant materials herbivores consume are harder to digest than meat. Despite such differences, mammalian organ systems are alike in a number of ways.

NERVOUS SYSTEM In addition to the cerebrum and the cerebellum, the mammalian brain consists of the *olfactory lobe*, the *optic lobe*, and the **medulla oblongata.** The medulla oblongata controls involuntary functions, such as heartbeat and breathing. The two parts of the cerebrum, called the *cerebral hemispheres*, account for 80% of the total weight of the brain. The cerebrum not only controls the activity of the animal, but it is also the center of memory and intelligence. The cerebellum, also very large, is directly connected to the cerebrum. This connection between the cerebrum and cerebellum is not found in other vertebrates. The olfactory lobe is small in mammals, such as the shrews, lemurs, monkeys, and human beings. The olfactory lobe receives impulses from the receptors in the nose that respond to smell. This lobe is large, however, in other mammalian groups. The optic

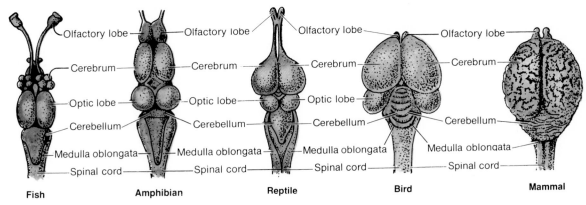

Figure 34-1 Comparison of Vertebrate Brains

In the figure, labels from left to right for each brain:

Fish: Olfactory lobe, Cerebrum, Optic lobe, Cerebellum, Medulla oblongata, Spinal cord

Amphibian: Olfactory lobe, Cerebrum, Optic lobe, Cerebellum, Medulla oblongata, Spinal cord

Reptile: Olfactory lobe, Cerebrum, Optic lobe, Cerebellum, Medulla oblongata, Spinal cord

Bird: Olfactory lobe, Cerebrum, Cerebellum, Medulla oblongata, Spinal cord

Mammal: Olfactory lobe, Cerebrum, Cerebellum

lobe receives impulses from the receptors in the eye that are responsible for sight.

The mammalian brain contains 12 pairs of *cranial nerves*. These paired nerves connect the brain with the head and neck, as well as with various organs. The cranial nerves have differing functions. Some, such as the optic and olfactory nerves, are *sensory nerves*, carrying sensory information to the brain. Other cranial nerves, such as those entering the eye muscles and certain facial muscles, are *motor nerves*. These nerves carry messages from the brain to the muscles. The mammalian nervous system also contains a *spinal cord*. *Spinal nerves* extend to and from the spinal cord, carrying impulses to various organs and muscles.

RESPIRATORY SYSTEM Mammals, like birds, need a great deal of oxygen for their high metabolic rates. The structure of the mammalian lung, however, is different from that of the bird lung. The *trachea* of mammals divides into two *bronchi* (BRAHNG-kī; singular: bronchus), one for each lung. Inside each lung, the bronchus subdivides into *bronchioles*. The bronchioles, in turn, end in clusters of *air sacs*. Each air sac contains a cluster of small sacs, called *alveoli* (al-VĒ-ə-lī; singular: alveolus). Gas exchange takes place in the alveoli, where there is a great deal of surface area.

The diaphragm is a large, dome-shaped muscle that separates the chest from the abdomen and controls breathing. When the diaphragm contracts, it makes the lung cavity bigger. The air inside the lungs spreads out to fill this larger space. This causes the air pressure in the lungs to drop. At this point, the air pressure outside the lungs is greater than the pressure inside. As a result, the air rushes from the outside through the trachea into the lungs. When the diaphragm relaxes and raises, it makes the lung cavities

Highlight

Structural characteristics of most mammals include a four-chambered heart, two pairs of limbs, a diaphragm that separates the thoracic cavity from the abdominal cavity, a vertebral column that is divided into five distinct regions, and a highly developed brain.

smaller. In so doing, the air inside the lungs is compressed. This makes the inside air pressure greater than the outside pressure. The air inside the lungs is then pushed out by the greater pressure.

Air flowing out of the lungs also plays a role in the vocal sounds that mammals make. Elastic vocal cords stretch across the *larynx*, or mammalian voice box that is made up of cartilage. When the animal tenses its vocal cords, the air passing over them produces sounds. The quality of the sounds depends on the structure of the larynx, how taut the vocal cords are stretched at the time, and the positions of the mouth and tongue.

CIRCULATORY SYSTEM The mammalian heart, unlike that of most vertebrates, has four chambers. Blood, circulating throughout the body, flows through the heart twice. First, oxygen-poor blood returning from the body enters the right side of the heart. It is then pumped to the lungs, where it picks up oxygen. Oxygen-rich blood then returns to the

Figure 34-2 Comparison of Vertebrate Hearts

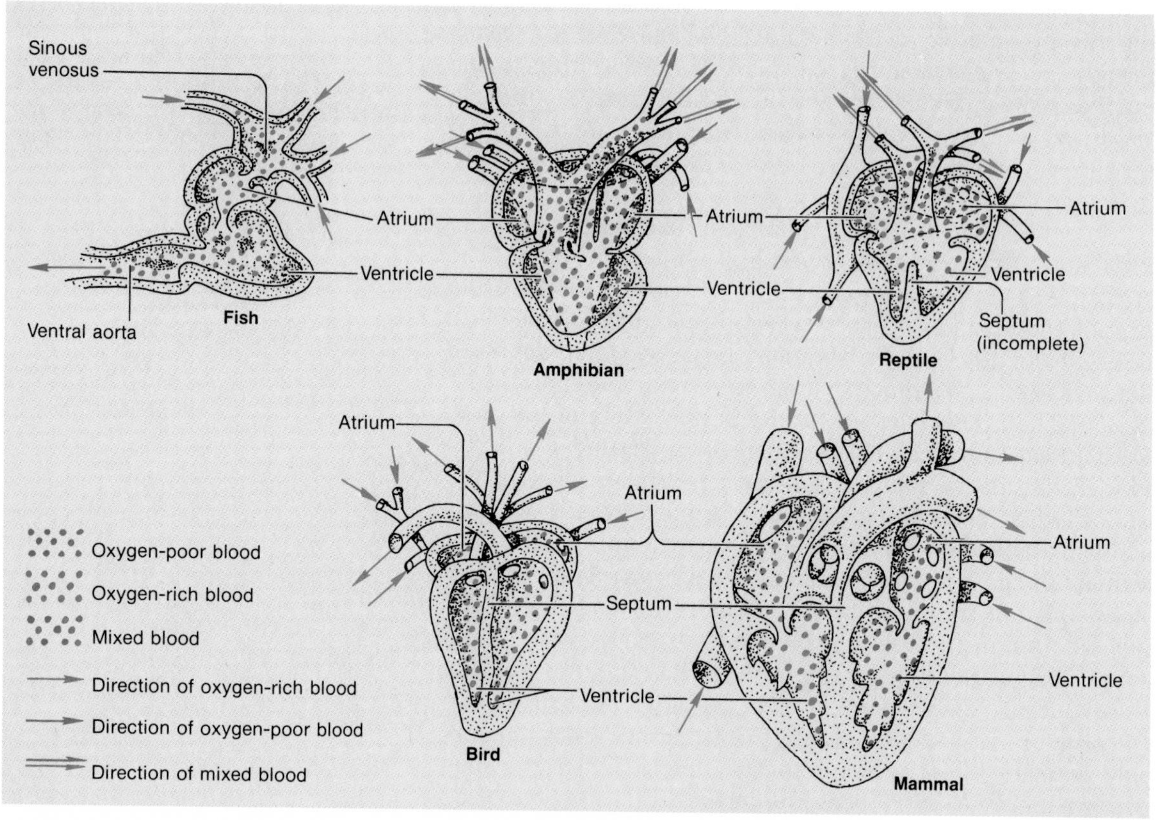

left side of the heart from the lungs. The heart then pumps this blood to the body.

All mammals are warm-blooded. In other words, their body temperatures remain constant, regardless of the temperatures of the environment. Mammalian body temperatures vary from species to species. For example, the average human body temperature is 37 °C. The average body temperature of dogs is 38.6 °C.

Reproduction and Parental Care

Fertilization in mammals is always internal. The *testes* of the male produce sperm, and the *ovaries* of the female produce eggs. During mating, the male deposits sperm within the female. In most mammals, if fertilization occurs, the resulting embryo becomes implanted in the *uterus*, or womb. The embryo then develops inside the uterus. The time required for the embryo to fully develop is called the **gestation period.** The gestation period varies greatly from one genus to another. For example, hamster embryos develop in 16 days. Elephant embryos take about 700 days to develop. In one group of mammals called the pouched mammals, the young only partially develop in the uterus. The partially developed embryo leaves the uterus, crawls up its mother's fur, and moves into the pouch of its mother, where it completes its growth.

Female mammals of all kinds feed their newborn young with milk secreted from their bodies. This milk provides all the nourishment that the young mammals need. The young therefore depend on at least their female parent for some time after birth. Baby elephants, for example, feed on their mother's milk for three years. In most mammals, the females rear the young. Only in a few mammals, such as the beavers and primates, do the males live with the females and young in a family group.

While the young are still in the mother's care, they are trained to carry out many activities, such as hunting for food. Mammals such as apes, which must devote a great deal of attention to their young during this initial period, bear only one or two offspring at a time. Mammals such as rodents, which pay little attention to their young, bear up to twelve offspring in one litter.

Migration and Hibernation

Some mammals *migrate*, or travel, thousands of kilometers each year, usually in search of warm weather and food. Many mammals migrate in groups. For example, during the

Sidelight

During the dry season in central Africa, thousands of zebras, wildebeests, and other animals are in constant migration searching for green grass.

558

You may want to have students draw maps showing the migration patterns of various mammals. These may be compared with the migration patterns of other animals, such as birds. Reasons for migration should also be investigated.

winter on the arctic tundra, herds of caribou move to less snowy areas in search of food. Some mammals migrate as individuals or in small groups. For instance, the California gray whale summers in the Bering Sea and the Arctic Ocean, but it swims to the warm southern waters as winter approaches. How fast a mammal migrates also varies. Some travel slowly, while others move quickly toward their destinations.

Mammals that do not migrate may survive the winter by *hibernation*. During hibernation, mammals live off the fat stored in their bodies. Their body temperatures drop, and their hearts slow down to as little as five beats a minute or less. Squirrels, chipmunks, and woodchucks, for example, all hibernate in protected spots when the cold weather sets in.

Some mammals go into a period of *dormancy* during the cold weather. In dormancy, the heartbeat and breathing slow down, but the body temperature remains unchanged. On a mild winter day, these mammals may leave their shelters. Bears, skunks, and raccoons, for example, go through dormant periods. Some mammals, including bears, have their young during the dormant period.

SECTION REVIEW   Answers on page T–87.

1. How does the mammalian heart differ from the heart of most vertebrates?
2. What is meant by the gestation period?
3. Distinguish between hibernation and dormancy.

Classification of Mammals

Despite the features that all mammals have in common, mammalian embryos develop in different ways. This difference can be used to divide mammals into three major groups. The groups are the **monotremes**, the **marsupials**, and the **placental mammals**.

Monotremes

The monotremes are primitive, egg-laying mammals that lack external ears. In these mammals, the intestine and genital duct both lead into a cloaca. Like other mammals, monotremes have hair, and they produce milk. The only two types of monotremes that are alive today are the duckbilled platypus and the spiny anteater. These two mammals build nests in burrows, where they nourish their newly hatched young.

Highlight

Fertilization is internal in all mammals. Development of the embryo is internal in all but the monotremes and marsupials.

Figure 34-3 The duckbilled platypus and the spiny anteater are the only living species of monotremes.

DUCKBILLED PLATYPUS The platypus is an excellent swimmer, with webbed forepaws, waterproof fur, and partially webbed hind paws. It is, however, only semiaquatic. Although it lives in streams, the platypus lives just as well on land. During the day, it hunts for snails, mussels, worms, fish, and crustaceans. Having no teeth, the platypus uses its bill to catch food. The platypus has a poison spur on its ankle for defense.

During the breeding season, the female platypus deposits one or two eggs in a den on a stream bank. Two weeks later, the young hatch. The hatchlings then feed on milk secreted from the mother's sweat glands.

SPINY ANTEATER The anteater, like most mammals, has hair all over its body. Mingled with the hair, however, are bristles and quills. When threatened by a predator, the anteater burrows into the ground until only its spines are exposed.

The mouth of this animal is at the tip of a long, beaklike structure. Inside the mouth is a sticky tongue that is used to probe rotting wood for ants and termites. The anteater also uses its strong claws to tear up ant and termite colonies.

In the mating season, a pouch develops on the abdomen of the female anteater. Into this pouch, the female deposits one or two eggs, where they incubate. Glands on the female's underbelly secrete milk for the young when they hatch.

Marsupials

Pouched mammals are called marsupials. The young marsupial, born only partially developed, climbs into a pouch on

560

Figure 34-4 Young opossums remain with their mother until they are old enough to go off on their own.

All of the world's marsupials, except for the opossums of the Americas, live in or around Australia. Students can do research to explain this zoogeographical mystery.

the abdomen of the mother. In the pouch, it attaches itself to a nipple for nourishment and completes its development. The opossum and the kangaroo are typical marsupials.

OPOSSUM The common opossum is the only North American marsupial. Most active at dawn and dusk, it lives in trees. The opossum eats fruits, insects, and small animals. It has five mobile fingers on each paw, and a tail that it uses for hanging onto trees.

Young opossums develop for 12 days in the uterus, where there are up to 13 nipples. Although as many as 18 young may be born in a litter, only 13 can feed and survive. The young stay in the pouch until fully developed. Even when they are completely developed, they may stay with the mother, riding on her back as she moves from place to place.

KANGAROO Kangaroos live in small herds in Australia and Tasmania, a large island off the southern coast of Australia. Some of these marsupials, such as the large red and grey kangaroos, can be as tall as 3 meters. Others, such as the rat kangaroo, can be as small as half a meter. Kangaroos have short forelimbs but long, muscular legs and tails. Their long feet have sharp claws. The tail helps the kangaroo to maintain its balance and to propel itself forward. Kangaroos are herbivores with flat teeth.

At birth, the partially developed kangaroo is only 2 centimeters long. At this time, the kangaroo is unable to see or to hear. Its forelimbs, however, are fairly well developed. With its forelimbs, it climbs to the pouch of its mother, probably guiding itself by sense of smell. The young kangaroo stays in the pouch, feeding for about nine months or until it can obtain its own food.

Placental Mammals

The mammalian egg is smaller than other vertebrate eggs, and it contains almost no yolk. To nourish the developing embryo, most mammals develop a new structure called the **placenta.** Animals with this structure are therefore called placental mammals. The placenta is made up of embryonic membranes, mainly the *chorion,* and the nearby tissues of the uterus. Within the placenta, the blood vessels of the mother and of the embryo lie very close together. Food and oxygen pass from the blood of the mother, through the placenta and umbilical cord, to the blood of the embryo. The bloodstreams of the mother and embryo, however, always re-

Highlight

Mammals can be divided into three major groups. Monotremes are primitive, egg-laying mammals. Marsupials are mammals that possess pouches in which the embryos develop. Placental mammals are those whose embryos develop totally within the female.

main separate. During the gestation period, the embryo develops fully before leaving the uterus.

There are more than 20 orders of placental mammals. They are classified according to various characteristics, such as what they eat, how they move about, or where they live. Of these orders, 13 are discussed in the sections that follow.

INSECT-EATING MAMMALS The *Insectivora*, or insect-eating mammals, include the mole, the prickly European hedgehog, and the shrew. Of all the members of this order, the shrew is perhaps the most familiar. The shrew is the smallest mammal in the world. The American pygmy shrew, for example, weighs only 20 grams. Although shrews thrive in woods and meadows, people rarely see them. For the most part undetected, they use their long snouts and sensitive facial whiskers to search for insects. Shrews can eat twice their own weight in insects every day.

Figure 34-5 Insectivores, such as these tiny shrews, eat insects, worms, or other invertebrates.

CLOSE-UP: *Helenette Silver*

In recent years, scientists and wildlife conservationists have been watching with interest the arrival of a new kind of coyote in the eastern United States. The Eastern coyote is larger than its western relative, the common coyote. Wildlife biologists think that the animal began migrating eastward some 80 years ago and that it has evolved into a new animal subspecies.

Helenette Silver, a New Hampshire wildlife biologist, is credited with the first scientific description of the Eastern coyote. Her research project began in 1960 and took six years to complete. On her farm in New Hampshire, she raised more than 50 Eastern coyote pups from several generations of litters. She kept careful records, often on a daily basis, of the growth patterns of the pups. She also kept records of their adult habits. Silver then compared the characteristics of the Western coyote with those of the Eastern coyote, as well as with those of the wolf. She was able to show beyond doubt that the Eastern coyote has become a subspecies different from the Western coyote.

The coyote research project is only one of many projects that Silver has worked on during

her many years as a wildlife biologist. She began her career in 1945 in the New Hampshire Fish and Game Department. Later, she became a research clerk for the department. After researching and publishing a book titled *A History of New Hampshire's Game and Furbearers,* she became research leader of a major study of metabolism in deer. Her pioneering efforts in the wildlife field have been the groundwork for other biological studies of wildlife, including further study of the Eastern coyote.

Figure 34-6 Bats navigate by emitting high-pitched sounds and listening for echoes that bounce off objects.

Figure 34-7 The teeth of carnivores are adapted for cutting and tearing.

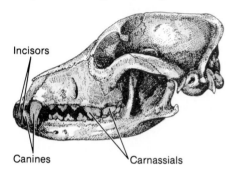

Incisors

Canines Carnassials

FLYING MAMMALS The only true flying mammals are the mammals in the order *Chiroptera*, or bats. Skin from the back and the abdomen of the bat stretches over the arms and long fingers to form wings. Like a bird, the bat has a large breastbone to anchor its powerful flying muscles, as well as a large pectoral area.

The eyesight of a bat is poor, but its hearing is excellent. To fly, it uses a sonarlike system. While flying, the bat emits high-pitched sounds that human beings cannot hear. The sounds bounce off objects in the path of the bat and return as echoes. By listening to these echoes, the bat knows where obstacles lie in its path.

Bats are divided into the fruit-eaters and the insect-eaters. Fruit-eating bats live in tropical and subtropical areas, such as Africa, India, Australia, and the Orient. Insect-eaters are found worldwide.

FLESH-EATING MAMMALS The *Carnivora*, or meat-eating mammals, include such animals as lions, skunks, bears, dogs, and otters. Carnivores are adapted for lives as predators. Their muscular legs help them to chase prey, and the sharp claws on their toes allow them to hold their prey. Their powerful jaws are adapted for tearing flesh. Carnivores use their *incisors*, or front teeth, for biting and their *canines*, or eyeteeth, for tearing. To cut through muscle tissue, these mammals use specialized teeth called *carnassials*.

Most carnivores can be divided into catlike and doglike animals. The catlike family includes lions, tigers, and domestic cats. The dog family includes wolves, jackals, foxes, and dogs. Most species of doglike carnivores are social animals, living together and hunting their prey in packs. The most primitive carnivores are the civets and mongooses. These animals live in the tropical forests of Africa and Asia. Mongooses have been imported into the Americas. Weasels, otters, and skunks are small, short-legged members of the carnivore group. Bears are also carnivores. Although they have no carnassial teeth, they have flattened teeth, called *molars*. These teeth are suitable for grinding many kinds of plants.

The raccoon of North and South America is related to the dog. Its diet, however, includes plants, and it cannot be considered a doglike carnivore. Raccoon teeth are better suited for grinding than for cutting and tearing. The giant panda is in the raccoon family.

There are some mammals that are flesh-eaters but they are not classified in the order *Carnivora*. Instead they are placed in the order *Pinnipedia* because they are adapted for living in the sea. Examples are seals and walruses.

TOOTHLESS MAMMALS The toothless mammals include the true anteaters, sloths, and armadillos. These mammals belong to the class *Edentata*. The true anteaters are not related to the spiny anteater. The long head of the true anteater ends in a pointed snout that curves toward the ground. At the tip of the snout is a mouth that does not contain teeth, but rather a long, sticky tongue. The anteater uses this tongue to catch insects. On the strong legs of the anteater are claws that curl backward. The anteater uses these claws to destroy nests of termites and ants.

Armadillos live in the southern United States and in Central and South America. These mammals have molars, teeth that are used for grinding, but they lack other types of teeth. They eat a variety of plants, insects, and small animals. The main feature of the armadillo is its protective shell, with its *scutes*, or small, bony plates. This shell develops from the deepest skin layer of the armadillo.

TRUNK-NOSED MAMMALS Trunk-nosed mammals are members of the order *Proboscidea*. The trunk on these mammals is actually a very long nose that includes part of the upper lip. At the tip of the trunk are nerve cells that are sensitive to smell and touch. In addition, 40,000 muscles in the trunk allow trunk-nosed mammals to use their trunks to carry food to their mouths and to lift heavy objects.

Only two types of trunk-nosed mammals are alive today. They are the African elephant and the Indian elephant. The African species, the largest land mammal, has huge, fanlike ears and a gray hide. This elephant can weigh about 5500 kilograms. The Indian elephant has smaller ears and a slightly smaller body, averaging about 3000 kilograms.

Elephants have two upper incisors, or front teeth, and twelve molars. In male elephants, the two incisors are developed into tusks that curve outward from the jaw. These tusks are a source of ivory. The tusks wear away with use, but they grow back constantly.

HOOFED MAMMALS Mammals with hoofs, called **ungulates,** can be odd-toed and even-toed. Horses, rhinoceroses, and zebras are odd-toed and are members of the order *Perissodactyla*. Even-toed ungulates include pigs, cows, goats, camels, and deer. These mammals belong to the order *Artiodactyla*. Most hoofed mammals are herbivores, feeding only on plants.

Figure 34-8 This anteater is an edentate, a toothless mammal. It is only distantly related to the spiny anteater, which is a monotreme.

Sidelight

Tiny mammals called hyraxes are about the size of a small rabbit or guinea pig. They are the closest living relatives of the elephants.

564

Ungulates are of great economic importance. Cattle, goats, pigs, and sheep have been domesticated, and people make use of their meat, milk, and hides. Horses and camels are also used for transportation and for bearing heavy loads.

Some even-toed ungulates, such as cows and sheep, are called **ruminants.** These ungulates have stomachs that are divided into four compartments. The first compartment, called the *rumen*, is a storage pouch for plant matter. Bacteria in this pouch produce enzymes that break down the *cellulose* in plant matter. The animal brings the semidigested food, called a *cud*, back into its mouth. After chewing it a while, the animal swallows the cud again. The food then travels through the other three compartments of the stomach. The food is further digested in the third compartment.

GNAWING MAMMALS The most numerous of all mammals are the animals in the order *Rodentia*. This order includes animals such as rats, mice, chipmunks, beavers, porcupines, and guinea pigs. Although many rodents live in burrows, the beaver builds its *lodge*, or home, of large branches and small tree trunks in streams. The largest rodent is the capybara of Panama and South America. Capybaras can grow to be 1.2 meters long, and they can weigh as much as 45 kilograms. Like all rodents, capybaras have two pairs of large chisel-shaped incisor teeth. These teeth grow continuously. If the incisors were not worn down by continuous use, they would grow so long that the animal could not close its mouth. Many rodents, such as mice and rats, are pests. Some, however, eat harmful insects and weeds.

RODENTLIKE MAMMALS. Rabbits and hares, classified in the order *Lagomorpha*, are like rodents in some ways and different in others. Like rodents, these animals gnaw, but they have an additional pair of small teeth behind their upper incisors. In addition, rodents grind their food by moving their jaws forward and backward, but a rabbit jaw moves sideways. Both rodents and lagomorphs reproduce quickly, and both are fast runners. As a result, rodents and lagomorphs thrive and multiply in spite of the fact that many other kinds of animals prey upon them.

WATER-DWELLING MAMMALS Two orders of mammals dwell completely in water. One of these orders is *Sirenia*, containing the manatees and dugongs. The other, *Cetacea*, includes the whales, dolphins, and porpoises. The manatees and dugongs have front limbs that are finlike. They have no hind limbs. They eat vegetation in the tropical Atlantic and Indian Oceans.

Figure 34-9 Water-dwelling mammals, such as the manatee, must come to the surface every so often to breathe.

Whales and porpoises, of the order *Cetacea*, are highly specialized mammals. Like the sirenians they have flippers instead of forelimbs, no hind limbs, dorsal fins, and tails. On the top of the head of these mammals is an opening through which warm moist air is blown from the lungs. Like all mammals, cetaceans breathe air, but some can remain underwater for 120 minutes.

Cetaceans obtain food in two ways. All porpoises, dolphins, and some whales have teeth, and they feed on animals, such as fishes and squids. All the whales without teeth, however, eat plankton organisms. These whales filter the plankton from the sea through rows of hard plates, called *baleen*, or whalebone. The 140,000-kilogram blue whale, for example, is the largest animal ever to live on the earth, but it has no teeth. Along with a number of other whales, the blue whale eats only plankton.

Cetaceans bear live young that are able to swim immediately after birth. For several months after birth, the mother feeds the young with a fatty milk. A female blue whale, for example, secretes about 200 liters of milk per day to feed a single offspring, or calf.

TREE-DWELLING MAMMALS   Members of the order *Primata*, or *Primates*, have several adaptations that are useful for living in trees. The eyesight of primates, especially their depth perception, is very good. Their hands have fingers that can grasp objects, such as tree limbs. Most importantly, the cerebrum is highly developed.

The primates are highly intelligent. Some chimpanzees, for example, have been taught to play tic-tac-toe. There is also evidence that chimpanzees can learn to use symbols to communicate with human beings. In the wild, chimpanzees use tools, such as broken branches, and they sometimes stand on two legs. Gorillas, the largest of the apes, can stand on two legs. They spend more time on the ground than do chimpanzees. New World monkeys have long tails that are used for climbing. Old World monkeys, such as baboons, have long tails that are not used for climbing. Human beings are also included in the order of *Primates*.

At this point, you may want your students to do the Laboratory Investigation at the end of this chapter.

Figure 34-10   The hands and feet of many primates, such as the tarsier, are adapted for grasping.

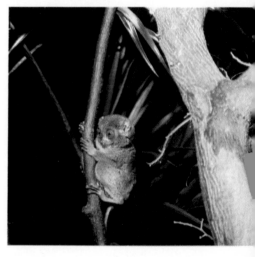

At this point, you may want to assign to your students the third of the Extensions and Applications at the end of this chapter.

SECTION REVIEW   Answers on page T–87.

1. What are monotremes?
2. Name the only North American marsupial.
3. What is a placenta?
4. Name four orders of placental mammals. Describe the general characteristics of each.

Figure 34-11 The Fourteen Major Orders of Mammals

Group Features	Order	Characteristics	Examples
Egg-laying mammals Internal fertilization External development	**Monotremata**	Teeth only in young Beaks	 Spiny anteater Duckbilled platypus
Pouched mammals Internal fertilization Development begins internally, completed externally	**Marsupialia**	Incisor teeth	 Kangaroo Opossum Tasmanian devil
Placental mammals Internal fertilization Internal development	**Insectivora**	Insect-eating mammals Sharp pointed teeth	 Shrew Mole
	Chiroptera	Flying mammals Sharp teeth Membranous forelimbs adapted for flying	 Bat
	Carnivora	Flesh-eating mammals Sharp teeth, canines modified into fangs Clawed toes	 Bobcat Dog Cat Bear Weasel
	Edentata	Toothless or teeth reduced to molars Clawed toes	 Sloth Anteater Armadillo
	Proboscidea	Trunk-nosed mammals Two upper incisors elongated into tusks Clublike feet	 Elephant

Group Features	Order	Characteristics	Examples
Placental mammals Internal fertilization Internal development	**Perissodactyla**	Odd-toed hoofed mammals Incisors and molars	Zebra Horse Tapir
	Rodentia	Gnawing mammals Chisel-like incisors Back and forth, lateral jaw motion Clawed toes	Porcupine Mouse Squirrel Rat
	Lagomorpha	Rodentlike mammals Extra pair of chisel-like upper incisors, no canines Lateral jaw motion Clawed toes	Pika Rabbit
	Sirenia	Water-dwelling mammals Molars Paddlelike forelimbs, no hind limbs	Manatee (sea cow) Dugong
	Cetacea	Water-dwelling mammals Teeth or plates Paddlelike forelimbs, no hind limbs	Dolphin Whale Porpoise
	Pinnipedia	Limbs formed as flippers or paddles Large canines Webbed toes	Seal Sea lion
	Primata	Tree-dwelling mammals Incisors, canines, premolars, and molars Innermost toes and thumbs usually opposable Capable of standing erect	Lemur Monkey Ape Human

LABORATORY INVESTIGATION 34

For additional information, see page T-87.

Classifying and Comparing Mammals

Purpose The class *Mammalia* is made up of a diverse group of animals. Some organisms in this class, such as the whales and porpoises look like fishes. Others, such as wolves, are entirely covered with hair. Some unusual mammals even lay eggs. The purpose of this investigation is to classify different mammals and to identify and compare the characteristics of mammals.

Materials *(per group)* ● Reference materials on mammals ● Pictures of mammals of different orders, cut from magazines, old texts, and so on ● 14 8″ x 12″ sheets of white construction paper ● Tape

Table 2

Identification Code	Name of Organism	Correct Order

Procedure **1.** Fold each sheet of construction paper in half along its width. **2.** Tape the sides of each sheet, forming a pocket envelope. Do not tape the top of the paper. **3.** Label each pocket envelope with an order name that is listed in Figure 34-12. **4.** Study the pictures of mammals provided by your teacher. **5.** Place each picture in the envelope you think represents that animal's order. **6.** Copy Table 1 on a sheet of paper. Place the identification code from each of your pictures in the proper space. **7.** In the second column of the table, fill in the order in which you classified each of the mammals. **8.** Then, fill in the characteristics of each of the animals based upon your study of the pictures. **9.** Re-evaluate your classification of the animals in each picture. Fill in the order in which you would classify the mammal after you have listed its characteristics. **10.** Copy Table 2 on the same sheet of paper as Table 1. Check with your teacher to find out the correct order and the name of each mammal. Fill in this information in Table 2.

Observations and Conclusions **1.** How do the monotremes differ from the marsupials? **2.** What feature distinguishes the marsupials from the other mammals? **3.** Which orders of mammals appear the most similar? Explain your answer. **4.** List the characteristics that all of the mammals have in common.

Table 1

Identification Code	Predicted Order	Characteristics	Re-evaluated Order

568

CHAPTER SUMMARY

History of Mammals The mammals probably descended from the therapsids, a group of ancient reptiles. The jaws of therapsids were similar to those of the reptiles. However, the limbs, teeth, and skull resembled those of mammals. The Cenozoic Era, or the Age of the Mammals, began about 65 million years ago.

Characteristics of Mammals Mammals are vertebrates with body hair. Most mammals bear live young and nourish their young with milk secreted by the mammary glands.

Mammals also have highly developed brains. The cerebrum controls activity and the cerebellum coordinates muscle movement. The medulla oblongata controls breathing and heartbeat.

In mammals, respiration occurs in the lungs. The lungs and the heart are separated from the abdominal cavity by a muscle called the diaphragm. Mammals have a four-chambered heart, two pairs of limbs, and a vertebral column that has five distinct regions.

In mammals, fertilization is internal. Mammals care for their young longer than do other vertebrates. During the winter, some mammals migrate and others hibernate.

Classification of Mammals The mammals can be divided into three groups based upon their type of embryonic development. These groups are the monotremes, marsupials, and placental mammals. Monotremes are primitive egg-laying mammals such as the duckbilled platypus and the spiny anteater. Marsupials are pouched mammals. The young of the marsupials are born only partially developed. They further mature in the pouch of the mother. The kangaroo and the opossum are typical marsupials.

In placental mammals, the placenta nourishes the developing embryo. In the placenta, the blood vessels of the mother and those of the embryo are very close together. The blood of one, however, does not mix with the blood of the other.

The more than 20 orders of living placental mammals include insect-eating mammals such as shrews, flying mammals such as bats, and flesh-eating mammals such as lions. Pinnipeds, such as seals, are also flesh-eaters but they live in the water. Edentates, such as the anteaters, are the toothless mammals. Elephants are examples of trunk-nosed mammals. The ungulates are hoofed mammals that are adapted to grazing. Gnawing mammals include mice and other rodents. Lagomorphs, or rabbits, are among the rodentlike mammals. Two orders of water-dwelling mammals, the sirenians and cetaceans, include manatees and whales, respectively. Human beings, monkeys, and apes are known as primates.

CHAPTER VOCABULARY

cerebellum	mammary gland	placenta
cerebrum	medulla oblongata	placental mammal
diaphragm	marsupial	ruminant
gestation period	monotreme	ungulate

REVIEW of FACTS and CONCEPTS Answers on page T–87.

On a separate sheet of paper, answer each of the following as completely as possible.

1. List ten characteristics of mammals.
2. Trace the path that air takes through the mammalian respiratory system.
3. How do mammals care for their young?
4. Why do mammals migrate?
5. What is a marsupial? Give two examples.
6. How are bats adapted for flight?
7. How are carnivores adapted as predators?
8. Name three types of mammalian teeth. Describe their functions.
9. What factors account for the fact that rodents and lagomorphs are so numerous?
10. How are cetaceans adapted for their way of life?
11. List fourteen orders of mammals.

EXTENSIONS and APPLICATIONS For additional information, see page T–87.

1. Write a report on the domestication of the horse, dog, or cat.
2. Visit a zoo, and study the different mammals. Compare their color adaptations, their limbs, the position of their eyes, and the functions of their tails.
3. Write a report on Washoe the Chimp and on the recent experiments on apes and language.
4. Obtain a preserved laboratory rat, cat, or fetal pig for dissection. Which structures do you see that are unique to mammals? Which structures occur in other vertebrates?

SUGGESTED READINGS

Beadle, M., *The Cat: History, Biology, and Behavior*. New York: Simon & Schuster.
   This book on the domestic cat should answer nearly every question one might have about this popular pet.
Carrington, R., and the Editors of Time-Life Books, *The Mammals*. New York: Time-Life Books.
   This illustrated volume offers an overview of the mammals, from shrews to primates.
Douglas-Hamilton, I., and O., *Among the Elephants*. New York: Bantam Books.
   These naturalists have written an exciting book on the biology and behavior of the largest land animal in the world.
Sanderson, I. T., *Living Mammals of the World*. Garden City, N.Y.: Doubleday.
   This reference book contains descriptions and photographs of the mammals of the world.

Language in the Higher Animals

The fact that animals communicate is well known. Honeybees, for example, perform a dance that tells other members of the hive where nectar can be found. True language, however, is learned, not inherited like the dance of the honeybee. It is also highly complex, made up of abstract spoken and behavioral symbols that express thoughts and feelings. It is therefore different from physical communication. Language has always been thought to be a human trait that makes human beings unique among organisms.

Recently, some scientists who study behavior suspect that other species may be able to communicate by means of language. In some cases, these scientists have experimented with language communication between other species and human beings. For example, marine mammals, such as dolphins and whales, are very intelligent, highly vocal, and social. They have therefore been considered likely candidates for language study.

John Lilly, a psychologist, studied the sounds produced by dolphins. One such sound is a high-pitched clicking that dolphins use to find their way around in deep water or at night. Other sounds, however, appear to be part of a language. Lilly tried to understand the code of this language, and he even claimed some success. Some researchers feel, however, that his claims are not well supported.

Roger Payne, a zoologist, has recorded and studied the elaborate songs of the humpback whale. Payne made the recordings with an underwater microphone lowered from the side of a boat. Although he is not certain that the songs are forms of communication, he has noted that they are complex and are repeated in cycles.

In the 1940s, several scientists tried to teach spoken language to chimpanzees. After a long period of training, one chimpanzee could speak four words, ma, pa, up, and cup. The vocabulary was limited because an ape does not have the same vocal anatomy as a human being.

Scientists Allen and Beatrice Gardner tried to communicate with a chimpanzee using Ameslan, a sign language that is used as a form of communication by deaf Americans. One of their chimpanzees was able to learn 160 words, and it could even communicate in complete sentences.

Some scientists argue that the apes in the experiment were not using true language. Instead, they had been conditioned to act in a certain way just to be rewarded. The Gardners disagree, and the debate seems to center on the definition of language. If people like the Gardners and John Lilly turn out to be correct, our relationships with some animals, such as apes and dolphins, may have to change.

Viewpoints

1. Find out the meanings of the terms "conditioned response," "learning," and "language." How do these terms apply to human behavior? To animal behavior? Based on your findings, write an essay expressing your views on the work of Roger Payne, John Lilly, and Allen and Beatrice Gardner. Read articles by and about these scientists and their work.

2. Research the ways children learn how to communicate. Means of communication you should investigate can include physical activities such as crying, gesturing and smiling, making various sounds, and spoken language. Repeat this line of research for a particular animal, such as a dolphin, or chimpanzee. Are there similar means of communication in animals and children? How are they similar? How are they different? What kinds of information do young children communicate that animals do not communicate? Prepare an oral or written report on your findings and conclusions.

3. Many people believe that they can talk with animals. Veterinarians have often said that their animal patients communicate their problems by the sounds they make and by their behavior. Can you understand a pet dog or cat by its actions? Draw up a chart of specific behaviors that your pet shows you. What do they mean? Would your analysis hold for all similar animals?

Human Structure and Function

For an overview of this unit, including field trip suggestions, a bibliography, and a list of audio-visual materials, see pages T–88 to T–98. You may want to check the Laboratory Investigations in this unit so that materials may be ordered, gathered, or prepared in advance.

The most complex organism on the earth is the human organism. Its cells, tissues, organs, and organ systems work in constant harmony. Encased in a protective envelope of skin is a mobile system of interconnected bones that gives the human body its shape. This skeleton is set in motion by the contractions of hundreds of specialized muscles. Other muscles drive the heart, while others help control the movement of blood and nutrients in the body. Blood moves through the circulatory system carrying oxygen and nutrients to almost all cells and carrying wastes away from them. Digestive, respiratory, and excretory organs make vital contributions to the smooth functioning of the body. All of these processes progress normally in a body provided with the proper nutrients and protected from the damage of disease and injury.

The movements of these figure skaters illustrate how different body structures work together in harmony.

35 Human Body Structure

Muscles and bones help to move and protect the body.

Chapter Objectives *After completing this chapter, you will be able to:*

a ■ Explain the relationships among cells, tissues, organs, and organ systems. p. 575
b ■ State the functions of the skeleton. p. 577
c ■ Name the two major divisions of the skeleton. p. 578
d ■ Describe the composition of a bone. p. 578
e ■ List the kinds of joints in the body. p. 581
f ■ Compare the structures and functions of three types of muscle tissue. p. 583
g ■ Describe the structure of the skin. p. 586
h ■ State the functions of the skin. p. 588

For teaching aids for this chapter, including a chapter overview and teaching strategies, see pages T–88 to T–90. The page number next to each chapter objective refers to the text page where the information needed to fulfill the objective begins.

Walking, jogging, smiling, and even standing upright may seem easy to do. The processes that underlie these movements, however, are very complex. A number of structures must work together smoothly to make these actions possible. Bones and muscles must move in harmony. The skin must be flexible enough to allow these movements to occur. Signals from the brain, which controls the movement of most muscles, must flow freely along nerves. When muscles receive a nerve impulse, they pull on bones to make the body move. More than 100 muscles, for example, are used to produce a single frown!

The movement of many muscles is often required in other activities. For example, think of the last time you played basketball. As you dribbled down the court, your hands, arms, and legs moved. You turned your head to watch for players of the opposite team. Perhaps you called to a teammate. You did all of these things almost without thinking. Your muscles, bones, and brain were *coordinating*, or working in harmony.

Organization in the Human Body

The human body is made of trillions of cells. These cells form different **tissues,** or groups of similar cells that perform the same function. The human body contains four basic types of tissues.

Connective tissue The *connective tissue* supports and connects different parts of the body. The various types of connective tissue have different properties. Bone and blood, for example, are two very different types of connective tissues. Bone, a solid tissue, makes up the skeletal system. The skeletal system gives a strong structural support for the body. Blood is often referred to as liquid tissue. It carries food, oxygen, and wastes throughout the body. Figure 35-1 lists the different types of connective tissue.

Muscle tissue The *muscle tissue* has the ability to contract. Three types of this tissue are found in the body. The first type makes the body move by pulling on bones. The second type makes up the walls of internal organs. The third type is a special muscle tissue that is found in the heart.

Epithelial tissue The *epithelial tissue* protects the body. Epithelial tissue forms the skin on the outside of the body. It also lines many body cavities. This tissue can absorb and secrete various substances.

Nerve tissue The *nerve tissue* has the ability to conduct messages. It is found in the brain, in the spinal cord, and

Highlight

Groups of similar cells that perform the same function are tissues. Several groups of different tissues form an organ, and several organs work together in an organ system.

You may want to illustrate the relationship of the structure of a tissue to its function in the body. For example, epithelial tissue has little intercellular material, and the cells are packed tightly together. Such a tissue would function well as a protective barrier against invading pathogens.

Figure 35-1 Types of Connective Tissue in the Human Body

Tissue	Functions
Bone	Provides support, stores minerals, and manufactures blood cells in the marrow
Cartilage	Provides firm but flexible support for some body parts, such as the ears
Loose fibrous connective tissue	Includes the tissue between body organs and fat tissue; serves as insulation and food storage
Dense fibrous connective tissue	Provides strong flexible connection betweeen body parts; examples include ligaments and tendons
Blood and lymph	Called liquid tissue; composed of red and white cells and fluid

System	Function
Skeletal	Protects and supports the body
Muscular	Movement and support of the body
Integumentary	Protects the body
Digestive	Receives, transports, breaks down, and absorbs food throughout the body
Circulatory	Transports oxygen, wastes, and digested food throughout the body
Respiratory	Permits the exchange of gases in the body
Excretory	Removes liquid and solid wastes from the body
Endocrine	Regulates various body functions
Nervous	Conducts messages throughout the body to aid in coordination of body functions
Reproductive	Produces sperm in males and eggs in females

Figure 35-2 Human Organ Systems and Their Functions

in all the nerves of the body. Nerve tissue is discussed in Chapter 41.

Groups of different tissues form **organs.** Some organs in the human body are the heart, the lungs, and the eyes. An **organ system** is made of groups of organs. The human body contains ten different organ systems. These are listed in Figure 35-2, along with their functions. Together, organ systems form an organism.

SECTION REVIEW   Answers on page T-89.

1. Name the four basic types of tissues in the human body.
2. What are the functions of blood?
3. Where is epithelial tissue found?
4. List the functions of the ten organ systems in the human body.

The Skeletal System

The human skeleton is made up of about 206 different bones. In addition, the human skeleton contains **cartilage** and **ligaments.** Both are tough and fibrous connective tissues, but they are not as hard as bone. Ligaments and cartilage differ in the kinds, number, and arrangement of fibers present. Ligaments hold organs in place and fasten bones together. Cartilage cushions long bones against shock and reduces friction between these bones. Cartilage is also found between the bones in the vertebral column, attaching ribs to the sternum or breastbone, and in the external ear, trachea, and nose. The bones, the connective tissues, and the muscles all work together to protect, to move, and to give shape to the body.

Because the skeleton is found beneath the skin and muscles, it is an **endoskeleton,** or internal skeleton. Unlike an exoskeleton, such as the shell of a lobster, an endoskeleton does not protect the skin and muscles. Although an exoskeleton provides such protection, it is relatively heavy and limits movement. An endoskeleton provides a strong supporting framework with the least possible mass.

Bones come in many shapes and sizes, and they have various functions. They can be as small as a few millimeters or as long as half a meter. Three of the smallest bones in the body are in the ear, where they make hearing possible. The largest bone in the body, called the *femur,* is the long bone of the thigh that supports the major portion of the body's mass. Other bones participate in movement or protect internal organs.

Functions of the Skeleton

The skeletal system serves several important functions. It manufactures blood cells, shapes the body, enables the body to move, protects the organs, and stores materials.

Support and shape of the body The internal system of bones is like the wooden frame of a house. Just as the house could not stand without its wooden frame, the human body would collapse without its endoskeleton.

Movement of the body Along with the muscles and other kinds of connective tissues, the arrangement of the bones permits many complex movements. For example, the long bones in the arms and legs act as levers that are pulled by muscles. In this way, the skeleton works with the muscles to make movement possible.

Protection of the internal organs Many bones protect the internal organs of the body. For example, the skull covers the brain. The ribs form a cage around the lungs, heart, and other chest organs.

Formation of blood cells   Some bones have a cavity with a soft tissue, called **marrow.** Most of the blood cells in the body are produced in the red marrow.

Storage of minerals   Stored in the bones are such minerals as calcium and phosphorus, which move back and forth constantly between the bones and the bloodstream.

Skeletal Divisions

The human skeleton can be divided into two major parts. The **axial skeleton** has 80 bones and runs through the central axis of the body. All the other bones are directly or indirectly connected to it. The three parts of the axial skeleton are the *skull,* the *vertebral column,* and the *thorax.* The skull has a movable jaw that gives the face its shape and a rigid bony shell that protects the brain. In the vertebral column, 33 small bones, called *vertebrae,* are stacked one upon the other. These bones not only protect the spinal cord, but they also form a strong support for the body.

The thorax is made up of 12 pairs of ribs attached to the vertebral column in the back. Seven of those pairs are attached directly to the *sternum,* or breastbone, by cartilage. These are the *true ribs.* The remaining five pairs of ribs are called *false ribs* because they are not directly attached to the sternum. Three of the false ribs are attached to the seventh true rib. The eleventh and twelfth false ribs, however, are attached to the vertebral column, but not to the sternum or to the seventh rib. These two pairs of ribs are often referred to as *floating ribs.*

The second major part of the human skeleton is the **appendicular** (ap-ən-DIK-yə-lər) **skeleton.** It contains 126 bones. The appendicular skeleton is attached to the axial skeleton by a group of connecting bones called *girdles.* One girdle is located in the shoulder, and the other is in the *pelvis,* or hips. The *shoulder girdle* is made up of the *clavicle,* or collar bone, and the *scapula,* or shoulder blade. The *pelvic girdle* is made up of three large bones held together tightly by cartilage. The major function of the pelvic girdle is support. The appendicular skeleton includes these two girdles, along with the bones of the arms and legs.

Formation of Bones

Bones are formed either from *membrane layers* or from cartilage. Almost all bones develop from cartilage. During the early stages of development before birth, the human

Highlight

The bones of the skull, vertebral column, and thorax make up the axial skeleton. The appendicular skeleton consists of the shoulder and pelvic girdles and the bones of the arms and legs.

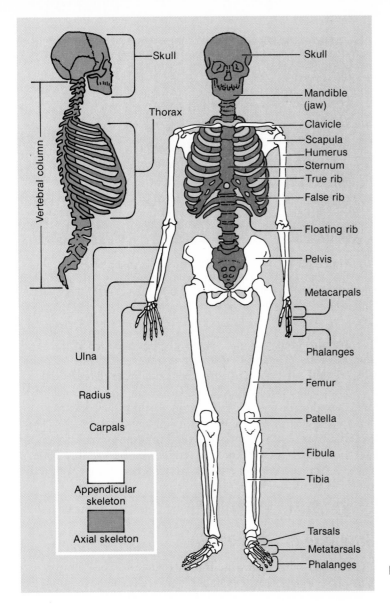

Skull

Skull

Mandible (jaw)

Clavicle

Scapula

Humerus

Sternum

True rib

False rib

Floating rib

Pelvis

Metacarpals

Phalanges

Femur

Patella

Fibula

Tibia

Tarsals

Metatarsals

Phalanges

Thorax

Vertebral column

Ulna

Radius

Carpals

Appendicular skeleton

Axial skeleton

Figure 35-3   Human Skeletal System

skeleton is made almost entirely of cartilage. During the second and third months of development, **ossification** (ahs-ə-fi-KĀ-shən), or the process of forming bone, takes place. During this process, bone cells replace cartilage cells, and calcium compounds are deposited between the bone cells.

Bone formation occurs throughout life, but most of it takes place during the first 25 years of growth. The ossification of cartilage occurs in most areas of the skeleton, especially in the arms, legs, and thorax. Some cartilage does not ossify. Even in adults, permanent cartilage is found at the tip of the nose and in the outer parts of the ears.

Highlight

Ossification is the process in which cartilage is transformed into bone.

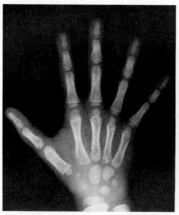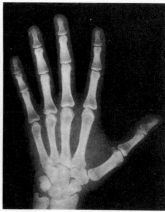

Figure 35-4 An X-ray of the hand of a young child (*left*) shows the absence of several bones in the wrist. In the adult hand (*right*), ossification is complete and all the bones of the wrist are fully formed.

Figure 35-5 At birth, the bones of the skull are not totally fused, leaving fontanels, or soft spots. In the adult, the fontanels ossify and are called sutures.

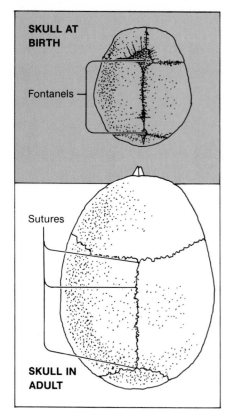

Membranous bone is formed in the flat areas of the skull and sternum. To form these bones, layers of connective tissue are laid one on top of the other and undergo ossification.

The *cranium*, the part of the skull that protects the brain, undergoes slow ossification. In newborn infants, the bones that make up the cranium have not yet fused. There are soft spots in the cranium, called **fontanels** (fahn-tə-NELZ). As the baby grows older, the edges of the cranium bones fuse. After the second year of development, the fontanels ossify completely. Irregular seams, called **sutures**, are formed where the cranium bones fuse.

Structure of a Bone

Human bone contains living tissue and nonliving materials. The living tissue includes bone cells, blood vessels, fat cells, and cartilage. The nonliving materials include water and minerals, such as calcium and phosphorus, in the form of phosphate. In fact, bones are hard and strong because they contain a great amount of calcium.

Bone has *compact bone tissue* and *spongy bone tissue.* Compact bone is very dense and hard. Compared to compact bone, spongy bone is softer, and it has many spaces in it.

Various bones of the body have different features. For example, a long bone, like the femur, has two enlarged ends with a long shaft connecting them. The ends are made of spongy bone, covered first with a thin layer of compact bone and second with a thin layer of cartilage. The cartilage cuts down on the friction between bones that touch each other.

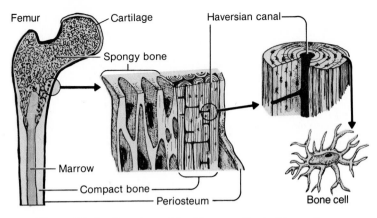

Femur — Cartilage — Haversian canal —
— Spongy bone
— Marrow
— Compact bone —
— Periosteum —
Bone cell

Figure 35-6 Structure of the Femur, a Typical Long Bone

The shaft is thick compact bone. A tough, fibrous membrane, called the **periosteum** (per-i-AHS-tē-əm), surrounds the shaft. The periosteum contains blood vessels and bone-forming cells, and aids in repairing and nourishing the bone.

Throughout compact bone tissue, there is a system of small channels, called the **Haversian** (ha-VER-shən) **canals.** These canals contain blood vessels and nerves. One of the functions of the canals is to carry food and oxygen to the living cells in the bone.

Many bones of the body contain a hollow space, called the *marrow cavity.* In the long bones, the marrow cavity extends the length of the shaft. The marrow cavity is filled with marrow, blood vessels, and nerves.

Two types of marrow are found in bones. *Red marrow* is responsible for the formation of most of the body's blood cells. This marrow gets its color from *hemoglobin* (HĒ-mə-glō-bin), the pigment found in red blood cells. Red marrow is found in the bones of the thorax, in the base of the cranium, in the vertebrae, and in the ends of some long bones. *Yellow marrow* is found in all other bones and contains stored fats. It is not actively involved in the formation of blood cells.

Skeletal Joints

The human body can make a wide range of movements because it has **joints,** or points where two or more bones meet. *Movable joints* permit full movement in one or more directions. Some joints are only partially movable. These are found in the pelvis and at the points where the ribs join the sternum. A few joints are fixed and are called *immovable joints.* The sutures in the adult skull, for example, are immovable joints.

Highlight

The point of contact between two or more bones is called a joint.

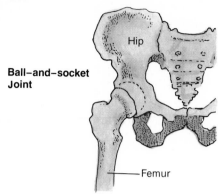

Ball–and–socket Joint

Hip

Femur

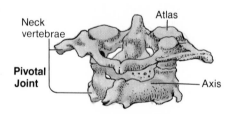

Humerus

Hinge Joint

Radius

Ulna

Elbow

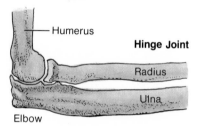

Neck vertebrae

Atlas

Pivotal Joint

Axis

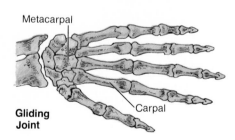

Metacarpal

Gliding Joint

Carpal

Figure 35-7 Four kinds of movable joints are found in the human skeleton. Describe the kinds of movement possible with each type of joint.

Hinge joints provide movement in one direction only. Pivotal joints provide rotating motion. Ball-and-socket joints provide circular motion. Gliding joints provide sliding or gliding motion of one bone past another.

When a person moves, pressure is often exerted on the ends of the bones. This pressure creates friction that is reduced in several ways. In addition to the cartilage that provides a kind of cushion between bones, a fluid called **synovial fluid** is found in joints. This fluid is secreted by a membrane found between the ends of bones in a joint and acts as a type of lubricant. In addition, fluid-filled sacs, called **bursae,** are found between bones. These sacs decrease the pressure on bones that are in contact with each other. An inflammation of the bursae is called *bursitis.*

BALL-AND-SOCKET JOINTS In a *ball-and-socket joint,* the rounded head of one bone fits into a cuplike socket of another bone. This type of joint permits a circular motion with free movement in all directions. Ball-and-socket joints connect the arms to the shoulder and the legs to the hips. A baseball pitcher, winding up for the pitch, shows the wide range of movement that this type of joint permits.

HINGE JOINTS Like the hinges on a door, the *hinge joints* in the body permit movement in only one direction. Hinge joints are found in the elbows and the knees.

PIVOT JOINTS In this type of joint, a ring-shaped bone surrounds a peglike pivot. These joints only permit a rotating motion. The head turns from side to side, for example, on a *pivot joint* between the first and second vertebrae.

GLIDING JOINTS In this joint, a bone with either a slightly curved or nearly flat surface slides along another bone with a corresponding shape. The flexibility of the wrists and ankles is made possible by *gliding joints.*

SECTION REVIEW   Answers on page T-89.

1. List four important functions of the skeleton.
2. Explain the differences between the axial and appendicular skeletons.
3. What is ossification?
4. Describe the structure of a long bone.
5. Explain the differences in structure and function between the four kinds of movable joints.

The Muscular System

The muscles of the body perform many functions. Human beings could not run, jump, or breathe if they had no muscles. Their hearts would not beat. Blood would not move efficiently through their veins and arteries. Food would not move through their digestive systems. All these activities are made possible by the functions of specialized muscle cells and muscle tissues.

Muscle tissue is made of bundles of long, thin cells called **muscle fibers.** These fibers are the only cells in the body that are able to contract, or shorten. Each muscle fiber contains smaller threads, called **myofibrils.** The myofibrils are visible under a light microscope. When seen under an electron microscope, however, the myofibrils are shown to contain bundles of protein filaments. There are two kinds of protein filaments that are arranged in a definite pattern. The thick ones are called *myosin filaments,* and the thin ones are called *actin filaments.* The functions of these filaments will be discussed in a later section of this chapter.

Muscle Types

There are three types of muscle tissue in the body. **Skeletal muscle** accounts for about 40% of the weight of the body. Skeletal muscle is made of long bundles of closely packed muscle fibers, each of which contains many nuclei. The bundles have light and dark bands called *striations.* The striations are formed by overlapped bundles of fibers. Due to this banded appearance, skeletal muscle is also called *striated muscle.* These muscles are connected to bones by ropelike structures called **tendons.** Still another name for

Figure 35-8 Muscles are made up of bundles of muscle fibers.

Figure 35-9 Skeletal muscles (*left*), smooth muscles (*center*), and cardiac muscles (*right*) are the three types of muscle tissue in the human body. Where in the body is each type found?

Skeletal, or striated, muscle is found in the skeleton. Smooth muscle is found in the blood vessels and digestive tract. Cardiac muscle is found in the heart.

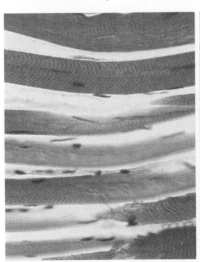
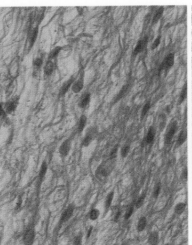
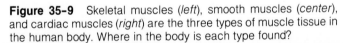

Sidelight

There are approximately 600 skeletal muscles in the human body. If all the skeletal muscles in the human body pulled in one direction, an average human being could lift 23,680 kilograms.

this type of muscle is *voluntary muscle*. These muscles cannot move on their own, but are controlled at will.

Smooth muscle is the second type of muscle tissue. It is made of long, spindle-shaped cells with a single nucleus in the center of each. This muscle tissue is found in the walls of some blood vessels and of the digestive system. Because these muscles move without conscious control, they are called *involuntary muscles.*

The third type of muscle, found only in the heart, is called **cardiac muscle.** These muscle cells are very unlike skeletal and smooth muscle cells. Cardiac muscle cells are branched, and they join to form a laced network. The striations in these cells are not as clear as those in skeletal muscle. This structure allows cardiac muscle to contract rhythmically, pumping blood out of the heart and through the blood vessels. The most important characteristic of cardiac muscle is that, under normal conditions, it contracts automatically.

CAREER: Biomedical Engineer

Biomedical engineers apply the principles of engineering to the medical and health sciences. In addition to conducting research, these engineers design and develop many types of life-support equipment and medical instruments. Artificial organs and pacemakers are only two examples of what biomedical engineers design.

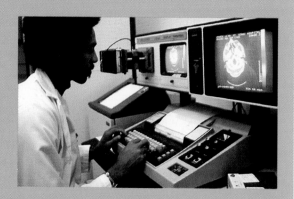

Some biomedical engineers develop ways to use computers in medical science. For example, these engineers have developed computer systems that monitor body functions of patients during operations. Other biomedical engineers may work closely with biologists, chemists, and physicians conducting research on the biology of human beings. Together, they develop new theories or facts about life systems. Some specialized biomedical engineers are called clinical engineers. They develop ways to make laboratory, hospital, and clinical procedures and techniques more modern and efficient.

To become a biomedical engineer, a person must receive a bachelor's degree in engineering from an accredited college or university. The requirements include courses in mechanical, electrical, chemical, or industrial engineering. Other courses are taken in biomedicine. Some engineers continue their education on the graduate level, usually specializing in a particular field of engineering.

Many biomedical engineers are employed as teachers in colleges and universities. Some biomedical engineers work for private industry, while others work for federal government agencies, such as NASA, or state agencies.

For further career information, write to Biomedical Engineering Society, PO Box 2399, Culver City, CA 90230.

Muscle Action

The kind of movement a skeletal muscle causes is determined by its places of attachment to bone. The fixed place of attachment is called the **origin,** and the movable point of attachment is the **insertion.** The body of the muscle between these two points is called the **belly.** Figure 35-10 shows the biceps and triceps, which are located in the upper arms and which move the forearms. Each of these muscles derives part of its name from the number of origin points. The *biceps* muscle has two origins, while the *triceps* muscle has three.

The biceps and triceps also show how muscles work in pairs. The biceps muscle is called a **flexor** because it bends a joint, while the triceps is an **extensor** because it straightens a joint. To flex, or bend the arm, the biceps contract, and the triceps relax. The opposite actions occur to extend the arm. The biceps relax as the triceps contract. These two muscles therefore flex or extend the arm by working in opposite ways. Skeletal muscles cause movement only in one way, by contracting.

Like all living cells, muscle cells need energy to perform their functions. Muscles get their energy from the breakdown of a substance called adenosine triphosphate (ATP).

You might want to tell students that the biceps are called the antagonists and the triceps the agonists.

Highlight

A flexor is a muscle that bends a joint and an extensor is one that straightens a joint.

Figure 35-10 The biceps and triceps are antagonistic muscles. That is, when one contracts, the other relaxes.

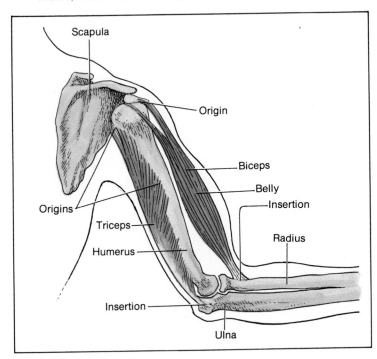

Scapula

Origin

Biceps

Belly

Insertion

Origins

Triceps

Radius

Humerus

Insertion

Ulna

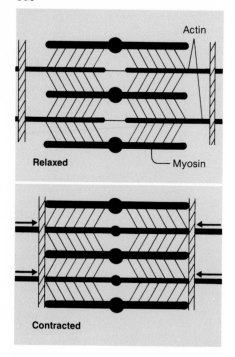

Figure 35-11 According to the sliding filament theory of muscle contraction, the actin filaments slide over each other and the myosin filaments do not move. What provides energy for muscle contraction?

ATP, or adenosine triphosphate

In addition to ATP, muscles need a nerve impulse to contract. To begin contraction, a nerve impulse is carried from a branched nerve cell to a few muscle fibers. The point where the nerve cell and the muscle fibers meet is called the *motor unit*. The impulse starts a chemical reaction that causes the myofibrils and muscle fibers to shorten. As the muscle contracts, the actin filaments slide past the myosin filaments, which do not move. Figure 35-11 shows how this action causes the muscle to contract.

When stimulated by an impulse, a muscle fiber contracts as much as possible or not at all. Only individual muscle fibers give this *all-or-none response*. Whole muscles do not.

The strength of the nerve impulse does not determine how forcefully muscle fibers contract. What does determine the force of the movement is the number of motor units that stimulate the muscle fiber. The force of the movement increases as more motor units are stimulated. As a simple example, for a softball batter to hit the ball into center field, more motor units are needed than to bunt a ball only a few meters.

You might want to tell students that, like muscle cells, nerve cells respond as much as possible or not at all.

SECTION REVIEW   Answers on page T-89.

1. Compare the structures and functions of the three types of muscle tissue.
2. When a muscle contracts, what happens to the myosin filaments and the actin filaments?
3. What are the functions of flexors and extensors?

The Integumentary System

The outer covering of the human body is called the **integument** (in-TEG-yoo-mənt), or skin. In addition to the skin, the integumentary system includes the hair, nails, and sweat glands. The skin is made up of many different types of tissues and is classified as an organ.

Structure of the Skin

The skin is a very thin covering on the body. At most, it is only about 4 millimeters thick. Despite its thinness, it is composed of two major layers that are divided into several sublayers. Each layer has a particular function, and the cells in each layer are different.

LAYERS OF THE SKIN   The skin has two layers. The outermost layer of the skin, the **epidermis**, is made of flat, interlocking cells, called *epithelial* (ep-ə-THĒ-lē-əl) *cells*. As new cells are produced in the bottom layer of the epidermis, old cells are pushed upward. At the outer surface of the skin, the food supply becomes poor, and the cells die. They become scalelike and form a waterproof protein material, called *keratin* (KER-ət-'n). These dead cells, containing keratin, make up the top layer of the epidermis. They are sloughed off and constantly replaced.

The lower layer of the epidermis has an irregular outline that forms ridges, called *papillae* (pə-PIL-ē), on the surface of the skin. On the fingertips, on the palms of the hand, and on the soles of the feet, numerous papillae form patterns. On the fingers, these patterns are known as fingerprints. Fingerprint patterns are so different from one person to another that they can be used for identification.

The lower layer of the epidermis also contains specialized cells that produce *melanin* (MEL-ə-nin). Melanin is a black, brown, or yellowish pigment that determines skin color. It also protects the skin from the sun by screening out the ultraviolet rays that can cause sunburn.

The second major layer of skin is the **dermis.** It is located below the epidermis. In comparison to the epidermis, the dermis is a thicker layer of skin that is made up of elastic connective tissue. It provides the skin with added strength and elasticity.

HAIR AND NAILS Hair and nails are derivatives of the skin. A hair is a thin strand of modified dead epidermal cells.

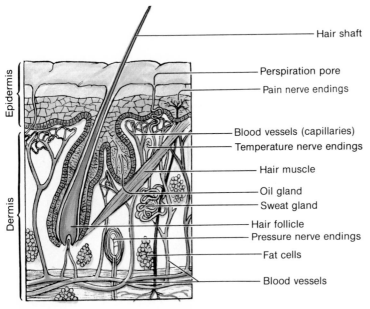

Figure 35-12 The skin, sweat glands, and hair form the integument. What is the main function of the skin?

It protects the body against disease and mechanical injury.

It is pushed through tubelike structures in the dermis called **hair follicles.** A typical hair consists of a *shaft* and a *root*.

Nails are produced by specialized cells in the skin. Made of thick deposits of keratin, the nails protect the tips of the toes and fingers.

SWEAT AND OIL GLANDS   Sweat glands are coiled tubes located in the dermis that connect to openings on the skin surface through pores. The palms of the hands contain many of these glands. Sweat glands rid the body of excess water, salts, and nitrogen wastes, all of which form a liquid called *perspiration*, or sweat. The secretion of perspiration helps to regulate body temperatures. As perspiration evaporates from the skin, the body is cooled.

Oil glands, also found in the dermis, are small, saclike structures that secrete oil. This oil keeps hair from becoming brittle, and keeps the skin soft. The clogging of these glands by dirt may cause skin blemishes.

Functions of the Skin

Highlight

The skin acts as a protective barrier against infection, helps to protect the internal organs from physical injury, serves as a storage area, and serves as a sense organ.

The appearance and structure of the skin can vary greatly from one part of the body to the other. For example, the *cornea* of the eye is made of transparent skin. On the feet, the skin is thick and relatively tough. The skin is also a temporary storage area for water, fats, glucose, and some salts. It can also convert some of its stored material to vitamin D, an essential vitamin for normal bone development.

The main function of the skin is protection. It is the first line of defense against infection by bacteria and other foreign bodies. The skin also protects the body against external injury by acting as a kind of shock absorber. For example, a blister is how the skin protects underlying tissue by forming a cushion of fluid over an injured area. The blister prevents further injury, and it also indicates that something is wrong.

Another function of the skin is to act as a sense organ. Within the layers of the skin are different types of nerves that permit the body to react to its surroundings. Each of these nerves responds to a particular stimulus, such as touch, temperature, pain, or pressure.

SECTION REVIEW   Answers on page T–89.

1. Where is melanin found? What is its function?
2. Why are sweat and oil glands important?
3. List some functions of the skin.

LABORATORY INVESTIGATION 35

For additional information, see pages T–89 to T–90.

Observing the Structure of Bones

Purpose   Bones have many different shapes and sizes. However, all bones are made up of living cells and nonliving material. The purpose of this investigation is to examine some representative bones and identify their structures.

Materials *(per group)*   ● Samples of bones such as various chicken, beef, and pork bones. ● Different bones soaked in vinegar ● Glass slides ● Cover slips ● Scalpels (or single-edge razor blades) ● Microscopes (compound and dissecting)

Procedure   **1.** Examine the bone samples provided by your teacher. Try to scrape away some of the bone with your fingernail. On a sheet of paper, record the color, texture, and hardness of each bone.
2. Examine the bone samples under the dissecting microscope. Identify the hard outer layer and the marrow cavity. In some bone specimens, you may observe the periosteum covering the outside surface. On the same sheet of paper, copy the table and record a check mark next to the features that you observed for each bone sample.   **3. CAUTION:** *Handle the scalpel or razor blade with extreme care and only under the supervision of your teacher.* Your teacher has soaked some bones in jars of vinegar for several weeks. Using a scalpel or razor blade, cut a very thin slice of soft bone from one of these specimens. Place the slice on a glass slide with a cover slip and examine it under low and high power of your microscope.
4. Try to identify the Haversian canals. These canals will appear as tiny openings in the compact bone.
5. Make a drawing of this bone slice and label all the structures you observe.   **6.** Examine several other slices of bone under the microscope.

Bone sample	Bone features				
	Cartilage	Spongy bone	Compact bone	Marrow cavity	Periosteum

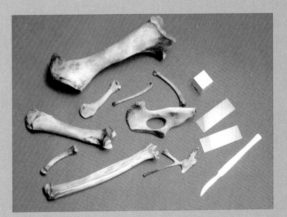

Observations and Conclusions   **1.** Do the long bones have soft cartilage tissue surrounding the ends? How is cartilage different from bone?   **2.** What happens to the texture of the bones after they have soaked in vinegar? Why?   **3.** What structures can you identify in the slices of the soaked bones? Can you find the same structures in each of the bones?   **4.** What differences do you observe among the bone slices? How might these differences be explained?

CHAPTER SUMMARY

Organization in the Human Body The human body contains four types of tissues. These tissues are connective, muscle, epithelial, and nervous. Tissues are organized to form organs and then organ systems. The skeletal, muscular, and integumentary systems are only three of the ten systems of the human body.

The Skeletal System Along with the muscles and connective tissues, the skeleton protects, moves, supports, and gives shape to the body. In addition, the skeleton manufactures blood and stores minerals. The human skeletal system has two divisions, the axial skeleton and the appendicular skeleton. The axial skeleton consists of the skull, vertebral column, and thorax. The appendicular skeleton is made up of the two girdles and the bones in the arms and legs.

Human bone is made up of nonliving and living materials. The living material is composed of compact tissue and spongy tissue. A system of small channels, called Haversian canals, allows blood vessels and nerves to come into contact with the living bone cell. Joints, which are found where two bones meet, may be movable or immovable.

The Muscular System Muscle tissue is made up of muscle fibers that enable the tissue to contract. The three types of muscle tissue are skeletal, smooth, and cardiac. The contraction of muscles is generated by a nerve impulse. The point where the nerve cells and the muscle fibers meet is called the motor unit.

The Integumentary System Protection is the main function of the skin, which is composed of two layers. The outer layer is called the epidermis, and the inner layer is the dermis. Hair and nails are derived from the skin. Two other structures found in the skin are the sweat and oil glands.

CHAPTER VOCABULARY

appendicular skeleton	fontanels	organ system
axial skeleton	hair follicles	origin
belly	Haversian canals	ossification
bursa	insertion	periosteum
cardiac muscle	integument	skeletal muscle
cartilage	joint	smooth muscle
dermis	ligament	sutures
endoskeleton	marrow	synovial fluid
epidermis	muscle fiber	tendon
extensor	myofibril	tissue
flexor	organ	

REVIEW of FACTS and CONCEPTS   Answers on page T–90.

On a separate sheet of paper, answer each of the following as completely as possible.

1. What are the four basic types of tissue found in the human body? What are their functions?
2. How do compact and spongy bone tissues differ?
3. What are the five functions of the skeletal system?
4. Name the two major divisions of the skeletal system. Which bones are found in each division?
5. Why is bone considered living material?
6. Explain the structure of a long bone.
7. What are the four types of joints in the body? Give an example of each.
8. What are the three types of muscle tissue? How are they alike? How do they differ?
9. What is the difference between extensor and flexor muscles? Give an example of each.
10. Explain how the muscles, bones, tendons, and ligaments are related.
11. What are the parts of the integumentary system?
12. Name places on the body where the skin has different appearances. Explain how the skin is adapted for its functions in these areas.

EXTENSIONS and APPLICATIONS   For additional information, see page T–90.

1. The next time that you have chicken or turkey for dinner, save the large bone from a drumstick. Clean the bone, and have an adult help you to cut off one end of the bone. Examine the bone carefully. What is the name of this bone? Identify and label as many parts of the bone as you can.

2. Make a working model of a muscle. Obtain two pieces of wood, two long balloons, some string, and some masking tape. Slightly blow up the balloons, and tie the ends to prevent the air from escaping. Using the balloons to represent the biceps and triceps muscles, make a working model to show how muscles work in opposing pairs.

3. Prepare an illustrated chart comparing parts of the human skeletal system to everyday objects. For example, you may want to start with the framework of a house and compare it to the entire skeleton. Use photographs from magazines or drawings to illustrate the chart. Some other parts of the skeletal system that you may wish to include in your chart are the cranium, the pelvis, the elbow, the spine, and a ball-and-socket joint.

SUGGESTED READINGS

Samachson, J., *The Armor Within Us: The Story of Bone.* New York: Rand McNally.
This entire book is about bones and the human skeleton. It includes many excellent photographs and illustrations.

Singer, S., and H.R. Hilgard, *The Biology of People.* San Francisco: W.H. Freeman.
The authors feel that biology and people are the two most interesting subjects in the world. In this book, they discuss the fundamentals of human biology. A separate chapter is devoted to each body system.

Spearman, R.I.C., *The Integument.* London: Cambridge University Press.
In this book, the author presents a comparison between the skin of invertebrates and vertebrates. There are also discussions of different skin coverings, such as scales, feathers, and hair.

36 Digestion

Chapter Objectives   *After completing this chapter, you will be able to:*

a ▪ List the parts of the digestive system and give their functions. p. 593
b ▪ Describe the digestive processes that occur in the stomach. p. 600
c ▪ Identify the various sections of the small intestine. p. 596
d ▪ Name the enzymes and the substances that they act upon in the small intestine. p. 600
e ▪ Describe the structure of the villi. p. 601
f ▪ Explain how absorption occurs in the digestive system. p. 601

For teaching aids for this chapter, including a chapter overview and teaching strategies, see pages T–90 to T–92. The page number next to each chapter objective refers to the text page where the information needed to fulfill the objective begins.

Digestion of food provides needed energy and building materials.

Human beings need energy as do all forms of life. Food supplies this energy, as well as the raw materials for the growth and repair of the body. All the structures in the human body, from the smallest part of a cell to the largest organ, use these raw materials.

Before the body can use this energy and these raw materials, it must change food into small molecules that the blood can then carry all over the body. While undergoing this change, food travels through a complex digestive tube that measures almost 10 meters from end to end. During this trip, the food is crushed, ground up, and moved along by special muscles. Along the way, the bits of food are also bathed in chemical solutions that break down the large molecules into small ones. These simple molecules contain the energy and nutrients that the bloodstream carries throughout the body.

The Digestive System

The breaking down of food into simple substances that can be absorbed into the bloodstream is called **digestion.** Digestion takes place in the digestive system, which is made up of two types of organs. *True digestive organs* are those through which the food actually passes. *Accessory digestive organs* play a role in digestion, but the food does not pass through them. Together, all of the digestive organs make up an efficient system for breaking down food and absorbing it. Without this system, the human body would be unable to release the energy from foods that it needs to carry out life functions. The body would also not be able to use the food for growth and repair.

The Mouth

The mouth is made up of a hard, bony part and a soft, muscular section. The **hard palate** (PAL-it) is located at the front of the roof of the mouth. The hard palate separates the mouth from the nasal cavity. Along the back of the mouth, there is a section of muscle tissue, called the **soft palate.** When a person swallows, the soft palates prevents food from entering the nasal cavity. A tiny knoblike structure, called the *uvula* (YOO-vyə-lə), is suspended from the soft palate.

SALIVARY GLANDS   The lining of the cheeks contain three pairs of **salivary glands.** The largest of these glands, the *parotid* (pə-RAHT-id) *glands*, are located in front of the ears. The *submaxillary* (sub-MAK-sə-ler-ē) *glands*, found beneath the tongue, open into the floor of the mouth. The third pair, the *sublingual* (sub-LING-gwəl) *glands*, are found in the front of the mouth below the tip of the tongue. They too have openings onto the floor of the mouth.

The three pairs of glands produce about 1.5 liters of *saliva* daily. Saliva is a mixture of water, **mucin** (MYOO-sin), and *ptyalin* (TĪ-ə-lin). Water makes up about 98% of saliva. Mucin is a slippery substance that lubricates food and makes it easier to swallow. Ptyalin is a digestive enzyme.

THE TONGUE   Attached at the back of the mouth, the tongue takes up most of the mouth floor. It is made up of skeletal muscle covered with epithelial tissue. Scattered over the tongue are the **taste buds,** or *taste receptors.* Various types of taste buds react with different types of dissolved food. The tongue is able to detect four basic tastes, either

Figure 36–1   The salivary glands are located around the mouth. They secrete saliva, which contains enzymes that begin the chemical digestion of food.

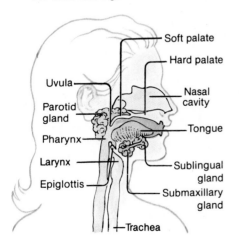

- Soft palate
- Hard palate
- Uvula
- Nasal cavity
- Parotid gland
- Tongue
- Pharynx
- Larynx
- Sublingual gland
- Epiglottis
- Submaxillary gland
- Trachea

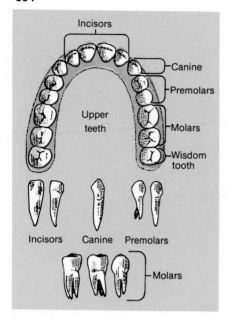

Figure 36-2 Different teeth do various jobs. Incisors and canines cut and tear food. Premolars and molars crush and grind food.

separately or in combinations. The four basic tastes are sweet, bitter, salty, and sour. In addition to tasting, the tongue aids in chewing. Either it pushes the food between the teeth or it moves the food toward the back of the mouth to be swallowed.

THE TEETH The human adult mouth contains 32 teeth, 16 in each jaw. There are, however, only 4 basic types of teeth. These basic types are the *incisors* (in-sī-zərs), the *canine teeth*, the *premolars*, and the *molars*. The four incisors are located at the center of the mouth, and they have sharp edges for cutting food. On each side of the incisors, there is a canine tooth. The canines, sometimes called the *eye-teeth*, are used to tear and shred food. There are two premolars behind each canine, followed by three molars. The third molars are called the *wisdom teeth*. Molars and premolars have flat surfaces that are used to grind and to crush food.

Each tooth is composed of the *crown*, the *root*, and the *neck*. The crown is the part of the tooth that is located above the gums. It is covered with *enamel*. Enamel is made of inorganic matter and is one of the hardest materials in the body. The root is below the gums, and it anchors the tooth in the jawbone. The root is covered with *cementum*, which holds the tooth firmly in its socket in the jaw bone. Another structure, called the *periodontal membrane*, also secures the

Figure 36-3 Structure of a Tooth

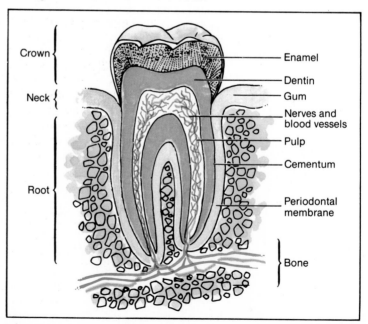

root in its socket. The area where the crown and root meet is called the neck.

Beneath the enamel and cementum, a hard substance, called *dentin*, makes up most of a tooth. A mass of dentin surrounds the *pulp*, or the innermost layer of the tooth. The pulp is made up of blood vessels, nerves, and connective tissue.

The Pharynx and Esophagus

From the mouth, food must pass through the **pharynx** (FAR-ingks) and the **esophagus** (i-SAHF-ə-gəs) on its way to the stomach. The pharynx is a muscular cavity at the back of the mouth. In addition to serving as a passageway for food and air, the pharynx aids in swallowing. The esophagus, or food tube, is a muscular tube that is 25 to 30 centimeters long and that connects the pharynx to the stomach. The main function of the esophagus is to conduct food from the mouth to the stomach. A lining on the inside of the food tube, called the *mucous* (MYOO-kəs) *membrane*, secretes *mucus*. This secretion lubricates the tube so that food can pass easily to the stomach. Between the pharynx and the esophagus is a flap of tissue, called the **epiglottis** (ep-ə-GLAHT-is). When a person swallows, the epiglottis flips down and stops food from going down the windpipe. When a person breathes, the epiglottis is in the open position.

In the esophagus, muscles contract in waves to move food from the esophagus to the stomach. These wavelike contractions, called **peristalsis** (per-ə-STAWL-sis), continue throughout the entire digestive system. Peristalsis is very strong. Even if a person ate or drank something while upside down, the food or liquid would still be moved to the stomach.

The Stomach

The esophagus is connected to the top of the **stomach.** The stomach is located in the *abdominal* (ab-DAH-mən'l) *cavity* beneath a sheet of muscle, called the **diaphragm** (DĪ-ə-fram). The stomach is a J-shaped, muscular pouch made up of several layers of muscles. Inside the stomach, many folds allow the organ to expand as it fills. Scattered throughout these folds are many gastric glands. These glands release *gastric fluid*. Gastric fluid is made up of enzymes, hydrochloric acid, and mucus.

The stomach empties the food into the intestines. At the intestinal end of the stomach, there is a valve called the **pyloric** (pī-LAWR-ik) **valve.** By opening and closing, this ringlike

Highlight

Peristalisis is the wavelike muscle contractions that move food through the digestive system. Food moves through the mouth, pharynx, esophagus, stomach, small intestine, and large intestine. Undigested materials pass out of the anus.

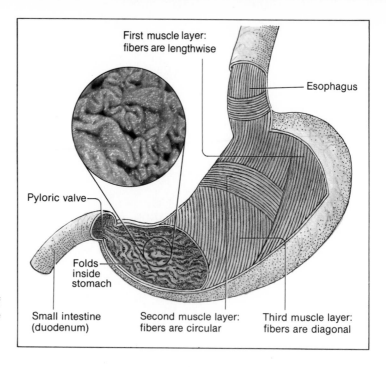

First muscle layer:
fibers are lengthwise

Esophagus

Pyloric valve

Folds
inside
stomach

Small intestine
(duodenum)

Second muscle layer:
fibers are circular

Third muscle layer:
fibers are diagonal

Figure 36-4 The stomach is made up of several layers of muscle. Inside the stomach are many folds called rugae.

muscular valve allows food to move into the small intestine. It also prevents food from backing up into the stomach.

The Intestines

Located in the abdominal cavity, the *intestines* are made up of two separate sections, the **small intestine** and the **large intestine**. The small intestine is much narrower but longer than the large intestine. The total length of both intestines is about 8 meters.

It might be difficult for students to comprehend the size of the small intestine. As a model, you can use a 7-meter section of 2.5-centimeter rope coiled and twisted to show how the small intestine fits into the abdominal cavity.

THE SMALL INTESTINE The small intestine is connected to the stomach at the pyloric valve. Coiled into many loops, this intestine fills a great part of the abdominal cavity. The small intestine is a long narrow tube that is a little more than 7 meters long and about 2.5 centimeters in diameter. It is held in place by a clear membrane, called the **mesentery** (MEZ-'n-ter-ē).

The small intestine is divided into three major parts. The first and shortest section, the *duodenum* (doo-ə-DĒ-nəm), is only about 25 centimeters long. The second part, called the *jejunum* (ji-JOO-nəm), is 2.5 meters in length. The last and longest part is the *ileum* (IL-ē-əm), which is almost 4 meters in length.

The small intestine stores, digests, and absorbs food. Food may remain in this intestine for up to five hours. In addition, the small intestine contains many intestinal glands, which secrete large amounts of digestive enzymes and intestinal fluid. These two substances aid in the complete digestion and absorption of foods.

THE LARGE INTESTINE   The ileum of the small intestine ends on the lower right side of the abdominal cavity. At this point, it is connected to the large intestine, or *colon*. This intestine is a tube that is about 1.5 meters long and 6.5 centimeters in diameter.

The large intestine forms an upside-down U over the coils of the small intestine. The right side of the U, which

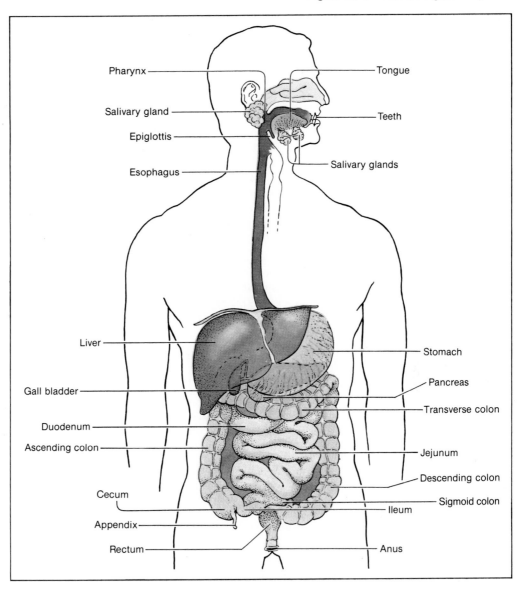

Figure 36–5   Human Digestive System

comes up from the ileum, is called the *ascending colon.* The part of the large intestine that runs across the top of the small intestine, from right to left, is the *transverse colon.* The *descending colon* drops down on the left side of the small intestines. In addition to these three sections, the colon includes the *sigmoid* (SIG-moid) *colon* and the **rectum.** The sigmoid colon is an S-shaped part of the intestine that follows the descending colon. The rectum is the last 15 to 20 centimeters of the large intestine. It narrows into the outside opening, called the *anus.*

At the point where the large intestine joins the small intestine, there is a blind pouch, called the *cecum* (SĒ-kəm). Hanging from the cecum is a deadend tube about 10 centimeters long, called the *appendix* (ə-PEND-diks).

The Liver and Pancreas

The **liver** is located largely on the right side of the body, directly underneath the diaphragm. Its four lobes weigh about 1.4 kilograms, making the liver the largest organ in the body. The liver takes part in digestion by producing **bile.** Bile moves through the *bile duct* to the **gall bladder,** where it is stored. The gall bladder releases bile only when food is present in the duodenum.

The **pancreas,** which is 14 to 15 centimeters long, lies between the stomach and the duodenum on the left side of the body. This organ looks like a slightly triangular cluster of grapes that is lying on its side. The pancreas has two functions. It produces *pancreatic* (pan-krē-AT-ik) *fluid* that contains several digestive enzymes. It also secretes *insulin,* which aids in regulating the use of *glucose,* or blood sugar, by the body.

SECTION REVIEW   Answers on page T–91.

1. What is saliva? Where is it produced?
2. What is the importance of the pyloric valve?
3. List the parts of the small and large intestines.
4. List the substances produced by the liver and the pancreas.

The Mechanisms of Digestion

Food is broken down during digestion both mechanically and chemically. *Mechanical digestion* is the physical breakup of food from larger to smaller pieces. This process begins in the mouth and occurs at several other sites in the digestive system. *Chemical digestion* takes place when digestive enzymes act on foods. At these sites, food is chemically changed or prepared for the next step in the digestive process.

Breaking Down Food

Digestion begins in the mouth. Mechanical digestion begins as the teeth chew food into small pieces. The tongue, the jaws, and the muscles of the cheeks all work together to move the food around in the mouth. Meanwhile, the teeth tear, grind, and crush the food. Chemical digestion also begins in the mouth. The saliva from the salivary glands aids digestion in several ways. The water moistens and partly dissolves the food, and the mucus lubricates it. At the same time, the ptyalin starts to digest the starches.

Highlight

Mechanical digestion is the physical breaking down of large pieces of food into smaller pieces. Mechanical digestion takes place in the mouth and stomach. Chemical digestion is the breakdown of food by chemicals, such as digestive enzymes and hydrochloric acid. Chemical digestion occurs in the mouth, stomach, and small intestine.

At this point, you may want to assign to your students the third of the Extensions and Applications at the end of this chapter.

CAREER: Dental Assistant

The job of dental assistants is to help dentists examine and treat patients. As patients come into the dentist's office, the assistants obtain the patients' records. The assistants then seat the patients in dental chairs, and prepare them for treatment. During the actual examination or treatment, assistants hand instruments and materials to the dentist. They also keep the mouth of the patient clear by using suction tubes or other devices. After treatment, dental assistants often provide patients with information on caring for their teeth.

Dental assistants make sure that all instruments are sterilized, and they may also process X-ray film. Assistants often prepare materials for making impressions of teeth. After the dentist has taken the impressions, the assistants may make casts of the teeth.

Some dental assistants are also responsible for managing the office. They arrange appointments, prepare and send out bills, and receive payments. As managers of the office, they keep patient records and order supplies and materials.

Dental assistants may learn their skills through on-the-job training, or by completing a 1- or 2-year program in dental assisting. These

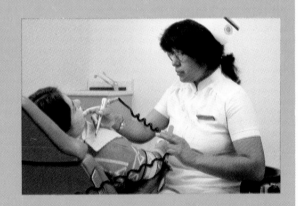

programs are given by many junior colleges, community colleges, and vocational schools. The programs include both classroom and laboratory instruction. Students get practical experience by working in offices, clinics, or dental schools that are affiliated with their programs.

Most dental assistants work for dentists in private practice, or group dental clinics. Part-time openings are often available.

For further career information, write to American Dental Assistants Association, Department of Education, Suite 1230, 211 East Chicago Avenue, Chicago, IL 60611.

As a simple experiment, put a piece of bread into your mouth. Chew it longer than you usually do, until the bread tastes sweet. This sweetness means that ptyalin has started to break down the starch in the bread into simple sugars. Usually, you do not notice this change because the food is in your mouth for only a short time before being swallowed.

DIGESTION IN THE STOMACH   The stomach secretes gastric juices that act on food in several ways. The water in these juices helps to dissolve certain food substances. The enzyme *pepsin* starts the digestion of protein. This enzyme splits protein into simpler groups of amino acids, called *peptones* and *proteoses*. The stomach also secretes hydrocholoric acid. This substance not only provides the proper environment for pepsin to act, but it also allows iron to be absorbed and destroys most bacteria.

Pepsin and hydrochloric acid are very strong chemicals. Ordinarily, they would be strong enough to digest the stomach itself. The inside of the stomach, however, is lined with *mucin*, which protects the stomach against these chemicals. When the mucin coating is absent, parts of the stomach wall are destroyed. The result is called an *ulcer*.

The muscle layers of the stomach churn the food. This churning action breaks up the food and mixes it with the gastric fluids. As a result of this action, the food is changed from a solid to a semifluid that is called **chyme** (kīm).

THE ROLE OF THE LIVER AND PANCREAS   The liver is a biochemical factory. Carbohydrates in the form of simple sugars are changed into glucose, which the body can then use for energy. Excess glucose can be changed to glycogen and stored in the liver. If there is too much glycogen, the liver can change it to fat, which can be stored in the body. The liver can also change waste products into **urea**, which is excreted by the kidneys.

As an accessory digestive organ, the liver produces bile. Although bile is not a digestive fluid, it contains the *bile salts* that aid digestion in a number of ways. These salts, for example, stimulate peristalsis. One bile salt, sodium bicarbonate, lowers the acidity level in the small intestine. Bile salts also *emulsify* fats. In other words, they break down large fat globules into smaller drops.

Another accessory digestive organ, the pancreas, secretes pancreatic fluid into the small intestine. Pancreatic fluid contains the three enzymes *trypsin, amylase,* and *lipase*. Trypsin continues the breakdown of proteins into groups of amino acids, called *peptides*. Amylase breaks down undigested starch into *maltose*, a type of sugar. Lipase acts

At this point, you may want to assign to your students the first of the Extensions and Applications at the end of this chapter.

Sidelight

After it is eaten, food stays in the stomach anywhere from two to six hours before entering the small intestine.

At this point, you may want to assign to your students the second of the Extensions and Applications at the end of this chapter.

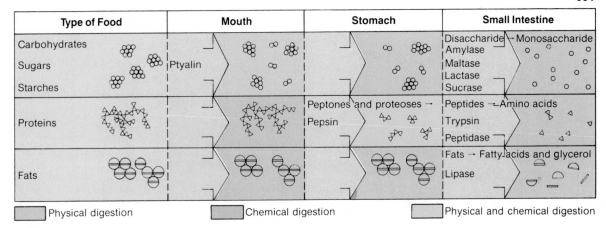

Type of Food	Mouth	Stomach	Small Intestine
Carbohydrates Sugars Starches	Ptyalin		Disaccharide – Monosaccharide Amylase Maltase Lactase Sucrase
Proteins		Peptones and proteoses → Pepsin	Peptides – Amino acids Trypsin Peptidase
Fats			Fats → Fatty acids and glycerol Lipase

☐ Physical digestion   ☐ Chemical digestion   ☐ Physical and chemical digestion

Figure 36-6 Nutrients are digested by different methods and enzymes in the organs of the digestive system.

on the emulsified fat drops, changing them to fatty acids and glycerol.

DIGESTION IN THE INTESTINES Bile, pancreatic fluid, and intestinal fluid complete about 90% of the digestive process in the small intestine. In addition to bile and pancreatic fluid, intestinal fluid is secreted from the intestinal wall. The intestinal fluid contains a number of enzymes. Each of these enzymes breaks down a different substance into simple sugars and amino acids. For example, amylase breaks down starches, sucrase breaks down sucrose (table sugar), and trypsin breaks down proteoses and peptones. Fats are broken down by lipase into fatty acids and glycerol.

Absorption of Food

After food has been broken down into its simplest form, it is absorbed into the bloodstream through the walls of the small intestine. These walls are covered with millions of tiny, fingerlike projections, called **villi** (singular: villus). The villi increase the surface area of the small intestine. In turn, this increases the rate of absorption.

Covering the outside of each villus is a layer of simple epithelial cells. Inside the villus, a network of capillaries surround a lymphatic vessel, called a **lacteal.** As completely digested foods are absorbed through the epithelial cells, the food molecules pass into the capillaries and lacteals. The blood and lymph then carry away the food molecules. Simple sugars and amino acids are carried by the blood. Glycerol, fats, and fatty acids are carried by the lymph. In addition, water, vitamins, and some salts are absorbed into the blood.

After absorption, what remains of the food passes into the large intestine. Although no digestion takes place in this

Highlight

The final phase of digestion is absorption of food molecules into the bloodstream. Absorption takes place in the villi of the small intestine.

At this point, you may want your students to do the Laboratory Investigation at the end of this chapter.

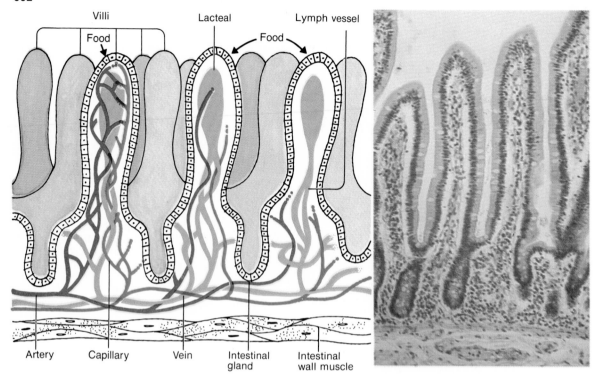

Villi   Lacteal   Lymph vessel

Food   Food

Artery   Capillary   Vein   Intestinal gland   Intestinal wall muscle

Figure 36-7   Molecules of digested food pass through the walls of the villi and enter the capillaries of the circulatory and lymphatic systems.

intestine, it absorbs water and bile salts. In fact, the colon absorbs about 6 liters of water each day and about 90% of the bile salts. This intestine also contains many helpful bacteria, which use some of the undigested organic material to make such vitamins as K_1, B_1, and B_2.

Substances that are not used by the large intestine make up the **feces** (FĒ-sēz). The feces are composed of water, bacteria, mucus, and undigested food that the body cannot use. This material is eliminated by the body through the anal opening.

Sidelight

The entire process of digestion can take anywhere from 12 to 24 hours.

SECTION REVIEW   Answers on page T-91.

1. What are the functions of pepsin and hydrochloric acid in the stomach?
2. List the functions of the liver.
3. Which enzymes are found in pancreatic fluid? List the function of each enzyme.
4. List the enzymes in the small intestine that break down sugars, starches, and proteins.
5. Explain how food is absorbed into the bloodstream.

The Effects of Surface Area on the Rate of Absorption

Purpose   Digested food products are absorbed in the small intestine. The rate of absorption is increased by the presence of tiny, fingerlike projections, called villi. By increasing the surface area of the intestine, the villi raise the rate of absorption. The purpose of this investigation is to compare how the amount of surface area of a membrane affects the rate of absorption through that membrane.

Time in Minutes	Differences in Jar A	Difference in Jar B
2		
4		
6		
8		
10		

Materials *(per group)*   ● Large glass jars (half-gallon or gallon size) ● Dialysis membrane (cut into 25-cm and 50-cm pieces) ● Graduated cylinders (25 ml) ● Iodine solution ● Glass stirring rods ● Starch solution ● Glass or plastic funnel ● String and scissors

Procedure   **1.** Take a piece of dialysis membrane of each length provided by your teacher. Place the membranes in tap water to soften them.   **2.** Tie one end of each membrane with string. Be sure that the knot is tight enough to prevent any material from leaking out of the membrane.   **3.** Using the funnel, add 25 mL of iodine solution to the longer tube. Tie the top with a string, making sure that the contents do not leak out. The knots in each end should be approximately 45 cm apart.   **4.** Repeat the procedure, using the smaller piece of tubing. Add 25 mL of iodine solution, and tie the top end so it does not leak. Space the knots approximately 15 cm apart.   **5.** Rinse both tubes in tap water to remove any traces of iodine from the outside.   **6.** Place each piece of tubing containing the iodine solution into separate glass jars that are half full of starch solution. Label the jar with the 50-cm membrane tube A. Label the jar with the 25-cm tube B.   **7.** Gently stir the contents of each jar at 2-minute intervals for 10 minutes. Copy the table on a sheet of paper. Record any differences that you observe in the starch solution in each jar.

Observations and Conclusions   **1.** What change is occurring in each jar? Why?   **2.** In which jar does the color change faster?   **3.** What causes the difference in the amount of color change?   **4.** Why is the iodine able to pass through the membrane?   **5.** Relate what you have observed to the functioning of the small intestine.

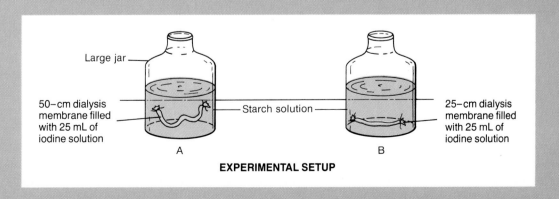

Large jar

50–cm dialysis membrane filled with 25 mL of iodine solution

Starch solution

25–cm dialysis membrane filled with 25 mL of iodine solution

A   B

EXPERIMENTAL SETUP

CHAPTER SUMMARY

The Digestive System   Digestion is the process of breaking down complex foods into simpler substances for use by the body. These substances may be used either for growth and repair or as a source of energy. The digestive tract extends from the mouth, through the esophagus and stomach, and into the small and large intestines. Food is moved through these organs by peristalsis. The secretion of mucus also helps to move food more easily through the digestive system. The accessory digestive organs include the teeth, tongue, salivary glands, liver, gall bladder, and pancreas. Each of these structures contributes in various ways to the completion of the digestive processes within the body.

The Mechanisms of Digestion   Food is acted on mechanically by the chewing of the teeth and by the churning movements of the stomach muscles. The liver, pancreas, stomach, and intestines secrete a variety of special fluids, including enzymes, that chemically change foods so they can be used by the body.

Digestion is completed in the small intestine, where the absorption of food also takes place. Digested foods enter the bloodstream through fingerlike projections, called villi. The large intestine absorbs water, as well as forming and absorbing some vitamins. Undigested food substances, along with water, bacteria, and mucus, are eliminated as feces through the anal opening of the large intestine.

CHAPTER VOCABULARY

bile	hard palate	pyloric valve
chyme	lacteal	rectum
diaphragm	large intestine	salivary gland
digestion	liver	small intestine
digestive enzymes	mesentery	soft palate
epiglottis	mucin	stomach
esophagus	pancreas	taste bud
feces	peristalsis	urea
gall bladder	pharynx	villus

REVIEW of FACTS and CONCEPTS   Answers on pages T–91 to T–92.

On a separate sheet of paper, answer each of the following as completely as possible.

1. What is digestion?
2. What is the difference between true digestive organs and accessory digestive organs?
3. During swallowing, how is food prevented from entering the nasal cavity? The windpipe?
4. Name the three pairs of salivary glands. What is the function of saliva?
5. Explain how the tongue functions as an accessory digestive organ.
6. Describe the structure of a tooth. What are the four basic types of teeth?
7. Why do you think it is helpful to chew your food before swallowing it?
8. List the organs of the digestive system in the order that food passes *through* them.
9. How is the stomach able to hold large amounts of food you may eat at a Thanksgiving dinner?

10. What are the three major parts of the small intestine? What are the parts of the large intestine?
11. What enzymes are secreted into the mouth? The stomach? The small intestine? Name the substance on which each enzyme acts.
12. Astronauts are able to eat and drink in space where there is no gravity. Explain how this is possible.
13. What are the roles of the liver and the pancreas in digestion?
14. Where does the absorption of food take place? Describe the structure of the villi and their role in absorption.
15. What is the function of the large intestine?
16. If you ate a slice of bread with jelly and drank a glass of milk, what would happen to each of these foods during digestion?

EXTENSIONS and APPLICATIONS For additional information, see page T–92.

1. Prepare a written report on the work done by Dr. William Beaumont in studying gastric digestion. List some of the observations made by Dr. Beaumont concerning the function of the stomach.

2. Bile can be called an emulsifying agent. Oil and water in the small intestine do not mix until bile is introduced. To examine this reaction, place water and oil in a test tube. The liquids do not mix. Add some liquid dishwashing soap and shake the test tube. What happens? How is the liquid soap like bile? Why is emulsification necessary for digestion?

3. Obtain two baby food jars. Fill each with 25 milliliters of water. Label one JAR A, and add a whole sugar cube. Label the second JAR B, and add a crushed cube. Carefully shake each jar, and observe how long it takes the sugar to dissolve. Relate this demonstration to the function of teeth in the digestive process.

SUGGESTED READINGS

Beaumont, W., *Gastric Juice and the Physiology of Digestion.* New York: Dover Publications.

A republication of one of the most remarkable documents in the history of medicine. From 1822 to 1829, a surgeon was able to make observations and experiments on a patient who, due to an accident, lived with a 3-inch hole in his abdomen, opening directly to the stomach. This book is the fascinating account of that story.

Collins, D.A., *Your Teeth.* Garden City, N.Y.: Doubleday.

A complete guide to the biology and care of teeth.

Nugent, N., *How to Get Along with Your Stomach.* Boston: Little, Brown.

An overall look at the digestive system and the ailments that affect individual organs.

37 Circulation

Chapter Objectives *After completing this chapter, you will be able to:*

a ■ List the functions of the human circulatory system. p. 607
b ■ Describe the components of the blood. p. 607
c ■ Explain the clotting process. p. 609
d ■ List the characteristics of the four blood groups and Rh factor. p. 609
e ■ Identify the parts of the circulatory system. p. 612
f ■ Trace the path of blood through the circulatory system. p. 615
g ■ Explain the importance of the lymphatic system. p. 618

For teaching aids for this chapter, including a chapter overview and teaching strategies, see pages T–92 to T–94. The page number next to each chapter objective refers to the text page where the information needed to fulfill the objective begins.

Like roads, blood vessels are vital transportation routes.

Picture a highway system that covers more than 96,000 kilometers. Imagine a network of roads that could go around the world nearly two and a half times. You have a system that big inside your body. Just as a modern roadway network connects small villages with big cities, the human **circulatory system** connects all the cells, tissues, and organs of the body. Instead of roadways, however, this human system uses blood vessels. Pumped by the heart, blood moves through these vessels throughout the body. Some vessels carry blood away from the heart and other vessels carry blood toward the heart. The circulatory system also carries many substances, such as food, water, enzymes, hormones, antibodies, oxygen, and carbon dioxide, toward or away from the body cells and tissues.

Closely connected with the circulatory system is the **lymphatic** (lim-FAT-ik) **system.** This system is made up of vessels and glands that filter fluids. The lymphatic system helps to maintain the proper fluid balance of the body.

The Circulatory System

The bodies of multicellular organisms, such as human beings, are made up of millions of specialized cells. Each type of specialized cell needs certain substances and conditions to work properly. The circulatory system meets these needs by performing several important functions. For example, most chemical reactions in cells can take place only within a narrow *acid-base* range. Acids contain more *hydrogen ions* than bases. A hydrogen ion is an electrically charged atom. A little too much acid or base can cause cells to perform improperly or not perform at all. To keep a proper acid-base balance, the circulatory system carries *buffers*. These substances prevent dramatic changes in the acid-base balance. The circulatory system also helps to maintain the correct water content and temperature of the body. Chemicals and cells of the circulatory system help fight infection. Most importantly, the circulatory system acts as a transport system, carrying substances throughout the body.

Blood Composition

Blood is a slightly *alkaline*, or basic, fluid tissue that accounts for about 7% of the total weight of the body. In an average person, this translates into 4 to 5 liters of blood. Blood is made up of liquid and solid parts.

Whole blood refers to both the liquid and solid portions of the blood. The liquid portion of the blood is called **plasma.** The solid portion of the blood is composed of cells. These cells include **red blood cells, white blood cells,** and **platelets** (PLĀT-lits). Plasma accounts for some 55% of whole blood, while the cells make up the remaining 45%.

PLASMA   Plasma is about 90% water and generally slightly yellowish in color. This fluid transports a wide variety of substances throughout the body. Some of these substances are the proteins called *fibrinogen, albumin,* and three *globulins*—alpha, beta, and gamma. Fibrinogen is necessary for blood clotting. Albumin is found in the greatest quantity in the plasma. This protein is important in maintaining the water balance between the blood and surrounding tissue and between the plasma and the solid portion of the blood. Alpha and beta globulin help in the transport of proteins and other substances throughout the body. Gamma globulin has immunizing properties and fights infections.

Plasma also transports food substances, such as carbohydrates, fats, and proteins. These substances provide energy and aid in building and repairing body tissues. Dissolved

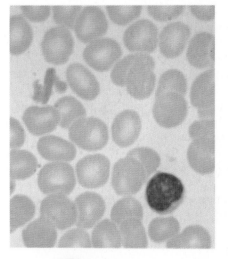

Figure 37-1   Blood is a complex body tissue made of several kinds of cells and various chemicals suspended in a liquid called plasma.

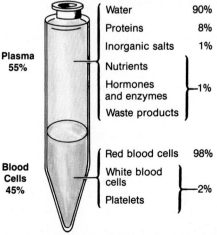

	Water	90%
	Proteins	8%
	Inorganic salts	1%
Plasma 55%	Nutrients	
	Hormones and enzymes	1%
	Waste products	
	Red blood cells	98%
Blood Cells 45%	White blood cells	
	Platelets	2%

At this point, you might ask your students where the food substances and gases in the blood come from. The answer, of course, includes both the digestive and respiratory systems. This question can be used to stress that the human body is a single functioning unit composed of many interdependent systems.

Red blood cells   Platelets

White blood cells

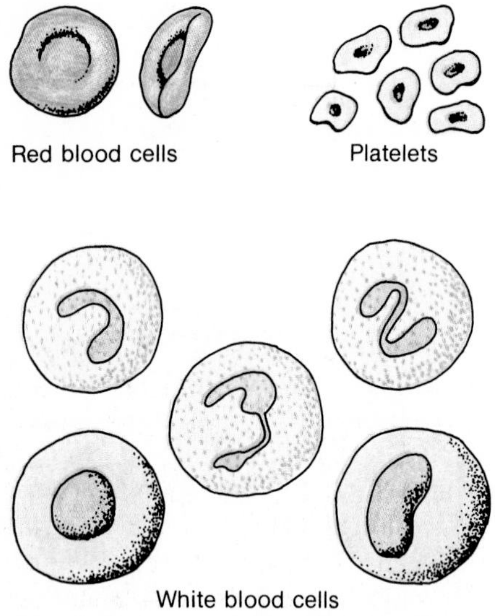

Figure 37-2 The blood contains three kinds of cells that each have their own unique structures and functions. These cells are red blood cells, white blood cells, and platelets.

Sidelight

In a cubic milliliter of blood are 5000 to 10,000 white blood cells, 300,000 to 400,000 platelets, and 5,200,000 red blood cells in males and 4,200,000 red blood cells in females.

mineral salts in the plasma include the element calcium that helps to build strong bones and teeth and plays a part in blood clotting. Also found in plasma are gases, such as oxygen and carbon dioxide, and metabolic waste products.

RED BLOOD CELLS   The most numerous of blood cells are the *erythrocytes* (i-RITH-rə-sītz), or red blood cells. They are so small that 10 million of them could fit into an area of about 6 square centimeters. Red blood cells look like doughnuts without a hole in the middle. Their centers are thin while their edges are thick.

Red blood cells carry oxygen and some carbon dioxide. Their ability to carry oxygen and their red color both come from an iron-containing molecule called **hemoglobin** (HĒ-mə-glō-bin). When oxygen combines with the hemoglobin in erythrocytes, the blood becomes *oxygenated* and bright red. When oxygen is released by the hemoglobin, the blood becomes *deoxygenated* and dark red.

Erythrocytes are produced in the *red marrow* of some bones, such as the ribs and the long bones of the upper arms and legs. The marrow is the inner soft part of a bone. Excess red blood cells are stored in the *spleen.*

The spleen is a large organ located on the left side of the abdominal cavity below the diaphragm. In times of emergency, the spleen supplies the blood with more red blood cells. This enables the body cells to obtain additional oxygen. The spleen, as does the liver, destroys worn-out blood cells and recycles their contents for later use. For example, the spleen reuses the iron from the hemoglobin of worn-out red blood cells to form new red blood cells. Other parts of the hemoglobin molecule are used to produce the bile that is made by the liver.

WHITE BLOOD CELLS   The *leukocytes* (LOO-kə-sītz), or white blood cells, are larger but less numerous than the erythrocytes. Small white blood cells are about 25% bigger than red blood cells. Large leukocytes can be twice the size of erythrocytes. Because white blood cells are colorless, they can be seen under the microscope only when they are stained with special dyes. White blood cells contain nuclei.

White blood cells help fight infection. With their ability to change shape, leukocytes can squeeze between the cells that make up the walls of tiny blood vessels and move into the surrounding tissue. Outside these blood vessels the white blood cells move about like amoebas. With this type of movement, called *ameboid movement*, white blood cells approach bacteria and engulf them. This process is known as *phagocytosis* (fag-ō-sī-TŌ-sis). The special type of white cells that

At this point, you may want your students to refer to the detailed explanation of how white blood cells help fight infection in Chapter 17.

perform phagocytosis are called *phagocytes*. Inside the white blood cell, the bacteria are digested and cause no further harm to the body. Phagocytes also have the ability to engulf and digest damaged red blood cells.

PLATELETS Platelets, or *thrombocytes* (THRAHM-bə-sītz), are not actually cells but only colorless fragments of cells. Platelets do not have a nucleus. Like red blood cells, they are produced in the red marrow of bones, but they are only half the size of red blood cells. Platelets serve two important functions in the blood. They initiate the clotting process, and they aid in sealing small leaks in the small blood vessels.

Blood Clot Formation

An injury to a blood vessel triggers the release of the chemical and the physical changes in the blood that result in clots. Figure 37-3 summarizes these changes. As platelets come into contact with the injured blood vessel, they release *thromboplastin,* an enzyme. In the presence of calcium ions in the plasma, thromboplastin acts on another substance, called *prothrombin.* Prothrombin is a protein that is continually formed in the liver in the presence of vitamin K. During this reaction, prothrombin is changed into a more active enzyme called *thrombin.* This more active substance then changes fibrinogen to *fibrin.* It is the fibrin that forms tiny threads over the injured blood vessel. This net of threads traps red blood cells and thus stops the bleeding. The *scab* that forms over an injury is actually a clot on the surface of the skin.

Normally, clotting within the blood vessels is prevented by a substance called *heparin* (HEP-ər-in) that is produced in the liver. Heparin is a natural *anticoagulant,* or substance that prevents clotting.

Blood Characteristics

In 1900, Dr. Karl Landsteiner, an American scientist, discovered that human beings have different blood groups. On the basis of his work, human blood is divided into four main blood groups or types. These are *A, B, AB,* and *O.* Together, these blood groups are known as the *ABO blood system.* The type of blood that a person has is determined by *multiple alleles,* or many genes. These genes do not change during the lifetime of a person. As a result, the blood type of a person stays the same for life.

The presence or absence of **antigens** (AN-tə-jənz) in the blood determines the specific ABO blood group. Antigens

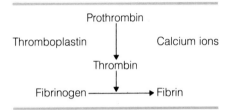

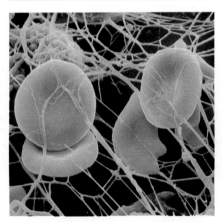

Figure 37-3 Clotting is the result of a complex chain of chemical reactions. Clotting stops a wound from bleeding. Blood clots when red blood cells are held together by threads of fibrin.

Blood group	Antigens on red blood cells	Antibodies in plasma
A	A	(tube, several dots)
B	B	(tube, few dots)
AB	B, A	(tube, empty)
O	(none)	(tube, many dots)

Figure 37-4 Each blood group is characterized by the antigens on the red blood cells and the antibodies in the plasma.

Figure 37-5 An Rh⁻ woman produces a small number of antibodies to her first Rh⁺ baby, which usually is not seriously harmed. However, a second Rh⁺ baby can trigger the production of many antibodies, which can be harmful to the baby.

are substances that are found on the surface of certain red blood cells. These substances are one of the factors that Landsteiner had found in 1900. For example, group A blood contains antigen A and group B blood contains antigen B. When antigens A and B are present, the blood group is AB. If neither antigen A or B is present, the blood group is O.

In addition to the antigens, the blood contains protein factors called **antibodies.** Antibodies are found in the plasma. They cause agglutination, or clumping, of red blood cells that contain foreign antigens. Foreign antigens are antigens not found in a person's blood. These antibodies are usually called anti-A and anti-B. Group B blood has anti-A antibodies and group A has anti-B antibodies. Each of these antibodies will attack a foreign antigen. If a person with group B blood is given group A blood, the recipient's anti-A antibodies attack the foreign antigen B. This causes the blood in the recipient's body to agglutinate and clog the small blood vessels.

Rh FACTOR In 1940, Landsteiner and Alexander Weiner, also an American scientist, discovered another antigen on red blood cells. This antigen is called the **Rh factor.** The Rh factor received its name because it was first isolated in the blood of the rhesus monkey. Like the ABO blood groups, the Rh factor is inherited. A person whose red blood cells have the Rh factor is said to be Rh positive, or Rh⁺. If the blood cells do not have the Rh factor, the person is Rh negative, or Rh⁻. In the United States, most of the population is Rh⁺.

The human body has no natural anti-Rh antibody in the plasma, but people with Rh⁻ blood can produce this antibody. This antibody is produced when foreign Rh⁺ red blood cells come into contact with the blood of an Rh⁻ person. For example, the child of an Rh⁻ mother and an Rh⁺ father may

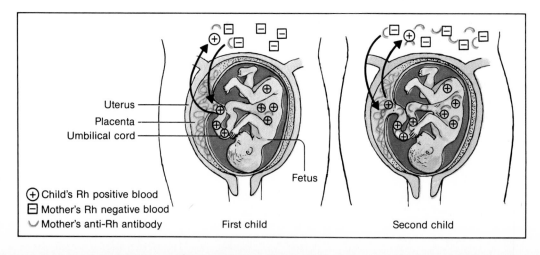

Uterus
Placenta
Umbilical cord
Fetus

⊕ Child's Rh positive blood
⊟ Mother's Rh negative blood
⌣ Mother's anti-Rh antibody

First child   Second child

inherit the Rh$^+$ gene from the father. The child would then be Rh$^+$. During the development of the child within the mother, the Rh$^+$ blood of the child may mix with the Rh$^-$ blood of the mother. This mixing occurs if there are tiny openings in the blood vessels of the mother and child. Normally, this mixing does not occur. However, if there is a mixing of the mother's and child's blood, the Rh$^-$ mother then develops antibodies against the Rh$^+$ blood of her child. Because the amount of antibodies produced is usually small, the blood of the baby is likely not to be damaged seriously. However, if the mother has a second Rh$^+$ baby and there is a mixing of their blood, the mother produces many anti-Rh antibodies. These antibodies, along with those produced during the development of the first child, can seriously harm the child.

To prevent harm to the baby, doctors can completely replace the Rh$^+$ blood of a child with Rh$^-$ blood. Today, this kind of treatment is usually not necessary. After the birth of the first Rh$^+$ child, an Rh$^-$ mother is given an injection of a substance that destroys any anti-Rh antibodies. As a result, few, if any, anti-Rh antibodies are present in the blood of the mother to harm a second Rh$^+$ baby.

BLOOD TRANSFUSIONS   People sometimes lose a great amount of blood in an accident or as the result of surgery. Other people do not produce enough of their own blood, perhaps as the result of a disease. Such people may need a *blood transfusion*. This process involves the taking of blood from one person and giving it to another. The person who receives the blood is called the *recipient* (rē-SIP-ē-ənt). The person who gives the blood is the *donor*.

Before transfusing blood, a doctor must determine whether the blood of the recipient matches that of the donor. Normally, the blood of the recipient and that of the donor are *cross-matched*. In this procedure, a blood sample from each individual is tested with the *serum* of the other. Serum is blood plasma that does not contain fibrinogen. If clumping does not take place, a transfusion between the two people is possible.

In general, individuals of blood group AB can receive blood from people with any of the other major blood groups. These people are therefore called *universal recipients*. People with blood group O can give blood to people of any other major blood group. Group O people are called *universal donors*.

Recently, scientists have experimented with artificial blood made from *fluorocarbons*, or substances containing the elements carbon and fluorine. These scientists have replaced

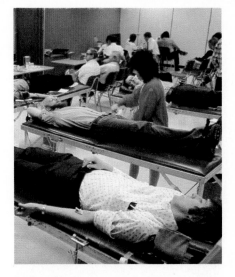

Figure 37-6   Donating blood to a blood bank is practically painless, takes only a few minutes, and may save a life.

up to 80% of the blood of experimental animals with artificial blood, and the animals have lived normal lives.

SECTION REVIEW   Answers on page T–93.

1. What is plasma?
2. Describe the structure and function of red blood cells, white blood cells, and platelets.
3. How does blood clot?
4. What are antigens and antibodies? Who discovered blood antigens?
5. What is the Rh factor?

The Path of Body Fluids

In the human circulatory system, the blood travels around the body through a network of blood vessels. As a result, the system is considered closed. Under normal conditions, the blood never leaves these vessels. Instead, it keeps circulating throughout the vessels, driven by the beating of the heart.

The Heart

The heart is about the size of a clenched fist and is the hardest working muscle in the body. With each beat, or contraction, the heart moves blood throughout the body. Even when the body is at rest, the heart pumps 5 liters of blood per minute. During strenuous exercise, this rate is increased to 25 liters per minute. In a normal adult, the heart beats about 70 times a minute, 101,000 times a day, 36,800,000 times a year, and about 2.7 billion times in an average lifetime.

The heart is almost centered in the chest between the lungs. The heart is covered with a sac called the *pericardium* (per-ə-KAHR-dē-əm). This sac is made up of two membrane layers that are separated by a fluid. The fluid acts as a cushion to prevent friction between the heart and the rib cage as the heart beats. The pericardium is also a means of attachment for the heart to surrounding tissues.

Inside the heart are four *chambers*, or hollow cavities. The two upper chambers, called **atria** (Ā-trē-ə; singular: atrium) are the receiving chambers of the heart. Blood from all parts of the body and the lungs enter the heart through these chambers. The two lower chambers are called the **ventricles** (VEN-tri-k'lz). The ventricles are pumping chambers that force the blood out of the heart. In addition, the heart is divided into right and left sides by a wall of tissue, called the

Highlight

The heart is the central organ of the circulatory system. Its function is to pump the blood through the entire body.

Figure 37-7   The human heart is a fist-sized muscle encased in a membrane called the pericardium. The heart pumps blood through the body at a rate of about 5 liters per minute.

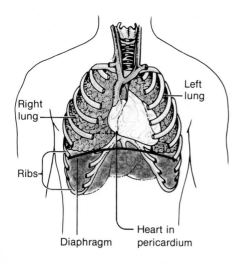

Right lung

Left lung

Ribs

Diaphragm

Heart in pericardium

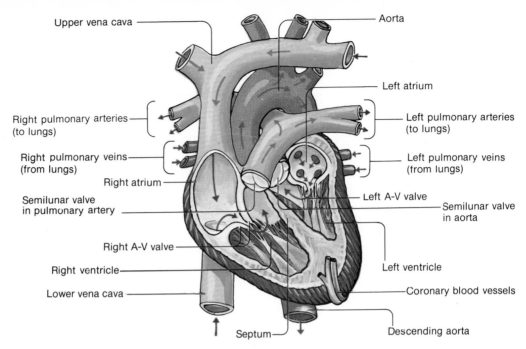

Upper vena cava

Aorta

Right pulmonary arteries
(to lungs)

Left atrium

Left pulmonary arteries
(to lungs)

Right pulmonary veins
(from lungs)

Left pulmonary veins
(from lungs)

Right atrium

Semilunar valve
in pulmonary artery

Left A-V valve

Semilunar valve
in aorta

Right A-V valve

Right ventricle

Left ventricle

Lower vena cava

Coronary blood vessels

Septum

Descending aorta

Figure 37-8 Circulation of Blood
Through the Heart

septum (SEP-təm). The septum divides the heart into right and left atria and right and left ventricles. Figure 37-8 shows the internal structure of the heart.

Between each atrium and ventricle is a flap of fiberlike tissue, called a **valve.** A valve prevents the blood from flowing backward. The valves between the atria and ventricles are called *atrioventricular* (ā-trē-ō-ven-TRIK-yə-lər), or *A-V,* valves. The valves between the ventricles and the blood vessels leaving the heart are called *semilunar valves.*

HEARTBEAT The rhythm of the heart, or the heartbeat, comes from the *sinoatrial* (sī-nō-ā-trē-əl), or *S-A, node.* This node, also referred to as the *pacemaker,* is located in the upper part of the right atrium. The sinoatrial node sets and regulates the heartbeat by sending impulses along the walls of the two atria to the *atrioventricular,* or *A-V, node.* The A-V node, located at the base of the right atrium, receives the impulses from the S-A node. In turn, these impulses spread down to the ventricles in a wavelike movement, causing them to contract.

The rate of the heartbeat is affected by how much oxygen the body needs. During strenuous exercising, such as swimming and running, the heart beats rapidly. The increased heartbeat rushes more oxygen to the body by pumping the blood faster. When the exercising stops, the heartbeat gradually slows down. Emotions, such as anger and fear, also increase the rate of heartbeat.

At this point, you may want to assign to your students the fourth of the Extensions and Applications at the end of this chapter.

At this point, you may want to assign to your students the third of the Extensions and Applications at the end of this chapter.

Sidelight

Engineers have designed artificial pacemakers that keep the heart beating in its proper rhythm even though the natural pacemaker may no longer be doing its job.

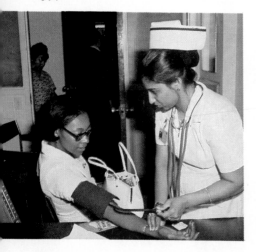

Figure 37-9 The sphygmomanometer measures the force with which the blood moves through the circulatory system. This force is called the blood pressure.

At this point, you may want your students to do the Laboratory Investigation at the end of this chapter.

BLOOD PRESSURE When blood is pumped through the blood vessels, a force is exerted against the walls of the vessels. This force is called *blood pressure*. This pressure is highest in the blood vessels that carry blood away from the heart, and it is the lowest in blood vessels that carry blood to the heart.

With an instrument called a *sphygmomanometer* (sfig-mō-mə-NAHM-ə-tər), a qualified person can measure blood pressure. The sphygmomanometer measures the pressure under two conditions, when the heart is contracting and when it is at rest, between contractions. The period of contraction of the ventricles is called the *systole* (SYS-tə-lē). The period of relaxation, or between the beats of the heart is called the *diastole* (dī-AS-tə-lē). The pressures of both of these periods are recorded and expressed as two numbers, such as 120/80. The first number is the systolic pressure, and the second number is the diastolic pressure. The blood pressure of a person varies slightly from day to day and from hour to hour. Other factors, such as age, sex, weight, heredity, physical activity, disease, and emotion, also affect blood pressure.

At this point, you may want to assign to your students the second of the Extensions and Applications at the end of this chapter.

Blood Vessels

In the human circulatory system, blood travels through three types of vessels. **Arteries** carry blood away from the heart, while **veins** carry blood to the heart. The **capillaries** are tiny blood vessels that connect the arteries and veins. Before the blood travels through the capillaries, it moves through small arteries, called *arterioles* (ahr-TĒR-ē-ōlz). As the blood leaves the capillaries to return to the heart, it moves through small veins, called *venules* (VEN-yoolz). Figure 37-10 shows the structures of the three main types of blood vessels.

ARTERIES The arteries are the strongest blood vessels in the body. They are composed of three layers of tissue. The outer layer is composed of connective tissue. The middle layer is smooth muscle, and the inner layer is lined with a special type of epithelial cell. Arteries can increase and decrease in diameter in response to certain body chemicals and nerve signals. By doing so, arteries can regulate blood flow.

CAPILLARIES The capillaries are tiny blood vessels made up of a single layer of epithelial cells. These cells allow such materials as nutrients, oxygen, carbon dioxide, and white blood cells to enter and to leave the bloodstream. As the capillaries perform this function, they form a bridge between

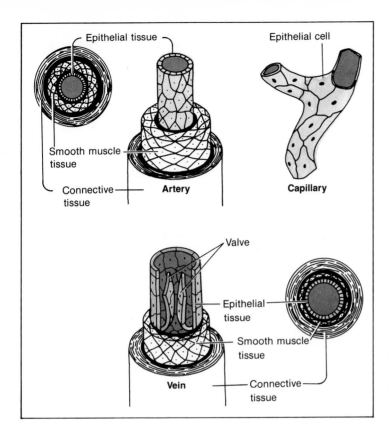

Epithelial tissue

Epithelial cell

Smooth muscle tissue

Connective tissue

Artery

Capillary

Valve

Epithelial tissue

Smooth muscle tissue

Connective tissue

Vein

Figure 37-10 Although arteries, capillaries, and veins are all blood vessels, they each have a unique structure that enables them to perform their different functions.

the arteries and the veins. The bridge, however, is microscopic. The average diameter of a capillary is 8 microns, or 8 millionths of a meter. Capillaries are so tiny that they permit only one red blood cell to pass through them at a time.

VEINS   Like arteries, veins have three layers of tissue. The muscle layer, however, is thinner in the veins than in the arteries. Another difference between arteries and veins is that the smooth inner layer of veins forms folds of tissue, called valves. The free ends of these valves point toward the heart. In this way, they help to prevent the back flow of blood into the capillaries.

Types of Circulation

The human circulatory system has two major divisions, the **pulmonary** (PUL-mə-ner-ē) **circulation** and the **systemic circulation.** In the pulmonary circulation, the blood flows between the heart and the lungs. As the blood enters the lungs, it releases carbon dioxide and picks up oxygen.

In the systemic circulation, the blood moves between the heart and all the organs and tissues of the body. Nutrients

Highlight

The circulatory system can be divided into two types of circulation. Pulmonary circulation refers to blood traveling between the heart and the lungs. Systemic circulation refers to blood traveling between the heart and the rest of the body.

and oxygen are brought to all the body cells, while waste products are removed from them. Approximately 79% of all the blood in the body is found in the systemic circulation.

The systemic circulation has a number of special branches, or networks. One of these is the *coronary* (KAWR-ə-ner-ē) *circulation*. In the coronary circulation, blood moves in the heart muscle. The flow of blood through the kidneys makes up another branch of the systemic circulation, called the *renal* (RĒn'l) *circulation*. Still another branch, the *portal circulation*, circulates blood between the liver and the digestive organs.

Blood flows continuously through the divisions of the circulatory system. Perhaps the best way to show how the blood circulates is to follow the path of one drop through the entire circulatory system. The journey begins in the lungs.

In the lungs, red blood cells pick up oxygen and leave by way of *pulmonary veins*. These veins bring the oxygenated

Sidelight

Doctors can examine the flow of blood through various parts of the circulatory system. This is done by injecting a chemical into the bloodstream that shows up on an X-ray. This type of procedure is called angiography.

CLOSE-UP: *Dr. Robert Geyer*

If you were to ask an auto mechanic the best way to learn how a car motor works, the mechanic would tell you to take a motor apart and then rebuild it yourself. This learning method is often referred to as the nuts-and-bolts approach. Medical researchers use this same approach to understand the systems of the human body. Sometimes, this approach has unexpected results.

A good example is the research of Dr. Robert Geyer at the Harvard School of Public Health in Boston, Massachusetts. Dr. Geyer is interested in the circulatory systems of human beings and of other animals. To learn about these systems, Geyer became one of the first researchers in the country to prepare and to experiment with artificial blood.

"We wanted to study the workings of human organs," he explains, "so we tried to develop an artificial system using animal organs." To fill the system, Geyer used artificial blood, a synthetic compound containing the elements fluorine and carbon.

In 1967, Dr. Geyer decided to run this preparation through the circulatory systems of living animals. It worked well in the living animals. As a result of the experiments, Geyer and other researchers around the world have been working to find ways of using artificial blood in the human

body. They have found that artificial blood is not rejected by the human body because the material is inert. That is, there is nothing in the blood that the body can recognize as a foreign protein.

Artificial blood was developed as a tool to examine circulatory processes. As a tool, it has aided Geyer's search for a better understanding of the circulatory system. Artificial blood has also been of direct benefit to some people. So far, only a few American patients have received artificial blood, Geyer reports. But in Japan, artificial blood has been used during emergencies and surgery on some 350 patients. Artificial blood was used after the supply of real blood had run out or the patients would not accept real blood.

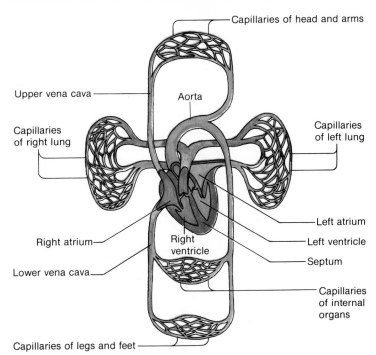

Capillaries of head and arms

Upper vena cava

Aorta

Capillaries of right lung

Capillaries of left lung

Left atrium

Left ventricle

Right atrium

Right ventricle

Septum

Lower vena cava

Capillaries of internal organs

Capillaries of legs and feet

Figure 37-11 Generalized Scheme of the Circulatory System. The path of oxygenated blood is shown in red. That of deoxygenated blood is shown in blue.

blood to the left side of the heart. The blood enters the left atrium and travels into the left ventricle. The left ventricle contracts, forcing the blood out of the heart through the largest artery in the body, the **aorta.** The aorta branches into a number of large arteries that carry the blood to the upper and lower parts of the body. As the blood gets farther and farther away from the heart, the arteries become smaller and smaller, finally becoming arterioles. Eventually, the blood enters the capillaries. In these microscopic vessels, the oxygen in the blood diffuses through the capillary membrane to the surrounding cells. At the same time, the blood picks up carbon dioxide from the cells. On the journey back to the heart, the blood travels through the venules to larger and larger veins.

Finally, the deoxygenated blood makes its way back to the heart. The large veins that bring the blood into the right atrium are the **venae cavae** (vēnē kā-vē; singular: vena cava). There are two of these large veins. The *upper vena cava* brings deoxygenated blood from the head region to the heart, and the *lower vena cava* brings the deoxygenated blood from the lower part of the body. After entering the right atrium, the blood passes into the right ventricle. By contracting, the ventricle pumps the deoxygenated blood back to the lungs by way of the *pulmonary arteries.* Inside the lungs, the blood gives up its carbon dioxide and takes on oxygen. At this point, the path of circulation begins again.

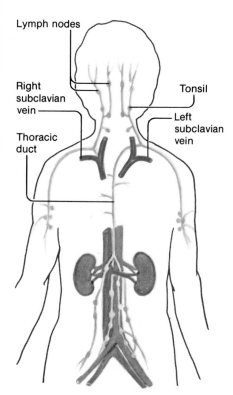

Lymph nodes

Right
subclavian
vein

Tonsil

Left
subclavian
vein

Thoracic
duct

Figure 37-12 The lymphatic system is composed of vessels, capillaries, glands, and ducts that contain lymph. Lymph is a plasmalike fluid that helps rid the body of disease-causing organisms.

Sidelight

Swollen glands, or swollen lymph nodes, are an indication that your body is fighting an invasion of foreign organisms, such as bacteria or viruses.

SECTION REVIEW   Answers on page T-93.

1. Name the four chambers of the heart, and explain the functions of each chamber.
2. Why are the S-A node and A-V node important?
3. Explain the difference between systolic and diastolic pressures.
4. List the functions of arteries, veins, and capillaries.
5. What are the functions of the pulmonary and systemic divisions of the human circulatory system?

The Lymphatic System

The lymphatic system acts as a secondary transport system. As a closed system, the circulatory system cannot transport or recirculate any fluid that leaves the bloodstream through the capillaries. The lymphatic system, however, is an open system. The lymphatic system can collect fluid from tissues and transport it back into the circulatory system.

The lymphatic system is made up of vessels, capillaries, glands, and ducts that carry *lymph*, a plasmalike fluid. The major lymph vessel is the *thoracic duct*. This duct is located in the right side of the chest. The thoracic duct collects lymph from most of the body and empties it into the surrounding veins. Every minute, this duct empties 4 to 10 milliliters of lymph into the veins. If lymph were not returned to the bloodstream, 60% of the plasma volume and 50% of the total plasma proteins would be lost in a day.

Throughout the lymphatic system are bean-shaped structures called *lymph nodes*, or glands. Lymph nodes filter the bacteria out of the lymph and enable white blood cells to destroy the bacteria. See Chapter 17.

Two familiar lymph nodes, the *tonsils* and *adenoids*, are located in the throat area. These glands protect the body against infection. Occasionally, the tonsils may become infected, resulting in *tonsillitis*. Tonsillitis is the inflammation of the tonsils. In the past, people who suffered from tonsillitis usually had their tonsils surgically removed. Today, tonsillitis is treated with antibiotics. By treating the infection in this way, the tonsils remain in the body to protect the digestive and respiratory tract against infection.

SECTION REVIEW   Answers on page T-93.

1. What are the functions of the lymphatic system?
2. What is the importance of the thoracic duct?
3. How do lymph nodes fight infection? Name two lymph nodes.

Observing Blood Circulation

Purpose Capillaries are the smallest vessels that transport blood in the body. Because their walls are only as thick as one cell, materials are exchanged rapidly between the body cells and the bloodstream. The purpose of this investigation is to examine the circulation of blood in the capillaries of a goldfish tail.

Materials *(per group)* ● Goldfish in an aquarium
● Absorbent cotton (approximately 5 cm long)
● Petri dish ● Glass slide ● Microscope

Procedure 1. Obtain a goldfish from your teacher. Wrap the fish in the wet cotton, leaving the head and tail exposed. **2.** Place the fish in the bottom half of a petri dish. Spread the tail out. Cover the tail with a glass slide as shown in the figure. **3.** Place the dish on the stage of the microscope, and examine the tail under low and high powers. **CAUTION:** *Keep the fish moist by adding aquarium water to the cotton as it dries out.* **4.** Observe the capillaries in the tail. Note the flow of blood through the capillaries. Blood enters the capillaries from tiny arterioles, and leaves through tiny venules. **5.** Trace a capillary back to an arteriole and forward to a venule. **6.** As soon as you have completed your observations, place the goldfish back into the aquarium.

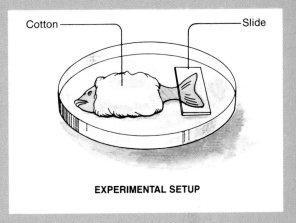

EXPERIMENTAL SETUP

Observations and Conclusions 1. How do blood cells travel through the capillaries? **2.** How thick are the walls of capillaries, compared to those of arteries and veins? **3.** Where in the head of the goldfish would you expect to find an extensive network of capillaries? Why?

CHAPTER SUMMARY

The Circulatory System The human circulatory system contains the blood that carries materials to and from the cells of the body. The blood is made up of a liquid portion called plasma and a solid portion containing red blood cells, white blood cells, and platelets. Red blood cells carry oxygen throughout the circulatory system, while white blood cells fight infection. The platelets are cell fragments that aid in the clotting of blood.

The process of clotting, or coagulation, begins when the platelets release thromboplastin. Thromboplastin acts on a protein, called prothrombin, changing it to thrombin. Thrombin converts the plasma protein, fibrinogen, to fibrin. In turn, the fibrin forms threadlike fibers over a cut, traps the red blood cells, and stops the bleeding. The scab that forms over a wound is a clot on the surface of the skin.

Human blood is classified into four groups, A, B, AB, and O. These types are based on the presence or absence of antigens, proteins found on the membranes of certain red blood cells. The blood also contains proteins, called antibodies, that are found in the plasma. When these antibodies come into contact with foreign antigens, the red blood cells clump up, or agglutinate. The ABO blood groups are inherited, as is another factor, called the Rh factor. People who have this factor have Rh$^+$ blood. Those who do not have the factor have Rh$^-$ blood. The ABO blood group system and Rh factor are important factors in matching the donors and recipients of blood transfusions.

The Path of Body Fluids The heart has four chambers, or hollow cavities. Two of these chambers are called atria, and two are ventricles. The atria are the upper chambers that receive blood, and the ventricles are the lower chambers that pump blood. A wall of muscle, called the septum, divides the heart into left and right sides. The heartbeat is controlled by a mass of tissue, called the sinoatrial, or S-A, node, that is located in the right atrium. The S-A node is also known as the pacemaker.

Blood travels through arteries, veins, and capillaries. Arteries carry blood away from the heart, while veins carry blood to the heart. Capillaries connect the arteries and veins.

The circulatory system has two major divisions, pulmonary circulation and systemic circulation. In pulmonary circulation, the blood flows between the heart and lungs. In systemic circulation, blood moves between the heart and all body organs and tissues.

The Lymphatic System The lymphatic system works closely with the circulatory system. The lymphatic system is made up of vessels and glands that filter fluid from the circulatory system. A plasmalike fluid, called lymph, flows through the vessels. The lymph picks up bacteria and other foreign substances that have escaped from the capillaries of the blood. Located along the lymphatic system are structures called lymph nodes, or glands. The adenoids and tonsils are examples of lymph glands.

CHAPTER VOCABULARY

antibody	hemoglobin	systemic circulation
antigen	lymphatic system	valve
aorta	plasma	vein
artery	platelet	vena cava
atrium	pulmonary circulation	ventricle
capillary	red blood cell	white blood cell
circulatory system	Rh factor	

REVIEW of FACTS and CONCEPTS   Answers on pages T–93 to T–94.

On a separate sheet of paper, answer each of the following as completely as possible.

1. What is the function of a circulatory system in a multicellular organism?
2. Why is blood considered a tissue?
3. Describe the functions of blood in the body.
4. Briefly describe the major components of human blood.

5. How do white and red blood cells differ?
6. What is the function of phagocytes?
7. Describe the events of the clotting process.
8. What are four blood types? How do they differ?
9. Explain the terms universal donor and universal recipient.
10. Discuss the importance of cross-matching blood for a blood transfusion.
11. Why is the human circulatory system considered a closed system?
12. Draw and label the internal structures of the heart.
13. Trace the passage of blood through the body.
14. Explain how the heart beats.
15. Where is blood pressure the highest? The lowest?
16. Name and briefly describe the two major divisions of the circulatory system.
17. List any subdivisions of these divisions.
18. How does the lymphatic system differ from the circulatory system?
19. How do the tonsils aid in protecting the body against infection?
20. Distinguish between the following pairs of terms: atrium and ventricle; artery and vein; and systole and diastole.

EXTENSIONS and APPLICATIONS   For additional information, see page T–94.

1. Visit a local blood donating center. What screening techniques are used for potential donors? Explain how the whole blood is treated and tested after it is donated. Present a report to your class.
2. Invite a doctor or nurse to your class to demonstrate the use of the sphygmomanometer to measure blood pressure. After observing this technique, try measuring the blood pressure of a classmate. As the cuff of the sphygmomanometer is loosened, what type of sounds do you hear through the stethoscope?
3. Research the topic of heart and valve transplants. Why is it necessary that donors and recipients be cross-matched before the transplant is made? What is the advantage of using artificial hearts and artificial valves in transplants? What is meant by bypass surgery? How is the problem of rejection solved in this form of surgery? Write a report to present to the class.
4. Obtain a beef heart from your local butcher. Carefully cut the heart lengthwise. Sketch and label the internal structure of the heart.

SUGGESTED READINGS

American Heart Association, *Heartbook*. New York: E.P. Dutton.
    This book contains an excellent collection of articles on how the heart works. The book covers the latest medical breakthroughs dealing with the prevention and treatment of heart problems.
DeBakey, M., and A. Gotto, *The Living Heart*. New York: David McKay Company.
    The operation of the cardiovascular system is explained by two renowned heart specialists. They also discuss the relationship of diet and exercise to maintaining a healthy heart.
Snively, W.D., and J. Thuerback, *The Sea of Life*. New York: David McKay Company.
    The authors present a discussion of the bodily fluids, including blood and lymph.
Vroman, L., *Blood*. Garden City, N.Y.: The Natural History Press.
    This is an informative and entertaining book about blood and its components.

38 Respiration and Excretion

The ability to inhale oxygen and exhale carbon dioxide is one necessity for life.

Chapter Objectives *After completing this chapter, you will be able to:*

a ■ Explain the processes of respiration. p. 623
b ■ Name and describe the respiratory organs and their functions. p. 623
c ■ Discuss the importance of diffusion in respiration. p. 625
d ■ Describe how breathing is controlled and the structures associated with it. p. 626
e ■ Define metabolism and its phases. p. 627
f ■ Describe the structure and function of the kidney and its parts. p. 629

For teaching aids for this chapter, including a chapter overview and teaching strategies, see pages T–94 to T–96. The page number next to each chapter objective refers to the text page where the information needed to fulfill the objective begins.

If you were in reasonably good health, you probably could survive for several weeks without eating. You could survive for a few days without water, but you could not live more than a few minutes without oxygen.

The importance of oxygen to the cells of the body cannot be overemphasized. Without this gas, life as we know it could not exist. At the level of the cell, oxygen makes possible the reactions that release energy from the food we eat.

The release of energy in your cells and their other functions result in the production of waste products, which are removed from the body. If they were not removed, the body would be poisoned by its own wastes. Many parts of the body are involved in the removal of wastes, including the kidneys, intestines, lungs, liver, and skin.

Respiratory System

Air is taken into the body by a process called *breathing*. By itself, breathing cannot deliver oxygen to all the cells of the body and bring about the release of energy. Delivery of oxygen to the cells, elimination of carbon dioxide, and the release of energy is called **respiration.** *External respiration* is the exchange of gases between the lungs and the blood. *Internal respiration* is the exchange of gases between the blood and the cells. *Cellular respiration* involves the release of energy in the cells. In complex multicellular organisms such as human beings, respiratory, circulatory, and excretory systems function together to supply the body cells with oxygen and to eliminate wastes.

You may want to review the process of respiration in one-celled organisms (Chapter 7). Discuss the reasons why a one-celled organism does not need a complex respiratory or excretory system.

Highlight

Respiration occurs in three phases. These phases are external repsiration, internal respiration and cellular respiration.

Respiratory Structures

The principal respiratory organs are the **lungs.** The lungs are divided into sections called *lobes*. The right lung has three lobes and the left lung has two lobes. The lungs are enclosed in a double membrane called the *pleura* (PLOOR-ə). A fluid between the membrane layers helps to prevent friction as the lungs move.

The passage of air to the lungs is complex. Air enters the body through two openings in the nose called **nares** (NER-ēz), or *nostrils*. The nares open into the *nasal chambers*, or spaces inside the nose. The nasal chambers are separated by the *septum*. The nasal chambers contain many blood vessels and are lined with cells that have cilia and secrete mucus.

Figure 38-1 The major organs of the respiratory system are the lungs. Oxygen-rich air in the lungs passes from the alveoli into the capillaries that lead to venules.

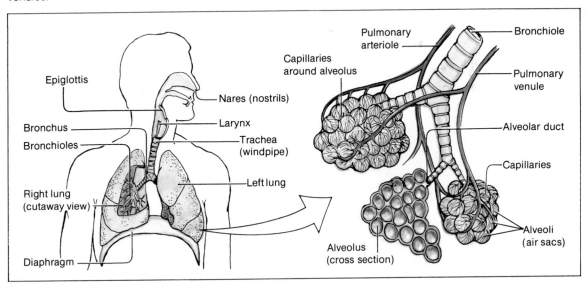

623

When air enters the nose it is moistened by the mucus and warmed by the blood flowing through the blood vessels. The mucus and cilia help to filter dust particles out of the incoming air.

The **pharynx** is a tube located below the nasal chambers in the back part of the mouth. This tube is a passageway for both air and food. From the pharynx, air passes into the **trachea,** or windpipe. The trachea is composed of alternating bands of cartilage and smooth muscle held together with connective tissue. The bands of cartilage prevent the collapse of the trachea. The trachea is lined with cilia and cells that secrete mucus. The cilia create an upward current that tends to keep inhaled dust particles from moving down into the lungs.

The **larynx,** or voice box, is located at the top of the trachea. The larynx is made of cartilage and is commonly called the Adam's apple. The opening into the larynx is called the **glottis.** The **epiglottis,** a flap of tissue at the base of the tongue, covers the glottis when swallowing occurs, preventing food from going into the larynx and trachea. Elastic fibers inside the larynx, called *vocal cords,* aid in voice production.

The lower end of the trachea divides into two **bronchi** BRAHNG-kī), each of which enters a lung. In the lungs, the bronchi further divide into smaller tubes called **bronchioles.** The bronchioles form a duct system that makes up most of the structure of the lungs. The smallest branches of the bronchioles are microscopic and are called the *alveolar* (al-vē-ə-lər) *ducts.* These ducts open into air sacs. Each air sac is made up of clusters of **alveoli** (singular: alveolus), microscopic sacs that are very elastic. The alveoli are surrounded by capillaries.

Mechanics of Breathing

The two basic actions of breathing are *inhaling,* or allowing air into the lungs, and *exhaling,* or pushing air out of the lungs. Air goes into the lungs when the air pressure in the chest cavity is less than the air pressure outside the lungs. Air is expelled from the lungs when the pressure of air in the chest cavity is greater than the outside air pressure.

Air pressure in the chest is changed when the volume of the chest cavity is changed. The volume of the chest cavity is changed by the action of the *diaphragm,* and by the action of *intercostal muscles* between the ribs. As the volume decreases, the pressure increases. As the volume increases, the pressure decreases.

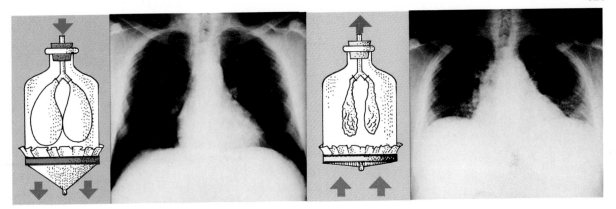

Figure 38-2 As the diaphragm contracts (*left*), air pressure decreases in the chest, causing the lungs to inflate. When the diaphragm relaxes (*right*), air pressure increases, causing the lungs to deflate.

The diaphragm is a sheet of muscle that forms a partition between the abdomen and chest. In its resting position, the diaphragm is bowed upward. When a human being inhales, the diaphragm contracts and is pulled downward. At the same time, the intercostal muscles pull the ribs upward and outward. These actions increase the volume of the chest cavity, decreasing the air pressure inside. The outside air pressure is now greater than the inside pressure and air flows into the lungs. When a human being exhales, the diaphragm relaxes and bows upward, and the ribs are pulled together and inward. The volume of the chest cavity is reduced, increasing the pressure and air moves out.

Gas Exchange

Gas exchange occurs in the lungs. This exchange is made between the alveoli and the capillaries surrounding them. The walls of the alveoli are only about one cell thick and are covered by a film of water. Oxygen in the alveoli dissolves in the water film and moves through the wall of the capillaries into the blood. Carbon dioxide moves from the blood through the capillary walls and into the alveoli. This exchange of gases takes place through *diffusion*. Diffusion is the movement of substances from an area of high concentration to an area of low concentration.

Oxygen is picked up by the *hemoglobin* in red blood cells. These oxygen-carrying cells are carried away from the lungs by the capillaries surrounding the alveoli. The oxygen-carrying blood enters larger blood vessels that take it to the heart. The heart pumps the blood into vessels that carry the blood to all the cells of the body. Carbon dioxide is carried from cells to the lungs by the blood. The carbon dioxide is removed from the lungs during exhaling.

Highlight

Diffusion is the process by which gases pass between the alveoli and blood vessels in the lungs.

Figure 38-3 Oxygen passes from the alveolus into the blood in the capillaries. Carbon dioxide moves in the opposite direction.

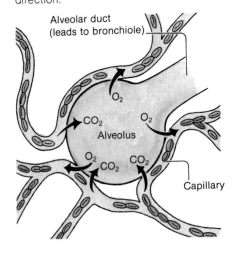

Alveolar duct (leads to bronchiole)

O_2

CO_2 O_2

Alveolus

O_2 CO_2

O_2 CO_2

Capillary

At this point, you may want to have your students do the Laboratory Investigation at the end of this chapter.

Sidelight

Most males have a larger average lung capacity than have females of the same age. For example, 18-year-old females have a lung capacity of 4.1 liters. Males of the same age have a lung capacity of 5.9 liters.

Control of Breathing

Breathing is controlled by the respiratory center in the *medulla oblongata* (mə-DUL-ə ahb-lawng-GAHT-ə) of the brain. Connected directly to this center are several nerves from the lungs, diaphragm, and the intercostal muscles. The nervous system automatically controls breathing all the time. A human being has only a limited amount of conscious control over breathing. A person can choose not to inhale or exhale but only for a limited time. Eventually chemical control causes the breathing to continue.

Chemical control of breathing is determined by the amount of carbon dioxide in the blood. As the level of carbon dioxide in the blood goes up, the blood becomes more acid. The change in the acidity of the blood stimulates the respiratory center to send out impulses that speed up the rate of breathing, in order to get more oxygen into the body and more carbon dioxide out. When the carbon dioxide level of the blood is reduced, the respiratory center slows down the breathing rate. When a person stops inhaling and exhaling, the carbon dioxide level of the blood rises. The respiratory center stimulates breathing again, no matter how hard a person tries to stop it.

Occasionally when a person engages in vigorous physical activities, the muscles may not get enough oxygen to meet their needs. Under these conditions, the muscle cells can temporarily obtain energy from **anaerobic respiration.** Anaerobic respiration is a chemical process in which glucose is converted to a substance called *lactic acid.* The lactic acid builds up in the muscle tissue, causing a feeling of weakness and, sometimes, pain. Oxygen is required to get rid of the lactic acid but the oxygen is not present. This shortage of oxygen is called an **oxygen debt.**

As the process of anaerobic respiration continues, muscle cells accumulate more and more of an oxygen debt. This stimulates the brain's breathing center to increase the rate of breathing. The increased breathing rate continues until the lactic acid is removed. At this point, the oxygen debt is "paid off," and breathing returns to normal.

During normal breathing, the amount of air entering and leaving the lungs is about half a liter. During intense inhaling and exhaling, the volume of air that moves through the lungs is much greater. The largest volume of air a person can breathe is called the **vital capacity** of the lungs. The capacity of the lungs varies with the age and the sex of the individual, and it increases from birth to adulthood.

Metabolism

The sum of all the chemical processes that occur in the body is called **metabolism.** Metabolism occurs in two phases. In *anabolism*, the building-up phase, energy is stored. Complex compounds are built up from simpler ones. An example of anabolism is the building of substances needed by the body. In *catabolism*, the breaking-down phase, complex compounds are broken down into simpler ones and energy is released. An example of this phase is the oxidation of food substances in the cells. When anabolism is greater than catabolism, growth occurs. When catabolism is greater than anabolism, weight loss occurs.

The work the body does in maintaining all life functions and their associated chemical reactions is called **basal metabolism.** The minimum amount of energy needed to accomplish these tasks is called the *basal metabolic rate*, or *BMR*. The BMR can be determined by measuring the amount of oxygen used up during a specific period of time.

CAREER: Emergency Medical Technician

Emergency medical technicians work as members of two-person medical teams. These technicians are responsible for administering first aid treatment to sick or injured people and transporting them to a proper medical facility. A medical technician team is sent to accident sites or other emergencies by a radio dispatcher. Team members drive specially equipped vehicles.

At the scene of an emergency, technicians must determine the extent of people's injuries or illness and decide what procedures should be followed. The technicians may control bleeding, administer oxygen, apply splints, and treat minor wounds and shock. They keep in close contact with medical professionals at hospitals or other treatment facilities by radio to receive instructions regarding possible treatment. Before reaching the hospital or emergency treatment facility, the technicians arrange to have medical personnel meet the emergency vehicle at the hospital or treatment center. Among the other duties of emergency medical technicians is maintaining vehicles, equipment, and supplies.

An 81-hour basic training program must be completed by a candidate for employment as an emergency medical technician. The program

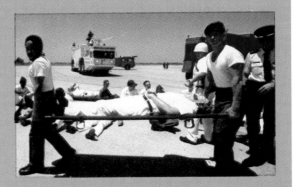

has been designed by the United States Department of Transportation to teach candidates how to handle various emergencies and medical equipment. People who want to take this program must be at least 18 years old and have a high school diploma and a valid driver's license.

Many emergency medical technicians work for police and fire departments and for private ambulance companies. Some are volunteers.

For career information, write to National Registry of Emergency Medical Technicians, 1395 East Dublin-Granville Road, P.O. Box 29233, Columbus, OH 43229.

At this point, you may want to assign to your students the first of the Extensions and Applications at the end of this chapter.

628

Figure 38-4 Before beginning mouth-to-mouth respiration, determine if there is an object obstructing the victim's air passages. If not, follow these steps. (1) Tilt the head back. (2) At the same time, pull the chin upward so that the jaw is jutting out. (3) Pinch the nostrils shut, while simultaneously opening your mouth and placing it tightly over the victim's mouth. Exhale into the victim's mouth every five seconds for one minute. (4) Listen for exhalation from the victim. Repeat the procedure until the victim is able to breathe.

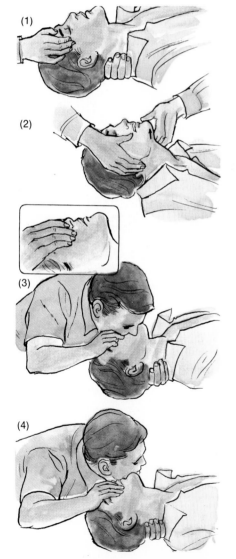

(1)

(2)

(3)

(4)

Respiratory Difficulties

Most respiratory difficulties are caused by environmental conditions. Others are symptoms of diseases caused by microorganisms or of other problems that originate within the body.

Many breathing difficulties are temporary. High altitude is one of the most common causes of temporary breathing problems. At higher altitudes there are fewer oxygen molecules in the air. The body needs to take in more air to supply its oxygen needs. The air pressure is lower at high altitudes. Therefore, it becomes more difficult to reduce the air pressure in the chest cavity so that air will readily move into the lungs.

Another respiratory difficulty occurs when abnormal amounts of carbon monoxide are present. Carbon monoxide is a colorless, odorless, poisonous gas released in automobile exhausts, cigarette smoke, and other products of combustion. Carbon monoxide combines more easily with hemoglobin than does oxygen. As a result, the amount of oxygen that goes to the cells is greatly reduced and oxygen deprivation occurs. Eventually, the cells die. An excessive intake of carbon monoxide can result in death.

Two somewhat related causes of respiratory difficulty are smoking and air pollution. Cigarette smoke and polluted air may damage the lining of the upper respiratory tract and the lungs. Cigarette smoke and air pollutants slow down and, in some cases, stop the cilia on the lining from removing foreign substances from the air. The harmful materials are left in close contact with various parts of the respiratory system. The conditions that may result vary from shortness of breath to diseases such as *emphysema* (em-fə-sĒmə). Emphysema is a disease in which the alveoli in the lungs are destroyed.

Sometimes, due to accident or illness, a person stops breathing. When this occurs *artificial respiration* is used. Artificial respiration is the manual or mechanical stimulation of respiratory movements and the exchange of gases until the victim can breathe naturally. The method most widely used today is called the *mouth-to-mouth method*. This method involves the steps shown in Figure 38-4.

SECTION REVIEW   Answers on page T–95.

1. Define respiration.
2. What are the principal respiratory organs?
3. Define diffusion.
4. What is artificial respiration?

At this point, you may want to assign to your students the second of the Extensions and Applications at the end of this chapter.

Excretory System

In carrying out its vital functions, the human body produces a variety of *metabolic wastes*. These wastes include salts, carbon dioxide, and pigments. The wastes are removed from the body by a process called **excretion.** If the wastes accumulate, serious cell damage can occur. The undigested food wastes that are excreted through the large intestine are not metabolic wastes. Therefore, the large intestine is not considered an organ of excretion and will not be discussed here. Many other parts of the body are involved in excretion.

Excretory Structures

The **kidneys** are the major organs of excretion. The kidneys are bean-shaped organs 10 to 15 centimeters long. They are embedded in *fat tissue* against the back wall of the abdominal cavity. The kidneys regulate the salt balance and control the fluid balance in the body. The kidneys also regulate the acid balance of the blood by removing acids produced during metabolic activities.

A kidney is composed of two major parts. The outer portion is called the **cortex.** The cortex is made up mostly of millions of **nephrons.** The nephron is the basic structural and functional unit of the kidney. The inner portion of the kidney is called the **medulla.** The medulla consists of cone-shaped structures called *pyramids.* The pyramids end in the *collecting tubules.* They carry the wastes of metabolism into an open area of the kidney called the *renal pelvis.* The renal pelvis narrows to form the **ureter** (yoo-RĒT-ər). A ureter leads from each kidney to the **urinary bladder.** The urinary bladder is a muscular, baglike organ that has a capacity of 250 milliliters. The urinary bladder stores liquid wastes before they are excreted through a tube called the **urethra** (yoo-RĒ-thrə). The urethra leads to the outside of the body.

Mechanics of Excretion

Inside each kidney more than a million nephrons function as filters. A nephron consists of a funnel-like **Bowman's capsule** surrounding the **glomerulus** (glah-MER-yoo-ləs). The glomerulus, consisting of a tuft of capillaries, is the actual filter. The Bowman's capsule is connected to a series of twisted and looped tubules. The *proximal convoluted tubule* leads from the Bowman's capsule into the *loop of Henle.* The loop of Henle runs down into the medulla of the kidney and then returns to the cortex. The *distal convoluted tubule* connects the loop of Henle with the collecting tubule.

Figure 38-5 Human Excretory System

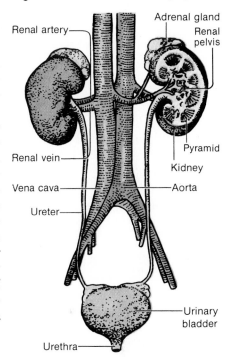

Renal artery — Adrenal gland — Renal pelvis — Pyramid — Kidney — Aorta — Urinary bladder — Renal vein — Vena cava — Ureter — Urethra

At this point, you may want to assign to your students the third of the Extensions and Applications at the end of this chapter.

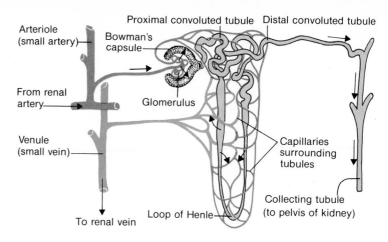

Figure 38-6 Structure of a Nephron

The nephrons remove nitogenous wastes from the blood through the processes of *filtration* and *reabsorption*. Filtration occurs in the glomerulus. Blood pressure within the capillaries in the glomerulus forces some substances in the blood into the Bowman's capsule. These substances, called the *filtrate*, diffuse into the Bowman's capsule. The filtrate includes water, glucose, amino acids, salts, and *urea*. Urea is a nitrogenous waste that is excreted by the liver. Blood cells and blood proteins remain in the capillaries.

The process of reabsorption occurs as the filtrate passes through the convoluted tubules and the loop of Henle. Digested food materials are reabsorbed from the tubules into the capillaries by *active transport*. Water is reabsorbed from the convoluted tubules and the loop of Henle into the capillaries by osmosis.

The remaining substances that empty into the collecting tubule compose the *urine*. Urine contains excess water and salts, urea, and uric acid.

Other Excretory Organs

The skin is often called an excretory organ. Its excretory function is carried out by structures called *sweat glands*. A sweat gland consists of a coiled tube that extends upward to the skin's surface to an opening called a *pore*. Sweat glands excrete water, salts, and urea.

The lungs and liver also have excretory functions. The lungs remove carbon dioxide and water vapor during exhalation. The liver removes bile pigments and some hemoglobin.

SECTION REVIEW   Answers on page T–95.

1. What is a nephron?
2. How are nitrogenous wastes removed from the blood?
3. Besides the kidneys, name three other excretory organs.

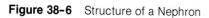

Sidelight

The skin of an adult human body is covered with over two million sweat glands. Sweat glands are found all over the body but are most heavily concentrated on the palms of the hands, the soles of the feet, and under the arms.

Measuring Pulse and Respiration Rates

Purpose   The pulse is an easily measured indicator of the heart's activity. The respiration rate indicates the lungs' activity in supplying oxygen to the blood and the removal of carbon dioxide from the blood. The purpose of this investigation is to determine the relationship between pulse and respiration rates by measuring the changes in these rates during rest and physical activity.

Materials *(per 2 students)* ● Watch or clock that shows seconds

Procedure   **1.** Find your partner's pulse by gently pressing two or three fingertips on the inside of your partner's wrist. Count the number of beats in one minute.   **2.** Determine your partner's respiration rate by counting the number of breaths in one minute.
3. Copy the table on a sheet of paper.   **4.** Count the number of your partner's pulse beats in one minute. Repeat the procedure two more times, and average the results. Record the average in the table.
5. Determine your partner's respiration rate for each of three minutes. Average the results and record the average in the table.   **6.** Repeat steps 4 and 5 after your partner has walked normally for one minute. Allow your partner to rest between trials.   **7.** Repeat steps 4 and 5 after your partner has run in place for one minute. Allow your partner to rest between trials.
8. Repeat the entire investigation again with you performing the activities and your partner recording the results.

Observations and Conclusions   **1.** What effect does walking have on pulse and respiration rates?   **2.** How does running affect pulse and respiration rates?
3. Are there any differences between the pulse and respiration rates of males and females? Explain.

	Resting	Walking	Running
Pulse Rate			
Respiration Rate			

CHAPTER SUMMARY

Respiratory System   The respiratory system brings oxygen to each of the cells during inhaling and removes carbon dioxide from them during exhaling. Oxygen is taken into the body by a process called breathing. Air passes through the nasal cavity, pharynx, larynx. trachea, and bronchi to the lungs, the principal organs of respiration. The bronchioles and alveoli of the lungs help transport oxygen to the blood.

The respiratory center is located in the medulla oblongata of the brain. Breathing is controlled by the nervous system and by the concentration of chemicals in the blood. The amount of carbon dioxide in the blood determines chemical control. The nervous system automatically controls breathing.

Metabolism is the sum of all chemical processes occurring in the body. The building-up phase is called anabolism while the tearing-down phase is known as catabolism. The work the body does in maintaining vital life functions is called basal metabolism.

The environment influences the ability to breathe. A number of environmental factors, such as air pollution, cigarette smoking, and high altitude, are responsible for a variety of respiratory difficulties.

Excretory System   Metabolic wastes include carbon dioxide, water, salt, urea, and bile pigments. These wastes are potentially harmful to the body. The excretory system removes metabolic wastes from the body through organs such as the kidneys, skin, lungs, and liver.

The kidneys are the principal organs of the excretory system. They also regulate the salt and fluid balance in the body. The basic structural and functional unit of the kidney is the nephron. The nephron is composed of a glomerulus, Bowman's capsule, and a convoluted tubule. Within the nephron nitrogenous wastes are removed by the process of filtration and reabsorption. In filtration, materials such as water, amino acids, urea, salts, and glucose, pass into the Bowman's capsule from the capillaries. In reabsorption, some of these materials are reabsorbed from the tubules back into the surrounding capillaries by active transport. The materials that remain in the tubules and travel to the collecting tubule are called urine. Urine travels via the ureter to the urinary bladder. Urine is stored in the bladder until it is expelled from the body through the urethra.

CHAPTER VOCABULARY

alveolus	glomerulus	oxygen debt
anaerobic respiration	glottis	pharynx
basal metabolism	kidney	respiration
Bowman's capsule	larynx	trachea
bronchiole	lung	ureter
bronchus	medulla	urethra
cortex	metabolism	urinary bladder
epiglottis	nares	vital capacity
excretion	nephron	

REVIEW of FACTS and CONCEPTS   Answers on pages T–95 to T–96.

On a separate sheet of paper, answer each of the following as completely as possible.

1. Explain the difference between external, internal, and cellular respiration.
2. List each respiratory organ and its functions.
3. Describe and give the location of the lungs.
4. What role do the diaphragm and intercostal muscles play in breathing?
5. Explain how oxygen and carbon dioxide are exchanged in the lungs.
6. When is anaerobic respiration used by the human body?
7. How is breathing controlled in human beings?
8. Define the term vital capacity.

9. What is oxygen debt?

10. Define metabolism. What are the phases of metabolism?

11. What happens when anabolism is greater than catabolism?

12. Why is the basal metabolism important to the body?

13. How does carbon monoxide affect the body?

14. What effect does cigarette smoke have on the respiratory system?

15. Describe the structure of the kidney.

16. Explain the mechanics of excretion.

17. How can the skin be classified as an excretory organ?

EXTENSIONS and APPLICATIONS   For additional information, see page T–96.

1. Prepare a bulletin board on respiration difficulties. Contact your local office of the Tuberculosis and Respiratory Disease Association to obtain materials on air pollution, emphysema, and respiratory allergies. Explain how cigarette smoke, allergies, and polluted air cause respiratory difficulties.

2. A deep-sea diver sometimes gets "the bends." What is this problem? Why does it happen? How can a diver avoid this problem? Using reference materials, write a short report about this topic.

3. Using reference materials, prepare a written report on how the artificial kidney machine works.

SUGGESTED READINGS

Cohen, J., *Kidney and Urinary Problems*. Wellesley, Mass.: Arandel.
An expert writes concisely about the treatment, medication, and prevention of disorders of the urinary system.

Collins, J.S., *Living with a Stranger*. New York: Braziller.
An interesting book by a nonmedical writer about the functions of the body. The section on respiration and excretion is very informative.

Reichman, S., *Breathe Easy*. New York: Crowell.
The effects of allergies and asthma upon the respiratory system are described.

39 Nutrition and Health

Chapter Objectives *After completing this chapter, you will be able to:*

a ■ Explain the differences among the six categories of nutrients. p. 636

b ■ List the major sources of carbohydrates, fats, and proteins. p. 636

c ■ List the vitamins and why each is important to the body. p. 637

d ■ Describe how exercise, sleep, and weight control contribute to good health. p. 640

For teaching aids for this chapter, including a chapter overview and teaching strategies, see pages T–96 to T–97. The page number next to each chapter objective refers to the text page where the information needed to fulfill the objective begins.

Exercise and proper eating habits contribute to good health.

The foods you eat are actually fuel and building materials for your body. As a result, your health depends on the kinds of foods you eat. These foods go to the nerve cells, blood cells, bone cells, muscle cells, and all the other cells of the body. These types of cells, however, need different kinds of foods. You must, therefore, eat foods that give the most benefit to all the cells of your body.

The study of nutrition reveals how the body uses food in growth, development, and repair. An understanding of nutrition also shows how foods with low nutritional value can be harmful to human health. In the last 50 years, *nutritionists*, or scientists who study nutrition, have made many advances. For example, they have discovered the sources and functions of many substances.

In addition to eating nutritious foods in proper amounts, good health involves the ability to resist sickness, cope with stresses, and exercise without tiring easily. Maintaining the proper weight and getting adequate rest and sleep are also necessary for good health.

Nutritional Substances

Highlight

Nutrients are substances that provide a source of energy and materials for growth and repair of body tissues.

At this point, you may want to assign to your students the second of the Extensions and Applications at the end of this chapter.

Food contains various **nutrients** that are needed to repair tissues, to supply energy, and to carry out life processes. The body needs and uses more than 50 nutrients. These nutrients are grouped into six categories. No single food, however, has all the nutrients needed for a strong, healthy body.

To stay strong and healthy, a person must eat a balanced diet. This type of diet contains all the nutrients that the body needs, and it is made up of four food groups. These groups are the *milk group*, the *vegetable-fruit group*, the *meat group*, and the *bread-cereals group*. For a daily balanced diet, an average young adult should eat the following.

Four or more servings from the milk group

Two or more servings from the meat group

Four or more servings from the bread-cereals group

Four or more servings from the vegetable-fruit group

Figure 39-1 A balanced diet contains nutrients from each of the four basic food groups. These are the milk group, the meat group, the bread and cereal group, and the vegetable and fruit group.

At this point, you may want to have your students do the Laboratory Investigation at the end of this chapter.

Proteins

Every living plant or animal cell contains **proteins.** Proteins help build and repair tissues. They also aid in the making of enzymes, some hormones, and antibodies. If other nutrients are not available, proteins can be used to provide energy.

Proteins are large molecules that contain carbon, hydrogen, oxygen, nitrogen, and several other elements. Each protein molecule is made up of *amino acids*, the building blocks of proteins. The kind and number of amino acids vary from one protein to another. About eight amino acids must be in the diet of almost all animals. These are called *essential amino acids*. Those amino acids that can be synthesized in the body without being present in food are called *nonessential amino acids*.

Some foods supply not only the essential amino acids, but also other substances that can be used to make the nonessential amino acids. These foods, such as soybeans, milk, eggs, fish, and lean meat, are called *complete protein foods*. Foods that supply only some of the amino acids needed in a balanced diet are called *incomplete protein foods*. Rice, potatoes, and corn are examples of incomplete protein foods.

Carbohydrates and Fats

To carry out the life processes in every cell, the human body has to get energy from food. The energy value of foods is measured in units called **Calories,** or *kilocalories*. One Calorie is equal to the amount of heat energy needed to raise the temperature of 1 kilogram of water by 1° C. How many Calories a person needs every day depends on the person's size, body build, occupation, type of physical activity, and age.

The molecules of **carbohydrates** contain carbon, hydrogen, and oxygen. Found mostly in cereals, breads, fruits, and vegetables, these molecules have a high Calorie value. Foods with large amounts of carbohydrates are very good sources of energy for the body.

If the body holds more carbohydrates than it needs to meet its energy requirements, the excess is stored in the muscles and liver. If these storage places become filled, the carbohydrates will then be stored in the body. Stored carbohydrates add weight to the body. As a result, a diet with an excess of carbohydrates can make a person overweight.

Carbohydrates take the form of sugars and starches. The simplest carbohydrates are the *monosaccharides*, or simple sugars, such as glucose or grape sugar, fructose or fruit sugar, and galactose. In fact, the digestive process breaks

Highlight

Proteins are made up of amino acids. People must obtain essential amino acids from the food they eat. Nonessential amino acids can be synthesized by the human body.

Highlight

Carbohydrates are the nutrients that are the body's major source of energy. Sugars and starches are the two kinds of carbohydrates.

At this point, you may want to have some of your students research and perform some of the simple tests to determine the presence of nutrients in foods. You might have them begin with the tests for sugars, starches, and fats.

down all carbohydrates into glucose for use by the body. The *disaccharides*, or double sugars, are more complex sugars, and include lactose or milk sugar, sucrose or table sugar, and maltose. The most complex carbohydrates, called *polysaccharides* include various starches, such as cellulose and glycogen.

Polysaccharides are useful to the body. Starch from the cellulose walls of fruits and vegetables can be broken down into glucose. Although humans cannot digest cellulose, it aids digestion by supplying *fiber*, or bulk. Fiber helps to increase *peristalsis*, or rhythmic muscular contractions in the digestive system.

Like carbohydrates, **fats** are made up of carbon, hydrogen, and oxygen. Fats, however, have much more carbon and hydrogen than do carbohydrates. Fats supply the body with twice as much energy as do equal amounts of carbohydrates or proteins. Fat stored in the body acts as insulation against the cold. Foods that are rich in fats come from both animals and plants. Common sources of fats are nuts, butter, vegetable oils, fatty meats, bacon, and cheese.

Vitamins

Each of the four basic food groups contains organic substances called **vitamins.** The body cannot make vitamins, and no single food contains all the vitamins that the body needs. As a result, the body must get its vitamins from a variety of foods.

Needed only in very small amounts, vitamins perform many complex functions. They help to regulate the body processes, promote growth, and aid in the general upkeep of the body. When the body does not have enough of a certain vitamin, the condition is called a *vitamin-deficiency disease.*

Vitamins are divided into two major groups. Vitamins A, D, E, and K are called the *fat-soluble vitamins.* These vitamins can be stored in the fatty tissues of the body. Vitamins that dissolve in water, called *water-soluble*, are not stored in the body. As a result, the body uses only as much of them as it needs, and it excretes the excess in the urine. The water-soluble group includes vitamin C and the B-complex vitamins, such as riboflavin.

Minerals

The body needs about 14 **minerals,** or inorganic substances. These substances usually take the form of elements or salts. As in the case of vitamins, no single food provides all the needed minerals.

Sidelight

Studies have shown that 1 gram of protein or carbohydrate provides 4 Calories and 1 gram of fat provides 9 Calories.

Highlight

The fat-soluble vitamins are A, D, E, and K. The water-soluble vitamins are C and B complex.

Figure 39-2 Important Sources and Functions of Nutritional Substances

Substances	Sources	Needed for
Organic nutrients proteins	soybeans, milk, eggs, lean meats, fish, beans, peas, cheese	growth, maintenance, and repair of tissues manufacture of enzymes, hormones, and antibodies
carbohydrates	cereals, breads, fruits, vegetables	energy source fiber or bulk in diet
fats	nuts, butter, vegetable oils, fatty meats, bacon, cheese	energy source
Complex organic substances vitamins	milk, butter, lean meats, leafy vegetables, fruits	prevention of deficiency diseases regulation of body processes growth efficient biochemical reactions
Mineral salts calcium and sodium compounds	whole-grain cereals, meats, milk, green leafy vegetables, vegetables, table salt	strong bones and teeth blood and other tissues
iron compounds	meats, liver, nuts, cereals	hemoglobin formation
iodine	iodized salt, seafoods	secretion by thyroid gland
Inorganic compound water	all foods	dissolving substances blood tissue fluid biochemical reactions

Highlight

Major mineral nutrients include sodium, calcium, phosphorus, and potassium.

Some minerals, called *major minerals*, are needed in large quantities. Examples of these minerals are sodium, calcium, phosphorus, and potassium. The body needs only small amounts of other minerals, such as iron, iodine, and copper. These minerals are called *trace elements*.

Minerals have a number of functions in the body. They give strength to soft tissues, bones, and teeth. They aid the growth of body cells, especially the formation of red blood cells. Minerals are also necessary ingredients of body fluids. Without minerals, heartbeat, nervous responses, and blood clotting would all be impossible.

The Importance of Water

The mass of the human body is made up of 60% to 80% of water. All of the biochemical reactions in the body take place in a watery environment. In addition, most substances can be carried throughout the body only if they are dissolved in

At this point, you may want to refer your students to Chapter 24 for comparisons that can be made between the nutritional requirements of plants and people.

Vitamins	Sources	Needed for	Deficiency Symptoms
A (fat soluble)	liver and kidney, fish-liver oils, eggs, butter, green and yellow vegetables, sweet potatoes, yellow fruit, tomatoes	maintenance of skin, eyes, and mucous membranes healthy bones and teeth growth	night blindness changes in skin and membranes retarded growth low resistance
D (fat soluble)	fish-liver oils, liver, fortified milk, eggs, tuna, sunlight	regulation of calcium and phosphorus metabolism healthy bones and teeth growth	rickets: faulty development of teeth soft bones extensive tooth decay
E (fat soluble)	milk, butter, vegetable oils	maintenance of cell membranes	undetermined
K (fat soluble)	tomatoes, soybean oil, leafy vegetables	blood clotting normal liver functioning	hemorrhages
Thiamine (B₁) (water soluble)	meat, yeast, whole-grain, cereals, green vegetables, nuts, peas, soybeans, seafood, milk	carbohydrate metabolism functioning of heart and nerves growth	beriberi: nerve disorders retarded growth loss of weight fatigue easily faulty digestion
Riboflavin (B₂ or G) (water soluble)	milk, cheese, fish, fowl, meat, green vegetables, liver, eggs, yeast	healthy skin growth eye functioning carbohydrate metabolism	premature aging sensitive to light retarded growth dimness of vision
Niacin (water soluble)	yeast, lean meats, liver, fish, whole grain, peanut butter, potatoes, leafy vegetables	growth healthy skin carbohydrate metabolism functioning of stomach, intestines, and nerves	pellagra: digestive disorders mental disorders skin eruptions
B₁₂ (water soluble)	eggs, meats, milk, green vegetables, liver	proper development of red blood cells	low number of red blood cells
C (ascorbic acid) (water soluble)	citrus and other fruits, tomatoes, potatoes, leafy vegetables	healthy bones, teeth, and gums growth maintaining strength of blood vessels	scurvy: bone hemorrhages bruise easily sore gums

Figure 39-3   Important Sources, Functions, and Deficiency Symptoms of Vitamins

water. In the digestive system, enzymes must also be dissolved in water before they can help to break down food.

How much water an individual needs every day depends on the temperature of the environment, the size of the individual, and the amount of physical activity. The average adult loses about 2.5 liters of water every day through respiration, perspiration, and excretion. This water usually is replaced as a person takes in fluids and foods that contain water. Only about 1 liter, however, is replaced by drinking fluids. If however, the body loses water without replacing it, *dehydration* can result. In dehydration, the fluid between cells is lost. Eventually, the cells lose the water in their cytoplasm, and they die.

SECTION REVIEW   Answers on page T–96.

1. What is the importance of carbohydrates, fats, and proteins to good health? List the food sources for each of these groups.
2. List six vitamins and state the function of each.
3. Explain the difference between major minerals and trace elements.

Maintaining Good Health

A person in good health can resist sickness, cope with physical and emotional stresses, and enjoy exercise without tiring easily. To be not only healthy, but also physically fit, a person must have good health habits. These habits include eating properly, getting enough sleep, and exercising regularly.

Exercise

To be physically and mentally healthy, you need a certain amount of **exercise,** or activity that uses the muscles. Such activities as jogging, swimming, bicycling, hiking, calisthenics, or even just walking fast are good ways to exercise. Persons who exercise regularly, have firm muscles and good posture. They also have general body strength, endurance, and a sense of balance.

All the internal systems of the body benefit from exercise. For example, in the circulatory system, the heart, like any other muscle, is strengthened by exercise. The heart can therefore pump more blood with each beat and rest longer between beats. Exercise also reduces the blood pressure and the level of cholesterol in the blood.

LABORATORY INVESTIGATION 38

For additional information, see page T–95.

Measuring Pulse and Respiration Rates

Purpose The pulse is an easily measured indicator of the heart's activity. The respiration rate indicates the lungs' activity in supplying oxygen to the blood and the removal of carbon dioxide from the blood. The purpose of this investigation is to determine the relationship between pulse and respiration rates by measuring the changes in these rates during rest and physical activity.

Materials *(per 2 students)* ● Watch or clock that shows seconds

Procedure **1.** Find your partner's pulse by gently pressing two or three fingertips on the inside of your partner's wrist. Count the number of beats in one minute. **2.** Determine your partner's respiration rate by counting the number of breaths in one minute. **3.** Copy the table on a sheet of paper. **4.** Count the number of your partner's pulse beats in one minute. Repeat the procedure two more times, and average the results. Record the average in the table. **5.** Determine your partner's respiration rate for each of three minutes. Average the results and record the average in the table. **6.** Repeat steps 4 and 5 after your partner has walked normally for one minute. Allow your partner to rest between trials. **7.** Repeat steps 4 and 5 after your partner has run in place for one minute. Allow your partner to rest between trials. **8.** Repeat the entire investigation again with you performing the activities and your partner recording the results.

Observations and Conclusions **1.** What effect does walking have on pulse and respiration rates? **2.** How does running affect pulse and respiration rates? **3.** Are there any differences between the pulse and respiration rates of males and females? Explain.

	Resting	Walking	Running
Pulse Rate			
Respiration Rate			

CHAPTER SUMMARY

Respiratory System The respiratory system brings oxygen to each of the cells during inhaling and removes carbon dioxide from them during exhaling. Oxygen is taken into the body by a process called breathing. Air passes through the nasal cavity, pharynx, larynx. trachea, and bronchi to the lungs, the principal organs of respiration. The bronchioles and alveoli of the lungs help transport oxygen to the blood.

The respiratory center is located in the medulla oblongata of the brain. Breathing is controlled by the nervous system and by the concentration of chemicals in the blood. The amount of carbon dioxide in the blood determines chemical control. The nervous system automatically controls breathing.

Metabolism is the sum of all chemical processes occurring in the body. The building-up phase is called anabolism while the tearing-down phase is known as catabolism. The work the body does in maintaining vital life functions is called basal metabolism.

The environment influences the ability to breathe. A number of environmental factors, such as air pollution, cigarette smoking, and high altitude, are responsible for a variety of respiratory difficulties.

Excretory System Metabolic wastes include carbon dioxide, water, salt, urea, and bile pigments. These wastes are potentially harmful to the body. The excretory system removes metabolic wastes from the body through organs such as the kidneys, skin, lungs, and liver.

The kidneys are the principal organs of the excretory system. They also regulate the salt and fluid balance in the body. The basic structural and functional unit of the kidney is the nephron. The nephron is composed of a glomerulus, Bowman's capsule, and a convoluted tubule. Within the nephron nitrogenous wastes are removed by the process of filtration and reabsorption. In filtration, materials such as water, amino acids, urea, salts, and glucose, pass into the Bowman's capsule from the capillaries. In reabsorption, some of these materials are reabsorbed from the tubules back into the surrounding capillaries by active transport. The materials that remain in the tubules and travel to the collecting tubule are called urine. Urine travels via the ureter to the urinary bladder. Urine is stored in the bladder until it is expelled from the body through the urethra.

CHAPTER VOCABULARY

alveolus	glomerulus	oxygen debt
anaerobic respiration	glottis	pharynx
basal metabolism	kidney	respiration
Bowman's capsule	larynx	trachea
bronchiole	lung	ureter
bronchus	medulla	urethra
cortex	metabolism	urinary bladder
epiglottis	nares	vital capacity
excretion	nephron	

REVIEW of FACTS and CONCEPTS Answers on pages T–95 to T–96.

On a separate sheet of paper, answer each of the following as completely as possible.

1. Explain the difference between external, internal, and cellular respiration.
2. List each respiratory organ and its functions.
3. Describe and give the location of the lungs.
4. What role do the diaphragm and intercostal muscles play in breathing?
5. Explain how oxygen and carbon dioxide are exchanged in the lungs.
6. When is anaerobic respiration used by the human body?
7. How is breathing controlled in human beings?
8. Define the term vital capacity.

Figure 39-4 Exercise contributes to good health.

Sleep

Everyone needs some rest and sleep. Sleep reduces fatigue, relieves tension, and restores energy, especially to the nervous system. During sleep, all activity decreases. The body muscles relax, the heart beats at a lower rate, and breathing slows down. The brain also seems to rest. During certain periods of sleep, however, the brain becomes more active, and the eyes move rapidly. Sleep during these times is called *dreaming sleep*, or *REM* (rapid eye movement) *sleep*. A typical eight-hour sleep period includes three to five intervals of REM sleep. The total amount of REM sleep per night is from one and one-half to two hours. The later dream intervals are usually longer than the earlier ones.

A person who is deprived of sleep suffers physical and mental harm. For example, when people do not sleep for two days, their attention span gets shorter, and they cannot think clearly. After three days without sleep, they have difficulty seeing, hearing, and talking. They may even have *hallucinations*, or see and hear things that are not actually present. REM sleep may help people keep their ability to learn and to solve problems.

Weight Control

The process either of losing excess body fat or of not putting on the weight in the first place is *weight control*. Weight control is based on a simple rule. The rule is that

642

Sidelight

A 68-kilogram person walking about 5.6 kilometers per hour uses up about 396 calories in 76 minutes. This number of calories is about as many as one serving of spaghetti contains. The same person could use up as many calories in 20 minutes of running or in 48 minutes of riding a bicycle.

At this point, you may want to assign to your students the first of the Extensions and Applications at the end of this chapter.

people should not take in more calories, or food, than they use up by their normal exercise every day. If they take in more calories than they burn up with exercise, then they generally add weight to their bodies. If they take in fewer calories than they use, then they usually lose weight. If they take in just as many calories as they need each day, their weight should remain the same.

To lose weight, people should eat a balanced diet, but slowly cut down on how much they eat. At the same time, they should either do as much exercise as they always did or gradually do a little more. For example, suppose a person needs about 4000 calories a day to stay at a certain weight while doing normal daily activities. If that person goes on a diet that contains only 3000 calories a day, he or she should lose about 0.9 kilograms a week. Although doctors warn that losing more than 0.9 kilograms a week is usually unhealthy, some people try to lose weight much faster. Before going on a weight control program, a person should see a doctor, get a

CLOSE-UP: Dr. Jacquelyne Jackson

Are city people as healthy as country people? How does the general health of the various ethnic groups in America compare to one another? How often do most people visit a doctor? These questions have no easy answers.

Information about the answers is beginning to come, however, from scholars like Dr. Jacquelyne Jackson. Jackson is a medical sociologist at Duke University in Durham, North Carolina. A sociologist studies general patterns of behavior in society. As a medical sociologist, Jackson is interested in health patterns.

One of her studies focused on the health of black Americans who live in cities. She wanted many questions answered. Which diseases did this group suffer from? How often did members of the group visit a doctor? How did they view the medical profession generally?

Jackson has also studied aging among black Americans and compared it to aging among whites and other ethnic groups. She wanted to discover whether race has an influence on the mental and physical health of the elderly.

To see general patterns, Jackson must examine information from many sources. For her ur-

ban black health project, she located and read more than 1000 articles on the subject. She also examined medical statistics and interviewed doctors and patients.

Often, Jackson spends months in study before she begins to draw her conclusions. The information that she provides about health patterns in the United States will be used by doctors, health organizations, and government agencies to improve American health standards and health care.

complete checkup, and discuss a weight reduction program with the doctor.

Three Major Health Problems

During the past 25 years, medical scientists have eliminated a number of diseases and health problems. Vaccines are used to prevent some viral diseases. Antibiotics are used to fight bacterial diseases. Some diseases, however, are still major health problems. In the United States, the three major health problems are heart disease, cancer, and mental illness.

Heart disease The two major causes of heart disease are *hypertension*, or high blood pressure, and arteriosclerosis, or hardening of the arteries. If blood pressure remains high for long periods of time, the blood vessels and the heart can be damaged. During arteriosclerosis, the supply of blood is reduced to the heart, causing severe heart pains. Special medication and diet are used to control hypertension and reduce the possibility of developing arteriosclerosis.

Cancer Cancer involves abnormal cell growth. Cancer cells multiply quickly and without control, forming a *tumor*. The tumor, or mass of cancerous cells, replaces the surrounding healthy tissue. Scientists are not sure why cancer develops. One possible factor may be repeated contact with cancer-causing substances called *carcinogens*. Another possible factor is that a person may inherit the tendency to have cancer. Doctors treat cancer with surgery, radiation, and drugs.

At this point, you may want to assign to your students the third of the Extensions and Applications at the end of this chapter.

Mental illness Mental illness includes a wide range of problems from extreme worry to losing contact with reality. Severe and prolonged periods of depression, worry, or anxiety may indicate emotional problems. Symptoms of more serious emotional problems are behaviors such as alcoholism, drug addiction, and criminal activity. Mental illness may be treated with drugs and therapy sessions.

SECTION REVIEW   Answers on page T–96.

1. How do exercise and sleep lead to better health?
2. Define weight control.
3. What are the three major health problems in the United States?

Determining Daily Energy Needs For additional information, see page T–97.

Purpose For a constant body weight, the number of calories taken in as food must balance the number of calories used up by the basal metabolism and physical activity. The purpose of this investigation is to determine how many kilocalories you take in and expend every day.

Materials *(per student)* ● Calorie chart ● Scales

Procedure **1.** Copy Table 1 on a sheet of paper. For 24 hours, keep a record of your food intake and your physical activities. **2.** Figure out the amount of energy that your body uses in a 24-hour period by completing the first line in Table 1. Your body weight should be given in kilograms (1 pound equals 0.45 kg). **3.** Use a calorie chart to list the number of kilocalories in each food item eaten. Determine the total number of kilocalories taken in during the 24-hour period. **4.** Use Table 2 to estimate the number of kilocalories that you used in each physical activity. Also indicate the duration of the activity. **5.** List this information along with your body weight in the appropriate place in Table 1. **6.** Multiply the number of hours times weight times kilocalories per kilogram per hour to obtain the number of kilocalories used in each physical activity. **7.** Enter the total kilocalories used for each activity in the right column. Add up the last column in Table 1 to obtain the total number of kilocalories used in a 24-hour period. **8.** Complete the summary section in Table 1 to determine your net gain or loss of kilocalories.

Table 2

Activity	kcal/kg/hr
Reading, writing, eating	0.9
Driving a car, walking 2 mph, typing, playing the piano	1.5
Horseback riding, bowling, walking 3 mph, cycling 6 mph	2.5
Walking 3.5 mph, cycling 8 mph, table tennis, volleyball	3.6
Walking 5 mph, cycling 11 mph, tennis, water skiing	4.2
Sawing, jogging 5 mph, cycling 12 mph, paddleball, basketball	4.8
Running 5.5 mph, cycling 13 mph	6.0
Playing handball or squash	9.5

Observations and Conclusions **1.** What happens to your weight when you take in more calories than you use? What happens to your weight when you use more calories than you take in? **2.** How can you maintain your weight?

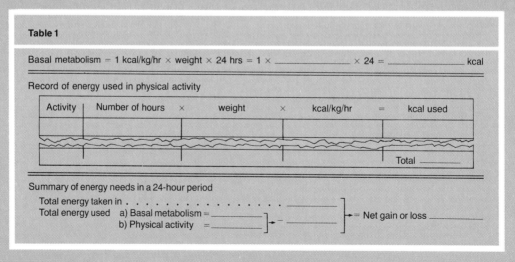

Table 1

Basal metabolism = 1 kcal/kg/hr × weight × 24 hrs = 1 × _____ × 24 = _____ kcal

Record of energy used in physical activity

Activity	Number of hours	×	weight	×	kcal/kg/hr	=	kcal used
						Total	_____

Summary of energy needs in a 24-hour period

Total energy taken in . . . . _____

Total energy used a) Basal metabolism = _____

b) Physical activity = _____] − _____ } = Net gain or loss _____

CHAPTER SUMMARY

Nutritional Substances   Nutrients providè fuel and building blocks for the body. The human body needs nutrients to repair tissues, to supply energy, and to carry out all the life processes. Nutrients are grouped into the six categories of proteins, carbohydrates, fats, vitamins, minerals, and water.

The body uses proteins to build and to repair tissues, as well as to help in manufacturing enzymes, some hormones, and antibodies. Proteins are abundant in such foods as milk, eggs, fish, and lean meats. Carbohydrates are a source of energy for the body. Such foods as fruits, cereals, breads, and vegetables are high in carbohydrates. Fats supply the body with twice as much energy as do equal amounts of carbohydrates or proteins. Fats are found mainly in such foods as nuts, butter, fatty meats, and cheese.

Vitamins are needed in small amounts to help regulate body processes, to promote growth, and generally to aid in maintaining the body. Each of the four basic food groups provides the body with vitamins. Minerals are used in making up body structures. They also make possible vital body processes, such as heart contractions, blood clotting, and the transmission of nerve impulses.

All chemical reactions in the body take place in a watery environment. The amount of water that a person needs varies with such factors as the size of the individual and the temperature of the environment. When water is lost from the body and not replaced, dehydration may result.

Maintaining Good Health   Good health habits make a person generally healthy and physically fit. Healthiness depends on regular exercise, getting the proper rest and sleep, and staying at a normal weight. Weight control is based on the rule that a person should take in as food only enough Calories as needed for normal daily activities.

The major health problems in the United States are heart disease, cancer, and mental illness. The two major causes of heart disease are hypertension and arteriosclerosis. Cancer may be caused by prolonged contact with carcinogens. Some people may also inherit the tendency to develop the disease.

CHAPTER VOCABULARY

calorie	**fat**	**protein**
carbohydrate	**mineral**	**vitamin**
exercise	**nutrient**	

REVIEW of FACTS and CONCEPTS   Answers on page T–97.

On a separate sheet of paper, answer each of the following as completely as possible.

1. What is a nutrient?
2. List the six categories of nutrients that the body needs and their important functions.
3. List the four basic food groups. Give a few examples from each group.
4. Describe a balanced diet.
5. List two examples each of monosaccharides, disaccharides, and polysaccharides.
6. What happens to excess amounts of carbohydrates that are not used by the body?
7. List the fat-soluble and water-soluble vitamins.
8. What is a vitamin-deficiency disease? Give an example.
9. Name some major minerals and trace elements.
10. Explain how exercise affects the circulatory and muscular systems.
11. Why is sleep needed for good health?
12. What should a person do to lose weight? Gain weight?
13. List two causes of heart disease.
14. What is cancer?
15. Define mental illness.

EXTENSIONS and APPLICATIONS For additional information, see page T–97.

1. Using reference materials, write a report about various kinds of weight-loss diets. How is each diet beneficial? What are the arguments against each diet?

2. Keep a daily record for one week of the foods you eat. Be sure to include between-meal snacks on your list. After completing this task, classify the foods according to the four basic food groups. How many of your meals are balanced? How often are you eating nutrition-poor food?

3. The three major health problems in the United States are cancer, heart disease, and mental illness. Go to your local office of the Mental Health Society, American Heart Association, or American Cancer Society. Obtain materials that show the work of these organizations. Put the materials on a bulletin board in your biology classroom so that everyone becomes familiar with the work of these important groups.

SUGGESTED READINGS

Corbin, C., *Nutrition*. New York: Holt, Rinehart and Winston.
 This is an outstanding reference and guide to good health and proper nutrition. It has a fine discussion about vitamins and minerals, their food sources, and their importance to good health.

Ford, B., *Future Food: Alternate Protein for the Year 2000*. New York: Morrow.
 The book discusses an anticipated worldwide protein shortage in the near future and describes research into finding alternative sources of protein.

Lappe, F.M., *Diet for a Small Planet*. New York: Ballantine.
 This book presents a logical argument for vegetarianism, with suggestions for high-protein, meatless meals.

Perl, L., *Junk Food, Fast Food, Health Food: What America Eats and Why*. Boston: Houghton Mifflin.
 The fast food phenomenon is presented. Food additives, various types of diets, and the health food movement are discussed.

Holistic Medical Treatment

With the initial discovery and investigation of microbes, scientists learned that many ailments are caused by the invasion of the body by micro-organisms. This knowledge led to the development of immunization techniques and antibiotics. Many of the most dreaded diseases, such as smallpox and polio, have been either conquered or brought under control by immunization. Medicine today uses a wide variety of drugs, surgical procedures, and nutritional controls to combat diseases ranging from cancer to the common cold.

There are critics, however, who believe that despite recent technological advances, modern medicine is not doing an adequate job in its fight against disease. For example, Americans spend more money per person on health care than do the citizens of any other country. However, Americans rank below the citizens of ten other countries in life span and infant and mother survival during child-birth. The percentage of deaths from cancer and heart disease in the United States is also greater than it is in many other developed countries.

Increasing numbers of critics, many of them physicians and patients, suggest that many diseases may involve the mind as well as the body. Some of these critics base their argument in part on the well-known "placebo effect." A placebo is a medically neutral substance, such as a sugar pill. Placebos are given to people who are led to believe the placebos are medicine. Evidence has shown that this kind of treatment has cured certain illnesses. Although the exact workings of this method remain unknown, the phenomenon suggests that the mind exercises a powerful influence over the body. This phenomenon supports the idea that a patient must be treated as a whole being rather than just a physical being.

Practitioners of holistic medicine stress the concept of wholeness. They argue that drugs and surgery alone cannot fight illness, and that acupuncture, chiropractic, and other approaches are worthwhile alternatives to more traditional medical procedures.

Preventive medicine is a large part of the holistic approach to illness. Accumulation of excess body weight, smoking, and drug and alcohol use are discouraged. A balanced, controlled diet and regular exercise are considered to be essential to good health.

Most medical professionals agree that preventive medical practices are important in maintaining good health. However, some argue that the use of techniques based upon unproven theories of health may do more harm than good.

Viewpoints

1. There are many alternative healing practices available to people. Some of these emerged from extensive cultural and historical traditions, whereas others are relatively new. Research several of the following medical practices: fasting, herbalism, osteopathy, yoga, chiropractic, acupuncture, and behavior modification. Set up a panel discussion in your class to discuss these practices.

2. The mind can strongly influence bodily functions. You can test this mind-over-body influence by performing the following demonstration. Sit down in a comfortable chair near a phonograph or radio and relax. Monitor your own pulse by pressing your first two fingers against your neck just below your jaw. A regular pulse can be detected as blood is pumped through arteries of the neck. Count these "beats" for several one-minute periods to obtain an average relaxation pulse. Now place a record of your choice, preferably loud and fast, on the phonograph, or tune in a similar piece on the radio. Settle back in the chair and repeat your pulse-taking. Does the mood of the music affect the rate of your heartbeat? Experiment with various styles of music. Explain how the results of your experiment relate to holistic medical concepts.

Human Response and Development

For an overview of this unit, including field trip suggestions, a bibliography, and a list of audio-visual materials, see pages T–98 to T–106. You may want to check the Laboratory Investigations in this unit so that materials may be ordered, gathered, or prepared in advance.

In order to survive, human beings must be able to respond to their environment. They must also develop and refine a set of behavior patterns to deal with all sorts of situations and problems. The ability of the body to respond to various stimuli depends largely on the functioning of two systems, the endocrine system and the nervous system. Certain chemical substances, such as those found in tobacco and in some drugs, can affect the operation of these systems.

The success of a species does not depend only upon the development of responses to stimuli. The members of the species must also be able to produce offspring of their own kind. The members of the human species must reproduce and must care for their young over a long period of time.

Human beings receive, interpret, and respond to changes in their environment.

40 The Endocrine System

The endocrine system regulates many body functions.

For teaching aids for this chapter, including a chapter overview and teaching strategies, see pages T–98 to T–99. The page number next to each chapter objective refers to the text page where the information needed to fulfill the objective begins.

The human **endocrine** (EN-də-krin) **system** is a chemical control system that regulates many body functions. The endocrine system consists of a number of glands located at various sites throughout the body. These glands secrete **hormones.** Hormones are chemical substances that regulate the activities of various organs. In this way, the endocrine system helps to maintain the stability of the body's internal environment. The maintenance of this steady state within the body is extremely important. The endocrine system also plays an important role in growth and development. Furthermore, hormones cause many changes in the human body.

Endocrine Structure

The endocrine system is composed of *ductless glands.* Ductless glands secrete hormones directly into the bloodstream. The hormones are carried by the blood or other body fluids throughout the body. The hormones carry a chemical message to stimulate or inhibit a particular organ. In contrast, the other glands in the human body are **exocrine** (EKS-ə-krin) **glands.** Exocrine glands release their secretions to specific areas of the body through ducts, or tubelike structures. Examples of exocrine glands are the salivary glands, the sweat glands, and the mammary glands.

The Thyroid

The **thyroid** (THĪ-roid) **gland** is shaped like a shield and located in the neck below the larynx, or voice box. The thyroid secretes the hormone *thyroxine* (thī-RAHKS-in). Molecules of thyroxine contain the element iodine. Thyroxine helps the body maintain and use energy from digested food. The thyroid also secretes the hormone *calcitonin.* Calcitonin affects the level of calcium found in the blood and the level of phosphate in bones.

Malfunctions of the thyroid gland can cause a number of disorders. **Hypothyroidism** (hī-pō-THĪ-roid-iz'm) is underactivity of the thyroid. A person suffering from hypothyroidism gains weight and becomes sluggish.

A condition called *cretinism* (KRĒ-tin-iz'm) is the result of a lack of thyroxine since birth. The face of an infant suffering from cretinism swells, the lips enlarge, and the tongue thickens. Physical and mental growth is stunted, and the limbs become short and thick, resulting in thyroid *dwarfism.* The same type of deficiency occurring in an adult is called *myxedema* (mik-sə-DĒ-mə). This condition results in changes in skin texture, puffiness of the face, and a decrease in mental processes. Cretinism and myxedema may be treated and corrected with the use of thyroid extract, if the treatment is begun early enough.

Overactivity of the thyroid is called **hyperthyroidism** (hī-pər-THĪ-roid-iz'm) A person suffering from hyperthyroidism loses weight and is nervous and restless. A *goiter* may result from hyperthyroidism or a lack of iodine in the diet. A goiter is an enlargement of the thyroid gland. The development of a goiter can be prevented if a person eats *iodized salt.* Iodized salt is table salt to which has been added an iodine compound. Drugs that slow down the production of thyroxine are often given to a patient to treat a goiter caused by

Sidelight

The cells of the body are very sensitive to hormones. As little as one-millionth of a milligram of a hormone per milliliter of blood can cause body cells to respond.

Figure 40-1   Endocrine Glands

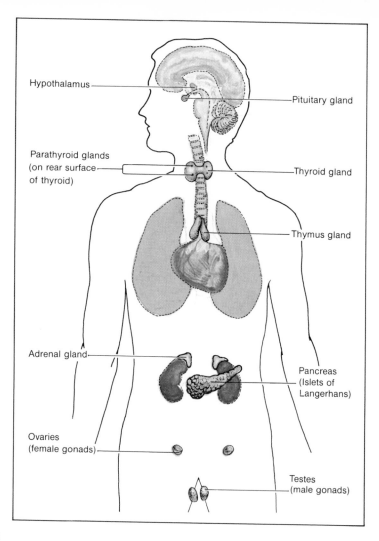

Hypothalamus

Pituitary gland

Parathyroid glands (on rear surface of thyroid)

Thyroid gland

Thymus gland

Adrenal gland

Pancreas (Islets of Langerhans)

Ovaries (female gonads)

Testes (male gonads)

Figure 40-2   A gamma ray detector permits physicians to monitor thyroid disorders in patients. The gamma rays given off by a patient who previously received radioactive iodine produce an image of the thyroid.

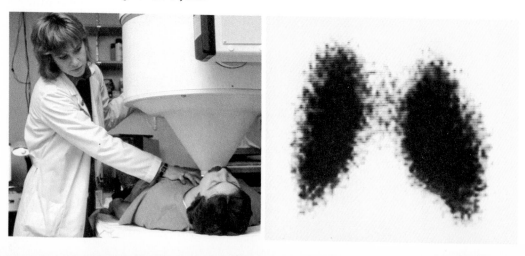

hyperthyroidism. Radioactive iodine is sometimes used to destroy some of the tissue of the thyroid gland and thus reduce the production of thyroxine.

The Parathyroids

There are four **parathyroid glands,** each about the size of a pea, located on the back of the thyroid gland. These glands secrete a hormone called *parathyroid hormone,* or PTH. Parathyroid hormone balances the calcium and phosphorus levels in the blood. If the parathyroids are injured or underactive, these levels drop and the muscles undergo *tetany,* or involuntary contractions or spasms. In a condition called *hyperparathyroidism,* the parathyroid glands become overactive, drawing calcium from the bones. This causes the bones to become soft and deformed. The muscles in the body are also weakened.

The Pituitary

Another term for pituitary is ''hypophysis.'' The anterior lobe is also known as the adenohypophysis and the posterior lobe as the neurohypophysis.

The **pituitary** (pi TOO-ə-ter-ē) **gland** is about 1 centimeter in diameter and is attached to the base of the brain by a stalk. This gland often is referred to as the "master gland" because the hormones that it secretes control all other endocrine glands and a variety of bodily processes.

The pituitary gland consists of an anterior, or front, lobe and a posterior, or back, lobe. The anterior lobe of the pituitary gland secretes several different hormones. Some of the hormones stimulate the secretion of hormones from other glands, such as thyroxine from the thyroid. A hormone called *human growth hormone,* or HGH, stimulates body growth and helps control metabolism.

An undersecretion of human growth hormone during childhood causes *pituitary dwarfism.* Body growth is stunted. However, the body parts are in the proper proportion to one another, and mental development is normal. The condition can be corrected by giving a person growth hormone before skeletal growth is completed.

An oversecretion of the growth hormone during the growth years causes *giantism.* The bones and tissues grow too fast. People affected by giantism grow very tall, but their body parts are in the proper proportion to one another. This condition may be caused by a *tumor,* or abnormal growth, in the pituitary gland. If the oversecretion of the growth hormone occurs in adulthood, the bones thicken, especially in the hands, feet, and face. The resulting condition is called *acromegaly* (ak-rō-MEG-ə-lē).

Highlight

Underactivity of the thyroid gland is hypothyroidism. Overactivity of the thyroid is hyperthyroidism. Overactivity of the parathyroid gland is hyperparathyroidism.

Highlight

The pituitary gland controls the functions of many other glands in the body. It is often called the "master gland." One of the main functions of the pituitary is the control of body growth.

Sidelight

One medical report of giantism described a person 3 meters tall.

654

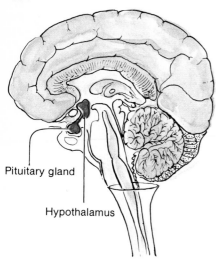

Pituitary gland

Hypothalamus

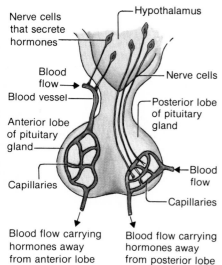

Nerve cells that secrete hormones

Hypothalamus

Blood flow

Blood vessel

Anterior lobe of pituitary gland

Capillaries

Nerve cells

Posterior lobe of pituitary gland

Blood flow

Capillaries

Blood flow carrying hormones away from anterior lobe

Blood flow carrying hormones away from posterior lobe

Figure 40-3 The pituitary gland and hypothalamus are located in the skull, just below the brain. The pituitary gland is attached to the hypothalamus by a stalk. The hypothalamus plays an important role in regulating pituitary function.

At this point, you may want to have your students do the Laboratory Investigation at the end of this chapter.

The posterior lobe of the pituitary secretes two important hormones. The hormone *oxytocin* (ok-sē-TŌ-sin) helps regulate blood pressure and stimulates the uterus to contract during childbirth. The hormone *vasopressin* controls reabsorption of water in the kidneys.

The Hypothalamus

The **hypothalamus** (hī-pə-THAL-ə-məs) **gland** is located under the cerebral hemisphere, below the thalamus. The thalamus is part of the brain. The hypothalamus serves as a sort of relay station, carrying impulses and information between various parts of the brain. It also controls body temperature, water balance, appetite, sleep, and certain aspects of digestion.

The hypothalamus is attached to the pituitary gland. Specialized nerve cells of the hypothalamus produce hormones that stimulate the posterior of the pituitary to produce its hormones. The hormones secreted by the hypothalamus are called *tropic hormones*. Tropic hormones act mainly on other endocrine glands.

The Adrenals

At this point, you may want to assign to several students the third of the Extensions and Applications at the end of this chapter.

There are two **adrenal glands.** An adrenal gland is located on top of each kidney. Each gland is divided into an outer portion, called the *cortex*, and an inner portion called the *medulla*.

The adrenal medulla secretes a hormone called *adrenaline* (ə-DREN-ə-lin), or *epinephrine* (ep-ə-NEF-rin). When released, adrenaline triggers various physiological changes in the body, such as an increased heart rate. These changes make the body better able to meet the challenge of sudden stress or danger.

The adrenal cortex secretes several hormones classified as *corticoids* (KOR-ti-koidz). The corticoids help synthesize glycogen in the liver. They also maintain a balance of salt and water in the body. These hormones also help prevent inflammation of body parts after an injury. The *glucocorticoids*, including *cortisone*, are among the most important corticoids. Cortisone is used to reduce muscle inflammation, and has been found helpful in treating allergies and rheumatoid arthritis.

An ailment called *Addison's disease* results from the hypofunctioning, or underfunctioning, of the adrenal cortex. The symptoms include low blood sugar and low blood sodium levels, increased blood potassium, low blood pressure, dehydration, fatigue, and yellowing of the skin. Corticoid hormones, including coritsone, are used to treat Addison's disease.

The Pancreas

You might want to use the term ''heterocrine gland'' when you refer to the pancreas. A heterocrine gland functions as both an endocrine and an exocrine gland.

The **pancreas** (PAN-krē-əs) is a gland located in the abdominal cavity below the stomach. The exocrine function of the pancreas is to secrete digestive enzymes. The pancreas also contains cells that have an endocrine function. These cells are organized into groups called *islets of Langerhans.* These cells are named after the German scientist, Paul Langerhans, who discovered them. The *alpha cells* in these

Highlight

The adrenal gland is divided into the outer cortex and the medulla. The adrenal gland secretes the hormones adrenaline and cortisone. The pancreas is both an exocrine gland and an endocrine gland. The islets of Langerhans secrete the hormones glucagon and insulin.

CLOSE-UP: *Dr. Donald Steiner*

At the University of Chicago, Dr. Donald Steiner, a biochemist, is a leader in insulin research. He is especially noted for his work that established how insulin is formed in the human body's islets of Langerhans.

In 1966, Dr. Steiner discovered that insulin is produced from a single chain of amino acids called proinsulin. The proinsulin chain folds and forms disulfide bridges. Then the chain splits, releasing the complex insulin molecule and a small peptide. This discovery was important to the study of diabetes, the condition that arises when the islets of Langerhans do not produce enough insulin.

"By learning how insulin is made, we begin to learn more about why it isn't being made normally in diabetics," Steiner explains.

Dr. Steiner's research has led the way for other discoveries. Building on his work, other scientists have shown that the many hormones and peptides that regulate nerve activities in the body are made from larger chains of amino acids. These large chains are processed in a manner similar to that for proinsulin.

Dr. Steiner was trained as a medical doctor at the University of Chicago and the University of Washington. Returning to the University of Chicago, he organized the insulin research project. He served as the chairman of the biochemistry

department between 1973 and 1979. Today he holds a special position in the department. He works mostly in the university laboratory, overseeing student research in the insulin program and furthering his own research on insulin-related problems.

Dr. Steiner's discovery has been put to use in the diagnoses, study, and treatment of diabetes by Dr. Arthur Rubenstein, chairman of the Department of Medicine at the University of Chicago.

"Taken together," Steiner says, "our work led to further basic discoveries and important clinical applications. Our work is a good example of the value of close interactions between basic scientists and clinical experts."

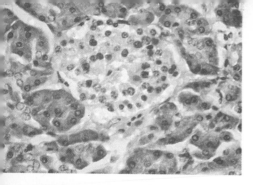

Figure 40-4 The islets of Langerhans contain two kinds of cells that secrete hormones. What are the major hormones secreted by these cells?

Alpha cells secrete glucagon. Beta cells secrete insulin.

You may want to explain to your students that there are two forms of diabetes. Diabetes mellitus is more common and is caused by insufficient insulin. Diabetes insipidus results when the posterior lobe of the pituitary secretes insufficient vasopressin.

At this point, you may want to assign to several students the first of the Extensions and Applications at the end of this chapter.

groups secrete a hormone called *glucagon* (GLOO-kə-gahn). This hormone allows the liver to convert the substance *glycogen*, an animal starch, to glucose, a sugar. The *beta cells* secrete the hormone *insulin*. Insulin is a substance that helps cells use glucose and helps to maintain normal levels of glucose in the blood.

Two disorders that result from improper amounts of insulin are *diabetes mellitus* and *hypoglycemia*. In diabetes mellitus, the beta cells fail to produce sufficient insulin. This causes abnormally high glucose, or blood sugar, levels. Symptoms include excessive thirst, hunger, and loss of weight. Treatment for this condition includes careful diet planning and monitoring of blood glucose levels. In many cases, people with diabetes must give themselves regular injections of insulin.

In hypoglycemia, abnormally low concentrations of glucose exist in the blood. This condition is usually the result of insulin overproduction. Treatment of hypoglycemia may involve a diet high in protein and low in carbohydrates.

The Gonads

The male **gonads**, or sex glands, are called *testes*. The female gonads are called *ovaries*. The testes and ovaries secrete sex hormones and produce the sex cells. During **puberty** (PYOO-bər-tē), usually occurring between the ages of 12 and 15 years, a number of changes caused by the production of certain hormones take place in males and females. The testes secrete a male sex hormone called **testosterone** (tes-TAHS-tə-rōn). Testosterone is responsible for the development of secondary sex characteristics, such as facial and body hair, broadening of the shoulders, and deepening of the voice. In the female, the ovaries secrete two kinds of hormones, **estrogen** (ES-trō-jən) and **progesterone** (prō-JES-tə-rōn). These hormones are responsible for the development of breasts and body hair, broadening of the hips, and the beginning of egg cell production and menstruation.

The Thymus

The **thymus** (THĪ-məs) **gland** is located in the chest cavity between the lungs. This gland slowly increases in size during childhood. Then, after puberty, the thymus decreases in size. The function of the thymus is not well understood. However, some scientists have found evidence that it is involved in immunological, or disease-preventing, activities.

Highlight

The testes and the ovaries produce sex cells and secrete hormones. The sex hormones affect the development of secondary sexual characteristics during puberty.

Figure 40-5 Endocrine Glands—Hormones and Functions

Gland	Location	Hormone Produced	Functions
Thyroid	Neck	Thyroxine	Increases rate of metabolism.
Parathyroids	Behind thyroid lobes	Parathyroid hormone	Regulates calcium and phosphate levels.
Pituitary gland Anterior lobe	Base of brain	Human Growth Hormone (HGH)	Stimulates body skeletal growth.
		Gonadotropic Hormone	Stimulates the development of male and female sex organs.
		Lactogenic Hormone	Stimulates the secretion of milk after childbirth.
		Thyrotropic Hormone	Proper functioning of the thyroid gland.
		Adrenocorticotropic Hormone (ACTH)	Proper functioning of the adrenal glands.
Posterior lobe		Oxytocin	Regulates blood pressure and stimulates smooth muscles; stimulates contractions of the uterus during childbirth; aids in flow of milk from mammary glands.
		Vasopressin	Increases the rate of reabsorption of water in the kidneys.
Adrenal gland Medulla	Above kidneys	Epinephrine (adrenaline)	Increased heart rate. Elevated blood pressure. Rise in blood sugar. Increased breathing rate. Decreased digestive activity.
Cortex		Mineralocorticoids	Maintains the balance of salt and water in the kidneys.
		Glucocorticoids — Cortisone	Breaks down stored proteins to amino acids. Aids in breakdown of adipose tissue. Promotes increase in blood glucose.
		Sex Hormones	Supplements the sex hormones produced by the gonads. Promotes development of sexual characteristics.
Pancreas Islets of Langerhans	Abdomen, near stomach	Insulin	Enables liver to store sugar. Regulates sugar oxidation in tissues.
Ovaries	Pelvis	Estrogen	Produces female secondary sex characteristics. Regulates female sexual functions.
		Progesterone	Growth of mucous lining of uterus.
Testes	Scrotal sac	Testosterone	Produces male secondary sex characteristics.

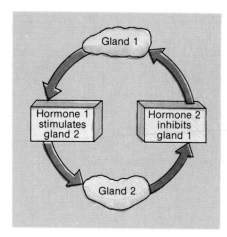

Figure 40-6 A Feedback Mechanism

At this point, you may want to assign to a group of students the second of the Extensions and Applications at the end of this chapter.

Highlight

The regulation of hormone secretion in the body is controlled by feedback mechanisms.

SECTION REVIEW Answers on page T-98.

1. What is a hormone?
2. What gland is called the master gland?
3. What is acromegaly?
4. What hormones are secreted by the ovaries?

Feedback Process

The glands of the endocrine system help maintain **homeostasis** (hō-mē-ō-STĀ-sis), or the internal stability of the body. They do so by keeping the hormones in the body in balance through a feedback process. In this process, one gland may secrete a hormone that stimulates another gland. This second gland in turn secretes a hormone that inhibits the production of a hormone from the first gland.

The operation of the feedback processes is somewhat analogous to the working of a home thermostat. A thermostat is set for a specific temperature. When the room temperature falls below this setting, the thermostat activates the furnace to operate until the temperature setting on the thermostat has been reached. The thermostat then turns the furnace off until the room temperature again falls below the thermostatic setting.

Endocrine feedback is illustrated by the relationship between the anterior lobe of the pituitary and the thyroid gland. The pituitary secretes a thyroid-stimulating hormone, or TSH, that stimulates the thyroid to secrete thyroxine. When the concentration of thyroxine reaches a certain level in the bloodstream, the anterior lobe of the pituitary slows down its production of TSH. In this way, a constant level of thyroxine is maintained in the body.

Another kind of feedback process exists between the endocrine system and the nervous system. In this case, tropic hormones produced by nerve cells of the hypothalamus cause the endocrine glands to secrete their own hormones. Once the proper level of these latter hormones is reached in the bloodstream, the hypothalamus stops producing the tropic hormones.

SECTION REVIEW Answers on pages T-98 to T-99.

1. What is meant by a feedback process?
2. Describe the feedback process between the thyroid and the anterior lobe of the pituitary.

Measuring the Effects of Adrenaline

Purpose   Adrenaline, or epinephrine, is a hormone produced by the medulla of the adrenal gland. In times of stress, this hormone is released rapidly into the bloodstream. The pulse rate, blood pressure, and blood sugar levels increase temporarily, enabling persons to perform "superhuman" feats, such as lifting heavy weights that they could not otherwise lift. The purpose of this investigation is to measure changes in blood pressure and pulse rate induced by physical exercise. The increase is analogous in certain respects to the increase caused by adrenaline release.

Materials (*per group*)   ● Stethoscope
● Sphygmomanometer   ● Clock or watch with second hand

Procedure   **1.** Work in groups of four. Two people in each group will serve as experimental subjects, one person as the observer, and one as the recorder. **2.** The observer should take the blood pressure and pulse rate of the first subject at rest. The recorder should copy the results in a data table, as shown in the table.   **3.** The first subject is to run in place for two minutes.   **4.** The observer should again take the subject's blood pressure and pulse rate. The recorder should add these results to the data table.   **5.** Have the second subject repeat procedures 2, 3, and 4. Record the data in the table for comparison.

Observation and Conclusions   **1.** How do the results of this investigation simulate an increase of adrenaline in the bloodstream?   **2.** Compare your data with those of other groups. Are there any significant differences between the blood pressure and pulse rate of different subjects performing this investigation? What would you expect the pulse and blood pressure readings to be five minutes after the test? Ten minutes?

Subject	Trial	Blood Pressure Reading	Pulse Rate (beats/minute)
1	Resting		
	Running		
2	Resting		
	Running		

CHAPTER SUMMARY

Endocrine Structures The endocrine system is made up of ductless glands that secrete chemical substances called hormones directly into the bloodstream. These hormones cause changes to occur in a specific organ somewhat distant from the site of the secreting gland.

The endocrine system includes a number of glands located in different parts of the body. The thyroid gland determines the amount of energy the body can obtain from the food ingested. The parathyroid controls the level of calcium and phosphorus in the blood. The anterior lobe of the pituitary gland controls skeletal growth, stimulates the development of sex organs in males and females, and controls the functioning of the thyroid and adrenal glands. The posterior lobe of the pituitary gland plays a role in childbirth and helps the body to retain water.

The inner cells of the adrenal medulla secrete adrenaline. This hormone increases heart and breathing rate and elevates blood pressure. The outer cells of the adrenal gland, called the cortex, secrete a variety of hormones that help the body to conserve water, and that increase blood glucose. The pancreas secretes insulin and glucagon, used to convert glucogen to glucose. The pancreas also secretes insulin used to promote the proper level and usage of the glucose. The gonad glands secrete hormones that stimulate the development of secondary sex characteristics in both males and females. The thymus gland is thought to aid in preventing disease in human beings.

Feedback Process The endocrine glands operate in cooperation with one another to maintain the internal stability of the body. This feedback process is most easily recognized in the relationship between the pituitary and thyroid glands. The endocrine system works with the nervous system in a similar feedback process.

CHAPTER VOCABULARY

adrenal gland	**hormone**	**pituitary gland**
endocrine system	**hyperthyroidism**	**progesterone**
estrogen	**hypothalamus gland**	**puberty**
exocrine gland	**hypothyroidism**	**testosterone**
gonad	**pancreas**	**thymus gland**
homeostasis	**parathyroid gland**	**thyroid gland**

REVIEW of FACTS and CONCEPTS Answers on page T–99.

On a separate sheet of paper, answer each of the following as completely as possible.

1. What is the endocrine system?
2. What is the difference between an endocrine gland and an exocrine gland?
3. Give the location and function of the thyroid gland.
4. Distinguish between the conditions of hypothyroidism and hyperthyroidism.
5. Differentiate between cretinism and myxedema.
6. How may injury to the parathyroid gland affect the muscles?
7. Why has the pituitary gland often been called the ''master gland'' of the body?
8. List the hormones secreted by the anterior and posterior lobes of the pituitary gland.
9. Contrast pituitary dwarfism and thyroid induced dwarfism.
10. How is the functioning of the hypothalamus related to the functioning of the pituitary gland?
11. List the secretions and functions of the adrenal cortex.
12. What is Addison's disease?
13. Why is the pancreas considered to be both an endocrine gland and an exocrine gland?
14. Define hypoglycemia.
15. What are the two functions of the gonads?
16. How does the secretion of adrenaline prepare the body for emergencies?
17. Illustrate feedback in the endocrine system.

EXTENSIONS and APPLICATIONS   For additional information, see page T-99.

1. Research the pioneer work of physiologists F.G. Banting and C.H. Best in the field of insulin research. Share your findings with the class by giving an oral report.

2. Prepare a report on the making of artificial hormones. Describe their uses.

3. Prepare a report on the work of Dr. Hans Selye on stress.

SUGGESTED READINGS

Hamburger, J.I., *Your Thyroid Gland—Fact and Fiction.* Springfield, Ill.: Charles C Thomas.
   In this book, a physician clearly explains the anatomy, normal functions, and disorders of the thyroid gland.

Nourse, A.E., and the Editors of Time-Life Books, *The Body.* New York: Time-Life Books.
   A chapter in this book concentrates on the endocrine glands, the great regulators of bodily function.

Wilson R., *How the Body Works.* New York: Larousse.
   This book contains an excellent explanation of the endocrine glands and how they function in response to everyday problems and experiences.

41 The Nervous System

For teaching aids for this chapter, including a chapter overview and teaching strategies, see pages T–99 to T–101. The page number next to each chapter objective refers to the text page where the information needed to fulfill the objective begins.

The nervous system works like an electronic switchboard.

Every living thing, no matter how large or small, how simple or complex, must be able to respond to conditions in the world around it. Thus, living things need a central process to inform them about their environment and allow them to respond. Nowhere is this more obvious than in human beings, who respond to and control their environment in many important ways. Maintaining this control process in human beings is the job of the **nervous system.** The nervous system is like a vast switchboard or computer system, relaying and receiving messages about the body's activities. The nervous system monitors and responds to internal changes, as well as external changes, in order to maintain homeostasis.

Structure and Functions of the Nervous System

The human nervous system is divided into two basic parts. The first part of the nervous system is the **central nervous system.** This system reacts to internal and external stimuli. It coordinates the activities of the body. The second part of the nervous system, the **peripheral** (per-IF-ə-r'l) **nervous system,** carries messages to and from the central nervous system. A part of the peripheral nervous system is the **autonomic** (aw-tə-NAHM-ik) **nervous system.** The autonomic nervous system carries impulses that regulate *involuntary activities.* Involuntary activities are those that do not require conscious control.

The Neuron

The basic unit of structure and function in the nervous system is the **neuron** (NOOR-ahn), or nerve cell. Neurons have three principal parts. The **cell body** contains the nucleus, or control center of the cell. The cell body is the base for receiving and sending impulses. The **dendrites** (DEN-drītz) are branching fibers that carry impulses toward the cell body. **Axons** are long fibers that branch at their ends. Axons carry impulses away from the cell body. In some neurons, the conducting core of the axon is covered by a *fatty myelin sheath* that serves as insulation.

Nerves are bundles of neuron fibers. The nervous system is composed of three types of nerves. **Sensory nerves** carry impulses to the brain and spinal cord. **Motor nerves** carry impulses from the central nervous system to the muscles and

Figure 41-1 A neuron's three principle parts are the cell body, the axon, and the dendrites. An axon of one neuron is separated from the dendrite of another neuron at the motor end plate. The space between the two neurons is called the synapse.

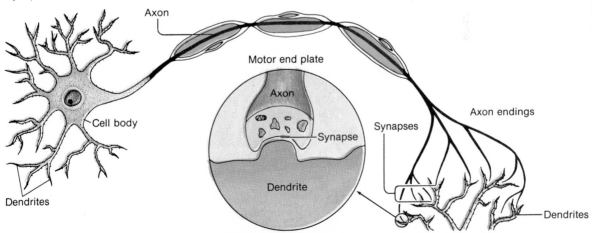

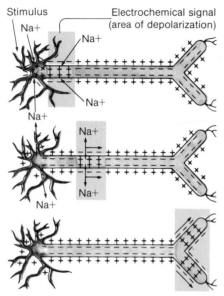

Stimulus

Electrochemical signal
(area of depolarization)

Figure 41-2 A nerve impulse moves along a neuron when positively charged sodium ions enter the axon and cause it to be depolarized.

At this point, you may want your students to do the Laboratory Investigation at the end of this chapter.

Figure 41-3 Acetylcholine is released from the motor end plate, causing the muscle to contract.

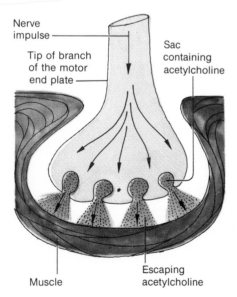

Nerve impulse

Tip of branch of the motor end plate

Sac containing acetylcholine

Muscle

Escaping acetylcholine

glands. **Mixed nerves** contain both sensory and motor nerve fibers.

Each neuron is a separate and distinct unit. The axon of one neuron does not make physical contact with the dendrite of another neuron. They are separated by a gap called a **synapse** (SIN-aps).

The Nerve Impulse

A **nerve impulse** is an electrochemical signal that moves along a neuron. The nerve impulse can be compared to an electric current. However, nerve impulses move much more slowly than does electricity in a wire. A nerve impulse travels at less than 100 meters per second. Electricity travels at nearly 300,000 kilometers per second.

A resting, or unstimulated, neuron has a positive electric charge on the outside of the cell membrane and a negative electric charge on the inside. The cell membrane in this state is *polarized*. When the neuron is stimulated, a section of the neuron is *depolarized*. The outside of the cell membrane becomes negatively charged and the inside becomes positively charged. This change in polarity moves down the axon in a wave. When this change occurs, positively charged sodium ions enter the neuron. The original polarity of the section returns after the impulse has passed.

In order for the nerve impulse from one neuron to reach the dendrites of the next neuron, the impulse must cross the synapse. Neurons release a number of **neurotransmitters,** or substances that bridge the synapse. These neurotransmitters include a chemical called *acetylcholine* (ə-sē-t'l-KŌ-lēn).

Acetylcholine plays a role in the transmission of nerve impulses to muscles. A muscle will not contract until it receives a stimulus from a motor neuron. The end of a motor neuron has many *motor end plates*. These end plates are close to the muscle fiber. As the nerve impulse travels down the axon, acetylcholine is released into the gap between the motor end plate and muscle fiber. The impulse is carried by the acetylcholine to the muscle fiber, causing the muscle to contract. An enzyme called *cholinesterase* (kō-lēn-ES-tər-ās) is then released, and breaks down the acetylcholine. This allows the muscle fiber to relax.

SECTION REVIEW   Answers on page T-100.

1. Name the three parts of a neuron.
2. Describe the roles of axons and dendrites.
3. When is a neuron polarized?

At this point, you may want to assign to your students the third of the Extensions and Applications at the end of this chapter.

Central Nervous System

The central nervous system consists of the *brain* and the *spinal cord*. Both of these structures are composed of nerve tissue. The brain is divided into sections, each of which controls particular functions of the body. Although the brain is the principal control center, the spinal cord also plays a major role in the transmission of motor and sensory impulses.

The Brain

The brain weighs about 1.4 kilograms. It is located in the cranial cavity of the skull. The brain is surrounded and protected by a series of three membranes called **meninges** (mə-NIN-jēz). The innermost membrane is the *pia mater*. It is a thin delicate membrane that closely adheres to the surface of the brain. The pia mater follows the *convolutions*, or folds, of the brain. The pia mater contains many small blood vessels that supply the brain with nutrients and oxygen. The middle membrane is the *arachnoid* (uh-RACK-noid) *mater*. It is a weblike, elastic membrane. A clear, watery substance called *cerebrospinal fluid* fills the space between the arachnoid mater and the pia mater. The cerebrospinal fluid serves as a pathway for the exchange of nutrients and wastes between the blood and brain cells. The outermost membrane is the *dura mater*. It is a thick, tough, and fibrous membrane that lines the inside of the cranial cavity.

The three meninges and the cerebrospinal fluid also act as a shock absorber for the brain. A severe blow to the head, however, can cause a brain bruise called a *concussion*. Individuals who have suffered concussions should be kept quiet and under observation until the bruise heals.

CEREBRUM The **cerebrum** is the largest part of the brain, and occupies most of the cranial cavity. It is divided into two *hemispheres*, or halves, by a deep groove. The left hemisphere controls the right side of the body. It is thought to affect the use of language, mathematics, and logical thinking. The right hemisphere controls the left side of the body. Scientists think it affects musical and artistic ability, and emotions.

The *cortex*, or outer surface, of the cerebrum consists of *gray matter*. Gray matter contains nerve cell bodies. There are many deep convolutions on the gray matter for increased surface area. The inner surface of the cerebrum contains *white matter*. The white matter is made up mostly of axons.

Highlight

The central nervous system reacts to stimuli and coordinates the body's activities. It consists of the brain and the spinal cord.

It is not possible to examine a human brain. Many companies, however, manufacture models of the brain for study. Also, butcher shops often have brains from cattle or sheep that can be dissected and examined in class.

Sidelight

The human brain contains more than 10 billion neurons.

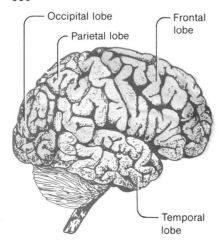

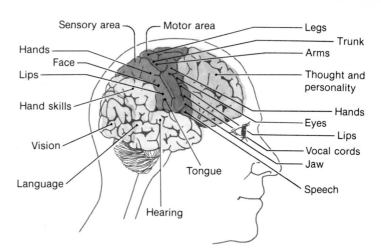

Figure 41-4 Specialized functions are controlled at specific sites in the lobes of the cerebrum.

The different regions of the cerebrum in each hemisphere are called *lobes*. The front region of the cerebrum is known as the *frontal lobe*. The region that lies behind this lobe that covers the top of the cerebrum is called the *parietal* (pə-RĪ-ə-t'l) *lobe*. The region in the back of the cerebrum is called the *occipital* (AHK-sip-ə-t'l) *lobe*. The region above the ears is called the *temporal lobe*. Each lobe contains specific sites that control specialized tasks.

CEREBELLUM The **cerebellum** is located below the occipital lobe of the cerebrum. It has two hemispheres com-

Figure 41-5 Structure of the Human Brain

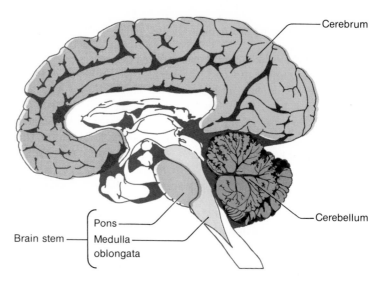

posed primarily of white matter, with a thin layer of gray matter on the outside. The cerebellum controls several important functions, including balance and coordination, and aids in posture by providing muscle tone. Whereas the cerebrum affects conscious activity, the cerebellum affects involuntary activities.

BRAIN STEM   The **brain stem** is composed of the **pons** and the **medulla oblongata.** These structures are bundles of nerve fibers located below the cerebrum. The pons, the more prominent swelling of the brain stem, serves as a bridge between the *cranial nerves.* An example of a cranial nerve is the olfactory nerve. The olfactory nerve conducts nerve impulses from the nose to the brain and is responsible for conveying information on odors.

The medulla oblongata is located between the pons and the spinal cord. The medulla oblongata serves as a conducting pathway between other parts of the brain. In addition, it maintains such vital activities as respiration, blood pressure, and heartbeat. It also controls sneezing, coughing, hiccoughing, vomiting, and swallowing.

The Spinal Cord

The *spinal cord* is a whitish, oval-shaped nerve cord that connects the brain and the rest of the nervous system. Its pathways carry messages to and from the brain. The spinal cord also regulates *reflexes,* such as blinking and sneezing. Reflexes are predictable, involuntary responses.

The spinal cord is protected by *vertebrae,* or small bones that make up the backbone. Near the middle of the cord is a

Sidelight

The human brain is often compared to a computer. However, the brain is more complex. In a single second, a computer can perform more than 4 million additions of 36 figures. In a single second of sleep, the brain sends out and receives more than 50 million messages.

Figure 41-6   Cross Section of the Spinal Cord

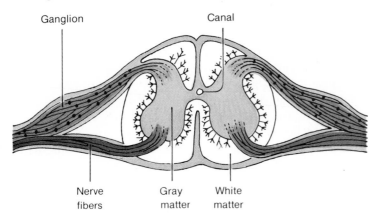

Ganglion   Canal

Nerve   Gray   White
fibers   matter   matter

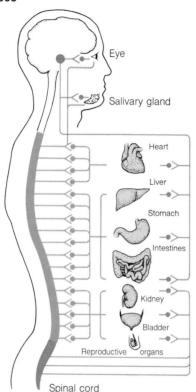

Eye

Salivary gland

Heart

Liver

Stomach

Intestines

Kidney

Bladder

Reproductive organs

Spinal cord

——— Sympathetic nervous system

——— Parasympathetic nervous system

Figure 41-7 The sympathetic nervous system (blue) has an accelerating effect on the body, while the parasympathetic nervous system (red) has an inhibiting effect.

Highlight

The peripheral nervous system carries messages between the central nervous system and the rest of the body. The autonomic nervous system controls the body's involuntary activities, such as heartbeat and breathing.

small canal called the *central canal*. The central canal is filled with *spinal fluid*. The interior of the spinal cord is composed of gray matter, and the exterior is composed of white matter. The spinal cord is about 42 centimeters long in adults.

SECTION REVIEW   Answers on page T–100.

1. What are the major parts of the brain?
2. What are the two parts of the brain stem?
3. Describe the function of the spinal cord.

Peripheral and Autonomic Nervous Systems

The peripheral nervous system is composed of 12 pairs of *cranial nerves* and 31 pairs of *spinal nerves*. The cranial nerves begin in the brain and extend fibers to the skin, skeletal muscles, and internal organs. The spinal nerves extend the length of the spinal cord. They provide a link between the central nervous system and the arms, legs, neck, and trunk.

A *reflex arc* is a pattern of stimulus and response that involves incoming sensory impulses and outgoing motor impulses. The "knee jerk" is an example of a simple reflex arc. As Figure 41-8 shows, the knee jerk response can be triggered by tapping the *patellar tendon* of the knee area. This action sends impulses through the sensory neurons to the spinal cord. Motor neurons then carry the impulses to the muscles. In this case, the muscle is the *quadriceps muscle*. The muscle contracts, and the lower leg lifts upward.

The autonomic nervous system conducts impulses to glands and certain muscle tissues. Activities, such as heartbeat, blood pressure, and secretions from various glands, are regulated by the autonomic nervous system. The autonomic nervous system is further divided into two systems.

The **sympathetic nervous system** controls many internal functions, such as an increase in heart rate during times of strenuous physical activity, anger, or stress. The **parasympathetic nervous system** controls the same body functions during rest. A decrease in heart rate is an example of this type of control. The sympathetic system and parasympathetic system work in opposition to each other. The central nervous system maintains the balance between the involuntary activities of these two systems.

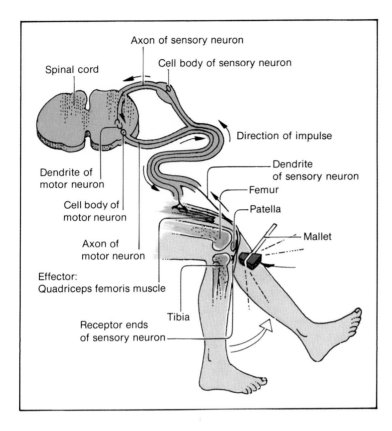

Figure 41-8 The knee jerk response is an example of a simple reflex arc.

Figure 41-9 The sympathetic and parasympathetic nervous systems work in opposition to each other.

AUTONOMIC FUNCTIONS

Structure	Sympathetic	Parasympathetic
Iris of eye	Dilation of pupil	Contraction of pupil
Salivary glands	Decreased salivation	Increased salivation
Heart	Accelerated activity	Depressed activity
Arterioles	Constriction of vessels	Dilation of vessels
Trachea and bronchi	Dilation	Constriction
Liver	Conversion of glycogen to glucose	Conversion of glucose to glycogen
Stomach	Depressed mobility	Increased mobility
Intestinal wall	Decreased peristalsis	Increased peristalsis
Adrenal medulla	Increased production of adrenaline	Decreased production of adrenaline
Urinary bladder	Contracts wall	Relaxes wall

SECTION REVIEW   Answers on page T–100.

1. Identify the two sets of nerves in the peripheral nervous system.
2. What is a reflex arc?
3. What are the two systems of the autonomic nervous system?

The Senses

Awareness of the external environment is obtained through the action of five **sense organs.** They are the eyes, nose, tongue, skin, and ears. The sense organs have highly developed, specialized *receptors* that respond to stimuli. These receptors are sensory nerve endings that receive information from the environment. The receptors carry messages about the environment toward the central nervous system. Through nerve impulses, *conductors* connect the receptors with structures called *effectors.* Effectors, such as muscles and glands, respond to the messages by carrying out certain activities.

Vision

The eye is composed of three layers. The *sclera,* the outer layer, is made of dense white connective tissue. At the front of the eye, the sclera is made of a transparent covering called the **cornea.** The middle layer of the eye is the *choroid,* containing black pigment and blood vessels. The black pigment aids in absorbing stray light. The middle layer also in-

Figure 41-10   Structure of the Human Eye

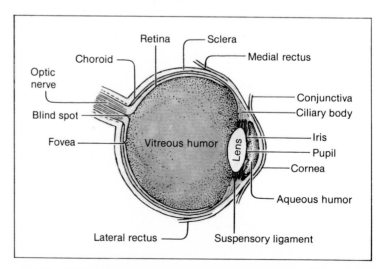

cludes the **iris,** or the colored part of the eye. The center of the iris contains an opening known as the **pupil.** The size of the pupil is regulated automatically by circular muscles found in the choroid. The pupil opens wider in dim light in order to admit more of the light. The opening of the pupil becomes narrower in bright light to prevent damage to delicate eye tissues. The *ciliary body* is a muscular part of the choroid layer that controls the shape of the **lens.** When the ciliary muscles contract, the lens can focus on objects. The lens is suspended by *suspensory ligaments* from the ciliary body. The area between the cornea and the lens is filled with a clear, watery fluid called the *aqueous humor.*

The inner layer of the eye is the **retina.** The lens focuses light images onto a small area of the retina. This area is called the *fovea.* Color vision is reduced when the image falls outside the fovea. A clear, jellylike fluid, called the *vitreous humor,* gives shape to the eye and is located between the lens and the retina. The retina contains *rods* and *cones,* or photoreceptor cells. Rods are sensitive to low-intensity light.

CAREER: Optician

Opticians prepare and fit eyeglasses and contact lenses. They follow prescriptions written by ophthalmologists or optometrists.

When a person brings a prescription for eyeglasses to an optician, the optician helps the person choose frames. The optician may grind the lenses and fit them into the frames. This also may be done by an optical mechanic, who specializes in this kind of work.

The optician adjusts the finished glasses to fit the customer. This is done with optical tools, including special pliers, screwdrivers, and files. It is important that the lenses be properly placed in relation to the person's eyes.

To prepare contact lenses, the optician measures the corneas of the customer's eyes. Using this information and a prescription, the optician writes specifications to be followed by a contact lens manufacturer. When the lenses are ready, the optician shows the customer how to place them into the eyes, how to remove them, and how to care for them. The optician examines the customer's eyes and contact lenses with special instruments to be certain that the lenses fit cor-

rectly. If minor changes are needed, the optician may make them. Major changes must be made by the manufacturer.

Many opticians learn their skills on the job. Others take a two-year course that includes instructions on how to grind and polish lenses.

Most opticians work for stores that sell eyeglasses and contact lenses. Some work for ophthalmologists or optometrists. A few work in hospitals and eye clinics.

For career information, write to Opticians Association of America, 1250 Connecticut Avenue, NW, Washington, DC 20036.

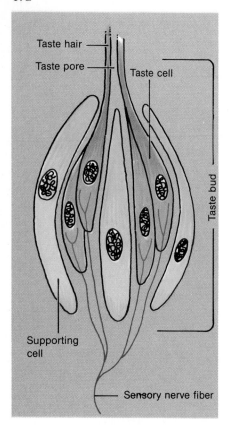

Figure 41-11 Taste buds are chemical receptors located in the tongue.

Figure 41-12 The taste buds for the four kinds of tastes are located in different parts of the tongue.

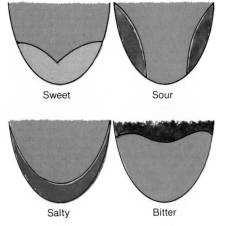

Cones are sensitive to bright light and to color. When light rays strike the rods and cones, the energy of the light is converted to nerve impulses. These impulses travel to the *optic nerve* which transmits the nerve impulses to the visual center of the brain. In the blind spot there are no cones or rods.

Smell

Most vertebrates have a highly developed sense of smell. Animals, such as dogs and deer, can detect odors from quite a distance. Relatively large areas of these animals' brains are involved in the process of receiving and interpreting odors. Odors are actually chemical molecules diffused through the air. Therefore, the sense of smell is a *chemical sense.*

Human beings do not have a highly developed sense of smell. The smell receptors, located in the upper part of the nasal cavity, are not especially numerous or extensive. These receptors connect directly to two small sections of the brain called the **olfactory bulbs.** Impulses from smell receptors travel from the olfactory bulbs to the olfactory tract and then to other portions of the brain.

Many of the sensations associated with taste are actually odor sensations. Molecules in food substances vaporize. These vapors stimulate smell receptors. Thus, human beings depend upon the sense of smell in order to detect the flavors in food. This is why, when a person has a cold, and mucus secretions cover the olfactory receptors, food seems to lose its flavor.

Taste

Taste is also a chemical sense. Organs of taste, called **taste buds,** are spread out over the surface of the tongue. Each taste bud consists of supporting cells surrounding a taste pore, from which taste hairs extend. Sensory nerve fibers carry the taste information to the brain in the form of nerve impulses.

In order for a substance to be tasted, its molecules must first be dissolved by the saliva in the mouth. The dissolved substance stimulates the taste buds. There are four basic types of taste to which the taste buds are sensitive. These four basic tastes are sweet, sour, salty, and bitter.

Touch

At this point, you may want to assign to your students the second of the Extensions and Applications at the end of this chapter.

The skin contains distinct receptors for touch, pressure, pain, heat, and cold. The receptors for touch and pressure are found all over the body. The nerves for touch are closer to

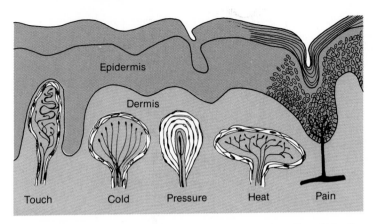

Epidermis

Dermis

| Touch | Cold | Pressure | Heat | Pain |

Figure 41-13 Five kinds of sensory receptors lie within the dermis.

the surface than are the pressure nerves. The pain receptors consist of bare nerve endings that are all over the body except in the brain. The sensation of pain is a warning that damage may be occurring.

The receptors for heat and cold lie deep within the skin. They are stimulated by high and low temperatures, and may produce a sensation of pain. The pain activates the body to respond.

Hearing and Balance

The ear is divided into three major parts. These parts are the *external*, the *middle*, and the *inner ear*. The external ear contains a funnel-like structure called an *auricle*. The auricle is made of cartilage and leads to the *ear canal*. The ear canal extends to the *eardrum*, or *tympanic membrane*. The eardrum separates the external ear from the middle ear. The middle ear contains a bony bridge composed of three small bones. These bones are the *malleus*, or hammer, the *incus*, or anvil, and the *stapes*, or stirrup. The stapes connects to the *oval window*. The oval window is a membrane that covers the opening to the inner ear. The *Eustachian* (yoo-STĀ-shē-'n) *tube* connects the middle ear with the throat. The Eustachian tube equalizes air pressure in the middle ear with that of the outside air pressure. In the inner ear, a series of *semicircular canals* connects with the *cochlea* (KAHK-lē-ə), a spiral-shaped tube that looks like a snail shell. Nerve endings in the cochlea lead to the auditory nerve. This nerve, in turn, leads to the brain.

Sound waves are created by vibrations of air. These vibrations travel to the ear and are directed into the outer ear

Sidelight

The fingertips have more than 200 nerve endings per square centimeter. The only parts of the body with more nerve endings are the lips, tongue, and nose. The human ear can respond to more than 300,000 different tones or sounds.

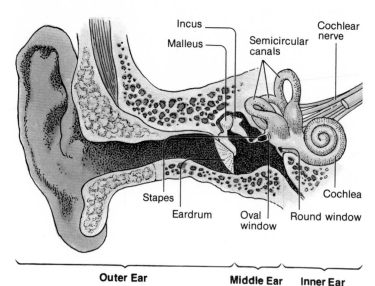

Figure 41-14 Structure of the Human Ear

Outer Ear Middle Ear Inner Ear

Some of your students might be interested in doing research into how sounds are produced and how they travel.

through the ear canal by the funnel-shaped auricle. The vibrations pass through the ear canal, causing pressure changes at the eardrum. The eardrum then vibrates, transmiting the vibration to the hammer, the anvil, and the stirrup of the middle ear. Finally, the stirrup vibrates against the oval window at the entrance of the inner ear. The vibrations are then transmitted to the fluid inside the cochlea. This fluid stimulates the *organs of Corti*, containing sense receptors for sound. The impulses pass from the organs of Corti to the cochlea and auditory nerves, and then to the brain. The cerebrum translates the impulses into sound.

The semicircular canals in the inner ear play an important role in maintaining balance, or equilibrium. These canals sit at right angles to each other in three different planes. They are filled with fluid. When a person's head changes position, the fluid moves, striking against hair cells located in the canals. The movement of fluid triggers impulses that travel to the cerebellum. The impulses carry information about the position of the head. This information allows the cerebellum to make the necessary adjustments throughout the body to maintain balance.

SECTION REVIEW   Answers on page T–100.

1. Describe the role of the lens in vision.
2. What are olfactory bulbs?
3. Describe the structure of the outer, middle, and inner ear.
4. Explain the role of the ear in maintaining balance.

Investigating Reaction Time

Purpose The nervous system coordinates a series of events that enables people to respond to changes. The length of time that elapses between perceiving a change and reacting to it is called reaction time. The purpose of this investigation is to determine relative lengths of reaction time in individuals.

Materials *(per pair of students)* ● Meter rulers

Trial	Distance ruler falls (mm)
1	
2	
3	
4	
5	
Average	

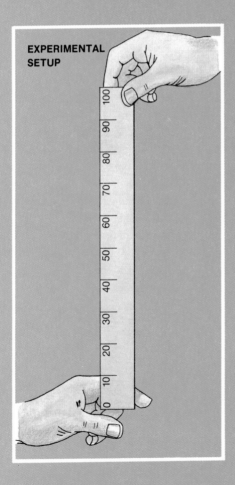

EXPERIMENTAL SETUP

Procedure **1.** Work in pairs of two students. The thumb and forefinger of the first student should be in position around the zero end of a ruler, but not touching it, as shown in the figure. The first student concentrates on catching the ruler when it is dropped by the second student, who holds the opposite end of the ruler. The first student must move only the thumb and forefinger, not the hand, to catch the ruler.
2. The second student drops the ruler when he or she chooses, and the first student tries to catch it as soon as it falls. Repeat the experiment five times and, in a table like the one illustrated, record the distance in millimeters from zero that the ruler falls until it is caught. Average the five trials to obtain an average distance for each student. Record the average distances on the chalkboard.

Observations and Conclusions **1.** Why does measuring the distance the ruler falls give a relative measure of reaction time? **2.** Compare the reactions of all the students. What do you conclude?
3. Consult a physics text or ask a physics teacher to translate the distance the ruler falls into the time taken to catch it. Make a chart of the reaction times for all the students and interpret the data.

CHAPTER SUMMARY

Structure and Function of the Nervous System

The nervous system is a communications network that allows people to respond to changes occurring within their bodies. It also allows people to react to changes in their environment.

The basic unit of structure and function in the nervous system is the neuron. Sensory neurons carry messages to the brain. Motor neurons carry impulses to effectors, such as muscles and glands. Nerve impulses are electrochemical signals that move from one neuron to another. These signals move across a space called a synapse, with the help of neurotransmitters.

Central Nervous System

The central nervous system is composed of the brain and the spinal cord. The brain is covered by membranes called meninges that, along with the cerebrospinal fluid, help protect it. The largest part of the brain, the cerebrum, is responsible for higher functions, such as thought, intelligence, and emotion. The cerebellum, the second largest portion of the brain, controls balance, equilibrium, and muscle coordination. The brain stem is composed of the pons and the medulla oblongata. The medulla oblongata contains centers that control vital functions, such as respiration, heartbeat, and blood pressure.

Peripheral and Autonomic Nervous Systems

The spinal cord is the connection between the brain and the peripheral nervous system. The peripheral system is made up of 12 pairs of cranial nerves and 31 pairs of spinal nerves. These nerves provide bridges between all parts of the body and the brain. The autonomic nervous system is divided into the sympathetic system and the parasympathetic system.

The Senses

Interaction with internal and external environment occurs through the senses. These senses are sight, smell, taste, touch, and hearing.

CHAPTER VOCABULARY

autonomic nervous system	lens	parasympathetic nervous system
axon	medulla oblongata	peripheral nervous system
brain stem	meninges	pons
cell body	mixed nerve	pupil
central nervous system	motor nerve	retina
cerebellum	nerve impulse	sense organ
cerebrum	nervous system	sensory nerve
cornea	neuron	sympathetic nervous system
dendrite	neurotransmitter	synapse
iris	olfactory bulb	taste bud

REVIEW of FACTS and CONCEPTS   Answers on pages T–100 to T–101.

On a separate sheet of paper, answer each of the following as completely as possible.

1. Name and give the functions of the two divisions of the human nervous system.
2. List and discuss the functions of the three types of nerves found in the nervous system.
3. Distinguish between a receptor, conductor, and an effector.
4. Describe the principal parts of a neuron and their roles.
5. What is a nerve impulse?
6. What role does the cerebrospinal fluid play in the nervous system?
7. What is a concussion?
8. List the three major divisions of the brain.
9. Describe the general structure of the cerebrum.
10. Contrast the gray matter and white matter found in the cerebrum.
11. State the location and functions of the cerebellum.

12. List the functions of the medulla oblongata.
13. Describe the functions of the spinal cord.
14. What is the role of the peripheral nervous system in carrying messages to and from the brain?
15. What is a reflex arc?
16. Briefly describe the three layers of the eye.
17. Identify the four kinds of taste buds and their locations on the tongue.
18. Name the two functions of the ear.
19. Explain the function of the Eustachian tube.

EXTENSIONS and APPLICATIONS For additional information, see page T–101.

1. The blind spot of the eye can be easily found. On a sheet of white paper, draw a small cross and a small circle about 8 centimeters apart. Hold the paper in front of you about 15 centimeters from your eyes. Be sure the cross and circle are held at the same level. Place an index card over one eye and look at the cross with the uncovered eye. The cross should be positioned toward the nose-side of your uncovered eye. Slowly move the paper toward you and then away from you until the circle seems to disappear. Using library research, discover what causes this blind spot.

2. The taste areas of the tongue can be mapped. Draw an outline of the human tongue. Use four different colors of pencils to record the four basic taste areas on your drawing. Use commercial quinine water beverage for the bitter taste, water and vinegar solution for the sour taste, water and salt solution for the salty taste, and water and sugar solution for the sweet taste. Place a cotton applicator in one of the solutions, then touch it to the tip, middle, and back of the tongue. Record on your diagram where the sensation of taste is the strongest in each case. Rinse your mouth with water between each test. Indicate your findings on the outline.

3. Prepare a report on one of the many types of nervous system disorders that may afflict human beings, such as cerebral palsy, Parkinson's disease, epilepsy, and multiple sclerosis.

SUGGESTED READINGS

Russell, P., *The Brain Book*. New York: Hawthorn Books.
This book describes how the human brain operates and involves the reader in many experiments and demonstrations.

Sagan, C., *The Dragons of Eden*. New York: Random House.
Speculations on the future of intelligence and on artificial intelligence are included in this book on the evolution of the vertebrate brain.

Shainberg, L., *Brain Surgeon*. Philadelphia: J.B. Lippincott.
This book provides an intimate view of the work of a brain surgeon.

42 Reproduction and Development

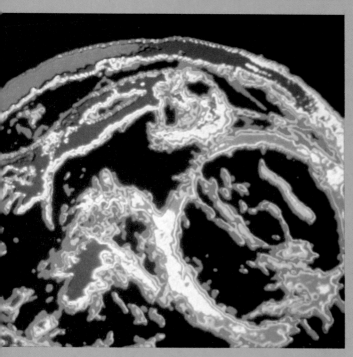

This ultrasonogram shows the outline of a human fetus.

For teaching aids for this chapter, including a chapter overview and teaching strategies, see pages T–101 to T–103. The page number next to each chapter objective refers to the text page where the information needed to fulfill the objective begins.

Human beings, like all other living organisms, must produce offspring to continue the species. This process is called **reproduction.** When this process involves the union of two **gametes,** it is called *sexual reproduction.* A gamete is a sex cell. Special structures in male and female human beings are involved in this form of reproduction.

Human beings pass through a series of stages throughout their lifetime. These stages are characterized by different levels and degrees of development.

The Reproductive System

Special reproductive organs, called **gonads**, produce male and female gametes. Other organs and structures in males and females carry out the different functions necessary for sexual reproduction.

Male Reproductive System

The male gonads, or **testes** (singular: testis) are found in the *scrotum*. The scrotum is a saclike structure located outside the body, behind the *penis*. The testes contain cells that produce the male hormone *testosterone*. The testes also contain *seminiferous* (sem-ə-NIF-ər-əs) *tubules* that are held together by connective tissue. Within these tubules, *sperm*, or male gametes are produced. Like all cells in the human body, sperm contain *chromosomes*. Chromosomes contain the genetic material. Each sperm cell has an oval head that contains a nucleus and a total of 23 chromosomes. A body or middle piece lies behind the head. A tail segment is connected to the body. This tail propels the sperm.

The seminiferous tubules lead into coiled tubes located on top of and behind each testis. These tubes function as storage places for sperm, while they mature. Each of these tubes is called an *epididymis* (ep-ə-DID-ə-məs). Each epididymis carries the sperm to a duct called a **vas deferens**.

With the permission of your students' parents, you may wish to invite a doctor to class to discuss the anatomy and physiology of the human reproductive system.

Sidelight

The overall length of a sperm is 0.06 millimeters.

Figure 42-1 Male Reproductive System

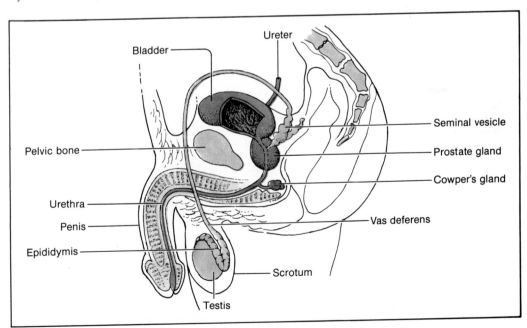

This duct takes sperm past a *seminal vesicle*, which provides nutrients to the sperm. The seminal vesicle empties into the vas deferens. The vas deferens conducts the sperm to the *urethra*. The urethra is a single tube that extends from the urinary bladder through the penis.

Several other structures are also part of the male reproductive system. The *prostate gland* is a small muscular gland located beneath the urinary bladder and surrounding the urethra. This gland produces a secretion that aids in sperm becoming *motile*, or able to move. A gland called *Cowper's gland* rests on either side of the urethra. This gland secretes a fluid that neutralizes any acid, such as that in urine, that might harm the sperm. The secretions of the prostate, seminal vesicles, Cowper's gland, and the sperm, make up the *semen*, or fertilizing fluid.

Female Reproductive System

The female gonads are called **ovaries.** These glands are about 3.5 centimeters in length and are located on the side wall of the abdominal cavity. The ovaries produce hormones that include the *estrogens* and *progesterone*. These hormones are responsible for secondary sex characteristics and for monthly changes in the female reproductive system. The primary function of the ovaries is to release the female gametes called *ova* (singular: ovum), or eggs. Like sperm, eggs contain 23 chromosomes.

The **Fallopian** (fə-LŌ-pē-ən) **tubes,** or oviducts, are located near the ovaries but are not directly connected to them. When an ovum is released, it travels through a Fallopian tube from the ovary to the *uterus*, or womb. The uterus is a hollow, inverted pear-shaped organ with thick muscular

Highlight

Gonads, or reproductive organs, produce the sex cells called gametes. Testes produce the male gametes, or sperm. Ovaries produce the female gametes called ova, or egg cells. The menstrual cycle is the monthly cycle of egg production in the female reproductive system.

Figure 42–2 Female Reproductive System

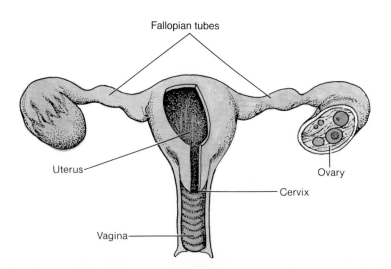

Fallopian tubes

Uterus

Ovary

Cervix

Vagina

walls. The uterus has a large middle portion called the *body*, and a narrow lower portion called the *cervix*, or neck. The function of the uterus is to serve as the site for the early development of the offspring. The cervix of the uterus narrows into an opening called the *vagina* (və-JĪ-nə). The vagina functions as the birth canal, through which the offspring passes to the outside.

Ovarian and Uterine Cycle

The monthly ovarian and uterine cycle of the female reproductive system is called the **menstrual cycle.** It has an average length of about 28 days, and consists of four stages. The first stage, the *follicle stage*, begins with the secretion of **FSH,** or *follicle-stimulating hormone*, by the anterior lobe of the pituitary gland. This hormone causes an ovum to ripen in a developing *follicle*, or pocket-like structure, within the ovary. The follicle is lined with specialized cells and holds a watery fluid containing the estrogens. The estrogens cause the lining of the uterus to begin to build up.

An increase in estrogen production signals the anterior lobe of the pituitary gland to produce and release **LH,** or *luteinizing hormone.* The increase of LH causes the follicle to rupture and release a matured ovum into the Fallopian tube. This process is called **ovulation** and it begins the second stage of the menstrual cycle. The ruptured follicle begins to change into a yellow body called the *corpus luteum.* During the corpus luteum, or third, stage of the cycle, the corpus luteum secretes progesterone. Progesterone finalizes the preparation of the uterus by causing a thickening of its lining. The thickened lining prepares the uterus for the attachment of the ovum if it has undergone **fertilization.** Fertilization occurs when a male and female gamete join in the Fallopian tube. After fertilization occurs, the corpus luteum continues to secrete progesterone. As a result, progesterone stimulates the lining of the uterus to thicken and accommodate the developing offspring.

If fertilization does not occur, the corpus luteum degenerates and no more progesterone is produced. The absence of progesterone causes the fourth stage called *menstruation.* During menstruation, soft uterine tissues and the unfertilized ovum are discharged through the vagina.

Figure 42-3 Fertilization occurs when one sperm cell enters and unites with an ovum.

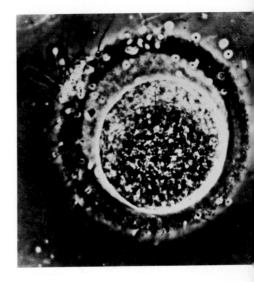

Some of your students might be interested in doing further research into the effects of hormones on the body.

SECTION REVIEW   Answers on page T–102.

1. Describe the structures of the male reproductive system and state their functions.
2. Describe the structures of the female reproductive system and state their functions.

Stages of Development

No fixed or rigid lines divide the stages of development in human beings. The stages, extending from fertilization to old age, overlap. Also, the ages at which different individuals begin and end stages of development vary.

Embryonic Development

The **zygote,** or fertilized ovum, represents the first stage of development of the **embryo.** The embryo is the unborn offspring during the first eight weeks of its development. The zygote travels through the Fallopian tube to the uterus. Here it will spend approximately 280 days growing and developing. This growth period is called **gestation.**

While the zygote is travelling through the Fallopian tube, the zygote undergoes a process called **cleavage.** During cleavage, the zygote divides into two equal cells.

After many more divisions, the zygote develops into a **morula.** A morula is a berrylike structure. As cleavage continues, a **blastula** (BLAS-tyoo-lə), or hollow sphere of cells surrounding a central cavity, forms. During the **gastrula** stage that follows, the **primary germ layers** are formed. These germ layers are the *ectoderm, mesoderm,* and *endoderm.* They form various tissues and organs of the body.

Highlight

Fertilization in human beings occurs when a sperm cell joins with an egg cell in a Fallopian tube to form a zygote. The zygote is the first stage of the development of the embryo.

At this point, you may want your students to do the Laboratory Investigation at the end of this chapter.

Figure 42-4 Primary Germ Layers

Germ Layer	Develops Into
Ectoderm	Nervous system Epidermis of skin
Mesoderm	Skeleton Muscles Circulatory system Excretory system Gonads
Endoderm	Digestive tract Respiratory system Liver Pancreas

ATTACHMENT OF THE EMBRYO Within ten days of fertilization, a zygote implants itself in the wall of the uterus. Four **extraembryonic membranes** develop during this important stage. One membrane, called the *chorion* (KOR-ē-ahn), surrounds the embryo. The chorion has fingerlike projections that attach the embryo to the uterus. Parts of the chorion and the uterus form the **placenta,** a membranous organ providing nourishment and oxygen for the embryo.

Another membrane, the *amnion,* contains amniotic fluid. This fluid surrounds the embryo, keeps it moist, and protects it from injury. The third membrane, the *yolk sac,* produces blood cells for the embryo until its own liver is able to perform the task. At that time, the yolk sac shrinks away.

The fourth membrane, the *allantois* (ə-LAN-tə-wis), also produces blood cells for the embryo and becomes part of the **umbilical cord,** which contains blood vessels. These blood vessels connect the embryo to the placenta where nutrients, wastes, and oxygen are exchanged between the mother and embryo. This exchange is by *diffusion.* There is no direct connection of the mother's and the embryo's blood supplies. None of the four membranes become a part of the embryo.

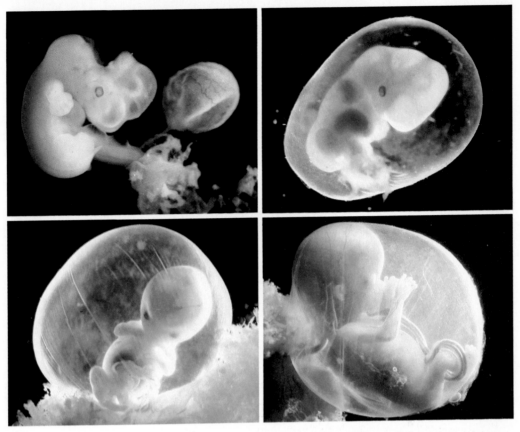

After two months of development, the embryo is called a **fetus**. When the fetus has fully developed, the process of birth begins. During this process contractions of the uterus occur. The amnion membrane breaks and amniotic fluid is released. Normally, the infant's head appears first through the birth canal. Finally, the whole infant emerges. The umbilical cord is cut and the placenta is expelled. The expelled placenta is called the afterbirth. A buildup of carbon dioxide in the baby's blood at birth causes the baby's lungs to take in air.

MULTIPLE BIRTHS In some cases, during cleavage the cells may divide into two separate parts. In this case, *identical twins* result. If, on the other hand, the ovary releases two ova, which are fertilized by different sperm, *fraternal twins* result. Fraternal twins, unlike identical twins, can be of different sexes and differ from one another in many other ways. This same possibility exists for other multiple births. For example, in the case of triplets, the three offspring may be either identical or fraternal.

Figure 42-5 The embryo develops quickly and undergoes many changes. These embryos are 5 weeks old (*top left*), 6 weeks old (*top right*), 7 weeks old (*bottom left*), and 16 weeks old (*bottom right*).

Figure 42-6 The structures within the uterus protect and nourish the developing fetus.

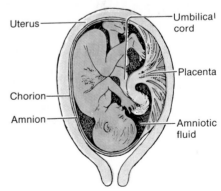

Uterus — Umbilical cord

Chorion — Placenta

Amnion — Amniotic fluid

At this point, you may want to assign to your students the second of the Extensions and Applications at the end of this chapter.

Infancy

Sidelight

The average baby weighs 3.25 kilograms at birth. The heaviest baby at birth weighed more than 10.5 kilograms.

The stage of development that begins with birth and that extends to the end of the first year is called **infancy.** Infancy is characterized by a tremendous rate of increase in weight and height. Often, the body weight of healthy infants triples in the first 12 months. A baby 50 centimeters in length at birth may often increase its length by 25 centimeters by the end of the first year. The infant's body proportions also change during the first year. Its arms and legs grow faster than its head and abdomen, both of which are quite large at birth. The sections of the soft skull slowly grow together, and teeth begin to appear.

Skills involving muscular movement, or motor skills, develop slowly. The infant is able to hold its head upright and reach for objects at about the age of three months. Muscle coordination improves at six months. At that point, the in-

Figure 42-7 Motor Development in Infancy

Age *(months)*	**Motor Activities**
1	Lifts chin when placed on stomach. Lifts chest when placed on stomach.
2	Lifts chest higher and more steadily when on stomach.
3	Reaches for objects. Holds head up.
4	Is able to roll easily from back to side. Actually grasps objects that are touched. Head control is more complete.
5	May be able to sit alone. Is able to reach and grasp objects.
6	Is able to turn completely over. Uses hands more efficiently for reaching, grasping.
7	Is able to sit up more steadily. Crawls, using squirming motion.
8	Is able to creep. May eat with fingers.
9	Walks when led. Is able to manipulate objects and pick up objects.
10	May stand by holding on to objects for support. Able to use a spoon. Able to grasp objects much more efficiently.
11	May walk around a supporting object with agility.
12	Stands alone. Is able to walk. Is able to use utensils, such as a cup.

fant can roll over and also move forward. At nine months, the infant can sit and pick up and handle objects. At the age of one year, the infant can walk or creep rapidly and is usually able to eat with a spoon and drink from a cup. Average expected motor development for the first year is outlined in Figure 42-7.

At this point, you may want to assign to your students the third of the Extensions and Applications at the end of this chapter.

Childhood

The period called **childhood** begins with the second year. This stage of development is characterized by a steady increase in height and weight and a variety of other changes.

During childhood, language facility develops rapidly. The child learns to understand and speak a language, and can be taught to read. Motor control improves. The child also learns a great deal about his or her environment, and is taught to behave in socially appropriate ways.

CAREER: Family Physician

A family physician provides comprehensive health care on a continuing basis. He or she treats people of all ages, that is, at all stages of development. Often the same doctor treats several or all members of a family.

The family doctor checks blood pressure, weight, and other factors that indicate a patient's state of health. The doctor may take blood and urine samples and perform various tests. If the tests reveal a problem, the doctor decides on the proper treatment. This may include prescribing medicine, a special diet, or certain exercises. The doctor keeps records of each patient's medical history. These records can be referred to if further problems arise.

A family doctor also advises patients on ways to prevent disease. The doctor vaccinates patients and gives them various types of injections to protect them from communicable diseases.

Sometimes, people have illnesses or other medical problems that cannot be treated by their family doctor. The doctor then refers these patients to medical specialists.

Family doctors graduate and receive a M.D. degree from a certified school. They must also

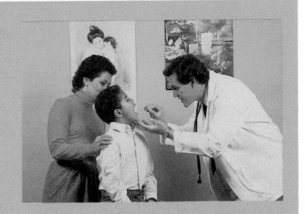

take and pass a special examination that enables them to practice medicine. In addition, they keep up to date on new developments in medicine through continuing-education programs.

Some family physicians have a private practice. Some work in hospitals and community health care centers. Some divide their time between private and community practice.

For career information, write to The American Academy of Family Physicians, 1740 West 92nd Street, Kansas City, MO 64114.

Adolescence

The stage of development between childhood and maturity is called **adolescence.** The beginning of adolescence is called *puberty*. During puberty, the sex organs develop rapidly. Menstruation begins in females, and sperm production begins in males. Secondary sex characteristics, such as the growth of breasts in females and beard growth in males, also develop. This growth period is characterized by body changes and a *growth spurt*. A growth spurt is a sudden increase in height and weight. Most females experience this rapid increase in height between the ages of 10 and 16. They may grow about 15 centimeters in height and gain about 16 kilograms or more. The growth spurt in males occurs between the ages of 11 and 17. During this period, males may grow about 20 centimeters and gain about 20 kilograms or more.

Adulthood

The final stage of human development extending from adolescence through old age is called **adulthood.** The body completes its growth in height, and the various body systems reach maturity.

The process called *aging* is a natural biological process that begins, in a sense, at the birth of an individual and continues throughout a lifetime. Women undergo a change known as *menopause*, which marks the end of their ability to reproduce. At menopause, estrogen production is reduced and menstruation ceases to occur. The secretion of FSH is drastically reduced, so that the ovary can no longer form and release ova.

During the final period of adulthood, a person's hair may thin out and turn gray. The adult's skin loses its firmness and elasticity, and wrinkles become more prominent on the face and hands. The body's muscles lose some of their strength. However, many changes associated with aging can be slowed or avoided if a proper plan of diet and exercise is followed.

SECTION REVIEW   Answers on page T–102.

1. What is the gestation period of human beings?
2. Describe the stages of embryonic development.
3. What changes occur during infancy?
4. What changes typically occur during adolescence and adulthood?

LABORATORY INVESTIGATION 42 For additional information, see page T-102.

Observing Human Growth

Purpose Human beings grow at varying rates from birth through adolescence. These rates include a growth spurt when the body grows at a very rapid rate. Although both males and females go through a growth spurt, they do not grow at the same rates and do not have their growth spurts at the same ages. The purpose of this investigation is to observe and interpret male and female growth statistics.

Materials *(per 2 students)*   ● Tape measure
● Graph paper   ● 2 pencils of different colors
● Ruler

Procedure   Part A   1. Copy Table 1 on a sheet of paper. **2.** Have your partner measure your height. Next measure your partner's height. Record this information on a sheet of paper. **3.** After all the students in your class have had their heights recorded, visit each pair of students and record their ages and heights. **4.** Compute the average height for males and females in each age group. Put your averages in the appropriate place in Table 1. **5.** Using this information, construct a line graph. **6.** Label the x-axis "Age in Years" and label the y-axis "Average Height in Centimeters." **7.** Use one of the colored pencils to draw the line graph for females and the other colored pencil to draw the line graph for males. **Part B   1.** Using the information in Table 2, construct another line graph. **2.** Repeat steps 6 and 7 in Part A.

Observations and Conclusions   1. Based on the graph of Table 2, at approximately what age do males and females double their size? **2.** At what ages do females grow more rapidly than males? At what ages do males grow more rapidly than females? **3.** Based on your observations, how many students in your class are above and below average height for their age? **4.** As a group, are the students in your class above or below average height? **5.** How many students are there in each of the age groups in Table 1? If there are very few in a particular group, how might this affect the reliability of your graph?

Table 1

Age group in years	Average height in centimeters Females	Males
13		
14		
15		
16		
17		

Table 2

Age group in years	Average height in centimeters Female	Male
At birth	50	51
2	87	88
4	103	104
6	117	118
8	128	128
10	139	139
12	152	149
14	160	162
16	163	172
18	163	174

CHAPTER SUMMARY

The Reproductive System The male gonads, or testes, produce sperm and also release testosterone. This hormone is responsible for the secondary sex characteristics in males. The female gonads, or ovaries, produce ova and release hormones called estrogens and progesterone.

The menstrual cycle prepares the female reproductive system for the release and passage of the ovum through the Fallopian tube to the uterus. If fertilization takes place in a Fallopian tube, the zygote proceeds to the uterus, where implantation occurs. If fertilization does not take place, the ovum and the soft walls of the uterus are shed.

Stages of Development The gestation period of human beings is about 280 days. A series of changes occur, starting with the division of the zygote, called cleavage, and proceeding through many stages, such as the morula, blastula, and gastrula. The body structures form from the three primary germ layers that are developed in these stages. These layers are the ectoderm, the mesoderm, and the endoderm. Four extraembryonic membranes aid in attaching the embryo to the uterus and in providing nutrients and protection. These membranes are the chorion, amnion, yolk sac, and allantois. The placenta forms from parts of the chorion and the uterus. The umbilical cord contains blood vessels and is a means of attachment between mother and child.

During the birth process, the fetus passes through the birth canal to continue life as an infant. The infant develops rapidly during its first year. Specific developments characterize the various stages through which human beings pass. These stages include infancy, childhood, adolescence, and adulthood.

CHAPTER VOCABULARY

adolescence	FSH	ovary
adulthood	gamete	ovulation
blastula	gastrula	placenta
childhood	gestation	primary germ layer
cleavage	gonad	reproduction
embryo	infancy	testis
extraembryonic membrane	LH	umbilical cord
Fallopian tube	menstrual cycle	vas deferens
fertilization	morula	zygote
fetus		

REVIEW of FACTS and CONCEPTS   Answers on page T–102.

On a separate sheet of paper, answer each of the following as completely as possible.

1. What are the specialized cells responsible for reproduction called?
2. Describe the structure of the testes.
3. Describe a sperm cell.
4. State the location and function of the ovaries.
5. What is the function of the Fallopian tubes?
6. What occurs during the menstrual cycle?
7. What occurs during fertilization?
8. List the stages that occur during embryonic development.
9. List the three primary germ layers. What body parts develop from each of the primary germ layers?
10. List and give the functions of the four extraembryonic membranes.
11. How does the development of fraternal twins differ from that of identical twins?
12. What is puberty?
13. Name and briefly describe the four stages of human development.

EXTENSIONS and APPLICATIONS For additional information, see page T–103.

1. Contact your local March-of-Dimes chapter or write March of Dimes Birth Defects Foundation, Public Health Education, 1275 Mamaroneck Avenue, White Plains, NY 10605, and obtain the film "Great Expectations." This film discusses nutrition during pregnancy. With your teacher's permission, show the film to your biology class. Have a class discussion on what you have seen.

2. Obtain information from the library on the effects of alcohol, cigarette smoking, and drugs on developing fetuses. Write an in-depth report on the subject.

3. Obtain permission from relatives or friends who have an infant to make observations of the infant in short time intervals over a period of several weeks. Study such things as (a) the ability to watch and follow an object with the eyes, (b) the ability to reach for and grasp an object after following it with the eyes, and (c) the ability to recognize favorite toys and human faces. Analyze and report your observations to the class.

4. Research the role of heredity in multiple births. Prepare a written report.

SUGGESTED READINGS

Nilsson, L., *A Child Is Born.* New York: Delacorte Press.
　　This book contains an extraordinary collection of photographs that illustrate the development of a human being within the uterus.
Rugh, R., and L.B. Shettles, *From Conception to Birth.* New York: Harper and Row.
　　This book presents a well-illustrated exploration of the development of a human fetus.
Tanner, J.M., G.R. Taylor, and the Editors of Time-Life Books, *Growth.* New York: Time-Life Books.
　　This illustrated volume explores human development from fertilization to adulthood.
Winter, R., *Ageless Aging.* New York: Crown.
　　This book describes recently discovered techniques that are used to help older people remain healthy.

43 Human Behavior

For teaching aids for this chapter, including a chapter overview and teaching strategies, see pages T-103 to T-104. The page number next to each chapter objective refers to the text page where the information needed to fulfill the objective begins.

Environmental stimuli partially influences human behavior.

The term **behavior** may be defined as anything that an organism does. In responding to a **stimulus,** or environmental change, behavior involves the actions of the muscles and glands. Usually the more complex an organism's nervous system and endocrine system, the greater the complexity of the organism's behavior. Behavior can be both involuntary and voluntary. Human behavior can involve thought, memory, feeling, and motivation, as well as physical activity.

Behavior is affected by both external and internal stimuli. An example of an external stimulus would be a sudden loud noise that might produce an alarm response. Internal stimuli include hunger, pain, and fatigue, each of which causes some type of response. Physical and psychological needs also affect human behavior.

Involuntary Behavior

You may want to review plant tropisms in Chapter 24 and compare them to simple stimulus/response behavior in human beings.

The most basic type of behavior is involuntary. That is, it does not depend upon will or choice. Involuntary behavior is also known as inborn, unlearned, unconscious, or automatic behavior. Involuntary behavior does not have to be learned, since it results from inborn patterns in the nervous system.

The ability of organisms to be affected by a stimulus and to respond to it is called **irritability**. The stimulus can be either internal or external. The response that arises because of this irritability is called a **taxis**. The response can be either toward or away from the stimulus. If the organism moves toward the stimulus, the response is called a *positive taxis*. The movement of a moth toward a light source is an example of a positive taxis. If the organism moves away from the stimulus, the response is called a *negative taxis*. The movement of a flatworm away from a light source is an example of negative taxis.

Simple automatic responses to stimuli are called **reflexes**. They usually involve only a small number of nerves. An example of reflex behavior is the secretion of juices by the salivary and gastric glands when food is smelled. Another example is the closing of the eye when an object comes near.

SECTION REVIEW   Answers on page T–103.

1. What is meant by involuntary behavior?
2. What is a taxis?

Figure 43–1 Moths being attracted to a light is an example of a positive taxis.

Figure 43-2 People use various kinds of shelters to protect themselves from the climate.

Basic Human Needs

There are many different theories on why human beings act as they do. Most *psychologists*, or scientists who study human behavior, feel that people act the way they do largely in order to satisfy certain needs. The most basic needs must be satisfied if the person is to survive and live a normal life. These needs are both physical and psychological.

The physical needs of an individual are those needs that must be satisfied in order for the individual to stay healthy and alive. People have a physical need for food, air, water, sleep, clothing, and shelter. People living in different parts of the world face different environments and therefore satisfy their physical needs in various ways.

The psychological needs of individuals are, in most respects, as important as the physical needs. Most psychological needs tend to vary from individual to individual more than physical needs do. However, some psychological needs seem to be common to most people. These include the need for social contact, the need to reach one's potential, and the need for self-esteem and the respect of others. People's attitudes toward themselves and others ultimately influence their behavior in general and, more specifically, their treatment of themselves and others.

SECTION REVIEW   Answers on page T–103.

1. Name three physical needs of human beings.
2. Name three psychological needs of human beings.

Emotional Behavior

Complex reactions that have both mental and physical elements, such as love, fear, and anger, are called **emotions.** Some psychologists define emotions as motives. Other psychologists define emotions as bodily changes. Still others define emotions in terms of the feelings experienced and reported by an individual.

Most emotions are usually complicated mixtures of feelings. However, emotions may be roughly divided into *positive* and *negative emotions*. Postive emotions are caused by things a person finds pleasant or appealing. Positive emotions are generally easier to express than negative emotions. Positive emotions include love, contentment, and joy. Negative emotions are caused by unpleasant or dissatisfying things. Negative emotions include anxiety, fear, and anger. In actual situations, positive and negative emotions usually contain elements of one another.

Basic Emotions

Love, fear, and anger are often considered to be the three basic emotions. Various combinations of these basic emotions account for a wide variety of emotional responses in people. For example, the complex emotion of jealousy includes elements of love, fear, and anger.

Highlight

The three basic human emotions are love, fear, and anger.

Figure 43-3 Human beings are unique in that they are able to experience a wide range of emotions.

694

Extremes of certain emotions, such as fear, can be harmful. Fears experienced over long periods of time may produce harmful anxiety in some individuals. If the anxiety is ill-founded and is not controlled or resolved, it may develop into a **phobia,** or irrational fear. Phobias include the fear of height, of close quarters, and of certain animals. Not all intense emotions are harmful. Some can aid in survival. For example, fear of running across a busy highway is reasonable and protective. Intense emotions become problems only when they lead people to do things they should not do, or keep them from doing things they should.

Physiological Reactions to Emotions

Emotional behavior patterns affect the body in different ways. For example, being in an embarrassing situation may cause the blood vessels in and around the face to dilate, or enlarge. The enlargement allows more blood to enter the

CAREER: Crime Lab Technician

Crime lab technicians help solve crimes. They gather, photograph, and preserve evidence that is used to reconstruct events or behavior. They carry out tests on the evidence. Some tests involve the use of chemical substances. Others involve the use of instruments, such as microscopes and spectroscopes.

Crime lab technicians work with many different kinds of evidence, such as fiber, bits of paper, paint, dirt, hair, skin, and blood. Firearms, bullets, shells, and explosives may serve as evidence in a criminal investigation. The technicians examine and classify these items. Evidence also includes impressions made by shoes, tires, or other objects. The technicians preserve these impressions by making casts of them. Crime lab technicians work closely with experts in other fields, such as fingerprinting, handwriting, ballistics, electronics, and biochemistry.

Technicians prepare reports on their findings. Sometimes they help reconstruct the scene of a crime. Other times they are asked to testify in court. They serve as expert witnesses on the evidence or on the techniques used in a crime laboratory.

Many crime lab technicians have a bachelor's degree. Others have completed a two-year program in a technical school or junior college. A good background in biology and chemistry is recommended for work in this field.

Crime lab technicians often work for police departments and other investigative organizations. They may also work for the federal government and for private investigators.

For career information, write to Federal Bureau of Investigation, U.S. Department of Justice, Washington, DC 20535.

face. This results in a flushed appearance called a *blush*. Other emotions, such as fear and anger, produce body changes such as sweating of the palms of the hands, rapid heartbeat, and queasy sensations in the stomach.

Such physiological reactions to emotions result from the high degree of interconnection between the various body systems. This interconnection includes the brain, in which the experience is consciously felt. The endocrine, nervous, and circulatory systems, for example, are closely related. Nervous anxieties can cause blood to be diverted from the digestive system. This action results in queasiness and a feeling of "butterflies" in the stomach. Prolonged anxieties can cause physical damage, such as heart problems or stomach ulcers.

Emotions can be caused by physiological factors. The size of the adrenal glands, for example, affects an individual's reaction to stress. The release of certain hormones, such as the sex hormones, for example, can also affect emotions and behavior.

SECTION REVIEW   Answers on page T–103.

1. Give examples of positive and negative emotions.
2. What are the three basic emotions?
3. Give an example of a physiological reaction to emotion.

Acquired Behavior

Intelligence and the ability to reason are distinguishing features of human beings. People can draw valid conclusions from situations they encounter. They also have the ability to learn and to base decisions on previous learning. Memory, or the ability to retain learning and experiences, plays an important role in the process of reasoning and response.

Many factors influence the intelligence of human beings, although these factors can be divided into two classes. Some factors relate to heredity, and others relate to environment. The roles that heredity and environment play in determining a person's intelligence are difficult to evaluate. As a result, it is extremely difficult to distinguish factors that are involved in the determination of intelligence. It is equally difficult to determine the true intellectual potential of individuals.

Intelligence plays a considerable role in determining behavior, especially *acquired*, or learned, *behavior*. Acquired behavior is conscious and voluntary. Acquired behavior is influenced by the physical environment. This behavior is

Sidelight

A polygraph, or lie detector, can pick up tiny physiological changes in the body caused by emotional responses. These changes sometimes indicate whether a person is being truthful or not.

Sidelight

Average intelligence, measured as IQ, or intelligence quotient, is 100. Albert Einstein's IQ was estimated to be over 180.

At this point, you may want to assign to your students the third of the Extensions and Applications at the end of this chapter.

696

Highlight

Acquired, or learned, behavior is complex, conscious, and voluntary.

At this point, you may want your students to do the Laboratory Investigation at the end of this chapter.

Figure 43-4 Doc, a chimpanzee, has been conditioned to smile when given a specific hand signal.

At this point, you may want to assign to your students the first and/or second of the Extensions and Applications at the end of this chapter.

influenced by the places and objects in the environment and by the interactions among people.

Examples of acquired behavior are *habits, mannerisms,* and *attitudes.* Habits are types of responses in which the response is repeated over and over again until it becomes almost automatic. The individual carrying out a habit response does so with little conscious thought. Habits can involve many kinds of learned behavior, such as whistling, typing, riding a bicycle, or brushing teeth. The advantage of automatic responses is that a person can do more than one thing at a time. For example, a person can whistle and ride a bicycle simultaneously. Habits become so automatic, they are difficult to break. However, because habits are learned, they can be broken.

Mannerisms are patterns of acquired behavior in which the individual develops an unusual or affected way of behaving or moving. Mannerisms can include ways of walking, ways of moving the hands while speaking, using particular speech patterns, and so on. Some psychologists feel that mannerisms are closely associated with hidden emotions. Therefore, psychologists think that mannerisms are a reflection of an individual's inner self.

Sometimes behavior is modified in such a way that a response once associated with a given stimulus becomes associated with an unrelated stimulus. This action is called **contioning.** For example, tickling an infant's foot causes the infant to move the foot. However, if a particular sound accompanies the stimulation, eventually the infant moves his or her foot whenever the sound is made. Therefore, this reaction occurs regardless of whether the tickling occurs. Conditioning can be unlearned.

An attitude is a readiness to respond in certain ways toward persons, events, or ideas. Many times an attitude exists without any personal experience of its object. *Stereotyping* and *prejudice* are examples of mostly negative attitudes. In stereotyping, an individual holds a fixed idea that involves casting certain groups of people in a mold. In the case of a prejudice, the individual holds an emotional, unfounded, and usually negative opinion of a person or group of people. This opinion is often formed before experiencing or considering the facts about the person or group of people. A person may also be prejudiced in favor of something.

SECTION REVIEW   Answers on page T-103.

1. What is acquired behavior?
2. What are habits?
3. What is prejudice?

Investigating Human Behavior

Purpose The human brain processes information from the internal and external environments and causes appropriate responses. Human beings depend to a large extent on learned behaviors in order to process information and solve problems. The purpose of this investigation is to examine types of human behavior demonstrated in a problem-solving activity.

Materials *(per group of six)* ● 1 large envelope containing 6 smaller envelopes of tangram, or Chinese geometric puzzle, pieces

Procedure **1.** The members of each team of six should sit in a circle. **2.** Each team receives a large envelope that contains six smaller envelopes. **3.** Each team member takes one small envelope from the larger envelope. **4.** When the teacher says to begin, team members open the small envelopes. **5.** Rules of the Game: **a.** Pieces of the puzzle are to be assembled in such a way that one large square results. **b.** Some team members may or may not have a complete set of tangram pieces in their envelopes when they begin. **c.** No team member is to speak to any other team member. **d.** Team members may give tangram pieces to one another. **e.** The first three members of each team to complete their puzzles win.

Observations and Conclusions **1.** What kind of behaviors can be observed in the problem-solving task? **2.** Which types of behaviors are supportive of team effort? Which types are nonsupportive of team effort? **3.** Which type of behaviors led to the solution of the puzzles? **4.** Why are communication and cooperation so important?

CHAPTER SUMMARY

Involuntary Behavior   Behavior is any activity of a person or other living thing. Human behavior is affected by both internal and external stimuli. The most basic type of behavior, involuntary behavior, is inborn, unlearned, unconscious, and automatic. An organism's ability to recognize and respond to a stimulus is known as irritability. Any resulting response is a taxis. A reflex is a simple, automatic reaction usually involving only a small number of nerves.

Basic Human Needs   Physical needs include food, air, water, sleep, clothing, and shelter. Psychological needs include the need for social contact, the need for self-respect, and the need to reach one's potential.

Emotional Behavior   Both mental and physical elements play a role in emotional reactions. Basic emotions include love, anger, and fear. Jealousy is a complex emotion containing elements of love, anger, and fear. Emotional behavior has physiological effects on the body. Physiological reactions to emotions result from the interconnection between various body systems. These factors can also bring about emotional reactions. Emotional extremes can be harmful to the body. Some extremes are protective.

Acquired Behavior   Human beings are able to think logically and intelligently. Memory aids in the process of acquiring modes of behavior. Intelligence is influenced by both heredity and environment. Acquired behavior is conscious, learned, and voluntary. Acquired behavior includes habits, mannerisms, and attitudes. Stereotyping and prejudice are negative attitudes.

CHAPTER VOCABULARY

behavior	**irritability**	**stimulus**
conditioning	**phobia**	**taxis**
emotion	**reflex**	

REVIEW of FACTS and CONCEPTS   Answers on page T–104.

On a separate sheet of paper, answer each of the following as completely as possible.

1. Define behavior.
2. List some of the external and internal stimuli that may influence the behavior of an organism.
3. What is involuntary behavior?
4. What is a taxis? Give an example of a taxis in both a lower animal and a human being.
5. Describe reflex behavior.
6. Distinguish between physical and psychological needs.
7. Define emotion.
8. Illustrate the relationship between physiological reactions and emotional behavior.
9. How do intelligence and reasoning distinguish human behavior from that of other organisms?
10. Describe what is meant by acquired behavior.
11. State the difference between habits and mannerisms.
12. What is conditioning?
13. What is an attitude?
14. Distinguish between stereotyping and prejudice.

EXTENSIONS and APPLICATIONS   For additional information, see page T–104.

1. Prepare a research paper on conditioning. Be sure to include accounts of the work of such scientists as Ivan Pavlov and B.F. Skinner in your research paper.
2. Using library materials, design an experiment that will illustrate conditioning. Try to include both experimental and control groups. After checking the experiment with your teacher, conduct it in class.
3. Obtain your teacher's permission to test the memory of various classmates. Using a deck of playing cards, select ten cards from the deck. Show the cards to the class members who wish to participate and then set the cards aside. Ask the subjects to list the ten cards selected. How good are their memories? Can you suggest ways to improve memory? Test your suggestions.

SUGGESTED READINGS

Dement, W.C., *Some Must Watch While Some Must Sleep*. San Francisco: San Francisco Book Co.

This introductory book describes what scientists know about the stages and disorders of sleep.

Fisher, J., *Body Magic*. New York: Stein and Day.

This informative book of "magic tricks" is designed to illustrate how people's minds affect their perceptions of the world.

Hall, E.T., *The Hidden Dimension*. Garden City, N.Y.: Doubleday.

People maintain spaces around themselves which are their "territories." The author of this book describes how the sizes of these spaces vary among members of different cultures.

Ornstein, R.E., *The Physiology of Consciousness*. New York: The Viking Press.

This book describes how the human mind deals with everyday problems.

44 Alcohol, Drugs, and Tobacco

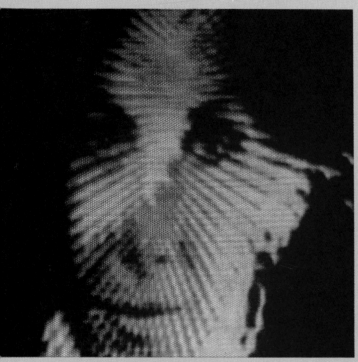

The abuse of certain drugs distorts reality.

For teaching aids for this chapter, including a chapter overview and teaching strategies, see pages T–104 to T–106. The page number next to each chapter objective refers to the text page where the information needed to fulfill the objective begins.

For thousands of years, people have used herbs and other plants for various purposes. The chemical substances, or **drugs,** in these plants had certain effects on the body, mind, or behavior of individuals. Some of these drugs continue to be used to treat diseases and wounds, and to reduce pain and fears. Such uses of these substances are beneficial to individuals and to society as a whole.

However, many people abuse these substances, that is, use them in ways that are dangerous to physical health or behavior. They may do so as an escape or as a way of reducing stress or tension. However, these practices are usually much more damaging to an individual than the problem the individual is trying to escape. Also, dependence upon a drug may continue long after the problem that led to the use of the drug has been solved.

Alcohol

An ingredient in alcoholic beverages is *ethyl alcohol,* or ethanol (C_2H_5OH). It is the only alcohol that is relatively safe for drinking. Other alcohols, such as isopropyl and methyl, are poisonous if taken internally. Isopropyl, or rubbing, alcohol is used as a disinfectant and for massages. Methyl, or wood, alcohol is used in such products as antifreeze and fuel.

Ethyl alcohol is produced by a process of *fermentation.* During this process, ethyl alcohol and carbon dioxide are produced when yeast cells act on the sugars found in fruits and berries. The chemical equation for this process is:

$$C_6H_{12}O_6 \xrightarrow{\text{Yeast}} 2C_2H_5OH + 2CO_2$$
Simple sugar $\qquad$ Ethyl alcohol $\qquad$ Carbon dioxide

Effects on the Body

Ethyl alcohol is a drug that is absorbed directly into the bloodstream from the stomach and small intestine. It takes only two minutes, or less on an empty stomach, for the alcohol to reach the bloodstream. The blood carries the alcohol to various parts of the body. The liver is the major organ that metabolizes ethyl alcohol to carbon dioxide and water and releases energy.

Alcohol affects the central nervous system when a person drinks the alcohol at a rate faster than the body can metabolize it. The accumulation of alcohol in the blood is called the **blood alcohol concentration, or BAC.** The concentrations are expressed as percentages. For example, a concentration of 0.05% indicates the presence of 50 milligrams of alcohol per 100 milliliters of blood. A concentration of 0.10% indicates the presence of 100 milligrams of alcohol per 100 milliliters of blood.

Alcohol acts as a **depressant** to the central nervous system. High blood alcohol concentrations tend to reduce the activity of bodily functions. The result is a numbing, or anesthetic, effect on the central nervous system. Research indicates that alcohol may reduce the ability of nerves to transmit impulses between the brain and the rest of the body. Alcohol affects the areas of the brain controlling judgment, memory, emotion, speech, vision, motor skills, muscular coordination, and balance. Heart, digestive, and respiratory rates slow down under the influence of alcohol. Figure 44-1 lists the general relationships between blood alcohol concentrations and behavioral responses.

Figure 44-1 Relationship Between Blood Alcohol Concentrations and Behavior

Percentage of Blood Alcohol Concentration	Symptoms
0.02%	Pleasant feeling. Sense of warmth and well-being. Minor impairment of judgment and memory.
0.03%	Time passes quickly. Person may feel superior. Does not worry.
0.04%	Motor skills may be impaired. Slight trembling of hands. Person acts energetic.
0.05%	Lowered alertness. Increase in reaction time. Loss of inhibition varies with individual. Driving ability impaired.
0.07%	Heavy pulse and slow breathing. Balance disturbed. Vision and hearing reduced. Person acts sluggish.
0.10%	Coordination badly affected. Less cautious. Staggers. Judgment, memory and concentration greatly affected.
0.20%	Has trouble standing up. Needs help to walk. Major disruption of motor and sensory skills.
0.40%	Unconscious. Alcohol has become strong anesthetic.
0.60%	Near death. Depressed circulatory and respiratory functions. This may occur at 0.50% or lower in some individuals.

Some students may be interested in researching the legal definitions of the terms "intoxication," "drunkenness," and "under the influence."

Ethyl alcohol is a drug. It is absorbed into the bloodstream through the stomach and instantly affects the nervous system. A depressant, alcohol slows down nerve impulses and affects every system of the body.

At this point, you may want to assign to your students the first of the Extensions and Applications at the end of this chapter.

Groups of students can request information from organizations that deal with alcoholism and its related problems.

Alcoholism

The excessive use of alcohol almost always causes health, social, or occupational problems. Such excessive use is called **alcoholism.** Alcoholism is recognized as a *loss of control* with respect to how often a person drinks as well as the amount of alcohol consumed.

Alcoholism is considered a *disease* because it causes disturbances of body functions and has characteristic symptoms. Recent research suggests that alcoholism may have a biochemical basis. This conclusion is based on the fact that alcoholics have certain substances in their bloodstream that nonalcoholics do not have. The reason for the presence of the substances is not known. Evidence does show that alcoholism tends to run in certain families. This does not necessarily mean that alcoholism is inherited, but that members of certain families may be more susceptible to the disease than are other people.

There are several identifiable stages of alcoholism. In early stages, *blackouts* or a temporary type of amnesia may occur. Another early symptom is an increasing dependence on and tolerance of alcohol. In later stages, **alcoholic psychosis** occurs. Symptoms of this condition include mental confusion, hallucinations, delusions, disorientation, convulsions, and violent tremors. This mental state is sometimes referred to as *delirium tremens*, or the *DT's*. The inability to recall recent events or form new memories is a further indication of alcoholic psychosis. The cause of this psychosis probably involves long-term effects of alcohol on brain cells.

Excessive amounts of alcohol in the bloodstream over a long period of time can result in a serious disease called *cirrhosis* (sə-RŌ-sis) of the liver. Normal-functioning liver tissue is destroyed and replaced by nonfunctioning scar tissue. A buildup of scar tissue causes the liver to malfunction. Many alcoholics develop serious vitamin deficiencies. This lessens their bodies' resistance to other diseases.

Treatment for alcoholism includes physiological and psychological therapy. The physiological therapy involves physical withdrawal from alcoholic dependence. This withdrawal causes symptoms that may include tremors, sweating, anxiety, and the DT's. Hospitalization is required during the withdrawal process. Psychological therapy may include working with a counselor in individual and group therapy sessions. These sessions help alcoholics understand and cope with their drinking and other problems. There are many organizations that assist alcoholics and their families, such as Alcoholics Anonymous, or AA.

SECTION REVIEW   Answers on page T–105.

1. Give the effects of alcohol on the body.
2. What is alcoholism? Alcoholic psychosis?
3. Name three identifiable symptoms of alcoholism.

Drugs

In general, a drug is any substance that causes a change in body function. Most drugs are used as medicines for internal or external use. Drugs can be placed into categories based on their use. Those used legally are either *over-the-counter drugs*, which are sold directly to the consumer, or *prescription drugs*, which are available to patients only through a licensed physician. Illegal drugs are those whose sale is forbidden. Such drugs are used other than as required medical aids. Abuse of drugs can cause serious health problems, or even death. When a person uses drugs and becomes physically or psychologically dependent on them, *addiction* occurs.

Drugs can be classified in seven groups. Drugs in these groups generally have varying effects on the user. Some of the different groups can have similar effects.

Inhalants

An **inhalant** is a substance that evaporates rapidly. Inhalants include products such as model glue, kerosene, and paint thinner. Intoxication can result when an individual inhales the fumes from these substances. If inhalation is continued, dizziness may result along with loss of muscular coordination, slurred speech, blurred vision, nausea, headaches, and depression. Continued use may cause drowsiness, unconsciousness, and sudden death. Habitual use can result in irreversible brain damage as well as damage to other organs, such as the kidneys and liver.

Depressants

Drugs that temporarily decrease the action of the central nervous system are called *depressants,* or sedatives. These drugs tend to reduce anxiety and tension, induce sleep, and act as muscle relaxants. The most commonly abused depressants are synthetic drugs called *barbiturates* (bahr-BICH-ər-its). The barbiturates most often prescribed by physicians are Seconal and Phenobarbital and are consumed in capsule form. Withdrawal symptoms, such as anxiety and

Highlight

A drug is a substance that causes a change in body function. There are a number of categories of drugs. Depressants, such as alcohol, barbiturates, and tranquilizers, slow down the body's systems. Hallucinogens distort perception. Stimulants, such as amphetamines, cocaine, and caffeine, speed up the body's systems.

At this point, you may want to assign to your students the second of the Extensions and Applications at the end of this chapter.

delirium tremens, can result if a heavy barbiturate user suddenly stops taking the drug. Barbiturates are a leading cause of death by poison, either by accidental overdose or by suicide. When alcohol is combined with barbiturates, the effect can be fatal.

Tranquilizers

Another group of drugs that has a calming or quieting effect on the central nervous system is the **tranquilizers** (TRAN-kwə-lī-zərs). When properly prescribed by a doctor, these drugs are useful in treating psychosomatic disorders, anxiety, and depression. When tranquilizers are abused, the results are lowered respiratory rate, dilated pupils, weak or rapid pulse, coma, and sometimes death. Examples of common prescription tranquilizers are Librium and Valium.

Hallucinogens

Drugs that can produce a variety of sensory distortions are called **hallucinogens** (hə-LOO-sə-nə-jens). Hallucinogens have no definitely known medical value as yet, but current research suggests a possible use in helping mentally ill patients.

The hallucinogen *LSD* affects the central nervous system. Some experts consider it to be the most dangerous hallucinogen because an individual's responses to this drug are very unpredictable. Some seemingly normal people have been known to commit suicide while under the influence of this drug. In general, LSD causes an individual's visual perception to be distorted. Other hallucinogens include mescaline, peyote, and psilocybin.

Phencylidine, or *PCP*, is a powerful drug that can be a stimulant, depressant, hallucinogen, or pain-killer. It has been banned for human use because of its dangerous side effects. These effects range from feelings of confusion, agitation, and depression to violent behavior that may result in murder or suicide. PCP is also known as "angel dust," "killer weed," and "hog."

Cannabis

The genus name for the Indian hemp plant is *Cannabis*. A natural drug called **marijuana** (mar-ə-WAH-nə) is obtained from the dried leaves and flowering stalks of this hemp plant. These parts of the plant are crushed, chopped, or shredded. Marijuana is rolled into cigarettes, smoked in pipes, sniffed, or taken in food.

Figure 44-2 These crystals of angel dust are magnified 250X.

Figure 44-3 Cannabis, or marijuana, is one of the most widely abused drugs.

The effects of marijuana vary with the individual. Effects also depend on the amount of a substance called *delta-9-tetrahydrocannabinol*, or *THC*, found in the marijuana. This ingredient causes a so-called "high," or feeling of intoxication. In the early 1960s, most marijuana was produced in this country and contained as little as 0.002% THC. Today, most marijuana is imported from Mexico and Colombia and has a THC level of 4% to 6%.

The effects of marijuana on the central nervous system include a feeling of well-being, impaired judgment, loss of inhibitions, distorted vision and hearing, relaxation, disoriented behavior, and increased appetite. There are many contradictory studies of the overdose effects from marijuana. More studies are needed to determine whether there are any long-term effects.

Current research indicates that marijuana may be as harmful as alcohol and tobacco. Some studies have shown that prolonged use of marijuana by adolescents can reduce motivation, increase feelings of being "left out," and reduce concentration and reasoning ability.

Stimulants

Drugs that temporarily increase the action of the central nervous system are called **stimulants.** These drugs create a feeling of alertness and wakefulness as well as a sense of self-confidence and well-being. Stimulants are used to decrease fatigue and mild depression.

The *amphetamines* (am-FET-ə-mēns) are a group of very powerful stimulants. They are also known as "uppers" or "pep pills." Medically, amphetamines are used to cure a disease known as narcolepsy and to calm down overactive children. Prolonged use of amphetamines can cause hallucinations, convulsions, and death.

A stimulant extracted from the leaves of the coca bush is called *cocaine.* It is used medically as a local anesthetic in eye

At one time, amphetamines were an ingredient of diet pills. Amphetamines are no longer used in diet pills because of the damaging side effects.

surgery. Cocaine causes increases in body temperature, heart rate, and blood pressure. This drug gives an individual a feeling of liveliness but can also cause feelings of persecution and hallucinations. Although cocaine does not cause physical addiction, it may produce a serious psychological dependence.

Narcotics

The **narcotics** are easily addictive and dangerous unless carefully administered. Narcotics depress the action of the central nervous system and are used medically to relieve pain. The narcotic codeine appears in a number of medicines, including cough suppressants. Other examples of narcotics include opium, heroin and pain-killing drugs such as morphine.

Opium comes from the juice of the unripe seed capsules of the white poppy plant. Morphine and codeine are produced from opium. Heroin is a semisynthetic substance produced from morphine. These drugs can be taken orally in pill, capsule, or powder form, or can be injected under the skin, into a muscle, or directly into a vein.

Heroin is extremely addictive, and deadly in overdoses. Possession or sale of heroin in the United States and Canada is illegal. Overdoses are frequent because when bought on the street the drug varies in concentration from package to package. Moreover, the body develops a tolerance to the drug so that increased and more frequent doses must be taken to try to get the same narcotic results. This increases the danger of overdose and death.

Treatment for Drug Abuse

Presently there are a number of methods used to treat drug abuse and addiction. Unfortunately, relatively few addicts are permanently cured of their addictions. One method that is used with quite limited success is the *methadone program* in which a heroin addict receives a synthetic drug called methadone. The drug is taken orally to relieve the desire for other narcotics, such as heroin. Addicts are given methadone in decreasing amounts until they overcome the physical need for narcotics. Other methods of treatment involve treatment-communities such as Hilltop, Phoenix House, and Odyssey programs. In these programs, the addicts spend varying periods of time in surroundings designed to aid in making them strong, self-reliant individuals who no longer are dependent upon drugs. These programs provide a drug-free social setting in which all activities are directed toward abstinence from drugs. Any individual with a drug abuse problem should seek assistance from a physician or drug treatment program.

SECTION REVIEW Answers on page T–105.

1. What is a drug?
2. Classify drugs into seven general groups.
3. What is a depressant? A stimulant?
4. Define hallucinogen.
5. What is a narcotic?

CAREER: Pharmacist

In the past, the work of a pharmacist included mixing and preparing ointments, pills, capsules, and solutions. However, today most drugs and medications are produced by large pharmaceutical companies. Preparing medication is only a small part of a pharmacist's responsibility. A pharmacist not only must know the uses, composition, and effects of hundreds of drugs, but must know how to bottle and dispense drugs and medicines. A pharmacist also tells the consumer how to use the prescription, any possible side effects that may result, and how the medication may affect a person's diet, sleep, and behavior. As new drugs are developed, a pharmacist must learn about them, and may advise doctors about their uses.

Many pharmacists own their own businesses. They must maintain an adequate inventory of drugs and decide what type of nonpharmaceutical merchandise to stock.

In order to practice pharmacy, a person must obtain a license. To qualify for a pharmacy license, a person must graduate from an accredited college of pharmacy and pass an examination. Most states also require that the person complete an internship or other on-the-job training program under the supervision of a registered pharmacist.

Some pharmacists work in hospitals and dispense medication to patients staying in the hospital and to patients who visit clinics. Pharmacists prepare some of the basic medications used in the hospital. They also help decide what drugs will be available in the hospital, and set up regulations under which the drugs are to be used.

Other pharmacists may work for drug manufacturers or wholesalers. Such pharmacists sell their company's products to retail pharmacies and hospitals. Part of their work involves informing other pharmacists and health personnel about new products. There are pharmacists who do research to try to develop new medications. Some research pharmacists also test the effectiveness and safety of drugs. Usually, research pharmacists have advanced degrees.

For further career information, write to American Association of Colleges of Pharmacy, 4630 Montgomery Avenue, Bethesda, MD 20014.

Figure 44-4 Uses and Effects of Drugs

Drug Type and Common Name	Medical Use	Possible Effects	Effects of Overdose
Tranquilizers			
Thorazine,	Reduce hallucinations, control psychotic behavior	Heavy sedation, disorientation, relief from anxiety, trancelike behavior	Severe muscle contractions, permanent damage to motor coordination
Miltown, Librium, Valium	Sedative, relief from muscle tension, anxiety, and symptoms of alcohol withdrawal	Mild sedation, produces sense of well-being, may cause headaches	Similar to barbiturate overdose
Hallucinogens			
LSD, Mescaline, Peyote, Psilocybin	None	Hallucinations, illusions, distortion of time and distance, rapid mood changes, loss of inhibitions	Longer more intense "trips," psychotic behavior, fatigue, possible death
PCP (Phencylidine)	Veterinary anesthetic	Dreamlike state, confusion, paranoid, psychotic, and aggressive behaviors, same effects as other hallucinogens Also considered a depressant, stimulant, and painkiller	
Stimulants			
Caffeine	Headache pain (in combination with pain killers)	Mild stimulation, wakefulness, increase in heartbeat and reaction time, ability to work longer	Stomach disorders
Nicotine	None	Mild stimulation, relaxation, increase in heartbeat	Lung damage, cancer, heart and respiratory disease
Amphetamines	Combat fatigue, depression, and hyperactivity in children	Strong stimulation, increased alertness, feeling of well-being, excitation, increased blood pressure and pulse rate	Agitation, increase in body temperature, hallucinations, convulsions, possible death
Cocaine	Local anesthetic for eye surgery	Similar to amphetamines	Prolonged use causes effects similar to amphetamine abuse

Drug Type and Common Name	Medical Use	Possible Effects	Effects of Overdose
Inhalants			
Amyl nitrite and Butyl nitrite	Smooth muscle relaxant, controls heart spasms by lowering blood pressure	Relaxation, rapid heartbeat, dizziness, headache	No known long-term effects
Nitrous oxide	Anesthetic	Intoxication and drowsiness	Possible damage to bone marrow after 12 hours of continuous use
Depressants			
(barbiturates) Amytal, Nembutal, Phenobarbital, Seconal, Tuinal	Sedative, relief from tension	Relaxation, sleep, disorientation, slurred speech, mild intoxication, loss of inhibition, decreased muscle coordination and alertness	Excessive sleepiness, confusion, weak respiration, weak and rapid pulse, coma, possible death
Alcohol — Wine, beer, spirits	Sedative, improved appetite and digestion, relieve anxiety, painkiller	Relaxation, loss of inhibition, feeling of well-being, talkativeness, decreased motor coordination and alertness	Malnutrition, ulcers, brain and liver damage, tremors
Cannabis			
Marijuana and Hashish	Under study for treatment of glaucoma, asthma, side effects of cancer medication	Feeling of well-being, impaired judgment, loss of inhibitions, distorted visual and auditory effects, relaxation, disoriented behavior, increased appetite	Many contradictory studies
Narcotics			
Opium, Morphine, Codeine	Painkiller	Feeling of well-being, drowsiness, respiratory depression, nausea	Shallow breathing, clammy skin, convulsions, coma, possible death
Heroin	None	Same as other narcotics	Same as other narcotics
Methadone	Painkiller and used to decrease addiction to heroin	Same as other narcotics	Same as other narcotics

710

Highlight

Tobacco smoking is linked to many diseases, including cancer, heart disease, and respiratory disorders.

At this point, you may want to have your students do the Laboratory Investigation at the end of this chapter.

Sidelight

In the United States alone, the tobacco industry produces more than 700 billion cigarettes and 3.5 billion cigars every year.

Tobacco

Tobacco leaves contain many substances, some of which have been shown by scientists to be harmful to people and animals. One component of tobacco is the drug **nicotine** (NIK-ə-tēn). This drug is a stimulant and may be responsible for the addictive quality of tobacco. Another component of tobacco is *tar*. Tars are sticky, brown organic substances that have been shown to cause cancer in animals. Finally, one of the gases produced by burning tobacco is carbon monoxide, which is found in very small quantities in cigarette smoke and can cause drowsiness and headaches.

Effects on the Body

In 1964, the United States Surgeon General issued a report stating that cigarette smoking was by far the most important cause of lung cancer in American males. Smoking was also linked with cancer of the larynx and coronary artery disease. In 1978, another report from the Surgeon General's office stated that smoking alters absorption and metabolism of several nutrients, such as proteins and vitamins C, B_6, and B_{12}. In addition, the report stated that pregnant women who smoked had infants of lower birth weight. Also, these infants were more susceptible to congenital abnormalities. Other findings proved that extensive tissue damage, especially to the lungs, results from cigarette smoking.

Immediate effects of smoking are increased heart rate, constriction of blood vessels, lowering of skin temperature, dilation of pupils of the eyes, and irritation of the lining of nose, throat, and mouth. Many of these effects are caused by nicotine. Nicotine causes blood vessels to constrict, leading to an increase in blood pressure. The heart then has to pump harder. The heartbeat may increase as much as 28 beats per minute after a cigarette is smoked.

Smoking-Related Diseases

Tobacco smoking is linked to many diseases including lung cancer and cardiovascular and respiratory illnesses. *Chronic bronchitis* occurs when the *cilia*, or tiny hairs in the *bronchi*, are destroyed. The bronchi are tubes that carry air in the lungs. The cells in the damaged area secrete excess mucus, clogging the bronchi and often leading to a "smoker's cough" and various infections.

Another lung disease is *emphysema*. It can result from continued smoke irritation, which causes the walls of the

Figure 44-5 The warning printed on packages of cigarettes is designed to alert people to the dangers of smoking.

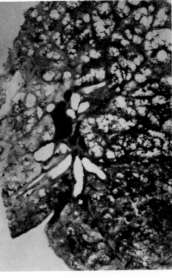

Figure 44-6 Healthy lung tissue (*left*) has small air sacs that are not visible with the unaided eye. The lung tissue of a heavy smoker (*right*) shows many enlarged and broken air sacs.

alveoli, or tiny air sacs in the lungs to thicken. Furthermore, air and mucus may get trapped in the lungs, causing the surface of the lungs to be greatly reduced. Advanced stages of emphysema may cause a person to use as much as 80% of the body's energy just to breathe.

Among cigarette smokers in the United States, cardiovascular disease is the leading cause of death. Cigarette smoking causes the heart to work harder because the arteries constrict, or get narrower. Many studies show that a person who smokes a pack of cigarettes a day is more than twice as likely to have a heart attack as is a nonsmoker.

Although some diseases caused by smoking can be successfully treated, many become incurable if not caught in time. Health professionals point out that the best way to avoid getting these diseases is not to smoke at all. These professionals also point out that it is easier not to begin smoking than it is to quit after the addiction has taken hold. However difficult it may be, quitting the habit can reverse the development of some smoking diseases, making the effort well worthwhile.

At this point, you may want to assign to your students the third of the Extensions and Applications at the end of this chapter.

SECTION REVIEW   Answers on page T–105.

1. Name some components of tobacco.
2. What immediate effects does cigarette smoking have on the body?
3. Why are smokers more likely to get certain diseases than nonsmokers?

Investigating the Hazards of Smoking

Purpose Smoking cigarettes produces many body changes. Tars are some of the many harmful chemicals in tobacco smoke that affect the body. Tars are brown sticky substances that damage lung tissues. The purpose of this investigation is to demonstrate the presence of these chemicals in tobacco smoke.

Materials *(per group)* ● Clear plastic squeeze bottle ● Old felt-tip pen with ends and insides removed ● Cotton balls ● Modeling clay ● 2 filter-tipped and 2 nonfilter-tipped cigarettes ● Tape ● Matches

Procedure **1.** Remove the center portion of the squeeze bottle top. **2.** Tape a cotton ball on the end of the felt-tip pen to be placed inside the bottle. Insert the pen through the hole in the top of the squeeze bottle. Seal around the hole with modeling clay. Be sure the seal is airtight so that air can only enter through the opening in the pen. **3.** Insert a cigarette in the outside end of the pen as shown in the figure. Seal the cigarette in the pen with modeling clay.
4. Caution: *Be very careful when using matches.* Light the cigarette and squeeze the bottle slowly and regularly to keep the cigarette burning. Stop pumping the bottle when the burning cigarette has reached the end of the pen. **5.** Unscrew the lid and examine the cotton ball for stains produced by the cigarette smoke. Pump out the cigarette smoke remaining in the bottle. Return the used cigarette to your teacher. **6.** Repeat steps 1-6 using a variety of filter-tipped and nonfilter-tipped cigarettes. Each cigarette should be burned to the same length.

Observations and Conclusions **1.** Which type of cigarette, filter-tipped or nonfilter-tipped, produced the most stain on the cotton? Why? **2.** Which type of cigarette produced the least stain on the cotton? Why? **3.** Relate the results of this investigation to what happens in the lungs of a smoker.

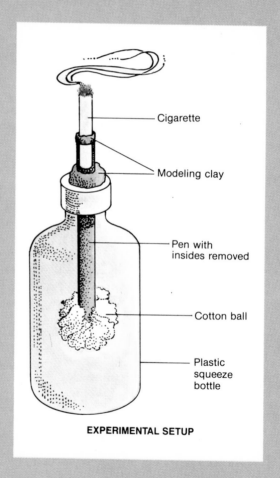

Cigarette

Modeling clay

Pen with insides removed

Cotton ball

Plastic squeeze bottle

EXPERIMENTAL SETUP

CHAPTER SUMMARY

Alcohol Ethyl alcohol is the main ingredient in alcoholic beverages and is produced by a process called fermentation. The accumulation of alcohol in the blood is measured in terms of the blood alcohol concentration, or BAC. Alcohol acts as a depressant to the central nervous system. Areas affected by alcohol include judgment, memory, emotion, speech, vision, motor skills, muscular coordination, and balance. Heart, digestive, and respiratory rates also slow down under the influence of alcohol.

Blackouts occur in early stages of alcoholism. Alcoholic psychosis occurs in later stages. The symptoms of this psychosis include confusion, hallucinations, convulsions, and violent tremors. Treatment for alcoholism includes physiological and psychological therapy.

Drugs A drug is any substance that causes a change in body function. Most drugs are used as a medicine or used in making medicines. Drugs can act as depressants, sedatives, stimulants, and pain-killers. The effects range from mild intoxication to distorted sensory effects, hallucinations, and psychotic behaviors.

Drugs can be classified in seven groups. Inhalants include kerosene, model glue, and paint thinner. Depressants include barbiturates and other sedatives, tranquilizers, and alcohol. Hallucinogens include LSD, mescaline, peyote, and psilocybin. *Cannabis*, the genus name for the Indian hemp plant, includes marijuana and hashish. Stimulants include amphetamines, cocaine, caffeine, and nicotine. Narcotics include heroin, morphine, codeine, and methadone.

Currently there are a number of methods for treatment of drug abuse. Included are community programs, such as Hilltop, Phoenix House, and Odyssey.

Tobacco Nicotine is the component in tobacco that may be responsible for its addictive quality. Tars, another component of tobacco, cause cancer in laboratory animals. Carbon monoxide is a poisonous gas produced by burning tobacco.

The United States Surgeon General's report of 1964 stated that cigarette smoking is the most important cause of lung cancer. The 1978 report stated that cigarette smoking alters the absorption and metabolism of nutrients.

Among the effects of cigarette smoking are increased heart rate, lowering of skin temperature, constriction of blood vessels, and irritation of the lining of the nose, throat, and mouth. Smoking has been linked to many cardiovascular and respiratory illnesses as well as various cancers. Cigarette smoking may be one cause of such diseases as chronic bronchitis and emphysema.

CHAPTER VOCABULARY

alcoholic psychosis	drug	narcotic
alcoholism	hallucinogen	nicotine
blood alcohol concentration (BAC)	inhalant	stimulant
depressant	marijuana	tranquilizer

REVIEW of FACTS and CONCEPTS Answers on pages T–105 to T–106.

On a separate sheet of paper, answer each of the following as completely as possible.

1. How is ethyl alcohol produced?
2. Describe the effects of alcohol on the nervous system.
3. Why is alcohol classified as a depressant?
4. Explain why alcoholism is considered a disease.
5. What effect does alcoholism have on the liver?
6. Describe two treatments for alcoholism.
7. Describe some effects that each group of drugs have in the body. Name a drug in each group.
8. Name some treatments for drug abuse.
9. Discuss the conclusions of the Surgeon General's reports on smoking.
10. Is there a relationship between cigarette smoking and cardiovascular disease? Explain.

EXTENSIONS and APPLICATIONS For additional information, see page T–106.

1. Go to the school library and prepare a report on the work of organizations such as Alcoholics Anonymous, Al-Anon, and Alateen for the rehabilitation of alcoholics.

2. Using resources from within your own community, prepare a panel discussion on topics related to drugs and their abuse that would interest students in your biology class. Invite outside experts from law enforcement groups, religious groups, social agencies, and the medical profession to discuss these topics.

3. Write to organizations such as the American Lung Association, American Heart Association, and American Cancer Society for information about the hazards of smoking. Using this information, prepare charts for a bulletin board display.

SUGGESTED READINGS

Modell, W., A. Lansing, and the Editors of Time-Life Books, *Drugs*. New York: Time-Life Books.
This volume explores the use and misuse of the most important and most commonly used drugs.

Nahas, G.G., *Keep Off the Grass*. New York: Thomas Y. Crowell.
This is a clearly written and well-documented account of the effects of marijuana.

Winter, R., *The Scientific Case Against Smoking*. New York: Crown.
This book includes a thorough, but nontechnical, discussion of the medical findings on the health effects of smoking cigarettes.

The ESP Debate

Most higher organisms, including human beings have five basic senses. The five senses are sight, hearing, touch, taste, and smell. Different organisms may rely on one particular sense more than another. Moreover, certain senses may be more highly developed in one organism than in another. For example, the sense of smell is more highly developed in dogs than in birds. However, the sense of sight is generally more highly developed in birds than in dogs.

Some people think that human beings possess a sixth sense. This sixth sense is referred to by several terms. One term is "extrasensory perception," or ESP. The scientific study of ESP is referred to as parapsychology.

Parapsychologists study a number of phenomena. Clairvoyance is the ability of a person to perceive things without the use of the five basic senses. The communication of thoughts between one person and another without use of any of the five basic senses is called telepathy. Precognition is the ability to predict an event. Psychokinesis is the ability to control physical events or objects with the mind.

Although studies of ESP have been going on for more than 50 years, there is still little evidence that ESP exists. Until the early 1930s, studies of ESP consisted only of collecting and comparing reports of psychic phenomena. Since that time, many methods have been developed to test ESP under laboratory conditions. Much of this testing has been performed at Duke University in North Carolina. The results appear to support the hypothesis that ESP exists.

In spite of the Duke University testing, most scientists think that ESP does not exist. These scientists think the phenomena can be explained in other ways. They often explain these events as coincidence, the result of an overactive imagination or

hallucinations, or as trickery. During the 1970s, a man called Uri Geller claimed he had psychokinetic powers. Geller claimed he could bend spoons and cause watches to stop running, using special mental powers. Since then, Geller's abilities have been studied under controlled conditions by scientists. No evidence was found to support his claims.

Despite such negative findings, there are still some scientists who are studying ESP. In the meantime, popular interest in the subject will continue as long as unexplained examples of ESP are reported. Perhaps new reliable methods will be discovered to test the phenomena of ESP.

Viewpoints

1. What are several types of psychic phenomena you have heard or read about? Cite specific examples. Do these examples have logical explanations? What do you think caused these phenomena?

2. Prepare a set of ESP cards by cutting out 25 rectangles that are 7 cm x 12 cm. Draw the following symbols on each of five cards: wavy lines, a star, a square, a circle, and a plus sign. Shuffle the deck and place it face down in front of you. Without looking at the faces of the cards, write down a list of the symbols as you think they are stacked. After you finish your list, turn the cards over and count how many of your guesses were correct. Pure chance should produce five correct answers out of 25. Repeat your experiment several times. What conclusions about ESP can you reach from your experiment?

3. Using the deck of ESP cards made for Viewpoint 2, devise an experiment to test for telepathy. You will need a partner. Run your test a number of times before you state a general conclusion. The law of chance stated in Viewpoint 2 also applies to this exercise.

Ecological Interactions

For an overview of this unit, including field trip suggestions, a bibliography, and a list of audio-visual materials, see pages T–106 to T–114. You may want to check the Laboratory Investigations in this unit so that materials may be ordered, gathered, or prepared in advance.

Life exists in a variety of places on the earth. Some places, such as the polar regions, do not provide the conditions that most life forms need to survive. The kinds of living things in these places are small. Other places, such as areas near the equator, are suitable to a great number of living things. However, wherever a particular form of life may live, it is adapted to its particular environment. Within each environment, all living things interact with one another. Thus, all organisms live in an ecological balance. This balance may be upset by abuse of resources, overcrowding, and pollution.

In an ecosystem, organisms interact with one another and their nonliving environment.

45 The Environment

The entire Earth is the environment of its living things.

Chapter Objectives *After completing this chapter, you will be able to:*

a ■ Define ecology, biosphere, and ecosystem. p. 718

b ■ Distinguish between a community and a population, and a habitat and a niche. p. 720

c ■ Explain how energy flows through an ecosystem. p. 722

d ■ Discuss the role of producers, consumers, and decomposers in a community. p. 721

e ■ Discuss commensalism, mutualism, and parasitism. p. 727

f ■ List four abiotic factors in the environment. p. 729

g ■ Describe the water, oxygen, carbon, and nitrogen cycles. p. 731

For teaching aids for this chapter, including a chapter overview and teaching strategies, see pages T-106 to T-108. The page number next to each chapter objective refers to the text page where the information needed to fulfill the objective begins.

The study of the relationships between living things and their environment is called **ecology.** The word ecology comes from Greek words meaning "the study of the home." The "home" includes the environment in which an organism lives, the interaction of organisms with one another, and the interaction of organisms with the nonliving environment. Scientists who study these interactions are called *ecologists*.

Ecologists have gained a great deal of knowledge about these interactions. This knowledge has led to a better understanding of the factors that affect all living things on the earth, including its human population. Ecologists use knowledge of these factors not only to understand the past and the present of an environment, but to predict what will happen to it in the future. For example, if conditions are naturally or artificially altered, an environment may no longer be able to support certain plants and animals. The effects of such an event may have far-reaching consequences for human beings.

The Biosphere

The **biosphere** is a thin zone that contains all living things on the earth. This zone extends down into the ground as far as the deepest caves. It penetrates into the oceans to depths greater than 9 kilometers. It stretches thousands of meters into the atmosphere. Although these distances may seem great, the biosphere is thin compared to the total size of the earth and its atmosphere.

Ecosystems

The biosphere is made up of many **ecosystems.** An ecosystem is an interacting system that consists of groups of organisms and their nonliving environment. Each ecosystem contains *biotic factors*, or living organisms, and *abiotic factors*, or nonliving or physical components. Abiotic factors include soil, water, temperature, and light.

Ecosystems vary in size. For example, a square meter of a garden, the edge of a lake, a small pond, a desert, a forest, and the entire biosphere are examples of ecosystems. Ecosystems are *self-sustaining*, or able to support themselves,

At this point, you may want to assign to several students the fifth of the Extensions and Applications at the end of this chapter.

Highlight

The biosphere is made up of many different environments called ecosystems. An ecosystem contains both biotic and abiotic factors. The biotic factors in a given area of an ecosystem make up a community.

Figure 45–1 An ecosystem is made up of biotic, or living, factors and abiotic, or nonliving, factors.

Biotic factors

+

Abiotic factors

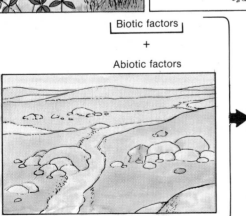

Ecosystem

if three conditions are met. First, there must be a source of energy, such as sunlight, in the ecosystem. Second, this energy must be converted into energy that is stored in chemical bonds, such as those in foods. Third, essential substances, such as water, oxygen, carbon, and nitrogen, must be recycled between the organisms and the environment.

Communities and Populations

Each ecosystem contains a **community.** A community consists of all the living organisms in a certain area. A forest containing birds, insects, small animals, and trees, and a pond containing fishes, insects, and microorganisms are examples of communities.

In a community, different types of animals and plants live together. Each member of the community has certain adaptations that enable it to stay alive. Within a community, some members feed upon others and some are fed upon. Others develop beneficial "partnerships." Many, such as certain plants, do not interact with other organisms to any great extent.

Communities are composed of **populations.** A population is a group of individuals of the same *species,* living together in the same area. Species are groups of organisms that interbreed. The lilies in a meadow, the earthworms in a lawn, the trout in a stream, and the spruce trees in a forest are all examples of populations.

Habitats and Niches

Each organism in a community has a **habitat,** or place where it lives. The habitat provides food and shelter for the organism. The habitat of a land snail is moist leaf litter that covers the ground. The habitat of a squirrel is the inside of a hollow tree trunk and the land around the tree that the squirrel uses. Some habitats may overlap. For example, the squirrel may look for nuts among the litter of leaves on the ground. The same area of ground may also be the habitat of the land snail. However, because these animals do not eat the same food, there is very little interaction from the overlap of their habitats.

In addition to having a habitat, each organism in a community plays a particular role. This role, or occupation, is called the **niche** (NICH). A niche is everything an organism does and everything the organism needs within its habitat.

Although organisms may share the same habitat, they cannot occupy the same niche. For example, in a grassland, prairie dogs, rabbits, and rattlesnakes have overlapping

Insects and birds might live in a wheat field. Snakes and scorpions might live in the desert. Monkeys and turtles might live in the rain forest. Many other answers are also acceptable.

Figure 45-2 A wheat field, a desert, and a rain forest are three examples of habitats. Name several organisms that might live in each of these habitats.

Assign a different animal to each student in your class. Have the students research the habitats and niches of the animals.

721

habitats. However, they eat different foods. As a result of this difference, these species occupy distinct niches in the grassland community. There are, of course, many other differences between the species. Each difference contributes to the separation of niches.

SECTION REVIEW   Answers on page T–107.

1. Define biosphere.
2. What is an ecosystem?
3. Distinguish between a habitat and a niche.

Biotic Interactions in the Environment

Every ecosystem contains a biotic portion. The organisms within this biotic portion can be divided into three groups. Each group is classified according to the way in which the organisms in it obtain their food from the ecosystem.

Producers, Consumers, and Decomposers

The first group of these organisms is green plants. Because these plants produce their own food they are called **producers.** Green plants are also called *autotrophs,* or self-feeders.

The second group of organisms in an ecosystem are the **consumers.** Consumers are organisms that feed directly or indirectly on producers. Consumers that feed directly upon producers are called *primary consumers.* Those consumers that feed upon primary consumers are called *secondary consumers.* For example, an insect that feeds upon plants is a primary consumer, a frog that feeds upon insects is a secondary consumer. In turn, there may be a third, fourth, or fifth level of consumers.

Primary consumers are also called *herbivores,* or plant eaters. Secondary and higher level consumers that feed on other animals are called *carnivores,* or flesh eaters. Those animals that feed on both plants and animals are called *omnivores.*

The third group of organisms in an ecosystem are the **decomposers.** Decomposers are organisms that break down organic material and return it to the environment, where it can be reused by producers. This process is known as *decay.* Examples of such decomposers are one-celled organisms called *bacteria* and fungi such as mushrooms. Fungi are plants that do not contain chlorophyll.

Highlight

The biotic factors in an ecosystem can be divided into producers, consumers, and decomposers. The flow of energy between the organisms of these groups is called a food chain. The complex of interrelationships among food chains is called a food web.

Some of your students might be interested in doing research into the differences between herbivores, carnivores, and omnivores.

Sidelight

Some of the largest decomposers, such as various species of fungi, are 1 meter in diameter.

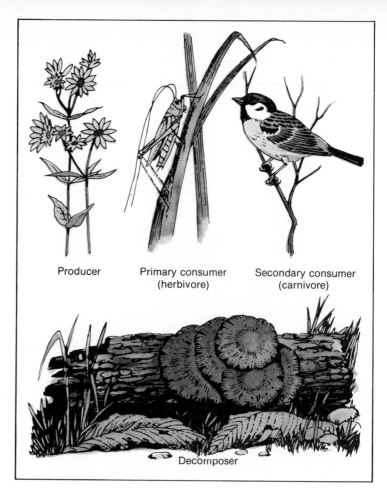

Producer Primary consumer Secondary consumer
(herbivore) (carnivore)

Decomposer

Figure 45-3 Organisms are classified as producers, consumers, or decomposers, depending on how they get their food. Producers are autotrophs. Consumers and decomposers are heterotrophs.

All consumers and decomposers are called *heterotrophs*, organisms that cannot make their own food. Heterotrophic plants that obtain their food from dead organisms or from the waste products of living organisms are called **saprophytes** (SAP-rə-fītz). Molds and mushrooms are examples of saprophytes. Animals that feed upon the bodies of dead animals are called **scavengers.** Jackals and vultures are examples of scavengers. Saprophytes and scavengers can be either consumers or decomposers.

Food Chains and Food Webs

In an ecosystem, producers convert light energy into the energy of chemical bonds of organic materials, such as food. The energy and organic materials are passed on through the rest of the ecosystem by consumers. This flow of energy and organic materials from organism to organism is called a **food chain.** An example of a food chain is a robin feeding on a caterpillar that fed on a leaf.

At this point, you may want to assign to several students the second of the Extensions and Applications at the end of this chapter.

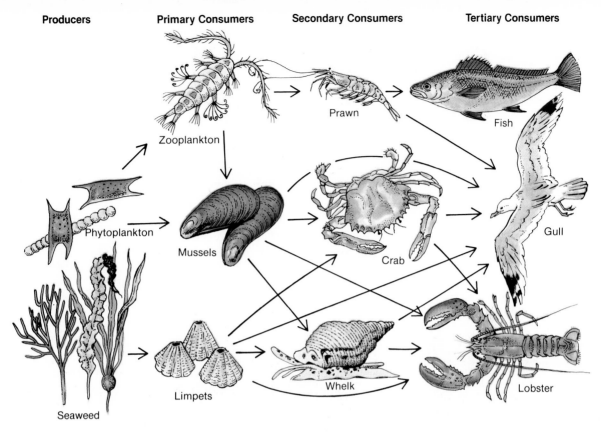

Producers	Primary Consumers	Secondary Consumers	Tertiary Consumers

Zooplankton

Prawn

Fish

Phytoplankton

Mussels

Crab

Gull

Seaweed

Limpets

Whelk

Lobster

Figure 45-4 This ocean food web is a complex overlapping of many individual food chains.

In a community, very few primary consumers feed upon just one kind of plant. Nor are primary consumers, in turn, generally eaten by only one type of secondary consumer. For example, in a saltwater environment, sea snails eat various types of seaweeds. However, the seaweeds may be eaten by many different primary consumers, including small fish and some shelled animals. In turn, these animals may become the prey of larger fish, birds, and octopuses. Omnivores are both primary and secondary consumers, depending on whether they are eating plants or animals. Because of these complex relationships, food chains interconnect or overlap to form a **food web.** The presence of many organisms interacting in a food web results in a more stable ecosystem.

Ecological Pyramids

Green plants capture only about 1% of the energy in sunlight. At each feeding level of a food chain, the amount of energy in plants that is passed on to consumers decreases.

Scientists call these feeding levels **trophic** (TRAHF-ik) **levels.** Trophic comes from a Greek word that means "food." All producers, or autotrophs, belong to the *first trophic level.* Primary consumers belong to the *second trophic level,* secondary consumers belong to the *third trophic level,* and so on.

Energy is lost at each trophic level for two reasons. First, each organism in a given trophic level uses some of the energy locked in the chemical bonds of its food to carry on its own life functions. Second, there is always a loss of energy in the form of heat in any system of energy transfer. The transfer of energy in a food chain may be shown as a *pyramid of energy.* In a pyramid of energy, the total amount of energy decreases at successively higher trophic levels.

Other aspects of ecosystems related to the transfer of energy may also be represented by pyramid models. Because the energy contained in organisms decreases at each trophic

CAREER: Environmentalist

Environmentalists are scientists who study, analyze, and try to solve environmental problems. They are concerned with the quality of air and water. They also study how land is used and the environmental impact of that use. Environmentalists examine the causes and effects of noise pollution and the sources and effects of radioactivity on the environment.

Environmentalists attempt to predict future environmental problems as well as identify present problems and their causes. For example, some lakes that once were filled with fish and other living things now hold very few forms of life. Environmentalists have traced the death of some of these lakes to acid rain. Acid rain forms when certain industrial pollutants enter the atmosphere and combine with precipitation. By monitoring air pollutants and wind factors, environmentalists can predict where acid rain will fall. Such predictions can lead to action that will prevent damage to the environment.

Many disciplines are involved in the study and solution of environmental problems. To understand the entire problem of acid rain, for example, one must understand fuel combustion, wind patterns, and plant and animal physiology.

Environmentalists usually work as a team, consulting with specialists in other fields.

A bachelor's degree is needed to obtain work in this field. A person may specialize in biology, ecology, chemistry, forestry, geology, engineering, geography, law, or even architecture.

Many environmentalists work for colleges and universities, combining research with teaching. Others work for federal, state, and local governments. Private research organizations and environmental groups also employ these scientists, as do manufacturers of pollution-control equipment.

For further career information, write to U.S. Environmental Protection Agency, Office of Public Affairs, Washington, DC 20460.

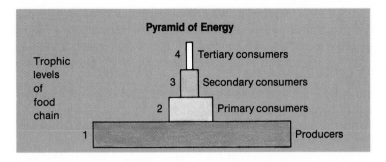

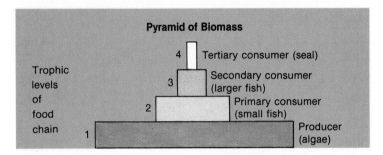

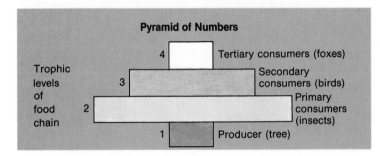

Figure 45-5 A pyramid of energy shows that the total amount of energy decreases at higher and higher trophic levels. A pyramid of biomass shows that the total mass of living things that can be supported decreases at higher and higher trophic levels. A pyramid of numbers shows that the total number of organisms may not necessarily decrease at higher and higher trophic levels.

level, it follows that the **biomass,** or amount of matter, that can be supported at each successive level will also decrease. A *pyramid of biomass* shows this relationship. For example, 1000 kilograms of algae may provide enough energy to support 100 kilograms of small fish. These small fish may provide enough energy to support 10 kilograms of larger fish. In turn, these larger fish may provide enough energy to support 1 kilogram of seal.

Relationships between trophic levels in food chains may also be represented by a *pyramid of numbers*. A pyramid of numbers shows the number of organisms at each level. Usually, the number of organisms decreases as the level increases. In some cases, as in Figure 45-5, the pyramid of numbers may not decrease because it reflects the number of organisms only, regardless of differences in their size.

Sidelight

In order to survive, a 50-kilogram wolf needs to consume approximately 2700 kilograms of moose per year. A moose, in turn, needs to consume about 35,000 kilograms of plants per year.

Pyramids of numbers may sometimes be inverted or unbalanced. For example, one tree at the first trophic level could provide enough energy to support a large number of insects at the second trophic level. In turn, these insects could provide energy needed to support many birds at the third trophic level. The birds could support only a few carnivores, such as foxes, at the next trophic level. Usually, however, if the producers are small in size, the producer level of the pyramid of numbers is large.

Competition

Often, members of a community interact with one another for the same materials. This interaction is known as *competition*. If this competition is among individuals of the same species, it is called *intraspecific competition*. Plants as well as animals may compete with members of their own species for such things as food, space, and light. For example, pine trees compete with one another for water, soil, light, and space. The individuals that are successful in this type of competition are those that are best adapted to their environment.

When two or more populations compete for needed resources another type of competition results. This is known as *interspecific competition*. An example is the competition between duckweed and cattail plants for water and space.

Predator-Prey Relationships

Generally, ecosystems maintain an *ecological balance*, or natural equilibrium. The relationships among members of a community help to maintain this balance. Intraspecific and interspecific competition affect the size and makeup of populations in a community. The effect of **predators** can also limit the size of populations. A predator is an animal that feeds upon another living animal. The animal that is fed upon is called the **prey.** The prey may be a herbivore or a carnivore. Together, these two organisms have what is called a predator-prey relationship. For example, snowshoe hares and lynxes have a predator-prey relationship. The lynx is the predator and the snowshoe hare is the prey. As the number of hares increases, the number of lynxes eventually tends to increase. An increase in the number of lynxes affects the number of hares, and the hare population declines. A lower number of hares cannot support the large number of lynxes, so then the lynx population declines.

At this point, you may want to assign to several students the first of the Extensions and Applications at the end of this chapter.

Sidelight

Before 1907, the Grand Canyon ecosystem had enough vegetation to support 4000 deer. The deer population was balanced by predators, such as mountain lions and wolves. In 1907, people began to kill the predators. By 1924, the deer population had increased to 100,000. The existing vegetation could not support so many deer, and the deer population decreased.

Have some students do research on how people affect specific predator-prey relationships.

Figure 45-6 This lion, a predator, is feeding on his prey, a zebra.

Symbiotic Relationships

The species in a community are all, to a greater or lesser extent, dependent upon one another. Sometimes the dependency is related to feeding and sometimes it is related to other functions necessary for survival. When two organisms interact in a way that affects the survival of one or both of them, their relationship is called **symbiosis** (sim-bī-ō-sis). Symbiotic relationships are divided into three types.

COMMENSALISM In **commensalism** one organism can benefit from another organism called a **host.** In this type of

Highlight

Symbiosis is an interaction of two organisms that contributes to the survival of one or both of them. The three types of symbiotic relationships are commensalism, mutualism, and parasitism.

Figure 45-7 The relationship between this gray whale and the barnacles on its surface is an example of commensalism. The barnacles benefit from their relationship with the whale host. The whale neither benefits from nor is harmed by the relationship.

Figure 45-8 The algae and fungi in this lichen benefit from each other. This relationship is an example of mutualism.

At this point, you may want to assign to several students the fourth of the Extensions and Applications at the end of this chapter.

Figure 45-9 The mistletoe benefits from its relationship with its pine tree host, but the pine tree is harmed. This relationship is an example of parasitism.

relationship, the host is not harmed. For example, in the ocean, whales provide a place of attachment for barnacles. The barnacles are able to obtain a steady supply of food as the whales move through the sea. In the process, the whales, or hosts, are unharmed by the barnacles.

Plants also exhibit commensalism. Some small green plants, such as orchids, grow in rain forests. The orchids grow on the upper branches of trees where there is sunlight. The roots of these orchids obtain water directly from the very moist atmosphere of the rain forest.

MUTUALISM   When two organisms benefit from each other, the relationship is called **mutualism.** For example, *lichens* are made up of two plants, a fungus and an alga. The alga is an autotroph and provides food for the fungus, a heterotroph. In return, the fungus supplies the alga with water, minerals, and physical support.

Another example of mutualism is the relationship between termites and a type of *protozoan*, or one-celled organism. Termites eat wood but are not able to digest *cellulose*, the chief substance in wood. The protozoa, living in the termites' digestive tract, digest cellulose. In return, the protozoa obtain food and water, from the termites.

PARASITISM   When an organism obtains its food from a host and harms the host by doing so, the relationship is called **parasitism.** Organisms that benefit from such a relationship are called parasites. At some point during the life cycle of a parasite, it completely depends upon the host for its needs. Many parasites cause diseases or injury in the organisms from which the parasites get food. For example, some fishes, such as lampreys, spend about one-sixth of their lives living off other fish. During this time, the lamprey bites into the fish, hangs on, and sucks food-containing blood from the fish.

Arthropods are animals with jointed legs. Some arthropods, such as ticks and mites, are parasites. These parasites live off people and animals, often causing injury and infections.

SECTION REVIEW   Answers on page T-107.

1. Define producer, consumer, and decomposer.
2. Distinguish between a food chain and a food web.
3. Name and describe three types of ecological pyramids.
4. Briefly describe a predator-prey relationship.
5. What is symbiosis? Name three types of symbiosis.

Abiotic Factors in the Environment

The abiotic factors of an ecosystem help determine the types of organisms that can live there. For example, a warm salty body of water will support certain organisms, such as sea urchins. A cool, clear stream will not support such living things, but will support freshwater plants and animals. Also, dry sandy soil may support organisms that are not able to survive in damp soil. There are four main abiotic factors.

Water

The kinds of plants and animals found in a particular region are determined in part by the amount of water present. Furthermore, these animals and plants have special adaptations to these particular environments. Cacti can survive in very dry areas because they have extensive root systems that pick up whatever water there is in the soil. Desert animals have special excretory systems that limit the loss of water from their bodies. Desert plants and animals cannot survive in very wet environments. Nor can plants that do well in very wet environments survive in dry areas.

Soil

The soil of the earth contains rocks that have been broken down into tiny particles by the process of *weathering.* Weathering is a slow, continuous process that wears away the land. Because rocks differ in their composition, weathering in different areas produces different soils. These soils

Highlight

Abiotic factors include water, soil, temperature, and light.

Sidelight

The roots of the desert mesquite tree grow as long as 12 meters straight down into the ground.

Figure 45-10 Plants grow even in the Sahara Desert if there is enough water.

contain varying proportions of minerals that influence the growth and development of various plants. In turn, these plants and animals influence the composition of the soil by adding organic materials.

Particles of weathered rock and organic materials are the two main ingredients of soil. Organic material consists of *humus*, or the decayed remains of plants and animals. Humus is vital to the growth of most plants, some small animals, and soil microorganisms.

Temperature

The earth's many environments show a wide range of temperatures. Animals and plants have adapted to many temperature extremes. Weddell seals, which are *endotherms*, or warm-blooded, live in the icy waters of the Antarctic. In general, endothermic animals, such as mammals and birds, can survive in a wide range of temperature conditions. They can do this because they have body processes that can maintain a constant internal temperature.

Cold-blooded animals, or *exotherms*, do not maintain a constant body temperature. Their temperature varies with that of the environment. Examples of exotherms are amphibians, reptiles, and fishes. They become sluggish at relatively high or low temperatures. Exotherms tend to be adapted to specific environments that have a narrow range of temperatures.

Light

Certain plants are better adapted to environments that have a great deal of sunlight. Other plants survive better where there is a great deal of shade. These different plant requirements affect the distribution on the earth of the many plants and of the animals that use them for food. The ocean environment responds in a special way to sunlight. As light penetrates the water, the light is rapidly absorbed, so that hardly any photosynthetic activity occurs at depths greater than 200 meters. Few, if any, green plants are found below such depths.

Sidelight

Desert plants must be able to survive drastic temperature changes. Daytime temperatures of over 38°C can drop by more than 25°C at night.

Some of your students might be interested in investigating marine ecosystems where there is no light from the sun.

SECTION REVIEW Answers on page T–107.

1. List four abiotic factors in the environment.
2. What are the two main ingredients of soil?
3. Distinguish between an exotherm and an endotherm. Give an example of each.

Important Cycles in the Environment

Energy flows through an ecosystem in only one direction. As energy comes from the sun, it is used in life processes and lost in energy transfer as it passes through food chains. In addition to energy, more than 20 different substances must be present in an ecosystem for the proper functioning of certain life processes. The main elements that are required are hydrogen, oxygen, carbon, and nitrogen. Unlike energy, these substances are constantly recycled within an ecosystem. The recycling of substances necessary for life is called a *nutrient cycle* or *biogeochemical cycle.*

Highlight

The recycling of substances necessary for life is called a biogeochemical cycle or nutrient cycle. Biogeochemical cycles include the water cycle, the oxygen cycle, the carbon cycle, and the nitrogen cycle.

The Water Cycle

The movement of water from the atmosphere to the earth and back to the atmosphere is called the **water cycle.** Movement of water from the atmosphere to the earth is called *precipitation.* Much of this water is lost to the atmosphere by *evaporation.* Evaporation occurs when some of the molecules on the surface of a liquid become a gas. The water that reaches the earth in the form of precipitation is eventually returned to the atmosphere through evaporation.

Most of the water that falls onto the earth runs along the surface of the ground. This *runoff* water joins lakes, streams, and rivers. Evaporation is constantly taking place at the surface of these bodies of water. Some of the water that falls to the earth soaks into the ground and is called

Figure 45-11 Water Cycle

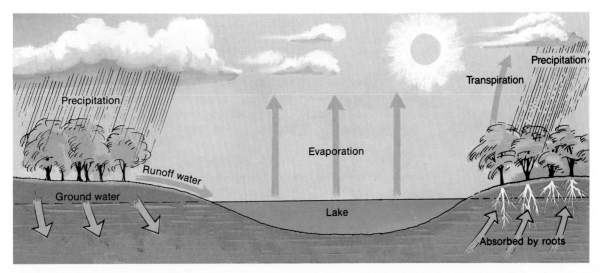

ground water. Some of this ground water flows into underground streams and lakes. Like runoff water, ground water may eventually reach a pond, a lake, or the ocean, where evaporation occurs.

The water vapor that is formed by evaporation is carried into the atmosphere. Here it condenses into water droplets that form clouds. When the clouds become saturated with water, rain or snow begins to fall, which completes the water cycle.

Plants and animals also recycle water, but to a lesser degree. Animals release small amounts of water during respiration and excretion. Green plants lose water from their leaves during *transpiration.*

At this point, you may want to have your students do the Laboratory Investigation at the end of this chapter.

The Oxygen Cycle

Oxygen is needed by most living things for respiration. Oxygen makes up about 20 percent of the air. It is also dissolved in water and makes up a part of water molecules themselves. The movement of oxygen through an ecosystem is called the **oxygen cycle.**

One phase of the oxygen cycle occurs during the process of photosynthesis. In this phase, molecules of water are split, releasing oxygen into the atmosphere. The oxygen is used by most organisms for respiration. One of the products of this respiration is water. The water can be absorbed by plants, which break down the water and release oxygen, thus continuing the oxygen cycle.

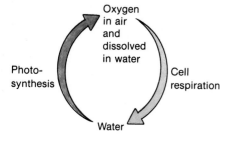

Figure 45-12   Oxygen Cycle

The Carbon Cycle

The element carbon is present as carbon dioxide, which makes up approximately 0.03% of the atmosphere. As carbon moves from the atmosphere to producers and consumers, and from these to decomposers and back to the atmosphere, it can be used over and over again. This process is called the **carbon cycle.** Scientists once considered the carbon cycle to be a perfect cycle that returned carbon to the environment as fast as it was removed. However, the increased burning of fossil fuels has added carbon dioxide to the atmosphere faster than it can be removed.

During photosynthesis, green plants use carbon dioxide from the atmosphere to help form glucose and other carbon-containing substances. Consumers and decomposers ingest these substances, some of which are broken down during respiration. One product of respiration is carbon dioxide. Carbon dioxide is released into the atmosphere, completing the carbon cycle.

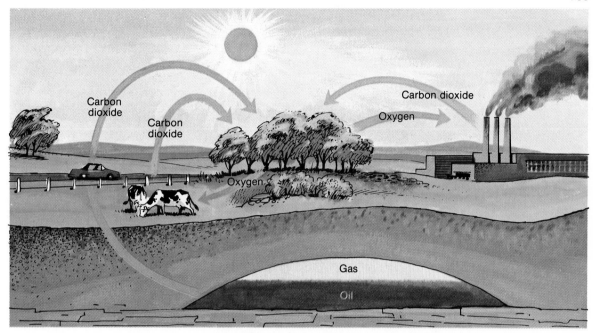

Figure 45-13 Carbon Cycle

The Nitrogen Cycle

Organisms need nitrogen to make proteins. Free nitrogen makes up about 79% of the atmosphere. However, free nitrogen cannot be used by most living things to build proteins. The process through which nitrogen passes from the atmosphere to organisms and back is called the **nitrogen cycle.** In the nitrogen cycle, nitrogen must first be in the form of *nitrates* so that it can be absorbed by plants. Nitrates are compounds that contain nitrogen and oxygen. These nitrates are used by plants to make plant proteins. Animals eat plants and use the plant proteins to make animal proteins. Nitrates are formed in several ways.

When plants and animals die, some bacteria cause the nitrogen in the decaying organism's protein to combine with hydrogen to form *ammonia.* The nitrogen that is found in the metabolic wastes of animals is also converted to ammonia by these bacteria. This process of forming ammonia is called **ammonification** (ə-mō-nə-fi-ΚĀ-shən). The ammonia is then oxidized by other bacteria to form *nitrites.* Eventually, other bacteria change these nitrites into nitrates. This process is called **nitrification.** The nitrates are absorbed by the roots of plants, and the nitrogen cycle continues.

Two types of bacteria can change atmospheric nitrogen directly into nitrates and nitrites. The process by which the bacteria do this is called **nitrogen fixation.** The bacteria are

Have some students report on the farming technique known as crop rotation and on its relationship to the nitrogen cycle.

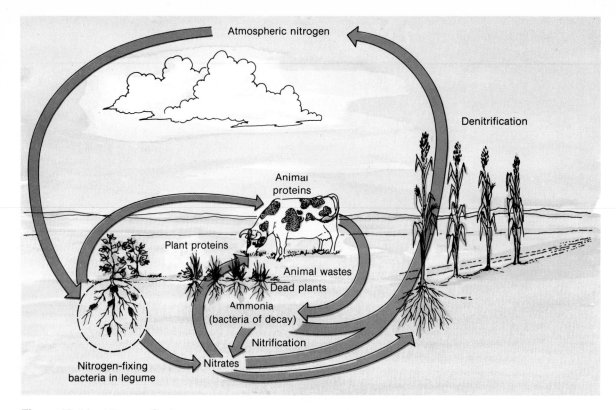

Figure 45–14 Nitrogen Cycle

called *nitrogen-fixing bacteria*. One type of nitrogen-fixing bacteria is widely distributed in the soil. The other type of bacteria lives on the roots of certain plants called *legumes*. These bacteria have a symbiotic relationship with the plants, providing them with nitrates. Peas, beans, peanuts, alfalfa, and clover are examples of legumes. Plants that are not legumes must obtain nitrogen from nitrates in the soil, which may be there naturally or placed there in fertilizers. Some aquatic plants obtain nitrogen from nitrates dissolved in water.

Nitrogen can pass from organisms to the soil and back many times before it is released into the atmosphere. The organisms that send nitrogen back to the atmosphere carry out a process called **denitrification.** *Denitrifyng bacteria* convert nitrites, nitrates, and ammonia into free nitrogen and release it. By returning free nitrogen to the atmosphere, the bacteria complete the nitrogen cycle.

SECTION REVIEW Answers on page T–107.

1. Distinguish between precipitation and evaporation.
2. Name four nutrient cycles.
3. What is nitrogen fixation? Denitrification?

The Role of Green Plants in the Water Cycle

Purpose Organisms use a variety of elements and compounds for their metabolism. All of these substances come from the environment and must be returned to it. One such substance, water, goes through a cycle from the environment to organisms and back. The purpose of this investigation is to observe the role of green plants in the water cycle.

Materials *(per 2 students)* ● 4 large clear plastic tumblers or wide-mouth glass containers ● 2 15-cm squares of wax paper ● 2 strips of blue cobalt chloride paper ● Dissecting needle ● Petroleum jelly ● Plant leaf with stem ● Wax pencil ● Tape

Procedure **1.** Label one of the tumblers A and the other B with the wax pencil. **2.** Fill both tumblers with water and apply a small amount of petroleum jelly around the rims of each. **3.** Place the wax paper over both tumblers containing the petroleum jelly and gently press down along the edges. **4.** With the dissecting needle, make a tiny hole in the center of the wax paper on tumbler A. **5.** Insert the plant leaf stem into the hole, so that the stem is in the water. **6.** Place a small amount of petroleum jelly around the stem where it emerges through the wax paper. See the figure. This provides an airtight seal. Be careful not to get any petroleum jelly on the blade of the leaf. **7.** Tape a piece of blue cobalt chloride paper to the inside bottom of each of the two remaining tumblers. **8.** Apply petroleum jelly to the rims of both of these tumblers. **9.** Invert each of these tumblers over tumbler A and B and gently press them together. Do not allow the leaf to touch the cobalt chloride paper. **10.** Place each of these sets of tumblers in a well-lighted area. **11.** Copy the table and record the changes in the cobalt chloride paper in each setup at one-minute intervals for 10 minutes. **12.** Allow the setup for A to remain untouched for 24 hours. Record any changes after this period.

Observations and Conclusions **1.** Which setup represents the control? Explain. **2.** Does the color of the blue cobalt chloride paper change? If so, what causes the change? **3.** After 24 hours, what substance collects on the interior of setup A? **4.** How does this experiment show the recycling of water by green plants?

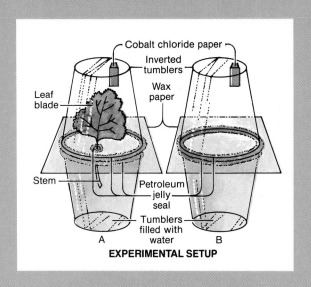

Cobalt chloride paper
Inverted tumblers
Wax paper
Leaf blade
Stem
Petroleum jelly seal
Tumblers filled with water
A
B

EXPERIMENTAL SETUP

Time (in minutes)	Color of cobalt chloride paper	
	A	B
0		
1		
2		
3		
4		
5		
6		
7		
8		
9		
10		

CHAPTER SUMMARY

The Biosphere   Ecology is the study of the relationships between living things and their environment. These relationships take place in the biosphere, which is divided into smaller units called ecosystems. An ecosystem is an interacting system that consists of groups of organisms and their nonliving environment. Each ecosystem contains biotic and abiotic factors.

Ecosystems are made up of communities that include all the living organisms in a certain area. Communities consist of a number of populations. A population is a group of individuals of the same species that live in the same area. Each organism in a community has a habitat, or place in which it lives, and a niche, or a particular role, within the habitat.

Biotic Interactions in the Environment   Organisms are divided into three groups according to the way in which they obtain their food. Producers, or green plants, make their own food by the process of photosynthesis. Producers are also called autotrophs. Consumers feed directly or indirectly upon producers. Those that feed directly upon producers are called primary consumers or herbivores. Those that feed upon primary consumers are called secondary consumers or carnivores. Animals that feed on both plants and animals are called omnivores. Decomposers are organisms that break down organic material and return it to the environment. Consumers and decomposers are also called heterotrophs. Heterotrophic plants called saprophytes feed upon dead organisms or the waste products of living organisms. Animals that feed upon dead organisms are called scavengers.

In an ecosystem, energy from producers passes through a system of consumers. This flow of energy and organic materials through a number of organisms is called a food chain. Food chains that interconnect or overlap form a food web. Each feeding level in a food chain is called a trophic level. Producers belong to the first trophic level, primary consumers belong to the second trophic level, secondary consumers belong to the third trophic level, and so on. Relationships among the different levels in food chains may be represented in ecological pyramids.

Members of a community interact with one another for the same materials. This is called competition. Intraspecific competition takes place among members of the same species. Interspecific competition results when two or more different species compete.

Certain factors help maintain an ecological balance in communities. Both competition and predator–prey relationships help to maintain the size of populations.

Symbiosis is the interaction between two organisms that affects the survival of one or both. There are three types of symbiotic relationships. These types of relationships are commensalism, mutualism, and parasitism.

Abiotic Factors in the Environment   Water, soil, temperature, and light are abiotic factors. All organisms need water to perform life functions. The type of soil determines the type of plants that grow in a given area. Average environmental temperatures affect the distribution of animals and plants around the world. The amount of sunlight determines the types of plants that can grow in an area. This, in turn, determines the types of animals that can live in the area.

Important Cycles in the Environment   In addition to energy, more than 20 different substances must be present in an ecosystem for living things to carry on vital processes. The four most important of these are the elements hydrogen, oxygen, carbon, and nitrogen. These substances are constantly recycled within an ecosystem. Nutrient, or biogeochemical, cycles include the water cycle, the oxygen cycle, the carbon cycle, and the nitrogen cycle.

CHAPTER VOCABULARY

ammonification	**denitrification**	**niche**	**prey**
biomass	**ecology**	**nitrification**	**producer**
biosphere	**ecosystem**	**nitrogen cycle**	**saprophyte**
carbon cycle	**food chain**	**nitrogen fixation**	**scavenger**
commensalism	**food web**	**oxygen cycle**	**symbiosis**
community	**habitat**	**parasitism**	**trophic level**
consumer	**host**	**population**	**water cycle**
decomposer	**mutualism**	**predator**	

REVIEW of FACTS and CONCEPTS Answers on page T–108.

On a separate sheet of paper, answer each of the following as completely as possible.

1. What is an ecosystem? Give an example of an ecosystem.
2. Why is sunlight needed to maintain an ecosystem?
3. What are the three groups of organisms that are classified according to the way in which they obtain their food? Give an example of an organism in each group.
4. Distinguish between an autotroph and a heterotroph.
5. Draw a food chain. Identify the different parts of the chain.
6. Describe an example of a food web.
7. Why does each trophic level in a food chain contain less energy than the level below it?
8. Explain how energy flows through a food chain in an ecosystem.
9. Why is it more energy-efficient for humans to eat plants instead of animals?
10. Briefly describe a predator-prey relationship.
11. Distinguish between the terms in each pair: habitat and niche; herbivore and carnivore; intraspecific competition and interspecific competition.

EXTENSIONS and APPLICATIONS For additional information, see page T–108.

1. Visit the library and research the effect of introducing certain foreign plants or animals into this country. Examples of some of these organisms are the Russian thistle, starling, English sparrow, gypsy moth, and European corn borer. Prepare an oral report showing how these organism benefited or harmed the environment.
2. Investigate the environment near your home. Identify the ecosystems and how they are related. Identify some food chains and food webs and illustrate them in a chart. Note any recent changes in the ecological balance of the area.
3. Collect three different samples of soil from three different areas. Compare the color, particle size, and capacity to absorb water for each of the soils. Also compare the smell and texture of the soils. In each type of soil plant some seeds, giving them sufficient water. In which soil did the seeds grow best? Explain.
4. Find a large tree near your school or home. Observe the tree for a week and make a list of plants and animals that use the tree for shelter or food. What would happen to this ecosystem if one kind of organism were removed? Explain.
5. Obtain a small aquarium. Place a 1-centimeter layer of small stones in the bottom of the aquarium and cover it with 10 centimeters of soil. Obtain a few small green plants and carefully place them in the aquarium. Gently put in more soil to anchor the plants, and moisten with water. Do not pack the soil down tightly. In one part of the aquarium, place a small dish of water. Collect some earthworms, land snails, and small insects and place them in the aquarium. Cover the top of the aquarium with thin screening to prevent the escape of the small animals. Observe this ecosystem for a few weeks. Prepare a written report on the changes that occur.

SUGGESTED READINGS

Farb, P., *Ecology*. New York: Time-Life Books.
  In this introductory book, the author, an experienced naturalist, explains how living organisms on the earth form communities. Many photographs and diagrams are included.
McCombs, L.W., and N. Rosa, *What's Ecology?* Menlo Park, Calif.: Addison-Wesley.
  The authors describe nutrient cycles and the flow of energy through ecosystems. They also explain the factors that affect populations.
Meeker, J.W., *The Spheres of Life: An Introduction to World Ecology*. New York: Scribners.
  The author offers simple explanations of the basics of ecology and discusses reasons for environmental problems such as pollution.

46 Succession and Population Changes

Plants begin to reappear soon after a volcanic eruption.

For teaching aids for this chapter, including a chapter overview and teaching strategies, see pages T–108 to T–110. The page number next to each chapter objective refers to the text page where the information needed to fulfill the objective begins.

Change is a characteristic of the natural world. Ponds and lakes become overgrown with plants. Trees and large shrubs invade meadowlands. Small streams become wider and deeper.

If you have lived in the same area for several years, you may have noticed changes taking place in a nearby vacant lot. First, small clumps of grass began to grow. Then, the lot may have become overgrown with small weeds. As the time passed, you may have noticed that taller and different types of weeds began to grow. Changes such as these tend to occur gradually over a number of years.

Other changes may occur quickly. In just a few days, a volcanic eruption can destroy a tree-covered mountain and fill nearby lakes with mud and ash. Floods, forest fires, and other natural disasters also cause rapid changes in the nature of ecosystems.

Ecological Succession

During the development of an ecosystem, the ecosystem goes through a series of changes known as **ecological succession,** or *ecosystem succession.* The changes happen within the structure of the community and usually are caused by the community itself. During succession, organisms tend to change their environment in such a way as to make conditions less favorable for themselves and more favorable for other organisms. The new organisms take over and, in turn, eventually make conditions unfavorable for their own survival and favorable for the survival of other organisms.

Abiotic factors also have a role in ecological succession. Temperature, amount of rainfall and light, geological features, or other abiotic factors may change gradually. These changes may also cause biotic changes. Some populations may be destroyed or may move out of an area. Other organisms may find the new conditions favorable and move in. Abiotic changes can speed up or slow down succession.

Succession in a Lake Ecosystem

Succession occurs in all ecosystems. A lake is an example of an ecosystem that is not permanent, and undergoes succession. The length of time required for a lake to undergo ecological succession varies. The size of the lake and abiotic conditions around the lake will affect this time.

A lake may begin as a cold, clear body of water that is surrounded by a forest. At this time, the lake contains very few nutrients and waste materials, and little decaying organic matter. Plants, such as water lilies and cattails, grow around the edge of the lake. Their root systems hold soil in place. Various species of algae are the main producers in the lake.

A succession process called **eutrophication** can occur. Streams that run into the lake carry *sediments,* such as silt and sand, into the lake. The sediments may contain additional nutrients, such as minerals. Flocks of migrating birds, such as ducks and geese, may stop at the lake, and leave large amounts of nitrogenous waste materials. The additional nutrients help to promote plant growth. New species of plants begin to establish themselves in the area. They are followed by new species of animals.

Gradually, the biomass of the lake increases, and the lake acquires a murky greenish color. Dissolved oxygen in the water is used up faster than it can be replaced. The amount of decaying material on the bottom of the lake increases. The soil washed into the lake by streams makes the

At this point, you may want to assign to several students the first of the Extensions and Applications at the end of this chapter.

Highlight

The stages an ecosystem passes through during ecological succession include pioneering, development, and the establishment of a climax community.

Figure 46-1 As sediments fill a lake, the kinds of plants able to grow there change.

Figure 46-2 Stages of Succession in a Lake Ecosystem

lake more shallow. The lake begins to fill with soil along the shoreline and small plants and shrubs begin to grow. Over a long period of time, the lake fills with soil and becomes a marsh. The succession will continue for many years, and a forest may finally develop where the lake once was.

During the succession of the lake, the species of animals and plants change. Fishes that live in cool, well-oxygenated water such as trout and sturgeon, are replaced by fishes that can live in warmer, less-oxygenated water, such as bass and perch. Frogs, snails, birds, and other land animals gradually move into the area as a marsh begins to form.

Human activity may also influence succession. For example, dumping organic wastes into lakes increases the nutrients available to plants. If grassland or forests around lakes are destroyed, more soil is washed into lakes because the rate of erosion increases. Dams may also cause the water level in a lake to rise or fall. Any of these activities would change the abiotic and biotic factors of the lake, and influence the succession of the lake.

Succession in a Sand Dune

Along the beaches of large lakes and oceans, winds blow sand inland. The sand is deposited in large mounds called *dunes.* Succession on a sand dune may take several hundred years.

PIONEERING STAGES First, organic matter from the lake or ocean is washed up on the beach. If it remains there, small sections of the beach are enriched with nutrients, and small patches of grass may begin to grow. The grasses are called **pioneer plants.** Pioneer plants are the first plants to dominate a developing ecosystem. As the grasses grow and spread, their roots trap the sand. As the grasses die and decay, they add more nutrients to the soil.

DEVELOPMENTAL STAGES Animals and the wind may carry seeds from shrubs onto the dune. These shrub seeds can now grow because the soil has been enriched with nutrients. These shrubs, in turn, prepare the way for small trees. Insects and birds begin to increase their use of the area. Decaying leaves and organic wastes from the insects and birds help increase the nutrients in the soil.

Pine trees may then be able to grow on the dune. Through the years, the pine trees become the dominant species. However, as the pines develop, older pine trees shade the younger pine trees. These younger trees do not receive enough sunlight and die. Eventually, the older pines dis-

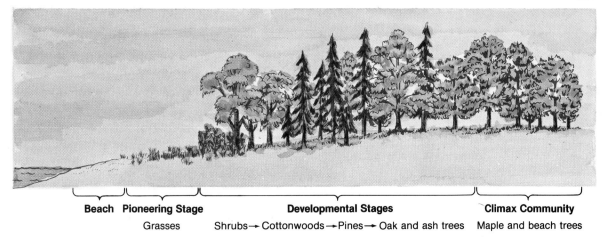

Beach | Pioneering Stage | Developmental Stages | Climax Community
Grasses | Shrubs→ Cottonwoods→Pines→ Oak and ash trees | Maple and beach trees

Figure 46-3 Stages of Succession in a Sand Dune

appear from the dune and die out because there are no young pine trees to replace the old ones.

During the growth and development of the pines, other tree seeds, such as acorns from oak trees and seeds from ash trees, may be carried into the area by squirrels or birds. These trees develop in shady areas and, eventually, grow taller than the pines. The pines cannot survive the shade and die. Other types of trees, such as sugar maple and beech, also begin to grow in the fertile soil.

CLIMAX COMMUNITY   Maple and beech seedlings thrive in the shade, and begin to crowd out the oak and ash trees. In this way, maple and beech become the dominant species. This can take many years. These trees are also called the **climax species.** The climax species continue to replace organisms with young of the same species. At this point, the community is stable and is called the **climax community.** In a climax community, no major changes will occur unless there are severe climate changes, natural disasters, or disturbances by people. Death and birth rates of the different organisms remain about the same. There are no major changes in the kinds of species or the structure of the community.

Types of Succession

The development of a community in an area where there has not been a community is called **primary succession.** Bare rock, lava-covered areas, and sand surfaces are examples of areas where new communities may begin. In an area that is undergoing primary succession on bare rock, lichens are the pioneer plants. The acids and other chemicals that lichens produce help change the rock chemically. Eventually, wind, rain, and other natural forces help break apart the rock,

Figure 46-4 Lichens are pioneer plants in most rock-covered environments.

Abandoned farmland

1-2 years

Grassland

3-20 years

Grassland with shrubs

25-100 years

Pine forest

Pine forest

100-150 + years

Oak and hickory climax community

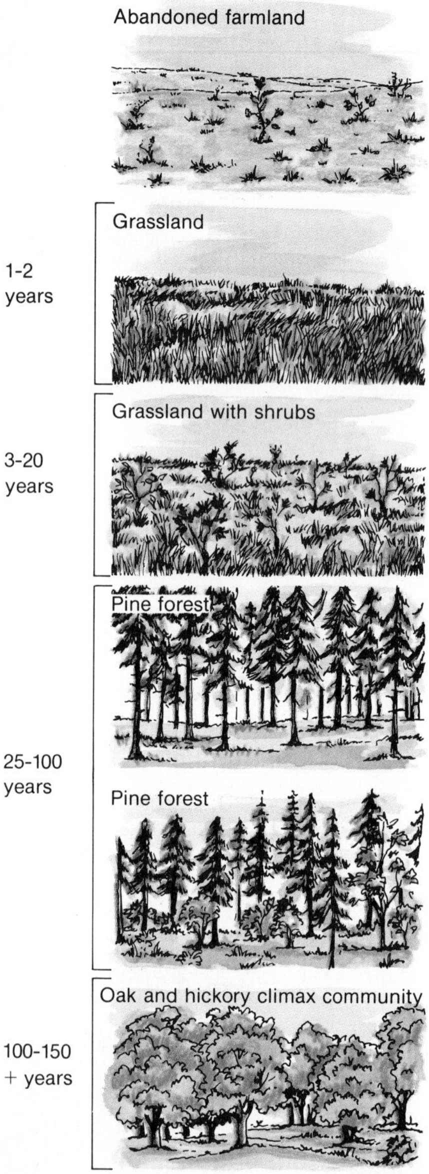

Figure 46-5 Secondary succession usually begins with grasses and proceeds until a climax community of hardwood forest develops.

At this point, you may want to assign to several students the third of the Extensions and Applications at the end of this chapter.

forming a thin layer of soil. Only a few species are in the community at this stage of primary succession. Mosses may develop as the soil becomes richer from tiny bits of organic material resulting from lichen decay. As the soil becomes more suitable for other organisms, new species move in and alter the environment in their own ways.

The development of a community in an area where a previous community was removed is called **secondary succession.** For example, secondary succession occurs in areas where forests are cut down or destroyed by fire, other natural disasters, and diseases. Abandoned farmland also undergoes secondary succession. Usually, secondary succession re-establishes the original community.

Secondary succession usually progresses more rapidly than primary succession because some plants and animals are already present and the soil contains nutrients. Grasses are usually the pioneer plants. Weeds and small shrubs usually follow. Later, fast-growing trees, such as poplars, begin to grow. Trees such as pines, which need a great deal of sunlight usually follow. Secondary succession proceeds until a forest develops, resulting in a climax community.

Climax communities vary in species composition from place to place. In some areas, the climax species may be oak and hickory trees. In others, maple and beech trees may be the climax species. Pines, fir trees, and spruces may be the climax species in still other regions.

Climax communities are more complex than the preceding stages. There are more species in climax communities and many more species interrelationships. In fact, at the beginning of succession, only five or six kinds of organisms may be involved in a food chain. Climax communities may have 30 to 40 kinds of organisms in a food web.

Some of your students might want to do research on the reasons a climax species differs from ecosystem to ecosystem.

SECTION REVIEW   Answers on page T–109.

1. What is ecological succession?
2. What is meant by pioneer plants? Climax species?
3. What is primary succession? Secondary succession?

Time Rhythms and Cycles in Biotic Communities

The activities of many organisms are tied to cycles of time. These activities may follow a daily, monthly, or annual cycle. The cycles are called *rhythmic* because they are regular and predictable. For example, many animals sleep or feed only at certain times of day. The release of an egg cell from the ovaries of a human female takes place in a cycle that is approximately one month long. For many kinds of birds, nest building, breeding, incubation, and caring for the young occur only once a year. Another annual cycle is found in monarch butterflies. Each year, groups of these butterflies travel more than 2800 kilometers. They start their journey in the northern United States and Canada and eventually land in Pacific Grove, California. The city, also known as Butterfly City, celebrates the arrival of the butterflies. The arrival is so regular and predictable that the people of Pacific Grove can plan the date of the celebration in advance, knowing that the butterflies will arrive on time.

Biologists have been attempting to determine how rhythmic behavior in organisms is controlled. One of the factors seems to be variations in light. For example, changes in

Highlight

The time rhythms organisms pass through include circadian rhythms, lunar rhythms, and annual rhythms.

CAREER: Animal Behaviorist

When a bee finds flowers with high nectar content, the bee can convey information on the location of the flowers to the other bees in the hive by performing a "dance." Lions will establish and defend a territory. Homing pigeons always find their way home. Salmon always go upstream to spawn, sometimes traveling many kilometers. Animal behaviorists study the reasons why animals act in particular ways, their instincts, intelligence, needs, and ability to learn.

Animal behaviorists who study the behavior of animals in their natural habitats are called ethologists. These scientists are interested in such behaviors as courtship and care of young. Ethologists want to find out how these behaviors help animal populations survive. Scientists also study animal communication. For example, some behaviorists record and analyze the whistles, barks, and clicks used by porpoises to communicate with one another.

Some animal behaviorists are interested in the intelligence of animals and in how the animals learn. Studies of these subjects are part of an area of zoology called comparative psychology. Comparative psychologists are interested in the relationship of the intelligence of an animal to its brain structure. They devise experiments to test an animal's ability to learn.

Some animal behaviorists study the social behavior of animals in their natural habitat. They study such topics as how animals in a population interact, and how animals in a population react when outsiders are introduced into the group.

A bachelor's degree in biology is needed to work in this field. However, an advanced degree is preferred. Animal behaviorists have strong backgrounds in genetics, physiology, evolutionary theory, and comparative psychology.

Most animal behaviorists work for colleges and universities, combining research with teaching. Some animal behaviorists work for natural history museums and zoos.

For further career information, write to American Society of Zoologists, Box 2739, California Lutheran College, Thousand Oaks, CA 91360.

the length of daylight as seasons change alters the secretion of certain hormones in birds. These hormones influence the activity of the birds. The hormones may influence cyclic breeding and nesting behavior. Temperature changes also influence the activities of organisms and may be responsible for biological cycles. In the Rocky Mountains, for example, elk move between high and low mountain areas as temperatures rise and fall.

Circadian Rhythms

The activities of many organisms, including people, are based on a 24-hour cycle. Such cycles are called **circadian** (sər-KĀ-dē-ən) **rhythms.** These cycles are controlled by an internal mechanism called a **biological clock.** Scientists are not sure where the control center is located. However, recent experiments provide evidence that protein production in cells may, in some way, control circadian rhythms.

These rhythms can result in an organism being active at night or during daylight hours. Animals that are active during the night, such as owls and bats, are called **nocturnal** (nahk-TER-n'l). Other organisms that are active during the day, such as hawks, are called **diurnal** (dī-ER-n'l).

Circadian rhythms can be observed in some flowering plants. Morning glories, for example, open every morning and close before night. Other plants, such as some cacti, flower at night. Marine *zooplankton*, or microscopic animals of the ocean, also exhibit circadian rhythms. They move toward the surface of the ocean at the end of the day and then move downward at dawn. Differing periods of activity permit many species to occupy the same habitat. However, they do not occupy the same niche. These alternating patterns of behavior help organisms survive.

In humans, pulse rate, body temperature, blood pressure, cell division, and the sleep-wake cycle are keyed to circadian rhythms. During a 24-hour period, a person's body temperature may rise and fall one or two degrees. It is higher toward evening and lower toward morning. Blood pressure is also lower in the morning than in the evening. Skin cells appear to divide most often between midnight and 4:00 A.M. Some people even sleep better between 4:00 A.M. and 11:00 A.M. than at night.

Figure 46-6 Circadian rhythms are observable in both plants and animals. Flowers of the morning glory close before evening. The owl is active at night.

Jet lag is a common problem among travelers. Some students may wish to investigate this problem in relation to circadian rhythms.

Lunar Rhythms

The gravitational pull of the moon on the earth causes tides. There is a pattern to the tides. In most places, a high tide occurs about every 12 hours. The tidal water rises gradually for six hours and then slowly falls back for six hours. The life activities of many organisms are affected by the rise and fall of the tides. During low tide, for instance, marine organisms left ashore must keep from drying out. Small fishes and *crustaceans*, such as crabs, survive in small, land-locked puddles of water called *tidal pools*. Mussels, clams, and barnacles close their shells until submerged once again at high tide.

The reproductive cycle of a small, silver fish called a grunion is affected by the tide. On three or four nights during the spring and summer, the tides are at their highest. At this time grunions come ashore to spawn.

The male grunions arrive ashore first, followed by the females about 20 minutes later. The fishes ride the waves up onto the beach as far as possible. As the tide moves out, the females dig into the sand and deposit from 1000 to 3000 eggs each. The males then fertilize the eggs.

When the tide comes in, the adult fishes are carried back into the ocean. The tide pulls sand over the eggs as it goes out again, burying the eggs to a depth of 20 to 40 centimeters. About 10 days later, the eggs hatch, and the small grunions are carried out to sea by the tides.

Figure 46-7 Grunions come ashore to spawn when the spring and summer tides are at their highest.

Annual Rhythms

Many plants and animals exhibit annual rhythms. A large number of plants flower and produce fruit only once a year. Some animals breed and raise young once a year. Other animals travel from northern areas to southern areas and return over the course of one year. Annual cycles are common in areas where there are definite winter and summer or wet and dry seasons.

Many annual rhythms are related to reproduction. In plants that reproduce sexually, the male sex cells must be mature at the same time as are the female sex cells. If pollen is carried from flower to flower by insects, it is important that the flowers mature when insects are present. New offspring must be born when temperatures are warm. There must be a proper amount of water and food. In some cases, certain types of shelter must be available. Correct timing of all the necessary factors promotes successful reproduction.

SEASONAL CHANGES Organisms have many adaptations to seasonal changes. Seasonal changes involve changes in such factors as food supply, water supply, and temperature. Some animals, such as bats, squirrels, chipmunks, woodchucks, and many reptiles and amphibians, reduce the effects of cold temperatures and food shortages by going

Sidelight

During hibernation, the body temperature of a woodchuck may drop to as low as 4°C. Its heart beats once every 10 or 15 seconds. The woodchuck breathes at the same slow rate.

A review of the key physiological points made in Unit Seven might be helpful in understanding the seasonal changes of hibernation, estivation, and migration.

Figure 46-8 The life processes of the chipmunk slow down during hibernation.

Sidelight

Small quantities of magnetized iron have been found in the brains of several animals. The presence of iron makes the animals in effect living compasses.

Figure 46-9 Herds of wildebeest migrate in search of new sources of food.

into **hibernation.** Hibernation is a state of inactivity that takes place in the winter.

During hibernation, the life processes of an organism slow down. The organism's breathing is slow and irregular. Its blood pressure becomes lower, and its body temperatures may drop to near freezing. The body organs and glands function only enough to keep the animal alive. The small amounts of energy that are needed are obtained from stored fat. As temperatures begin to rise with the changing seasons, the animal comes out of hibernation. However, several hours must pass before metabolic processes speed up enough for the animal to become alert.

Some animals, such as bears, opossums, and skunks, spend much of their time sleeping during the winter months. However, these animals do not really hibernate. Although their metabolic rates slow down, their sleep is normal but deep. These animals wake up from time to time to search for food.

Some animals must escape the hot temperatures of summer. These animals, such as desert pocket mice, frogs, and turtles, go through a period of **estivation.** Estivation is a period of summer inactivity. During estivation, animals conserve water as well as energy.

The life cycles of many plants correspond closely with seasonal changes in the availability of water. Plants that live only for one season are called *annuals*. In North America, there are two types of annuals. Summer annuals germinate and develop in the summer and early fall. Winter annuals germinate and develop in the winter and spring. For instance, many winter annuals grow in the Mojave Desert, where rain falls during the winter. Summer annuals are common in the Chihuahuan Desert, which has its rainy season in summer. However, the Sonoran Desert has rains during both summer and winter. Therefore, both summer and winter annuals grow in this area.

MIGRATION The movement of animals from one region to another and back is called **migration.** Many animals migrate seasonally in search of warmth, water, and food. Birds usually migrate to escape cold temperatures and poor food supplies. The African wildebeest and other herbivores migrate from dry areas to those where rain is plentiful to meet their requirement of at least 680 kilograms of green grass per hectare. Some of the carnivores that feed on wildebeest migrate along with them.

Many mysteries surround migration. Scientists do not know how long-distance migrating organisms find their way from one area to another and back. Scientists have found

At this point, you may want to assign to several students the second of the Extensions and Applications at the end of this chapter.

evidence that animals may navigate by using the sun, moon, stars, and the magnetic field of the earth. Temperature, odors, and the amount of food or moisture present in an environment also seem to help determine the routes of migrating organisms.

SECTION REVIEW   Answers on page T–109.

1. What is a circadian rhythm?
2. How does the moon affect the rhythmic cycles of some organisms?
3. What is the difference between hibernation and estivation?
4. List three reasons why animals migrate.

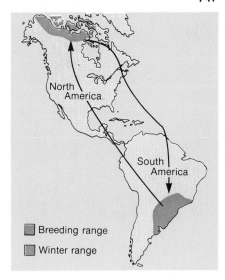

Figure 46-10   The round-trip migration route of the golden plover is more than 19,000 kilometers long. The plover breeds in northern Canada and then migrates to South America.

Population Changes

Many factors affect the size of populations. For instance, new offspring and **immigrants,** or organisms moving into an area, increase the size of a population. Deaths and **emigrants,** or organisms that move out of an area, reduce the size of a population. Change in population size can be expressed in a mathematical formula.

$$\text{Change in population size} = (\text{Births} + \text{Immigrants}) - (\text{Deaths} + \text{Emigrants})$$

For example, a population of rabbits produces 150 offspring per season. During the same period, 10 rabbits move in, 50 die, and 20 leave the area. The net change in population size is an increase of 90 rabbits.

In a climax community, the population size of any given species stays about the same because birth rates and death rates remain about the same. In developing communities, populations may change in size. Food supply, changes in temperature or amount of rainfall, or the introduction or elimination of animals or plants into or out of a community are also factors that may affect the size of any population.

People can also affect the sizes of populations. When land is cleared to build homes and factories, the living space of certain animals and plants is reduced, and food webs may be interrupted. Increased use of insecticides and fertilizers, and changes in abiotic factors, such as soil, air, and water quality, may also occur with land use by people. Changes in these factors have increased the size of some populations and decreased the size of others.

Highlight

The change in the size of a population of organisms is affected by the number of new organisms entering the population by birth or immigration and the number of organisms leaving the population by death or emigration.

Biotic Potential and Carrying Capacity

Every population has a **biotic potential** that can be attained if there is enough food and living space to support the population. In addition, no other factors can be present that would slow the rate of population growth. Therefore, the biotic potential of a species is the possible size a population would reach if all offspring survive and produce young. For example, under ideal conditions, a pair of elephants would have 19 million descendants after 750 years. However, neither an elephant population nor any other population ever achieves its biotic potential. Factors such as food supply, living space, and water supply prevent organisms from reaching their biotic potential. These factors are called **limiting factors,** or *environmental resistance.*

If you were to investigate the growth of a population you would notice that there is a pattern to the growth. On a graph, this pattern appears as an S-shaped curve called a **population growth curve.** A population growth curve shows that, at first, a population increases slowly in size. Then, the increase becomes more rapid. Eventually, the population growth levels off. There may be small declines and increases in the size of the population, but these variations remain within a specific range. At this stable level, the population has reached the **carrying capacity** of the environment. Carrying capacity is the size of a population that the environment can support. The carrying capacities of different areas vary based on the limiting factors in each area.

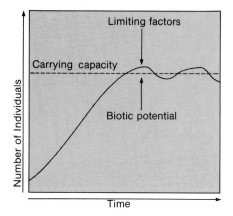

Figure 46-11 A population growth curve shows the growth of a population related to time. The population of a species is prevented from reaching its biotic potential by various limiting factors. A population becomes stable at its carrying capacity.

Population Density

The number of individuals of a certain species per unit area is called **population density.** For example, the density of earthworms can be as high as 700 per square meter of soil. A recent survey of the lion density in an African wildlife preserve showed 1.5 lions per square kilometer. In the same area, the density of hunting dogs was 0.02.

If a population density is higher than the carrying capacity of an area, many individuals may die. Subsequently there may be a great drop in population density. However, high population density that does not surpass carrying capacity has some advantages.

In sexually reproducing organisms, there is greater *genetic diversity* in large populations than in small ones. That is, there is a wider variety of inherited traits within the population. Such diversity increases the chances of the population adapting to environmental changes. High genetic diversity thereby increases a population's probability of survival.

Highlight

Carrying capacity is the maximum size of a population that a particular ecosystem can support. Population density is equal to the number of organisms in a particular ecosystem divided by the area of that ecosystem.

High population densities provide other benefits to living things. For example, many herbivores that move in herds, such as zebras and wildebeest, can better protect themselves and their young when they are in a large group. Grasses must grow in very dense populations to keep soil from eroding, or washing away. A dense grass population also keeps other plants from growing in the area and competing for resources.

If population density becomes too low, the population may die out. If such a population holds all the remaining members of a species, the species may become *extinct*. Scientists think that the California condor will become extinct because of its low population density. A recent survey showed that there were fewer than 50 of these condors alive in the world. Their low numbers make it difficult for condors to find suitable mates. Scientists estimate that a minimum population of 500 individuals is necessary to guarantee long-term survival in nature. The size of a population and, therefore, the probability of its survival is affected by a number of factors.

DENSITY-DEPENDENT FACTORS The effect of limiting factors on a population are often directly related to the density of the population. If the intensity of the factor depends on the population density, it is called a **density-dependent factor.** An example of a density-dependent factor is *predation*. For example, when the population density of deer is very high, the food supply of grass, twigs, and shrubs is inadequate to feed all of the deer. Some of the deer become weak. Predators, such as wolves, have less trouble finding and killing deer. As a result, the deer population density declines.

Most biotic factors, such as disease, availability of food, predation, competition, and parasitism, are density dependent. That is, the effects of these factors increase as the population density increases. These factors do not usually eliminate an entire population. Instead, density-dependent limiting factors help to keep the population density of a species near the carrying capacity of the environment. When factors such as these reduce the population, more food and space become available. There is less competition, and the population increases again.

DENSITY-INDEPENDENT FACTORS Some limiting factors have an effect on populations regardless of the population densities. These factors are called **density-independent factors.** Density-independent factors are generally abiotic factors. These factors include temperature, rainfall, wind speed

750

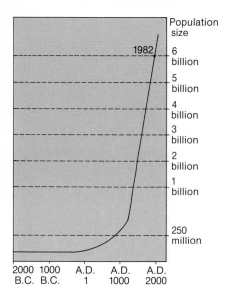

Figure 46-12 For the last 1000 years, the human population has increased at a tremendous rate.

At this point, you may want to assign to your students the fourth of the Extensions and Applications at the end of this chapter.

Figure 46-13 The human population density varies greatly from continent to continent.

Human Population Density by Continent

Europe		66 per km²
Asia		61 per km²
Africa		16 per km²
North America		15 per km²
South America		14 per km²
Australia		5 per km²

At this point, you may want to have your students do the Laboratory Investigation at the end of this chapter.

and direction, air quality, and the amount of available light. For example, ideal moisture conditions for tomatoes also provide the best conditions for molds to grow on the tomatoes. The mold growth takes over regardless of the density of the tomato plants. Slow changes, such as the erosion of a canyon, are also density independent. Catastrophic events, such as earthquakes and volcanic eruptions, also affect populations, regardless of their densities.

Human Populations

Scientists estimate that, worldwide, 230 babies are born and 90 people die every 60 seconds. Therefore, under these conditions, the human population of the earth increases by approximately 140 people per minute. If this *natality rate*, or birth rate, remains higher than the *mortality rate*, or death rate, until the end of the century, scientists predict that by the year 2000 there will be more than 6.2 billion people living on the earth. This is twice the population of the world in 1960 and six times the size of the population in 1850. The growth rate seems to be slowing down, however. It was 2% per year between 1960 and 1965 and is now about 1.7% per year. Scientists predict an annual increase of 1.6% by the year 2000.

Scientists estimate that the carrying capacity of the earth is from 8 to 11 billion people. This number is difficult to predict because many factors are involved, including living space, food supply, and use of resources. However, most of the limiting factors that affect other organisms also affect people. If this estimate is correct, the human population density is approaching the upper limit of the carrying capacity of the earth. At the current 1.7% growth rate, the world's human population will reach 9 billion people in the year 2020 and 18 billion in the year 2060. New technologies, medical practices, and sources of food, and new kinds of housing, communications, and transportation networks will have to be developed to support such a population.

SECTION REVIEW   Answers on page T-109.

1. What are immigrants? Emigrants?
2. What factors prevent a population from reaching its biotic potential?
3. What is meant by carrying capacity?
4. What is meant by density-dependent factors? Density-independent factors?
5. What do scientists predict that the earth's human population will be by the year 2000?

Succession and Population Density in Microorganism Cultures

Purpose   The gradual replacement of one group of organisms in an ecosystem with another group is called succession. The purpose of this investigation is to observe the stages of succession in a microorganism culture and to observe the interaction of population density and environmental factors.

Materials *(per group)* ● Microscope ● Microscope slides ● 2 400-mL beakers or glass jars ● No. 12 large cork ● Medicine droppers ● Aged tap water ● Some grass, hay, small stones, and twigs ● Labels ● Masking tape ● Graph paper ● Several different cultures of labeled microorganisms ● Single-edge razor blade

Procedure   **Part A** *Succession*   **1.** Label one beaker "A" and the other "B."   **2.** Observe each of the cultures under a microscope and sketch them. These drawings will serve as a reference key later in the investigation.   **3.** On a sheet of paper, copy the table shown in the investigation.   **4.** Add half a medicine dropper measure of each culture to beaker A. **Note:** *Use a clean medicine dropper for each culture.* Then, fill the beaker with aged tap water to the 300-ml mark.
5. CAUTION: *Be very careful when working with a razor blade.* Cut a slit into the center of the narrow end of the cork. The slit should extend approximately half way through the length of the cork.   **6.** Insert one end of a clean microscope slide into the slit. Tape the slide securely in place. On the wide end of the cork, label the cork A and B to identify the two sides of the microscope slide.   **7.** Float the cork carefully in beaker A. If the slide touches the bottom of the beaker, add a little more aged tap water.   **8.** Set the beaker aside for 24 hours. After 24 hours, remove the slide, and dry the A side of the slide. Examine the B (wet) side under the low and high powers of your microscope. **Note:** *Do not remove the slide from the cork.* Identify any organisms on the slide and count the organisms of each type. Use your key sketch as a reference. Place the information in your table. Replace the cork with its slide in the beaker.   **9.** Observe the slide at two-day intervals for two weeks. Each time, identify and record your observations in your table.
Part B *Population Density*   **1.** In beaker B, place some grass, hay, small stones, and twigs. Fill the beaker to

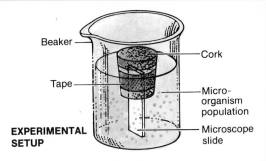

Beaker

Cork

Tape

Micro-organism population

EXPERIMENTAL SETUP

Microscope slide

Day	Organisms	Quantity	General Observations
2			
4			
6			
8			
10			
12			
14			

the 200-mL mark with aged tap water. This will be a grass infusion.   **2.** After 24 hours, examine a drop of the infusion under the low power of a microscope. Count and record the approximate number of organisms in the microscope field.   **3.** Repeat this procedure every day for two weeks.   **4.** After the two weeks, graph the growth of the community. The vertical (y) axis of your graph will represent the number of organisms and the horizontal (x) axis will represent the age of the populations in days.

Observations and Conclusions   **Part A 1.** How many different organisms did you observe after 24 hours? 48 hours? One week?   **2.** Which organisms dominated the slide on the third and fifth days?   **3.** How can you explain the changes that take place during the observation period?   **Part B 1.** What happens to the number of organisms present in the infusion for the first few days?   **2.** Is there a large increase in the number of organisms at some point? If so, on what day?   **3.** What happens to the number of organisms present towards the end of the observation period? Explain your answer.   **4.** What is the general shape of the graph?

751

CHAPTER SUMMARY

Ecological Succession In the development of ecosystems, communities undergo a series of changes called ecological succession. These changes are caused by the communities themselves. Organisms alter their environments in ways that make conditions unfavorable to themselves but favorable to others. A lake is not a permanent ecosystem and undergoes succession. The lake begins to fill up with sediments. Eventually, the lake may become a marsh and finally a forest. Throughout its succession, many different plant and animal populations develop and are replaced. During a period of several hundred years, a sand dune may also undergo ecological succession. Pioneer plants, such as grasses, are the first plants to grow. As more and more nutrients and decaying organic matter are added to the sand, it becomes better suited to plant growth. Shrubs and small trees will begin to grow. Eventually, a succession of different types of trees occurs. On the sand dune, the climax species may be maple and beech. At this point, the community is called a climax community because no more major changes will occur in species composition and community structure. There are two types of succession. These types of succession are primary succession and secondary succession.

Time Rhythms and Cycles in Biotic Communities The activities of many organisms are linked to daily, monthly, or annual cycles. These cycles are referred to as rhythmic because they are regular and predictable. The rhythmic behavior of organisms appears to be affected by light variations, temperature changes, amount of rainfall, and other factors.

Cycles that are based on 24 hours are called circadian rhythms. Some organisms are nocturnal, and others are diurnal. Certain basic body functions are keyed to circadian rhythms. Other rhythms are based on the lunar cycle. Organisms in tidal areas respond to the rise and fall of the tides. Grunions are examples of this type of organism.

Other rhythms are annual. Many reproductive cycles are related to annual rhythms. Hibernation and estivation are responses to seasonal changes. Migration is also a response to seasonal changes. As the winter months begin or wet or dry seasons begin, animals migrate to escape unfavorable weather and to find adequate food supplies.

Population Changes The size of a population depends on the birth rate, death rate, the number of immigrants, and the number of emigrants. Each population has a biotic potential that could be achieved if there were enough food and living space. However, such conditions do not exist. The limiting factors present prevent any population from reaching its biotic potential.

If a population's growth is plotted on a graph, the resulting population growth curve is S-shaped. The curve shows a slow increase in population size followed by a rapid increase. Eventually, the population size stabilizes near the carrying capacity of the environment.

The number of individuals of a species per unit area is called population density. The population density is affected by a number of factors. Density-dependent factors are those whose effectiveness is directly related to the density of a population. They include predation, availability of food, competition, and parasitism. Other factors, such as temperature, rainfall and moisture, wind speed and direction, and air quality are density independent. These factors will affect the size of a population regardless of its density.

CHAPTER VOCABULARY

biological clock	**ecological succession**	**pioneer plant**
biotic potential	**emigrant**	**population density**
carrying capacity	**estivation**	**population growth curve**
circadian rhythm	**eutrophication**	**primary succession**
climax community	**hibernation**	**secondary succession**
climax species	**immigrant**	
density-dependent factor	**limiting factors**	
density-independent factor	**migration**	
diurnal	**nocturnal**	

REVIEW of FACTS and CONCEPTS   Answers on pages T–109 to T–110.

On a separate sheet of paper, answer each of the following as completely as possible.

1. What causes succession of a community?
2. What is the role of pioneer plants in succession?
3. List the characteristics of a climax community.
4. Compare primary and secondary succession.
5. What is meant by a biological clock?
6. Define the terms nocturnal and diurnal. Give examples of nocturnal and diurnal animals.
7. Identify the type of rhythm that each of the following examples exhibits. (a) A skunk searches for food at night. (b) Crabs move under ledges covered by seaweed during low tide. (c) A mouse spends the winter in an underground nest. (d) A poppy flower opens during the day and closes at night. (e) Grunions move to the beaches at high tide and return to the sea at the next high tide.
8. How are hibernation and estivation alike? How do they differ?
9. List three reasons why animals migrate. Give three examples of animals that migrate.
10. What four factors determine the change in the size of a population? What would the change in a

deer population be if 25 deer are born, 5 deer join the herd, 15 deer die, and 15 deer leave?
11. List several factors that prevent organisms from reaching their biotic potential.
12. If a population growth curve showed only small declines and increases in the size of a population in a given area, what could you tell about the population size in relation to the environment?
13. Sketch a population growth curve that would represent a population introduced into a natural environment. Sketch a curve for a population introduced into a closed environment.
14. If three deer live in an eight-hectare area, what is their population density?
15. What are some advantages of a high-density population that does not exceed the carrying capacity of the environment?
16. Why is competition a density-dependent factor? Why are floods density-independent factors?
17. What are some of the limiting factors in human population growth?

EXTENSIONS and APPLICATIONS   For additional information, see page T–110.

1. Visit a pond, lake, or some other natural area. **CAUTION:** *Do not go alone.* Look for evidence that ecological succession is occurring. Identify some plants and animals that appear to be increasing in population and others that are decreasing. Talk to some people who have lived in the area for many years. Ask them how the area is changing and whether they have noticed any changes in the physical environment. Find some old photographs of the area and compare the former conditions of the area with present conditions. Prepare a written or oral report.
2. Using reference materials in the library, look up the migration patterns of the golden plover, wilde-

beest, northern fur seal, lemming, Atlantic salmon, and desert locust. Prepare a map that shows the migration patterns of each organism.
3. The eruption of Mount St. Helens in 1980 destroyed an ecosystem. Find out how ecological succession has been taking place on Mount St. Helens since the eruption. Prepare a report.
4. Develop a demographic profile for a nation of your choice. Include the population size, birth rate, death rate, immigration and emigration rates, rate of population change, age and sex distribution of the people in the country, major causes of death, and life expectancies of males and females.

SUGGESTED READINGS

Ehrlich, P., *The Population Bomb*. New York: Ballantine Books.
   The author describes the problem of overpopulation and explains how it affects the ecological systems of the earth.
Emmel, T.C., *An Introduction to Ecology and Population Biology*. New York: W.W. Norton.
   This book offers a basic study of population dynamics in ecology.
Weston, I., *Body Rhythm*. New York: Harcourt Brace Jovanovich.
   This book is a good introduction to the study of body rhythms.

47 Biomes

For teaching aids for this chapter, including a chapter overview and teaching strategies, see pages T–110 to T–112. The page number next to each chapter objective refers to the text page where the information needed to fulfill the objective begins.

A shoreline constitutes part of an aquatic environment.

The various regions of the world have different climates. Therefore, the animal and plant populations are not the same from place to place. The climate of a region is determined by its average yearly temperature and rainfall.

The *latitude*, or distance north or south of the equator, influences temperature. Areas closer to the equator are warmer than areas farther from the equator. The *altitude*, or the distance above sea level, also affects temperature. Temperatures tend to decline with increasing altitude. Both rainfall and temperature are affected by nearness to mountains and to large bodies of water. This is due to the fact that warm or cold ocean currents can either raise or lower the temperature of the air over nearby landmasses.

The interaction of all of these abiotic factors helps define the types of plants and animals that live in a region. Biologists classify and describe large geographic regions on the basis of their climate and characteristic plant and animal life. These geographical areas are called **biomes.**

Biogeography

As early explorers sailed to different parts of the world or to previously unexplored areas, they began discovering plants and animals that were new to them. Each of the geographic regions they visited had some kinds of plants and animals that were not found anywhere else. For example, kangaroos were found only in Australia. Giraffes and zebras were found only in Africa. Sloths and anaconda snakes were found only in South America. Potatoes grew only in South America, and sunflowers grew only in North America. The discovery of these different plants and animals led to the development of a branch of biology called **biogeography**. Biogeography is the study of the distribution of plants and animals throughout the world.

Dispersal of Plants and Animals

The movement of organisms from one habitat or environment to another is called **dispersal**. Birds fly from one area to another. Herds of elk or deer make their way down from upper mountain areas to lower areas. Fishes swim from streams to rivers into lakes. The movement of organisms by their own energy is referred to as *active dispersal*.

Some organisms are carried from place to place by animals, wind, moving water, or other physical factors. This type of movement is referred to as *passive dispersal*. There are many examples of passive dispersal among animals. Parasitic organisms are carried on or in other animals. These parasites may drop off their host, be excreted in waste products, or be released in the decaying remains of other animals. Most plants are dispersed from area to area by passive dispersal. They have many adaptations that permit passive dispersal.

People have had a great influence on the distribution of plants and animals. Some of the effects of this distribution are positive while others are negative. For example, rabbits, buffaloes, camels, goats, and pigs are among the many animals that people have taken to Australia. Some of these eventually caused problems, such as destruction of grassland.

People have also distributed many useful animals and plants throughout the earth's continents. Corn, tomatoes, and sweet potatoes are examples of food crops that have been taken by people from Mexico and other areas in the Western Hemisphere to other parts of the world. All of these crops are now grown in many other regions of the world.

Figure 47-1 The structure of a seed determines the method of its dispersal. Burrs (*top*) stick to the fur of animals. Milkweed seeds (*center*) are carried on the wind. Coconuts (*bottom*) float in ocean water.

At this point, you may want to assign to your students the first of the Extensions and Applications at the end of this chapter.

755

756

Barriers

Plants and animals cannot spread freely across the surface of the earth. There are *barriers* that prevent their dispersal.

Geographical barriers Oceans, rivers, lakes, deserts, and mountains are examples of geographical barriers. For example, an ocean is a geographical barrier to a freshwater organism because this kind of organism cannot survive in salt water.

Ecological barriers Climate, type of soil, and availability of food are examples of ecological barriers. Every organism has specific needs that are met in its environ-

CAREER: Biogeographer

Certain organisms only live in one area of the world. Other organisms are found in many places. Biogeographers study the distribution of organisms and the factors that account for this distribution.

Biogeographers who specialize in the distribution of plants must study climatic conditions, such as temperature, wind patterns, and amount of rainfall. They must also study the composition of the soil and rocks. The distribution of animals is largely dependent on the distribution of plants. Each species of plant and animal requires a certain kind of habitat. Biogeographers study the animals found in different biomes. They then try to determine how each biome meets the needs of each animal.

Because conditions on the earth are always changing, shifts in the distribution of plants and animals are always occurring, too. Biogeographers keep records of these shifts. Sometimes, their findings are important economically. For example, biogeographers keep farmers informed of the spread of weeds and insect pests. These scientists can also explain why schools of fishes suddenly move out of certain commercial fishing grounds.

Some biogeographers concentrate on the history of the distribution of organisms. For example, biogeographers have discovered that redwood trees were common in the American Arctic 100 million years ago. Gradually, the red-

woods died out. Today, they are only found in California.

A bachelor's degree is needed to work in this field. However, most positions require more advanced degrees. Biogeographers must study biology, geology, meteorology, and geography. If they specialize in a particular area, they must take courses in their area of specialization. For example, biogeographers who specialize in ocean life must acquire an in-depth understanding of oceanography.

Some biogeographers work for colleges and universities, teaching and doing research. Others work for government organizations, such as the agricultural departments.

For further career information, write to American Institute of Biological Sciences, 1401 Wilson Boulevard, Arlington, VA 22209.

ment. These same needs are not met in all environments. For example, if the seed of an apple tree were dropped in a desert, the ecological conditions would probably not permit the seed to germinate.

Behavioral barriers Many organisms or groups of organisms have *territories*. Territories are areas that individual organisms or groups of organisms occupy and protect. Territoriality produces barriers in several ways. First, many organisms do not leave their territories, even though they are physically able to do so. In most cases, these organisms will fight to keep other organisms out. This type of behavior creates a barrier for those animals that might otherwise have entered the territory. In addition, many animals, such as birds, will occupy only those territories that provide the particular materials they need to build their nests or shelters.

SECTION REVIEW   Answers on page T–111.

1. Define biogeography.
2. What is the difference between active dispersal and passive dispersal?
3. List the three types of barriers that prevent the dispersal of organisms.

Terrestrial Biomes

The *terrestrial biomes* are those ecosystems that are located on the earth's landmasses. The terrestrial biomes are determined by climate and the climax species. There are three

Sidelight

Many rabbits have territories less than 0.5 kilometers across. A mountain lion's territory can be more than 25 kilometers across.

Figure 47-2 The Northern and Southern Hemispheres are each divided into tropical, temperate, and polar climatic zones.

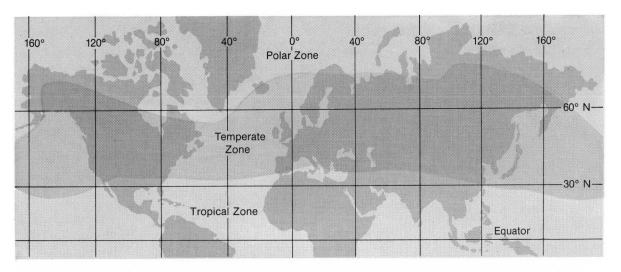

major climate zones that extend around the earth in bands. The *tropical zone* is the region that lies within 30° latitude north and south of the equator. The *temperate zone* is found between the 30° and 60° latitudes of both the Northern and Southern Hemispheres. The *polar zone* extends from the pole to the 60° latitude of each hemisphere.

Local factors, such as the presence of mountain ranges and the proximity of bodies of water, also influence the climate of an area. These factors also affect the characteristics of biomes. They also affect the boundaries of biomes and make it difficult to establish exact boundaries between biomes. Between biomes, there are transition zones, called **ecotones,** that contain species from both biomes.

Tundra

The **tundra** is a large terrestrial biome that borders the Arctic Ocean and surrounds the North Pole. This biome covers about 5.5% of the earth's landmass. There is no similar

Figure 47-3 Major Terrestrial Biomes of the World

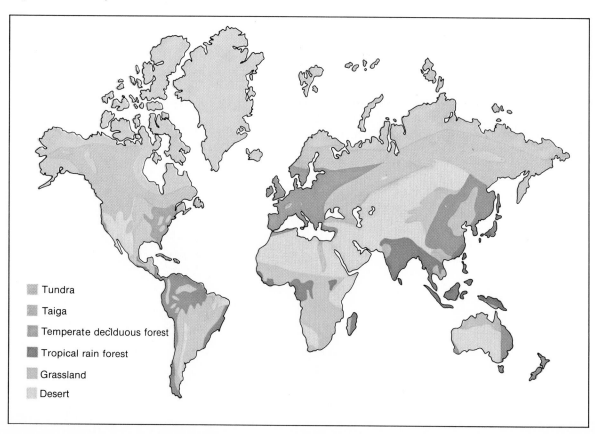

- Tundra
- Taiga
- Temperate deciduous forest
- Tropical rain forest
- Grassland
- Desert

terrestrial biome in the southern latitudes. The corresponding geographical area north of Antarctica is ocean. However, some high mountain areas also have a tundra landscape.

The climate of the tundra is very cold and dry. Winter lasts nine months of the year, with temperatures remaining below freezing most of this time. Spring and summer together last only three months, and the growing season is only 60 days. During this period, the soil thaws to a depth ranging from a few centimeters to 10 to 20 centimeters. Below this depth the soil remains permanently frozen. This permanently frozen soil is called **permafrost.**

During the Arctic summer, grasses, lichens, mosses, and short, woody shrubs grow. There are no trees in the tundra because the growing season is too short. Also, the permafrost prevents trees from rooting and developing.

Examples of animals that live in the tundra are the Arctic fox, the polar bear, the weasel, the shaggy muskox, and the moose. Large herds of migrating caribou, as well as small rodents called lemmings, are also quite common in the tundra. Certain birds, such as ptarmigans and snowy owls, remain on the tundra throughout the year. However, most birds that live on the tundra during the summer migrate to warmer areas in the autumn.

Coniferous Forests

South of the tundra, there is an ecotone. This transition zone reaches into the northern parts of Europe, Asia, and North America where the **coniferous forest** biome begins. This biome consists of *cone-bearing trees*, such as pines, firs, spruces, cedars, and redwoods, hence, the name *coniferous*.

Many kinds of animals live in the coniferous forest biome. Its small mammals include squirrels, beavers, porcupines, mice, and snowshoe hares. Larger mammals include deer, moose, caribou, foxes, and wolves. Many varieties of birds also live in this biome. Some examples are ducks, loons, eagles, and owls. One species of bird called the red crossbill is especially well adapted for life in the coniferous forest biome. Its beak is adapted for splitting open pine-cone seeds. Another species of bird, called the spruce grouse, thrives in this environment. The spruce grouse is able to exist solely on a diet of spruce tree needles.

Within the coniferous forest biome, there are areas that are different in terms of climate and vegetation. The northernmost area of the coniferous forest is called the **taiga** (TĪ-gǝ), a Russian word meaning "swamp forest." Although precipitation in this area is low, the taiga is warmer and wetter than the tundra. In the spring and summer months,

Figure 47-4 The tundra is characterized by low temperatures and low average rainfall.

Figure 47-5 The northernmost coniferous forests (*top*), or taiga, support needleleaf evergreens such as spruce and pine. The warmer, wetter coniferous California forests support redwood trees (*bottom*).

Some of your students might be interested in examining the needles of various coniferous trees with a hand lens or a microscope. The results can be compared and contrasted with the results of the examination of broad leaves in Chapter 22.

Figure 47-6 The trees in deciduous forests have no leaves in winter and have leaves during the warmer seasons.

the soil of the taiga thaws completely. Usually, the soil is soaked and swampy by early summer. This produces many *bogs*, or areas of wet spongy ground.

Many evergreens, such as black spruce, white pine, and balsam fir, are common in the taiga. These trees are adapted to low moisture levels and cold temperatures. They have needlelike leaves that are covered with a waxy layer. The waxy layer prevents loss of water and enables the needles to withstand freezing temperatures.

The coniferous forest that extends from the coast of Alaska to central California receives a great deal of precipitation. Rainfall ranges from 45 to 375 centimeters per year. Heavy fogs also cover this region. The average temperature of this area of coniferous forest is higher than that of the taiga. The soil in the area remains free of frost for 120 to 300 days. Thus, this moister and warmer climate can support larger trees, such as the Douglas fir, the giant sequoia, and the redwood. Mosses, ferns, and many different kinds of flowering plants grow on the floor of these forests.

Deciduous Forests

The temperature and the amount of rainfall increase in the region south of the coniferous forests. This region has a temperate climate made up of definite seasons that include warm summers and cold winters. This temperate region, known as the **deciduous forest** biome, receives about 75 to 125 centimeters of rainfall per year. A deciduous forest is composed mostly of trees that shed their leaves in the fall. Oak, maple, hickory, beech, and elm are examples of the types of trees found in deciduous forests. The eastern part of North America, most of Europe, and eastern Asia are the principal areas in which large deciduous forests grow. There are variations in soil and climate conditions in these areas. As a result, there are differences among the dominant types of trees found in each area. Beech and maple trees, for example, are dominant in most northern deciduous forests. Oak and hickory trees are the most common trees in southern deciduous forests.

In the deciduous forest, as in all forests, there is *vertical stratification*. That is, different kinds of plants grow to different heights above the forest floor.

Canopy The top layer of a forest is the **canopy,** or the upper reaches of the taller trees. The canopy of a deciduous forest is about 30 meters high.

Understory Beneath the canopy is the *understory*. The understory is made up of shorter trees.

Shrub Layer   The next layer of a forest is the *shrub layer*. This layer is made up of woody plants that have more than one stem, but that do not grow as tall as trees.

Herb Layer   Beneath the shrub layer is a layer made up of small, soft-stemmed plants, such as grasses and ferns. This layer is the *herb layer*.

Forest Floor   The lowest layer of the forest is the *forest floor*. It is covered with decaying plants and animals, moss, and fallen leaves.

Each layer of vertical stratification contains organisms particular to it. For example, in the deciduous forests of North America, squirrels and many varieties of birds, including woodpeckers and crows, are common in the canopy branches. Tree frogs, opossums, and some types of mice may be found climbing in the shorter trees that make up the understory. Snails and slugs are found on the moist forest floor or on the trunks of trees. Many types of insects are also common. Elk, white-tailed deer, cottontail rabbits, and beavers are some herbivores found there. Bobcats and different types of weasels are common carnivores.

Tropical Rain Forests

The **tropical rain forest** biome is located in areas near the equator in central Africa, southern Asia, and Central and South America. Tropical rain forests are characterized by the highest biomass of any biome. They receive 200 to 225 centimeters of rain per year. Their warm temperatures change very little throughout the year.

This warm, moist climate is ideal for the growth of many plants. As a result, this biome has the greatest variety and number of plants. The tropical rain forest around the Amazon River in South America, for example, contains at least 25,000 different kinds of plants. Plant growth is very rapid in the tropical rain forest. Many of the broad-leafed trees grow 38 to 45 meters tall. Bamboo, a grass, may grow at a rate of 30 centimeters per day. In only a few months, the bamboo reaches its full height of 30 meters. Many flowering plants of the tropical rain forest flower and produce fruit and seeds all year round.

Vertical stratification occurs in the tropical rain forest, as it does in the temperate deciduous forest. Each layer of stratification differs in temperature and in the amount of light and humidity. However, the so-called **emergent layer** is found only in the tropical rain forest. The emergent layer is

Figure 47-7   Vertical Stratification in a Deciduous Forest

Figure 47-8   The tropical rain forest is characterized by high temperatures and high average rainfall.

Figure 47–9 Vertical Stratification in a Tropical Rain Forest

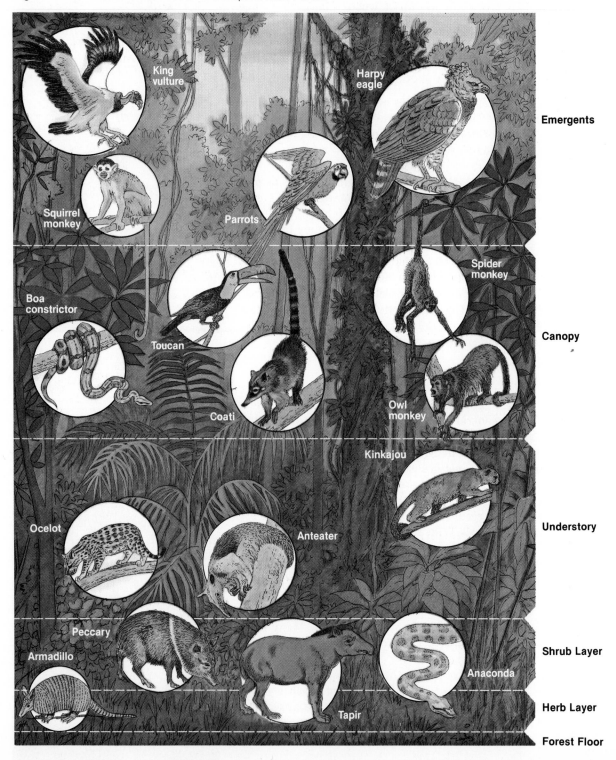

made up of the individual tops of the tallest trees. The canopy, or second-highest layer of the tropical rain forest, is a layer of broad leaves and branches that make up a continuous mass of greenery. The tree tops of the emergent layer protrude from this mass of greenery.

The animal life of the tropical rain forest also tends to be vertically stratified. Flying squirrels, different kinds of monkeys, boa constrictors and other snakes, bats, and chameleons are found at the various layers. Many different kinds of birds, such as toucans, parakeets, and birds of paradise, live in the upper layers. Some of these animals never climb down to lower levels or to the forest floor.

Some of the animals that occupy the lower levels and floor are anacondas, giant anteaters, jaguars, armadillos, and tapirs. Ants, termites, and many *decomposers* are found on the forest floor.

Surprisingly, the rain forests do not have fertile soil. Although rapid decomposition adds humus to the soil, the nutrients are quickly used up by the lush plant growth or drained by heavy rains. As a result of these poor soil conditions, efforts to cut down tropical rain forests and then grow crops often fail.

Grasslands

The **grasslands** biome is the largest of North America's various biomes. The grasslands stretch west from the Mississippi River to the Rocky Mountains and south from central Canada to the Gulf of Mexico. This biome also occurs in parts of Africa, Asia, and South America. In these areas, the grasslands are known as *veldts, steppes,* and *pampas,* respectively.

The climate of the grasslands is similar to that of the deciduous forests. However, grasslands receive less rainfall than deciduous forests, usually between 25 and 75 centimeters per year. Grasslands also experience *droughts,* or long periods without rain. These conditions do not permit trees to develop in most grasslands. The most common types of vegetation are many varieties of grasses.

The grasslands in different parts of the world do not contain the same kinds of animals. Antelope dominate the African veldts. Kangaroos dominate the Australian grasslands. Pronghorns, elks, gophers, prairie dogs, and jackrabbits are common in the North American grasslands, as are foxes, coyotes, and wolves. The common insects of the North American grasslands are locusts and grasshoppers. These grasslands also support quail, hawks, falcons, meadowlarks, and many seed- and insect-eating birds.

Figure 47–10 Grasslands, such as this prairie (*top*), are large, flat areas covered with grasses and shrubs. Savannahs (*bottom*) are grasslands scattered with trees.

764

Despite the large numbers and kinds of animals in the grasslands, there is a natural balance. The amount of rainfall determines the amount of grass that grows. The amount of grass determines, in turn, the size of the population of herbivores. If the population were not controlled by this factor, it would soon destroy the grass and cause the grassland to become desert. Therefore, each kind of animal has its niche within the grasslands biome. For example, zebras eat the tops of grasses. The wildebeest eat the leaves and stems of grasses, and the gazelles nibble at the remaining parts.

Some areas of the world contain **savannahs**, grasslands that are scattered with trees. One example of a savannah is the Serengeti Plain in Africa. The Serengeti is famous for its many different kinds of animals. More than 200,000 zebras, 700,000 gazelles, and 1.4 million wildebeest inhabit it. Other animals found there include elephants, giraffes, rhinoceroses, antelope, lions, cheetahs, and leopards.

Desert

The **desert** biome is usually located inland. It is isolated from oceans by high mountain ranges. As a result, the air moving over desert areas does not carry much water. Most deserts receive less than 25 centimeters of rain per year. Some do not receive rain for several years at a time.

The largest desert in the world is the Sahara. Parts of it are 1900 kilometers long and 4800 kilometers wide. Other large deserts cover nearly half of the island-continent of Australia and sizable portions of western and southwestern United States. Many of the Middle Eastern countries are made up almost entirely of deserts.

Some deserts are referred to as *hot deserts*. These deserts do not experience cold winters. Daylight hours are extremely hot, and nights may become very cool. The dominant vegetation in hot deserts is the creosote bush. *Cool*, or *cold*, *deserts* also experience hot daylight hours and cool nights. During winter months, these deserts become very cold and may even have snow. The dominant vegetation in cold deserts is sagebrush.

There are three main types of desert vegetation. The plants of each type are specially adapted to survive desert conditions.

Succulents   Succulents, such as cacti, can store water in their stems. They are covered with a thick outer skin that prevents the stored water from evaporating. The leaves of the cacti are modified *spines*, or sharp, needle-like structures, that reduce evaporation.

Have your students find out what a wadi is and how wadis affect life in the desert.

Sidelight

The highest temperature ever recorded, 58°C, occurred in the Libyan part of the Sahara Desert.

At this point, you may want to assign to several students the second of the Extensions and Applications at the end of this chapter.

Perennial plants Perennial plants are plants that live for more than two years. In the desert, perennial plants consist of the desert shrubs, such as sagebrush and creosote. These shrubs have a waxy covering on their leaves that reflects heat and prevents water loss. During droughts, these plants often appear to be dead because their leaves become quite dry.

Annuals Annual plants are plants that live for only one season. In the desert, this type of plant often grows to maturity in only a few days. This occurs at a time when enough water is present. The annuals rapidly flower and produce seeds. Then they wither and die.

Desert animals use and lose very little water. To conserve water, many are able to burrow into the ground during the hottest part of the summer. Others are active only at night. Many reptiles, including iguanas, Gila monsters, and horned lizards, live in deserts. Kangaroo rats, pocket mice, and gopher tortoises are also common. Cicadas, scorpions, and spiders are found in desert communities. Burrowing owls, vultures, cactus wrens, and roadrunners are among the few species of birds that live in the deserts.

Figure 47-11 The desert biome is characterized by very low average rainfall. Deserts can be either hot or cold.

At this point, you may want to have your students do the Laboratory Investigation at the end of this chapter.

SECTION REVIEW Answers on page T-111.

1. What are the three major climate zones of the earth?
2. What is an ecotone?
3. What is meant by permafrost?
4. What is the difference between the trees in a coniferous forest and those in a deciduous forest?
5. What is meant by vertical stratification in a forest?
6. What is a savannah?
7. List the major terrestrial biomes.

Aquatic Biomes

The *aquatic biomes* are the water ecosystems. The aquatic biomes support more living things than do the terrestrial biomes. The main abiotic factors that affect the types of organisms found in the aquatic biomes are the amount of oxygen and carbon dioxide available, the temperature, the presence of dissolved materials, and the amount of sunlight. The temperature variations of the aquatic biomes are not as great as those of the terrestial biomes. In fact, aquatic biomes are in a general sense more stable ecosystems than are terrestrial biomes.

Highlight

The aquatic biomes include the marine and freshwater biomes. The marine biome consists of the intertidal, neritic, and open sea zones. The freshwater biome includes ponds, lakes, rivers, and streams.

The Marine Biome

The ocean and sea environments are referred to as the *marine biome*. The ocean is the largest biome. This biome is divided into two environments. The open sea is known as the **pelagic environment.** The floor of the ocean is known as the **benthic environment.**

As many as 200,000 different kinds of plants and animals may live in the marine biome. Marine organisms are classified into three groups according to their habits and environment. The largest group of animals and plants are called **plankton.** Plankton are organisms that float and drift on or near the surface of the ocean. Algae, diatoms, protozoans, copepods, and the larvae of many animals are examples of plankton. Organisms that swim freely through the water are called **nekton.** Whales, porpoises, squids, and fishes are examples of nekton. Organisms that live on the ocean floor are called **benthos.** Barnacles, clams, starfishes, crabs, and many seaweeds are examples of benthos.

Many factors affect the environment of the marine biome. These factors determine, in turn, the kinds of life that occur there.

Amount of Sunlight Sunlight penetrates the marine biome to a depth of about 200 meters.

Temperature Ocean water ranges from −2° C at the bottom of the ocean near Antarctica to 30° C at the equator. In general, the temperature of ocean water decreases as depth increases.

Salinity Salinity is the amount of dissolved salts in ocean water. The average salinity is about 35 parts salts per thousand parts water.

Water Pressure Water pressure increases as depth increases.

The marine biome can be divided into different life zones. Each life zone has its own marine organisms that are adapted to the conditions found there.

INTERTIDAL ZONE The life zone in which it is most difficult for organisms to live is the **intertidal zone.** The intertidal zone is the area between the high-tide line and the low-tide line. This zone is periodically covered and uncovered with water as the tides come in and go out. The zone is also exposed to direct sunlight at low tide. Organisms that live in the intertidal zone must be able to live without water for

Sidelight

The Dead Sea is the saltiest body of water in the world. Its salinity is about 200 parts per thousand.

Figure 47-12 The marine biome consists of a vast number of species of floating, swimming, and bottom-dwelling organisms.

some of the time. They must also be able to attach themselves to rocks or burrow into the sand to keep from being washed out to sea. Some organisms that live in the intertidal zone are clams, barnacles, starfishes, crabs, and seaweeds.

NERITIC ZONE   The **neritic zone** is the area of the ocean that extends from the low-tide line to the edge of the true open sea. Sunlight penetrates this zone. Water pressure is low, and the water temperature is relatively constant. Marine life is most abundant in the neritic zone. This zone is inhabited by many different kinds of animals and plants, including plankton, nekton, and benthos. Fishes, such as flounder and rays, as well as crabs, clams, and mussels, are common.

OPEN SEA ZONE   The *open sea zone* has different conditions at different depths. As was mentioned earlier, sunlight can penetrate this zone to a depth of about 200 meters. The top 200-meter layer of the open sea zone, together with the neritic zone, is called the **photosynthetic zone.** Many types of producers live in the photosynthetic zone. Some light penetrates below the photosynthetic area. Many large organisms such as sharks, whales, octopuses, and squids swim in this region of limited light.

The *abyssal zone* of the open sea zone begins at a depth of about 2000 meters. In this zone, there is no sunlight, great water pressure, and little food. The organisms in this zone

Figure 47–13   Life Zones of the Marine Biome

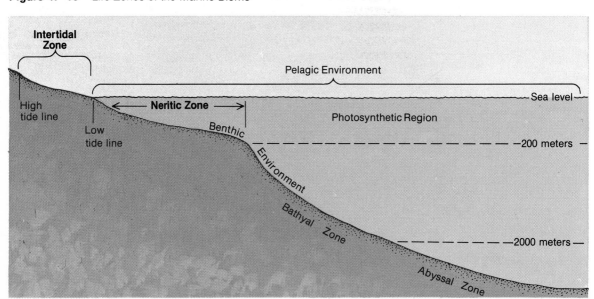

must be able to withstand extreme pressure and cold temperatures. They feed largely on dead organisms that sink from above.

Some of your students might be interested in studying the animal and plant life of the abyssal zone.

Freshwater Biome

Bodies of water that contain little or no salt and other minerals make up the *freshwater biome*. The freshwater biome includes bodies of standing water, such as lakes, ponds, swamps, and bogs. It also includes bodies of moving water, such as rivers, streams, and springs.

LAKES AND PONDS   A lake is a deep depression in the earth that is filled with fresh water. Some very deep areas of a lake are not penetrated by sunlight. Ponds are shallow depressions filled with fresh water. All areas of a pond are penetrated by sunlight, and have more plant growth. The physical and chemical factors that determine the types of plant and animal life differ from lake to lake and from pond to pond.

Some deep lakes may have a low population of plankton and few plants along their shores. Lakes of this sort have small amounts of nutrients and are called **oligotrophic** (ahl-ə-gō-TRŌ-fik) **lakes**. Oligotrophic lakes have a good oxygen supply and contain bottom-dwelling fishes, such as lake trout.

Shallower lakes may have large populations of plankton and many plants along their shores. Lakes of this sort contain many nutrients and are called **eutrophic** (yoo-TRŌ-fik) **lakes**. Because eutrophic lakes have a large biomass of animal life, their oxygen supply is sometimes low. Fishes that need an oxygen-rich environment may not survive in eutrophic lakes. Carp and catfish are examples of fishes that can survive in eutrophic lakes.

STREAMS AND RIVERS   The water environment in streams and rivers is affected by the movement of water and by the type of *bed*, or bottom, of the stream or river. These factors also determine the types of organisms that live in such environments. In some streams and rivers, the *currents*, or movements of the water, are rapid. If the beds of these bodies of water are covered with sand and silt, these materials will shift with the currents. This movement makes it difficult for life forms to establish themselves.

Other streams or rivers with rapid currents have hard beds covered with many stones and rocks that are unaffected by the movement of the water. Plants and animals are able to remain in place by attaching themselves to the

Figure 47-14 Lakes may be oligotrophic (*top*) or eutrophic (*bottom*), depending on their depth, nutrient content, and other factors.

Some of your students might be interested in doing research on the changes that occur in a meandering stream and how these changes affect the organisms that live in the stream.

Figure 47-15 The kinds of organisms that can survive in a stream or river are affected by the speed of the currents and the temperature of the water.

At this point, you may want to assign to your students the third of the Extensions and Applications at the end of this chapter.

stones and rocks. In these rivers and streams with harder, more stable beds, mosses and algae are common. Many small organisms, such as protozoans, worms, and insect larvae, are found among these plants. Actively swimming animals, such as darters and minnows, also live in rapidly moving streams and rivers that have hard beds.

The water in fast-moving streams and rivers is constantly mixing with air. This allows it to absorb large amounts of oxygen and carbon dioxide. Slow-moving water tends to absorb less oxygen and carbon dioxide. Cold water can dissolve more oxygen than warm water. Therefore, fast-moving, cold streams or rivers have more oxygen than slow-moving, warm streams or rivers. The oxygen content and temperature of the water help determine the kind of life found in it. For example, trout require oxygen-rich water. Therefore, they are found in mountain streams, but not in warm, slow-moving rivers, such as the Missouri.

Estuaries

The zone between a freshwater biome and a marine biome is called an **estuary** (ES-choo-wer-ē). Lagoons, sounds, mangrove swamps, tidal marshes, and the mouths of rivers that empty into the ocean are estuaries. These areas contain brackish water, a mixture of fresh water and salt water. Estuaries are usually rich in nutrients. The nutrients are constantly circulated by the rising and falling of the tides.

Estuaries support a variety of life forms. They are usually shallow and sunlight penetrates the water. Therefore, photosynthesis occurs at all levels, making estuaries a good environment for many different types of producers. However, most of the plants in estuaries either are marsh grasses, seaweeds, or phytoplankton.

Animals that people use for food are often found in great abundance in estuaries. Shrimp, oysters, clams, crabs, and many kinds of fish are found in this environment. Many fish also *spawn*, or lay their eggs, in estuaries. Estuaries are also the habitats of numerous kinds of birds. Some estuaries are the homes of large animals, such as elephants and crocodiles.

SECTION REVIEW   Answers on page T-111.

1. What are the two marine environments?
2. List four factors that affect life in the marine biome.
3. What is the difference between freshwater and saltwater biomes? List several freshwater environments.
4. What is an estuary?

Climatograms

Purpose The climate and the plants and animals of a region form major geographical ecosystems called biomes. Climatograms are graphs that summarize the measurements of temperature and rainfall in an area. The purpose of this investigation is to construct and interpret climatograms.

Materials *(per student)* ● 6 sheets of graph paper
● Ruler ● Several reference books

Procedure **Part A 1.** Study the climatogram in Table 1. **2.** Complete the questions in Part A of the Observations and Conclusions. **Part B 1.** Using the information in Table 2, construct a climatogram for each biome. The top figures in Table 2 are the

Table 2

Biome	J	F	M	A	M	J	J	A	S	O	N	D
A	-20.0	-19.5	-14.0	-1.0	7.0	11.0	16.0	15.0	10.0	4.0	-6.5	-14.0
	3.3	2.3	2.8	2.5	4.2	5.4	6.1	8.8	7.5	4.9	2.6	2.8
B	1.0	2.0	3.0	6.5	12.5	17.5	22.5	25.0	20.5	14.0	7.5	3.4
	8.2	7.6	7.9	8.9	8.4	9.3	9.9	11.1	7.9	7.9	6.4	7.8
C	-3.5	5.0	12.0	15.5	19.0	24.5	26.0	21.5	15.0	12.5	7.5	2.0
	1.4	2.3	3.0	4.6	6.0	5.5	6.4	10.3	9.9	7.6	5.3	3.0
D	-23.0	-23.0	-21.5	-16.5	-1.5	2.0	5.0	5.5	0	-9.5	-16.5	-21.5
	1.0	1.4	1.8	1.5	1.6	1.5	2.2	2.7	2.8	2.8	1.5	1.8
E	-0.5	-1.0	2.0	5.0	10.5	12.5	16.5	23.0	13.5	10.0	4.5	2.0
	1.7	1.3	1.2	1.3	1.0	0.8	0.7	0.4	1.5	0.9	0.8	1.2
F	30.5	30.0	30.8	30.8	30.8	30.8	30.8	30.8	30.8	31.0	31.0	30.5
	27.5	27.0	33.0	28.5	19.4	21.0	15.2	13.0	12.9	20.9	17.0	27.0

temperatures in °C for the biome. The bottom figures are the amounts of rainfall in centimeters. **2.** After you have completed the climatograms, identify the biome that each climatogram represents. Use the reference books if necessary. **3.** Obtain the average monthly rainfall and temperatures for your area or a nearby city, and construct a climatogram for the area.

Observations and Conclusions **Part A 1.** What is the warmest month in Albuquerque, New Mexico? In Columbus, Ohio? **2.** What are the driest months in each city? **3.** What is the coldest month in Albuquerque? In Columbus? **4.** In which month in Albuquerque is the amount of rainfall lowest? In Columbus? **5.** Which city has warmer summers? Colder winters? **6.** Which city has the higher annual rainfall? **7.** Which city has greater fluctuations in average monthly rainfall? **8.** In which biome is Albuquerque located? Columbus? **Part B 1.** Copy the names of the following biomes and match the letter of the climatograms to the proper biome: temperate deciduous forest, tundra, tropical rain forest, desert, taiga (coniferous forest), grassland. **2.** Which climatogram is most similar to the climatogram for your area? **3.** In which biome is your area located?

Table 1

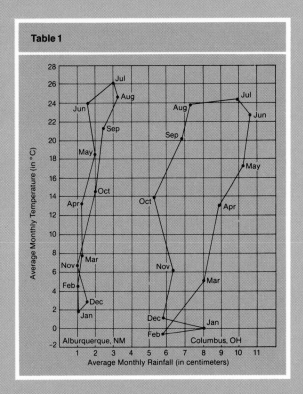

CHAPTER SUMMARY

Biogeography The study of the distribution of plants and animals is called biogeography. The movement of organisms from one area to a new area is called dispersal. The movement of organisms by their own energy is referred to as active dispersal. If the organisms are carried from place to place by animals, wind, water, or other physical factors, the movement is called passive dispersal. Most plants are moved from area to area by means of passive dispersal. Humans often carry plants and animals to different places around the world. However, barriers prevent the free dispersal of plants and animals across the surface of the earth. These barriers are geographical, ecological, and behavioral.

Terrestrial Biomes The characteristics of a biome are determined by the climate in an area. The three major climate zones are the tropical, temperate, and polar zones. The factors that influence climate also affect the characteristics of biomes.

There are six major terrestrial biomes. The northernmost terrestrial biome is called the tundra. The coniferous forest biomes lie to the south of the tundra. Some areas of the coniferous forest biome are included in the taiga biome. The deciduous forest biomes are found in the temperate climate zone. The deciduous forests grow in a variety of soils and climate conditions. The tropical rain forest biomes are located in areas near the equator. The largest biome is the grasslands. Although most areas of this biome support only grasses, some grasslands, called savannahs, are also scattered with trees. Desert biomes are usually located inland. Their lack of moisture is due to the fact that they are isolated from oceans by mountain ranges.

Aquatic Biomes Aquatic biomes are more stable than terrestrial biomes and thus support more life forms. There are three types of aquatic biomes. The marine biome includes the ocean and sea environments. The amounts of sunlight, water temperature, salinity, and water pressure in the various zones of the marine biome help determine the kinds of life found there. Various forms of plankton, nekton, and benthos are adapted to different ocean life zones.

The freshwater biomes include standing bodies of water, such as lakes and ponds, and moving bodies of water, such as rivers and streams. Physical factors, such as the amounts of oxygen, nutrients, and sunlight, help determine the types of plant and animal life found in these environments.

Estuaries are located between freshwater and marine biomes. The water in estuaries is brackish. Conditions in estuaries support many kinds of organisms.

CHAPTER VOCABULARY

benthic environment	**ecotone**	**pelagic environment**
benthos	**emergent layer**	**permafrost**
biogeography	**estuary**	**photosynthetic zone**
biome	**eutrophic lake**	**plankton**
canopy	**grassland**	**savannah**
coniferous forest	**intertidal zone**	**taiga**
deciduous forest	**nekton**	**tropical rain forest**
desert	**neritic zone**	**tundra**
dispersal	**oligotrophic lake**	

REVIEW of FACTS and CONCEPTS   Answers on pages T–111 to T–112.

On a separate sheet of paper, answer each of the following as completely as possible.

1. List five ways that organisms are dispersed from one habitat or environment to another.
2. What type of barrier would prevent each of the following from being dispersed? (a) A fern spore landing in the desert. (b) A starfish moving into a freshwater lake. (c) A kangaroo migrating to Africa. (d) A snowshoe hare going more than 0.4 kilometers from where it was born.
3. What are the dominant forms of vegetation in the tundra? Why are there no trees in the tundra?

4. What is the taiga? What is the dominant group of trees in coniferous forests?

5. List and explain the different layers of vertical stratification in a deciduous forest.

6. What factors account for the fact that tropical rain forests have the highest biomass of any biome?

7. What is the difference between a grassland and a savannah?

8. Explain how some plants and animals are adapted to living in the desert biome.

9. In which terrestrial biome would you find sagebrush? Caribou? Sequoias? Kangaroos? Beech and maple trees?

10. List the main abiotic factors that affect the types of organisms in aquatic biomes.

11. What special adaptations do organisms in the intertidal zone of the oceans have?

12. What characteristics of the neritic zone make it the most productive life zone in the ocean?

13. What conditions limit the kinds of organisms that can live in the abyssal zone?

14. What is the difference between an oligotrophic lake and a eutrophic lake?

15. What environmental conditions affect the types of organisms living in streams and rivers?

16. What plants and animals live in estuaries?

EXTENSIONS and APPLICATIONS For additional information, see page T–112.

1. Make a list of ten kinds of plants and ten kinds of animals. Then go to the library and determine the distribution of these organisms in the world. Find out where they originated. Prepare a map that shows their places of origin and their distribution.

2. Identify the type of biome in which you live. Make a collection of the plant life there. Dry, mount, and identify the plants. Place them in a herbarium. Are these plants typical of the biome? What animals would you expect to find there?

3. Construct a miniature freshwater aquatic or terrestrial biome. On the outside of the aquarium or terrarium keep a list of the plants and animals that you used. Observe the biome for one week. Keep records of the activities and movements of animals in the biome. Prepare a written report that includes descriptions of the interactions of the animals, and records of the growth of the animals or plants. Include a chart that illustrates the locations of the various organisms.

SUGGESTED READINGS

Andres, W.A., ed., *Freshwater Ecology*. Englewood Cliffs, N.J.: Prentice-Hall.
    This guide to freshwater ecology includes descriptions of simple techniques for collecting and studying organisms.

Brown, L., *The Life of the African Plains*. New York: McGraw-Hill.
    The ecology of the African grasslands, with their large and varied animal populations, is explored. The book includes many photographs.

Carson, R.W., *The Sea Around Us*. New York: Oxford University Press.
    An introduction to the study of the oceans and their inhabitants is presented in this easy-to-read book.

Teal, J. and M., *Life and Death of the Salt Marsh*. Boston: Little, Brown.
    A description of the ecology and importance of the salt marsh biome is presented.

48 Conservation

Chapter Objectives *After completing this chapter, you will be able to:*

a ■ Define conservation. p. 774
b ■ Distinguish between renewable and nonrenewable resources. p. 775
c ■ List the effects of soil and water erosion. p. 776
d ■ Name four methods of soil conservation. p. 776
e ■ Define pollution. p. 781
f ■ Identify the causes of atmospheric, water, and land pollution. p. 782
g ■ Discuss some methods of pollution control. p. 787

For teaching aids for this chapter, including a chapter overview and teaching strategies, see pages T–112 to T–114. The page number next to each chapter objective refers to the text page where the information needed to fulfill the objective begins.

Urban development affects the nature of an environment.

The earth has a limited supply of materials to support its forms of life. Because the earth's human population is constantly growing, more and more land, resources, and food are needed to sustain it. Unfortunately, the needs of human beings are often satisfied at the expense of the environment and the animals and plants that live in it. *Conservation* is an activity in which attempts are made to find ways of satisfying the needs of human beings while doing the least damage to the environment and the organisms that live in it.

People who study the environment in an attempt to protect its resources are called *conservationists*. They search for ways of managing the forests that supply timber and of sheltering wildlife. They also attempt to keep farmlands productive and to find solutions to the problems of city life. Conservationists are also called environmentalists or ecologists. They try to find ways to obtain resources such as coal and oil and to meet the world's energy needs without destroying the beauty or ecological balance of the land.

Natural Resources

Highlight

Natural resources are divided into renewable and nonrenewable resources. Renewable resources include food crops, wildlife, and forests. Nonrenewable resources include fossil fuels.

Conservationists divide *natural resources,* or the living and nonliving "materials" of the earth, into two groups. Those resources that can be used and replaced are called **renewable resources.** Plants, animals, soil, water, and air fall into this group. Because many renewable resources are living things, they interact with each other. Therefore, changes in one renewable resource often cause changes in other renewable resources.

The second type of resources, **nonrenewable resources,** cannot be replaced. These resources include such materials as coal and petroleum. The formation of these substances has taken millions of years. Unless substitutes for them are found, they will soon be used up.

Food

Although food is a renewable resource, its availability varies from year to year and even from season to season. Many factors in the environment affect the production of food. Just the right balance of rain and sunlight produces large yields of a crop. On the other hand, floods and droughts can lead to serious shortages of a crop. A food shortage occurs when the food supply is too small to feed the people who depend on it.

Food supplies are dependent upon conditions in the environment that vary from country to country. In some developing countries, for instance, food shortages are a common occurrence. Thousands of people die yearly of starvation. Geographical factors are in part responsible for the inadequate supply of food in these countries. Many of the countries lie close to the equator, where the soil and climate are not suited to the production of large amounts of food. Other countries are too cold, or receive too much or not enough rain.

Sometimes a country lacks food because its population is growing at a faster rate than its food supply. The country also may not have developed efficient means of preserving, processing, storing, and transporting foods. As a result, many foods spoil before they can be eaten.

Developed countries generally suffer from few food shortages. The population of a developed country tends to increase at a slower rate than that of a developing country. Unlike most developing countries, the developed countries lie in areas that are more suitable for large food production. In addition, developed countries have modern systems for preserving, processing, storing, and transporting foods. In spite of these factors, some people in developed countries still go hungry because of uneven or ineffective distribution of the food supply to the population.

Soil

Soil is needed to grow plants, which in turn provide food for people and animals. Soil is made up of minerals and plant and animal matter. Fertile soil, formed over thousands of years, covers much of the surface of the earth in a thin layer. Natural forces, such as rain and wind, gradually carry away the soil. This carrying away process is called **erosion.** Fortunately, a number of factors in nature tend to control erosion. For instance, the root systems of small and large plants, such as grasses and trees, hold the soil so that it cannot be blown or washed away. If too many of these plants are removed to make room for housing, mining, and industry, the rate of erosion of the soil increases. Plants can also reduce erosion by absorbing rainwater, so that less of the soil around them is washed away. In areas where there are few or no plants, much of the eroded soil is deposited in streams, lakes, and rivers. If these bodies of water become clogged or too shallow, they may no longer be able to support life.

Organic matter and minerals may also be removed from the soil by the process of **depletion.** Depletion is caused by excess water, which carries away organic matter and minerals from the soil. Constantly growing a single kind of crop on the same land may also cause depletion. This practice reduces the fertility of the soil because it deprives the land of specific organic materials and minerals that the crop uses to grow. Depletion can be prevented by using **crop rotation.** Crop rotation is the practice of alternating the growing of different crops each year on the same land. One of the rotating crops should be a legume, such as clover or alfalfa. Legumes add chemicals called *nitrates* to the soil, while crops such as corn and wheat remove the nitrates. Sometimes *fertilizers* are added to restore minerals to the soil. They may consist of organic materials, such as decaying plants or processed manure, or inorganic chemicals, such as nitrates.

Other methods of soil conservation include the following.

Contour farming In *contour farming,* the land is plowed around a slope rather than up and down the slope. The ridges that are formed act as small dams that allow water to soak into the soil instead of running off.

Terracing The separating of a long slope into a series of small level surfaces is called *terracing.* A terraced slope resembles a staircase. Each step is separated from

Figure 48-1 Soil erosion is caused by the action of moving water and wind.

At this point, you may want to review Chapter 24. Students might then better understand what materials and minerals are being removed from the soil.

another by a bank. Terracing reduces soil erosion on hill-sides and makes sloping land more efficient for farming.

Strip cropping Alternating strips of cover crops between bands of corn or other grain crops is called *strip cropping*. Cover crops are close-growing plants whose roots spread out to hold the soil. By holding the soil, these plants cut down on the loss of soil by erosion.

Windbreaks During wind storms, large amounts of soil are blown away. Wind erosion is especially a problem in dry areas, such as plains and prairies. In order to prevent wind erosion, farmers plant *windbreaks*. These are rows of trees that act as a barrier to the wind.

Water

All organisms, including people, need fresh water. People use fresh water not only for drinking, but also for cooking, irrigation, and bathing. Because the world's human population is increasing, the need for fresh water is also increasing. The earth as a whole has an abundant supply of fresh water. Because people in some areas do not receive adequate rainfall, they have had to develop special ways of conserving or obtaining water.

Drilling wells is a common method of obtaining underground water. However, over a long period of time, the use of wells may create a problem because it reduces the level of the *ground water*. Ground water is water that has accumulated in the ground. Sometimes these underground sources of water can be refilled by collecting water during heavy rainfalls and pumping it into the ground.

Dams are an effective means of conserving surface water. By building dams on rivers, new reservoirs can be created. Dams also control flooding. Unfortunately, dams also threaten animal life in the area. The water that builds up behind a dam may flood and destroy wildlife habitats.

Another way in which water can be conserved is by reducing the amount that runs off the land. This can be done by covering hilly and mountainous areas with trees and other plants that block the free flow of water. Such areas are called **watersheds**. Watersheds replenish ground water and permit drainage of an area into a major river or river system. They also prevent soil erosion and flooding.

Some communities along dry seacoasts meet some of their freshwater needs by removing the salt from seawater. This process is called **desalination** (dē-sal-ə-NĀ-shən). The major drawback of desalination is its expense, because it uses up large amounts of energy.

Figure 48-2 In strip cropping, close-growing plants (dark bands) are grown between ribbons of farm crops (light bands).

Figure 48-3 Dams help to conserve water and soil. However, the buildup of water behind a dam can destroy wildlife habitats.

Energy

Approximately 95% of all the energy used by people throughout the world comes from *fossil fuels*. Examples of these fuels are coal, oil, and natural gas. The remaining 5% of the earth's usable energy comes mainly from the sun and from running water. A very small amount is produced by nuclear power plants.

Scientists and engineers are trying to develop several renewable sources of energy to reduce the world's dependence on dwindling fossil fuels. These sources include heat from the earth's interior, ocean waves, wind, and sunlight. However, until these energy sources are fully developed, the world's people will have to find some way of conserving the supply of fossil fuels that still remains.

The tapping of energy from the interior of the earth may well become an almost unlimited source of energy. This type of energy is called *geothermal*, meaning "earth heat." Geothermal energy is usually tapped as steam that is formed deep in the earth when natural ground water comes into contact with hot rock. Sometimes the steam reaches the surface of the earth through natural steam vents, such as the geysers in Yellowstone National Park. The steam can then be piped into generators to make electricity.

Another way to tap geothermal energy is to drill wells into the hot, dry rock beneath the earth's surface. When water is pumped into the wells, it returns as steam. The steam is then piped to generators to produce electricity. This method of producing energy is useful, although it does present some problems. It can only be used where geothermal energy is relatively close to the earth's surface. Moreover, the hot steam that is brought to the surface often contains large amounts of sulfur compounds that can corrode equipment and pollute the air and water. Ridding the steam of these impurities adds to the expense of using geothermal energy.

The use of wind as a source of energy is not a new idea. More than 50 years ago, most farms in the United States used windmills to pump water and to generate small amounts of electricity. However, these windmills could not supply enough energy to meet the increasing needs of farmers. It was not until recently that people began to reconsider wind as a renewable and nonpolluting source of energy.

Although the use of wind energy seems promising, there remain some disadvantages. One disadvantage is that the wind does not blow constantly in most places. During times when there is no wind, users of windmills have to rely on other sources of energy. Another disadvantage involves the

Sidelight

Temperature in the earth's crust can reach 870°C.

size of the windmills necessary to produce enough energy. In 1975, scientists performed numerous tests on large windmills. In one such test, the windmill blades developed small cracks and the tower on which the windmill rested began to vibrate. Because of these problems, scientists suggest that several more years of testing are needed before it is known whether large windmills that are safe and efficient producers of energy can be designed.

One of the most promising sources of energy to date is the sun. After solar energy has been captured, it can be changed to electrical energy. Moreover, solar energy produces no pollution and its supply is virtually unlimited.

Solar energy can be captured in devices called *collecting units*. One type of unit is a *flat-plate collector*. A flat-plate collector consists of a black surface over which there is a plastic or glass window. The function of the black surface is to absorb the sunlight. The window prevents the captured heat from escaping. Air or water flows constantly over or behind the black surface and removes heat from it. Then the heated air or water is circulated through a house or other building to provide warmth. Many homes and factories are already making use of these flat-plate solar collectors.

Wildlife

In the past, human activities caused many forms of wildlife to become extinct. For example, uncontrolled hunting threatened the existence of many animals. In the nineteenth century, snowy egrets were hunted for their plumage. This caused the number of these birds to decrease rapidly. To prevent these animals from becoming extinct, John Audubon, the American naturalist who headed the Audubon Society, campaigned against the hunting of snowy egrets. Eventually, laws were passed to protect these birds as well as other wildlife. However, these controls came too late to save other organisms, such as the passenger pigeon, the dodo, and the great auk.

Today, the destruction of habitats is the main cause of the extinction or near extinction of living things. As more homes, farms, factories, and industries are built, more wildlife habitats are destroyed. Industrial wastes, fertilizers, and pesticides build up in lakes, streams, and soil. These chemicals contribute to the destruction of wildlife. In addition, the introduction of a foreign species into the habitat of a plant or animal sometimes causes the extinction of the original species. As foreign species are introduced into an area, they may become more aggressive competitors than the existing species. As a result, the existing species may be

Figure 48-4 Wind can drive the blades of an electric generator. Sunlight can be collected and used to heat water and warm a house.

Sidelight

More than 200 species of animals have become extinct since the year 1600 A.D.

Figure 48-5 The hunting of wildlife such as buffalo is prohibited in many areas in order to preserve endangered species.

An interview with a forest or park ranger would provide firsthand information on forest management.

Figure 48-6 Five-month-old fir seedlings grown in a hothouse will be planted in destroyed woodland areas.

driven into extinction. An organism that is close to extinction is called an **endangered species.**

In order to preserve the growing numbers of endangered species, preserves, or wildlife refuges, have been established. These areas protect wildlife so that they may live without any threat from people. Hunting and fishing laws conserve wildlife by limiting the size, number, and method of capture of various animals. The restocking of ponds and streams with fish is also effective. Perhaps the most basic method of wildlife conservation is noninterference by people in the predator-prey balance of an ecosystem. People who support this method suggest that neither predators nor their prey should be destroyed and that natural processes should be allowed to take their course.

Plant Life

Plant life, especially in forests, protects the supply of water and prevents soil erosion by acting as a watershed. Forests also prevent flooding, serve as sources of timber, and provide habitats for some wildlife. Because of an ever increasing human population, forests are decreasing in size. Forest land is being cleared to build houses and factories, and great quantities of trees are being cut down to be made into wood and paper.

One of the major causes of the destruction of forests is improper forestry management, that is, removal of trees without proper replacement of them. One method of combating this problem is **reforestation.** Reforestation is the practice of renewing the forest by seeding and planting new trees to replace the mature trees that have been cut down. Younger trees are allowed to continue to grow until they are ready for harvesting. Some forests have been named as national forests by the United States Forest Service. Generally, their timber cannot be cut down, nor can their land be developed for houses or factories.

Another cause of the destruction of forests is forest fires. These fires destroy not only plant life but wildlife as well. A significant number of fires are caused by the carelessness of people. Others are caused naturally by lightning. Although forest fires are destructive, they do have some benefits. Fire returns minerals to the soil when the burned parts of trees fall to the soil and decay.

SECTION REVIEW   Answers on page T–113.

1. What is conservation?
2. What is a renewable resource? A nonrenewable resource?

3. Distinguish between erosion and depletion.
4. Name four soil conservation methods.
5. What is desalination?

Environmental Pollution

The contamination of the atmosphere, water, or soil with undesirable materials is called **pollution.** These undesirable materials, known as *pollutants*, endanger the health of plants, animals, and human beings. Although people have always polluted their environment, it was not until fairly recently that the problem became serious. Years ago, the buildup of pollutants was slow enough for natural processes to break the pollutants down. There were fewer industries, less crowded cities, no cars and buses, and no great demands for products such as oil and pesticides, which now often pollute the environment.

Highlight

Pollution is the contamination of the soil, water, or air by undesirable materials. Most atmospheric pollutants are products of the combustion of fossil fuels. Some water pollutants come from sewage disposal, agriculture, and industry. Land pollutants include pesticides and solid wastes.

CLOSE-UP: *Dr. F. Wayne King*

What do the Bali tiger, the Sumatra elephant, and the Java rhinoceros have in common? They are all in danger of becoming extinct. These three animals are among hundreds of animal species whose numbers have dwindled drastically in recent years. They are on the "endangered species" list. There are also some 20,000 plants on the list.

The endangered species list is a chief concern of Dr. F. Wayne King, a conservation biologist whose work is known internationally. King is the director of the Florida State Museum, a natural history museum. He is also an important figure in the International Union for Conservation of Nature and Natural Resources (I.U.C.N.).

I.U.C.N. is an organization of government officials, biologists, environmentalists, and other scientists that directs conservation programs all over the world. King feels that this worldwide approach to conservation is necessary. The number of endangered species is steadily growing. Only if experts from many countries pool their knowledge and work together can this trend be reversed.

King and others have already saved some species. Several years ago, conservationists discovered that crocodiles and alligators everywhere were being destroyed for their hides. King worked with several governments to establish laws to limit international trade in crocodile and alligator hides. He also worked to set up land refuges for these reptiles. "Hopefully we've turned the alligator situation around, but other species still need help," King says.

To help other endangered species survive, King and other conservationists helped set aside land in Africa, Asia, and Latin America where the animals can live safely. "We hope we will be able to stabilize their populations and save them from extinction."

Figure 48-7 Temperature inversions trap pollutants in the lower atmosphere where they are most harmful to living things.

Normal City Air

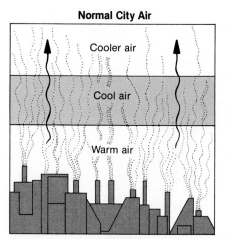

Temperature Inversion

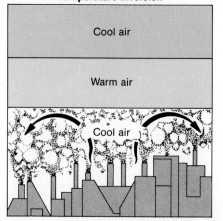

Pollutants or other substances that are naturally broken down by living things in the environment are said to be **biodegradable.** After these substances are decomposed, or broken down, their parts are recycled and used by other organisms. Today, many products that people use are **nonbiodegradable.** When these pollutants are discarded, they cannot be decomposed.

Pollutants of all kinds can build up in air, water, and soil. Polluted air can make people ill. Polluted water can harm or kill aquatic organisms as well as people. Soil pollution decreases the amount of land available for growing food.

Atmospheric Pollution

The atmosphere of the earth is a mixture of many gases. These gases include oxygen, nitrogen, carbon dioxide, and water vapor. Many pollutants also occur naturally in the atmosphere. For example, pollen, dust from erosion, and gases produced by volcanoes are all natural pollutants. However, some atmospheric pollutants are of artificial origin. Most of these are products of the *combustion*, or burning, of fossil fuels, such as gasoline and coal. The pollutants produced by the combustion of fossil fuels range from colorless, poisonous gases to tiny solid particles, such as those found in smoke.

Air pollution has been linked directly to certain lung, throat, and eye irritations. The symptoms of these conditions were found to increase during an atmospheric phenomenon called a **temperature inversion.** Normally, the temperature of the air decreases with increasing altitude. The warm air near the ground rises because it is less dense than cold air. As this warm air rises and cools, it carries air pollutants to the upper atmosphere. A temperature inversion works in just the opposite way. It occurs when a cool layer of air pushes in below the warm layer. Then pollutants become trapped in the cool air near the ground, where people live and work. Temperature inversions may last for several days, the pollutants in the air becoming more and more concentrated. In the past, temperature inversions have caused *pollution episodes* that resulted in many deaths, especially among the elderly and people with respiratory problems.

Some pollutants are of more concern to environmentalists than others. One such pollutant is carbon dioxide. Due to a great increase in the burning of fossil fuels, this gas has been building up rapidly in the atmosphere. Although carbon dioxide permits sunlight to pass through it to the surface of the earth, this gas prevents the sunlight's heat from leaving the atmosphere. As a result, a buildup of carbon dioxide increases the average temperature of the atmosphere. An accumulation of carbon dioxide in the atmosphere acts like the glass of a greenhouse. Both allow sunlight to pass in and both tend to keep heat from passing out. Therefore, the phenomenon of temperature increase due to carbon dioxide buildup is called the *greenhouse effect.* Accumulations of water vapor have a similar effect.

PHOTOCHEMICAL SMOG   During the middle of the twentieth century a new and serious type of pollution developed. This pollution was made up of a combination of smoke, gases, and fog. In the presence of sunlight, these substances formed **photochemical smog.**

One of the causes of photochemical smog is the automobile. Ideally, carbon dioxide and water should be the only waste products that result from the burning of *hydrocarbons,* substances composed of hydrogen and carbon. But in automobiles, gasoline is incompletely burned, permitting some hydrocarbons to escape in the exhaust. Various nitrogen oxides also form, as does carbon monoxide, a poisonous gas. In the atmosphere, these gases undergo a series of reactions with each other and with oxygen and water vapor to form many substances that are irritating or poisonous to plants, animals, and human beings.

RADIATION   *Radioactive particles* form another group of atmospheric pollutants. These particles are released into the atmosphere during nuclear reactions. In the past, the major sources of such pollutants were the explosions of nuclear bombs in the atmosphere.

However, nuclear power plants are now a source of possible radioactive pollution. Such plants use radioactive materials to produce electricity. Accidents in these power plants can and have released small amounts of radiation into the environment. In addition, the improper disposal of radioactive wastes from uranium mines can release radiation into the atmosphere.

Conservationists are concerned about radiation because it can injure or kill all kinds of organisms. It can interfere with the ability of cells to function and reproduce normally. Once certain kinds of radioactive substances are released into the atmosphere, they may take hundreds or thousands of years to become harmless.

Water Pollution

All organisms depend upon water for survival. Although water is a renewable resource, changes in its quality and availability affect all life on the earth.

Sidelight

The greenhouse effect causes temperatures on some areas of Venus to be about 480°C.

At this point, you may want to assign your students the first of the Extensions and Applications at the end of this chapter.

Figure 48-8   A nuclear power plant conserves fossil fuel resources but may also cause radioactive pollution.

Figure 48–9 When chemical pollutants, such as those containing nitrogen and phosphorous, are dumped into lakes or streams, large amounts of algae grow. As the algae die, oxygen in the water is used up. The process is called eutrophication.

At this point, you may want your students to do the Laboratory Investigation and the second of the Extensions and Applications at the end of this chapter.

Only about 3% of the earth's water is fresh water. Most of this fresh water cannot be used because it is frozen in polar ice caps. The remaining 97% of the earth's water is salt-water found primarily in our oceans. Like the atmosphere, water can be affected by pollutants. These pollutants come from many sources, including sewage and garbage systems, farms, and industries.

SEWAGE POLLUTION Sewage systems carry organic wastes from homes, offices, and industries into nearby bodies of water. As these wastes decay in the water, they use up large amounts of oxygen. As a result, many aquatic plants and animals die due to lack of oxygen. Harmful organisms, such as some kinds of bacteria, are also sometimes found in sewage. These organisms can cause typhoid fever, cholera, and other infectious diseases.

Many cities have waste treatment plants that remove some of the organic wastes from water. Despite this precaution, the treated sewage still contains other harmful substances. Two of the most common are *nitrates* and *phosphates*. When these chemicals are introduced into lakes and streams, they cause *algae*, or one-celled plants, to grow excessively. As these algae die and decay, they use up oxygen in the water. This oxygen-depletion process is called **eutrophication.** Detergents containing large amounts of nitrates and phosphates have caused eutrophication in lakes and streams.

AGRICULTURAL POLLUTION Rainwater that runs off farmland into nearby bodies of water may contain animal wastes, fertilizers, and *insecticides*. Insecticides are chemicals that destroy harmful insects. These chemicals can also injure harmless or beneficial insects, various other animals, and human beings. Once in the water, these poisonous substances are eaten by small aquatic animals and stored in their bodies. The poisons are carried along a food chain and become more concentrated at each step. As a result, the carnivores at the end of the food chain may become poisoned. This buildup of chemicals in members of a biological system is called **biomagnification.** Biomagnification occurs when a substance is taken into an organism and is not excreted or metabolized.

An example of biomagnification involves the insecticide DDT (*d*ichloro-*d*iphenyl-*t*richloroethane). The properties of DDT as an insecticide were discovered shortly before World War II. Over the next few decades, the use of DDT to control household, garden, and agricultural pests became widespread. Most people at the time believed that DDT broke up

At this point, you may want to assign to your students the third of the Extensions and Applications at the end of this chapter.

in the environment and disappeared. However, this was not the case. As the DDT was sprayed into the air, it fell to the ground, remained there, or was washed into streams and other bodies of water that emptied into the oceans. The DDT remained in the environment and entered the food chains of animals. Recently, minute amounts of DDT were found in animals as far away as the Antarctic.

Eventually, evidence began to be found that DDT was poisoning birds and other animals. Traces of it were also found in the bodies of human beings. Consequently, in 1972, the United States Environmental Protection Agency banned the use of DDT in the United States. However, this insecticide is still in use in other countries of the world.

Figure 48-10 Industrial wastes are a major source of water pollution.

INDUSTRIAL POLLUTION Many of the pollutants that are poured into water systems come from factories. These pollutants include chemicals of all kinds. Some industrial pollutants, such as mercury and lead, can be deadly to all living things. Through biomagnification, these substances may be passed along a food chain from fish to people.

Mercury is introduced into the environment when the wastes from some industries, such as mining, electrical manufacturing, and fossil-fuel power plants, are dumped into bodies of water. If large amounts of fish containing mercury are eaten by people, serious bone and nerve damage may occur. Lead may enter the environment from the dumping of batteries into lakes and streams. As lead accumulates in the bodies of human beings, severe retardation or death may result.

Some industries may pollute water by heating it. For example, electrical and nuclear power plants use large amounts of water to cool equipment. As the water circulates through the equipment, the water becomes hot. Then the water is discharged into a lake or river, causing an increase in temperature in the body of water. This addition of undesirable heat to the water is called **thermal pollution.** Thermal pollution harms aquatic plants and animals by causing eutrophication to occur.

Figure 48-11 Oil spilled in the ocean is a threat to living things of all kinds. Sea birds coated with oil cannot fly.

Another source of industrial water pollution is oil spills. These spills occur in the oceans and other large waterways. Spills are caused by oil being dumped by tankers or offshore oil wells into the ocean or other large waterways. The spilled oil is carried through the ocean by currents. If the oil spill covers areas where there are aquatic or bird populations, many of these animals may die.

Another industrial pollution problem arises when moisture in the air combines with nitrogen oxide gases and sulfur dioxide gas. These gases are produced by automobiles

785

Figure 48-12 Piles of solid wastes destroy the natural beauty of the land and can become the breeding grounds of disease-causing organisms.

that burn gasoline and by factories that burn coal or oil. The reaction of these two gases with the moisture in the air produces nitric and sulfuric acids. Both of these substances then fall to the earth mixed with rain or snow in a form of pollution called **acid rain.**

Acid rain pollutes not only the atmosphere, but lakes, rivers, and soil as well. Acid pollution of bodies of water results in the destruction of aquatic ecosystems and the contamination of drinking water. Acid rain also increases the rate of corrosion of many metal structures, such as bridges. Acid rain can also dissolve limestone and marble. This has resulted in the destruction of valuable statues made of these materials.

Land Pollution

In nature, soil is kept fertile by the cycles that occur among organisms. For example, as dead plant matter accumulates in the soil, *decomposers,* such as bacteria and fungi, break the matter down into nitrates, phosphates, and other substances. In turn, these substances nourish growing plants. When these plants die, the cycle continues.

As people use more and more pesticides and fertilizers to grow crops, these materials soak into the soil. Not only do some of the pesticides kill weeds and insects that harm plants, but they also destroy some of the helpful organisms in the soil. In this way, the natural cycle described above is interrupted.

A more obvious type of land pollution is the accumulation of solid wastes. These wastes include old cans, automobiles, home appliances, and paper. Each year people throw away billions of metric tons of solid wastes. The wastes pile up on roadsides, in streams and lakes, and in dumps. Not only do solid wastes make the surrounding area unattractive, they also become the homes of disease-carrying animals. Burning is often carried out to reduce the amount of combustible solid wastes. Unfortunately, this method produces smoke, causing air pollution.

SECTION REVIEW Answers on page T-113.

1. What is pollution?
2. Distinguish between biodegradable and nonbiodegradable substances.
3. Define biomagnification.
4. Name one effect each of atmospheric, water, and land pollution.
5. What is thermal pollution?

Pollution Controls

Pollution can be controlled if the potential signs of pollution are recognized. Then methods can be devised and implemented to control pollution. Some air pollution control methods involve the trapping or filtering of wastes. Organic wastes can be removed by passing the air or water containing these wastes through charcoal filters. Some industries use a chemical filter to trap the sulfur dioxide that is produced during the combustion of coal. The sulfur dioxide passes through a spray of lime that chemically combines with it. This reaction produces a *precipitate*, or solid, of calcium compounds. These calcium compounds can then be easily filtered out of the system.

A second method of controlling air pollution involves chemically changing the pollutant into a harmless compound. For example, poisonous carbon monoxide gas and unburned hydrocarbons released by automobiles can be made almost harmless by a device called a *catalytic converter*. As the automobile exhaust passes through this device, a substance called a catalyst causes oxygen to react rapidly with the carbon monoxide and unburned hydrocarbons. As a result, these compounds are changed into water vapor and carbon dioxide. High-temperature incinerators can oxidize unburned hydrocarbons from power plants, changing them into carbon dioxide, water, and other relatively harmless compounds.

Some water pollution control methods call for the banning of certain products. The sale of high-phosphate detergents was banned in some areas where eutrophication had become a problem. Low-phosphate detergents that do not tend to cause eutrophication were put on the market as a substitute. Many pesticides have been banned from general use and other, safer, pesticides have been substituted. In addition, biological control methods are also being used to decrease the number of insect pests. In these methods, a natural predator of the pest is introduced into the environment. The praying mantis is an example of a pest predator because it eats many plant-eating insects. Sterilizing male insect pests and releasing them into the environment is another biological control method. When these sterile males mate with females, no offspring are produced. As a result, the insect population decreases.

Highlight

Pollution can be controlled by first recognizing its signs and then devising methods for its control.

SECTION REVIEW Answers on page T–113.

1. What is a catalytic converter?
2. Name a control method for atmospheric pollution.

Densities of Polluted and Unpolluted Water

Purpose   Water is essential to all forms of life. Polluted water contains undesirable substances, whereas unpolluted water does not. Polluted and unpolluted water may be distinguished from each other through comparison of their densities. Density is the mass of an object per unit volume. The purpose of this investigation is to determine the densities of samples of polluted and unpolluted water and to remove solid wastes from polluted water.

Materials *(per group)*   ● Distilled water ● Sample of "polluted" water ● 2 graduated cylinders ● Triple-beam balance ● Glass funnel ● Glass beaker ● Ring stand with ring clamp ● 2 pieces of filter paper ● Dissecting needle ● Glass slide ● Microscope

Procedure   Part A 1. Copy the table.   **2.** On the balance, weigh the empty graduated cylinder to the nearest tenth of a gram. Record this mass in the table.   **3.** In the graduated cylinder measure 25 mL of distilled, or pure, water. This is the volume of the distilled water.   **4.** Place this graduated cylinder containing the distilled water on the balance and find its mass. Record the mass in the table.   **5.** To obtain the mass of the distilled water, subtract the mass of the empty cylinder from the mass of the cylinder with distilled water. Record this information.   **6.** To calculate the density of the distilled water, divide the mass of the water by the volume. The formula for this calculation is

$$\text{density} = \frac{\text{mass}}{\text{volume}}.$$

Record this information in the table.   **7.** Obtain a sample of "polluted" water from your teacher and repeat steps 3 to 6 using the "polluted" water instead of the distilled water.   **Part B 1.** Place the filter paper in the glass funnel and put the funnel in the ring clamp that is attached to the ring stand.   **2.** Place an empty beaker under the funnel. (See the experimental setup figure.)   **3.** Carefully pour all of the "polluted" water from the graduated cylinder into the funnel and collect the liquid in the beaker.   **4.** Rinse the graduated cylinder. Remove the filter from the funnel and allow it to air dry.   **5.** Repour the liquid collected in the beaker into the graduated cylinder.   **6.** Record the volume of the liquid.   **7.** Determine the density of the

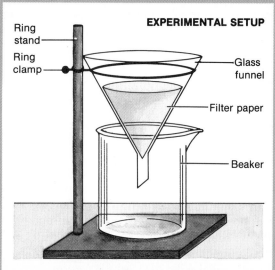

EXPERIMENTAL SETUP

Ring stand — Ring clamp — Glass funnel — Filter paper — Beaker

	Distilled water	Polluted water	
		Before filtering	After filtering
Mass of empty graduated cylinder	g	g	g
Mass of graduated cylinder and water	g	g	g
Volume of water	mL	mL	mL
Mass of water	g	g	g
Density of water	g/mL	g/mL	g/mL

filtered "polluted" water by repeating steps 4 to 6 in Part A.   **8.** Record your results in the table.   **9.** With the dissecting needle, gently remove a small amount of the material from the filter paper.   **10.** Make a wet mount of this material.   **11.** Examine it under the low and high powers of the microscope. Make sketches of what you see.

Observations and Conclusions   1. Describe the appearance of each water sample   **2.** Which sample of water has the higher density?   **3.** Describe the particles of "polluted" water that are trapped in the filter.   **4.** Refilter the "polluted" water. Is the density of this water now closer to or further from that of the distilled water? Explain.

CHAPTER SUMMARY

Conservation Conservation is the wise use, protection, and proper management of natural resources. Renewable resources are those that can be used and replaced. Nonrenewable resources are those that cannot be replaced.

Food is an example of a renewable resource. The food supply varies everywhere from year to year as a result of rainfall, floods, and droughts. Food shortages occur in areas where the human population grows at a faster rate than the food supply.

Soil is composed of minerals and decayed plant and animal matter. Soil is needed for the proper growth of plants. However, natural forces, such as wind and rain, are gradually wearing away the soil by erosion. In addition, depletion removes organic matter and minerals from the soil. By practicing crop rotation the fertility of the soil can be restored. Other methods of conserving the soil are contour plowing, terracing, strip cropping, and the planting of windbreaks.

Although the earth has an abundant supply of fresh water, much of it is not readily available. Therefore, wells must be dug and dams must be built to supply people with new water sources. Watersheds are used to block the free flow of water, reducing the amount of water that runs off into lakes and rivers. The water that is held by the trees refills the underground sources of water. Some seacoast cities add to their water supply by a process called desalination.

Most of the energy used to power machines and to provide electricity comes from the burning of fossil fuels. Because fossil fuels are a nonrenewable resource, people are turning to renewable resources such as nuclear, geothermal, wind, solar, and ocean wave energy.

Wildlife and plant life also need to be conserved because they are part of the natural cycles of the earth. To protect endangered animal species from extinction, they are placed in preserves, or wildlife refuges. Reforestation is used to renew forests by reseeding and replanting areas where mature trees have been cut down.

Environmental Pollution Pollution is the contamination of the atmosphere, water, and soil with undesir-able materials. Those pollutants that can be broken down naturally by the environment are called biodegradable substances. Pollutants that cannot be broken down are considered nonbiodegradable.

Most atmospheric pollution results from the burning of fossil fuels. Temperature inversions increase the effects of air pollution by trapping the pollutants in the air near the ground. Other types of atmospheric pollution include photochemical smog and radiation.

Water pollutants come from many sources, including some sewage systems, farms, and industries. Disease-causing bacteria are found in polluted water. In addition, both treated and untreated sewage contain substances that cause algae in small bodies of water to grow at alarming rates. As the algae decay, they use up the oxygen that other forms of aquatic life need to survive. This process is called eutrophication. Sometimes wastes enter the water supply and are carried along an aquatic food chain. The wastes may become more concentrated at each organism level in a process called biomagnification.

Some industries pollute our environment by discharging large amounts of hot water into streams and lakes. Raising the temperature of the body of water can threaten the lives of many of its organisms. This is called thermal pollution. Another kind of industrial pollution is acid rain, which is formed when moisture in the air combines with oxides of nitrogen and sulfur to produce acids. These acids then fall to the earth along with rain or snow.

Pesticides and fertilizers are examples of land pollutants. When pesticides are used, they soak into the soil and destroy helpful soil organisms, such as bacteria.

Pollution Controls In order to limit the amount of environmental pollution, people must be able to recognize the potential signs of pollution, devise some methods to control it, and enact these controls. Some methods of pollution control include trapping pollutants before they can enter the atmosphere, developing methods for the more complete burning of fossil fuels, and substituting biological controls for chemical controls as a means of killing insect pests.

CHAPTER VOCABULARY

acid rain	**endangered species**	**pollution**
biodegradable	**erosion**	**reforestation**
biomagnification	**eutrophication**	**renewable resource**
crop rotation	**nonbiodegradable**	**temperature inversion**
depletion	**nonrenewable resource**	**thermal pollution**
desalination	**photochemical smog**	**watershed**

REVIEW of FACTS and CONCEPTS   Answers on pages T–113 to T–114.

On a separate sheet of paper, answer each of the following as completely as possible.

1. What is a natural resource?
2. Name two renewable and two nonrenewable resources.
3. Why does soil erosion occur in areas where trees are removed?
4. What happens to farmland if only one crop is planted year after year?
5. How do windbreaks stop soil erosion?
6. What is desalination? Give a disadvantage of this process.
7. Name three fossil fuels.
8. Name three alternate sources of energy other than the burning of fossil fuels.
9. What is an endangered species? Name two.
10. Describe reforestation.
11. How does a temperature inversion form?
12. Why does an increase in the amount of carbon dioxide in the air increase the average temperature of the earth? What is this process called?
13. What is photochemical smog?
14. Define eutrophication.
15. Pesticides have been found in animals in the far southern regions of the earth where there is no plant life. Explain.
16. How does acid rain form?
17. Describe three methods of pollution control.

EXTENSIONS AND APPLICATIONS   For additional information, see page T–114.

1. To determine the amount of particles in the air around your school and home, cut out four 10 cm x 10 cm pieces of cardboard. Cover one side of each piece of cardboard with cellophane wrap. Apply a thin layer of petroleum jelly to the surface of the cellophane wrap. Place one of these pieces, petroleum jelly side up, outside your home. Place another inside. Take the other two pieces of cardboard and place one piece on a shelf in your classroom. With tape, attach the other piece to the outside of your classroom window. Allow these pieces of cardboard to remain in place for 48 to 72 hours. Then remove the cardboard pieces and examine them. What types of materials were trapped by the petroleum jelly? Which cardboard pieces have the most trapped materials? Explain.

2. Visit a local sewage treatment facility. Ask the plant manager how the phosphates and nitrates are removed from the water. Also, ask if there are any plans being made for better sewage treatment. If so, what are the plans? Report your findings to your class.

3. You may want to visit the library to find more information on pesticides. Are they necessary? Are there other available methods of pest control? If so, describe them. Present your findings in a written report.

SUGGESTED READINGS

Carson, R., *Silent Spring.* Boston, Mass.: Houghton Mifflin.
   The author explains the hazards of pesticides for people and for animals.
Commoner, B., *The Closing Circle.* New York: Alfred A. Knopf.
   The author, who is an ecologist, discusses and explains the environmental crisis.
La Bastille, A., *Woodsman.* New York: E.P. Dutton.
   This book tells the story of a person who builds a cabin in the wilderness and learns to live off the land without altering it.

Oceans as a Food Resource Versus Ecological Balance

The ocean is the largest biome on earth. It covers 71% of the earth's surface and has an average depth of 4 kilometers. Representatives of nearly every phylum of plant, animal, and protist live in large numbers within this vast aquatic environment. The total number of oceanic species is in the hundreds of thousands. There are more than 20,000 species of fish alone. Given these facts, it is not surprising that, in a time of expanding population and dwindling food resources, some people are suggesting use of the sea as a major source of food.

Some experts estimate that an annual catch of nearly one billion metric tons of food will be possible once the necessary "harvesting" technology is developed. Fish, mollusks, and crustaceans would make up the major part of the catch. Plankton, the major bulk of the ocean's biomass, might become a valuable food source. The various algae, drifting larvae, and other animals and plants that make up the plankton contain many important nutrients. The plankton also contain shrimplike crustaceans called krill that are found in tremendous numbers in the ocean. Food technologists in some countries are experimenting with ways to use this abundant plankton food source. Krill meal, krill butter, and krill cheese-spread products are already being marketed in these countries.

Many critics point out that the sea simply cannot provide much more food than it does currently. Despite popular beliefs, only a fraction of the total oceanic volume is productive. The shallow waters off the continental coasts are examples of relatively small but extremely productive regions. These regions contain mineral and nutrient runoff from the nearby land. These nutrients support the phytoplankton that are eaten in turn by large numbers of other organisms in the marine food chain. The nutrients largely are absent or in low concentration in the open ocean away from land, so life is more sparse there.

Critics who contend that the ocean's food resources are limited also point out that photosynthesis cannot occur below the maximum depths to which light can penetrate. Depending on the water's clarity, the photic zone, or region of light penetration, extends for only a tiny fraction of the 4-kilometer average ocean depth. The unlit deep-sea region contains relatively small numbers of organisms. These organisms feed largely upon the organic matter and dead organisms that descend from the photic zone. Therefore, the popular notion that the deeper levels of the sea are teeming with life is a false one.

Critics emphasize that only a small percentage of available ocean life is actually edible or palatable. Many species of fish are poisonous. Others repel people by their appearance, smell, or taste. Also, the people of many cultures almost completely avoid seafood for traditional reasons.

Two human factors may further decrease the nutritive yield of the sea. Overfishing hinders natural populations from replenishing themselves. The annual catches of several fish species have actually been declining recently due to overfishing. Ocean pollution can also seriously reduce productivity. Oil spills from tankers, human sewage dumped offshore, and toxic chemical runoff are some of the major sources of this pollution.

Viewpoints

1. Alternative food sources must be developed if global food-shortage problems are to be solved. Algae and various seaweeds are plentiful in many regions of the sea. Research the nutritive value and possible uses of these plants. How are they currently used as a food source by non-Western cultures?

2. Expanded use of the sea as a food source will require the development of new harvesting technologies. Do research to determine the difficulties and costs involved in this development. Do you feel that the advantages outweigh the disadvantages?

Reference Section

The Compound Microscope

One of the most essential tools in the study of biology is the microscope. With the help of different types of microscopes, biologists have developed detailed concepts of cell structure and function. The type of microscope used in most biology classes is the compound microscope. It contains a combination of lenses and can magnify objects normally unseen with the unaided eye.

The eyepiece lens is located in the top portion of the microscope. This lens usually has a magnification of $10 \times$. A compound microscope usually has two other interchangeable lenses. These lenses, called objective lenses, are at the bottom of the body tube on the revolving nosepiece. By revolving the nosepiece, either of the two objectives can be brought into direct line with the body tube.

The shorter objective is low power in its magnification, usually $10 \times$. The longer one is high power, usually $40 \times$ or $43 \times$. The magnification is always marked on the objective. To determine the total magnification of a microscope, multiply the magnifying power of the eyepiece by the magnifying power of the objective being used. For example, the eyepiece magnifying power, $10 \times$, multiplied by the low power objective, $10 \times$, equals $100 \times$. The total magnification is $100 \times$.

A microscope also produces clear contrasts to enable the viewer to distinguish between objects that lie very close together. Under a microscope the detail of objects is very sharp. The ability of a microscope to produce contrast and detail is called resolution, or resolving power. Although microscopes can have the same magnifying power, they can differ in resolving power.

Learning the name, function, and location of each of the microscope's parts is necessary for proper use. Use the following procedures when working with the microscope.

1. Remove the microscope from its storage area by placing one hand beneath the base and grasping the arm of the microscope with the other hand.
2. Gently place the microscope on the lab table with the arm facing you. The microscope's base should be resting evenly on the table, approximately 10 centimeters from the table's edge.
3. Raise the body tube by turning the coarse adjustment knob until the objective lens is about 2 centimeters above the opening of the stage.
4. Revolve the nosepiece so that the low-power objective ($10 \times$) is directly in line with the body tube. A click indicates that the lens is in line with the opening of the stage.
5. Look through the eyepiece and switch on the lamp or adjust the mirror so that a circle of light can be seen. This

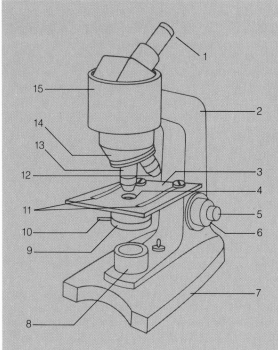

Microscope Parts and Their Function

1. **Eyepiece** Contains a magnifying lens
2. **Arm** Supports the body tube
3. **Stage** Supports the slide being observed
4. **Opening of the stage** Permits light to travel up to the eyepiece
5. **Fine adjustment** Moves the body tube slightly to sharpen the focus
6. **Coarse adjustment** Moves the body tube up and down for focusing
7. **Base** Supports the microscope
8. **Illuminator** Produces light or reflects light up through the body tube
9. **Diaphragm** Regulates the amount of light entering the body tube
10. **Diaphragm lever** Opens and closes the diaphragm
11. **Stage clips** Hold the slide in position
12. **Low-power objective** Provides a magnification of $10 \times$ and is the shorter of the objectives
13. **High-power objective** Provides a magnification of $43 \times$ and is the longer of the objectives
14. **Revolving nosepiece** Contains the low- and high-power objectives and can be rotated to change magnification
15. **Body tube** Maintains a proper distance between the eyepiece and objective lenses

is the field of view. Moving the lever of the diaphragm permits a greater amount of light to come through the opening of the stage.

6. Place a prepared slide on the stage. Position the specimen over the center of the opening of the stage. Fasten the stage clips to hold the slide in position.
7. Look at the microscope from the side. Carefully turn the coarse adjustment knob to lower the body tube until the low-power objective almost touches the slide or until the body tube can no longer be moved. Do not allow the objective to touch the slide.
8. Look through the eyepiece and observe the specimen. If the field of view is out of focus, use the coarse adjustment knob to raise the body tube while looking through the eyepiece. When the specimen comes into view, use the

fine adjustment knob to focus the specimen. Be sure to keep both eyes open when viewing a specimen. This helps prevent eye strain.

9. Adjust the lever of the diaphragm to allow the right amount of light to enter.
10. To view the specimen under high power ($43 \times$), revolve the nosepiece until the high power objective is in line with the body tube and clicks into place.
11. Look through the eyepiece and use the fine adjustment knob to bring the specimen into focus.
12. After every use, remove the slide. Clean the stage of the microscope and the lenses with lens paper. Do not use other types of paper to clean the lenses, as they may scratch the lenses.

Preparing a Wet-Mount Slide

1. Obtain a clean microscope slide and a cover slip. A cover slip is very thin, permitting the objective lens to be lowered very close to the specimen.
2. Place the specimen in the middle of the microscope slide. The specimen must be thin enough for light to pass through it.
3. Using an eyedropper, place a drop of water on the specimen.
4. Lower one edge of the cover slip so that it touches the side of the drop of water at a 45° angle. The water will spread evenly along the edge of the cover slip. Using a dissecting needle or probe, slowly lower the cover slip over the specimen and water. Try not to trap any air bubbles under the cover slip. Air bubbles interfere with the view of the specimen. If air bubbles are present, gently tap the surface of the cover slip over the air bubble with a pencil eraser.

5. Remove any excess water at the edge of the cover slip with a piece of paper towel. If the specimen begins to dry out, add a drop of water at the edge of the cover slip.

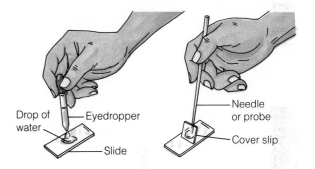

Drop of water — Eyedropper

Slide

Needle or probe

Cover slip

Staining Techniques

1. Obtain a clean microscope slide and cover slip.
2. Place the specimen in the middle of the microscope slide.
3. Using an eyedropper, place a drop of water on the specimen.
4. Place one edge of the cover slip so that it touches the side of the drop of water at a 45° angle. After the water spreads along the edge of the cover slip, use a dissecting needle or probe to lower the cover slip over the specimen.
5. Add a drop of stain at the edge of the cover slip. Using forceps, touch a small piece of lens paper or paper towel to the opposite edge of the cover slip. The paper causes the stain to be drawn under the cover slip and stain the cells. Some common stains are methylene blue, iodine, fuchsin, and Wright's stain.

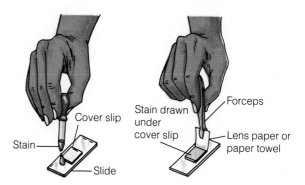

Cover slip

Stain

Slide

Forceps

Stain drawn under cover slip

Lens paper or paper towel

The Metric System

The metric system is an international decimal system of measurement that was developed in France in 1790. Today, over 90 percent of the nations of the world use the metric system. In these nations, the metric system is used by the general public as well as in trade, commerce, and scientific studies. In the United States, both the metric system and the U.S. customary equivalents are used.

The metric system is based on units of ten. Within the metric system, there are three commonly used units. The unit for length is the meter, the unit for volume is the liter, and the unit for mass is the gram. Prefixes are added to each of these units to indicate larger or smaller units. Each unit in the system is ten times larger than the next smaller unit and ten times smaller than the next larger unit.

Common Uses for Metric Units

Length (distance from one point to another)

millimeter (mm) used in industry and for small dimensions

centimeter (cm) used to express clothing sizes and body measurements

meter (m) used to measure larger dimensions and short distances

kilometer (km) used to measure long distances

Area (measure of space on a surface)

square centimeters (cm²) used to measure small areas

hectare (ha) used to measure farm land

square kilometers (km²) used to measure large areas

Volume (amount of space that an object occupies)

milliliter (mL) used to measure small quantities of liquids

cubic centimeter (cm³) used to measure drugs in a pharmacy or pharmaceutical company

liter (L) used to measure the volume of a liquid

Mass (amount of matter in an object)

milligram (mg) used to measure vitamins and medications

gram (g) used to measure food or small objects

kilogram (kg) used to measure larger objects, including the mass of a person

Temperature (measure of the degree of warmth or coldness of an object or substance)

degrees Celsius (°C) used for commercial, scientific, and everyday purposes

Reference points: 0°C = freezing point of water, 100°C = boiling point of water

Some Metric Prefixes and Definitions

micro-	= 0.000001	deka-	= 10
milli-	= 0.001	hecto-	= 100
centi-	= 0.01	kilo-	= 1000
deci-	= 0.1	mega-	= 1,000,000

Metric Relationships

Unit and Symbol	Relationship	
kilometer (km)	1 km	= 1000 m
meter (m)	1 m	= 100 cm
centimeter (cm)	1 cm	= 10 mm
millimeter (mm)	1 mm	= 0.1 cm
hectare (ha)	1 ha	= 10,000 m²
liter (L)	1 L	= 1000 mL
milliliter (mL)	1 mL	= 0.001 L
tonne (t)	1 t	= 1000 kg
kilogram (kg)	1 kg	= 1000 g
gram (g)	1 g	= 1000 mg
milligram (mg)	1 mg	= 0.001 g

Metric-U.S. Customary Equivalents

2.54 cm	= 1 inch	1 kg	= 2.2 pounds
1 m	= 39.37 inches	28.35 g	= 1 ounce
1 km	= 0.62 miles	°C	= 5/9 x (°F − 32)
1 L	= 1.06 quarts	°F	= (9/5 x °C) + 32
236.6 mL	= 1 cup		

Five-Kingdom System for Classifying Organisms

KINGDOM PROTISTA

Unicellular and colonial organisms; prokaryotic or eukaryotic; heterotrophic

PHYLUM SARCODINA   Unicellular; amoeboid motion; eukaryotic; reproduction by fission; pseudopodia; no pellicle; marine and fresh water (*Amoeba, Foraminifera,* and *Radiolaria*)

PHYLUM CILIOPHORA (ciliates)   Unicellular; locomotion by cilia; eukaryotic; reproduction by binary fission; pellicle; many have macronucleus and micronucleus (*Paramecium, Vorticella,* and *Stentor*)

PHYLUM MASTIGOPHORA (flagellates)   Mostly unicellular, some colonial; locomotion by one or more flagella; eukaryotic; reproduction by longitudinal binary fission; pellicle usually present (*Euglena, Volvox,* and *Trypanosoma*)

PHYLUM SPOROZOA (sporozoans)   Unicellular; no means of locomotion; eukaryotic; reproduction by spores; parasitic (*Plasmodium*)

KINGDOM MONERA

Unicellular organisms; prokaryotic; mostly heterotrophic; reproduction by fission; some conjugation

Subkingdom Schizophyta

Unicellular or cells in chains or clusters; motile forms with flagella; prokaryotic; mostly saphrophytic or parasitic; some photosynthetic and chemosynthetic

PHYLUM EUBACTERIACEA (true bacteria)   Unicellular or cells in chains; mostly saphrophytic; some medically and economically important parasites (*Escherichia coli* and *Diplococcus pneumoniae*)

PHYLUM CHLAMYDOBACTERIAE (mycelial bacteria)   Cells have fungal-like mycelial filaments; flagellated; medically important in production of antibiotics (*Aureomyces* and *Actinomyces*)

PHYLUM SPIROCHAETAE   Corkscrew-shaped; large cells; flagellated; parasitic (*Treponema pallidum*)

PHYLUM MYCOPLASMAE   Some form colonies resembling mycelia; small cells; no cell walls (mycoplasmas)

Subkingdom Cyanophyta

Unicellular, colonial, or filamentous; motile and nonmotile; autotrophic; reproduction by fission, spores, and fragmentation

PHYLUM CYANOPHYTA (blue-green algae)   Photosynthetic; cells contain chlorophyll masked by phycocanins; chlorophyll not organized in plasmids; food stored as starch

(*Gloeocapsa* and *Oscillatoria*)

KINGDOM FUNGI

Mostly multicellular; eukaryotic; heterotrophic; cells form a mycelium; cell walls with cellulose or chitin; many with no known sexual reproduction; reproduction by spores

Subkingdom Gymnomycota

Acellular types have large, multinucleate plasmodium; cellular types have unicellular plasmodium; heterotrophic; spores produced by sporangia; shapeless (slime molds)

Subkingdom Dimastigomycota

Mycelium made up of very few cells; saphrophytic and parasitic; flagellated asexual spores; large oogonia and fingerlike antherida (downy mildews)

Subkingdom Eumycota

Mostly multicellular; heterotrophic; composed of hyphae (true fungi)

PHYLUM ZYGOMYCETES (conjugating molds)   Extensive mycelia; asexual reproduction by spore formation; sexual reproduction by conjugation and formation of diploid zygospores (bread molds)

PHYLUM ASCOMYCETES (sac fungi)   Ascus usually contains eight ascospores formed by sexual reproduction (yeasts, morels, cup fungi, and powdery mildews)

PHYLUM BASIDIOMYCETES (club fungi)   Basidium contains basidiospores formed by sexual reproduction (mushrooms, rusts, and smuts)

PHYLUM DEUTEROMYCETES (imperfect fungi)   Reproduction by spores on simple hyphae (*Penicillium* and *Aspergillus*)

KINGDOM PLANTAE

Unicellular, colonial, filamentous, and multicellular organisms; eukaryotic; autotrophic, asexual and/or sexual reproduction; cell walls contain cellulose; cells contain chlorophyll organized into plastids; multicellular plants have tissues and organs

Subkingdom Thallophyta

Thallus or plant body does not have true roots, stem, or leaf; no vascular tissue; gametes enclosed by cell wall; autotrophic and heterotrophic

DIVISION CHLOROPHYTA (green algae)   Unicellular,

colonial, or filamentous; motile, sessile, or free-floating; eukaryotic; reproduction by fission, spores, and gametes; autotrophic; cells contain chlorophyll and other pigments organized into plastids; food stored as starch (*Protococcus, Spirogyra, Ulothrix, Oedogonium,* and desmids)

DIVISION CHRYSOPHYTA (golden algae) Unicellular, colonial, or filamentous; motile and free-floating; eukaryotic; reproduction by fission and gametes; autotrophic; cells contain chlorophyll, orange carotenes, yellow xanthophylls, and brown fucoxanthins organized into plastids; cell walls contain silica; food stored as complex carbohydrates and oils (yellow-green algae, golden-brown algae, and diatoms)

DIVISION PHAEOPHYTA (brown algae) Multicellular; sessile or free-floating; eukaryotic; reproduction by spores and gametes; autotrophic; cells contain chlorophyll masked by brown fucoxanthin organized into plastids; food stored as complex carbohydrates or oils (*Fucus* and *Sargassum*)

DIVISION RHODOPHYTA (red algae) Multicellular; usually sessile; eukaryotic; reproduction by fission and gametes; autotrophic; cells contain chlorophyll masked by red phycoerythrins; food stored as starch (*Nemalion* and *Polysiphonia*)

DIVISION PYRRHOPHYTA (fire algae) Unicellular; two flagella; eukaryotic; reproduction by fission and gametes; autotrophic; cells contain chlorophyll, orange carotenes, and yellow xanthophylls organized into plastids; food stored as starch or oil (dinoflagellates)

Subkingdom Embryophyta

Zygote develops into a multicellular embryo that is enclosed within the female sex organ or within an embryo sac; autotrophic

DIVISION BRYOPHYTA (nonvascular plants) Multicellular; alternation of generations, with unbranched sporophyte generation attached to conspicuous gametophyte generation; terrestrial green plants found in moist places; no vascular tissues or true roots, stems, and leaves; multicellular sex organs

Class Hepaticae (liverworts) Sporophyte made up of capsules containing spores; leafy or thalluslike gametophyte, usually prostrate (*Marchantia*)

Class Anthocerotae (hornworts) Sporophyte elongated; thalluslike gametophyte

Class Musci (true mosses) Sporophyte on leafy gametophyte that is usually erect (*Polytrichum, Sphagnum,* and *Andreaea*)

DIVISION TRACHEOPHYTA (vascular plants) Conspicuous sporophyte generation; vascular tissues; true roots, stems, and leaves

Subdivision Psilopsida No leaves and roots; mostly extinct; only one living order (*Psilotum*)

Subdivision Lycopsida (club mosses) Sporangia formed on special spore-bearing leaves; small, mostly simple leaves spirally arranged in vertical rows on stem (*Lycopodium* and *Selaginella*)

Subdivision Sphenopsida (horsetails) Small simple leaves arranged in whorls; stems contain silica; mostly extinct (*Equisetum*)

Subdivision Pteropsida Leaves usually large and complex

Class Filicineae (ferns) Sporophyte generation produces fronds that usually bear sporangia; germinating spore becomes the prothallus of the gametophyte generation

Subdivision Spermopsida Embryo enclosed by seed covering

Class Gymnospermae (gymnosperms) Mostly large and woody; seeds not enclosed in a protective wall; pollen deposited in or near ovules

Order Cycadophyta (cycads) Palmlike or fernlike; male and female reproductive structures usually in cones (*Zamia*)

Order Gingkophyta (gingkoes) Large tree with bilobed fan-shaped leaves; male and female reproductive structures found on separate plants; one living species (*Gingko biloba*)

Order Coniferophyta (conifers) Mostly evergreens; leaves usually needlelike; reproductive structures in cones (pines, cedars, cypresses, firs, hemlocks, larches)

Order Gnetophyta Mostly fossils; only three genera (*Ephedra, Gnetum,* and *Welwitschia*)

Class Angiospermae (angiosperms) Flowering plants; seeds enclosed in an ovary that develops into a fruit; pollen deposited on stigma

Subclass Monocotyledonae (monocots) Parallel-veined leaves; embryo with one cotyledon; flower parts in threes; fibrovascular tissues scattered in stem (grasses, orchids, irises, lilies, and palms)

Subclass Dicotyledonae (dicots) Net-veined leaves; embryo with two cotyledons; flower parts mostly in fours or fives; fibrovascular tissues of the stem in a cylinder (cacti, beeches, roses, maples, walnuts, peas, and beans)

KINGDOM ANIMALIA

Multicellular organisms with tissues and, in most cases, organs and organ systems; heterotrophic; undergo larval or embryonic development

PHYLUM PORIFERA (sponges) Body wall made up of two cell layers with many pores; reproduction by buds, gemmules, and gametes; protective skeleton made of calcium carbonate spicules, silica spicules, or spongin; marine and fresh water

Class Calcispongiae Spicules composed of calcium carbonate; shallow waters (*Grantia*)

Class Hylospongiae Spicules composed of silica; deep waters (Venus's flower baskets)

Class Demospongiae (large soft sponges) Skeleton of spongin or spongin and silica spicules; marine and fresh water (bath sponges and boring sponges)

PHYLUM COELENTERATA (coelenterates) Individual or colonial forms; reproduction by buds and gametes; cup-shaped body of two cell layers; digestive cavity with one opening; stinging cells and most with tentacles; free-swimming; marine and fresh water

Class Hydrozoa Individual or colonial; usually polyp form; marine and fresh water (*Hydra* and *Obelia*)

Class Schyphozoa Jellylike middle layer; usually medusa form; mostly marine (*Aurelia*)

Class Anthozoa   Individual or colonial; only polyp form; many tentacles; marine (sea anemones and corals)

PHYLUM CTENOPHORA   Comblike structures formed from fused cilia; reproduction by gametes; hermaphroditic; jellyfishlike; radially symmetrical; digestive cavity; free-swimming; marine (comb jellies and sea walnuts)

PHYLUM PLATYHELMINTHES (flatworms)   Three cell layers; flat ribbonlike bodies; reproduction by gametes; hermaphroditic; unsegmented; bilaterally symmetrical; lack body cavity; respiratory, circulatory, and skeletal systems; nervous system made up of two long nerve cords; sense organs located in head area

Class Turbellaria   Cilia on ventral surface of many; reproduction by gametes and fragmentation; mostly free-living aquatic or terrestrial (*Planaria*)

Class Trematoda   No cilia; parasitic; complicated life cycle (liver flukes)

Class Cestoda   Body is made up of a series of proglottids; hooked scolex; parasitic (tapeworms)

PHYLUM ROTIFERA (rotifers)   Mostly cylindrical; presence of a wheel organ (circle of cilia around mouth); jaws; bilaterally symmetrical; body ends in a foot; mostly free-living; fresh water, marine, and in moist areas on land

PHYLUM ACANTHOCEPHALA   Slightly flattened body; head contains recurved spines; reproduction by gametes; no digestive tract; parasitic in vertebrates (spiny-headed worms)

PHYLUM NEMATOMORPHA   Long slender body; reproduction by gametes; reduced digestive tract; parasitic as larvae and free-living in water as adults (hairworms)

PHYLUM CHAETOGNATHA   Arrowlike body; mouth contains chitinous teeth; marine (arrow worms)

PHYLUM NEMATODA (roundworms)   Long slender flattened bodies; unsegmented; reproduction by gametes; opening at anterior end (mouth) and opening at posterior end (anus); bilaterally symmetrical; body cavity present; many parasitic (*Ascaris, Trichinella,* and hookworms)

PHYLUM NEMERTEA   Long flattened body; no body cavity; reproduction by gametes and fragmentation; ciliated epidermis; bilaterally symmetrical; proboscis extends through mouth opening in anterior end; circulatory system; mostly marine (ribbon worms)

PHYLUM BRACHIOPODA (brachiopods)   Mollusklike with bivalve shell; pair of coiled arms with tentacles inside the shell; marine

PHYLUM ANNELIDA (segmented worms)   Coelom; reproduction by gametes; ventral nerve cord and dorsal brain; circular and longitudinal muscles in body wall; closed circulatory system; terrestrial, fresh water, and marine

Class Polychaeta   Paddlelike appendages called parapodia; eyes and tentacles present; setae; marine (*Nereis*)

Class Archiannelida   Body covered with cilia; some with no external segmentation; no parapodia; marine (*Dinophilus*)

Class Hirudinea   Anterior and posterior suckers; some are hermaphroditic; no setae; parasitic; terrestrial and fresh water (leeches)

Class Oligochaeta   Setae; closed circulatory system; hermaphroditic; terrestrial and fresh water (earthworms)

PHYLUM MOLLUSCA (mollusks)   Soft, unsegmented bodies; reduced coelom; reproduction by gametes; muscular foot used for locomotion; most secrete a hard shell substance from a mantle; marine, fresh water, and terrestrial

Class Amphineura   Long body with reduced head; no tentacles; many with shells containing eight plates; marine (chitons)

Class Pelecypoda   Hatchet-shaped foot; bivalve shell; gills in mantle cavity; fresh water and marine (clams, oysters, and scallops)

Class Gastropoda   Most have univalve shells; some have reduced shells or no shell; head, eyes, and tentacles present; marine, fresh water, and terrestrial (snails, slugs, and whelks)

Class Scaphopoda   Long toothlike body found in tubular shell; shell opened at both ends; threadlike tentacles; no gills; marine (tooth shells)

Class Cephalopoda   Large head; well-developed brain; foot adapted into a ring of tentacles; closed circulatory system; marine (octopuses, squids, and nautiluses)

PHYLUM ECHINODERMATA (echinoderms)   Spiny exoskeleton; reproduction by gametes; most have tube feet for locomotion; radially symmetrical; marine

Class Crinoidea   Five branched rays; no suckers on tube feet; fossil forms (sea lilies)

Class Asteroidea   Five rays on body; two rows of tube feet on each ray; eyespot at tip of each ray (starfishes)

Class Ophiuroides   Slender flexible rays; poorly developed tube feet without suckers (brittle stars)

Class Echinoidea   No rays; spherical, oval, or disk-shaped bodies; tube feet with suckers; spines (sea urchins and sand dollars)

Class Holothuroidea   No spines or rays; long, thick body; mouth surrounded by tentacles (sea cucumbers)

PHYLUM ARTHROPODA (arthropods)   Segmented body; jointed appendages; bilaterally symmetrical; chitinous exoskeleton; reproduction by gametes, some reproduce parthenogenetically; dorsal heart; ventral nervous system; aerial, terrestrial, and aquatic

Subphylum Trilobita (trilobites)   Skeleton forms a three-lobed shield; antennae on second segment and remaining segments have two-branched limbs; all extinct; marine

Subphylum Chelicerata   No antennae; first pair of appendages modified into pincerlike chelicerae; six pairs of appendages; fresh water, marine, and terrestrial

Class Eurypterida   Body with six pairs of ventral appendages; first pair of appendages have chelicerae, next four are walking legs, and last are large paddles; all extinct; marine (sea spiders)

Class Xiphosurida   Body flattened with anterior segments forming a shield; no antennae; ancient forms with only a few living representatives; marine (horseshoe or king crabs)

Class Pycnogonida   Short body with long legs; marine (sea spiders)

Class Arachnida   Head and thorax fused into cephalothorax; four pairs of legs; no antennae; book lungs or tracheae for respiration (spiders, scorpions, ticks, and mites)

Subphylum Mandibulata   Appendages near mouth are

modified into mandibles or jaws

Class Crustacea (crustaceans) Head and thorax fused into cephalothorax; five pairs of legs; two pairs of antennae; respiration by gills; limy exoskeleton (crayfishes, crabs, shrimps, lobsters, and barnacles)

Class Chilopoda (centipedes) Flattened body; 15 to 170 segments; one pair of legs attached to each segment; poison claws

Class Diplopoda (millipedes) Cylindrical body; 20 to 100 segments; two pairs of legs attached to each segment; no poison claws

Class Insecta (insects) Head, thorax, and abdomen regions; one pair of antennae; three pairs of legs; respiration by tracheae; complete or incomplete metamorphosis; most have wings

Order Thysanura Wingless; chewing mouthparts; no metamorphosis (silverfishes and bristletails)

Order Odonata Two pairs of membranous wings; toothlike biting mouthparts; large compound eyes; aquatic larvae; incomplete metamorphosis (dragonflies and damselflies)

Order Ephemeroptera Two pairs of wings, hind ones smaller; vestigial mouthparts in adults; incomplete metamorphosis (mayflies)

Order Phasmida Many wingless; grinding mouthparts; incomplete metamorphosis (stick and leaf insects)

Order Embioptera Females and some males wingless; chewing mouthparts; forelegs have silk-spinning organs; incomplete metamorphosis (web spinners)

Order Orthoptera Usually two pairs of wings; biting mouthparts; many with leaping hindlegs; incomplete metamorphosis (grasshoppers, crickets, and katydids)

Order Isoptera Usually two pairs of identical wings, some wingless; chewing mouthparts; incomplete metamorphosis (termites)

Order Anoplura Wingless; piercing-sucking mouthparts withdrawn into head when not feeding; eyes reduced or absent; parasitic in mammals; incomplete metamorphosis (sucking lice)

Order Dermoptera Wingless or two pairs of wings; hindwings folded under forewings when at rest; chewing mouthparts; incomplete metamorphosis (earwigs)

Order Hemiptera Two pairs of wings or wingless; leathery forewings and membranous hindwings; hindwings folded under forewings when at rest; piercing-sucking mouthparts; incomplete metamorphosis (true bugs)

Order Homoptera Wingless or one or two pairs of membranous wings; wings roofed over body when at rest; piercing-sucking mouthparts; incomplete or complete metamorphosis (aphids and cicadas)

Order Coleoptera Two pairs of wings or wingless; horny covered forewings and membranous hindwings; chewing mouthparts; complete metamorphosis (beetles, ladybugs, and fireflies)

Order Neuroptera Two pairs of crossed-veined wings; biting mouthparts; complete metamorphosis (lacewings and ant lions)

Order Diptera Membranous forewings, short knobbed hindwings; piercing-sucking or sponging mouthparts; complete metamorphosis (true flies, mosquitoes, and midges)

Order Siphonaptera Wingless; piercing-sucking mouthparts; no compound eyes; hind legs adapted for jumping; parasitic in birds and mammals; complete metamorphosis (fleas)

Order Lepidoptera Two pairs of scaly wings; tube-shaped sucking mouthparts coiled when not in use; large compound eyes; long antennae; complete metamorphosis (butterflies and moths)

Order Hymenoptera Most with two pairs of wings, some wingless; chewing, lapping, or sucking mouthparts; complete metamorphosis (ants, bees, and wasps)

PHYLUM CHORDATA (chordates) Tube within a tube body plan; notochord present in all embryos and sometimes in adults; paired gill slits at some stage of life cycle; dorsal nerve cord; terrestrial, marine, and fresh water

Subphylum Hemichordata Body divided into proboscis, collar, and trunk; wormlike; primitive dorsal nervous system; marine (acorn worms)

Subphylum Urochordata (Tunicata) Larvae have notochord, lost in adults; reproduction by budding and gametes, some are hermaphroditic; adult has primitive circulatory system; marine (tunicates)

Subphylum Cephalochordata Well-developed coelom; prominent muscle segments; marine (*Amphioxus* or lancelet)

Subphylum Vertebrata (vertebrates) Internal skeleton of cartilage or bone, or both; spinal column composed of vertebrae enclosing dorsal nerve cord, replaces notochord; terrestrial, marine, and fresh water

Superclass Pisces (fishes) Gills; cartilaginous or bony skeleton, or both; marine and fresh water

Class Agnatha (Cyclostomata) Jawless fishes; eel-like body; no scales or fins; cartilaginous skeleton; marine and fresh water (lampreys and hagfishes)

Class Chondrichthyes (Elasmobranchii) True jaws; paired fins; cartilaginous skeleton; openings of gills through gill slits; mostly marine (skates, rays, and sharks)

Class Osteichthyes Scales; paired fins; operculum over gills; cartilaginous and bony skeleton; swim bladder; marine and fresh water (bony fishes)

Subclass Actinopterygii Streamlined body; paired fins are fan-shaped; nostrils not connected with mouth cavity (ray-finned fishes)

Subclass Choanichthyes Nostrils open into mouth cavity; paired fins have enlarged median lobes; most species extinct (lobe-finned fishes and lungfishes)

Superclass Tetrapoda Vertebrates that usually have two pairs of limbs

Class Amphibia (amphibians) Moist, smooth skin; scales absent in most; gills present in larva and lungs present in adult; external fertilization; metamorphosis; aquatic and terrestrial

Order Apoda Wormlike body; some dermal scales; short tail or no tail; legless (caecilians)

Order Caudata Tailed body; front and hind legs equal in size (newts, salamanders, and sirens)

Order Salienta Tailless body; small front legs and large hind legs used for leaping; gills in larva and lungs in adult (frogs and toads)

Class Reptilia (reptiles) Body covered with horny scales or plates; dry skin; respiration by lungs; internal fertilization; young develop in leathery shelled egg; aquatic and terrestrial

Order Rynchocephalia   Only one living species; parietal eye in roof of skull; terrestrial (*Sphenodon,* or tuatara)

Order Chelonia (Testudinata)   Body enclosed between two bony shells; short legs, beak (turtles, terrapins, and tortoises)

Order Squamata   Long body; smooth or horny scales covering body (lizards and snakes)

Order Crocodilia   Large lizardlike body; valves in nostrils and ears that close when under water (crocodiles and alligators)

Class Aves (birds)   Feathers covering body; wings; beak; four-chambered heart; lungs; warm-blooded; internal fertilization; young develop in shelled egg; aerial, terrestrial, and aquatic

Superorder Palaeognathae   Modern toothless birds; flightless

Order Struthioniformes   Huge flightless birds; small wings; no feathers on head and neck (ostriches)

Order Rheiformes   Large flightless birds; head and neck feathered (rheas)

Order Casuariiformes   Large flightless birds; small wings; long hairlike feathers (cassowaries and emus)

Order Apterygiformes   Medium-sized flightless birds; vestigial wings (kiwis)

Superorder Neognathae   Modern birds

Order Gaviformes   Diving birds; webbed feet; reduced tail; compressed and sharply pointed bill (loons)

Order Sphenisciformes   Flightless birds; pointed beaks; webbed feet; wings modified as paddles (penguins)

Order Pelecaniformes   Swimming birds; large bills; webbed feet (pelicans, gannets, cormorants, and water turkeys)

Order Ciconiiformes   Wading birds; long pointed bill; long legs and neck (herons, storks, and ibises)

Order Anseriformes   Swimming and diving birds; short legs and webbed feet; bill usually broad and flat (ducks, geese, and swans)

Order Galliformes   Seed- and plant-eating birds; short wings; heavy feet with short, strong claws; short, stout bill (chickens, turkeys, quails, and partridges)

Order Columbiformes   Short legs; short slender bill (pigeons and doves)

Order Psittaciformes   Feet adapted for grasping; heavy hooked bill; often brilliantly colored plumage (parrots)

Order Strigiformes   Nocturnal birds of prey; strong hooked bill; sharped, curved talons (owls)

Order Apodiformes   Fast flying birds with long narrow wings; small legs and feet (hummingbirds)

Order Piciformes   Tree-dwelling birds that nest in holes; chisel-like or very large beaks (woodpeckers and toucans)

Order Passeriformes   Perching birds and songbirds (larks, crows, jays, chickadees, wrens, bluebirds, sparrows, and robins)

Class Mammalia (mammals)   Mammary glands secrete milk to nourish young; hair present; warm-blooded; four-chambered heart; internal fertilization; terrestrial and aquatic

Order Monotremata (monotremes)   Most primitive mammals; egg-laying (duck-billed platypuses and spiny anteaters)

Order Marsupalia (marsupials)   Primitive placenta; young complete development in female's pouch (kangaroos, koala bears, and opossums)

Order Insectivora   Insect-eating mammals; long pointed snouts, claws (shrews, moles, and hedgehogs)

Order Chiroptera   Flying mammals; forelimbs modified into wings; sharp teeth and claws (bats)

Order Carnivora   Flesh-eating mammals; large canine teeth; clawed toes (dogs, cats, and bears)

Order Pinnipedia   Flesh-eating mammals; marine (seals and walruses)

Order Edentata   Many toothless; others lack canines and incisors (anteaters and sloths)

Order Proboscidea   Nose and lip modified into trunk; upper incisor teeth enlarged to form tusks (elephants)

Order Perissodactyla   Odd-toed hoofed mammals (horses and tapirs)

Order Artiodactyla   Even-toed hoofed mammals; ruminants with four-chambered stomachs (cows, camels, and deer)

Order Rodentia   Gnawing mammals; well-developed and chisel-like incisors; no canines (squirrels and hamsters)

Order Lagomorpha   Rodentlike mammals; chisel-like incisors; no canines (rabbits and hares)

Order Sirenia   Aquatic mammals; forelegs developed into flippers and hindlegs absent (sea cows)

Order Cetacea   Marine mammals; forelegs modified into flippers; no neck, very little hair (whales and porpoises)

Order Primates   Erect mammals; five digits on hands and feet (monkeys, lemurs, gibbons, gorillas, and human beings)

Glossary

Pronunciation Key

SYMBOL	KEY WORD	RESPELLING	SYMBOL	KEY WORD	RESPELLING
a	act	(act)	uh	cup	(kuhp)
ah	star	(stahr)	ə	a as in along	(ə-LAWNG)
ai	dare	(dair)		e as in moment	(MŌ-mənt)
aw	ball	(bawl)		i as in modify	(MAH-də-fi)
ā	ate	(āt)		o as in protect	(prə-TEKT)
e	end	(end)		u as in circus	(SER-kəs)
ē	eat	(ēt)	ch	chill	(chil)
er	learn	(lern)	g	go	(go)
	sir	(ser)	j	joke	(jōk)
	fur	(fer)		bridge	(brij)
i	hit	(hit)	k	kite	(kīt)
ī	ice	(īs)		curve	(kerv)
ir	deer	(dir)	ng	bring	(bring)
	fear	(fir)	s	sum	(suhm)
ō	bone	(bōn)		cent	(sent)
oi	foil	(foil)	sh	sharp	(shahrp)
	boy	(boi)	th	three	(thrē)
or	horn	(horn)	z	zebra	(ZE-brə)
ow	out	(owt)		pose	(pōz)
	clown	(clown)	zh	treasure	(TRE-zhər)
oo	hoot	(hoot)			
	rule	(rool)			
yoo	few	(fyoo)			
	use	(yooz)			
u	book	(buk)			
	put	(put)			

abdomen part of the human body between the diaphragm and pelvis; in arthropods, the last body section

abiogenesis (ā-bī-ō-GEN-ə-sis) development of living things from nonliving materials; commonly called spontaneous generation

aboral (ā-BOR-'l) **surface** upper surface of a starfish

abscission (ab-SIZH-'n) shedding of a leaf or other plant organ

acid rain pollution in which acids formed from gaseous pollutants fall to the ground

acoelomate (ā-SE-lō-māt) organism lacking a body cavity

acquired trait physical trait developed during the lifetime of an organism

activation energy energy needed to break chemical bonds in a chemical reaction

active absorption movement of water into a plant by the process of osmosis

active immunity acquired immunity that can be brought about by injecting vaccines into an organism

active transport movement of substances into and out of a cell that requires the use of cellular energy

adaptation process by which an organism or species becomes better suited to a change in its environment

adaptive shift change in the frequency of occurrence of certain genes due to changes in the environment

adolescence stage of human development beginning with puberty and extending to adulthood

ADP adenosine diphosphate, a molecule similar to ATP that contains only two phosphate groups

adrenal gland endocrine gland on the top of each kidney

adsorption attachment of a virus to a host cell

adulthood final stage of human development that extends from adolescence through old age

adventitious (ad-vən-TISH-əs) **root** plant root developing from a stem or leaf

aerial root exposed plant root that obtains water and minerals from the air

aerobe (ER-ōb) organism that uses the aerobic phase of cellular respiration as its major energy source; requires oxygen for its survival

aerobic (er-ō-bik) **phase** second phase of cellular respiration requiring oxygen

air sac in grasshoppers, structure that pumps air into the trachea; in birds, spaces for storage of air; in human beings, clusters of alveoli

albinism condition in which an organism is unable to produce an enzyme needed to make the pigments that are responsible for the color of skin, hair, other body coverings, and eyes

alcoholic psychosis mental illness due to excessive use of alcohol over an extended period of time

alcoholism excessive use of alcohol

alga (AL-gə), *pl.* **algae** (AL-jē) simple form of plant life that includes "seaweeds" and "pond scums"

allantois (ə-LAN-tə-wis) saclike membane in a reptilian egg that stores nitrogen waste products

allele (ə-LĒL) one specific form of a gene for a single trait

alternation of generations process by which an organism reproduces asexually in one generation and sexually in the next generation

altricial bird species of bird in which the young must be cared for by their parents

alveolus (al-VĒ-ə-ləs), *pl.* **alveoli** microscopic sac in the lungs surrounded by capillaries

amino acid organic compound that is the building block of proteins

ammonification (ə-mō-nə-fi-KĀ-shən) formation of ammonia by bacterial decay of nitrogenous organic material

amniocentesis (am-nē-ō-sen-TĒ-sis) process of removing amniotic fluid from the amniotic sac; also, test using this process to determine some genetic disorders in a fetus

amnion sac in which an embryo develops

amniotic egg hard-shelled egg containing an amnion filled with a watery fluid used for protection and food

amoebocyte amoebalike cell that makes up the middle layer of a sponge

AMP adenosine monophosphate, lowest energy compound that contains only one phosphate group, used in the building of ADP and ATP

anabolic (AN-ə-bahl-ik) **reaction** biochemical reaction that builds up molecules and stores energy

anabolism (ə-NAB-ə-lizm) formation of complex substances from simple substances

anaerobe (an-ER-ōb) organism that uses the anaerobic phase of cellular respiration as its sole energy source; carries out its life processes without oxygen

anaerobic (an-er-ō-bik) **phase** phase of cellular respiration in which oxygen is not required

anal fin unpaired fin on the ventral surface of a fish

analogous organs organs similar in appearance and function but not in origin

anal pore opening in the paramecium through which undigested food particles leave the organism

anaphase stage in which the two sets of chromosomes move to opposite ends of the cell

angiosperm (AN-jē-ə-sperm) plant that develops seeds inside a fruit

animal pole upper hemisphere of an amphibian egg containing very little yolk

annual plant whose entire life cycle takes place within one growing season

annual ring layer of xylem that grows each year out of the previous layer of xylem

antenna, *pl.* **antennae** organ extending from the head of many arthropods used for touch and taste

antennule short appendage on many crustaceans, used for balance, touch, and taste

anther pollen-containing structure on a stamen

antheridium (an-thə-RID-ē-'m), *pl.* **antheridia** male reproductive organ of bryophytes

anthropology study of the origin, culture, and physical development of human beings

antibiotic chemical substance that slows or stops growth of a microbe

antibody protein produced by an organism in response to an antigen, a disease-fighting substance

antigen (AN-tə-jən) foreign protein that invades an organism; in human beings, protein on surface of red blood cells that determines blood type

antitoxin special antibody that counteracts the effects of bacterial toxins

anus opening at the posterior end of the digestive system through which wastes are excreted

aorta main artery leading directly from the heart, branching into smaller vessels

aortic arch structure in the circulatory system of some lower organisms that helps move the blood

apical dominance effect of plant auxins that causes terminal rather than lateral buds to grow

appendicular (ap-ən-DIK-yə-lər) **skeleton** part of the human skeleton that includes the shoulder and pelvic girdles, the arms, and the legs

applied genetics practical use of the science of genetics

aquatic root plant root adapted to life in the water

arboreal (ahr-BAWR-ē-əl) **heritage** theory that a group of animals descended from tree-dwelling ancestors

archegonium (ahr-kə-GŌ-ne-əm), *pl.* **archegonia** female reproductive organ of bryophytes

artery vessel that carries blood away from the heart

ascus, *pl.* **asci** spore-containing sac on some fungi

asexual reproduction formation of offspring from a single parent

assimilation production of living materials from chemical substances of food that are used for growth, repair, and maintenance

aster starlike pattern of microtubules extending from the centrioles in mitosis

aster rays microtubules that form the radial arms of the aster during the prophase stage of mitosis

atom smallest particle of an element

ATP adenosine triphosphate, a coenzyme composed of a base, a sugar, and three phosphate groups that stores and controls the release of energy within a ce¹l

atrium (Ā-trē-əm), *pl.* **atria** upper chamber of a heart

autonomic (AW-tə-NAHM-ik) **nervous system** part of the human nervous system that regulates involuntary activities

autosome any chromosome except a sex chromosome

autotroph (AWT-ə-trawf) producer; organism that makes its own food *adj.* **autotrophic**

auxin (AWK-sin) plant hormone regulating cell growth

axial skeleton part of the human skeleton, composed of the skull, the vertebral column, and the thorax

axon part of a neuron that carries messages away from a cell body

bacillus (bə-SIL-əs), *pl.* **bacilli** rod-shaped bacterium

bacterium, *pl.* **bacteria** simple, one-celled prokaryotic organism

bacteriophage (bak-TIR-ē-ə-fāj) virus that infects a bacterium; commonly called a phage

bacteriostat substance that slows down or prevents the growth and reproduction of bacteria

barb thin extension of the shaft of a feather

barbule structure that hooks barbs on a feather to one another

bark protective covering of a mature woody stem

basal disc structure in a hydra that secretes a sticky substance used for attachment to a rock or an aquatic plant

basidium (bə-SID-ē-əm), *pl.* **basidia** club-shaped sexual reproductive structure of some forms of fungi

behavior anything that an organism does

belly body of a muscle between its origin and insertion

benthic environment ocean floor

benthos group of marine organisms living on the ocean floor

biennial (bī-EN-ē-əl) plant whose entire life cycle takes place over two growing seasons

bilateral symmetry condition in which right and left sides of an organism are mirror images

bile substance produced in the liver that stimulates peristalsis and emulsifies fats

binary fission mitotic asexual reproduction in which a parent cell divides into two cells of equal size

binomial nomenclature two-word system for naming all organisms

biodegradable substance substance that can be broken down by natural, environmental processes

biogenesis development of living things from other living things

biogeography study of plant and animal distribution throughout the world

biological clock internal mechanism that controls circadian rhythms

biology study of living things

biomagnification buildup of chemicals in organisms within an ecosystem

biomass amount of living matter within an ecosystem

biome large geographic area determined by climate and characteristic plant and animal life

biosphere zone where all living things exist on the earth

biosynthesis process of building new, larger chemical compounds in living things

biotic potential largest size a population can reach provided all offspring survive and reproduce

biped animal able to walk upright on two legs *adj.* **bipedal**

bipinnaria starfish larva

bivalve mollusk of the class *Pelecypoda* having a two-part shell

blade thin, flat part of a leaf

blastopore hole that develops in a blastula

blastula (BLAS-tyoo-lə) stage of embryonic development resembling a hollow ball of cells

blood alcohol concentration (BAC) relative amount of alcohol in the blood

book lung structure in most spiders used for respiration

botany study of plants

botulism food poisoning caused by bacilli in improperly canned foods

Bowman's capsule structure in the nephron of a kidney that collects the filtrate from the glomerulus

brain stem part of the brain composed of the pons and the medulla oblongata

bristle short, hairlike feather with few or no barbs

bronchiole one of many smaller tubes into which the bronchi divide inside the lungs

bronchus (BRAHN-kəs), *pl.* **bronchi** air tube leading from the trachea to each of the lungs

bryophyte (BRĪ-ə-fīt) plant without vascular tissue

budding mitotic asexual reproduction in which a projection formed on a parent develops into another individual; also, form of grafting using a bud as the scion

bulb underground stem with scalelike leaves that contains food for the plants

bundle scar mark left on a stem after a leaf falls

bundle sheath structure that surrounds and supports the smaller veins in a leaf

bursa, *pl.* **bursae** (BUR-sē) fluid-filled sac between bones in movable joints

calorie unit of heat energy used to measure the energy value of foods

calyx (KĀ-liks) flower structure formed by all of the sepals on a receptacle

cambium (KAM-bē-əm) area containing meristematic tissue and causing an increase in root and stem diameter

canopy top forest layer

capillarity tendency of water to rise in a narrow tubelike structure

capillary blood vessel that connects arteries and veins

capillary beds groups of blood vessels found in warm-blooded animals

capsid (KAP-sid) protein layer surrounding viruses

capsomeres (KAPS-ə-mirz) protein units that combine to form the capsid of a virus

capsule definite boundary coating on the outside of the cell wall of some bacteria

carapace hard, protective outer shell of turtles, tortoises, and some arthropods

carbohydrate nutrient composed of carbon, hydrogen, and oxygen that provides energy to cells

carbon cycle movement of carbon through an ecosystem

cardiac muscle muscle tissue found only in the heart

carrying capacity size of a population that can be supported by the environment

cartilage tissue that attaches bones, cushions them and reduces friction between them

catabolic (KAT-ə-bahl-ik) **reaction** biochemical reaction that breaks down molecules and releases energy

catabolism (kə-TAB-ə-liz'm) breaking down of complex substances that results in the release of energy

catalyst chemical that helps to speed up reactions without itself being changed

caudal fin unpaired fin attached to the tail and used to propel a fish forward; also called tail fin

cell basic structural and functional unit of all living things

cell body part of a neuron containing the nucleus

cell lysis bursting of a host cell infected by a virus

cell membrane outermost living structure of an animal cell

cell metabolism breaking down of foods and building up of cell substances

cellular respiration energy-releasing process by which a cell uses potential energy to form molecules of ATP.

cell wall outermost nonliving structure of most plant cells

central nervous system part of the human nervous system composed of the brain and spinal cord

centriole (SEN-trē-ōl) organelle in most animal and some plant cells that is involved in the process of cell reproduction

centromere structure that holds together a pair of chromatids

cephalization (sef-ə-li-ZĀ-shən) localization of sense organs in the head area of an organism

cephalothorax part of a crustacean body made up of a combined head and middle section

cerebellum part of the human brain that controls balance, coordination, and other unconscious activities

cerebrum part of the human brain that controls the senses, thought, and conscious activities

cervical vertebra bone of the spine located in the neck

chelicera (kə-LIS-ə-rə), *pl.* **chelicerae** appendage of an arachnid; in spiders, a poisonous fang; in other arachnids, a clawlike appendage

cheliped (KĒ-lə-ped) appendage of a crustacean used for food getting and protection; also called pincer

chemistry study of the interaction of substances

chemosynthesis (kem-ō-SIN-thə-sis) process of making food by using energy from chemical reactions involving sulfur, iron, and nitrogen

chemotherapy (kēm-ō-THER-ə-pē) treatment of disease with chemical substances

chemotropism response to certain chemicals

childhood stage of human development from about one year of age to the onset of puberty

chitin (KĪT-'n) substance of which an arthropod exoskeleton is made

chlorenchyma (klor-EN-ki-mə) parenchyma cells that contain chlorophyll and undergo photosynthesis

chlorophyll green pigment in plants necessary for photosynthesis

chloroplast chlorophyll-containing organelle in which photosynthesis occurs

chorion outermost membrane in the egg of a bird or reptile that lines the shell; in mammals, membrane that encloses the amniotic sac and attaches it to the wall of the uterus

chromatid strand of DNA, two of which make up a chromosome

chromatin material irregular mass of thin threads of DNA, RNA, and proteins that form the chromosomes

chromatophore special cell containing various pigment granules that enable some organisms to change their coloration

chyme (kīm) semifluid substance into which foods are changed in the stomach

cilia short, hairlike projections of cytoplasm

circadian rhythm activities based on a 24-hour cycle

circulatory system body system that moves blood to all of the organs, tissues, and cells

citric acid cycle series of reactions in the aerobic phase of cellular respiration that form citric acid

class major taxonomic subdivision of a phylum

cleavage early divisions of a fertilized egg

climax community final stage of ecological succession, in which no major changes occur in the kinds of species or the structure of the community

climax species dominant plant species in the final stage of ecological succession

clitellum reproductive structure in an earthworm that appears as a swollen area near the anterior end

cloaca (klō-Ā-kə) chamber in the body of many organisms into which the digestive, excretory, and reproductive systems empty

cloning production of genetically identical organisms

clutch group or set of bird's eggs

cnidoblast (NĪ-də-blast) Stinging cell in the tentacles around the mouth of coelenterates

coccus (KAHK-əs), *pl.* **cocci** spherical bacterium

cocoon silklike protective covering around maturing eggs of an earthworm or the pupa of an insect

codon combination of three bases on a strand of messenger RNA that determines the order of amino acids needed to make specific proteins

coelenteron (si-LEN-tə-rahn) digestive cavity of all coelenterates

coelom (SĒ-luhm) liquid-filled body area

coenzyme organic molecule that bonds with an enzyme

coleoptile (kō-lē-AHP-t'l) covering of a plumule

collar cell specialized cell that makes up the inner layer of the body wall of a sponge; also called choanocyte

colloid (KAHL-oid) homogeneous mixture containing insoluble particles suspended in a medium

commensalism symbiosis in which one organism benefits from another but does not harm the host

community all of the living things in an ecosystem

companion cell cell that helps a sieve-tube element cell carry out function

complete metamorphosis insect metamorphosis including the egg, larva, pupa, and adult stages

compound substance containing two or more chemically bonded elements

compound eye eye containing many lenses

compound light microscope instrument that uses light to illuminate various specimens and objects

conditioning form of learned behavior in which a response to a specific stimulus becomes associated with a different stimulus

cone seed-bearing structure of a gymnosperm; in the retina, structure sensitive to bright light and color

coniferous forest terrestrial biome containing mostly cone-bearing trees

conjugation sexual reproduction in which cellular material is exchanged

consumer organism that feeds on other organisms; also called heterotroph

contour feather largest feather of a bird providing the streamlined shape necessary for flight

control part of an experiment to which the experimental set-up can be compared

convergent evolution process in which unrelated species develop similar characteristics

cork waxy outer tissue of woody stems and roots

cork cambium layer of secondary tissue from which cork grows

corm vertical underground stem enclosed by thin, scalelike leaves

cornea transparent covering of the eye

corolla (kə-RŌL-ə) structure composed of all the petals of a flower

cortex primary root tissue just inside the epidermis; also, outer portion of a kidney

cotyledon (kaht-'l-ĒD-'n) first leaf developed by the plant embryo of an angiosperm

covalent bond bond formed by atoms sharing electrons

cranial nerve nerve leading from the human brain to various areas of the head, neck, and sensory organs

cretinism (KRĒ-tin-iz'm) condition in infancy that results from severe thyroid deficiency and stunts physical and mental growth

crop thin-walled storage structure in the digestive system of some organisms; in a bird, sac in the esophagus in which food is moistened

crop rotation practice of alternating the growing of different crops each year on the same land

crossing-over exchange of genetic material from one chromosome to another

cuticle waxy coating on leaves that slows water loss; in roundworms, protective coating that prevents the worm from being digested inside the body of a host

cutting method of vegetative propagation in which

part of a plant is cut from the parent plant and then rooted in water or moist soil

cyanophyte prokaryotic moneran, blue-green alga

cyst structure formed by some protists when they enter a dormant stage; in some parasites, protective structure formed when inside a host

cytokinin (sī-tə-KĪ-nin) plant hormone that stimulates cell division

cytoplasm protoplasm outside the nucleus of a cell

dark reactions photosynthetic reactions that do not require light energy

deciduous forest temperate terrestrial biome containing mainly broad-leafed trees

decomposer organism that breaks down organic matter

dehydration synthesis formation of large molecules from the bonding of small molecules with the release of water

dendrite (DEN-drīt) part of a neuron that carries messages toward the cell body

denitrification process by which some bacteria convert nitrites, nitrates, and ammonia into free nitrogen

density-dependent factor factor limiting population size and dependent on the density of organisms in an environment

density-independent factor factor limiting population size but not affected by the density of organisms in an environment

depletion process of removing organic matter and minerals from the soil

depressant drug that decreases the action of the central nervous system; also called sedative

dermis lower layer of human skin

desalination (dē-sal-ə-NĀ-shən) process of removing salt from seawater

desert tropical or temperate terrestrial biome characterized by extremely low annual rainfall

development series of changes in form and function

diaphragm muscle in mammals separating the lungs and heart from the abdominal cavity that assists in breathing

diatom golden alga having cell walls made of silica

dicot angiosperm having two cotyledons

diffusion passive transport by which substances move from a region of higher concentration to a region of lower concentration; in respiration, process by which oxygen and carbon dioxide pass between alveoli and capillaries in the lungs

digestion process by which food is broken down into simple molecules by physical and chemical means

digestive enzyme chemical substance produced by the body that assists the process of digestion

digitigrade animal that walks on its toes with its heels not touching the ground

dihybrid cross cross involving two different pairs of alleles or two sets of traits

dinosaur group of extinct reptiles

dioecious (dī-Ē-shəs) containing male or female reproductive organs, but not both

diploid number normal number of chromosome pairs

disinfectant chemical substance used to kill microbes on nonliving things

dispersal movement of organisms to another habitat

diurnal (dī-ER-n'l) active during the day

divergent evolution process by which many different species developed from a common ancestor

division major taxonomic grouping of the plant kingdom

division of labor situation in which various cells of an organism, or various organisms in a population, perform different functions

DNA deoxyribonucleic acid, coiled double-stranded molecule that carries the genetic code

dominant gene gene that expresses itself over another gene in determining a trait

dorsal fin unpaired fin on the upper surface of a fish

dorsal surface upper surface or back of an organism

down feather simple feather; the only type of feather on an immature bird; found beneath the breast contour feathers of a mature bird

Down's syndrome condition caused by trisomy of the twenty-first chromosome

drug substance that causes a change in body function

dual-host virus virus transmitted from one host to another by a vector

eclipse (ē-KLIPS) third stage of the lytic cycle, in which the nucleic acid of the virus causes the host cell to form new viral parts

ecological succession series of changes in an ecosystem

ecology study of the relationships between living things and their environment

ecosystem any interacting system containing organisms and their nonliving environment

ecotone transition zone between terrestrial biomes

ectoderm outer cell layer of an organism, a primary germ layer in embryonic development; also called epidermis

ectoplasm thin, almost clear cytoplasm near the cell membrane

electron negatively charged particle outside the nucleus of an atom

electron microscope instrument that uses a beam of electrons to distinguish various specimens and objects

electron transport chain series of coenzymes along which an electron moves between chlorophyll molecules

element substance containing only one type of atom

elongation region   section of a root in which newly formed cells increase in length

embryo (EM-brē-ō)   developing organism

emergent layer   tops of the tallest individual trees protruding through the canopy of a tropical rain-forest

emigrant   organism that moves out of an area

emotion   complex reaction having both mental and physical elements

endangered species   organism close to extinction

endocrine (EN-də-krin) **system**   body system composed of glands that secrete hormones directly into the bloodstream

endocytosis (en-dō-sī-TŌ-sis)   active transport that moves large particles through the cell membrane

endoderm   inner cell layer of an organism, a primary germ layer in embryonic development

endoplasm   thick, grainy cytoplasm

endoplasmic reticulum   canal-like membrane system within the cytoplasm

endoskeleton   internal skeleton

endosperm   structure that stores food materials for a plant embryo

endosperm nucleus   structure formed by the joining of a sperm with two polar nuclei

endospore   spherical structure that protects the DNA and other structures of a dormant bacterium

endotoxin   poisonous substance produced by a bacterium and released when it dies

enzyme   biochemical catalyst enabling chemical reactions to take place

epicotyl (ep-ə-KAHT-'l)   structure in a plant seed made up of embryonic leaves

epidermal hair   structure on the outside of leaves that slows down surface water evaporation

epidermal tissue   outermost layer of cells

epidermis   outermost tissue of an organism; also called skin

epiglottis (ep-ə-GLAHT-is)   flap of tissue at the base of the tongue that covers the glottis and prevents food from entering the larynx and the trachea

erosion   process of carrying away of soil and rock by water and wind

esophagus (i-SAHF-əgəs)   muscular tube connecting the mouth to the internal digestive organs; also called food tube

estivation (es-tə-VĀ-shən)   state of inactivity in the summer during which the life processes of an organism slow down

estuary (ES-choo-wer-ē)⁻   zone between a freshwater biome and a marine biome

eukaryote (YOO-kar-ē-ōt)   cell with a well-defined nucleus enclosed in a nuclear membrane

eucoelomate (YOO-sē-lō-māt)   organism that has a coelom

Eustachian (yoo-STĀ-shən) **tube**   canal connecting the middle ear to the mouth cavity

eutrophication (yoo-trahf-i-KĀ-shən)   process by which oxygen is depleted in a body of water

eutrophic lake   shallow lake with large amounts of nutrients and a poor oxygen supply

evolution   change over a period of time

excretion   removal of waste products from an organism

excurrent siphon   tube which removes water from a bivalve

exercise   activity involving the work of muscles

exocrine (EKS-ə-krin) **gland**   gland with a duct that secretes substances directly into an organ

exocytosis (ek-sō-sī-TŌ-sis)   active transport in which particles too large for passive transport are removed from a cell

exoskeleton   external skeleton

exotoxin   poisonous bacterial secretion

experimental factor   condition being tested in an experiment

extensor   muscle that straightens a joint

extraembryonic membrane   one of four membranes that protect and nourish the human embryo

eyespot   light-sensitive organ in many lower organisms

facultative bacteria   bacteria that can live with or without oxygen

Fallopian (fə-LŌ-pe-ən) **tube**   tube that conducts an ovum from an ovary to the uterus

family   major taxonomic subdivision of an order

fang   extended tooth in the front of an organism's mouth; in some species, a hollow, curved tooth that conducts poison

fat   nutrient that provides energy and also insulates the body against cold

feces (FĒ-sēz)   mixture of undigested food, water, bacteria, and mucus that is the waste product of digestion

fermentation   form of cellular respiration that does not require oxygen

fertilization   uniting of a sperm and an ovum

fetus   stage of human development between embryo and birth

fibrous root   threadlike, branched root developing from a secondary root in some plants

fibrovascular bundle   vein in a leaf; also, a kind of leaf tissue that contains the xylem and phloem

filament   stalklike part of a stamen

filoplume   simple, hairlike feather containing only a few barbs at its tip; also called pin feather

filterability   property of a virus to pass through filters

flagellum, *pl.* **flagella**   whiplike structure of some protists used for locomotion

flame bulb   cell in a planarian that secretes water and wastes through pores

flexor   muscle that bends a joint

flower   structure of an angiosperm containing the reproductive organs

follicle   opening in the skin through which a feather or hair protrudes

fontanel (fahn-tə-NEL)   soft spot in a baby's skull

food chain   flow of energy and organic materials from organism to organism

food web   complex relationship formed by interconnecting and overlapping food chains

foot   organ on many organisms used for locomotion; in a mollusk, a body region

fossil   remains or trace of an organism that lived in the past

fragmentation   asexual reproduction in which pieces of an organism break off and undergo regeneration to form a new organism

frond   leaf, as of a fern, palm, lichen, or seaweed

fruit   seed-bearing structure of an angiosperm

FSH   follicle-stimulating hormone, a hormone made by the anterior lobe of the pituitary gland that causes an ovum to develop in the ovary

fungus (FUHN-gəs), *pl.* **fungi** (FUHN-j i) simple form of life including molds, toadstools, and mushrooms

gall bladder   organ of the digestive system that stores bile

gamete   sperm or ovum; also called sex cell

gametogenesis (ga-mēt-ə-JEN-ə-sis)   development of sex cells by meiosis

ganglion, *pl.* **ganglia**   bulblike enlargement of nerve tissue that makes up the ventral nerve cord in many invertebrates

gastric caeca (SĒ-kə)   gland in the stomach of an insect secreting an enzyme that digests food

gastrodermis   inner layer of cells; also called endoderm

gastrula   stage of embryo development forming layers of cells and various organs

gemma (JEM-ə) **cups**   small structures attached to a bryophyte in its gametophyte generation that contain chlorophyll and gemmae

gemmule (JEM-yool)   in a sponge, group of amoebocytes surrounded by a protective coat formed during unfavorable environmental conditions

gene   structure on a chromosome that determines hereditary traits; basic unit of heredity

gene pool   all of the genes of a given population

generative nucleus   part of a pollen grain that develops into two sperm nuclei

genetic (je-NET-ik) **breeding**   selectively breeding only individuals that have a particular trait

genetic drift   random changes in gene frequency in which the Hardy-Weinberg Law may not apply

genetic engineering   technology of adding or removing specific genes in an organism

genetics   study of heredity

genotype (JĒN-ə-tīp)   combination of alleles for a trait

genus   major taxonomic subdivision of a family; in binomial nomenclature, capitalized first name before the species name

geotropism   in plants, growth response to gravity

gestation   period of growth and development of an embryo or fetus in the uterus

gibberellin (jib-ə-REL-in)   plant hormone that promotes stem growth

gill   respiratory organ that absorbs dissolved oxygen in water

gill filament   structure containing thin disks that makes up the gills of a fish

gill raker   structure that stops food or dirt from clogging the gill filaments of a fish

girdling (GER-d'ling)   process of completely removing a ring of bark from a tree

gizzard   thick-walled structure in the digestive system in which food is ground up through muscular action

glomerulus (glah-MER-yoo-ləs)   filtering structure inside a nephron

glottis   opening in the pharynx leading to the larynx

Golgi (GŌL-jē) **apparatus**   organelle made up of a series of closely stacked, flattened sacs that packages substances to be secreted from the cell

gonad   sex organ, either a testis or an ovary, that secretes hormones affecting body development

grafting   propagation in which a cutting from one plant is attached to another plant

grana   membrane in a chloroplast that is made up of layers of chlorophyll, proteins, and lipids

granule   structure in a bacterium that stores food

grassland   temperate terrestrial biome characterized by flat, treeless areas; also called veldt, steppe, or pampas

green gland   excretory gland of most crustaceans

growth   increase in size; also, increase in the amount of protoplasm in an organism; also, increase in the number of organisms in a population

guard cell   one of a pair of cells that regulates the flow of gases into and out of a leaf

gullet   funnel-shaped structure in the paramecium extending from the mouth pore into the cytoplasm

guttation   process through which a plant eliminates excess liquid water

gymnosperm (JIM-nə-sperm)   plant that develops seeds externally on a cone

habitat   place an organism occupies in an ecosystem

hair follicle   tubelike structure through which a hair grows

half-life   time it takes for one-half of any quantity of a radioactive element to decay

hallucinogen   drug that can cause sensory distortions

haploid number one-half the diploid number of chromosomes

hard palate (PAL-it) hard structure that separates the mouth from the nasal cavity

Hardy-Weinberg Law theory stating that the frequency of dominant and recessive genes in a population remains constant from generation to generation

Haversian (ha-VER-shən) **canals** system of channels in bone tissue that nerves and blood vessels pass through

hemocoel (HEM-ə-sēl) largest part of the coelom of an arthropod

hemoglobin (HĒ-mə-glō-bin) iron-containing molecule in red blood cells that loosely combines with oxygen

hemophilia (hē-mə-FIL-ē-ə) inherited, sex-linked disease caused by defective genes in which minor injuries may result in severe bleeding

hemotoxin poisonous substance that destroys red blood cells and impedes blood clotting

herbivore animal whose diet consists of plants

heredity passing of traits from parent to offspring

heterotroph (HET-ər-ə-trawf) organism that depends on other organisms as food and energy sources; also called consumer *adj.* **heterotrophic**

heterozygote (het-ə-rə-ZĪ-gōt) zygote not having identical alleles *adj.* **heterozygous**

hibernation state of inactivity in the winter during which the life processes of an organism slow down

hilum (HĪ-ləm) scar formed when a seed pod breaks off from its stalk

holdfast special cell that grows from a zoospore and then becomes attached to an object

homeostasis (hō-mē-ō-STĀ-sis) internal stability and chemical balance in an organism regardless of external changes in the environment

homology (hō-MAHL-ə-jē) state of being identical or similar in form, as chromosomes, organs, or structures *adj.* **homologous**

homozygote (hō-mō-ZĪ-gōt) zygote having identical alleles *adj.* **homozygous**

hormone gland secretion that causes changes in organs

horny outer layer outermost layer of a bivalve

host in commensalism or parasitism, organism not benefited by the relationship

humus mixture of roots and decayed organic matter usually found in topsoil

hybrid organism organism with two different genes for a particular trait; also called heterozygous organism

hybridization (hī-brəd-i-ZĀ-shən) crossing of two genetically different species

hydrolysis process that breaks down larger molecules of carbohydrates when water is added

hydrophyte plant adapted to a watery environment

hydrotropism in plants, growth response to water

hyperthyroidism (hī-pər-THĪ-roid-iz'm) disorder caused by an overactive thyroid gland

hypertonic solution solution in which the concentration of a dissolved substance is higher outside than inside a cell

hypha (HĪ-fə), *pl.* **hyphae** branching filament found in a true fungus

hypocotyl (hī-pə-KAHT-'l) seed structure that produces the embryonic stem

hypothalamus (hī-pə-THAL-ə-məs) **gland** endocrine gland beneath the brain that secretes hormones and emits impulses affecting the pituitary gland

hypothesis (hī-PAHTH-ə-sis) tentative explanation for a problem that accounts for and agrees with known information

hypothyroidism (hī-pō-THĪ-roid-iz'm) disorder caused by an underactive thyroid gland

hypotonic solution solution in which the concentration of a dissolved substance is lower inside than outside a cell

immigrant organism that moves into an area

immunity resistance to disease

inbreeding method of genetic breeding using individuals that are closely related

incomplete dominance condition in which neither gene of a pair is dominant

incomplete metamorphosis insect metamorphosis consisting of the egg, nymph, and adult stages

incubate heating an egg to a temperature that enables embryo development to occur

incurrent siphon tube through which water enters a bivalve

infancy stage of human development that begins at birth and lasts for about one year

ingestion process of taking in substances such as oxygen and food

inhalant substance that evaporates rapidly

inorganic compound substance composed of elements other than carbon

insectivorous (in-sek-TIV-ər-əs) **plant** plant adapted to catch and digest insects

insertion movable point of attachment of a skeletal muscle

integument (in-TEG-yoo-mənt) outer covering of the human body, such as skin, hair, and nails

interferon antiviral substance produced in cells invaded by a virus

interkinesis (in-tər-ki-NĒ-sis) stage of meiosis between the first and second divisions

internode gap between two nodes

interphase stage between the completion of mitosis in one cell and the beginning of mitosis in the newly formed cells

intertidal zone life zone of the marine biome between the high-tide and low-tide lines

ion electrically charged atom

ionic bond bond formed when electrons are transferred from one atom to another

iris colored part of the eye

irritability ability of an organism to be affected by a stimulus and to respond to it

isolation separation of a population from other members of that species

isotonic solution solution in which the concentration is equal inside and outside a cell

isotope any of two or more forms of an element having different numbers of neutrons

jaundice human condition in which the skin, eyeballs, and urine become a deep yellow color

joint point where two or more bones meet

juvenile hormone insect hormone that causes the development of the larva

kidney major organ of excretion in most vertebrates

kinetic energy energy of motion; also, energy available to do work

kingdom largest taxonomic division

Klinefelter's syndrome human condition in which a male has one or more extra X chromosomes

labium lower lip of the mouth of an insect

labrum upper lip of the mouth of an insect

lacteal lymphatic vessel inside a villus that absorbs glycerol, fats, and fatty acids

large intestine tube of the digestive system in which liquids are absorbed and undigested food is stored; also called colon

larynx structure containing the vocal cords at the opening of the trachea; also called voice box or Adam's apple

lateral line series of pits running along a fish's body used as organs of taste

law of independent assortment rule stating that gene pairs on different chromosomes assort independently

law of segregation rule stating that a pair of alleles separates during gamete formation

layering method of propagation in which adventitious roots grow from stems cut from a plant

leaf external structure of a plant in which photosynthesis, respiration, and transpiration occur

leaflet section of a compound leaf

lens transparent structure in the eye that can focus an image on the retina

lenticel opening in a woody stem through which oxygen may enter the plant

LH luteinizing hormone, a hormone made by the anterior lobe of the pituitary gland causing the release of a matured ovum from the ovary

lichen (LĪ-kən) combination of algae and fungi living in a symbiotic relationship

ligament tissue that holds organs in place and fastens bones together

light reactions photosynthetic reactions that use light energy; chemical reactions that convert light energy into chemical energy

limiting factors any factors that prevent a population from reaching its biotic potential

lipid group of oily, greasy, waxy, or fatty organic compounds

liver organ that produces bile

lung principal organ of the respiratory system where gas exchange occurs

lymphatic (lim-FAT-ik) **system** body system that filters body fluids and helps maintain proper fluid balance

lymphocyte (LIM-fə-sīt) white blood cell capable of producing antibodies

lysosome (LĪ-sə-sōm) round organelle containing enzymes, found mainly in the cytoplasm of animal cells

lysozyme (LĪ-sə-zīm) viral enzyme that destroys the chemical bonds of a bacterial cell wall

lytic (LIT-ik) **cycle** process by which a cell is infected and destroyed by a virus

macroevolution development of a new species

macronucleus nucleus in the paramecium that controls all functions other than reproduction

macrophage white blood cell that destroys bacteria

Malpighian (mal-PIG-ē-'n) **tubule** tube that removes wastes from the body cavity of most arthropods

mammary gland milk-producing gland in mammals

mandible jaw of many arthropods and higher organisms

mantle membrane covering the visceral mass of a mollusk that usually secretes a material that forms the mollusk shell

marijuana (mar-ə-WAH-nə) drug obtained from the dried leaves and stalks of the Indian hemp plant

marrow soft tissue in the central cavity of bones

marsupial group of mammals whose young are born immature and develop inside a pouch

matter anything that occupies space and has mass

maturation region section of a root in which cells mature and become specialized in their functions

maxilla (mak-SIL-ə), *pl.* **maxillae** in arthropods, mouth structure that holds food and draws water over the gills; in vertebrates, the upper jaw

maxillary tooth one of many teeth that line the edge of the upper jaw of a frog

maxilliped (mak-SIL-i-ped) appendage of a crustacean that tastes and holds food during chewing

medulla inner portion of a kidney

medulla oblongata part of the brain stem serving as a passageway between other parts of the brain and controlling certain involuntary activities

medusa   coelenterate with a bell-shaped or cup-shaped body

megaspore   mother cell in each ovule in a flower

meiosis (mi-Ō-sis)   process that results in cells containing one-half the normal number of chromosomes

meninges (mə-NIN-jēz)   series of three membranes that surrounds and protects the brain

menstrual cycle   monthly cycle of the human female reproductive system

meristematic (mer-ə-stə-MAT-ik) **region**   section of a root that produces new cells

meristematic tissue   plant cells that grow causing an increase in length of roots and stems

mesentery (MEZ-'n-ter-ē)   clear membrane holding the small intestine in place

mesoderm   middle cell layer of an organism, a primary germ layer in embryonic development

mesoglea (mes-ō-GLĒ-a)   jellylike cell layer between the ectoderm and endoderm of a coelenterate

mesophyll   middle leaf tissue

mesophyte   plant adapted to a moist environment

mesothorax   part of the thorax of an insect

messenger RNA   RNA that brings the coded message from the DNA to the ribosomes in a cell; also called mRNA

metabolism (mə-TAB-ə-liz-'m)   total of all the chemical processes occurring in an organism

metaphase   stage of cell mitosis and meiosis during which the chromatids divide and move to the equatorial plane

metathorax   part of the thorax of an insect

metazoan   multicellular organism

microevolution   gradual change in a species

microfilament   protein fibers in a cell's cytoplasm involved in changes in the cell's shape

micronucleus   nucleus in the paramecium that controls reproduction

micropyle (MĪ-krə-pīl)   opening in the embryo sac of an ovule

microspore   cell produced in the anther that develops into a pollen grain

microtubule (mi-krə-TOOB-yool)   hollow, cylindrical structure in the cytoplasm of animal cells that maintains cell shape and transports substances

migration   movement of an organism into or out of a population or area

milt   sperm-containing fluid released by male fishes

mimicry (MIM-ik-rē)   close resemblance of an organism to an object or another organism that serves as a form of camouflage

mineral   nutrient needed to form body tissues

mitochondria (mīt-ə-KAHN-drē-ə)   complex oval and rod-shaped structures in the cytoplasm that function during cellular metabolism

mitosis   process in which a cell divides into two new cells, each of which has the original number of chromosomes; also called simple cell division

mixed nerve   nerve that carries messages to and from the human central nervous system

mixture   combination of two or more ingredients in which no chemical reaction takes place

molecule   bonded set of atoms forming the smallest particle of a compound able to exist and behave like that compound

molting   process of shedding an exterior layer of skin, feathers, or an exoskeleton

moneran   prokaryotic organism, such as any of the bacteria and cyanophytes

monocot   angiosperm having one cotyledon

monohybrid cross   cross involving only one pair of alleles or set of traits

monosomy (MAHN-ə-sō-mē)   condition in which a zygote is missing a chromosome

monotreme   group of mammals whose young hatch from eggs

morula   berrylike stage of embryo development

motile organism   organism that can move from place to place by its own energy

motor nerve   nerve that carries messages from the human central nervous system to muscles or glands

mouth pore   opening in the paramecium leading from the oral groove to the gullet

mucin (MYOO-sin)   slippery salivary substance that lubricates food to make it easier to swallow

multiple alleles   more than a single pair of alleles that control a single trait

muscle fiber   cell that forms bundles of muscle tissue

mutation   sudden change in the DNA pattern passed from one generation to the next

mutualism   symbiosis in which both organisms benefit from the relationship

mycelium (mī-SĒ-lē-əm), *pl.* **mycelia**   fruiting body of a fungus composed of many hyphae

myrofibril   thread found in muscle fibers

NAD   nicotinamide adenine dinucleotide, a hydrogen-accepting coenzyme necessary for anaerobic respiration

NADP   nicotinamide adenine dinucleotide phosphate, a hydrogen-accepting molecule necessary for photosynthesis

nanometer   one-millionth of a millimeter

narcotic   depressant drug that often causes strong physical addiction

naris (NAR-is), *pl.* **nares** (NAR-ēz)   opening in the nose or nasal cavity; also called nostril

nastic movement   plant growth response not directed toward or away from stimulus

natural selection   process by which organisms best suited to their environment survive and reproduce

nekton   group of free-swimming marine organisms

nematocyst (NEM-ə-tō-sist)   spearlike thread within a cnidoblast

nephridium (ne-FRID-ē-əm) *pl.* **nephridia**   one of two excretory organs in all but four segments of an earthworm

nephron basic structural and functional unit of the kidney

neritic zone life zone of the marine biome extending from the intertidal zone to the edge of the open sea

nerve impulse electrochemical signal that moves through the nervous system

nerve net network of nerves in a hydra

neuron (NOOR-ahn) basic structural and functional unit of the nervous system; also called nerve cell

neurotoxin poisonous substance that interferes with the normal functioning of the nervous system

neurotransmitter chemical substance that permits a nerve impulse to pass from one neuron to another

neutron atomic particle having no charge

niche (nich) role an organism plays in an ecosystem

nicotine (NIK-ə-tēn) stimulant drug in the leaves of the tobacco plant

nictitating membrane transparent protective covering of skin over the eye of some amphibians

nitrification process by which some bacteria convert ammonia to nitrites and nitrates

nitrogen cycle movement of nitrogen through an ecosystem

nitrogen fixation process by which some bacteria change nitrogen into nitrites and nitrates

nocturnal (nahk-TER-n'l) active during the night

node connecting link between a stem and leaf

nonbiodegradable unable to be broken down by natural environmental processes

nondisjunction failure of a homologous pair of chromosomes to separate during mitosis or meiosis

nonrenewable resource natural resource that cannot be replaced after use

nucleic acid any of an essential group of complex organic acids found in the nucleus of all living cells

nucleic acid core hereditary material of a virus

nucleolus (noo-KLĒ-ə-ləs) body within the nucleus made up of RNA and protein

nucleoplasm protein-rich protoplasm in the nucleus of a cell

nucleotide section of a DNA molecule consisting of a sugar, a phosphate group, and a nitrogen base

nucleus oval or spherical structure within a cell that contains most of the hereditary material necessary for growth and reproduction and is the cell's control center; also, the center of an atom made up of protons and neutrons

nutrient substance needed by an organism

obligate aerobe organism that can live only in the presence of oxygen

obligate anaerobe organism that can live only in the absence of oxygen

ocelli (ō-SEL-ī) specialized group of nerve cells in jellyfishes that responds to light

olfactory (awl-FAK-tər-ē) **bulb** section of most mammalian brains that interprets nerve impulses involving the sense of smell

olfactory lobe section of the brain of most vertebrates that receives sensory information from the nasal cavity

oligotrophic (ahl-ə-gō-TRŌ-fik) **lake** deep lake that has few nutrients and a good oxygen supply

omnivore organism whose diet consists of both plant and animal foods

ootid (ō-ə-tid) cell produced during oogenesis that later develops into an egg

operculum (ō-PER-kyoo-ləm) hard movable flap covering the gill openings in a fish

opposable thumb finger that works in a direction opposite to that of the other fingers

optic lobe brain section of most vertebrates that receives sensory information from the eyes

optimum temperature temperature at which growth and life processes occur most rapidly and efficiently

oral groove channel or indentation of the paramecium through which food is brought to the mouth pore

order major taxonomic subdivision of a class

organ group of different tissues working together to perform the same function or functions

organelle organized structure within a cell that carries out a life function of the cell

organic compound usually any substance containing carbon

organism living thing

organ system group of organs working together to perform a certain function

origin fixed point of attachment of a skeletal muscle

osculum opening in a sponge through which water and wastes leave

osmosis passive transport in which water diffuses through a selectively permeable membrane

osmotic pressure pressure exerted on a cell by water outside the cell

ossification (ahs-ə-fi-KĀ-shən) process of bone formation during the early stages of embryo development

ostium (AHS-tē-əm), *pl.* **ostia** in crustaceans, opening in the heart through which blood enters; in sponges, pore through which water passes

ovary female reproductive organ; in plants, structure at the base of a pistil

oviduct coiled tube through which ova pass out of the ovary

oviparity (ō-vi-PAR-ə-tē) reproduction process in which offspring hatch from eggs outside the body of the mother *adj.* **oviparous** (ō-VIP-ər-əs)

ovipositor (ō-vi-PAHZ-i-tər) structure at the rear of a female insect used to lay eggs

ovisac thin-walled structure in amphibians that

develops from an oviduct and stores eggs until they are laid

ovoviviparity (ō-vō-vī-və-PAR-ə-tē) reproduction process in which offspring hatch from eggs within the body of the mother *adj.* **ovoviviparous** (ō-vō-vī-VIP-ər-əs)

ovulation process of producing and releasing an ovum

ovule structure that develops into a seed

ovum, *pl.* **ova** female gamete; also called egg cell

oxygen cycle movement of oxygen through an ecosystem

oxygen debt shortage of oxygen in muscle cells

palisade mesophyll upper layer of the mesophyll in a leaf

palmate leaf compound leaf in which the leaflets radiate from one end of the petiole

pancreas (PAN-krē-əs) organ of the digestive system that has both endocrine and exocrine functions

parabronchus, *pl.* **parabronchi** branch of the bronchi and secondary bronchi within the lung

parapodium (PAR-ə-pod-əm), *pl.* **parapodia** paddle-like appendage on each segment of some segmented worms used for swimming or burrowing

parasite organism that obtains its food from a host and harms the host in the process

parasitism symbiosis in which one organism benefits from and one is harmed by the relationship

parasympathetic nervous system part of the human autonomic nervous system that controls many internal body functions during times of rest

parathyroid gland endocrine gland on the back of the thyroid gland that balances the levels of calcium and phosphorus in the blood

parenchyma (pə-REN-ki-mə) **tissue** plant tissue in which food and water are stored

parietal (pə-RĪ-ə-t'l) **body** sensory organ under the surface of the skin that can detect light

parthenogenesis (par-then-ō-JEN-ə-sis) development of an egg without fertilization *adj.* **parthenogenetic**

passive absorption movement of water into a plant due to transpiration

passive immunity acquired immunity brought about by injecting antibodies into an organism

passive transport movement of substances into and out of a cell without the use of energy

pathogen microbe capable of causing disease

pearly layer inner layer of the shell of a bivalve

pectoral fin one of a pair of fins behind the gill openings on a fish used for swimming

pedicel (PED-i-s'l) supportive structure that serves as the stalk on which a flower rests

pedipalp (PED-i-palp) appendage attached to the cephalothorax of an arachnid used for chewing and sensory functions

pelagic environment open sea

pellicle hard membrane covering the outer surfaces of some protists

pelvic fin one of a pair of fins on the ventral side of a fish used for swimming

perennial (pə-REN-ē-əl) plant that lives for more than two growing seasons

periosteum (per-i-AHS-tē-əm) tough, fibrous membrane surrounding the shaft of a long bone

peripheral (per-IF-ə-r'l) **nervous system** part of the human nervous system that carries messages between the central nervous system and the rest of the body

peristalsis (per-ə-STAWL-sis) muscular contractions that push food through the digestive system

permafrost soil that is permanently frozen

permanent wilting sagging of a plant due to lack of water caused by damage to the roots

petal usually colorful leaflike structure that grows from the receptacle and encloses a flower

petiole (PET-ē-ōl) stalk of a leaf

PGA phosphoglyceric acid, a 3-carbon molecule produced by photosynthesis

PGAL phosphoglyceraldehyde, a 3-carbon molecule formed when hydrogen atoms combine with PGA to form the intermediate product of photosynthesis

phagocyte (FAG-ə-sīt) specialized human white blood cell that helps fight disease

phagocytosis (fag-ō-sī-TŌ-sis) endocytosis in which pseudopodia surround particles such as food and antigens

pharynx (FAR-ingks) muscular cavity at the rear of the mouth that connects the trachea and esophagus; long tube used to draw food into the mouth

phenotype (FĒ-nə-tīp) visible characteristics of an organism produced by a particular genotype

pheromone (FER-ə-mōn) chemical substance emitted by females of a species to attract males

phloem (FLŌ-əm) vascular tissue that conducts nutrients throughout a plant

phobia irrational fear

photochemical smog air pollution containing smoke, gases, and fog that forms in the presence of sunlight

photoperiodism plant response to the lengths of light and dark periods

photosynthesis process by which green plants convert light energy into chemical energy

photosynthetic zone life zone in the marine biome composed of the neritic zone and part of the open sea zone where many producers live

phototropism in plants, growth response to light

phylum taxonomic division of the animal kingdom

physiology study of bodily processes and functions of an organism

pinnate leaf compound leaf with leaflets arranged along the sides of an extended petiole

pinocytosis (pē-nō-cī-TŌ-sis) endocytosis in which

particles collect on the cell membrane, which then folds inward around the particles

pioneer plant   first plant to dominate an ecosystem

pistil (PIS-t'l)   female reproductive organ of a flower

pith   area at the center of a stem used for the storage of food

pituitary (pi-TOO-i-ter-ē) **gland**   endocrine gland in the human skull beneath the brain that secretes hormones affecting many body functions; also called master gland

PKU   phenylketonuria, an inherited disease in infants in which a vital enzyme is not produced

placenta   thin membrane formed inside the uterus to transport oxygen and nutrients between the mother and the developing embryo

placental mammal   mammal whose young develop fully inside the uterus of the mother

placoid scale   disklike fish scale with a hard, sharp point

plankton   organisms that float or drift on or near the surface of the ocean

planula   free-swimming larva of a coelenterate

plasma   liquid portion of blood

plasmid   separate segment of DNA in some bacteria

plasmodium (plaz-MŌ-dē-əm)   nonreproductive stage formed when many individual slime mold cells join

plasmolysis   loss of turgor pressure in a plant cell due to the movement of water out of the cell

plastid   organelle that makes or stores food

plastron   underside of a turtle or tortoise shell

platelet (PLĀT-lit)   cell-like part of the blood that begins clotting and prevents leaks in the capillaries; also called thrombocyte

plumule (PLOOM-yool)   structure formed by the epicotyl and its young leaves

polar body   one of three haploid cells produced during oogenesis

pollen tube   outgrowth of a pollen grain that permits the generative nucleus to enter the embryo sac

pollination   process by which pollen is transferred from an anther to a stigma

pollution   contamination of the environment

polyp   tube-shaped coelenterate

polyploidy (PAHL-i-ploi-dē)   condition of an organism having more than two sets of chromosomes

pons   part of the human brain stem that functions as a bridge between the cranial nerves

population   all of the individuals of one species in a community

population density   number of individuals of a population per unit of area

population genetics   genetic study of a group of organisms

population growth curve   graph representing the growth of a population

population sampling   genetic study of a random group of individuals within a population of organisms

porocyte   epidermal sponge cell that forms the ostium

potential energy   energy stored within a cell that can be released to do work

precocial   active and well formed; of baby birds, able to follow the parents out of the nest almost immediately after hatching

predator   organism that hunts and feeds on other living organisms

prehensile tail   tail adapted for grasping

prey   organism fed upon by a predator

primary germ layer   any of many groups of cells from which various tissues and organs form during the gastrula stage of development

primary root   first root to develop from a seed

primary succession   development of a community in an area where there had not been a community before

primary tissue   first kind of cells that form in a root

principle of biogenesis   idea that living things develop only from other living things

prismatic (priz-MAT-ik) **layer**   middle layer of the shell of a bivalve

producer   organism, usually a green plant or a bacterium, that produces its own food; also called autotroph

proglottid (prō-GLAHT-id)   one of many nearly square sections that make up the body of the tapeworm

prokaryote (PRŌ-kar-ē-ōt)   cell without a true nucleus; cell in which the nuclear material is not enclosed in a nuclear membrane   *adj.* **prokaryotic**

prophase   stage of mitosis in which chromosomes become visible; stage of meiois in which synapsis occurs

prostomium (prō-STŌ-me-əm)   small lip covering the mouth in an earthworm

protein   substance composing every living cell; a nutrient necessary for cell growth and repair

protein synthesis   process by which cells combine amino acids to manufacture proteins

prothallus (prō-THAL-əs)   heart-shaped green plant that grows from a germinating spore

prothorax   part of the thorax of an insect

proton   positively charged particle in the nucleus of all atoms

protonema (prōt-ə-Nē-mə)   green threadlike structure that develops on some plant spores

protoplasm   material in a cell made up of many different substances and structures that function together to carry out the chemical activities of life

protozoan   simple, microscopic, one-celled, animal-like protist

pseudopodium (SOO-de-PAHD-əm), *pl.* **pseudopodia** (SOO-de-PO-de-ə) projection of cytoplasm in some protists and amoebalike cells

pulmonary (PUL-mə-ner-ē) **circulation**   division of

the circulatory system in which blood flows between the heart and the lungs

pupil central opening in the iris of the eye

purebred organism organism with like genes for a particular trait; also called homozygous organism

purine (PYOOR-ēn) one of the two kinds of nitrogen bases in a DNA molecule

pyloric caecum (pī-LAWR-ik sē-kəm), *pl.* **pyloric caeca** intestinal pouch that increases the surface area through which absorption can occur

pyloric valve ringlike muscular valve at the base of the stomach that controls the amount of food entering the intestines

pylorus opening at the lower end of the stomach controlled by a muscular valve

pyrenoid (pī-RĒ-noid) protein body on chloroplasts that functions as a storage area for the cell

pyrimidine (pi-RIM-ə-dēn) one of the two kinds of nitrogen bases in a DNA molecule

quarantine separation of infected individuals from noninfected individuals

quill base or attachment point of a contour feather

radial canal in a starfish, one of five passages of the water-vascular system that extends into a ray

radial symmetry regular circular arrangement of body parts around a central area

radicle embryonic root in a plant seed

radula tonguelike structure of a mollusk used for scraping food from an object

RDP ribulose diphosphate, a 5-carbon sugar molecule involved in the photosynthetic dark reaction

receptacle supportive structure at the tip of a pedicel

recessive gene gene masked when the dominant allele is present

recombinant DNA new strand of DNA produced by recombining segments from separate DNA strands

rectum section of large intestine leading to the anus

red blood cell blood cell that carries oxygen; also called erythrocyte

reflex simple automatic response to a stimulus

reforestation practice of planting new trees to replace those cut down

regeneration asexual reproduction in which an organism is able to grow back missing or broken parts

renewable resource natural resource that can be used and replaced

replication process of making an exact copy of a DNA molecule

reproduction process of producing offspring

reservoir in *Euglena,* large area into which excess water is pumped

respiration process by which oxygen is delivered to a cell and in which energy is released

retina inner layer of the eye on which the lens focuses an image

Rh factor antigen in red blood cells used to determine blood type

rhizoid (RĪ-zoid) cluster of short hyphae that develops on the stolon of a fungus

rhizome (RĪ-zōm) horizontal underground stem that looks like a root

ribosomal RNA RNA that makes up part of the ribosomes in a cell; also called rRNA

ribosome organelle that makes proteins

RNA ribonucleic acid, a single-stranded molecule involved in the manufacture of proteins by a cell

root structure of a plant that anchors the plant, absorbs water and minerals, and stores food

root cap structure made up of several layers of cells that protects the root tip

root hair microscopic projection of a root cell on the surface of a root

root pressure force of water within a root

ruminant even-toed ungulate with a four-chambered stomach

sacral vertebra bone of spine near hip or leg joint

salivary gland gland that secretes the saliva used to moisten food and start the digestive process

saprophyte (SAP-rə-fīt) organism that feeds on dead organisms or the wastes of living organisms

savannah grassland biome containing scattered trees

scavenger animal feeding on the remains of dead animals

scion (SĪ-ən) plant cutting used in grafting

sclerenchyma (skli-REN-ki-mə) plant tissue that supports and strengthens parts of a plant

sclerenchyma fiber supporting structure that strengthens the larger veins in a leaf

scolex knob-shaped head area of a tapeworm

scutes scalelike plates covering a turtle or tortoise shell

scyphistoma (sī-FIS-tə-mə) polyp that develops from a planula after attaching to an object

secondary root root that grows from the primary root

secondary succession development of a community in an area where a previous community has been destroyed or removed

secondary tissue cells that form in a root after primary tissue has matured

seed plant reproductive structure formed by the joining of a male and female gamete

seed dispersal process by which seeds are spread from one place to another

selection process of choosing and breeding organisms with desired traits

seminal vesicle saclike structure that surrounds the testes and stores sperm

sense organ any of five organs that respond to environmental stimuli, including eye, nose, tongue, skin, and ear

sensory lobe sense organ in some organisms that responds to touch, chemicals, or other stimuli

sensory nerve nerve that carries messages to the central nervous system

sensory receptor nerve ending in the skin that responds to an environmental stimulus

sepal (SE-p'l) leaflike structure that develops from the receptacle and encloses the bud

sessile (SES-il) **leaf** leaf without a petiole

sessile organism organism not able to move spontaneously; organism attached to an object

seta (SE-tə), *pl.* **setae** (SE-te) one of a pair of bristles on each segment of most segmented worms

sex chromosome chromosome that determines an organism's sex; called X or Y chromosome

sex-linked trait trait carried by genes on the sex chromosome for a characteristic other than sex

sexual reproduction formation of offspring requiring two parents

shadow casting electron microscopy technique used to study the structures of very small organisms; also called electron-shadow micrography

shaft central part of a feather growing out of the quill and supporting the barbs

shoot part of a plant that includes the stem, leaves, flowers, and fruits

shoot apex new tissue at the tip of a bud

sickle-cell disease inherited disease usually found in people of African or Hispanic origin in which the red blood cells become deformed

sieve tube part of a plant's phloem

sieve-tube element cell from which the phloem of angiosperms and gymnosperms is made

skeletal muscle muscle tissue responsible for all voluntary movement; also called striated muscle

slime layer diffuse coating on the outside of the cell wall of a bacterium with no distinct boundary

small intestine narrow, hollow tube through which food is absorbed into the bloodstream

smooth muscle muscle tissue responsible for all involuntary movement

soft palate (PAL-it) soft muscle tissue in the mouth that prevents food from entering nasal cavity

solution homogeneous mixture in which one substance is dissolved in another substance

sorus (SO-rəs), *pl.* **sori** round, reddish-brown structure on the underside of a fern frond in which spores are produced

spawn in fishes, to lay eggs

speciation development of a new species

species major taxonomic subdivision of a genus, a group of closely related organisms that interbreed; in binomial nomenclature, uncapitalized second name after the genus name

sperm male gamete

spermatophore (sper-MAT-ə-for) packet of sperm deposited by some species of amphibians

sperm nucleus structure formed from a pollen grain that fertilizes either the egg or the polar nuclei

spicule (SPIK-yool) sharp, pointed, noncellular projection that makes up the skeleton of some sponges

spinal nerve nerve leading from the spinal cord to other sections of the body

spine in many desert cacti, modified, sharply pointed leaf; in vertebrates, backbone

spinneret web-spinning organ of a spider

spiracle (SPI-rə-k'l) opening in the abdomen of an arachnid used for respiration

spirillum (spI-RIL-əm), *pl.* **spirilla** spiral-shaped bacterium

spirochete (SPI-rə-ket) form of bacteria that moves by rotating with a spiral motion

spongin (SPUHN-jin) protein material that makes up the skeleton of some sponges

spongy mesophyll lower mesophyll layer in a leaf

sporangium (spaw-RAN-je-əm), *pl.* **sporangia** asexual reproductive structure in which a fungus produces and stores spores

spore protist or plant reproductive cell

stamen (STA-men) male reproductive organ of a flower

statocyst saclike structure near the base of the antennule of a crustacean that controls balance

statolith (STAT-ə-lith) specialized group of nerve cells in jellyfishes that responds to gravity

stem external plant structure that supports the plant, produces leaves, and carries materials between the roots and the leaves

stimulant drug that temporarily increases the action of the central nervous sytem

stimulus any change in an organism's environment

stipule (STIP-yool) scalelike protective structure at the base of some leaves

stock plant stem to which a scion is grafted

stolon horizontal stem that grows on the ground or just under the surface; also called runner

stoma, *pl.* **stomata** opening formed by two guard cells, through which gases pass into or out of a leaf

stomach organ in which foods are digested physically and chemically

strobilation process by which a strobila develops into a mature jellyfish

succulent leaf thick, fleshy leaf that can store large quantities of water

suspension mixture containing undissolved particles in a medium

suture seam that forms where the bones of the skull fuse together

swim bladder organ in a bony fish that fills with air and enables the fish to rise or sink in the water; also called air bladder

swimmeret   appendage on the abdomen of a crustacean used for swimming and respiration

symbiosis (sim-bī-Ō-sis)   relationship between two organisms of different species

sympathetic nervous system   part of the autonomic nervous system that controls many internal body functions during increased physical or mental activity

synapse (SIN-aps)   gap between the axon of one neuron and the dendrite of another

synapsis   process in which double-stranded homologous chromosomes pair up and twist around each other

synovial fluid   lubricating fluid found in joints

syrinx   organ at the lower end of the windpipe of a bird used to produce sounds

systemic circulation   division of the circulatory system in which blood flows between the heart and all the tissues of the body other than the lungs

taiga (TĪ-gə)   northernmost area of a coniferous forest biome

talon   sharp claw on the feet of some birds

taproot   primary root that remains the main root of a mature plant such as a beet or carrot

taste bud   sensory receptor that reacts with chemicals in food

taxis   movement toward or away from an external stimulus

taxonomy   science of classifying plants and animals

tegument   protective coating on some parasites that prevents them from being digested by a host

telophase   last stage of mitosis and meiosis in which nuclear membranes form around the chromosomes and the cytoplasm divides to form new cells

telson   triangular structure in the middle of the uropod of some crustaceans

temperature inversion   condition in which a cool layer of air becomes trapped beneath a warmer layer

temporary wilting   sagging of a stem due to loss of turgidity occurring when the rate of transpiration is greater than the rate of absorption

tendon   tissue that connects skeletal muscles to bones

tendril   coiled supportive structure on the tip of some compound leaves

testa   outer part of a seed coat

test cross   test to determine whether an organism is heterozygous or homozygous for a specific trait

testis, *pl.* **testes**   male reproductive organ

tetrad   pair of double-stranded chromosomes containing a total of four chromatids

thallophyte (THAL-ə-fīt)   simple plant that lacks true roots, stems, and leaves; alga or fungus

thallus, *pl.* **thalli**   body of a thallophyte

theory   proposed explanation that is supported by considerable experimentation

thermal pollution   addition of undesirable amounts of heat energy to a body of water

thigmotropism (thig-MAHT-rə-piz'm)   in plants, response to contact or touch

thymus (THĪ-məs) **gland**   endocrine gland in the chest that may affect the body's disease-preventing activities

thyroid (THĪ-roid) **gland**   endocrine gland in the neck that affects the use of energy by the body

tissue   group of specialized cells that are alike in structure and function

topsoil   uppermost layer of soil containing humus

trachea (TRĀ-kē-ə), *pl.* **tracheae**   main air tube from the pharynx to the lungs; also called windpipe

tracheid (TRĀ-kē-id)   pointed, thick-walled plant cell from which the xylem of gymnosperms is made

tracheophyte (TRĀ-kē-ə-fīt)   plant with vascular tissues

tranquilizer (TRAN-kwə-lī-zər)   drug that has a calming effect on the central nervous system

transcription   process of making messenger RNA using DNA molecules as the pattern

transduction   process by which a virus transfers DNA from one bacterium to another

transfer RNA   RNA that carries amino acids to the messenger RNA at the ribosomes; also called tRNA

transformation   process by which living bacteria take in part of the DNA from dead bacteria

translation   process by which the original code of DNA makes a protein molecule in the cytoplasm

translocation   movement of materials within a plant

transpiration   process by which a plant eliminates excess water vapor through its leaves

transpiration-cohesion theory   theory used to explain translocation of materials in plants

trichinosis   disease caused by the trichina worm contracted by eating undercooked, infected pork

trichocysts (TRIK-ə-sists)   poison-containing structures in the pellicles of some protists used to anchor and defend the organism

trisomy (trī-SŌ-mē)   condition in which a zygote has an extra chromosome

trochophore (TRAHK-ə-fawr)   larval stage of a mollusk

trophic (TRAHF-ik) **level**   feeding level within a food chain or ecological pyramid

tropical rain forest   terrestrial biome characterized by large biomass and high annual rainfall

tropism (TRŌ-piz-'m)   in plants, growth response either toward or away from stimulus

trunk vertebra   bone of the spine in the main section of the body

tube foot   external suction disk of the water-vascular system of an echinoderm

tube nucleus   part of a pollen grain that controls the growth of the pollen tube

tuber   modified stem that is actually an enlarged section of an underground stolon

tumor uncontrolled growth of cells

tundra polar terrestrial biome

turgidity (ter-JID-i-tē) condition caused by turgor pressure that maintains the shape of a plant cell

turgor pressure pressure exerted against the cell wall by the contents of a plant cell

Turner's syndrome condition in which a gamete is missing a sex chromosome; results in genotype XO

tympanum membranous sensory organ used in hearing

umbilical cord structure containing blood vessels that connects the embryo or fetus to the placenta

ungulate order of hoofed mammals

unicellular organism living thing that is made up of only one cell

univalve mollusk of the class *Gastropodia* with a one-part shell

urea waste product made by the liver and excreted by the kidneys

ureter (yoo-RĒT-ər) tube leading from the kidneys to the urinary bladder

urethra (yoo-RĒ-thrə) tube leading from the urinary bladder to the outside of the body

urinary bladder saclike structure that stores urine

uropod (YOOR-ə-pahd) appendage on a crustacean used for swimming; also called flipper

urostyle several fused vertebrae at the posterior end of the spine

uterus, *pl.* **uteri** body cavity or tube in which eggs are stored or incubated or in which a fetus develops

vaccine substance injected into an organism to increase the organism's resistance to disease-causing microbes

vacuole (VAK-yoo-ōl) cavity within the cytoplasm of a cell often filled with food, water, enzymes, and other materials needed by the cell

valve flap of tissue between an atrium and a ventricle that prevents blood from flowing backward

variation difference in the structure or characteristics of similar organisms

vascular cambium meristematic tissue between the xylem and phloem in the vascular cylinder

vascular cylinder central core that carries water and other essential substances throughout a plant

vascular tissue interior network of conducting tubes in some plants

vas deferens sperm-carrying duct in the male reproductive system

vector organism carrying and transmitting a virus but not affected by it

vegetal pole lower hemisphere of an amphibian egg containing a large quantity of yolk

vegetative organ structure of a plant that carries out one or more of the plant's life functions, including root, leaf, and stem

vegetative propagation (prohp-ə-GĀ-shən) asexual reproduction in many flowering plants

vein blood vessel carrying blood to the heart

vena cava (VĒ-nə KĀ-və), *pl.* **venae cavae** (VĒ-nē KĀ-vē) vein bringing blood into the right atrium

venation arrangement of the veins in a leaf

ventral surface underside of an organism

ventricle (VEN-tri-k'l) lower chamber of the heart

vessel in angiosperms, a tube up to 1 meter long made of vessel elements

vessel element cell from which the xylem tissue of angiosperms is made

vestigial (ves-TIJ-ē-əl) **organ** organ or structure that once had a function but no longer has it

viability (vī-ə-BIL-ə-tē) ability of a seed to germinate

villus, *pl.* **villi** tiny projection in the small intestine that increases intestinal surface area and absorbs simple foods into the bloodstream

viral reservoir source of a virus

virology (vi-RAHL-ə-jē) study of viruses

virus particle that contains hereditary material and is able to reproduce; a disease-causing microbe

visceral mass part of a mollusk containing the gonads, digestive system, excretory organs, and heart

vital capacity largest volume of air an organism can inhale

vitamin any of several nutrients that regulate bodily processes or promote growth

viviparity (viv-ə-PAR-ə-tē) reproduction process in which offspring are born live *adj.* **viviparous** (vī-VIP-ər-əs)

vomerine tooth one of two teeth in the roof of the mouth of a frog used to hold prey

walking leg appendage of a crustacean

water cycle movement of water between the atmosphere and the earth

watershed drainage area of river or river system in which trees and other plants prevent excess water runoff

water-vascular system coelom of an echinoderm that obtains food and provides locomotion

white blood cell cell that helps fight infection; also called leukocyte

wood section of a woody stem composed of different forms of xylem tissue

xerophyte (ZIR-ə-fīt) plant adapted to a dry climate

xylem (ZĪ-ləm) vascular tissue that conducts water throughout a plant

yolk egg fluid containing food for embryo

zoospore (ZŌ-ə-spawr) single reproductive cell released during asexual reproduction

zygote (ZĪ-gōt) fertilized ovum

Nobel Prize Winners

In the late 1800s, the Swedish chemist Alfred Nobel established the awarding of prizes for outstanding breakthroughs by scientists in the fields of physiology or medicine, chemistry, and physics. The first prizes were awarded in 1901. Both men and women have received Nobel Prizes, including James D. Watson and Francis H.C. Crick for finding the structure of DNA (1962), Rosalyn Yalow for research on human hormones (1977), and Barbara McClintock for work in plant genetics (1983).

To enrich your study of biology, a chart, containing the year the prize was awarded; to whom; the achievement for which the prize was given; and the reference to the textbook chapter to which the achievement relates, is given below. The chart contains all of the prizes in physiology or medicine and those in chemistry and physics that relate to biology. You are encouraged to research the scientists listed here and to discover the impact of their contributions upon biology.

Physiology or Medicine

Year	Recipient(s)	Achievement(s)	Chapter Reference(s)
1901	von Behring, Emil (German)	Discovery of diphtheria antitoxin	17
1902	Ross, Ronald (British)	Discovery of how malaria is transmitted	17
1903	Finsen, Niels R. (Danish)	Treatment of diseases using concentrated light rays	17
1904	Pavlov, Ivan P. (Russian)	Research on the physiology of digestion	36
1905	Koch, Robert (German)	Research on tuberculosis and discovery of tubercule bacillus and tuberculin	16, 17
1906	Golgi, Camillo (Italian) Ramon y Cajal, Santiago (Spanish)	Studies of nerve tissue	41
1907	Laveran, Charles L.A. (French)	Study of protozoan diseases	16, 17
1908	Ehrlich, Paul (German) Metchnikoff, Élie (Russian)	Research on immunity	17
1909	Kocher, Emil T. (Swiss)	Research on pathology, physiology, and surgery of thyroid gland	40
1910	Kossel, Albrecht (German)	Study of cell chemistry, proteins, and nucleic materials	4, 5, 8
1911	Gullstrand, Allvar (Swedish)	Research on light refraction through the eye	41
1912	Carrel, Alexis (French)	Technique for blood vessel surgery and transplanting tissues and organs	37
1913	Richet, Charles R. (French)	Study of allergies caused by foreign substances	17
1914	Bárány, Robert (Austrian)	Research on the function of equilibrium organs in the inner ear and their diseases	41

Year	Recipient(s)	Achievement(s)	Chapter Reference(s)
1915-1918	No award		
1919	Bordet, Jules (Belgian)	Discoveries on immunity	17
1920	Krogh, August (Danish)	Discovery of the action system of blood capillaries	37
1921	No award		
1922	Hill, Archibald V. (British)	Discovery of heat production by muscles	7, 35
	Meyerhof, Otto F. (German)	Theory on lactic acid production in muscles	7, 35
1923	Banting, Frederick G. (Canadian) Macleod, John J.R. (Scottish)	Discovery of insulin	40
1924	Einthoven, Willem (Dutch)	Invention of the electrocardiograph	37
1925	No Award		
1926	Fibiger, Johannes (Danish)	Discovery of parasite (nematode) that causes a type of cancer	26, 39
1927	Wagner–Jauregg, Julius (Austrian)	Discovery of the fever treatment for paralysis	17
1928	Nicolle, Charles (French)	Research on typhus	17
1929	Eijman, Christiaan (Dutch)	Discovery of the vitamins that prevent beriberi	39
	Hopkins, Frederick G. (British)	Discovery of vitamins that aid growth	39
1930	Landsteiner, Karl (Austrian)	Discovery of four main blood groups	10, 37
1931	Warburg, Otto H. (German)	Discovery of enzymes that aid in tissue respiration	6, 7
1932	Sherrington, Charles S. (British) Adrian, Edgar D. (British)	Discoveries on the function of neurons	41
1933	Morgan, Thomas Hunt (American)	Study of the function of chromosomes in heredity	10
1934	Whipple, George H. (American) Murphy, William P. (American) Minot, George R. (American)	Discoveries on liver treatment for anemia	36, 37
1935	Spemann, Hans (German)	Discovery of organ-forming influences exerted on tissues by nearby embryo parts	42
1936	Dale, Henry H. (British) Loewi, Otto (Austrian)	Discoveries on the chemical transmission of nerve impulses	41
1937	Szent-Györgi von Nagyrapolt, A. (Hungarian)	Discoveries concerning oxidation in tissues, vitamin C, and fumaric acid	7, 39
1938	Heymans, Corneille (Belgian)	Discoveries concerning the control of respiration	7
1939	Domagk, Gerhard (German)	Discovery of the first sulfa drug	17

Year	Recipient(s)	Achievement(s)	Chapter Reference(s)
1940-1942	No award		
1943	Doisy, Edward (American)	Synthesis of vitamin K	39
	Dam, Henrik, C.P. (Danish)	Discovery of vitamin K	39
1944	Erlanger, Joseph (American)	Research on single nerve fibers	41
	Gasser, Herbert S. (American)		
1945	Fleming, Alexander (British)	Discovery of penicillin	17
	Chain, Ernst B. (British)		
	Florey, Howard W. (British)		
1946	Muller, Hermann J. (American)	Discovery that X-rays can cause mutations	10
1947	Cori, Carl F. (American)	Research on insulin	40
	Cori, Gerty (American)		
	Houssay, Bernardo A. (Argentine)		
1948	Müller, Paul H. (Swiss)	Discovery of the insecticidal properties of DDT	29, 48
1949	Hess, Walter R. (Swiss)	Discovery of how certain areas of the brain regulate body organs	41
	Moniz, Antônio (Portuguese)	Origination of prefrontal lobotomy	41
1950	Hench, Philip S. (American)	Discoveries on cortisone and ACTH	40
	Kendall, Edward C. (American)		
	Reichstein, Tadeus (Swiss)		
1951	Theiler, Max (South African)	Development of yellow fever vaccine	17
1952	Waksman, Selman A. (American)	Discovery of streptomycin	17
1953	Krebs, Hans Adolf (British)	Discoveries in biosynthesis and metabolism	4, 6, 7
	Lipmann, Fritz A. (American)		
1954	Enders, John F. (American)	Discovery of a simple method of growing polio virus in test tubes	14, 17
	Weller, Thomas H. (American)		
	Robbins, Frederick C. (American)		
1955	Theorell, A. Hugo T. (Swedish)	Discoveries on the nature and action of oxidation enzymes	6
1956	Cournand, André F. (American)	Use of a catheter to map the inside of the heart	37
	Forssmann, Werner (German)		
	Richards, Dickinson W. Jr. (American)		
1957	Bovet, Daniel (Italian)	Discovery of antihistamines	17
1958	Beadle, George Wells (American)	Research in biochemical genetics	10
	Tatum, Edward Lawrie (American)		
	Lederberg, Joshua (American)	Studies of bacterial genetics	10, 15
1959	Ochoa, Severo (American)	Production of nucleic acid artificially	8
	Kornberg, Arthur (American)		

Year	Recipient(s)	Achievement(s)	Chapter Reference(s)
1960	Burnet, F. Macfarlane (Australian) Medawar, Peter B. (British)	Research in human organ transplant	37
1961	von Békésy, George (American)	Demonstration of how the ear distinguishes between various sounds	41
1962	Crick, Francis H.C. (British) Watson, James D. (American) Wilkins, Maurice H.F. (British)	Research on nucleic acid	8
1963	Eccles, John Carew (Australian)	Research on the transmission of nerve impulses	41
	Kodgkin, Alan Lloyd (British) Huxley, Andrew Fielding (British)	Description of nerve impulse behavior	41
1964	Bloch, Konrad E. (American) Lynen, Feodor (German)	Research on fatty acid metabolism and cholesterol	4, 39
1965	Jacob, François (French) Lwoff, André (French) Monod, Jacques (French)	Discoveries concerning genetic regulation of enzymes and virus synthesis	6, 10, 14
1966	Rous, Peyton (American)	Discovery of a cancer-producing virus	14, 39
	Huggins, Charles B. (American)	Discovery of the uses of hormones in cancer treatment	39, 40
1967	Granit, Ragnar (Swedish) Hartline, H. Keffer (American) Wald, George (American)	Research on the physiological and chemical processes that occur in the eye	41
1968	Holley, Robert W. (American) Khorana, H. Gobind (American) Nirenberg, Marshall W. (American)	Explanation of how genes determine cell function	5, 10
1969	Delbrück, Max (American) Hershey, Alfred D. (American) Luria, Salvador E. (American)	Research on bacteriophages	14
1970	Katz, Bernard (British) von Euler, Ulf Svante (Swedish) Axelrod, Julius (American)	Discoveries of the part played by certain chemicals in nerve impulse transmission	41
1971	Sutherland, Earl W. Jr. (American)	Discovery of methods of hormone action	40
1972	Edelman, Gerald M. (American) Porter, Rodney R. (British)	Discovery of the chemical structure of antibodies	17, 37
1973	von Frisch, Karl (Austrian) Lorenz, Konrad (Austrian) Tinbergen, Nikolaas (British)	Studies on animal behavior	29, 30, 33

Year	Recipient(s)	Achievement(s)	Chapter Reference(s)
1974	Claude, Albert (American) de Duve, Christian (Belgian) Palade, George E. (American)	Research in cell biology	5, 6, 7
1975	Baltimore, David (American) Dulbecco, Renato (American) Temin, Howard M. (American)	Research on how certain viruses affect cancer cell genes	14, 39
1976	Blumberg, Baruch S. (American) Gajdusek, D. Carleton (American)	Discoveries concerning the origin and spread of infectious diseases	17
1977	Guillemin, Roger (American) Schally, Andrew (American) Yalow, Rosalyn (American)	Research concerning the role of hormones in body chemistry	40
1978	Arber, Werner (Swiss) Nathans, Daniel (American) Smith, Hamilton O. (American)	Discoveries in molecular genetics	10
1979	Cormack, Allan Macleod (American) Hounsfield, Godfrey Newbold (British)	Contributions to the development of the computerized axial tomographic (CAT) scanner	35–42
1980	Benacerraf, Baruj (American) Dausset, Jean (French) Snell, George D. (American)	Discoveries concerning the genetic control of the body's immune system	10, 17
1981	Sperry, Roger W. (American) Hubel, David H. (American) Wiesel, Torsten N. (Swedish)	Research on organization and function of the brain	41
1982	Bergström, Sune K. (Swedish) Samuelsson, Bengt I. (Swedish) Vane, John R. (British)	Research on hormonelike substances (prostaglandins)	40
1983	McClintock, Barbara (American)	Research on plant genetics	9, 10, 11
1984	Jerne, Niels K. (Danish) Milstein, César (Argentine) Köhler, Georges (German)	Contributions to the theory and techniques of modern immunology	17

Chemistry (Biology Related)

Year	Recipient(s)	Achievement(s)	Chapter Reference(s)
1901	Van't Hoff, Jacobus H. (Dutch)	Discovery of laws of osmotic pressure	6, 21
1902	Fischer, H. Emil (German)	Synthesis of sugars, purine derivatives, and peptides	4
1914	Richards, Theodore W. (American)	Determination of atomic weights of many elements	4
1915	Willstätter, Richard M. (German)	Research concerning chlorophyll and other coloring substances in plants	7, 22
1928	Windaus, Alfred O.R. (German)	Study of sterols and their connection with vitamins	39
1929	Harden, Arthur (British) von Euler-Chelpin, Hans A.S. (German)	Research on sugar fermentation and enzymes	6, 7
1930	Fischer, Hans (German)	Study of the coloring substances of blood and leaves and synthesis of hemin	7, 22, 37
1937	Haworth, Walter N. (British)	Research on carbohydrates and vitamin C	4, 39
	Karrer, Paul (Swiss)	Study of carotenoids, flavins, vitamins A and B_2	7, 22, 39
1938	Kuhn, Richard (German)	Research on carotenoids and vitamins	7, 22, 39
1939	Butenandt, Adolph F.J. (German)	Study of sex hormones	40, 42
1946	Sumner, James B. (American)	Discovery of enzyme crystalization	6
	Northrop, John H. (American) Stanley, Wendell M. (American)	Preparation of pure enzymes and virus proteins	6, 14
1947	Robinson, Robert (British)	Research on penicillin, flower pigments, and hormones	17, 23, 40
1948	Tiselius, Arne W.K. (Swedish)	Discovery of the nature of serum proteins	37
1955	du Vigneaud, Vincent (American)	Discovery of the process for making synthetic hormones	40
1957	Todd, A.R. (British)	Research on protein composition of cells	5
1961	Calvin, Melvin (American)	Research on photosynthesis	7, 22
1962	Perutz, Max F. (British) Kendrew, John C. (British)	Study of globular proteins	4, 39
1964	Hodgkin, Dorothy C. (British)	Study of X-rays of substances such as penicillin and vitamin B_{12}	17, 39
1970	Leloir, Luis (Argentine)	Discovery of chemical compounds that affect chemical energy storage in living things	6, 7

Year	Recipient(s)	Achievement(s)	Chapter Reference(s)
1972	Anfinsen, Christian B. (American)	Contribution to the chemistry of enzymes	6
	Moore, Stanford (American)		
	Stein, William H. (American)		
1978	Mitchell, Peter (British)	Studies of cellular energy transfer	6, 7
1980	Berg, Paul (American)	Studies of chemical structure of nucleic acids	4, 8
	Gilbert, Walter (American)		
	Sanger, Frederick (British)		
1982	Klug, Aaron (British)	Explanation of biologically important nucleic acid-protein complexes	4, 8
1984	Merrifield, R. Bruce (American)	Research on the study of proteins leading to development of new drugs	4

Physics (Biology Related)

Year	Recipient(s)	Achievement(s)	Chapter Reference(s)
1922	Bohr, Niels (Danish)	Study of the structure of atoms	4
1923	Millikan, Robert A. (American)	Measurement of charge on electrons	4
1935	Chadwick, James (British)	Discovery of the neutron	4
1953	Zernike, Frits (Dutch)	Invention of the phase contrast microscope for cancer research	1, 39
1963	Wigner, Eugene Paul (American)	Contributions to the understanding of atomic nuclei	4
	Goeppert-Mayer, Maria (American)	Work on atomic nuclei structure	4
	Jensen, J. Hans D. (German)		
1968	Alvarez, Luis W. (American)	Contributions to the knowledge of subatomic particles	4
1975	Bohr, Aage (Danish)	Work on the structure of the atomic nucleus	4
	Mottelson, Ben (Danish)		
	Rainwater, James (American)		
1984	Rubbia, Carlo (Italian)	Development of a single theory to account for all natural forces	4
	van der Meer, Simon (Dutch)		

Index

asexual reproduction, 34, 141, 142, 368, 369
assimilation, 33
aster, 136
aster ray, 136–137
atmospheric pollution, 782–783
atomic mass, 61
atomic number, 61
atoms and elements, 60–61
ATP (adenosine triphosphate), 97–99, 114, 585
  in cellular respiration, 116–117, 119, 121, 123, 124
atria (atrium), 491, 508, 612
attitude, 696
auditory nerve, 674
Aurelia (jellyfish), 406, 409
Australopithecus afarensis, 226–227
Australopithecus africanus, 226–227
Australopithecus robustus, 226–227
autonomic nervous system, 663, 668–670
autosome, 170
autotroph, 49, 111, 252, 269, 297, 721
auxin, 357, 385–387
avoidance reaction, 268
axial skeleton, 578
axon, 663

B

bacilli, 250
bacteria, 15, 77, 79, 237, 248–261, 721
  classification of, 250
  denitrifying, 734
  DNA transfer in, 256–257
  life functions in, 251–257
  movement of, 251
  nitrogen-fixing, 734
  size of, 249
  structure of, 250–251
bacterial disease, 282–284
bacterial growth, requirements for, 254
bacterial toxin, 278
bacteria spore formation, 256
bacteriochlorophyll, 113
bacteriology, 15
bacteriophage. *See* phage
bacteriostat, 277
balance, 673–674
balanced diet, 635
baleen, 565
ball-and-socket joint, 582
barb and barbule, 542
barbel, 482
barbiturate, 703–704
bark, 331, 350
barnacle, 452, 453
basal disk, 407
basal metabolic rate (BMR), 627

basal metabolism, 627
basidium in fungi, 307
beak, 539
bed, stream or river, 769
behavior, 690
  acquired, 695–696
  emotional, 693–695
  involuntary, 691
  in plants, 384, 391–393
behavioral barrier, 757
behavioral characteristics, human, 225
Beijerinck, Martinus, 237
benthic environment, 766
benthos, 766
biennial plant, 333
bilateral symmetry, 414, 433
bile, 490, 598, 600
bile duct, 418
binary fission, 142, 254, 265, 268, 270–271
binomial nomenclature, 44
biochemical evidence of evolution, 206
biochemical similarities, 45
biodegradable substance, 782
biogenesis, principle of, 27–31, 77
biogeochemical cycle, 731
biogeography
  barriers, 756–757
  dispersal, 755
biological clock, 744
biological control of insects, 473
biological investigation, 17–22
  measurements, 19–20
  scientific method, 17–19
  tools, 20–22
biology, 13–25
  classification in, 42–55
  living organisms in, 26–41
bioluminescence, 303
biomagnification, 784
biomass, 725
biomes, 37, 754–773
  aquatic, 765–770
  terrestrial, 757–765
biosphere, 37, 719–721
  communities and populations, 720
  ecosystems, 719–720
  habitats and niches, 720–721
biosynthesis, 80
biotic communities, rhythms and cycles in, 742–747
biotic factors in ecosystems, 719
biotic interactions in the environment, 721–728
  competition, 726
  ecological pyramids, 723–726
  food chains and food webs, 722–723
  predator-prey relationships, 726
biotic potential, 748
bipedal, 222, 518
bipinnaria, 441
birds, 536–551

anatomy of, 540–548
characteristics of, 538–540
history of, 537–538
types of, 538–539
birth, 683
bivalve, 434
bladder, 507
blade of the leaf, 358
blastopore, 500
blastula, 409, 500, 682
blood
  characteristics of, 609–612
  composition of, 607
  types of circulation, 615–618
blood alcohol concentration (BAC), 701
blood pressure, 614
blood serum, 278
blood transfusion, 611–612
blood type and alleles, 176–177
blood vessel, 614–615
blushing, 695
bogs, 760
bones, 578–581
bony fishes (*Osteichthyes*), 484–494
  perch, 486–494
book lung, 460
botany, 16, 296
botulism, 253, 283
Bowman's capsule, 629–630
brain, 665–667
  capacity of human, 224
brain stem, 667
branching pattern in stems, 348
bread-cereals group, 635
breathing, 624–626
breeding habits. *See* reproduction.
bristle, 542
brittle star, 441
broad-leafed plant, 357
bronchi, 508, 624
bronchiole, 624
bronchitis, 710
Brontosaurus, 518
Brownian movement of atoms and molecules, 101
bryophytes, 315–318, 369
budding, 142, 306, 371, 404
buds, types of, 347
bulb, 351
bundle scar, 347
bundle sheath, 361
bursa, 582

C

caecilians, 499
caecum, 598
calorie, 636
calyx, 372
cambium, 331
Cambrian Period, 204

Down's syndrome (trisomy-21), 180–181
drone, 470
Drosophila, 45, 169, 170–173, 212
drought, 763
drug abuse, treatment of, 706–707
drugs, 700, 703–709
dual-host virus, 243
duck-billed platypus, 558–559
ductless glands, 651
ductus deferens, 546
dune, 740
duodenum, 506, 596
dysentery, amoebic, 284–285

E

ear, parts of, 673
earthworm, 424–427
Echinodermata (echinoderms), 432, 439–442
ecological balance, 726
ecological barrier, 756–757
ecological interactions
  biomes, 754–773
  conservation, 774–791
  environment, 718–737
  succession and population changes, 738–753
ecological pyramid, 723–726
ecological succession, 739–742
  climax community, 741, 742
  developmental stages, 740–742
  in lake ecosystem, 739–740
  pioneering stages, 740, 741
  in a sand dune, 740–741
  types of, 741–742
ecologist, 718
ecology, 718
ecosystem, 719–720
ecotone, 758
ectoderm, 406
ectoplasm, 263
Edentata (toothless mammals), 563
egg and sperm cells, formation of, 139–141. *See also* reproduction.
egg stage, 467–468
Ehrlich, Paul, 288
electron(s), 21, 60, 61
electron microscope, 21–22
electron-shadow micrography, 238
electron transport chain, 114
elements, 60–61
elongation region, 342
embryo, 205, 371, 682–683
embryological evidence of evolution, 205
embryology, 17
embryonic development, 682–683
embryo sac, 374
emergent layer, 761
emigrants, 747

emotions, 693–695
emphysema, 628, 710
Endamoeba histolytica, 284–285
endangered species, 780
endocrine structure, 651–658
endocrine system, human, 650–661
  feedback process in, 658
endocytosis, 105–106
endoplasm, 263
endoplasmic reticulum (ER), rough and smooth, 86
endoskeleton, 439, 577
endosperm, 376
endospore, 256
endotherm, 730
endotoxin, 283
energy, 37–38, 59, 94, 778–779
  cell, 95–99
  conservation of, 95
  types of, 95
energy level, 60, 61
entomologist, 468
environment, 34, 718–737
  biosphere, 719–721
  biotic interactions in, 721–728
environmental pollution, 781–786
environmental resistance, 748
enzyme(s), 71, 96, 206, 304, 490, 598, 600–601
  and chemical reactions, 95–97
  restriction endonucleases, 193
enzyme-substrate reactions, theories of, 96–97
epicotyl, 377
epidermal hairs, 360
epidermal tissue, 329
epidermis, 342, 360, 401, 526, 586–587
epiglottis, 595, 624
epinephrine, 654
epithelial tissue, 575
epochs, 202
equatorial plane of the cell, 137
equine encephalitis virus and host, 244
era, 202
erosion, 776
erythrocyte (red blood cell), 607, 608
Escherichia coli, 193, 241–242, 254
esophagus, 424, 449, 465, 490, 595
estivation, 502, 746
estrogen, 656, 680
estuary, 770
ethyl alcohol, 701
eucoelomate, 423
euglena, 34, 81, 270–271
eukaryote, 90, 262, 299
Eumycophyta (fungi), 304
Eustachian tube, 503, 673
eutrophication, 739, 784
eutrophic lake, 769
evaporation, 64, 731
evolution, theory of, 15–16, 206–210

anatomical evidence, 204–205
biochemical evidence, 206
convergent, 216
Darwin's theory, 208–210
DeVries' theory, 210
divergent, 214–216
embryological evidence, 205
fossil evidence, 200–201
Lamarck's theory, 207–208
pathways, 214–216
processes, 211–214
evolutionary processes, 211–214
  adaptive shifts, 212
  gene mutation, 211–213
  Hardy-Weinberg law, 211
  isolation, 213–214
  migration, 212–213
excretion, 33, 81, 629–630
excretory system, 466, 491, 506–507, 529, 544, 629–631
excurrent siphon, 435
excurrent stem, 348
exercise, 640
exobiology, 17
exocrine glands, 651
exocytosis, 106
exoskeleton, 447, 462
exotherm, 730
exotoxin, 283
extensor, 585
extinct species, 202, 749
extraembryonic membrane, 682
eye, 451, 466, 670–672
eye spot, 79, 270, 416, 440

F

facultative bacteria, 253–254
Fallopian tube, 680, 682
family in classification, 46
fangs, 521
fats, 71, 636–637
fatty acids, 71, 277
feather, 537, 542
feces, 285, 418, 602
feedback processes, 658
Felis domesticus, classification of, 46
female genital pore, 427
female reproductive system, 680–681
femur, 464, 577
fermentation, 122–123, 253, 306, 701
ferns (*Pteropsida*), 319–321
fertility in DNA transfer (F factors), 256
fertilization, 34, 142, 376, 681
fetus, 683
fibers in stems, 347
fibrin, 609
fibrous root, 341
fibrovascular bundle, 361
filament, 297, 298, 372
filoplume, 542

filterability of virus, 237
filter feeder, 483
filtration, 64
fin, 481
fishes, 479–498
  bony, 484–494
  cartilaginous, 482–484
  classification of, 481–486
  jawless, 481–482
fission, reproduction by, 81, 297–299
flagella, 251, 269
flagellate, 269–271
flame bulb, 416
flatworms (*Platyhelminthes*), 415–419
  flukes, 417–419
  planarians, 415–417
  tapeworms, 419
Fleming, Alexander, 289
flesh-eating mammals (*Carnivora*),
  562
flexor muscle, 585
flight, structures used in, 540–542
flowers, 327–329, 371–375
fluid mosaic model of lipids and
  proteins, 83
flukes (*Trematoda*), 417–419
flying mammals (*Chiroptera*), 562
follicle, 542
fontanel, 580
food, 38, 281
  absorption of, 601–602
  as a resource, 775–776
food chain, 38, 722
food group, 635
food industry and bacteria, 257–258
food poisoning, 283
food web, 723
foot, 433
foot-and-mouth disease, 244
Foraminifera, 263
forest floor, 761
form in classification, 46
formula, 63
fossil, 200–202
fossil cast, 201
fossil fuel, 778–779
fossil mold, 201
fragmentation, 297, 417
freshwater biome
  lakes and ponds, 769
  streams and rivers, 769–770
frog, 502–512
frond, 320
fructose, 67
fruit, 327, 329, 377–378
fruiting body, 304, 307, 311
FSH (follicle-stimulating hormone),
  681
Fungi, 296, 303–309
  club (*Basidiomycetes*), 307-308
  conjugating (*Zygomycetes*), 304-305
  imperfect (*Deuteromycetes*),
    308-309

morels and cup (*Ascomycetes*),
  306–307
sac (*Ascomycetes*), 305
fungi kingdom, 48, 49, 50, 296

G

galactose, 67
gall bladder, 490, 598
gametes, 34, 138, 151, 271, 297, 299,
  371, 405, 678, 679
gametogenesis, 138
gametophyte generation, 315
gamma globulin, 287
ganglia, 424, 450
gas, 59
gas exchange, 625
gastric caeca, 465
gastric fluid, 595
gastrodermis, 406
Gastropoda (one-shelled mollusks),
  436–437
gastrula, 501, 682
gecko, 524
gemmae cups, 318
gemmule, 404
gene(s), 152, 154, 168
  chromosomes and, 166–183
  crossing over, 172
  mapping and linkage, 169–170
  Morgan's investigations of, 170–171
  nature of, 168–173
  nondisjunction, 172–173
  transformation, 168–169
gene frequency, 211
gene linkage, 169–170
gene mutation, 212
gene pair, 154
gene pool, 211
generative nucleus, 375
genetic breeding, 187
genetic changes, 173–182
  amniocentesis and ultrasound,
    181–182
  influence of environment, 182
  inherited diseases, 177–178
  multiple alleles, 176–177
  nondisjunction in chromosomes,
    179–181
  sex-linked traits in, 178–179
genetic code, 191
genetic continuity, 136
genetic diversity, 748
genetic drift, 211
genetic engineering, 191–194
genetic isolation, 214
genetic recombination, 256
genetics, 16, 150
  applications of, 186–197
genetic similarities, 45
genetic variability, 188
genotype, 156

genus in classification, 44, 46
geographical barriers, 756
geologic time, 202–204
geothermal energy, 778
geotropism, 392–393
German measles, 282
germination, 297, 327
gestation, 682
gestation period, 557
gibberellic acid (GA), 387
gila monster, 524
gill bailer, 450
gill chamber, 450, 491
gill filament, 491
gill raker, 491
gills, 433, 481
gingko, 334–335
girdles, 488, 578
girdling, 350
gizzard, 424, 465, 544
gliding joints, 582
glomerulus, 629
glottis, 508, 624
glucagon, 656
glucose, 67
glutathione, 407
glycerol, 71
glycogen, 68
glycolipid, 83
glycoprotein, 83
gnawing mammals (*Rodentia*), 564
Golgi apparatus, 87–88
gonad, 433, 656, 679
gonorrhea (*Neisseria gonorrhoeae*),
  281
grafting, 370
grana, 89, 113
granule, 251
grasshopper (*Orthoptera*), 462,
  463–467
grassland, 763–764
green gland, 450
greenhouse effect, 783
groundwater, 732, 777
group, 46
growth, 33, 384, 385–391
growth spurt, 686
grub, 468
guard cells, 360
gullet, 267
guttation in leaves, 362–364
gymnosperm, 327, 334

H

habitat, 720
habits, 696
hagfish, 482
hair and nails, 587–588
hair follicles, 588
half-life of elements, 202
hallucination, 642

hallucinogen, 704
haploid megaspore, 374
haploid micronucleus, 268
haploid number, 138, 190
haploid organisms, 142
Hardy-Weinberg law, 211
Haversian canals, 581
head, 462
head-footed mollusks (*Cephalopoda*),
    438–439
health, maintaining good, 640–643
hearing, 673–674
heart, human, 612–613
heartbeat, 613
heart disease, 643
Heliozoa, digestion in, 264
Hemiptera, 462, 467
hemocoel, 447
hemoglobin, 177, 581, 608, 625
hemophilia, 179
hemotoxin, 523
heparin, 609
hepatitis, viral, 282
herbaceous stem, 328, 346–347
herbivore (primary consumer), 518,
    554, 721
herb layer, 761
heredity, 16, 35, 150–165
    concepts of, 155-162
hermaphrodite, 405
heroin, 706
herpetologist, 519
heterogeneous mixtures, 64
heterotroph, 49, 111, 252–253, 270
    304, 722
heterozygous zygote, 156
hibernation, 502, 558, 746
hilum, 378
hinge joint, 582
holdfast, 300
homeostasis, 83, 99–100, 658
    active transport and, 104–106
    diffusion, 101–102
    endocytosis, 105–106
    exocytosis, 106
    osmosis, 102–103
    passive transport and, 99–104
    plasmolysis, 103–104
Hominidae family, 221
Homo erectus, 228
homogeneous mixture, 64
Homo habilis, 227–228
homologous chromosomes, 169
homologous organs, 204–205
homologous structures, 45
Homoptera, 462, 467
Homo sapiens, 226, 228, 229
homozygous plant, 189
homozygous zygote, 156
honeybee, 469
hoofed mammal (ungulate), 563–564
Hooke, Robert, 15, 77
hookworm, 421–422

hormone, 385, 468, 650
horny outer layer, 434
horsetails (*Sphenopsida*), 322
hosts, 239, 417, 727
human behavior, 690–699
    acquired, 695–696
    basic needs, 692
    emotional, 693–695
    involuntary, 691
human beings
    characteristics of, 221–225
    disease defenses in, 278–279
    biological history of, 225–229
    plasmodium life cycle in, 271–272
human body
    alcohol in, 701
    muscular system, 582–586
    organization in, 575–576
    skeletal system, 576–582
    structure, 574–591
    tobacco in, 710
human growth hormone (HGH),
    193–194, 653
human history, 220–233
    early forms, 227–229
    fossil records, 226–227
human microbial disease, 276–293
human needs, basic, 692–695
human populations, 750
human response and development,
    649–713
    alcohol, drugs, and tobacco,
        700–715
    behavior, 690–699
    endocrine system, 650–661
    nervous system, 662–677
    reproduction and development,
        678–689
human structure and function,
    573–647
    body structure, 574–591
    circulation, 606–621
    digestion, 593–605
    nutrition and health, 634–647
    respiration and excretion, 622–633
humus, 341, 730
hybrid, 155
hybrid vigor, 189
hydra (*Hydrozoa*), 406–408
hydrochloric acid, 600
hydrogen, 60–63, 66–71
hydrolysis, 68
hydrophyte, 390
hydrotropism, 393
hydroxyl group, 71
Hydrozoa (hydra), 406–408
Hymenoptera, 462, 467
hypertension, 643
hyperthyroidism, 651
hypertonic solution, 102
hyphae of fungi, 304
hypocotyl, 377
hypoglycemia, 656

hypothalamus gland, 654
hypothesis, 18, 154
    Oparin's, 72
hypotonic solution, 102

I

ichthyologists, 481
identical colonies, 79, 262
identical twins, 182
ileum, 506, 596
immigrant, 747
immunity, types of, 286–289
imprint fossil, 200
incisor, 562
incomplete dominance, 161–162
incubated eggs, 547
incurrent siphon, 435
independent assortment, law of, 155,
indoleacetic acid (IA), 387
induced fit theory, 96–97
industrial pollution, 785
infancy, development during,
    684–685
infectious disease, 279
influenza and the common cold, 282
ingestion, 33
inhalants, 703
inorganic compound, 66–67
Insecta (insects), 446, 458, 462–473
    anatomy, 462–467
    behavior, 469–472
    control, 472–473
    development, 467–469
insect-eating mammals (*Insectivora*),
    561
insectivorous plant, 362
insulin, 81, 194, 656
    produced by bacteria, 258
integumentary system (skin), 586–588
interferon, 194, 279
interkinesis, 139
internode, 347
intertidal zone, 766
intestine, 415, 596–598, 601–602
invertebrate hosts for viruses,
    242–243
invertebrates
    arachnids and insects, 458–477
    crustaceans and myriapods,
        446–457
    mollusks and echinoderms, 432–445
    sponges and coelenterates, 400–413
    worms, 414–431
involuntary muscle, 584
ion, 63, 345
ionic bonds and bonding, 63
iris of eye, 670
irritability, 34, 691
islets of Langerhans, 655
isolation, 213
isopod, 447

rays (*Chondrichthyes*), 483
RDP (ribulose diphosphate), 114
reactive site of substrate reaction, 96
receptacle, 371
recessive trait, 152–154
recombinant DNA, 192–193
recombination of genetic material, 172
rectilinear movement, 528
rectum, 465, 544, 598
red blood cell (erythrocyte), 607, 608
Redi, Francesco, 27–28
"red tide," 303
reflex, 667, 691
reflex arc, 668
reforestation, 780
regeneration, 404–405, 441, 452, 501, 526
relative age, 202
REM (rapid eye movement) sleep, 642
renal circulation, 616
replication of viruses, 240–242
reproduction, 34–35, 678
    in algae, 297–303
    in amoebas, 265
    in amphibians, 500
    in bacteria, 254, 256
    in birds, 546–548
    as cell function, 81
    in club mosses, 322
    in crayfishes, 452
    in earthworms, 426–427
    in euglenas, 270
    in ferns, 320–321
    in flatworms, 416, 417, 419
    in flowering plants, 368–383
    in the frog, 511–512
    in fungi, 304–307
    in grasshoppers, 466
    human, 678–681
    in hydras, 408
    in liverworts, 317–318
    in mammals, 557
    in mollusks, 434
    in mosses, 316–317
    in paramecia, 268–269
    in perch (bony fishes), 492–494
    in reptiles, 530–532
    in roundworms, 420–421
    in skates and rays, 483
    in sponges, 404–405
    in toads, 501–502
reproductive stage in plants, 368
reproductive system, 510–511
    female, 680–681
    male, 679–680
Reptilia (reptiles), 516–535
reservoir in euglena, 270
resources
    natural, 775–781
    nonrenewable, 775
    plant life, 780
    renewable, 775

respiration and respiratory system, 33, 38, 80, 110, 117–124, 253–254, 328, 362–363, 450, 464, 491, 508, 529–530, 545, 555
    difficulties, 628
    human, 622–628
    mechanics of breathing, 624–625
    structures, 623–624
response, 34, 81, 265, 267–268, 270, 391–393, 691
retina, 671
R group in proteins and amino acids, 70
Rh factor, 610–611
rhizoid, 305, 315–316
rhizome, 320, 351
Rhodophyta (red algae), 302–303
ribonucleic acid. *See* RNA
ribosomal RNA (rRNA), 131
ribosome, 86, 251
rickettsia, 249, 253
RNA (ribonucleic acid), 71, 85, 130–132, 237–239
rock moss (*Andreaea*), 315
Rodentia (gnawing mammals), 564
rodentlike mammals (*Lagomorpha*), 564
rods, 671–672
root(s), 328, 340, 341–345
    stems and, 340–355
root adaptation, 344
root cap, 342
root hair, 342
root pressure, 345
root tip, 342
roundworms (*Nematoda*), 420–423
    Ascaris, 421
    hookworms, 421–422
    Trichina, 422–423
rubella, 282
rumen, 564
ruminants, 564
runners, 369
runoff water, 731
rusts and smuts, 308
Rynchocephalia (tuatara), 519, 520

S

Sabin vaccine (OPV), 286
sacral vertebrae, 504, 527, 543
salamanders (*Caudata*), 499–501
saliva, 599
salivary gland, 465, 593
Salmonella, 283
sand dollar, 441–442
sandworm (*Nereis*), 427
sap, 352
saprophyte, 253, 303, 722
Sarcodina (sarcodines), 263–265
saturated solution, 65
savannah, 764

scab, 609
"scale of nature," 207
scallop, 435–436
scanning electron microscope (SEM), 22
scavenger, 483, 722
science, definition of, 14
scientific method, 17–19
scientific name, 44
scion stock, 370
sclerenchyma, 332, 361
scolex, 419
scorpion, 461
scute, 521, 563
scyphistoma, 409
Scyphozoa (jellyfishes), 406, 408–410
sea anemones and corals (*Anthozoa*), 406, 410
sea cucumber, 442
seasonal changes, 745–746
sea urchin, 441
seaweed and kelp, 302
secondary cell walls, 82
secondary consumers (carnivores), 721
secondary growth tissue in stems, 349–351
secondary root, 341
secondary root tissue, 342–344
secretion as cell function, 80
sedimentary rock, 200
seed, 326, 371
seed-bearing plant, 326–339
seed dispersal, 378–379
seed dormancy, 379
seed germination and growth, 379–380
seed structure, 377–378
seed viability, 379
segmented worms (*Annelida*), 423–428
    earthworms, 423–427
    leeches, 427–428
    sandworms, 427
segregation, law of, 154–155
selectively permeable membrane, 82–83, 101, 345
self-pollination, 151, 189
semen, 680
semicircular canal, 673
seminal receptacle, 460
seminal vesicle, 426, 511, 680
sense organs, 670–674
sensory lobe, 416
sensory receptor, 489
sensory receptor cell, 408
sepal, 329, 372
septum, 530
sessile leaf, 358
sessile organism, 266
sessile sponge, 401
setae, 425
sewage pollution, 784

terrestrial mollusks, 432
terrestrial plants, 314
territories of organisms, 757
testa, 377
test cross, 171
testes, 140, 466, 492, 557, 656, 679
testosterone, 656, 679
thallophyte, 296
thallus, 296, 317
THC (9-tetrahydrocannabinol), 705
theory, 19, 154
therapsid, 553
thermal pollution, 785
thigmotropism, 393
thorax, 462
thrombocyte (platelet), 607, 609
thumb, human, 222
thymus, 656
thyroid gland, 651–653
thyroid-stimulating hormone, TSH, 658
thyroxine, 651
tibia, 464
tick, 462
tidal pool, 745
time rhythms and cycles in biotic communities, 742–747
tissue, 36–37, 329–333, 575–576
toad, 45, 501
tobacco, 710–711
tobacco mosaic virus (TMV), 237
tongue, 593–594
toothless mammals (*Edentata*), 563
topsoil, 341
touch, 672–673
trace element, 639
trachea, 453, 555, 624
tracheid, 331, 347, 361
tracheole, 464
Tracheophyta (tracheophytes), 318–322
traits or characteristics, 34, 136, 150
tranquilizers, 704
transduction in DNA transfer, 257
transfer RNA (tRNA), 132
transformation in DNA transfer, 257
translocation in the stem, 352, 361
transmission electron microscope (TEM), 22
transpiration, 345, 362, 363–364, 732
transpiration-cohesion theory, 352
transport as cell function, 80
tree-dwelling mammals (*Primata*), 565
Trematoda (flukes), 417–419
tribe in classification, 46
Triceratops, 518
trichina (*Trichinella spiralis*), 422–423
trichinosis, 422
trichocysts in *Paramecium*, 267–268
trisomy-21 (Down's syndrome), 180–181

trochophore, 433
trophic level, 724
tropical rain forest, 761, 763
tropical zone, 758
tropic hormone, 654
tropism, 392
trunk-nosed mammals (*Proboscidea*), 563
trunk vertebrae, 505
trypanosoma, 270, 284
trypsin, 96
tuatara (*Rynchocephalia*), 519, 520
tube feet, 441
tube nucleus, 375
tuber, 351
tuberculosis, 284
tubule bacillus, 284
tumors, plant, 242
tundra, 758
Turbellaria (planarians), 415–417
turgidity, 346
turgor pressure, 103, 346
Turner's syndrome, 181
turtles and tortoises (*Chelonia*), 519, 520–521
twins, identical and fraternal, 683
tympanum, 466, 503
Tyrannosaurus, 518

U

ulcer, 600
Ulothrix, 300
ultrasound test, 182
umbilical cord, 682
understory, 760
ungulates (hoofed mammals), 563–564
unicellular algae, 297
unicellular organisms, 36, 79
univalves, 436
"universal solvent," 66
urea, 67, 426, 600, 630
ureter, 544, 629
urethra, 629, 680
urinary bladder, 529, 629
urinary duct, 507
urogenital opening, 492
uropod, 449
urostyle, 505
uterus, 557, 680
in flukes, 417

V

vaccines, 258, 286
vacuole, 87, 103, 251, 263–264
vagina, 681
valve, 613
variations, 35, 199, 209

through time, 198–219
variety in classification, 46
vascular bundle, 346
vascular cambium, 343, 350
vascular cylinder, 342–343
vascular tissue, 315, 331
vas deferens, 679
vasopressin, 654
vector (transmitter of virus), 243
vegetable-fruit group, 635
vegetal pole, 500
vegetative organs of the plant, 328–329
vegetative propagation, 369–371
vegetative state, 368
vein, 359–360, 492, 614, 615
veldt, 763
venae cavae, 617
venom, 521
ventral nerve cord, 450
ventral surface, 415
ventricle, 491, 508, 612
vernalization, 389–390
vertebrae, 488, 504, 578
spinal cord and, 668
vertebrate(s), 46, 205
amphibians, 498–515
birds, 536–551
fishes, 479–498
mammals, 552–571
reptiles, 516–535
vertebrate host, 242–243
vertical stratification, 760–761
vesicle, 87
vessel elements, 331
vessel in vascular tissue, 331
vestigial organ, 208
villi, 601
viper, 522–523
viral anatomy, 237–239
viral disease, 281
viral reservoir, 244
viroid, 237
virulence of a virus, 281
viruses, 32, 236–247
classifying, 239
discovery of, 237
disease and, 242–244
size and shape, 239
structure of, 238–239
viral replication and lytic cycle, 240–242
visceral mass, 433
vision, 670–672
vital capacity of the lungs, 626
vitamin, 97, 637
viviparity, 483
viviparous organism, 532, 554
volume, 20, 59
voluntary muscle, 584
volvox, 79, 270
vomerine teeth, 506
vorticella (*Ciliophora*), 266